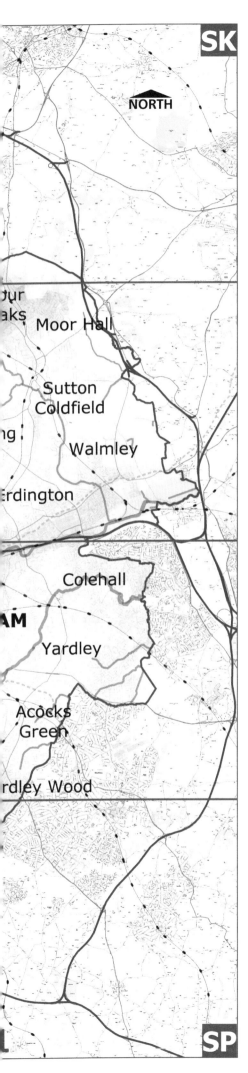

SK

NORTH

ur
aks

Moor Hall

Sutton
Coldfield

ng

Walmley

Erdington

Colehall

AM

Yardley

Acocks
Green

rdley Wood

SP

District boundaries

- · - · - Railways

Motorways

A-roads

Canals

Rivers and streams

Open space

Urban

**Elevation (m)**

271

59

# Flora of Birmingham and the Black Country

Ian Trueman, Mike Poulton and Paul Reade

*With chapters edited by*
David Antrobus & Bill Moodie, Martin Godfrey, Peter James and Peter Jarvis

*And contributions by*
Simon Atkinson, Stefan Bodnar, Sara Carvalho, Sue Collingswood, Anna Coward, Peter Coxhead, Alan Cutler, Anne Daly, Nicola Farrin, John Gerrard, Jane Hardwick, Margaret Kingsbury, David Mitchell, Chris Parry, Simon Phipps, Antony Ratcliffe, Peter Shirley, John Shrimpton, Andy Slater, Paul Wilkinson and Chris Young

*Drawings by*
Teresa Bailey, Anne Bebbington, Anne Daly, Aidan Edwards, Gemma Edwards, Sue Nicholls and Neville Walters

*Maps by*
Sara Carvalho and Andy Slater of EcoRecord. The atlas distribution maps were prepared with the DMAP software written by Dr A. J. Morton. "Early English Birmingham and the Black Country" map by John Hemingway

*Design by*
NatureBureau with contributions from Chris Gardner of Design Bridge

*Photographs by*
David Antrobus, Simon Atkinson, Birmingham Museums Trust, Morgan Bowers, Sue Collingswood, Peter Creed, Anne Daly, Gemma Edwards, Martin Godfrey, Dan Hunt, Rudi Pilsel, Mike Poulton, Andy Purcell, Andy Slater, Ian Trueman, Mike Waller, Chris Wishart and Tony Wood

The publication of the Flora was greatly assisted by the generous financial help given by the Birmingham Natural History Society, the Sutton Coldfield Natural History Society, The Sandwell Valley Naturalists' Club, The Grimmitt Trust, Land Care Associates, several small donors and the Black Country Community Living Landscapes Project [1]

 1*The Wildlife Trust for Birmingham and Black Country's Black Country Community Living Landscapes Project was awarded £442,000 by Natural England as part of its Access to Nature Programme, funded by £28.75m from the Big Lottery Fund's Changing Spaces Programme
LOTTERY FUNDED

The Birmingham and Black Country Botanical Society

EcoRecord
the ecological database for Birmingham and the Black Country

THE wildlife TRUSTS
Birmingham & Black Country

piscespublications

Published 2013 by Pisces Publications on behalf of EcoRecord, The Wildlife Trust for Birmingham and the Black Country and the Birmingham and Black Country Botanical Society

British-Library-in-Publication Data
A catalogue record for this book is available from the British Library

ISBN 978-1-874357-55-1

Designed and published by Pisces Publications

Pisces Publications is the imprint of NatureBureau, 36 Kingfisher Court, Hambridge Road, Newbury, Berkshire RG14 5S
www .naturebureau.co.uk

Printed and bound in the UK by Gomer Press Ltd

FSC
www.fsc.org
MIX
Paper from
responsible sources
FSC® C114687

# Flora of Birmingham and the Black Country
# Contents

# Flora of Birmingham and the Black Country
# Authorship

**Chapter 1 Introduction** by Paul Reade, Ian Trueman & Mike Poulton

**Chapter 2 Wild flowers in Birmingham and the Black Country**
 Section 1 **Botanical walks** Edited by Mike Poulton & Sara Carvalho, with contributions from Sue Collingswood, Anna Coward, Anne Daly, Jane Hardwick, Simon Phipps, Paul Reade, Peter Shirley, & Ian Trueman.
 Section 2 **Finding wild flowers** Edited by Ian Trueman & Mike Poulton, with contributions from Stefan Bodnar, Peter Coxhead, Nicola Farrin, Peter Millett, Simon Phipps & John Shrimpton
 Section 3 **Neophytes (and where to see them)** by Mike Poulton
 Section 4 **A register of nature conservation sites** Edited by Ian Trueman based on EcoRecord and Natural England wildlife site information with contributions from Chris Parry, Andy Slater, Simon Atkinson, Alan Cutler and Antony Ratcliffe

**Chapter 3 Background to the Flora** edited by Peter Jarvis
 Section 1 **Geology and geodiversity** by Alan Cutler
 Section 2 **Climate** by David Mitchell
 Section 3 **Relief, drainage and soils** by John Gerrard
 Section 4 **Hydrology and water quality** by David Mitchell
 Section 5 **Habitats and vegetation** by Peter Jarvis
 Section 6 **The garden habitat** by Chris Young
 Section 7 **The history of human occupation** by Margaret Kingsbury

**Chapter 4 Exploring the flora records** Ian Trueman, with contributions from Sara Carvalho, Andy Slater & Paul Wilkinson

**Chapter 5 Fungi** by David Antrobus and Bill Moodie

**Chapter 6 Lichens** by Peter James

**Chapter 7 Bryophytes** by Martin Godfrey

**Chapter 8 Vascular plants** by Mike Poulton, Paul Reade & Ian Trueman

**Indexing** by P. Creed, P. Jarvis & the editors

# Foreword

A new Flora is always an exciting prospect, but for me this one is particularly special. Birmingham and the Black Country is one of the most industrialised areas of Britain, yet it retains within its intensely built-up environment a wealth of natural history. The richness and variety of habitats caught up within Birmingham's urban sprawl were well described in *The Endless Village* published by the Nature Conservancy Council in 1978. Indeed the case was so well made that it set the scene for a national programme of urban nature conservation that spread throughout the land. Now we have another trailblazer in the form of this new Flora, which takes our knowledge and understanding of urban ecology to new levels.

What is so special about this Flora? Firstly it makes botany accessible to ordinary people. Descriptions of local botanical walks provide an engaging introduction to the floristic possibilities that exist close to your own doorstep. These are put in context by chapters describing the main ecological features of different parts of the metropolis, which bring the whole subject to life for local residents. Added to which is a register of the best nature conservation sites, which must be a crucial appendage for anyone with an interest in local natural history.

Then there is the Flora itself with its comprehensive treatment of vascular plants. The individual entries are clearly a labour of love; so much detail packed into so small a space. Amazingly the number of species found represents 43% of the flora recorded in the whole of Britain, which gives some measure of the diversity of habitats involved. But the book also includes details of fungi, lichens, mosses and liverworts, which makes this one of the most comprehensive of local Floras.

For me a special feature is the way that plant records have been used to classify and interpret the urban landscape. Whilst much of the conurbation is predominantly sub-urban in character other parts have very different origins. Some have a strong legacy of industrialisation, whilst others owe their origins to long established semi-natural landscapes of ancient woodland, heath and even bog. The analysis shows a scattering of post-industrial landscapes throughout the urban matrix, with canals and abandoned mineral workings rich in plant diversity sitting cheek by jowl with residential and commercial districts. More natural habitats include the remarkably extensive swathe of Sutton Park, one of the most impressive examples of encapsulated countryside of any British city. But there are also many smaller patches that together provide a rich array of wildlife habitats. I could go on at great length, but urge you to read it for yourself. The maps too provide an endless source of fascination and inspiration.

Preliminary results from the new Flora have already been put to practical use. Identification of biodiversity hotspots offers possibilities for links to be made through stepping-stones and improved habitat management. This approach provided the basis for a successful bid for Birmingham and The Black Country to become a national *Nature Improvement Area,* where the aim is to improve linkages between habitats on a regional scale. That's quite a challenge, but the new Flora will help enormously.

I much enjoyed a day spent with Mike Poulton and Simon Atkinson, visiting some of the most extraordinary habitats including post-industrial landscapes of Rowley Hills, with colourful mixtures of Mullein, Mugwort, clovers and vetches; the disused and now wooded Parkhead Viaduct where Stinking Hellebore and Pale Toadflax grow between the abandoned railway tracks; vestiges of our rural past in Ploughman's-spikenard still surviving rooted in the calcareous mortar of a canal bridge at Bumblehole; and most unforgettable the two botanists assiduously recording maritime plants such as Danish Scurvygrass and some very scarce species of clover on the central reservation of a major dual-carriageway near Oldbury, despite being continuously drenched by spray from passing lorries.

I can only applaud all those involved in the production of this book, especially Professor Ian Trueman and Mike Poulton, together with Paul Reade and Sara Carvalho and a huge supporting cast. The result is a remarkable blend of meticulously detailed plant recording and a far-sighted model for the future of nature conservation in towns and cities.

*David Goode February 2013*

*Formerly Head of Environment for London and Director of the London Ecology Unit*

# Preface

At the end of the 1970s, George Barker of the then Nature Conservancy Council, Chris Baines and the other founders of the Urban Wildlife Group were already campaigning to recognise and protect the wildlife sites of Birmingham and the Black Country. In 1978 Bunny Teagle produced *The Endless Village*, a ground-breaking survey of our sites, brought up to date in 2007 by Peter Shirley supported by Ellen Pisolkar. In 1980 the Urban Wildlife Group, which in 2004 became The Wildlife Trust for Birmingham and the Black Country, was founded and its ecologists and planners, particularly Chris Parry and Mike Dando, began the task of identifying and describing all our wildlife sites. In 1991 the local biological records centre EcoRecord was founded and has since thrived.

Our book has, as its purpose, the systematic description of the botanical background to all these activities. It also lays the foundation for the conurbation to be seen and understood as an ecological entity. We recorders also wanted to celebrate its often unnoticed beauty and complexity. We hope it will give the reader as much pleasure as we have had in preparing it. We also hope, fervently, that just a few of you will be stimulated to take up this unfinished and ever-changing challenge in all the groups we have attempted to cover.

We are not the first to record the flora of Birmingham and the Black Country. The three botanical vice-counties which cover our area are vc. 39 (Staffordshire), which produced a new Flora in 2011 and involved our collaboration, vc. 38 (Warwickshire), which has a ground-breaking Flora from 1971 and an excellent wildflowers book from 2009, and vc. 37 (Worcestershire), which will also soon produce a new Flora. We have left it to these publications to celebrate the botanists of the past, many of whom recorded within the conurbation, although many of their most important records are remembered here. There is however a long tradition of biological recording in the midlands that is often forgotten and which we remember a little in chapter 1.

There is still much to do. We expect the Flora to stimulate lots of new records and there are several habitats which still require much more detailed investigation. Railways, golf courses and the remnants of our system of hedgerows come to mind, and also our national treasure, Sutton Park, which needs surveying inch by inch. This Flora is very much focused on the one kilometre square as a unit and now the vegetation of its sites needs to be thoroughly investigated. In particular we need to complete the evaluation of the remains of our very special industrial revolution before it all disappears. Perhaps most of all we need a campaign of exploration of our private gardens, possibly our last frontier, probably only to be adequately penetrated by you, its owners.

Birmingham and the Black Country is a place for people and it is people who will decide what they want and need here. We think that everyone here, from the young mother with a pushchair, to the gentlemen in high-vis jackets and safety helmets, should recognise, enhance and be able to enjoy a resilient and boundlessly diverse green background to city life.

## A message from Neil Wyatt, Chief Executive of The Wildlife Trust for Birmingham and the Black Country

I'm sitting in Edgbaston; this new Flora is the third to come out of this part of Birmingham, appropriately known as the 'place where the trees begin'. William Withering, writer of the first British Flora to follow the Linnaean system lived at Edgbaston Hall. Cadbury, Hawkes and Readett produced the first ever computer-mapped Flora, using then-revolutionary technology at Birmingham University. I should record appreciation of the work of James Bagnall, who catalogued the floras of Warwickshire and Staffordshire, but he lived far away in Aston. This new volume lives up to the standard set by its illustrious predecessors, forging a new path, combining meticulous and dedicated recording of our botanical heritage with an unprecedented level of objective interpretation that will set the standard for future Floras everywhere.

Conservation, like medicine and public policy, is at its best and most effective when our actions are based on evidence and understanding, informed by experience. Even before publication, the work carried out to produce this Flora has materially shaped the work of the Wildlife Trust and that of our partners, creating a better future for people and wildlife. Our vision for Birmingham and the Black Country is one where wildlife and the natural world are a vital, diverse and valued part of the landscape, helping clean the air, temper the climate and lift the spirits of those who live here.

So, in your hands you hold concrete proof that the wildlife of an urban area can be as diverse, surprising and rewarding to study as that of anywhere else. It shows urban habitats are not degraded shadows of their rural cousins. They are unique and fascinating, and as this Flora shows, they challenge us to understand the processes and principles that shape them.

I see this book as a gift to those who work to make the future a better place, a handbook to help us better understand the raw material with which we work – urban wildlife.

▲ 'A Lane at Hamstead, Staffordshire' by William Ellis (1747–1810). This painting depicts a location close to the very centre of Birmingham and the Black Country. The Garman Ryan Collection, The New Art Gallery Walsall.

Image courtesy of The New Art Gallery, Walsall via Wikimedia Commons

# Acknowledgements

Many people and organisations helped us in all kinds of ways in preparing this Flora, almost all without any payment or recompense, and we thank you all.

In particular EcoRecord, the Biological Records Centre for Birmingham and the Black Country, has been our mainstay throughout. In the early years Craig Slawson, then the project officer, helped us design our recording forms, organised its entry and analysed the early results. These roles were later taken on by Sara Carvalho, still later joined by Andy Slater, both of whom played a huge part in preparing the Flora for publication. Thanks are also due to the members of the EcoRecord Steering Group – volunteers, representatives of all five Local Authorities, Natural England, the Wildlife Trust and recently the Environment Agency - who have all supported our efforts for well over a decade.

The Wildlife Trust for Birmingham and Black Country, the host organisation of EcoRecord, has also been a strong supporter, allowing access to all its records, hosting practically all our indoor meetings and generally by being quietly supportive.

Generous financial support for publishing the Flora came mainly from the Birmingham Natural History Society, EcoRecord, the Black Country Living Landscapes project of The Wildlife Trust for Birmingham and Black Country and the Sutton Coldfield Natural History Society, with further generous donations from the Sandwell Valley Naturalists' Club, the Grimmitt Trust, Land Care Associates, Peter Coxhead, Andy Slater and Trueman Ecology.

We would also like to express our grateful thanks to the many EcoRecord volunteers who helped enter the data, Lynn Morgan who helped check the entries and Luke Reade of The Approach Design Group who gave crucial help with sorting the database.

Particular thanks must go to all those who were involved in collecting the records. Most of our recorders are thanked personally at the beginnings of the four Atlas chapters and we are very much in their debt. We should particularly mention the Botanical Society of the British Isles vice-county Recorders who allowed us to dismember and reassemble parts of their empires. We would particularly like to remember Bryan Fowler (vc. 39) and both Pam Copson and James Partridge (vc. 38) who all sadly died during our recording period. James in particular helped us a great deal with the recording, as has John Hawksford (vc. 39) and John Day and Bert Reid (vc. 37). A.R. 'Matt' Busby, vice-president of the British Pteridological Society, also gave us useful support. Mark Powell played a particularly important part in the Lichen chapter by working with Peter James to record Sutton Park. We feel we must also thank personally Anne Daly, Jane Hardwick and Sue Collingswood, who were out recording with enormous productivity throughout the project. Chris Parry and Paul Stephenson of the Wildlife Trust, Sue Timms and Chris Westall also contributed a huge amount of records. Rudi Pilsel made a special and abundant contribution to our photographs, for which we are particularly grateful. All our photographers and all our artists provided their photographs and drawings without charge and deserve much gratitude. We would also like to record our appreciation of Clive Stace's Flora and all the other works of identification and description which we used.

We would also like to thank the people of Birmingham and the Black Country, who tolerated our curiosity and gave us access to often private sites, always benignly (if sometimes with a little puzzlement). We would not have hoped for a nicer set of people! We wish to thank the Local Authority allotment officers, site secretaries and plot holders who supported the allotments survey.

A group which helped us patiently throughout were the BSBI specialist referees and we would particularly like to thank them. They include J.R. Akeroyd, J. Bevan, J.C. Bowra, R.K. Brummitt, J.F.M. Cannon, Arthur Chater, Eric Clement, John Day, Dr Ian Denholm, Mrs J. Fryer, A. Grenfell, John Hawksford, A.C. Jermy, V. Johnstone, S. Knapp, A.C. Leslie, Roger Maskew, Dr J. L. Mason, G.A. Matthews, D.J. McCosh, J.M. Mullin, J.R. Palmer, J. Poland, C.D. Preston, the late Rev. A.L. Primavesi, A. Radcliffe-Smith, M. Rand, the late Frances Rose, Bert Reid, Tim Rich, A.J. Richards, N.K.B. Robson, Fred Rumsey, A. Rutherford, A.J. Wilmott, B.Z. Wurzell and P.F. Yeo. We would also want to record our special thanks to Bill Thompson and Bert Reid, who sorted out *Hieracium* and *Taraxacum* for us.

Many people helped us to analyse and interpret the records and read and reviewed parts of Flora and we particularly thank EcoRecord staff, who did much more than produce maps! The list also includes Adam Atkins, Dave Bishop of Mott McDonald, Eleanor Cohn, Sue Collingswood, Lucy Bastin, Brian Dakin, James Hale, Sue Lawley, Alex Lockton, Chris Parry, Simon Phipps, Ellen Pisolkar, Lynn Poulton, Antony Ratcliffe, Peter Shirley, Paul Smith, Robin Stuttard and Neil Wyatt. Margaret Kingsbury would like to record her grateful thanks to the Local Authority Archaeologists John Hemingway, Dr Michael Hodder and Paul Quigley for their advice and help in answering her queries relating to the history chapter and also for their willingness to pass on relevant information not gleaned from her background reading; we would also like to thank them warmly.

To those we have omitted, we can only apologise. We thank them all.

We also wish to thank and apologise to our families, who have supported us for so long and so patiently in this enterprise.

# Chapter 1
# Introduction

◀ Bugle *Ajuga reptans*

## The place

This book is a celebration of the plants which spontaneously occupy Birmingham and the Black Country (B&BC), a cluster of towns and cities in the West Midlands of England (see Figure 1.1), in the centre-west of lowland Britain. For much of the book we will refer to the Birmingham and Black Country conurbation as a whole as B&BC.

▲ Figure 1.1 An outline of UK showing location of Birmingham and the Black Country

This diversity goes much further. The northern part of the City of Birmingham, Sutton Coldfield, was also an independent municipality until 1974, and in 1966 a large number of locally-beloved small towns were subsumed into the four "Black Country" Metropolitan Districts of Dudley, Sandwell, Walsall and Wolverhampton. The actual boundaries of the true Black Country lie within these four districts and are the subject of intense (and usually joyful) argument. Three nationally recognised vice-counties, the basic units for botanical recording, have borders within the conurbation: vc. 37 (Worcestershire), vc. 38 (Warwickshire) and vc. 39 (Staffordshire).

Despite all these divisions, the combination forms a whole, a continuous "endless village" (Teagle 1978). It is a business-like place; its history is focused on the industrial age, in which it has played a significant role, although many of the main centres originated as mediaeval market towns. The mineral wealth which supported its industrial age is concentrated in the Black Country, but Birmingham is the largest centre of population.

Inside the front cover is the main Flora reference map. Figure 1.2 shows vice-county and District boundaries. The Ordnance Survey Landranger 1:50,000 map no. 139 *Birmingham and Wolverhampton* covers the same area.

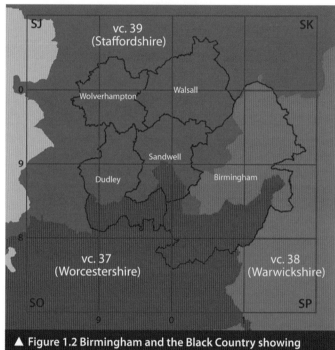

▲ Figure 1.2 Birmingham and the Black Country showing Metropolitan District and vice-county boundaries

The centre of Birmingham is at latitude 52°29′, longitude 01°52′, central Ordnance Survey grid reference SP066869. The area covered by the Flora is made up of five separate municipalities (Metropolitan Districts), each with its own local government. Populations (census 2011) and areas of these are given in Table 1.1.

The commercial centres of Birmingham, Dudley, Walsall and Wolverhampton are shown on these maps. The commercial centre of Sandwell is West Bromwich. Many of the other centres named in the Black Country such as Willenhall, Bilston, Wednesbury, Kingswinford and Stourbridge are towns in their own right; others, and most of the smaller centres in Birmingham, have their origins as rural villages.

Today, practically the entire area of B&BC is urbanised, and the urban area almost exactly lies within its outside boundaries. The major open spaces in the conurbation are concentrated in Walsall, Sutton Coldfield and the Sandwell Valley (see main Flora map). The landscape is fairly flat or only moderately undulating, although there is a well-marked ridge of high ground running between Sedgley in the north-west and Rubery and Longbridge in the south, also another area of higher ground in the area of Aldridge and Sutton Park.

### Table 1.1 Areas and populations of the districts of B&BC

| Metropolitan Districts | Population | Area (km$^2$) |
|---|---|---|
| City of Birmingham | 1,073,000 | 267.8 |
| Metropolitan Borough of Dudley | 312,900 | 97.96 |
| Metropolitan Borough of Sandwell | 308,100 | 85.58 |
| Metropolitan Borough of Walsall | 269,300 | 104 |
| City of Wolverhampton | 249,500 | 69.44 |

B&BC is at a central point in the transport systems of the British Isles: major roads, canals and railways linking south and north Britain pass through it. In the 20th century the motorway system also developed a central junction within the conurbation.

Opinions on our area have often been rather mixed! In 1813, at the age of about 13 years, the girl later to become Queen Victoria wrote about the Black Country in her diary:

"The men, women, children, country and houses are all black….The country is very desolate. Everywhere….The grass is quite blasted and black. Just now I saw an extraordinary building flaming with fire. The country continues black, engines flaming, coals, in abundance, everywhere smoking and burning coal heaps, intermingled with wretched huts and carts and little ragged children."

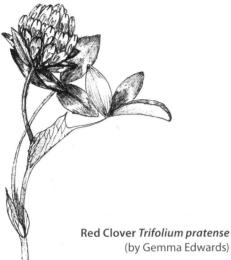

Red Clover *Trifolium pratense* (by Gemma Edwards)

▲ Guelder-rose *Viburnum opulus*

▲ Russell Lupin *Lupinus × regalis*

## The Flora

The Flora is essentially a survey. The unit of the survey is the one kilometre square of the Ordnance Survey National Grid. This is a smaller unit than the usual one in a vice-county Flora, but B&BC is a smaller area than a vice-county and the 'texture' of the landscape is particularly fine and detailed in the urban environment. The current (2012) political boundaries of the five Districts forming the conurbation impinge on about 717 one kilometre squares (henceforth referred to as 'monads'), but there are only recordable areas in 715 monads, which have all been surveyed for the Flora. More information about the recording structure and timing is given in the Atlas chapters, but the period for records started in January 1995 and ended in December 2012.

In **Chapter 2 – Wild flowers in Birmingham and the Black Country**, our objective is to introduce the best botanical sites in B&BC. A great deal of work remains to be done before we can refer all our sites to the National Vegetation Classification (Rodwell 1991–2000) so the sites are introduced in general terms. Also we are particularly keen to attract newcomers to botany with this chapter. All plants are described using their English names. Section 1 *Botanical walks* is a selection of sites described by means of guided walks in which many key plants are introduced. In section 2 *Finding wild flowers* we first attempt to describe the plants of our two largest continuous sites, Sutton Park and Sandwell Valley. The second section continues with a brief description of the botanical treasures of each of the five municipalities. One particular source of interest in populated areas is the plants which are coming out of cultivation or which have been recently establishing themselves in the wild by other means. These are often given little attention in surveys such as our section 2, so

▲ Gooseberry *Ribes uva-crispa*

▲ Harebell *Campanula rotundifolia*

section 3 **Neophytes** deals with them specifically. The chapter ends with section 4 ***A register of nature conservation sites,*** a brief inventory, District by District, of all the sites in B&BC which have been given national statutory protection, plus the upper tier of non-statutory sites which have been locally selected and approved as sites of wildlife interest, the so-called Sites of Importance for Nature Conservation (the SINCs).

**Chapter 3 – The background to the Flora** is an exploration, topic by topic, of a selection of the physical and biological factors behind the distribution of our flora. The presentation is necessarily more technical than in chapter 2 but we have tried to make the information understandable to the non-specialist. Section 1 ***Geology and geodiversity*** shows its profound influence on almost everything in the conurbation. Section 2 ***Climate*** describes our climate in general terms and also deals with variation in climatic factors at the monad level within the conurbation. Section 3 ***Relief, drainage and soils*** discusses their variation across the conurbation, and Section 4 ***Hydrology and water quality*** focuses on our river systems**.** Section 5 ***Habitats and vegetation*** is a survey of the habitats which occur in the conurbation and the types of vegetation which may be found there. The garden is a ubiquitous, ever-varying habitat which is very difficult to survey systematically. We have given it its own section 6 ***The garden habitat***. Finally we study the profound influence of human beings on the flora by exploring the history of the landscape in section 7 ***The history of human occupation***.

A principal outcome of the Flora project has been the huge set of analysable data. The database amounts to more than 240,000 records over the recording period, but when these are reduced to monad records of the 1449 species, hybrids and mappable subspecies, there are 128,361 monad records spread over 715 monads.

These data have been subjected to some simple analysis in **Chapter 4 – Exploring the Flora records.** In section 1 ***The botany of the urban landscape*** the data is used to describe types of monad, map them and evaluate the patterns shown. Section 2 ***Influences on the urban landscape*** examines the contribution of some influences such as geology and some habitat types such as canals and rivers to the botany of the urban landscape. In section 3 ***Implications of the analysis*** the significance of these investigations for conservation is discussed. This chapter has to mention the names of many scientifically identifiable plants and therefore Latin names are used throughout.

The rest of the Flora is taken up with the species Atlases. The project has concentrated on the so-called vascular plants: Flowering Plants, Conifers, Ferns, Horsetails and Clubmosses. However, in the conurbation, there is much data available for the other groups, and more has been collected for the present Flora so it has been possible to assemble checklists as a first step in describing the distribution of three further groups of plants and plant-like organisms.

In **Chapter 5 Fungi, Chapter 6 Lichens** and **Chapter 7 Bryophytes**, specialists in the groups present information about all the species and subspecific categories known from B&BC.

In **Chapter 8**, following an introduction to the recording scheme, with the exception of some critical groups and arrays of microspecies, the distribution and ecology of every vascular plant species, interspecific hybrid and many subspecies and varieties recorded from B&BC are described. All except the commonest and rarest are mapped at the monad level.

The Flora ends with a gazetteer and separate species indexes to the four Atlases.

## Bygone days of this fair field (by Paul Reade)

The present *Flora of Birmingham and the Black Country*, a first for the area, was made possible only by the collaboration of numerous individuals, many of whom are members of local societies and institutions. They gave generously of their time and knowledge so that their investigations could be put together in one place and published for the benefit of conservation and interested persons. While this Flora may be a first, a collaboration of similar sorts has happened here before: coming into being during the 1870s and encompassing a much larger region and a wider field of investigation. This was the Midland Union of Natural History Societies and their journal was called *The Midland Naturalist*. The subtitle of early volumes refers to this group as the Associated Natural History, Philosophical, and Archaeological Societies and Field Clubs of the Midland Counties.

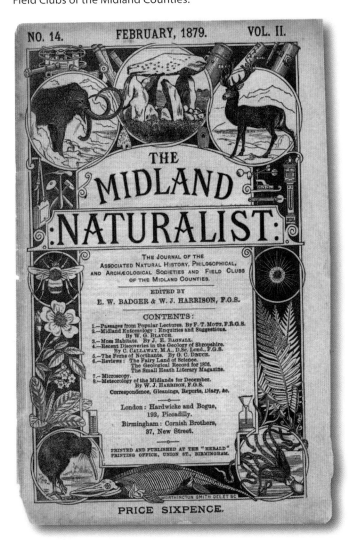

▲ Wild Daffodil *Narcissus pseudonarcissus*

In the Opening Address of the first volume of *The Midland Naturalist*, January 1878, there are listed seventeen societies already in the newly formed Midland Union of Natural History Societies. They are all listed below, together with four which joined later the same year.

Birmingham and Midland Institute Scientific Society.
Birmingham Natural History and Microscopical Society.
Birmingham Philosophical Society.
Birmingham School Natural History Society.
Burton-on-Trent Natural History and Archaeological Society.

▲ Bogbean *Menyanthes trifoliata*

▲ Herb-Paris *Paris quadrifolia*

▲ Bog Asphodel *Narthecium ossifragum*

Caradoc Field Club.
Cheltenham Natural Science Society.
Derbyshire Naturalists' Society.
Dudley and Midland Geological and Philosophical
Society and Field Club.
Evesham Field Naturalists Club.
Leicester Literary and Philosophical Society.
Northampton Naturalists' Society.
Nottingham Literary and Philosophical Society.
Nottingham Naturalists' Society.
Rugby School Natural History Society.
Oswestry and Welshpool Naturalists' Field Club.
Severn Valley Naturalists' Field Club.
Shropshire Archaeological and Natural History Society.
Stroud Natural History and Philosophical Society.
Tamworth Natural History, Geological, and Antiquarian Society.
Woolhope Naturalists' Field Club.

Many of these organisations persist to this day, but at that time
it was not uncommon for a field excursion to attract hundreds of
participants.

There follow a few snippets of botanical interest from an
assemblage of early copies of the Journal. Equivalent modern plant
names are given in square brackets.

Mathews (1888a) quotes an interesting record of Herb-Paris *Paris
quadrifolia* growing near Dudley Castle prior to 1825. It is in a fine
list of plants, referred to as 'the first collected record of the plants of
Castle Hill', from an 1825 publication, "A Descriptive and Historical
Account of Dudley Castle and its surrounding scenery" by the Rev.
Luke Booker, LL.D. This is the only account of this ancient woodland
species of calcareous ground which we have in B&BC. It was
growing on a limestone hill that had been quarried for centuries,
surely a hanger-on from an earlier time, a time before the industry,
before the spread of the town, a plant from a truly ancient wood.

Clues to what grew here in the 19th century lie with our
axiophytes, which are listed in Chapter 4 where the concept is
explained. Today they can be thought of as plants indicating
where the old vegetation is hanging on, places where these
species have enjoyed unbroken residence throughout the many
decades of upheaval around them. It follows therefore that old
records and accounts of axiophytes are showing us the greater
extent this vegetation had in the past. A good example is The
Lemon-scented Fern *Oreopteris limbosperma* which today has just
two extant sites (probably only two individual plants); looking
back into the 20th century we find there are a few more records,
and further back into the 19th century it is "fairly abundant" as this
next extract from the Midland Naturalist shows.

"*Nephrodium oreopteris* [*Oreopteris limbosperma*] was recorded
by Bree from near Coleshill and Allesley, in 1818, *vide* Purton's
*Midland Flora*, Vol. II., page 508. As a Warwickshire plant it may be
considered as comparatively rare now; twelve years ago [1868] it
was fairly abundant on marly soils all round Birmingham, more
especially in Sutton Park. I still find it in Bree's old districts, and in
the Middleton and Kingsbury districts." (Bagnall, 1880).

The next extract celebrates the glorious past of what we now
know, as a remnant, as Moseley Bog.

"About a mile to the south-east of Moseley Church, but in the
parish of Yardley, was an open tract of common, partly covered
with bog, called Moseley Common, the remnant of a still larger
tract, known as Moseley Wake Green. It produced some of the
rarest plants in the county, such as *Drosera rotundifolia*, *Radiola
millegrana* [*R. linoides*], *Hypericum elodes*, *Parnassia palustris*, *Carduus
pratensis* [*Cirsium dissectum*], *Vaccinium oxycoccos*, *Menyanthes
trifoliata*, *Scutellaria minor*, *Anagallis tenella*, *Centunculus minimus*,

*Narthecium ossifragum, Rhynchospora alba, Eriophorum vaginatum, Osmunda regalis, Lycopodium selago [Huperzia selago]*[1]. The Commons Preservation Society not being that time in existence, the Common was enclosed and drained in or about the year 1842, and all its characteristic plants destroyed." (Mathews, 1888b).

Nowadays we continue to lose habitats to both development and neglect, but in the past collecting was as big a threat as these. There were a number of exchange clubs that existed so that members could fill their herbariums with rarities. Then as now, there were conservationists who took steps to mitigate the damage. Things were discussed in 1884: "Some time ago I brought before the members of the Birmingham Natural History and Microscopical Society the subject of the reckless Vandalism which threatens many of our native plants with speedy extermination, and the subject having been referred to the Committee, Mr. W.R. Hughes, F.L.S., and myself [A.W. Wills] were deputed to attend the recent meeting of the Midland Union at Peterborough in order to urge upon the Council the importance of taking such steps as might appear practicable in order to arrest, if possible, the progress of this destruction." (Wills, 1884)

"Again, in the markets of our own and of other large towns even the commoner plants of the district are daily exposed for sale by hundreds, usually in full leaf or flower, so that the lanes and hedgerows for miles round are completely stripped, and even the Daffodil and the Male Fern have become scarce." (Wills, 1884).

"The large dimensions which this traffic has assumed are indicated by the number of such advertisements which appear in some of the gardening periodicals, offering ferns from Devonshire, Cornwall, Somerset, the Wye Valley, &c., at from 4s. to 7s. 6d. per 100, in named varieties; *Hymenophyllum tunbridgense* and *H. unilaterale* [*H. wilsonii*][2] at 2s. per square foot; various species of Orchis, Saxifrage, &c., at from 2s. to 5s. per 100; Bog Asphodel at 2s. per doz.; or inviting tenders for Primroses and Daffodils at so much per 100,000." (Anon., 1885).

Then this appeal was published in 1885.

"They [Council of the Midland Union] therefore earnestly urge the following considerations upon botanists, members of Field Clubs, Natural History and other Scientific Societies, upon all lovers of nature and upon the public generally:

First. – That they should rigidly abstain from encouraging or countenancing the purchase from professional plant-hunters of any native plant, for the sake either of their rarity or of their decorative value.

Second. – That botanists should resort to the assistance of Exchange Clubs, if at all, only for the purpose of obtaining single specimens necessary to fill up blanks in their herbaria, using such assistance with discrimination, and excluding from their operations plants of great rarity.

Third. – That all teachers should inculcate upon their pupils, by precept and example, the lamentable consequences of the wholesale or indiscriminate gathering of plants, especially with their roots or when in seed.

Fourth. – That individual botanists should seriously reflect on these consequences, and abstain from taking more than the smallest number of specimens indispensible for the purpose of genuine study, and even from taking any where the extermination of a particular species from a restricted habitat is threatened.

Fifth. – That tourists and amateurs should be urged to refrain from collecting plants of any degree of scarcity, especially when in flower or seed, it being impossible that ten per cent. of those gathered under such conditions can possibly live after removal.

Finally, the Council earnestly appeals to the editors of all journals devoted to Science and Art as well as to Horticulture and Floriculture and to those of the leading London and provincial papers to assist it in creating a healthy public opinion on this subject by the expression of their sympathy with the effort which the Council is making, and by refusing insertion to advertisements from professional plant-hunters." (Anon., 1885).

Here is a heart-felt exposition of the joys of natural history: "Each creature that swims in the waters of our noble river, each flower that blooms on its banks, each hill that looks out over its verdant meadows, is a microcosm of wonders; and as the prophet beheld horses of fire and chariots of fire where the common eye saw nothing, so the true student of nature expatiates in a world of beauty and marvel which is invisible to the untrained sense. A Newton perceives laws where other men had seen only aimless motions. To a Darwin, a buttercup is a wonder whose glory derives a tenfold charm from the mysteries which still lie hidden in its nectaries or its carpels, but to most men it is a buttercup and nothing more. Surely it is worth making an effort to penetrate the secrets which hide themselves in the common objects that lie about us." (Callaway, 1889).

Henry Boyden (1886) gave this account of the River Rea: "From careful investigation of the locality, and personal enquiries among old residents, I came to the conclusion that the [River] Rea has its highest source in a spring which rises midway on one of the Lickey hills, popularly called "The Shoulder of Mutton Hill," approached by a narrow footpath through the cultivated fields of Wetty Farm. The water from the spring trickles down by the side of a hedge, disappears underground, accumulates by a field drain, emerges in its descent towards Rubery, flowing through the village parallel with the Bromsgrove Road, and then round by the Lunatic Asylum, till it is joined midway between Rubery and Long Bridge by a babbling tributary. This takes it rise at the foot of a field descending from Frankley Beeches, flowing through a deep, narrow, shrub-entangled dingle; receiving on its right bank the waters discharged from a drain-pipe, passing in a tortuous course through woods, and then by the railway, till it joins the Rea. After this junction the Rea flows on as a conspicuous stream beneath Long Bridge, through Northfield, King's Norton, and Lifford, receiving at the Pebble Mill, Pershore Road, the tributary stream of Bournbrook, and passing there out of the county of Worcester into Warwickshire. From thence it flows by Cannon Hill and Calthorpe Park, where it enters on its town conditions, unfavourable to the Botanist, and passes through the older part of Birmingham across Deritend, to join the Tame in the neighbourhood of Aston. The Tame, thus augmented, flows into the Trent beyond Tamworth, near to Croxall, and this finds its way into the estuary of the Humber, and so into the North Sea."

"I said that the Rea enters on its town conditions where it leaves Calthorpe Park, and this reminds me of the rapid growth of the town in this direction; for I can remember when the river was crossed by stepping stones where the Gooch Street Bridge now stands; when Barford Street was barred by gates, beyond which were Dester's fields, where I gathered my first wild-flowers, now the populous parish under my ministerial charge; when snipe were shot in the marshy places that became Bishop Street; and when the Rea ran betwixt smiling meadows till it reached the old Apollo Gardens of Moseley Street. But if we consult maps dated 1731, copies of which we can see in Dr. Langford's "Century of Birmingham Life," we shall find that the Rea was a country river

---

[1] The English names for these species, in the same order are: Round-leaved Sundew, Allseed, Marsh St John's-wort, Grass-of-Parnassus, Meadow Thistle, Cranberry, Bogbean, Lesser Skullcap, Bog Pimpernel, Chaffweed, Bog Asphodel, White Beak-sedge, Hare's-tail Cottongrass, Royal Fern and Fir Clubmoss, all of which are nowadays rare or absent in B&BC.
[2] Tunbridge Filmy-fern and Wilson's Filmy-fern

▲ Meadow Saffron *Colchicum autumnale*

▲ Small Teasel *Dipsacus pilosus*

through nearly the whole of its course, the main street of Deritend being the only strip of town that intervened; we shall see meadows by Deritend Chapel, divided by hedgerows, diversified by trees, rendered picturesque by an occasional homestead and a windmill, and personally interesting by the couples who stroll on the banks of the Rea in the summer gloaming." (Boyden, 1886).

Some of the flora Henry Boyden observed in the Rea Valley: "The Pebble Mill Pool is a station that is doomed to pass away, as it is being gradually filled up – a loss to the botanist, but a gain to society, as the scene of some suicides and pregnant with malaria. If thoroughly searched its yield, I think, would be good. I have obtained there *Nymphaea alba*, though not in flower; *Nasturtium amphibium* [*Rorippa amphibia*], of luxuriant growth; *Lychnis githago* [*Agrostemma githago*], a colonist; *Artemisia vulgaris*; *Iris pseudacorus*, the Yellow Flag; *Carex riparia*; and of grasses, *Digraphis arundinacea* [*Phalaris arundinacea*] and *Phalaris canariensis*."[3] (Boyden, 1886).

"The Dog Pool Lane and adjoining fields have supplied me, among other plants, with *Orobus tuberosus* [*Lathyrus linifolius*], *Prunus domestica*, *Adoxa moschatellina*, *Dipsacus pilosus*, the Shepherd's Teazle, *Petasites vulgaris* [*P. hybridus*], frequent along the sandy banks of the Rea; and *Colchicum autumnale*, the Meadow Saffron."[4] (Boyden, 1886).

"Among many plants obtained there [Northfield] I select for mention *Ranunculus aquatilis*, *R. sceleratus*, *R. arvensis*, *Cardamine amara*, a good local plant; *Chelidonium majus*, *Lychnis vespertina* [*Silene latifolia*], common, but rare in the Rea Valley; *Malva moschata*, *Pyrus malus* [*Malus sylvestris*], *Circaea lutetiana*, *Sedum acre*, *Centaurea cyanus*, a colonist; *Achillea ptarmica*, *Hieracium umbellatum*, rare; *Campanula latifolia*, the Giant Bell Flower, abundant and luxuriant on the railway bank; *Convolvulus sepium* [*Calystegia sepium*], *Orchis maculata*, *Listera ovata* [now *Neottia ovata*], and *Narcissus pseudo-narcissus*, the latter a common plant which deserves special mention here as giving a name to a locality, – the Daffodil Fields – meadows on either side of the Rea, made golden by a profusion of these glorious wild flowers, these early gleams of a returning spring. Of the grasses of this district I would name *Aira caespitosa* [*Deschampsia cespitosa*], *Melica uniflora*, *Triticum caninum* [*Elymus caninus*], and *T. repens* [*Elytrigia repens*][5]. Several members of the Society also report the Snowdrop for this locality." (Boyden, 1886).

Cannon Hill Park: "As soon as the site of the garden [Students' Garden, Cannon Hill Park] was decided upon I saw that the pool adjoining would form a very valuable adjunct, and that not only aquatic but possibly also marsh and bog plants might be grown there. Accordingly a series of 'pockets' have been constructed around the margin of the pool, and these, as well as the 'bays' between them, will, I hope, soon be stocked with water-loving plants. The naming of the trees and shrubs, too, was a part of my original suggestion to the Park Committee, and the labels are in course of preparation. They will give the botanical and common names, together with the natural order and the countries of which the tree or shrub is native, so that while helpful to the student

---

[3] These plants, in order, have the English names: White Water-lily, Great Yellow-cress, Corncockle, Mugwort, Yellow Iris (or Yellow Flag), Greater Pond-sedge, Reed Canary-grass and Canary-grass.

[4] These are Bitter-vetch, Wild Plum, Moschatel, Small Teasel, Butterbur and Meadow Saffron.

[5] The species from Northfield, in order, have the following English names: Common Water-crowfoot, Celery-leaved Buttercup, Corn Buttercup, Large Bittercress, Greater Celandine, White Campion, Musk Mallow, Crab Apple, Enchanter's-nightshade, Biting Stonecrop, Cornflower, Sneezewort, a Hawkweed, Giant Bellflower, Field Bindweed, Heath Spotted-orchid, Common Twayblade, Wild Daffodil, Tufted Hair-grass, Wood Melick, Bearded Couch and Common Couch.

of botany it is hoped that they may also prove instructive and interesting to the general visitor." (Oliver, 1886).

Some old records of Fungi: "I was surprised to-day, on examining some fungi, collected at Sutton last March [1884], to find that one of them was a species of *Helminthosporium*, new to Great Britain. It resembles *H. hirudo*, Sacc. (Fung. Ital. 54), but differs in being nearly twice as large; the spores are about 400μ long, very dark, with about 60 septa. I propose to name it var. *Anglicum*." (Grove, 1885).

"A not uncommon species, according to my experience, is *Boletus badius*; it occurs in large quantities in Sutton Park, and at Bradnock's Hays, Middleton, Coleshill Pool, Streetley, Hints, Edgebaston Park, and the Lickey Hills it can be found sometimes in considerable numbers. This is the species referred to as not being currently reputed edible, and it must be confessed that the disagreeable blue-green tint assumed by the pores (and to a less extent by the flesh) on touching them is not at all inviting. This discoloration, however, passes away in a short time. By itself, this fungus is not to be recommended, but its thick and substantial flesh makes it a welcome addition to that mixture of species in which the confirmed fungus-eater usually indulges. Cooked with a quantity of [edibles], such as can nearly always be gathered at the same time and place, it makes a delicious dish. The tubes and stem should be removed (the tubes separate remarkably easily), and the pileus cut into slices as one would cut a loaf of bread, and fried in the rich liquor yielded by the other species and a lump of butter; pepper and salt to taste." (Grove, 1886).

Next, an early account by Bagnall (1881) of the moss *Dicranum montanum* from 1870. Despite the name, it is a lowland species.

"On Saturday, April 16th [1881], whilst searching in some of the woods near Coventry for Hepaticae, I came across a fine growth of the rare moss, *Dicranum montanum*. This moss I first found, in 1870, in Sutton Park; it was then new to the British Flora, and for some little time the Sutton Park locality was the only known British station. Subsequently, Mr. E.M. Holmes, one of the most indefatigable of English Bryologists, found it in Abbey Wood, Kent, from whence he sent me nice specimens."

"Unfortunately, in 1871, the oak upon which this moss was abundant in Sutton Park was felled, and so my first station was destroyed; the same year, however, I found it sparingly on another oak near to the original station, and here I saw it, still growing sparingly, a few days since."

Its spread in recent years may have been a response to acid rain (Hill *et. al.*, 1992); was the same happening in the 1870s due to the coal smoke of industry?

Today atmospheric pollution is on the decline and because of this we are starting to see a return to our area of Lichen species that have had a long absence. Just how long is illustrated by this advice given to the reader in August of 1880.

"Where to collect Lichens will now require a few remarks. Supposing the student to have provided himself with the necessary appliances just enumerated, he will now undertake his first excursion in pursuit of specimens. He must get well away into the country, at a distance from towns and smoke, for the Lichens loves pure air and free ventilation. It has long since been remarked that they rarely, if ever, attain their perfect maturity in the vicinity of cities or manufactories, where much smoke is found in the atmosphere." (Phillips, 1880).

"*Lycopodium clavatum*[6] has also been found in this locality by Miss Ethel Stone, of Erdington, a young lady who takes great interest in botanical science, and whose more keen observation has enabled her to find a plant for which I have searched hitherto

---

[6] *Lycopodium clavatum* has the English name Stag's-horn Clubmoss

in vain. *Lycopodium clavatum* is recorded for 'Sutton' by Samuel Freeman in the *Phytologist* for July, 1842, page 262, but as Miss Stone had never heard of this record her discovery of the plant in Sutton Park is as truly an original one as was Freeman's." (Bagnall, 1885).

The absence of algae in the present flora is to its detriment. Luckily Wills (1880) has left us with a list of the most noble gentlemen in all of botany, the Desmids...

List of Desmidieae Found in Sutton Park, Warwickshire [published in 1880].
(* species not hitherto recorded in England)

*Hyalotheca*
　*dissiliens, mucosa*
*Didymoprium*
　*borreri* [*Bambusina borreri*], *grevillei* [*Desmidium grevillei*]
*Desmidium shwartzii*
*Sphaerozosma excavatum* [*Teilingia excavata*]
*Micrasterias*
　*americana, angulosa** [*denticulata*], *crenata, crux-melitensis,*
　*denticulata, fimbriata, jenneri, papillifera, rotata, truncata*
*Euastrum*
　*ansatum, binale, didelta, elegans, oblongum, rostratum*
　[*bidentatum*], *verrucosum*
*Cosmarium*
　*bioculatum, biretum, botrytis, brebissonii, conspersum, cucumis,*
　*cucurbita* [*Actinotaenium cucurbita*], *margaritiferum,*
　*pyramidatum, pseudopyramidatum**, *ralfsii, tinctum, undulatum*
*Xanthidium*
　*armatum, cristatum*
*Arthrodesmus*
　*convergens* [*Staurodesmus convergens*], *incus* [*Staurodesmus incus*]
*Staurastrum*
　*asperum, dejectum* [*Staurodesmus dejectus*], *dilatatum, hirsutum,*
　*margaritaceum, muricatum* [*hirsutum var. muricatum*], *muticum,*
　*orbiculare, polymorphum, punctulatum, sexcostatum, spinosum*
　[*furcatum*], *spongiosum*
*Tetmemorus*
　*brebissonii, granulatus, laevis*
*Penium*
　*brebissonii* [*Cylindrocystis brebissonii*], *closterioides* [*Closterium*
　*closterioides*], *cylindrus, digitus* [*Netrium digitus*], *interruptum*
　[*Netrium interuptum*], *jenneri, margaritaceum, nägelii** [*Netrium*
　*naegelii*], *navicula** [*Closterium navicula*]
*Docidium*
　*clavatum* [*Pleurotaenium clavatum*], *ehrenbergii* [*Pleurotaenium*
　*ehrenbergii*], *nodulosum* [*Pleurotaenium nodulosum*], *truncatum*
　[*Pleurotaenium truncatum*]
*Closterium*
　*acerosum, acutum, attenuatum, cornu, costatum, dianae,*
　*didymotocum var. baileyanum* [*baileyanum*], *directum**,
　*intermedium, juncidum, leibleinii, lineatum, lunula,*
　*pritchardianum**, *rostratum, setaceum, striolatum*
*Spirotaenia*
　*condensata, obscura* [*Tortitaena obscura*]
*Pediastrum*
　*boryanum, tetras*
*Scenedesmus*
　*obliquus* [*Acutodesmus obliquus*], *obtusus, quadricauda*
　[*Desmodesmus communis*]

The modern names (in square brackets) are from John *et al.* (2011) with additional species from Guiry & Guiry (2013).

▲ **Lesser Celandine** *Ficaria verna*

## References

Anon. (1885) Appeal. *The Midland Naturalist* VIII: 227.

Bagnall, J.E. (1880) *Nephrodium oreopteris. The Midland Naturalist* III: 202.

Bagnall, J.E. (1881) *Dicranum montanum*, New Warwickshire Habitat. *The Midland Naturalist* IV: 116.

Bagnall, J.E. (1885) Additions to the Flora of Sutton Park. *The Midland Naturalist* VIII: 56.

Boyden, H. (1886) Notes on the River Rea and the Flora of the Rea Valley. *The Midland Naturalist* IX: 150.

Callaway, C.H. (1889) The work of field clubs. *The Midland Naturalist* XII: 109.

Caswell, J. (1880) Notes from Oscott College. *The Midland Naturalist* III: 119.

Hill *et al.* (1992) *Atlas of the Bryophytes of Britain and Ireland Volume 2 Mosses (except Diplolepideae)* p. 161. B. H. & A. Harley Ltd., Colchester, Essex for the British Bryological Society.

Grove, W.B., (1885) New British Fungi. *The Midland Naturalist* VIII: 269.

Grove, W.B. (1886) The Boleti of the Birmingham District. *The Midland Naturalist* IX: 264.

Guiry, M.D. & Guiry, G.M. (2013) AlgaeBase. World-wide electronic publication, National University of Ireland, Galway. http://www.algaebase.org; searched on 30 January 2013.

John, D.M., Whitton, B.A. & Brook, A.J. (eds) (2011) *The Freshwater Algal Flora of the British Isles*. Second edition. Cambridge University Press, Cambridge.

Mathews, W.M. (1888a) History of the County Botany of Worcester. *The Midland Naturalist* XI: 57.

Mathews, W.M. (1888b) History of the County Botany of Worcester. *The Midland Naturalist* XI: 303.

Oliver, J.W. (1886) Students' Garden, Cannon Hill Park. *The Midland Naturalist* IX: 225.

Phillips, W. (1880) British Lichens: How To Study Them. *The Midland Naturalist* III: 196.

Rodwell, J.S. (1991–2000) *British Plant Communities Vols. 1–5*. Cambridge University Press, Cambridge.

Teagle, W.G., (1978) *The Endless Village: The Wildlife of Birmingham, Dudley, Sandwell, Walsall and Wolverhampton*. Nature Conservancy Council, West Midlands Region, Attingham Park, Shropshire.

Wills, A.W. (1880) List of Desmidieae Found in Sutton Park, Warwickshire. *The Midland Naturalist* III: 265.

Wills, A.W. (1884) The Preservation of Native plants. *The Midland Naturalist* VII: 209.

"Notes from Oscott College [Chester Road, Sutton Coldfield. May 1880]. – The cold of the last fortnight has somewhat checked the opening buds, and it will be some time before the trees are fully out. The Larch, Chestnut, and Lime show signs of returning summer; but the Beech, Oak, and Ash are very backward, and it will be some weeks before they are fully out. The following are the notes recorded for the month:– March 21st [1880], Thrush's nest with eggs, Humble Bee seen, Daffodil and Jonquil in flower; 23rd, Honey and Sand Bees seen, Willow and Furze in flower; 26th, Shepherd's Purse in flower, *Vanessa urticae* [Small Tortoiseshell] seen; 29th, Dandelion, Strawberry-leaved Cinquefoil, White and Purple Dead-Nettle, Musk Ivy [Ground Ivy?], Lesser Celandine, Marsh Marigold, Whitlow Grass, Golden Saxifrage, Ivy-leaved Veronica and Osier in flower, Chiff-chaff singing; 30th, several Vanessa, Common White, and Brimstone Butterflies seen; April 5th, Pansy and Lady's Mantle in flower, Swallow first seen; 8th, two Swifts seen; 18th, Sand Martins seen; 20th, Garden Warbler seen and heard singing, House Martin seen, Cuckoo heard; 24th, *Cerastium arvense* and *Prunus avium*[7] in flower." (Caswell, 1880).

And to end with, this is recorded in the *Midland Naturalist* volume I, page 174…

"Our midland district is rich in the objects of the study of the Botanist and Zoologist; their branches of natural science are within the reach of every one, and the favourite pursuits of many. Of the almost infinite variety of vegetable and animal life, afforded by this fair field, much is unrecorded; aid in supplying this deficiency." – from the Inaugural Address of the President of the Union, Mr Edmund Tonks, B.C.L., read at the first general meeting of the Associated Natural History, Philosophical, and Archaeological Societies and Field Clubs of the Midland Counties, in the Lecture Theatre of the Birmingham and Midland Institute, on Monday, 27 May 1878.

It is still resonant today.

---

[7] Field Mouse-ear and Wild Cherry

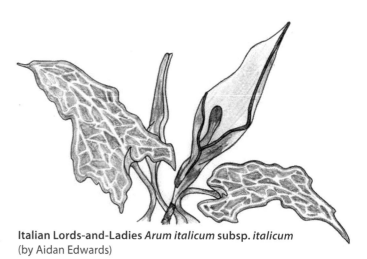

**Italian Lords-and-Ladies** *Arum italicum* **subsp.** *italicum*
(by Aidan Edwards)

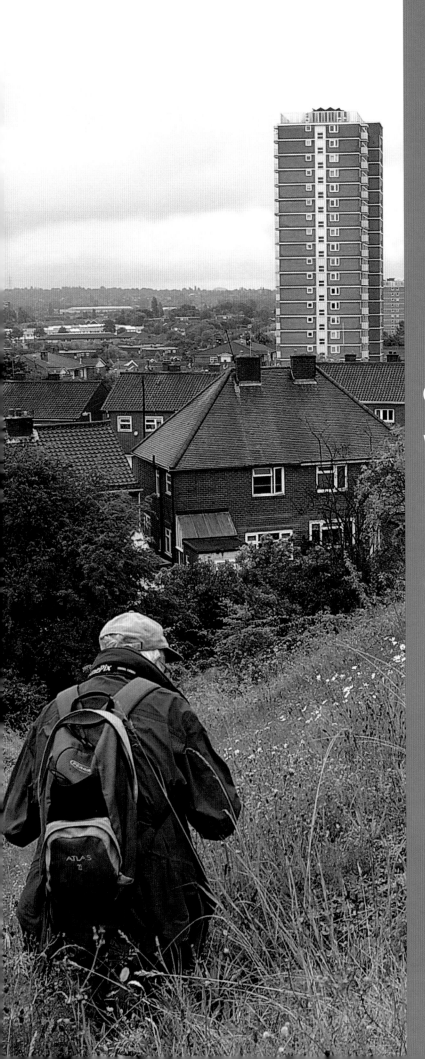

# Chapter 2

# Wild flowers in Birmingham and the Black Country

# Section 1 • Botanical walks

This section is an invitation to readers to 'dip their toes' into the amazing botanical wealth present in Birmingham and the Black Country and see its relationship with heritage and its wider value and significance generally. The invitation takes the form of 'conducted tours' of some especially chosen beauty spots right across the conurbation. They are all of interest the year round, but obviously many of the plants named have their own seasons and will not always be apparent. In most cases the wonderful ability of semi-natural sites to change as the year progresses and reveal a succession of treasures means that many visits at different seasons will be equally enjoyed.

We hope that you enjoy your visits and the observations of our contributors, and that some of you will find this an irresistible introduction to the rest of our book and to a deeper knowledge about the bottomless store of natural diversity which is present all around us!

The information given generally refers to features visible at different times of the year, however, what you will see will be determined to some extent by the season of your visit.

The sites in this chapter have been carefully chosen for your enjoyment, however, many do not have surfaced pathways and shelter is limited, so please wear suitable footwear and clothing. There are no public toilets on most sites. Most sites are also unlit, so time your visit to avoid getting caught out at dusk. Help may not be on hand in the event of illness or injury, so it makes sense to enjoy your visit with a companion. The authors accept no responsibility for any loss or injury, howsoever caused, to anyone visiting any of the sites included in this book.

The information included in this chapter has been produced in good faith, however, we cannot guarantee all information is accurate and recommend that parking, facilities etc. are checked in advance of any visit. Site maps have been produced for site location purposes only, and do not necessarily reflect the true extent of the publicly accessible site. No legal right of access is inferred by the site location maps.

Although every effort has been made to ensure that all parts of the walks are accessible, this may have changed by the time the book is published and access may have changed or no longer be possible.

# STUBBERS GREEN CANAL – SHORT WALK

## Description
The canal towpath and marginal vegetation along this short stretch of canal is at its floral best during June and July and involves walking from Hopley's Bridge to the bridge on Stubbers Green Road and back.

**Distance and walking time** Approximately ¾ mile. The walk takes about 1 hour at a gentle pace.

**Starting point** Hopley's Bridge (OS grid reference: SK046009).

**Parking** There is roadside parking in Dumblederry Lane, situated north-west of the crossroads with Westgate.

**Getting there by public transport** Bus routes 935A and 35 (Walsall) stop in nearby Wharf Approach.

**Access/conditions** The towpath is in good condition making this an easy walk.

**Facilities and further information** None

## THE WALK

→ **Approach the bridge ❶ and take the grassy path to its right to gain access to the canal-side. Turn left (east) at the canal-side and walk along the towpath to the next bridge ❷ then return.**

There is a selection of emergent and moisture-loving species in the margins of the canal and in its column (the built edge of the canal). Species preferring drier situations should be sought on the other side of the path from the canal – so you could look to one side going out and to the other when returning.

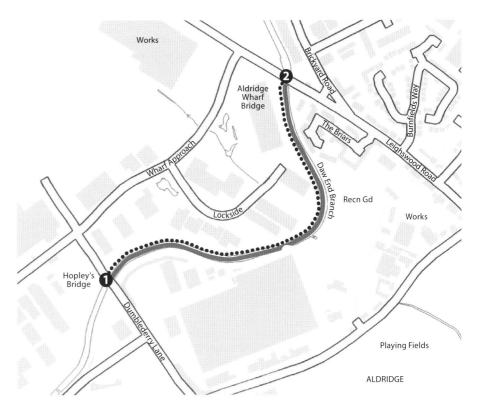

On the canal side look for Southern Marsh-orchid, Branched Bur-reed, Arrowhead, Shining Pondweed, Skullcap, Yellow Water-lily, Marsh Thistle, Water Dock, Yellow Iris, False Fox-sedge, Hemlock Water-dropwort, Meadowsweet, Clustered Dock, Remote Sedge, Narrow-leaved Water-plantain, Water Mint, Reed Sweet-grass, Cyperus Sedge, Hemp-agrimony and Water Forget-me-not among others.

On the hedge side of the towpath are American and Great Willowherb, Oxeye Daisy, Fairy Flax, Perennial Sowthistle, Common Centaury, Hedge Bedstraw, Common Ragwort, Red Clover, Goat's-beard, Common Bird's-foot-trefoil, and Hedgerow Crane's-bill among others.

### Species mentioned in the text
Arrowhead *Sagittaria sagittifolia*
Bedstraw, Hedge *Galium album*
Bird's-foot-trefoil, Common *Lotus corniculatus*
Bur-reed, Branched *Sparganium emersum*
Centaury, Common *Centaurium erythraea*
Clover, Red *Trifolium pratense*
Crane's-bill, Hedgerow *Geranium pyrenaicum*
Daisy, Oxeye *Leucanthemum vulgare*
Dock, Clustered *Rumex conglomeratus*
Dock, Water *Rumex hydrolapathum*
Flax, Fairy *Linum catharticum*
Forget-me-not, Water *Myosotis scorpioides*
Fox-sedge, False *Carex otrubae*
Goat's-beard *Tragopogon pratensis*
Hemp-agrimony *Eupatorium cannabinum*
Iris, Yellow *Iris pseudacorus*
Marsh-orchid, Southern *Dactylorhiza praetermissa*
Meadowsweet *Filipendula ulmaria*
Mint, Water *Mentha aquatica*
Pondweed, Shining *Potamogeton lucens*
Ragwort, Common *Senecio jacobaea*
Sedge, Cyperus *Carex pseudocyperus*
Sedge, Remote *Carex remota*
Skullcap *Scutellaria galericulata*
Sowthistle, Perennial *Sonchus arvensis*
Sweet-grass, Reed *Glyceria maxima*
Thistle, Marsh *Cirsium palustre*
Water-dropwort, Hemlock *Oenanthe crocata*
Water-lily, Yellow *Nuphar lutea*
Water-plantain, Narrow-leaved *Alisma lanceolatum*
Willowherb, American *Epilobium ciliatum*
Willowherb, Greater *Epilobium hirsutum*

▲ Southern Marsh-orchid

## PARK LIME PITS WALK

### Description

The quarry was closed in Victorian times and now forms a nature reserve with deep pools surrounded by beech forest and a wealth of interesting species.

The walk takes in the fields of Lime Pits and Stencills Farms, the Lime Pits pools and a stretch of canal along the Beacon Way.

Choose a springtime walk to get a feel for the area and take in the early-flowering plants and birdlife to be seen in the hedgerows and along the canal. From June onwards the arable weed flora provides interest and is a good time to search for Corn Buttercup, whose numbers fluctuate from year to year. Later in the summer many late-maturing species can be seen and the emergent flora along the canal reaches its peak.

**Distance and walking time** Approximately 2 miles. The walk takes 1½–2 hours at a gentle pace.

**Starting point** The footpath between the houses on the northern side of Stencills Road at the junction with Mellish Drive (OS grid reference: SP029996).

**Parking** There is roadside parking near the junction of Stencills Road and Mellish Drive.

**Getting there by public transport** There are five buses from Walsall town centre going along Mellish Road to a stop called Fernleigh Road which is very near Mellish Drive. Bus number 32 goes to Rugeley. The 366, 367 and 368 go to Sutton Coldfield and the 381 goes to Lichfield.

**Access/conditions** There are no access restrictions. The walk is fairly flat but the route can be slippery and muddy and there are some quite steep flights of steps. Sturdy footwear is recommended.

**Facilities and further information** Refreshment and toilet facilities at The Dilke public house.

### THE WALK

This is a circular walk around Park Lime Pits Local Nature Reserve, which is the site of a former large limestone quarry.

→ **From the junction of Stencills Road and Mellish Drive ❶, take the footpath (north-north-east) opposite Mellish Drive, between the houses, to a kissing gate and signpost pointing to 'Daw End'. Pass through the kissing-gate and continue along the track with the fields of Lime Pits Farm to both left and right. These are managed for wildlife and produce an ever-changing display of wild flowers throughout spring and summer.**

→ **After about 160 metres, at a way-marked gap in the wooden railings, turn left and follow the undulating path to a T-junction ❷.**

→ **Turn left and follow the path clockwise around the pool edge.**

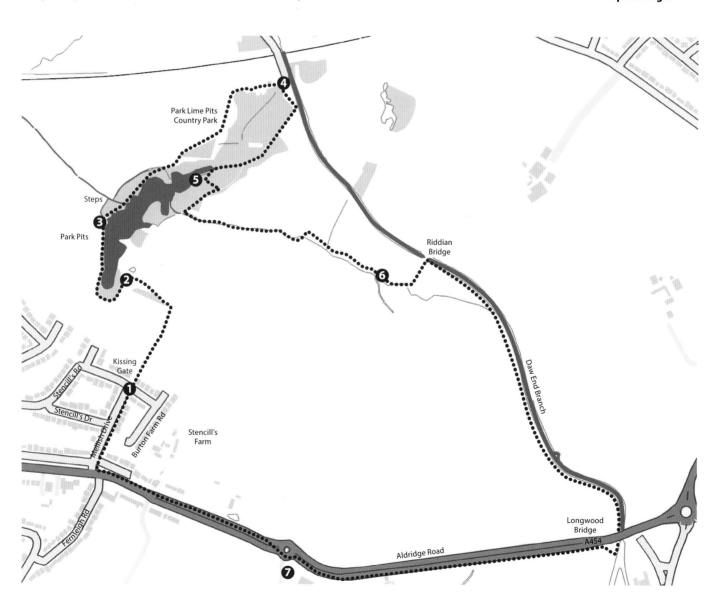

In early spring there are magnificent displays of Cherry Plum blossom in the hedges beside the track. There are also views over the pool and an occasional Kingfisher may be glimpsed darting across the water.

→ **At a gap in the woodland ❸, where a broad flight of steps leads down into the pool, there are wet fields on your left used for grazing horses.**

In summer a short diversion here is worthwhile for the damp-loving plants to be found, including Betony, Ragged-Robin and Devil's-bit Scabious.

→ **Return to the path and continue around the pool, across a stream, up and down steps, before climbing a steep set of 17 steps up a bank to your left.**

At the top of these steps you will reach a small meadow where Timothy, Tufted Vetch and Spear Thistle grow.

→ **Bear right and follow the path alongside the hedge.**

Southern Marsh-orchid and Bee Orchid have been found recently in the adjacent field.

→ **You will then reach a green metal gate with yellow stripes at the edge of a car park. Cross towards the entrance of the car park and take the path to the right of the cattle grid ❹.**
→ **Follow the path for about 50 metres with the hedge and canal parallel on the left. The track then swings away from the canal across a meadow and towards a wooded area.**

In spring Dog's Mercury, Bluebell and Lords-and-Ladies can be seen under the hedge and on the right patches of non-native Daffodils can be found. In the marshy area Tufted Hair-grass with its sharp, prickly-edged leaves is present alongside Hard Rush. As you approach the wood edge you will find False Brome and Ramsons.

→ **About 100 metres into the wood take the four small steps to your right and follow the path that leads to wooden decking at the edge of the pool.**

Bulrush grows in the pool and Mare's-tail can be seen breaking the surface in the summer and into autumn.

→ **With care, follow the path clockwise around the pool and shortly after**

▲ Park Lime Pits pool

**leaving the decking, on a small rise, there is a gap in the hawthorns to your right ❺.**

Look out for the fragrant blooms of Hoary Plantain, accompanied by Quaking-grass and Pignut.

→ **Retrace your steps for a few metres and take the narrow path to your right which very shortly takes you back to the main track through the woods.**
→ **Turn right (south-west). Continue along this track until you come to a point where it crosses a stream and the wood opens out on to a field on your left.**

This field contains many arable weeds and is a botanist's delight at almost any time of the year. Plants to look out for include Long-headed and Common Poppies, Oxeye Daisy, Prickly Lettuce, Weld, Teasel and the scarce Corn Buttercup, a decreasing cornfield weed occurring nowhere else in Birmingham and the Black Country.

→ **Follow the track which goes up the left side of this field and it will take you over the stream to your left, so that you walk up the right side of the adjacent field.**

By August the path is lined with Perennial Sowthistle.

→ **You will come to a bridge made of railway sleepers crossing the stream ❻.**

It is worth pausing here, especially in spring, when the stream banks are shining with Lesser Celandine and Hazel is covered with catkins. Later in the season Remote Sedge, a plant which grows in places where water levels fluctuate, can be seen stretching out over the water.

→ **Pass through a wooden gate by an information board, and here the track skirts the right edge of a field known to locals as 'Goldfinch Field', after the flocks that can be seen feeding on thistle heads in autumn.**
→ **Continue (left) towards Riddian Bridge which spans the canal and can be seen in the near distance.**

Approaching the bridge, look for Fool's Parsley and Field Bindweed, whilst in the field on the right, the presence of Sainfoin indicates its arable history.

→ **Take the path to the left, just before the bridge and descend onto the canal towpath.**
→ **Turn right to go under the bridge – notice the marks in the brickwork left by the bargee's ropes but**

▲ Arable field, Lime Pits Farm

**mind your head! Continue along the towpath for about 1 kilometre towards Longwood Bridge and Longwood Boatyard.**

Lapwings, Yellowhammers and Fieldfares have been seen in the field to the right of the towpath and a Little Owl spotted perching in the single oak tree across the canal not far from Riddian Bridge. In summer Skullcap, Gypsywort, Arrowhead, Narrow-leaved Water-plantain, Branched and Unbranched Bur-reed can be seen flowering at the canal edge.

→ **Just after passing under Longwood Bridge turn right up the access road and turn left onto Aldridge Road.**

Alternatively you may want to take a look along the next stretch of canal, where very soon you will encounter colonies of Fringed, White and Yellow Water-lilies forming mats across the surface of the water and below them the slender, submerged leaves of Fennel Pondweed.

→ **Return to Aldridge Road where you can catch a bus or continue for about 1km to Mellish Drive.**

During spring many flowers of the salt-tolerant Danish Scurvy-grass can be seen along the kerbs near the carriageway.

→ **About halfway between Longwood Boatyard and Mellish Drive is The Dilke pub ⑦ which will provide refreshments and toilet facilities if required.**

### Species mentioned in the text

Arrowhead *Sagittaria sagittifolia*
Betony *Betonica officinalis*
Bindweed, Field *Convolvulus arvensis*
Bluebell *Hyacinthoides non-scripta*
Brome, False *Brachypodium sylvaticum*
Bulrush *Typha latifolia*
Bur-reed, Branched *Sparganium erectum*
Bur-reed, Unbranched *Sparganium emersum*
Buttercup, Corn *Ranunculus arvensis*
Celandine, Lesser *Ficaria verna*
Daffodil *Narcissus* sp.
Daisy, Oxeye *Leucanthemum vulgare*
Gypsywort *Lycopus europaeus*
Hair-grass, Tufted *Deschampsia cespitosa*
Hazel *Corylus avellana*
Lettuce, Prickly *Lactuca serriola*
Lords-and-Ladies *Arum maculatum*
Mare's-tail *Hippuris vulgaris*
Marsh-orchid, Southern *Dactylorhiza praetermissa*
Mercury, Dog's *Mercurialis perennis*
Orchid, Bee *Ophrys apifera*
Parsley, Fool's *Aethusa cynapium*

Pignut *Conopodium majus*
Plantain, Hoary *Plantago media*
Plum, Cherry *Prunus cerasifera*
Pondweed, Fennel *Potamogeton pectinatus*
Poppy, Common *Papaver rhoeas*
Poppy, Long-headed *Papaver dubium*
Quaking-grass *Briza media*
Ragged-Robin *Silene flos-cuculi*
Ramsons *Allium ursinum*
Rush, Hard *Juncus inflexus*
Sainfoin *Onobrychis viciifolia*
Scabious, Devil's-bit *Succisa pratensis*
Scurvy-grass, Danish *Cochlearia danica*
Sedge, Remote *Carex remota*
Skullcap *Scutellaria galericulata*
Sowthistle, Perennial *Sonchus oleraceus*
Teasel *Dipsacus fullonum*
Thistle, Spear *Cirsium vulgare*
Timothy *Phleum pratense*
Vetch, Tufted *Vicia cracca*
Water-lily, Fringed *Nymphoides peltata*
Water-lily, White *Nymphaea alba*
Water-lily, Yellow *Nuphar lutea*
Water-plantain, Narrow-leaved *Alisma lanceolatum*
Weld *Reseda luteola*
Wild-oat *Avena fatua*

## CUCKOO'S NOOK, THE DINGLE AND HAY HEAD WOOD WALK

### Description

This walk explores the largely wooded nature reserves of Cuckoo's Nook, the Dingle and Hay Head Wood. These are some of the most diverse woodlands in Birmingham and the Black Country. The walk also shows the importance of geology in influencing vegetation where it crosses the Eastern Boundary Fault in the Dingle. Spring is by far the best time to enjoy the woodland flowers although the wetlands and grassland at Hay Head are at their best in summer but form only a small part of this walk. Leaving aside the botany, the scenery is attractive at any time of the year.

**Distance and walking time** Approximately 3 miles. The walk takes about 2–2½ hours at a gentle pace.
**Starting point** Cuckoo's Nook and the Dingle Local Nature Reserve on the north side of the Sutton Road (OS grid reference: SP047982).
**Parking** There is roadside parking on the wide service road opposite the start of the walk on Sutton Road (B4151). There is also a car park at Hay Head Wood off Longwood Lane (OS grid reference: SP041990) and the walk could start and finish here, which could serve as an alternative start and finish point for this walk.

**Getting there by public transport** There are two bus services from Walsall town centre stopping on the Sutton Road. The nearest bus stop is outside the former Three Crowns public house close to the start of this walk. Bus number 77 goes from Walsall to Sutton Coldfield via Streetly and New Oscott. The 935 service goes from Walsall to Birmingham via Streetly and Kingstanding.
**Access/conditions** This circular walk is generally flat but there are numerous short flights of steps, boardwalks, stiles and footbridges. Most of the paths are well made, although some places are muddy in wet weather. Sturdy footwear is recommended.
**Facilities and further information** The Three Crowns Garden Centre (OS grid reference: SP051982) ⑫ has a coffee shop. Cuckoo's Nook, the Dingle and Hay Head Wood are managed by Walsall Council as nature reserves. Several leaflets about the reserves are available.

### THE WALK

→ **The starting point of the walk is the well-signposted entrance to Cuckoo's Nook and the Dingle Local Nature Reserve on the north side of the Sutton Road.**
→ **Go through the kissing gate into the reserve.**

You are now in the Dingle ❶. On your left, almost hidden from view by Hawthorn and Elder scrub, is a former limestone quarry. The quarry was in use from the 1760s until the 1860s and provided limestone as a flux for iron making. The quarry is linear and the walk explores its entire length of 1,250 metres or ¾ mile. Ramsons and Dog's Mercury soon become apparent in increasing numbers. A variety of typical hedgerow plants are seen including: Cowslip, Hedge Woundwort, Hogweed, Lesser Celandine, Raspberry, Tansy and Teasel. Butterflies abound.

→ **After 400 metres you cross a wide farm track. Climb over the stile ahead to rejoin the Dingle ❷.**

Ramsons becomes the dominant plant in spring with its characteristic garlic fragrance. Dog's Mercury and Lesser Celandine are also common. Early Dog-violet and Sanicle, both uncommon in Birmingham and the Black Country, are present but much less frequent. The tree canopy comprises Ash and Sycamore

▲ Ramsons

while Hawthorn is the dominant shrub, although Dogwood and Gooseberry are occasionally seen.

→ **After about 300 metres take the first obvious side path to your left ❸, which quickly brings you to the edge of the woodland.** (If you are short of time, you can omit this diversion by continuing straight through the Dingle – go forward to stage ❼.)

→ **Follow the path along the field edge for about 100 metres before turning**

left over a stile onto a boardwalk across a shallow stream ❹.

→ **Follow the path through an open grassland area ❺ with a low lying wet core.**

Here a diverse grassland has avoided the 'improvement' of modern agriculture. This field is best seen in early summer but several plants flower in the spring at the same time as those in the woodland. The lowest parts of the field are permanently wet and dominated in the summer by the tall, pink-flowered Great Willowherb. Rushes are also common.

As the grassland becomes less wet, the spring-flowering Cuckooflower (sometimes known as Lady's-smock) and Glaucous Sedge will be seen. The upright clumps of Tufted Hair-grass will flower later in the summer, together with scattered Wild Angelica and Common Figwort. These three plants are at home in more shaded tall herb plant communities which indicate past clearance of scrub and grassland restoration.

In the drier grassland near the path Bugle, Common Sorrel and Tormentil flower

early in the summer while Betony, Common Knapweed and Meadow Buttercup appear later. Pignut is found in the shadier areas. Most of these plants indicate old grassland with low nutrient levels. Fine grasses such as Sweet Vernal-grass and Red Fescue are abundant, although the coarser Cock's-foot is also very common.

→ **The path will bring you to a stile and a footbridge over a stream ❻ taking you into Hay Head Wood.**

→ **Climb the steps and turn left immediately. Continue along the main path and ignore minor side-paths to left and right.**

→ **After a few metres, in a woodland clearing, turn left onto the path in front of you into an area of open woodland. Bear right and continue along a winding woodland path.**

You are now entering an area of ancient woodland dominated by Pedunculate Oak. Ancient woodland is believed always to have been woodland since earliest historical times, although this can rarely be proven. The earliest

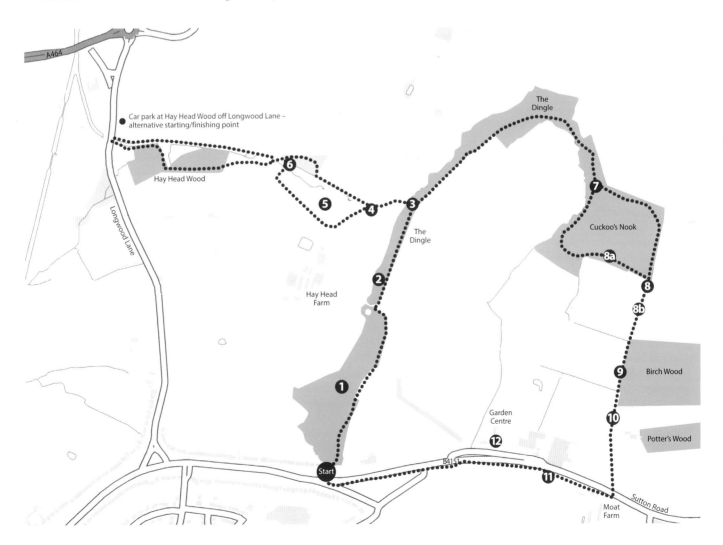

▲ Yellow Archangel

In the shallow marginal areas, the yellow flowers of Marsh-marigold stand out in the spring. Other plants include: Bulrush, Great Willowherb, Reed Sweet-grass and Yellow Iris. Lesser Pond-sedge and Pendulous Sedge are also present. Less welcome is the invasive Indian Balsam.

Along the edge of the canal, Ramsons is often dominant. There are also the occasional flower spikes of the non-native Spanish Bluebell together with small areas of Enchanter's-nightshade.

→ **With the canal basin now behind you, turn right onto the path ahead of you and immediately left. You soon see the stile and footbridge which brought you into the wood below you. ❻**

→ **Instead of retracing your steps across the stream, follow the path ahead through the woodland, keeping the stream on your right.**

→ **Bear left at a path junction close to brick masonry.**

This arm of Hay Head Wood once contained the shaft to an underground limestone mine. The remains of brickwork from associated buildings are visible. Limestone was extracted here sporadically from at least 1593 until use finally ceased in 1921.

Dog's Mercury is abundant with occasional Early Dog-violet.

→ **After less than 100 metres take the right fork over the knobbly roots of an old Ash before turning left over a footbridge. The path leaves the woodland and continues along a field edge with the stream on your right.**

→ **After a further 150 metres pass by the stile and boardwalk you crossed earlier ❹ and retrace your steps back into the Dingle ❸.**

→ **Once in the Dingle, immediately turn left and continue along the well constructed path keeping the seasonally wet areas on your left.**

Although the flora in the Dingle indicates old woodland, it is officially classified as secondary woodland because it grew up on a disused quarry and could not have been any older than the date of the quarry.

→ **After less than 200 metres the path crosses a railway sleeper footbridge over a stream bed coming in from the right. (You will have crossed three railway sleeper bridges over wet depressions before reaching this point.)**

The stream bed is often dry and gives a good view of the pavement-like nodular limestone beds which were laid down within the grey Wenlock shales in the Silurian period some 400 million years ago. The underlying limestone rock provides a lime-rich soil which supports the rich ground flora seen in both Hay Head Wood and here in the Dingle. In this area, there is more Pedunculate Oak in the canopy and Hazel starts to appear in the shrub layer. The field layer also becomes more diverse, with scattered Wood Anemone and Wood Melick growing amongst the Ramsons.

→ **After a further 250 metres there is a moss-covered concrete cross in the hollow on your left.**

Gradually the path rises onto a steep-sided bank with the former quarry on your left and the stream bed below to your right. By the time you pass the concrete cross in the quarry below, the tree canopy begins to be dominated by mature Beech which was planted following the closure of this northern part of the quarry in 1843. Horse-chestnut, Large-leaved Lime and Sycamore were also planted and many are now over-mature. The non-native Snowberry is also flourishing at shrub level. On either side of the path Sanicle is frequent.

Beyond the concrete cross is an exposed quarry face with its layers of limestones and siltstones. This is the heart of the visible geological interest of the Dingle and a geological information leaflet is published by Walsall Council.

Shortly afterwards you cross the Eastern Boundary Fault, a 50-mile long geological fault running across the Midlands from Bromsgrove in the south to the Potteries in the north. Here in the Permian period 248 to 286 million years ago the land to the east of the fault dropped by hundreds of metres. Millions of years of erosion removed any difference in levels on either side of the fault. While the fault is not visible at ground level, the transition from calcareous Wenlock shales to acidic Carboniferous shales is seen in changes to the vegetation as the lime-rich soils encountered so far on the walk blend into acidic soils as you cross into Cuckoo's Nook.

You will even smell the difference as the pungent garlic smell of the Ramsons gives way to the perfumed fragrance of massed Bluebells. The underlying geology commonly influences the vegetation growing on the surface, but it is unusual to see this demonstrated quite so obviously.

→ **Continue along the path, passing some stone-filled gabions on the left.**

documentary evidence for the age of Hay Head Wood dates from the 1760s. The ground flora is not dominated by any one species, but Bluebell, Wood Anemone, Wood-sedge, Wood-sorrel and Yellow Archangel are all present. Growing together they indicate old and probably ancient woodland. The rare Violet Helleborine has been recorded in this area, but not for some 20 years.

→ **Keeping the wet woodland on your right, follow the path in a westerly direction.**

While walking through the ancient woodland you will soon be aware of wet woodland dominated by Alder and Willow scrub on your right. This is the overgrown canal basin where once limestone was loaded into canal barges. The walk follows the edges of the canal basin where a range of swamp and open water habitats can be seen.

→ **After about 250 metres, with the traffic on Longwood Lane very audible, turn right along the embankment supporting the former canal basin. Here the land falls steeply to your left.**

→ **Follow the edge of the canal basin towards Longwood Lane. A few metres short of Longwood Lane, the path crosses the former canal arm and immediately turns abruptly right along the canal edge.**

→ **Keeping the canal basin immediately on your right, continue for about 350 metres on a straight path.**

Down the steps on your right is a wet swampy area with extensive beds of Large Bitter-cress. The white spring flowers have distinctive violet anthers. Marsh-marigold is also present. Nearby, in the drier areas, Greater Stitchwort, Wood Anemone, Wood Melick and Woodruff can be seen. Away from the wettest areas, Bluebells dominate, but Wood Anemone, False Brome and Tufted Hair-grass are also frequent. Sanicle is now very rare. The tree canopy in the drier areas is dominated by Oak with a Hazel shrub layer but Ash is also present. Downy Birch is found in the damper areas.

You are now on the edge of Cuckoo's Nook, which is believed to be an ancient woodland. It was present on old maps of the area by at least 1799.

→ **Continue along a boardwalk, passing a stile on your left and cross a footbridge. After about 130 metres you reach a major path junction where there is a timber bench. Take the left fork 7.**

The Bluebell woodland has gradually given way to a less diverse ground flora dominated by Bramble and Creeping Soft-grass. Large Oaks dominate the tree canopy but both Silver and Downy Birch are present and Holly dominates the shrub layer. Rowan saplings are also frequent.

→ **Follow the path around the edge of the woodland and bear right shortly before a boardwalk. Soon the path joins a wet ditch. At the edge of the wood you come to a sign board and a bench marking the south-east entrance to Cuckoo's Nook 8.**

▲ Cuckoo's Nook

**Here there is a choice.**

→ **8a Retrace your steps about 25 metres and turn left at the first path. Follow the path along the edge of the woodland back to the path junction with the timber bench 7 where you turn left and retrace your steps through the Dingle back to Sutton Road. This is the longer alternative by about ¼ mile.**

At first the woodland is noticeably younger with smaller oaks forming the canopy and a field layer dominated by Bramble, Creeping Soft-grass and Tufted Hair-grass, with occasional patches of Wavy Hair-grass. The shrub layer is a mixture of Birch, Hawthorn, Holly and Rowan. As the woodland becomes damper (and you start crossing boardwalks, footbridges and ditches), Bluebell becomes increasingly common with patches of Wood Melick and occasional Ramsons, Wood-sorrel, Wood Anemone and Yellow Archangel.

→ **8b Follow the track to the south towards Sutton Road.**

Leaving the woodland you walk along a straight track lined with Oak. The Wavy Hair-grass beneath demonstrates the acidic conditions to the east of the geological fault.

Soon you reach Birch Wood 9, an old rectangular plantation woodland, which may have been planted in the 17th century when this land was enclosed. It is privately owned with no public access. At its fringes you will see several Aspen and a pond is just visible through the dense hedge.

Twenty years ago the margins of this pond provided habitat for a variety of uncommon plants including: Bottle Sedge and Cyperus Sedge along with Water Horsetail, Water Forget-me-not and Bog Moss (*Sphagnum* species). These have been lost due to increased shading by trees and shrubs which shows how precarious the survival of the local flora can sometimes be.

Immediately after Birch Wood is a field 10 containing grassland similar to the one visited earlier near Hay Head Wood. The land here is private and can only be glimpsed through a few gaps in the hedge. Among the species found here are Betony, Common Bird's-foot-trefoil, Common Knapweed, Bugle, Glaucous Sedge and Devil's-bit Scabious. In the spring, Bluebells spill out from the adjacent woodland and hedgerows into the grassland.

→ **Follow the track until it reaches a stile on the Sutton Road. Cross the road and turn right along the wide verge 11 back to the start of the walk.**

Along the verge Common Stork's-bill, Sweet Vernal-grass, Common Field-speedwell, Bulbous Buttercup and Field Wood-rush are present amongst the mown sward. Danish Scurvy-grass forms a white border on the roadside in early spring, while Cow Parsley dominates the base of the hedge in summer.

**Species mentioned in the text**

Alder *Alnus glutinosa*
Anemone, Wood *Anemone nemorosa*
Angelica, Wild *Angelica sylvestris*
Archangel, Yellow *Lamiastrum galeobdolon*
Ash *Fraxinus excelsior*
Aspen *Populus tremula*
Balsam, Indian *Impatiens glandulifera*
Beech *Fagus sylvatica*
Betony *Betonica officinalis*
Birch, Downy *Betula pubescens*
Birch, Silver *Betula pendula*
Bird's-foot-trefoil, Common *Lotus corniculatus*
Bitter-cress, Large *Cardamine amara*
Bluebell *Hyacinthoides non-scripta*
Bluebell, Spanish *Hyacinthoides hispanica*
Bramble *Rubus fruticosus*
Brome, False *Brachypodium sylvaticum*
Bugle *Ajuga reptans*
Bulrush *Typha latifolia*
Buttercup, Meadow *Ranunculus acris*
Celandine, Lesser *Ficaria verna*
Cock's-foot *Dactylis glomerata*
Cowslip *Primula veris*
Cuckooflower *Cardamine pratensis*
Dog-violet, Early *Viola reichenbachiana*
Dogwood *Cornus sanguinea*
Elder *Sambucus nigra*
Enchanter's-nightshade *Circaea lutetiana*

Fescue, Red *Festuca rubra*
Figwort, Common *Scrophularia nodosa*
Forget-me-not, Water *Myosotis scorpioides*
Gooseberry *Ribes uva-crispa*
Hair-grass, Tufted *Deschampsia cespitosa*
Hair-grass, Wavy *Deschampsia flexuosa*
Hawthorn *Crataegus monogyna*
Helleborine, Violet *Epipactis purpurata*
Hogweed *Heracleum sphondylium*
Holly *Ilex aquifolium*
Horse-chestnut *Aesculus hippocastanum*
Horsetail, Water *Equisetum fluviatile*
Iris, Yellow *Iris pseudacorus*
Knapweed, Common *Centaurea nigra*
Lime, Large-leaved *Tilia platyphyllos*
Marsh-marigold *Caltha palustris*
Melick, Wood *Melica uniflora*
Mercury, Dog's *Mercurialis perennis*
Oak, Pedunculate *Quercus robur*
Pignut *Conopodium majus*
Pond-sedge, Lesser *Carex acutiformis*
Ramsons *Allium ursinum*
Raspberry *Rubus idaeus*
Rowan *Sorbus aucuparia*
Sanicle *Sanicula europaea*
Scabious, Devil's-bit *Succisa pratensis*
Sedge, Bottle *Carex rostrata*
Sedge, Cyperus *Carex pseudocyperus*
Sedge, Glaucous *Carex flacca*
Sedge, Pendulous *Carex pendula*
Sedge, Wood *Carex sylvatica*
Snowberry *Symphoricarpos albus*
Soft-grass, Creeping *Holcus mollis*
Sorrel, Common *Rumex acetosa*
Stitchwort, Greater *Stellaria holostea*
Stork's-bill, Common *Erodium cicutarium*
Sweet-grass, Reed *Glyceria maxima*
Sycamore *Acer pseudoplatanus*
Tansy *Tanacetum parthenium*
Teasel *Dipsacus fullonum*
Tormentil *Potentilla erecta*
Vernal-grass, Sweet *Anthoxanthum odoratum*
Willowherb, Great *Epilobium hirsutum*
Woodruff *Galium odoratum*
Wood-sorrel *Oxalis acetosella*
Woundwort, Hedge *Stachys sylvatica*

## LADYMOOR POOL WALK

### Description

Ladymoor Pool, one of the Sites of Importance for Nature Conservation (SINC) sites of Wolverhampton, is best approached from Ladymoor Road in Bilston. Take the Coseley Road south off the Black Country Route in Bilston, or turn east off the Birmingham New Road down Shaw Road. Both roads become Ladymoor Road in the middle.

You are in the middle of an area of great importance in the industrial history of the Black Country. Across the road you will see the forbidding high bank which

once formed the boundary of the vast Bilston Steelworks, lost at the end of the 1970s, but this whole area was occupied by generations of mines and blast furnaces going back to the 18th century and the dawn of the industrial age.

Ladymoor Pool is a mining subsidence pool. It is currently much beset by Canada Geese, but Mallard, Coot, Moorhen, Mute Swans and Tufted Duck also breed there. The landscape around the pool was reshaped in the mid-1980s, but the lawns have not been able to withstand goose grazing; note the scarcity of grasses and the abundance of Ribwort Plantain, Selfheal, Daisy, Weld and other low plants evidently not to the taste of the geese! Despite the eutrophication caused by the geese some specialities such as the winter annual Little Mouse-ear have been recorded in the gravelly soil by the road. There is a thin reedswamp, mainly of Great Willowherb, and practically no submerged flora.

**Distance and walking time** Less than one mile. 2 hours at a very gentle pace.
**Starting point** Best approached from Ladymoor Road in Bilston (OS grid reference: SO94269516).
**Parking** Park on Ladymoor Road in the lay-by by the row of houses immediately by the pool and close to the junction with Highfields Road.
**Getting there by public transport** Bus number 126 along the Birmingham New Road: alight at Hessian Close and walk down Shaw Road to Ladymoor Road. The 229 bus runs from Bilston Bus Station: alight on Highfields Road close to the junction with Ladymoor Road; alternatively, Coseley train station is also fairly close by.

**Access/conditions** Open access, with many paths but ground uneven and much developing scrub.
**Facilities and further information** None.

### THE WALK

→ **Start the walk at Ladymoor Road. Skirt the pool clockwise and head south-east up the bank between the first two tree plantings round the back of the pool.**

Coal spoil ❶ comes to the surface on steep slopes down to the pool here, and has developed a moderately acid grassland of Common Bent, Red Fescue and Sheep's Sorrel. The tree plantings are full of Traveller's-joy, suggesting that not all the substrate is so acid, and you will find the path skirting a deep wooded gully with outcrops of limy spoil.

→ **The path travels along a sort of causeway ❷ to the south of the pool, (which was built and planted with trees by the old West Midlands County Council in the 1980s. It marks the boundary between Wolverhampton City Council (Bilston), which has the SINC, and Dudley Metropolitan Borough Council (Coseley) where the site has been used for landfill).**
→ **Follow the fence around the landfill.**

Look out for the yellow crucifer Hoary Mustard, a recent addition to our wasteland flora now becoming much commoner. Head towards the canal.

→ **You will cross further landfill ❸ (canal dredgings), now grazed**

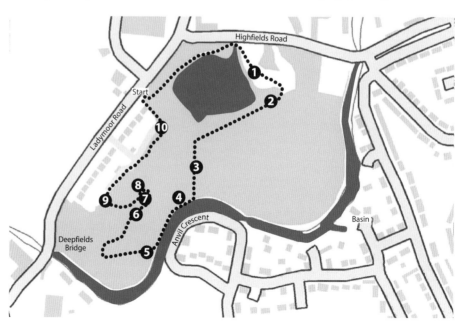

**by tethered ponies into passable pasture and with a self-set thicket of very mixed willow scrub. Continue until you meet the canal.**

Here ❹ can be found Purple Willow as well as the commoner Grey and Crack-willows. The canal is a feeder for the Birmingham Canal which is only a few hundred yards to the west. The feeder canal water is sweet and clean (don't drink!), though it is pumped up from deep mine workings and can become cloudy with iron deposits. The flora is typical, with a reedswamp of Reed Sweet-grass, Bulrush and Branched Bur-reed, with plenty of Gypsywort, False Fox-sedge, Mint, Hard Rush, Clustered Dock etc. The submerged flora can be interesting, with much Broad-leaved Pondweed and Fennel Pondweed, but sometimes you can find the Black Country hybrid speciality Linton's Pondweed. Little Grebes sometimes breed here.

Across the canal rise the new houses of the future; turn the other way to see uneven banks, mounds and ditches self-grown with Goat Willow and Hawthorn, and finally a glimpse of a deep hollow with mounds of old blast furnace spoil. This is one of the last remnants of the post-industrial landscape which was once so common hereabouts and is almost impossible to find elsewhere now. It seems to be the remains of a huge spoil tip left over from the early years of iron-making in Bilston. Much was dug up for roadstone in the early 20th century but these huge boulders were too difficult to move.

➜ **As the towpath veers to the right (south), turn even sharper right ❺ onto a footpath across more open, undulating spoil.**

Note the characteristic stands of tall herbs: Tansy, Mugwort and Wormwood etc. but also patches of open vegetation on shallow, droughty soils with Perforate St John's-wort, Mouse-ear-hawkweed, lichens and mosses.

➜ **Keep close to the edge of excavation until you can get down to the spoil mounds ❻ (the best paths down are currently blocked by brambles and scrub).**

The zone around the spoil is a marsh very rich in biodiversity, but it is now getting very wooded. Nevertheless you will still see interesting remnants of a rush-marsh, with (mainly) Hard Rush, but also Slender Rush as well as Jointed Rush, Soft-rush, and Compact Rush, some very scarce liverworts and four species of *Sphagnum* moss. Look out for Southern Marsh-orchid,

▲ **Mound of furnace spoil boulders**

and other uncommon wetland species such as Marsh Arrowgrass ❼. Beyond the marsh are the huge slag boulders, almost indistinguishable from volcanic slag, and lower areas of finer material with a drought-tolerant flora including several microspecies of Hawkweed, Oxeye Daisy, Fairy Flax and the winter annual Silver Hair-grass, which produces its exquisite silvery inflorescences in the early spring and then dies before the summer drought.

You can climb right over the big spoil boulders, bare except for patches of Biting Stonecrop, Ivy-leaved Toadflax and that escapee from the volcanoes of south Europe, Oxford Ragwort. There are also at least 20 lichen species which you will find listed elsewhere in this Flora. As you descend on the shady northern side ❽ there are ferns: Maidenhair Spleenwort (almost always on walls in the urban area), Hart's-tongue and, lower down, Male-fern and Lady-fern.

➜ **Head to the left (west) through the scrub back into the wetland.**

In this area many sedges – False Fox-sedge, Prickly Sedge, Glaucous Sedge and Common Sedge may be found.

➜ **On leaving the marsh and entering a dryer area, turn right (north-west) through the trees ❾ (planted as a screen by the locals and the Bilston Conservation Association in 1985 and now in need of thinning) onto the track behind houses.**

Colt's-foot flowers here, also Woodruff and the hybrid of our native Bluebell and the Spanish Bluebell (presumably garden escapes).

➜ **Follow the track north-east to the car barrier ❿ and back onto the pool area close to Ladymoor Road.**

### Species mentioned in the text

Arrowgrass, Marsh *Triglochin palustris*
Bent, Common *Agrostis capillaris*
Bluebell, Hybrid *Hyacinthoides* × *massartiana*

Bulrush *Typha latifolia*
Bur-reed, Branched *Sparganium erectum*
Colt's-foot *Tussilago farfara*
Crack-willow *Salix fragilis*
Daisy *Bellis perennis*
Daisy, Oxeye *Leucanthemum vulgare*
Dock, Clustered *Rumex conglomeratus*
Fescue, Red *Festuca rubra*
Flax, Fairy *Linum catharticum*
Fox-sedge, False *Carex otrubae*
Gypsywort *Lycopus europaeus*
Hair-grass, Silver *Aira caryophyllacea*
Hart's-tongue *Asplenium scolopendrium*
Hawkweed *Hieracium* section Vulgata
Hawthorn *Crataegus monogyna*
Lady-fern *Athyrium filix-femina*
Male-fern *Dryopteris filix-mas*
Marsh-orchid, Southern *Dactylorhiza praetermissa*
Mint *Mentha* spp.
Mouse-ear, Little *Cerastium semidecandrum*
Mouse-ear-hawkweed *Pilosella officinarum*
Mugwort *Artemisia vulgaris*
Mustard, Hoary *Hirschfeldia incana*
Plantain, Ribwort *Plantago lanceolata*
Pondweed, Broad-leaved *Potamogeton natans*
Pondweed, Fennel *Potamogeton pectinatus*
Pondweed, Linton's *Potamogeton* × *lintonii*
Ragwort, Oxford *Senecio squalidus*
Rush, Compact *Juncus conglomeratus*
Rush, Hard *Juncus inflexus*
Rush, Jointed *Juncus articulatus*
Rush, Slender *Juncus tenuis*
Rush, Soft *Juncus effusus*
Sedge, Common *Carex nigra*
Sedge, Glaucous *Carex flacca*
Sedge, Prickly *Carex muricata* subsp. *pairae*
Selfheal *Prunella vulgaris*
Sorrel, Sheep's *Rumex acetosella*
Spleenwort, Maidenhair *Asplenium trichomanes*
St John's-wort, Perforate *Hypericum perforatum*
Stonecrop Biting *Sedum acre*
Sweet-grass, Reed *Glyceria maxima*
Tansy *Tanacetum vulgare*
Toadflax, Ivy-leaved *Cymbalaria muralis*
Traveller's-joy *Clematis vitalba*
Weld *Reseda luteola*
Willow, Goat *Salix caprea*
Willow, Grey *Salix cinerea*
Willow, Purple *Salix purpurea*
Willowherb, Great *Epilobium hirsutum*
Woodruff *Galium odoratum*
Wormwood *Artemisia absinthium*

## GREAT BARR – URBAN SAFARI WALK

### Description

Discover the hidden wildlife of suburbia in this undulating but easy walk around part of the Great Barr area on the borders of Birmingham, Walsall and Sandwell. The intensive development of the past two centuries has obscured the series of gently rolling hills and wide flat valleys upon which the 'Endless Village' of the Black Country was built. This walk takes in the ridge of one of these hills forming the eastern side of the Tame Valley. It allows good views of the Rowley Hills in the middle of the Black Country, and the Clent Hills which mark the return to open country to the west. The route takes in a Victorian town park, a fragment of forgotten woodland, an old farm, old hedgerows and pastures. A peaceful stretch of canal completes a surprisingly rich walk.

**Distance and walking time** Approximately 3 miles. The walk takes about 2½ hours at a gentle pace.

**Starting point** Red House Park (OS grid reference: SP040945).

**Parking** There is a car park in Hill Lane or on the roadside nearby.

**Getting there by public transport** Buses 16A, 28, 51, 451, 651 and 886 all call at the Scott Arms, a short distance to the east of Red House Park.

**Access/conditions** This walk can be very muddy. In places the Beacon Way has become overgrown with bramble. Near the end of the walk there is a steep ascent from the canal towpath to the road.

**Facilities and further information** None.

### THE WALK

→ **From the car park in Hill Lane, walk into Red House Park ❶ and past the old house ('Red House') with the formal rose beds to the right.**

→ **Turn right ❷ to pass beneath the avenue of limes and turn right again near the end of the path by the private gardens to go down the hill to the two pools.**

→ **Go between the pools ❸ and follow the second pool round to the right and make for Wilderness Lane to go beneath the motorway bridge ❹.**

Red House Park is a typical Victorian town park complete with formal flower beds, acres of closely mown grass, mature specimen trees, and uninspired modern tree planting. One of the real characters

of the park is a tough old Black Mulberry tree which leans at the corner of the main path by the house. Thousands of miles from its home in West Asia, with its orange and grey bark fissured and flaked, a steel band holding it together, fire damaged and beetle infested, it still manages to flower and fruit.

The path continues through an imposing avenue of limes. These trees are Common Limes, hybrids between the Small-and the Large-leaved Limes. By mid-summer they take on a lovely yellow-green hue as thousands of star-shaped flowers open.

Common Figwort will be found on the left of the path: an odd looking plant which numbers amongst its close relatives flowers as diverse as Snapdragons, Foxgloves, Mulleins and Speedwells. Just after passing beneath the motorway and opposite the school, make a detour into the enchanting sliver of wet woodland to the right of the footpath. The patch of woodland, scrub and grassland, nestling beneath the motorway and houses, covers about ten acres and is typical of many such forgotten corners of suburbia. It is home to many trees, flowers, birds and insects, a link with the rural past

and a hope for a more sympathetic future. Dark reflections through the trees reveal the presence of shallow pools. Above them, Marsh Cinquefoils and Yellow Iris bloom whilst young oak and hawthorn scrabble skywards.

→ **Cross the road to turn left into Peak House Road ❺.**

→ **Turn left again at the main road and walk down the hill until the university playing fields car park is reached on the left. Enter here and find the 'Beacon Way' signs ❻.**

→ **Follow them around the edge of the playing fields, behind the school, over the metal footbridge ❼, eventually to reach the Tame Valley Canal ❽.**

Peak House Farm, on the corner of the main road is now derelict, and next to it a solid Georgian farmhouse faces the busy traffic on the main Birmingham to Walsall road. Peak House is well named, sitting as it does on a high ridge overlooking the Tame Valley. Just past the house, before the start of the hedge, a view opens up

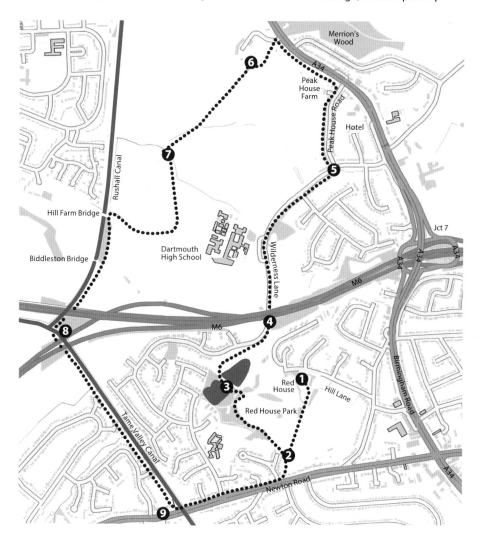

▲ Bittersweet

to the Rowley Hills and beyond that Clent Hills on the Worcestershire side of the West Midlands. The hedge on the left of the footpath sits on a bank, partly supported by an old drystone wall. It is fairly tall now, but the horizontal branches at its base are evidence that it was once laid, a stockproof barrier which would have prevented any animals on the other side from getting under the wheels of the carts and carriages which once passed this way. Wild flowers fairly tumble out of it: Mugwort, Hogweed and Garlic Mustard in one place, Hedge Woundwort, Brambles and Bittersweet in another. The last named climbs through the Hawthorn to appear above head-height with its bright purple petals surrounding yellow anthers.

The nightshades are all members of a generally poisonous family (Solanaceae) which nevertheless provides two of our most widespread foods: tomatoes and potatoes. The berries of Bittersweet which go from green to yellow to brilliant red are indeed poisonous. Just before the car park the main hedgerow plant changes from Hawthorn to Blackthorn.

After skirting the car park the land to the right changes from playing fields to rough herbage, back to playing fields and then to hay fields, while on the left is a beautiful old hedge. Now tall and unlaid it has enough variety of woody species to suggest it could be very old, if not ancient. In places forming a double hedge over a deep ditch, it contains Oak, Ash, Willow, Wych Elm, English Elm, Elder, Hazel, Sycamore, Wild Rose, Field Maple and Hawthorn.

The herbaceous plants include Black Bryony, Bittersweet and Great Willowherb.

Many of the trees are now so large that the hedge is more like a narrow strip of woodland. In comparison to the average hawthorn hedge this is a rich ribbon of foliage winding across the fields.

A particularly attractive fungus which grows here is Oyster Mushroom. This spectacular toadstool produces masses of grey-blue fruiting bodies and is more usually seen on living trees, especially beech.

As the blocks of flats are approached, spend a few minutes leaning over the five-bar gate on the right of the path. Survey the peaceful scene in front: flats to the left and the low school buildings to the right there may be, both half hidden by greenery, but in front is a field of grasses and clovers, and all around are those fabulous hedgerows punctuated with mature trees. Depending on the time of year, there could be an accompaniment of birdsong or the humming of insects. It requires some effort to recall that this bucolic setting is about half way, and in a direct line, between the centres of Birmingham and Walsall. Turning away from the gate, a colourful corner is revealed where white Hogweed, mauve-pink Rosebay Willowherb and bright yellow Perforate St John's-wort delight the eye.

The thin, relatively poor soil along this part of the route is strewn with many different sorts of flowers and even a cursory examination reveals that many of them are members of the pea family. With White and Red Clover, yellow Bird's-foot-trefoil, Meadow Vetchling, and purple Tufted Vetch it is easy to forget that, as well as being

very attractive, the pea family (Fabaceae) is probably second only to the grass family in economic importance to man. With about 17,000 species worldwide it is not surprising that we should find a use for some of them. Many varieties of peas and beans are eaten, while indigo dye, gum-arabic and gum-tragacanth are obtained from others; some produce timber, others (clovers, Sainfoins and Lucernes) are utilised as fodder, while Laburnum and Wisteria decorate our gardens.

Where the path passes above the canal a search of the field to the left should be rewarded with the discovery of two wild gentians. One of them – Common Centaury – is not rare but it does have a delicate beauty with its fresh green leaves and bright-pink, five-petalled flowers in umbel-like heads. The other is more unusual as it is normally found in limestone areas. It is Yellow-wort, noted as having grown on Silurian limestone a few miles away in the vicinity of Dudley in 1801.

→ **Pass beneath the motorway bridge and at the junction of the canals turn left and almost immediately right over the bridge.**

→ **Do NOT follow the 'Beacon Way' signs which point straight ahead but turn left along the canal towpath.**

→ **After some way, just before the high road bridge, take a right fork and go up the embankment ❾ onto the pavement and turn left over the bridge.**

→ **Walk on to the park gates on the left, turn into the park and return**

▲ Hogweed

**beneath the avenue of limes to the Red House and the car park.**

This deep, cool, shady cutting, filled with birdsong, lined with luxuriant vegetation and buzzing with insect life provides a complete change of atmosphere to the open landscapes around Peak House Farm. The sudden transition at the little gate from peace and seclusion to noise and bustle is startling to say the least. Crossing the bridge soon aids recovery as it is realised that the highway authority has kindly built an aerial walkway through the tops of the tallest trees in the canal cutting. At any time it is quite an experience to look down into the trees instead of up as is usual; their shape, perspective and character are all completely changed. Passing back through the park our old friend the Black Mulberry tree can be seen screening the Red House as it is approached beneath the limes.

## Species mentioned in the text

Alder *Alnus glutinosa*
Ash *Fraxinus excelsior*
Beech *Fagus sylvatica*
Bird's-foot-trefoil, Common *Lotus corniculatus*
Bittersweet *Solanum dulcamara*
Blackthorn *Prunus spinosa*
Bramble *Rubus fruticosus* agg.
Bryony, Black *Tamus communis*
Centaury, Common *Centaurium erythraea*
Cinquefoil, Marsh *Comarus palustre*
Clover, Red *Trifolium pratense*
Clover, White *Trifolium repens*
Elder *Sambucus nigra*
Elm, English *Ulmus procera*
Elm, Wych *Ulmus glabra*
Figwort, Common *Scrophularia nodosa*
Hawthorn *Crataegus monogyna*
Hazel *Corylus avellana*
Hogweed *Heracleum sphondylium*
Horse-chestnut *Aesculus hippocastanum*
Iris, Yellow *Iris pseudacorus*
Lime *Tilia × europaea*
Maple, Field *Acer campestre*
Mugwort *Artemisia absinthium*
Mulberry, Black *Morus nigra*
Mustard, Garlic *Alliaria petiolata*
Oak, Red *Quercus rubra*
Oak, Sessile *Quercus petraea*
Oak, Turkey *Quercus cerris*
Rowan *Sorbus aucuparia*
Spruce, Norway *Picea abies*
St. John's-wort, Perforate *Hypericum perforatum*
Sycamore *Acer pseudoplatanus*
Vetch, Tufted *Vicia cracca*
Vetchling, Meadow *Lathyrus pratensis*
Willowherb, Great *Epilobium hirsutum*
Willowherb, Rosebay *Chamerion angustifolium*
Woundwort, Hedge *Stachys sylvatica*
Yellow-wort *Blackstonia perfoliata*

# SANDWELL VALLEY CIRCULAR WALK

## Description

Sandwell Valley Country Park is a large open green space in the heart of Birmingham and the Black Country. The 'Valley', as it is referred to by locals, is partially in Birmingham and partially in Sandwell and is virtually surrounded by dense urban sprawl. The busy M5 motorway cuts through the Valley from north to south.

Sandwell Valley has never been developed but much of its past and present history can be traced by walking around the Valley, or visiting the two visitors' centres: Forge Mill Farm and Sandwell Park Farm.

An exhibition at Sandwell Park Farm tells the story of the 12th century Sandwell Priory, of which the remains were excavated in the early 1980s. The Priory was built near to a spring known as the Holy Well or Sand Well. After the suppression of the priory in 1525 a dwelling known as Priory House stood on the site. This was later acquired by the Earl of Dartmouth and the building became known as Sandwell Hall. When the building was demolished a new Sandwell Hall was built in its place which stood up until 1928 when it too was finally demolished. A substantial part of Sandwell Valley once formed part of the Earl's estate until it was sold to the council in 1947.

Although no longer to be seen, the spoil heaps from Sandwell and Jubilee Collieries once blotted the landscape towards the northern end of the Valley. The only evidence remaining today is one of the bridges which spanned the railway line that was used to transport coal from the mines to the main railway line in Handsworth.

Remains of a World War II gun emplacement can be found on the

Birmingham side of the Valley at Hill Top.

Today there are three Local Nature Reserves in the Country Park and it is home to the first urban RSPB Reserve.

**Distance and walking time** Approximately 2½ miles. 2–2½ hours at a gentle pace.
**Starting point** Sandwell Park Farm car park (OS grid reference: SP01889138).
**Parking** Follow signs for Sandwell Valley Country Park, where there are ample parking facilities in the car park near Park Farm. The car park can be very busy at weekends and during public holidays.
**Getting there by public transport** West Bromwich town centre is served by a Metro service from Birmingham and Wolverhampton. There are bus services from most other areas of the Black Country. Sandwell Park Farm is a 10–15 minute walk from the town centre.
**Access/conditions** No access restrictions. The route is mostly on the flat along well-defined paths, but does include an ascent and descent on a poor path towards the end of the walk. Sturdy footwear is recommended.
**Facilities** Toilets and refreshments are available inside Sandwell Park Farm buildings, for opening times and admission charges visit www.sandwell.gov.uk. and at the RSPB building (subject to opening times) at the entrance to the reserve off Tanhouse Avenue. Leaflets giving information about Sandwell Valley and other local sites are available in the reception area of Park Farm buildings.

## THE WALK

The walk starts and ends at Sandwell Park Farm car park and takes in a range of different habitats including woodland, riverside valley, lakes, pools and meadows.

▲ Marsh-marigolds in Park Farm Wood

→ **From Sandwell Park Farm car park ❶, take the path through Park Farm Wood and ascend the flight of steps to the main concreted track near the motorway bridge.**

→ **Turn left crossing over the M5 and continue east, passing a track on the left that runs parallel with the motorway.**

→ **After reaching the bottom of the slope, turn left through a wooden kissing-gate and follow the obvious woodland path to the west bank of Ice-house Pool.**

Originally this pool extended further west towards Park Farm but part of it was lost to make way for the M5 motorway.

Several Silver Maple trees, with their characteristic silvery underside to the leaf have been planted near the path along the western side of the pool. A close examination of their leaves may reveal that some are infected with the mite *Vasates quadripedes,* whose feeding on the leaf causes the leaf tissue to grow out and form a gall around each mite. This gall causer was first recorded in Britain in the London area as recently as 2002.

→ **Continue along the north bank of the pool and look across to the trees on the island.**

A sizeable heronry has been established here for several years, and herons are usually to be seen perched in the branches.

→ **The path continues to the north-west corner where it meets a smaller body of water known as Cascade Pool.**

Fringed Water-lily was introduced into the pool some years ago and now forms large, dominant patches around the margins. Growing with it is the larger-leaved Yellow Water-lily, with its characteristic brandy bottle-shaped fruit. The floating leaves of the aquatic form of Amphibious Bistort reach out on to the water surface in some places around this pool.

→ **Follow the path in a clockwise direction round to the east side of Cascade Pool until you reach the small footbridge.**

As you proceed there are large patches of Great Horsetail, and in the muddy margins of the pool near the footbridge look for Butterbur. The small pool to the east of the footbridge is known as Cypress Pool, and growing directly from the water is a mature Swamp Cypress which gives the pool its name.

→ **Retrace your steps past the Butterbur and take the second path to the right (north-east).**

→ **After approximately 80 metres there is a mature Horse-chestnut to the right of the path. Continue along this path until it meets a wider track and then turn right.**

After 50 metres look on the right of the track for a well-established patch of Early Goldenrod whose leaves and stem are virtually hairless, unlike the similar looking Canadian Goldenrod, which is noticeably pubescent throughout and is found elsewhere in the Valley.

→ **This track meets a wider track after 80 metres ❷. Turn left (west) at this point and head towards Swan Pool which is in view straight ahead to your right.**
→ **Follow the track until you reach a crossroads and then turn right skirting Swan Pool in a clockwise direction along its western bank.**

▲ Island in Swan Pool

In the marginal vegetation of the pool there are patches of Yellow Iris and Southern Marsh-orchid. The orchids become more frequent as you proceed further along the path.

Directly ahead to the north of Swan Pool is an extensive wooded area known as Jubilee Mound. The pit mounds of Diamond Jubilee Colliery once dominated the landscape where the wood now stands and the whole area looked very different. A colliery tramway carried coal from the pit southwards to the railway and canals in Smethwick.

→ **Shortly before reaching the landing stage at the northernmost point of Swan Pool, leave the track and go through the gate towards the car park. Immediately before entering the car park, turn right and proceed past the buildings until you reach Forge Lane.**
→ **Cross the road and follow the sign for Beacon Way, Forge Mill Lake and Nature Centre. Continue until you cross the River Tame ❸ and take**

the track to the right with Forge Mill Lake to your left.

A mixed plantation of deciduous trees and shrubs obscures the view of the lake for the first 200 metres or so. In places Italian Alder, which was part of the original planting scheme, has self-sown here and a second generation of young trees has sprung up to form extensive patches. The river flows swiftly between steep-sided banks lined with Indian Balsam and along this stretch of the river many sightings of Kingfisher have been made in recent years. Views of the new hide replace the tree plantation and on the nearside bank, patchy scrub and tall vegetation now line the water's-edge. Along the path the pinkish flowers of Red Bartsia become apparent as the end of the lake is approached.

→ **Stay on the track between the lake and river until you reach the end of the lake, and then follow the lower path which winds its way around the marsh and up to the remains of the old RSPB Visitor Centre.**

In June and July large patches of Crown Vetch and Chicory can be seen flowering in the grassland between the building and the marsh. Crown Vetch is an attractive member of the pea family and is well established on the Reserve. Along with Chicory it was originally introduced as part of an acid grassland seed-mix sown shortly after the opening of the reserve in the early 1980s.

→ **Take the obvious path to the right (east) of the building and continue down a gentle slope until the path becomes a boardwalk.**

On the right of the path is an area of open grassland containing a variety of common plants including Common Knapweed, Tufted Vetch, Great Burnet, Meadow Vetchling, Common Bird's-foot-trefoil, Ribwort Plantain and Perforate St John's-wort. On warm sunny days in summer this is an excellent place to observe butterflies.

→ **Just before reaching the metal gate leading to the hide, turn to the right and leave the reserve. When open, the hide is an excellent viewpoint for birdwatching in the scrape and along the margins of the lake.**
→ **Proceed along the path with Forge Mill Lake on your left.**

Bee Orchids have been recorded in three places between the path and lake with mid-June being the best time to search

for plants in flower. Common Centaury is also quite common along the banks of the lake, and a white-flowered variety, growing mixed in with the more typical pink-flowered form, can be seen here.

Where an opening appears leading up into a meadow immediately before a track lined with a wooden fence, turn into this opening and walk for a few metres. An obvious damp area is apparent almost immediately to your left. During early summer, many Southern Marsh-orchids can be seen flowering here and it is also home to an extensive colony of Brown Sedge.

→ **Continue along the path to the far north of the lake where it meets the track that follows the River Tame.**
→ **Head back south along the west side of the lake.**

The island in the lake, known as North Island, once contained a small colony of Twiggy Mullein, a plant found nowhere else in Birmingham and the Black Country. Although it has not appeared recently it is worthwhile looking across to the nearside bank of the island during July and August in the hope of catching a glimpse of its tall, wand-like spikes of yellow flowers.

Large predatory Pike are often seen in the water along this stretch of the lake, and it is not unusual to catch a fleeting glimpse of a Kingfisher skimming the surface of the water.

→ **Cross the footbridge over the river ❸ and retrace your steps to the south-west corner of Swan Pool ❹.**
→ **Turn right and go over the motorway via the footbridge.**
→ **Immediately after descending the slope from the footbridge, turn left ❺ taking the narrow path up the bank. Go past a small plantation of pine trees and follow the obvious path to the left.**

Look for Medlar ❻ on the right of the path after approximately 50 metres. In the early 1990s a small specimen was discovered

▲ Medlar fruits

growing near the base of a Silver Birch. The birch has gone but the Medlar has layered extensively from its many tangled branches to form a dense, mangrove-like thicket. Its large white, hawthorn-like flowers appear during May and June, followed by solitary fruit which in some years are abundant and remain on the branches well into late autumn.

→ **Continue along the path and descend the bank which leads out onto a wide track.**
→ **Turn left to return to Park Farm and the car park beyond.**

There is much more to see at Sandwell Valley, and visitors are recommended to explore other parts throughout the different seasons of the year.

### Species mentioned in the text

Alder, Italian *Alnus cordata*
Balsam, Indian *Impatiens glandulifera*
Bartsia, Red *Odontites vernus*
Birch, Silver *Betula pendula*
Bird's-foot-trefoil, Common *Lotus corniculatus*
Bistort, Amphibious *Persicaria amphibia*
Burnet, Great *Sanguisorba officinalis*
Butterbur *Petasites hybridus*
Centaury, Common *Centaurium erythraea*
Chestnut, Horse *Aesculus hippocastanum*
Chicory *Cichorium intybus*
Cypress, Swamp *Taxodium distichum*
Goldenrod, Canadian *Solidago canadensis*
Goldenrod, Early *Solidago gigantea*
Horsetail, Great *Equisetum telmateia*
Iris, Yellow *Iris pseudacorus*
Knapweed, Common *Centaurea nigra*
Maple, Silver *Acer saccharinum*
Marsh-orchid, Southern *Dactylorhiza praetermissa*
Medlar *Mespilus germanica*
Mullein, Twiggy *Verbascum virgatum*
Orchid, Bee *Ophrys apifera*
Plantain, Ribwort *Plantago lanceolata*
Sedge, Brown *Carex disticha*
St John's-wort, Perforate *Hypericum perforatum*
Vetch, Crown *Securigera varia*
Vetch, Tufted *Vicia cracca*
Vetchling, Meadow *Lathyrus pratensis*
Water-lily, Fringed *Nymphoides peltata*
Water-lily, Yellow *Nuphar lutea*

## GALTON VALLEY WALK

### Description
A walk along canal towpaths in the Galton Valley – a man-made cutting – in the heart of the industrial Midlands. Natural and industrial history share this renowned site which was a vital transport artery during the Industrial Revolution.

Despite being within yards of Smethwick High Street and a main railway

▲ **Winter view of Galton Valley**

line this is a surprisingly peaceful and green oasis. It has not one but two canals, their banks changing colour with the seasons as the grasses, flowers, shrubs and trees bloom and fade; and birds, animals and fish find a living here. The clamour and smoke of the 19th century and the massive upheavals of the 18th century are but a memory. Many of the bridges and locks around the valley are listed buildings or scheduled ancient monuments. The jewel in the crown is the ornate Galton Bridge, spanning the deepest part of the cutting made to accommodate Telford's New Main Line in 1829.

**Distance and walking time** Approximately 1.5 miles. The walk takes about 1 hour at a gentle pace.
**Starting point** Galton Valley Canal Heritage Centre (OS grid reference: SP020890).

**Parking** Car park in Great Arthur Street near Galton Valley Heritage Centre.
**Getting there by public transport** Bus routes 80, 87, 129, 438, 444, 446, 448A, 450 and 478 all stop in the nearby Smethwick High Street. A regular rail service is available at Smethwick Galton Bridge and Rolf Street station.
**Access/conditions** There is a steep bank and some steps to negotiate; the towpath can be muddy.
**Facilities and further information** For more information visit www.sandwell.gov.uk

### THE WALK

→ **From the car park ❶ pass the Galton Valley Heritage Centre and cross the two canals. Climb the footbridge linking Brasshouse Lane with Smethwick High Street.**

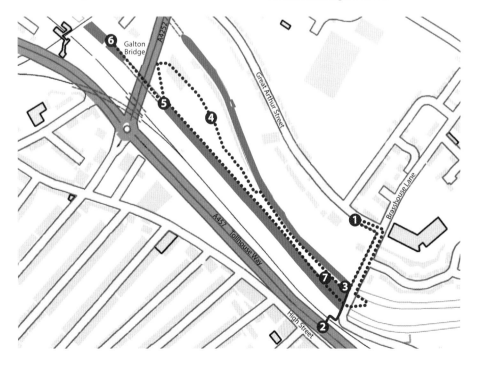

From the footbridge ❷ the nation's transport history is laid out across the valley: Smethwick High Street, a dual carriageway, a main railway line, and two canals will be seen. The canals lie in a deep cutting, the sides of which are covered in a variety of grasses, wild flowers, shrubs and trees.

Each transport system has left its mark upon what used to be an area of heathland. So much so that almost all trace – but not quite all – of the original habitat has disappeared. It is still possible, for example, to find plants like Heather and Broom growing on the sides of the cutting, the remnants of the vegetation which once flourished undisturbed for centuries on this part of the Birmingham Plateau.

→ **Go back down the steps, cross the first canal and turn left down the steps ❸ and proceed along the towpath past the Pump House.**

Leaving the High Street and railway line behind and dropping down to the canal towpath, takes you into another world within minutes. Late on a summer's evening, with the setting sun illuminating the stands of Rosebay Willowherb, the area takes on the appearance of a remote hillside covered in Heather – a curious irony when it is remembered there is now very little Heather left here and the Rosebay Willowherb is a relative newcomer. If you are fortunate and observant you might catch a fleeting glimpse of a Kingfisher as it flashes by in search of a suitable perching platform on which to alight in readiness for a rapid dive into the canal to capture any unfortunate stickleback that might be lurking below the water surface. In recent years sightings of this highly colourful bird have become more frequent along the Old Canal Level.

The Reed Sweet-grass which fringes the opposite bank provides a perfect dwelling place for Moorhens. In addition, the roots and stems of the grasses act as a sort of shock-absorber against the wash of slow-moving narrowboats.

→ **Follow the 'Nature Trail' signpost to the left of the brick wall (here is the derelict garden of Galton House) and follow the path uphill ❹ for some way to the road.**

Hedge Bedstraw has found a home among the old brickwork foundations of Galton House and the glorious tangle of vegetation all around provides a home for countless insects which buzz, crawl and jump around this mini-jungle. The great thing about places such as canal banks and derelict gardens is that because nobody comes along to mow or tidy them every couple of weeks, hundreds of plants and animals are able to thrive. The long grass favoured by the grasshoppers is also used by the beautiful dark-grey and red day-flying burnet moth. These creatures use the stems as supports for their papery cocoons, which can be found, sometimes in large numbers, high on the stalks of Cock's-foot or Timothy. The stems are not, as is sometimes thought, used as food: the caterpillars in fact feed on clovers and vetches, while the adult moths, which fly in July and August, take their nectar from flowers such as Teasel and thistles. This use of various species of plants at different times in an animal's life-cycle illustrates the importance of diversity in the urban landscape to a great number of creatures.

Near the straggly remains of an old hawthorn hedge the scarlet-berried Bittersweet scramble through the branches of other plants. The berries are the final metamorphosis from purple and yellow flowers through green and then yellow berries. The light-brown stems of a miniature forest of Raspberry canes stand out against the bright green of those of the Broom.

At the top of the hill is a small plateau and a grove of trees which include Horse-chestnut, Pedunculate Oak, Beech and Turkey Oak. The latter is an exotic oak, being a native of Southern Europe and South-west Asia which was introduced to this country in the first half of the 18th century. It is now common in parks and large gardens and is easily distinguished from other oaks by the hair-like growths at each bud and the soft moss-like covering of the acorn cups. Along the side of the path, Ground-ivy forms extensive patches rooting as it spreads across the ground. Contrary to its common name this is not an ivy at all, but in fact a pungent smelling member of the Labiate or Dead-nettle family producing 2–4 blueish-purple flowers at each node. Often found growing around here is a beautiful little cup-lichen – a type of *Cladonia*.

→ **Just before the road turn left inside the fence and find your way down to the towpath. Turn right ❺ through the tunnel and walk as far as the second bridge over the canal ❻. Turn here and walk back along the towpath to the Pump House ❼.**

This egg-shaped tunnel is the newest on the canal, having been created in 1974. Unlike conventional tunnels it was not driven through a hillside to make way for the canal, but rather placed in position and the hill then put on top to carry a new road. It is ironic to think of all the effort taken with pick, shovel and barrow to dig out the cutting only to have it filled in again. Walking through the tunnel provides a wonderful surprise view of one of the most beautiful pieces of canal hardware in the country – Galton Bridge. The next bridge along, a solid brick structure, is clearly visible before the nearer but higher and lighter Galton Bridge suddenly appears, soaring over 70 feet above the water. Built in 1829 to take the now redundant road over Telford's New Main Line, its 150-foot span arches elegantly overhead. It was the state-of-the-art when it was built – a designer bridge bringing art to artefact. It was once the world's longest single-span metal bridge, crossing the world's largest man-made earthwork.

The results of all that shovelling and burrowing are clear to see in the deep cutting through which the canal now passes. In effect the hill which formed Smethwick Summit has been turned inside-out. The original slopes around this part of the Birmingham Plateau have been built on, but they have been replaced by these artificial inclines which allow wildlife to flourish in the very heart of the industrial landscape.

On the bank to the left, Bracken, Foxgloves, Common Knapweed and Tansy may be seen. Tansy was much used by

▲ Foxglove

herbalists in the treatment of sciatica, toothache, gout and worms. It grows to about three feet and has fern-like leaves, and is one of those members of the daisy family whose flowers only have disc florets. To the right of the path, in the cracks of Telford's stone-coping at the water's edge, a plant with opposite pairs of leaves with whorls of pale, purple-spotted flowers at the bases of the leaves will be found. This is Gypsywort, a typical water's edge plant which finds canal sides very amenable.

→ **Just past the Pump House, go under the bridge and turn left and left again up a brick ramp. Cross the road and return to the car park.**

The Pump House is relatively new compared to many of the other canal buildings in the area, having been opened in 1892 to house two steam-engines. These lifted water from the New Main Line to the Old Main Line to replenish losses from the higher canal at the nearby locks. Its restoration is part of the recreational development of the canal cutting which is now named the Galton Valley Canal Park.

In October and November the water mirrors the autumn tints of the trees along the banks, white gulls wheel and mew, and hawthorns stand adorned with rich red fruit ready to feed the blackbirds and thrushes.

**Species mentioned in the text**
Bedstraw, Hedge *Galium album*
Beech *Fagus sylvatica*
Bittersweet *Solanum dulcamara*
Bracken *Pteridium aquilinum*
Broom *Cytisus scoparius*
Cock's-foot *Dactylis glomerata*
Foxglove *Digitalis purpurea*
Ground-ivy *Glechoma hederacea*
Gypsywort *Lycopus europaeus*
Heather *Calluna vulgaris*
Horse-chestnut *Aesculus hippocastanum*
Knapweed, Common *Centaurea nigra*
Oak, Pedunculate *Quercus robur*
Oak, Turkey *Quercus cerris*
Raspberry *Rubus idaeus*
Sweet-grass, Reed *Glyceria maxima*
Tansy *Tanacetum vulgare*
Teasel *Dipsacus fullonum*
Timothy *Phleum pratense*
Willowherb, Rosebay *Chamerion angustifolium*

## WREN'S NEST NATIONAL NATURE RESERVE WALK

### Description
Wren's Nest National Nature Reserve is situated to the north of Dudley town centre and is one of four limestone hills in Dudley

Borough, the others being Castle Hill to the south and Hurst Hill and Sedgley Beacon to the north.

The Silurian Limestone is home to an assemblage of lime-loving plants, some of which are extremely rare in Birmingham and the Black Country.

The mantle of green that now cloaks much of the Wren's Nest hides many of the man-made scars inflicted by the extensive quarrying carried out in this area during the industrial revolution. It is now a place of tranquillity and a haven for many species of plants and animals. Wren's Nest has gained recognition as a site of international importance for both its geology and fossils, the most notable of them being the trilobite known as the 'Dudley Bug' which features as the centrepiece of the town's coat of arms.

**Distance and walking time** Approximately 1½ miles. The walk takes about 1½ hours at a gentle pace.
**Starting point** Dudley College, Mons Hill campus car park, Wrens Hill Road, DY1 3SB (OS grid reference: SO937927).
**Parking** Visitors to Wren's Nest National Nature Reserve are currently permitted to park in the grounds of Mons Hill Campus in Wrens Hill Road.
**Getting there by public transport** Buses on routes 206 and 207 run at 30 minute intervals (from Dudley Bus Station) stopping near to the college.
**Access/conditions** For safety reasons some areas of Wren's Nest are fenced off and inaccessible. The walk is undulating and can be slippery and muddy in places. It also includes a steep flight of ascending steps. Sturdy footwear is recommended.
**Facilities and further information** Toilets and refreshments are available inside the college buildings, but for security reasons it is advisable to report your presence to security at the office as you enter the building.

The following leaflets giving information about the reserve are available from Dudley Council and can usually be obtained from the college:
• *The Wildlife of Wren's Nest National Nature Reserve*
• *The Geology of Wren's Nest Nature Reserve*
• *The Limestone Way Countryside Walks in Dudley*
• *Wren's Nest Geological Trail Guide.*
See also Dudley Metropolitan Borough Council websites;
• www.dudley.gov.uk/countryside
• www.dudley.gov.uk/wrensnest
• www.dudley.gov.uk/walks

**THE WALK**
The walk starts from the college and includes a section of Mons Hill and a circular walk around Wren's Nest. Wren's Hill Road divides Mons Hill and Wren's Nest Hill.

→ **Leave the college grounds into Wren's Hill Road ❶ and turn right (east). After a short distance, cross the road to the north side (Mons Hill) through a metal gate with a signboard welcoming visitors to Wren's Nest.**
→ **Follow the footpath until it reaches its highest point where there is a fine viewpoint ❷. On the side of the path at this point an open grassy area slopes up to a low ridge.**

The woodland comprises mainly Ash, Sycamore and Hawthorn, and patches of delicate Wood Anemone or 'Windflower' cover the banks during the spring months. Elm was once a common component of the woodland here until it was virtually wiped out by Dutch Elm Disease.

In the grassland near the ridge, to reduce fertility and encourage species diversity, much of the topsoil has been

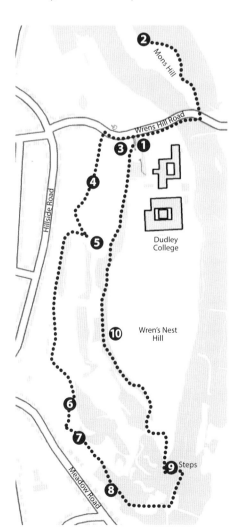

scraped away, leaving only a sparse covering over the underlying rock. A June/July visit will reward the visitor with flowering displays of Hoary Plantain, Quaking-grass, Common Centaury and Common Spotted-orchids. Cutting back and removal of the vegetation after flowering and seed-set maintains the low fertility preferred by species that grow here. This annual regime is a task carried out by the dedicated team of rangers who manage the site. At the back of this scraped area, growing along the top of the low ridge near the fence, is a small colony of Common Gromwell. This inconspicuous, pale-green-flowered herbaceous perennial occurs elsewhere on the reserve but is found nowhere else in Birmingham and the Black Country. The reasons for this are unclear, as equally suitable-looking locations exist on the other limestone hills nearby.

→ **Retrace your steps back to the road and pass the college entrance and Caves public house ❸ and take the left entrance through a metal barrier into the reserve on the south side of the road. Follow the footpath to the second rock exposure ❹ on the left at Geological trail marker 3.**

Betony and Hedge Bedstraw grow alongside each other at the base of the exposure near to the path.

→ **Continue along the path and take the left fork into the main quarry area ❺. Geological trail marker 4.**

Common Milkwort and Small Scabious can be found on the lower slopes and are relatively frequent here, although both are rare elsewhere in Birmingham and the Black Country. Quaking-grass and Bee Orchids also grow in the quarry and patches of Hoary Plantain occur on the east side near to the bottom of the long flight of steps. Slender Trefoil has also been recorded in this area in the past. In recent years Pyramidal Orchid has appeared and may be on the increase.

→ **Go back to the footpath and continue towards the viewing platform for the Ripple Beds. Geological trail marker 5. Take time to read the information board and view the Ripple Beds which are amongst one of the best examples of their kind in Europe.**
→ **Continue along the path but do not take the left fork up the steps for the Geological Trail, instead continue through the gate and past the old Lime Master's cottage on the right and lime kilns on the left.**

▲ Path descent to Geological trail marker 6

→ **Shortly after passing the occupied bungalow on the right take the path up a slight slope on the left. Pass through the wooden fence opening and turn right. Almost immediately, go up a low bank and straight ahead (not left), taking the less obvious path between Hawthorn shrubs.**
→ **Follow this path with the security fence on your left towards a metal barrier ❻.**
→ **Just beyond the barrier follow the path to the right which descends to Geological trail marker 6.**

A small colony of Bee Orchids regularly appears in the turf near the metal barrier. Near the descending steps, False Brome and Traveller's-joy clothe the bank.

→ **Continue along the track to the exposed limestone slope with a sign warning of falling rocks. For safety reasons the slope is fenced off from the public.**

Lime Master's cottage
(by Neville Walters)

→ **Descend the flight of steps ❼ and continue along the track passing some large, moss-covered, decomposing tree trunks on the right of the path ❽.**

Colonies of Wild Strawberry grow around the rock piles just inside the security fence and it was on this slope that Wall Brown butterfly was last recorded at Wrens Nest. Hereabouts Enchanter's-nightshade and Lords-and-Ladies are frequently encountered, and a little further on to the left of the path, is a specimen of Flowering Currant which could have been originally planted.

→ **At the point where the paths cross at geological trail marker 7, turn left and after 60 metres on the left ascend the 99 steps (actually 77 – count them) to Murchison's Viewpoint at the top ❾.**

Sir Roderick Murchison was a founder member of the Geological Society of

Lime kilns (by Neville Walters)

London and was the author of 'The Silurian System', based on the study of Dudley's fossils.

You can enjoy excellent views of nearby Dudley Castle and the surrounding area from this spot.

→ **Continue along the path and at the point where the path forks ❿ go straight on, passing through a gap in a low stone wall. After a further 20 metres turn left up a slight slope and go through a metal gate. Turn right and continue for 20 metres or so.**

In late March and early April the wooded bank at the side of the path is the place to search for Toothwort. Toothwort belongs to the Broomrape (Orobanchaceae) family of plants, which are entirely lacking in chlorophyll. In early spring, the waxy-white stems with scale-like, stalkless leaves sprouting tiers of whitish-cream, purple-tinged flowers push through the leaf-litter and appear around the roots of various shrubs and trees in this area. Hazel appears to be the preferred host but plants also occur beneath Hawthorn and Sycamore, suggesting they are parasitic on these species too. This is undeniably a Wren's Nest speciality plant and this is probably the most dependable site in which to see it in Birmingham and the Black Country, but even here its appearance can be erratic. In some years many hundreds of spikes appear, in other years a thorough search will be fruitless – the reasons for this are unclear.

→ **Proceed along the path until you reach the green painted metal fence overlooking the rubble-filled openings to the Seven Sisters, considered to be the last remaining surface-opening limestone cavern in the world.**

At the end of the fence is a viewing platform looking down into the quarry. Near the bottom is a grid-covered entrance which leads into a cave opened up as an alternative roost to accommodate the large bat population which was prevented from returning to its original winter-roosts when the entrances to the Seven Sisters were filled in.

On the banks nearby, showy Wood Anemone intermingles with less conspicuous Dog's Mercury and occasional patches of Early Dog-violet, which comes into flower earlier in the spring than its similar-looking cousin, Common Dog-violet. In late summer two conspicuous woodland grasses dominate both sides of

▲ **View towards Ripple Beds and Fossil Coral Reef**

the path; False Brome, with yellow-green hairy leaves, and the much taller Hairy-brome, with its conspicuous flat, drooping, hairy leaves.

→ **Continue to the top of the quarry viewpoint at Geological trail marker 10 with the steep-sided, tree and shrub covered bank on your left.**

Take time to read the board which provides interesting information about the rocks, fossils and lime-loving plants found at Wren's Nest National Nature Reserve.

→ **Continue along the path which skirts the top of the steep-sided wooded quarry edge.**

Wayfaring-tree, a medium-sized deciduous shrub of woodland edges and hedgerows in base-rich soils, is relatively frequent in this part of the reserve. Elsewhere in Birmingham and the Black Country it is considered to be introduced, but here at Wren's Nest its naturally occurring status is less clear.

Toothwort often occurs on the exposed roots of Hazel on the steep-sided, densely-wooded bank, but great care should be taken as the banks fall away very steeply in this area.

→ **Continue along the path, passing a small pond containing patches of Marsh-marigold. Shortly afterwards regain Wrens Hill Road near the Caves public house and so return back to the start of the walk ❸.**

**Species mentioned in the text**

Anemone, Wood *Anemone nemorosa*
Ash *Fraxinus excelsior*
Bedstraw, Hedge *Galium album*
Betony *Betonica officinalis*
Brome, False *Brachypodium sylvaticum*
Centaury, Common *Centaurium erythraea*
Currant, Flowering *Ribes sanguineum*
Dog's Mercury *Mercurialis perennis*
Dog-violet, Early *Viola reichenbachiana*
Enchanter's-nightshade *Circaea lutetiana*
Gromwell, Common *Lithospermum officinale*
Hairy-brome *Bromopsis ramosa*
Hawthorn *Crataegus monogyna*
Hazel *Corylus avellana*
Lords-and-Ladies *Arum maculatum*
Marsh-marigold *Caltha palustris*
Milkwort, Common *Polygala vulgaris*
Orchid, Bee *Ophrys apifera*
Orchid, Pyramidal *Anacamptis pyramidalis*
Plantain, Hoary *Plantago media*
Quaking-grass *Briza media*
Scabious, Small *Scabiosa columbaria*
Spotted-orchid, Common *Dactylorhiza fuchsii*
Strawberry, Wild *Fragaria vesca*
Sycamore *Acer pseudoplatanus*
Toothwort *Lathraea squamaria*
Traveller's-joy *Clematis vitalba*
Trefoil, Slender *Trifolium micranthum*
Wayfaring-tree *Viburnum lantana*

## FENS POOLS WALK

**Description**

Fens Pools is one of the jewels in the crown of Dudley's nature reserves. Its many pools and ponds, in addition to disused canals, comprise the largest area of open water in the borough, amazingly rich in both flora and fauna. Amphibians are well represented by frogs and toads, Smooth Newts and Great Crested Newts – the latter forming one of the largest populations in Britain. It is for this reason the reserve is designated a Site of Special Scientific Interest (SSSI) and in part a Special Area of Conservation (SAC). Many birdwatchers are drawn to the area where they regularly see Great Crested Grebe (and possibly their courtship dance in the spring), Little Grebe, and a wide variety of waterfowl. They are also occasionally rewarded with sightings of Bittern, Osprey, Phalarope, and Jack Snipe and many other birds including raptors, owls, warblers – in fact the Pensnett Wildlife Group have listed 183 bird species in their excellent book of 2005 –'The Story of The Pensnett Wildlife Group'. This is a book on the history of the reserve, and of the Pensnett Wildlife Group that founded it, and which lists the fauna and flora to be found there.

The surrounding landscape – a mosaic of grassland, scrub, and incipient or remnant woodland – was formed incidentally through the activities of man as he exploited the rich natural resources of the area. The coal and iron industries have left a legacy of tipped waste and slag heaps rich in minerals, and with the lime from the blast furnaces this provides for a very interesting and varied flora, with Southern

Marsh-orchid, Field Mouse-ear, the unusual Adder's-tongue, and White Mullein as some of the stars. Over 450 plant species have been recorded here in recent years, including trees and shrubs, grasses, sedges, rushes, ferns, and pondweeds, as well as the more colourful flowering plants.

You may be sure that at whatever season you visit, you will not be disappointed – and there is always something new to see.

**Distance and walking time** 2–2½ miles. You can complete this walk under two hours if you ignore the diversions and just walk steadily enjoying what you see but not stopping long to look for hidden treasures. However, if you are keen to see all this reserve has to offer, do bring a drink and a sandwich and take your time over it.

**Starting point** The car park (by the children's playground) at the junction of Pensnett Road (B4179) and Bryce Road on the northern edge of Dell Stadium (OS grid reference: SO911881).

**Parking** There is ample parking in the car park. There is also a car park at Chapel Street, near the Fens Pool Community Centre, and the walk could start from there.

**Getting there by public transport** Buses 222, 254, and 255 all stop near the site.

**Access/conditions** Walking is fairly easy on the whole, but please note that there is a long series of wide steps down (and some up) at the south-east corner of Middle Pool. Since it is a wetland reserve you should expect to find mud in places (except in a very dry season). Strong footwear recommended.

**Facilities and further information**
The facilities at Fens Pools include a warden's base. There are no specific opening times for public access to this building and therefore visits should be by appointment. There are toilet facilities available whenever a warden is in attendance (which does not include weekends). Fens Pools and Buckpool Nature Reserve is managed by Dudley Council. Information can be found on the Website and on leaflets available at public libraries in the Dudley area.

**THE WALK**
A circular walk around the Fens Pools (with optional diversions) starting and ending at the warden's office.

→ **From the car park, turn right and walk a few hundred yards up the main road to the crossing point; after crossing, continue uphill for a short distance to an entrance on the left into Fens Pools and Buckpool Nature Reserve ❶.**

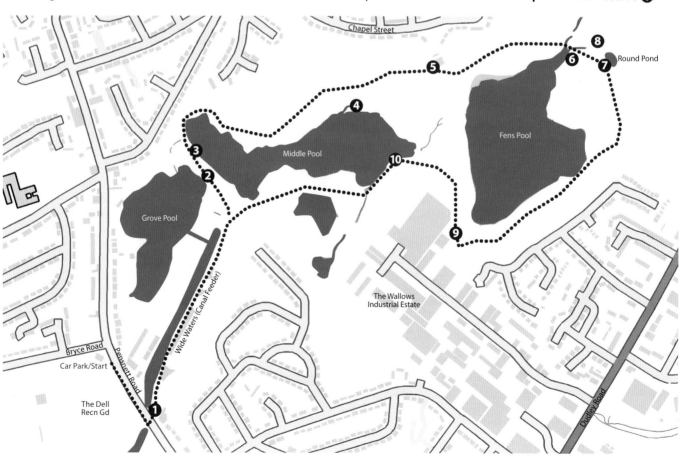

▲ Wide Waters

The stretch of canal on your left is known as Wide Waters. On the banks are many trees, such as Field Maple, Hazel, Alder, Rowan and several species of willow including Crack-willow and Osier. Within minutes of leaving the busy road you will find here an amazing sense of tranquillity. Pause to take in the beauty of the trees reflected in the water and to watch for Coot and Moorhen bobbing about.

In the gaps between trees, look for waterside plants such as Gipsywort, Yellow Iris, and Lesser Water-parsnip. Aquatic plants include Water-starwort, Nuttall's Waterweed, Ivy-leaved Duckweed and the pretty Fringed Water-lily, which has yellow fringed flowers in summer; the tall Reed Sweet-grass with its graceful feathery heads grows near the bank. Across the canal, look for a stunning Mock-orange full of snow-white blossom in June, and a beautiful wild rose bush cascading down to the surface of the water and reflected there.

A large stand of Bulrush marks the end of this short stretch of canal. A few yards further on brings the first view of Grove Pool ❷, another tranquil scene with swans and other water fowl. Down the steps is a large patch of the yellow Dotted Loosestrife.

→ **In a few yards, pass through the green barrier-gate. Middle Pool lies just ahead, with a bench ❸ affording a good view of the waterfowl**.

Little Grebe and Great Crested Grebe may be found here at times, as well as Tufted Duck. Plants to be found around here include Wild Carrot, Common Toadflax, Colt's-foot and Weld.

→ **Walk on to the left until the road bends left. At this point turn right onto a track passing between two posts**.

As you go, note the light grey-green leaves of the aromatic plant Wormwood on your right; leaves of this plant were chewed by furnace-stokers in the forges to keep the saliva running, as it was such hot work.

The larva of an uncommon moth, "The Wormwood" (*Cucullia absinthii*), which feeds on the flowers of Wormwood and Mugwort, was found in summer 2010 at Fens Pools by local naturalists. It is a rather local species, occurring in scattered locations throughout England and Wales.

→ **Bear right at the next green barrier and follow the path round to the right to Middle Pool, watching for honeysuckle in the hedge. Purple Willow also grows along here.**

The path takes you close to the pool, with Hard Rush and Common Spike-rush at the water's edge, and Common Bird's-foot-trefoil (sometimes called 'eggs-and-bacon' because of its red buds and yellow flowers) on the verge amongst Red and White Clovers. On your left you will pass three small ponds named "the Perry Ponds" in honour of the late naturalist Alan Perry, one of the two local men (the other being Brian Jones) who had the vision of saving the Fens as a nature reserve, and started the Pensnett Wildlife Group, without which the reserve may never have been created.

Here too, is an opportunity to compare two plants that might seem confusing: one is Mare's-tail, growing in the pool – an aquatic flowering plant, its tiny green flowers hidden at the base of whorls of soft narrow leaves; and the other is Field Horsetail, on which you are probably standing as you look at the mare's-tail! Horsetails are very primitive plants related to ferns, and so propagate by spores produced in cones, rather than seeds in fruits. The stems and the whorls of thin branches are jointed, and at the joints are very small triangular leaves.

In the second pond there is Jointed Rush, more Common Spike-rush, and an interesting emergent plant, Branched Bur-reed (whose flowers form bur-like clusters). There are various sedges in the grassland near the ponds.

→ **Follow this path slightly uphill to an open grassy area where Common Knapweed grows (the pylon ahead is a useful landmark).**

There is much hawthorn scrub on the right. At a break in the hawthorn the grassy area is colourful with purple-flowered Tufted Vetch, Yellow-rattle and Meadow Buttercup.

**Diversion 1**:
→ **After passing the pylon you will come to a clear view of Middle Pool on your right. Head towards the next patch of hawthorn and, immediately before it, wander down ❹ over the grass.**

On the left is a wet flush with wetland species such as Ragged-Robin, Common Fleabane, Greater Bird's-foot-trefoil, Water Mint, Hemp-agrimony, various ferns, sedges, and rushes, and (especially in June) the deep pink/purple spikes of Southern Marsh-orchid.

Back on track, over on the left there are some cindery mounds covered in vegetation. These have been colonised by Field Mouse-ear, a low-growing plant found mainly in the east of England but occasionally cropping up elsewhere. It flowers in spring, the large white flowers similar to those of the garden plant Snow-in-summer. Also there is Thyme-leaved Speedwell, Oxford Ragwort, Common Knapweed and Lady's Bedstraw.

→ **Walking over the grass, in a few yards veer left on a cindery track. There is a nice patch of Creeping Cinquefoil as you reach a junction of small paths by the Fens Pools Community Centre ❺. Turn left towards the Centre, then bear right following the footpath.**

Cut-leaved Crane's-bill is on the left hand corner before the turn, and in the hedge is Wild Privet, with longer, narrower leaves than the garden variety and creamy flowers in June.

→ **This path takes you along the north side of Fens Pool, though the water is not yet in view. Head towards some buildings seen above the trees ahead. The hedges are full of wild roses. After a while the path veers right skirting the hawthorn hedge. Where there is a little track left, look for the pretty grey-pink 'furry' heads of Hare's-foot Clover – but stay on the main track.**

**Diversion 2:**
→ **When you reach a break in the dense hawthorn, follow the little path on the right towards the edge of the pool ❻ where there is a stream and marshy ground.**

Look here for the blue-flowered Brooklime, Water Mint, Hoary Willowherb, Selfheal, Trifid Bur-marigold and two similar looking plants, often mistaken for each other, Fool's-water-cress (an umbellifer) and Water-cress (a crucifer). Red Goosefoot has also been seen here.

**Return to the path.**
→ **Continue along the path until you reach Round Pond on your left ❼.**

In this pond, Water-crowfoot, Water-plantain, Floating Sweet-grass, and Broad-leaved Pondweed can be found. Amphibious Bistort is abundant, its pink spikes of flowers held above its floating leaves. When growing on land, the leaves of Amphibious Bistort are more erect and hairy. Curled Dock and Marsh Yellow-cress grow at the edge of the pond, with Common Toadflax and White Campion nearby. Moving on, Tansy and Yellow-rattle grow beside the path.

**Diversion 3:**
→ **The Ridge and Furrow Meadow ❽. A few paces back from Round Pond, look at the grassland to the left of it and you will see an area known to locals as "the bumpy field" because the ridges and furrows of a by-gone agricultural system are still very evident.**

Around this area of damp grassland, colourful in summer with Meadow Buttercup, Common Knapweed and Common Ragwort, there are various

ponds where dragonflies and amphibians may be found. Look near or under the Bracken edging the sides and top end of this area and you may find Adder's-tongue, an unusual little fern that is indicative of unimproved grassland.

**Diversion 4:**
→ **Look across the Ridge and Furrow Meadow to the grey roofs of the nearby factory and walk towards it. A path leads uphill along metal railings onto a wide level area known as 'the Plateau'.**

This area is the result of years of tipping of furnace waste and the storage of lime and coal, so that an interesting well-drained soil with some lime content has been produced. A walk to the top is rewarded by extensive views of the whole reserve and over to the south, the Shropshire hills, in the distance. Many interesting plants have been found here, including calcicoles such as Ploughman's-spikenard and Blue Fleabane. Others include Fairy Flax, Small Toadflax, and Thyme-leaved Sandwort. Dappled Hawkweed and Small-flowered Evening-primrose have appeared, and the rare White Mullein has also been seen – although this plant is now appearing in other areas as well.

The vegetation of this man-made habitat is changing as natural succession takes its course, so that many of the small plants are being replaced by larger perennials, shrubs and trees.

→ **After either or both of these diversions, return to the path, pass the Round Pond and continue, rounding the south-east corner of Fens Pool and continuing along the south side of it.**

On the sloping banks of the pool is a tapestry of wild flowers including Oxeye Daisy, Musk-mallow, Common Bird's-foot-trefoil, various clovers, Goat's-beard (a dandelion-type flower that forms the largest "clock"), Hairy Tare, Selfheal, and Bloody Crane's-bill. Amphibious Bistort is also found here in its terrestrial form, upright, having long narrow leaves with stiff adpressed hairs.

→ **As you near the southwest corner of Fens Pool, walk (on upper or lower paths) towards the pylon until you ascend a slope and are facing a graffiti-decorated concrete wall.**
→ **Turn right by the pylon, and almost at its feet pause to look at an old wheel, an industrial relic, half-buried in solid slag ❾.**

**Visible remains of wheel** (by Anne Daly)

This half-wheel now serves on the Reserve's logo. Wild Mignonette, Charlock, and White Mullein have been seen close by.

→ **Continue through some posts along the side of the boundary wall of Sunrise Medical.**

Where the wall turns a corner look for a tall crucifer, Hoary Mustard, and you may also find White Mullein which has been seen in the past at the base of the steep slope.

→ **From here, one can either follow the main path northwards back to the Community Centre, and retrace steps to the car park; but our more interesting route lies along the southern edge of Middle Pool. To get there, proceed down a long series of wide and not-too-steep steps that leads down to the water's edge.**

A break in the trees ❿ gives a lovely view of the full length of Middle Pool. Under the trees are Soft Shield-fern, Hart's-tongue and Broad Buckler-fern. More examples of industrial waste can be seen on the left.

→ **At the end of this path, cross the small wooden bridge and turn to look at the wet patch to the right of it.**

More Southern Marsh-orchids may be seen here, with Gypsywort, Tufted Forget-me-not, Water-plantain, Common Fleabane, Meadow Vetchling, Common Spike-rush, Toad Rush and Marsh Foxtail. Common Club-rush and Cuckooflower grow by Middle Pool.

→ **From here, walk over the grass and slightly to the right to the crest of the hill. Walk up to the smaller pool ahead of you and as you move along the edge to the right watch out for Water-plantain.**
→ **Cross the concrete sluice* and a bit further on you may find the little**

▲ View across two of the pools

starry flowers of Lesser Stitchwort.
[* should this be too wet, retrace your
steps and go left round the pool and
straight ahead to join the main path.]
→ **Walk a few yards across the grass to
the right, then turn left on a narrow
track** (in summer there is a clump of
Bladder Campion on the corner)**, until
you reach the main track.**
→ **Go left a few yards to a narrow track
downhill** (a patch of Meadow Crane's-
bill grows on the corner)**.**
→ **Carefully follow the steep track into
an open meadow across which you
can walk back to the start. Continue
to the main road and the car park. If
the track is too steep, go back right
along the main track to the green
barrier where you came in, turn left
onto the lower path and follow it
back to the main road.**

### Species mentioned in the text
Adder's-tongue *Ophioglossum vulgatum*
Alder *Alnus glutinosa*
Bedstraw, Lady's *Galium verum*
Bird's-foot-trefoil, Common *Lotus corniculatus*
Bird's-foot-trefoil, Greater *Lotus pedunculatus*
Bistort, Amphibious *Persicaria amphibia*
Brooklime *Veronica beccabunga*
Buckler fern, Broad *Dryopteris dilatata*
Bulrush *Typha latifolia*
Bur-marigold, Trifid *Bidens frondosa*
Bur-reed, Branched *Sparganium erectum*
Buttercup, Meadow *Ranunculus acris*
Campion, Bladder *Silene vulgaris*
Campion, White *Silene latifolia*
Carrot, Wild *Daucus carota*
Charlock *Sinapis arvensis*
Cinquefoil, Creeping *Potentilla reptans*
Clover, Hare's-foot *Trifolium arvense*
Club-rush, Common *Schoenoplectus lacustris*
Colt's-foot *Tussilago farfara*
Crane's-bill, Bloody *Geranium sanguineum*
Crane's-bill, Cut-leaved *Geranium dissectum*

Crane's-bill, Meadow *Geranium pratense*
Cuckooflower *Cardamine pratensis*
Daisy, Oxeye *Leucanthemum vulgare*
Dock, Curled *Rumex crispus*
Duckweed, Ivy-leaved, *Lemna trisulca*
Evening-primrose, Small-flowered *Oenothera biennis*
Flax, Fairy *Linum catharticum*
Fleabane, Blue *Erigeron acris*
Fleabane, Common *Pulicaria dysenterica*
Fool's-water-cress *Apium nodiflorum*
Forget-me-not, Tufted *Myosotis laxa*
    subsp. *caespitosa*
Foxtail, Marsh, *Alopecurus geniculatus*
Goat's-beard *Tragopogon pratensis*
Goosefoot, Red *Chenopodium rubrum*
Gypsywort *Lycopus europaeus*
Hart's-tongue *Asplenium scolopendrium*
Hawkweed, Dappled *Hieracium* cf. *scotostictum*
Hazel *Corylus avellana*
Hemp-agrimony *Eupatorium cannabinum*
Honeysuckle *Lonicera periclymenum*
Horsetail, Field *Equisetum arvense*
Iris, Yellow *Iris pseudacorus*
Knapweed, Common *Centaurea nigra*
Loosestrife, Dotted *Lysimachia punctata*
Maple, Field *Acer campestre*
Mare's-tail *Hippuris vulgaris*
Marsh-orchid, Southern *Dactylorhiza praetermissa*
Mignonette, Wild *Reseda lutea*
Mint, Water *Mentha aquatica*
Mock-orange *Philadelphus* sp.
Mouse-ear, Field *Cerastium arvense*
Mullein, White *Verbascum lychnitis*
Musk-mallow *Malva moschata*
Mustard, Hoary *Hirschfeldia incana*
Osier *Salix viminalis*
Ploughman's-spikenard *Inula conyzae*
Pondweed, Broad-leaved *Potamogeton natans*
Privet, Wild *Ligustrum vulgare*
Ragged-Robin *Silene flos-cuculi*
Ragwort, Common *Senecio jacobaea*
Ragwort, Oxford *Senecio squalidus*
Rowan *Sorbus aucuparia*
Rush, Hard *Juncus inflexus*
Rush, Jointed *Juncus articulatus*

Rush, Toad *Juncus bufonius* agg.
Sandwort, Thyme-leaved *Arenaria serpyllifolia*
Selfheal *Prunella vulgaris*
Shield-fern, Soft *Polystichum setiferum*
Speedwell, Thyme-leaved *Veronica serpyllifolia*
Spike-rush, Common *Eleocharis palustris*
Stitchwort, Lesser *Stellaria graminea*
Sweet-grass, Floating *Glyceria fluitans*
Sweet-grass, Reed *Glyceria maxima*
Tansy *Tanacetum vulgare*
Tare, Hairy *Vicia hirsuta*
Toadflax, Common *Linaria vulgaris*
Toadflax, Small *Chaenorhinum minus*
Trefoil, Bird's-foot *Lotus corniculatus*
Vetch, Tufted *Vicia cracca*
Vetchling, Meadow *Lathyrus pratensis*
Water-cress *Nasturtium officinale* agg.
Water-crowfoot *Ranunculus aquatilis sensu lato*
Water-lily, Fringed, *Nymphoides peltata*
Water-parsnip, Lesser *Berula erecta*
Water-plantain *Alisma plantago-aquatica*
Water-starwort *Callitriche* sp..
Waterweed, Nuttall's *Elodea nuttallii*
Weld *Reseda luteola*
Willow, Crack *Salix fragilis*
Willow, Purple *Salix purpurea*
Willowherb, Hoary *Epilobium parviflorum*
Wormwood *Artemisia absinthium*
Yellow-cress, Marsh *Rorippa palustris*
Yellow-rattle *Rhinanthus minor*

## SALTWELLS WOOD AND DOULTON'S CLAYPIT WALK

### Description
This is wonderfully varied woodland, its
history is as rich as its wildlife, and the
geology of the disused claypit is of such
value that it has been notified as a Site of
Special Scientific Interest (SSSI). The wood
and the claypit together were declared the
first Local Nature Reserve in the county of
West Midlands in September 1981. There is
a great contrast between the open aspect
around the lip of the claypit and the dark
recesses of the wood. Although some of the
trees now present were planted about 200
years ago, woodland has probably been on
the site for many centuries.

**Distance and walking time** Approximately
    1.5 miles. The walk takes about 1–1½
    hours at a gentle pace.
**Starting point** Reserve car park near Saltwells
    Inn. (OS grid reference: SO93418691).
**Parking** Follow the signs off Saltwells Road
    to Saltwells Inn and park either in the
    reserve car park (open until 4.00pm) or
    on the space between the car park and
    the inn.
**Getting there by public transport**
    Services 217, 258, 276 and 282 all stop
    nearby in Saltwells Road.

**Access/conditions** An undulating walk on good paths, but including the descent and ascent of steps that can be wet and slippery.

**Facilities and further information** Refreshments and toilet facilities are available at Saltwells Inn.

### THE WALK

→ **Go through a five-bar gate to the right of the entrance to the car park ❶ with a small factory at your back.**
→ **Walk straight ahead past the claypit on the right.**

The tides of history may have flowed over and around this last remaining fragment of a once-great forest stretching from Cannock in the north to the Wyre Forest in the south, but, rock-like, the woodland is here still.

To the right of the path is a stand of Blackthorn. The blackthorn leaves are covered with hundreds of galls. These galls are tiny white pustules caused by tiny relatives of the spider, called gall mites, which live inside the pustules, so gaining a degree of protection from predators. On the left of this path is a meadow, golden with buttercups in summer. Almost without warning the land to the right falls away and a stunning view of Doulton's Claypit is revealed. As its name suggests this mighty

▲ View across Doulton's Claypit

excavation, now about 50 feet shallower than it used to be after partial infilling, was used to supply clay for Doultons. The mineral taken from here was not destined for the dining rooms of high society, but for bathrooms – it was used in the making of sanitary earthenware and clay pipes. Since clayworking ceased in the 1940s the slopes of the pit have become clothed in shrubs and trees, consisting mainly of birch, oak and hawthorn.

The most spectacular features of the claypit, and the reason for its designation as an SSSI, are the sections of exposed

rock showing the different layers which underlie the area. Each level shows where succeeding tropical swamps played host to plants and creatures even more varied and fantastic than those enjoying our more temperate climate today.

→ **Agile climbers can easily descend into the claypit ❷ and out again to rejoin the path.**

For those wishing to explore the flora of the claypit, go over the stile and down the path. As you descend into the claypit,

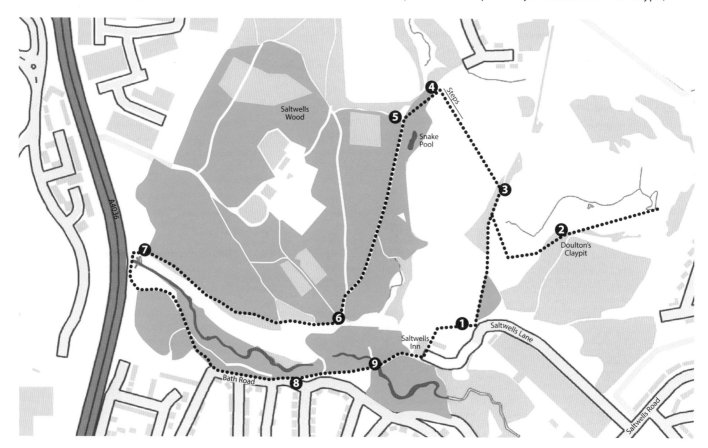

Salad Burnet frequents the sides of the path intermingled with Creeping Cinquefoil and Bird's-foot-trefoil. Near the bottom of the slope, from around mid-summer onwards, the erect, reddish-purple, whorled flower-spikes of Betony protrude between patches of willow scrub. Nearby, a small stream and a continuous seepage of water from the hillside have created constantly moist ground conditions in which the attractive, roundish, violet-blue flower-heads of Devil's-bit Scabious can be seen. The moist ground found in the bottom of the claypit provides ideal growing conditions for moisture-loving species such as Southern Marsh-orchid and Yellow Iris which produce a glorious flowering display of purple and yellow blooms during June and July. They are followed by Hemp-agrimony, Purple-loosestrife, Marsh Thistle, Sharp-flowered Rush and many others, ensuring a continuous flowering display well into autumn. Lesser Bulrush is dominant in the margins of one of the small ponds in the claypit, but down here is reluctant to produce its unmistakable, narrow, cylindrical inflorescence. Sharing its watery habitat are Common Club-rush, Broad-leaved Pondweed, Fool's-water-cress, Lesser Water-parsnip and in the vegetation surrounding the pond the pinkish-white, vanilla-scented flowers of Common Valerian, a generally scarce plant in Birmingham and the Black Country.

At the far end of the claypit is a small clear pond, which has shoals of small fish darting in all directions on one's approach. Unbranched Bur-reed frequents its muddy margins, and just below the water surface Ivy-leaved Duckweed shelters a wealth of pond creatures that live here.

Natural succession over many years has resulted in the claypit becoming increasingly more wooded. In the few remaining open areas Zigzag Clover, Bird's-foot-trefoil, Common Knapweed, Angelica, Betony and stands of Rosebay and Great Willowherb colonise the sides of the path. Soft Lady's-mantle, which originates from the Carpathian Mountains, has found conditions here very much to its liking and in places lines the sides of the path.

→ **Retrace your steps out of the claypit and continue along the path.**
→ **Just before the path splits, turn left ❸ up a ramp by a Sycamore tree on to a flat open area.**
→ **Go straight across and descend a long flight of steps, turning left at the bottom ❹, passing a pool on the left.**

The flat area – locally called the 'Table Top' – is the top of one of the spoil heaps which was thrown up when the pit was excavated and used as a football pitch by the workers. Today it is dotted with Oxeye Daisies and takes on a soft-red hue because of the low-growing flowers of Sheep's Sorrel. The bright-yellow flowers of Mouse-ear-hawkweed and the white umbels of Elder add more colour to the scene. At the top of the steps a distant view of Netherton Top Church perched upon the next hill will be glimpsed. At the foot of the steps on the left, there is a dark and mysterious woodscape where Ivy scrambles over the ground beneath a low, dense canopy of Hawthorn, whilst on the right there is another meadow gleaming brightly with a million buttercups.

→ **At the T-junction turn left ❺ along the 'Sculpture Trail'.**

Soft pink Dog-roses mark the way here and moths, flowerbugs, bees and hoverflies make their own erratic journeys through the wood. Dragonflies and damselflies also frequent this area, a pool providing a home for their nymphs. Great Diving Beetles, frogs and toads breed here in Snake Pool – a name not at all fanciful because there is a thriving colony of Grass Snakes in this part of Saltwells Wood. These harmless reptiles are one of only three species of snake found wild in Britain.

→ **At the five ways ❻ take the path second right and continue straight ahead at the crossroads.**
→ **Continue along this path passing a five-bar wooden gate ❼ on the right, ascend five wooden sleeper steps and follow the path with a hedge and the road above you to the right.**

The clearing where the five paths meet is a good place for watching butterflies in summer. About two dozen types have been found in the wood including Speckled Wood, and both Green and Purple Hairstreak.

The path now runs along the line of an old railway, once used to take coal to the Earl of Dudley's steelworks at Brierley Hill, later to become the Round Oak Steelworks, which is now where Merry Hill Shopping Centre stands. Taking a detour along the path to the right of the brick culvert, you'll see the yellow flowers and red spiky fruits of Wood Avens intertwined with Greater Stitchwort, Cleavers and the evil-smelling Hedge Woundwort, all overlooked by the flat-topped umbels of Hogweed.

→ **Turn left just where the steps come down from the road on the right.**
→ **Walk straight on, keeping the stream on the left.**

The stream is screened at first by the remnants of an old hedge, close inspection

▲ Junction of 'Sculpture Trail'

of which reveals that it is mainly composed of Garden Privet. It is the remains of a garden hedge which belonged to a cottage which stood by the Tipsyford Brook. On the other side of the path deep shadows hide the interior of the woodland, bringing an air of mystery and darkness. In some places around here grows the plant with perhaps the most magical name of any in Britain, Enchanter's-nightshade. Curiously it is not a nightshade at all but a willowherb, sending up spikes of tiny white flowers. It is often in fruit at the base of the stem whilst still in bud at the top. This characteristic can be seen displayed by its more prominent cousin, Rosebay Willowherb.

→ **Go through a five-bar gateway onto the road and then through another five-bar gateway ❽ and continue straight on down the path, passing over a footbridge ❾.**

This part of the wood is close to the site of the enterprise which gave it the name of Saltwells. (It has been variously called part of Pensnett Chase, Ladywood and Casson's Wood, the latter being the name of one of the keepers who lived at Saltwells House). Long before the Industrial Revolution the whole area was used for supplies of timber, clay and coal. One unsuccessful coal mining venture may have led to the discovery of brine as the pit flooded and became unworkable. In the *Natural History of Staffordshire* by Robert Plot, published in 1636, the following appears:

"In Pensnet Chase south from Dudley about a mile and a half there is another weak brine belonging to the right Honorable Edward Lord Ward of which his lordship once attempted to make salt; but the brine proving too weak, he thought fit to desist, though possibly it might have been advanced to profit by the Art of Tunnelling much used in Cheshire to keep out the freshes."

Extract quoted in *The Saltwells Near Dudley*, by E. Blocksidge

Making salt by evaporation may not have been profitable, but operating baths in later centuries certainly was. Saltwells became a spa, the most important in this part of the Midlands, and people travelled from miles away to 'take the waters'.

→ **Ascend the short slope to Saltwells Inn on the left.**
→ **At the Saltwells Inn go between the inn and the houses to return to the car park.**

## Species mentioned in the text

Angelica *Angelica sylvestris*
Avens, Wood *Geum urbanum*
Betony *Betonica officinalis*
Bird's-foot-trefoil, Common *Lotus corniculatus*
Blackthorn *Prunus spinosa*
Bluebell *Hyacinthoides non-scripta*
Bulrush, Lesser *Typha angustifolia*
Burnet, Salad *Poterium sanguisorba* subsp. *sanguisorba*
Bur-reed, Unbranched *Sparganium emersum*
Cinquefoil, Creeping *Potentilla reptans*
Cleavers *Galium aparine*
Clover, Zigzag *Trifolium medium*
Club-rush, Common *Schoenoplectus lacustris*
Daisy, Oxeye *Leucanthemum vulgare*
Dog-rose *Rosa canina* agg.
Duckweed, Ivy-leaved *Lemna trisulca*
Elder *Sambucus nigra*
Enchanter's-nightshade *Circaea lutetiana*
Fool's-water-cress *Apium nodiflorum*
Hawthorn *Crataegus monogyna*
Hemp-agrimony *Eupatorium cannabinum*
Hogweed *Heracleum sphondylium*
Iris, Yellow *Iris pseudacorus*
Ivy *Hedera helix*
Knapweed, Common *Centaurea nigra*
Lady's-mantle, Soft *Alchemilla mollis*
Marsh-orchid, Southern *Dactylorhiza praetermissa*
Mouse-ear-hawkweed *Pilosella officinarum*
Pondweed, Broad-leaved *Potamogeton natans*
Privet, Garden *Ligustrum ovalifolium*
Purple-loosestrife *Lythrum salicaria*
Rush, Sharp-flowered *Juncus acutiflorus*
Scabious, Devil's-bit *Succisa pratensis*
Sorrel, Sheep's *Rumex acetosella*
Stitchwort, Greater *Stellaria holostea*
Thistle, Marsh *Cirsium palustre*
Valerian, Common *Valeriana officinalis*
Water-parsnip, Lesser *Berula erecta*
Willowherb, Great *Epilobium hirsutum*
Willowherb, Rosebay *Chamerion angustifolium*
Woundwort, Hedge *Stachys sylvatica*

## THE EASTSIDE OF BIRMINGHAM WALK

### Description

This is a circular walk that begins and ends at Moor Street Railway Station ❶ and includes many buildings of historical significance. It can be undertaken at any time of the year. To appreciate the flora colonising the areas of dereliction fully, the best time for a visit is considered to be from June to late October. Birmingham's Eastside is changing rapidly, and some of the buildings mentioned may have gone or could soon disappear.

### Distance and walking time
Approximately 3.7 miles. The walk takes about 2½ hours at an easy pace.

**Starting point** Moor Street Railway Station (OS grid reference: SP07358675).
**Parking** There are several car parks near to Moor Street Station but they fill quickly, particularly on Saturdays. Pay and Display parking is available in many of the side roads near to the station, but check for restrictions which may apply.
**Getting there by public transport** Travelling into Birmingham by public transport is recommended. There are regular train services into Moor Street Station, and New Street Station is only a few minutes walk. Buses from all directions terminate in Birmingham City Centre.
**Access/conditions** No restricted areas. Good quality footpaths and canal towpaths, mainly on the level.
**Facilities and further information** Toilets are available at the station and in the Custard Factory. There are public houses, cafés and shops in various places, particularly on the later stages of the walk.

### THE WALK

→ **Leave the station ❶ through the main entrance and turn right past the station building and immediately into the adjoining car park.**
→ **Walk across the car park to Freeman Street, a short road which terminates in the car park.**

Some of the old buildings which once lined the road have been knocked down and the ground levelled in anticipation of future development. This has resulted in colonisation by a range of plants associated with disturbance, some of which, although now very common and widespread in Birmingham and the Black Country, originate from distant parts of the world.

▲ Guernsey Fleabane and Butterfly-bush

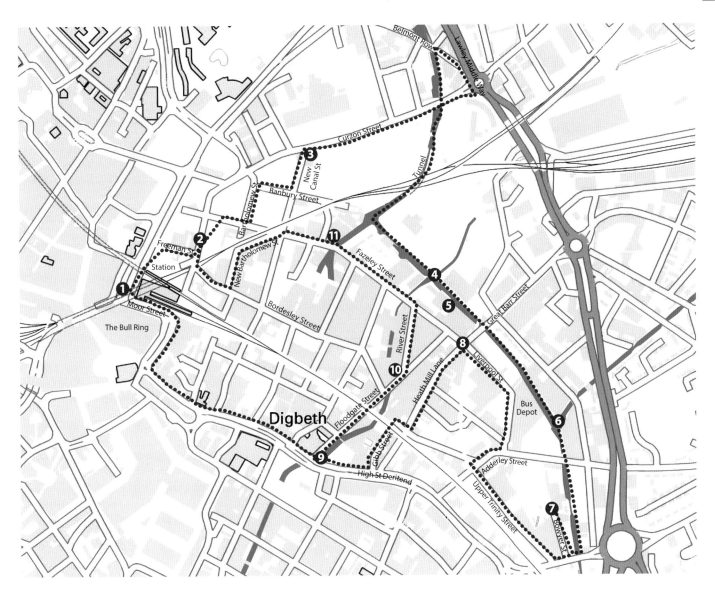

Four of the most frequently encountered plants in the inner-city are Butterfly-bush from China, Guernsey Fleabane from sub-tropical South America, Eastern Rocket from Eastern Europe and Canadian Goldenrod from North America. Of these, Guernsey Fleabane has been with us for only the last few years, but is spreading rapidly and fast becoming a common weed of disturbed ground in the urban area.

→ **Walk to the end of Freeman Street and cross the road into Park Street Gardens ➋.**

In Victorian times the park was much larger than it is today, and tombstones in the park are a reminder of its past link to St Bartholomew's Church, which stood nearby and was demolished in the 1960s. Further back in time, this tiny bit of parkland formed part of a vast park used by royalty for deer hunting. Nowadays, mature London Plane and Poplars line

its boundaries and the grass is regularly mown. A careful search of the short grassland during the summer months may reveal one of the few known Birmingham and Black Country sites for Slender Trefoil, the tiny, yellow pea-flower, growing mixed in with patches of Lesser Trefoil with which it can easily be confused (you will need to consult a wild flower identification reference book for this one).

→ **Follow the path into Fazeley Street. Turn right and cross over the road.**
→ **Turn left into Bartholomew Street and then first right into Banbury Street.**

Temporary car parks have replaced the buildings that once stood on this land, but now they too stand empty awaiting the next phase of the Eastside redevelopment. In this interim period, colonisation by Butterfly-bush, Guernsey Fleabane, Tall Melilot and a medley of plants associated with disturbance has taken place, bringing

an abundance of colour to an otherwise drab area.

→ **Continue along Banbury Street for a short distance and then turn left into New Canal Street towards the front of Curzon Street Station building ➌.**

At the eastern end of Banbury Street, the Birmingham Gun Barrel Proof House is largely unchanged since it was established in 1813 by an Act of Parliament at the request and expense of the Birmingham Gun Trade. Tours of the building can be arranged by appointment.

Curzon Street Station building is the oldest surviving example of monumental railway architecture in the world, and acted as the terminus for the London and Birmingham Railway and Grand Junction Railway, which connected Birmingham with London, Manchester and Liverpool. The station was opened in 1838 but its heyday was short-lived; in 1854 the London and North Western Railway and Midland

Railway completed New Street Station, and the use of Curzon Street as a passenger terminal began to decline, although holiday excursions continued until 1893. It remained in use as a goods station until eventually closing in 1966.

→ **Turn right into Curzon Street passing Millennium Point and continue along this road to the junction with Lawley Middleway at Curzon Circle.**
→ **Turn left at this road island and almost immediately fork left into Belmont Row which is blocked-off to vehicular traffic.**
→ **Proceed along this road for approximately 100 metres to the triangular-shaped house near the canal bridge.**

Looking further along Belmont Row, the derelict remains are all that is left of the Co-op furniture factory which was a locally listed building, built in 1899 and destroyed by fire on 11 January 2007. This building was known to house one of the biggest bat roosts in the Eastside of Birmingham.

The triangular house is one of the few remaining residential properties in the Eastside. Now empty, it once had a pleasant canal-side garden, the remains of which are still evident.

→ **Access the canal towpath opposite the triangular house and turn left (south), passing beneath Belmont Row Bridge.**
→ **Continue down a series of locks past a reed-dominated basin with a good view towards the city centre, passing beneath Curzon Street Bridge and through Curzon Street Tunnel beneath the railway.**

Emerging from the tunnel, the banks on both sides of the canal are densely vegetated. The southern (nearside) bank was originally landscaped with trees and shrubs and is now semi-mature woodland. Ivy and brambles dominate the understorey providing a cover and foraging site for small birds and mammals. Along the far bank from the tunnel to the rear of the Proof House there is an almost continuous cover of Bracken and Butterfly-bush with patches of Common Reed forming the marginal vegetation.

→ **At the canal junction, pass beneath the footbridge and go left towards the abandoned Banana Warehouse situated on the opposite side of the canal. Look out for an information board headed 'Warwick Bar'.**

The stop lock or 'bar' is a physical barrier minimising water loss from one private canal to another. The Digbeth branch of the Birmingham Canal Navigations and the Grand Union Canal met at this point; as canal barges transferred from one body of water to the other the bar ensures that only a miniscule amount of water would flow from the canal with the higher water level into the other. Today the canal system is under common control so the gates are chained permanently open.

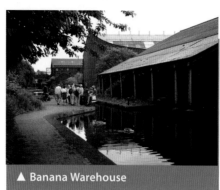

▲ Banana Warehouse

The overhanging canopy of the Banana Warehouse, so called because it was once owned by Geest, is Grade II listed along with Warwick Bar, and plans to renovate this whole area are included in the regeneration of the Eastside. Next to the Banana Warehouse the curved-walled Fellows, Morton and Clayton building was built in 1935 as a late show of confidence in the canals. The nearside banks are landscaped with shrubs and include a range of exotic plantings such as Barberry, Forsythia and Butterfly-bush as well as native shrubs. Red Campion and Guernsey Fleabane are frequent in the canal towpath brickwork along this stretch.

→ **Continue along the towpath to the point where the canal crosses the river Rea ❹.**

Ivy-leaved Toadflax with its palmately-lobed leaves and small lilac and yellow flowers has gained a foothold in the brickwork mortar of the canal bridge above the river, in places cascading down the brickwork for several feet. If you are fortunate you might catch a fleeting glimpse of a Kingfisher darting along the river corridor from this spot. In recent years Kingfisher sightings have increased in Birmingham and Black Country.

The raised bank along the canalised river has become densely vegetated with the invasive Japanese Knotweed and Bracken, and an assortment of exotic shrubs and herbs introduced over many years. Of the introductions, one has particular botanical interest; a few metres along the path above the river there is a specimen of a hybrid of Butterfly-bush and Orange-ball-tree. It has the common name of Weyer's Butterfly-bush, and its intermediate, loose-globose, yellow-flushed-purple flowers continue well into autumn, long after the flowers have faded on the typical and ubiquitous Butterfly-bush.

→ **Continue along the towpath for a few more metres to The Bonded Warehouse on the opposite side of the canal ❺.**

Originally comprising Victorian factory buildings, the Bonded Warehouse (known as The Bond) has now been transformed into a canal-side cafeteria and offices.

As you continue along the towpath, Butterfly-bush has colonised the old brickwork of the building on the opposite side of the canal. Shortly after passing beneath the railway viaduct and Great Barr Bridge, look on the opposite bank for a large, self-sown Fig tree which has undoubtedly been growing here for many years.

▲ River Rea

→ **Continue along the towpath, crossing the footbridge at the junction of the Grand Union Canal ❻ and continue south, passing beneath Adderley Street and through Camp Hill locks to exit the canal at the Coventry Road bridge.**

→ **Turn right towards the railway viaduct, passing the entrance into Bowyer Street. (Alternatively go up Bowyer Street to the very end to see the old lock-keeper's cottage ❼ which is privately owned but can be viewed from the road.)**

→ **Turn right into Upper Trinity Street, which runs parallel with the railway viaduct.**

High up on the brickwork and now largely obscured by Butterfly-bush, is the direction sign BR(W) Bordesley Cattle Station. This was the major cattle station when railways were the means of transport used for bringing livestock to Birmingham Cattle Market. It is interesting to note the signage at this point, as similar signage on the bridge parapet at the far end of Upper Trinity Street, at its junction with Adderley Street, replaces BR(W) with GWR.

The Staffordshire blue bricks used in the viaduct construction are extremely dense and heavy and of low porosity. Any moisture is absorbed into the mortar, and in many places colonisation by Butterfly-bush has taken place.

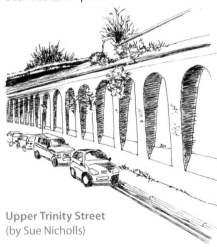

**Upper Trinity Street**
(by Sue Nicholls)

Midway along Upper Trinity Street below the curious 'overhang', the purpose of which is unclear, additional moisture seeping from above has enabled a colony of Hart's-tongue to become established in the damp brickwork mortar.

→ **Continue to the end of Upper Trinity Street to the junction with Adderley Street.**

→ **Turn right into Adderley Street and continue into Liverpool Street. Pass**

**Birmingham Central Bus Garage on the right and proceed to the junction with Heath Mill Lane ❽.**

The section of railway viaduct to the left, the small section to the right above the building on the corner of the road, and the section on the northern side of Great Barr Street all form part of the Duddeston Viaduct, known locally as 'the Viaduct to Nowhere'. Partly constructed by the Birmingham and Oxford Joint Railway (B&OJR) but never completed, the viaduct was an architectural masterpiece branching from Bordesley and intended to make a link with the Grand Junction Railway into Curzon Street. However, parliamentary lobbying, rivalry between railway companies and the opening of New Street Station resulted in the abandonment of the project before completion. The condition of the brickwork is a testament to the quality of the bricklayers of the day; stretching 1,100 yards, it never carried a through train. Over the years it has become colonised by vegetation which has resulted in the formation of a natural green roof, a secluded retreat for wildlife high above the Eastside.

→ **Turn left into Heath Mill Lane and head towards the railway viaduct.**

→ **Immediately before the viaduct, turn right into Gibb Street.**

Before turning right, take a look at the unusual entrance to the car park in Heath Mill Street which is constructed solely of crushed cars. No habitat seems too harsh for Butterfly-bush; at the time this walk was being compiled one plant was detected growing from the top of a lump of crushed metal to the right of the entrance – is it still there now?

→ **Continue along Gibb Street to the Custard Factory complex where refreshments and toilet facilities are available.**

→ **Proceed to the end of Gibb Street, which is now pedestrianised, and turn right heading back towards the City Centre to the junction with Floodgate Street, the point where High Street, Deritend crosses the River Rea and becomes Digbeth ❾.**

Nowadays, most people travelling in and out of Birmingham are unaware that the River Rea flows swiftly by beneath the road at this point, largely because it is virtually hidden from view behind advertisement boards. It is hard to conceive that this insignificant point was the birthplace of what was to become the City of

Birmingham. Historically the land to the east of the river was in the Parish of Aston and the land to the west in the Parish of Birmingham. The area around Deritend and Digbeth was at one time the most industrialised in the city, attracting famous companies such as Typhoo Tea, Brylcreem and Alfred Bird, the inventor of egg-free, instant custard.

At this point there is a choice of returning directly to Moor Street Station by continuing along Digbeth towards the new Selfridges building which stands next to the historic St Martins-in-the-Bullring. You can access the station by a short flight of steps at the southern entrance. Alternatively, to explore more of the Eastside, turn into Floodgate Street and continue as follows.

→ **From the Digbeth/Floodgate Street junction, walk along Floodgate Street, beneath the railway arches and take a left fork into River Street ❿. At the end of River Street turn left into Fazeley Street.**

On the opposite side, a little way to the right along Fazeley Street, is the front entrance to The Bond, the rear of the complex which was viewed earlier from the canal towpath. Continuing along Fazeley Street towards the City Centre the River Rea is once again crossed over and shortly afterwards the front of the Fellows, Morton and Clayton building is reached. Immediately next to this building, along the roadside, it is worth examining the ferns growing from the blue-brick wall mortar. There are four species to be seen all growing in close proximity to each other – Maidenhair and Black Spleenworts, Wall-rue and Polypody. A little further along this road, the imposing block of blue brick buildings which once housed a gymnasium and boxing ring is Grade II listed and awaits renovation.

→ **Continue along Fazeley Street crossing the canal ⓫ to the junction with Andover Street.**

The graffiti-covered building on the corner of this road is quite impressive but now stands empty, its fate uncertain.

→ **Continue along Fazeley Street to the junction with New Canal Street.**

→ **Cross this road and walk south-west into New Bartholomew Street, passing Birmingham Dogs Home on the left, and continue round the bend to the end of the road where it meets Bordesley Street.**

→ **Turn right into Bordesley Street and continue to the end where it meets Park Street.**

→ **Turn right into Park Street and left into Freeman Street and the car park next to the station. Moor Street Station is a few metres further on.**

Moor Street Railway Station was a second Birmingham station on the main Great Western Railway (GWR) line from Paddington through to Birkenhead and formed a terminus for trains from Warwickshire. Initially targeted for closure during the time of the Beeching Axe, when most of the main line services were diverted into New Street, the tunnel into Snow Hill was closed along with Snow Hill Station, and Moor Street was due to follow suit. However, capacity at New Street was not sufficient to take all of the extra services, so Moor Street survived and was utilised as a terminus for local trains from Stratford and Leamington Spa. In 1986 when a decision to run cross-country services was made, a new station was built on the path of the old line next to the old Moor Street Station, and this also led to the re-opening of Snow Hill Station and the connecting tunnel.

In 2002, at a cost of £11million, the original and now crumbling Grade II listed building was renovated, with most of the original architecture retained, including some from the old demolished Snow Hill Station.

A preserved GWR 2800 class locomotive no. 2885, on loan from nearby Tyseley Locomotive Works, is a reminder of the days of steam locomotives and contributes to the general interest of the newly restored Moor Street Station.

**Species mentioned in the text**

Barberry *Berberis* sp.
Bracken *Pteridium aquilinum*
Butterfly-bush *Buddleja davidii*
Butterfly-bush, Weyer's *Buddleja* × *weyeriana*
Campion, Red *Silene dioica*
Elder *Sambucus nigra*
Fig *Ficus carica*
Fleabane, Guernsey *Conyza sumatrensis*
Forsythia *Forsythia* sp.
Goldenrod, Canadian *Solidago canadensis*
Hart's-tongue *Asplenium scolopendrium*
Knotweed, Japanese *Fallopia japonica*
Melilot, Tall *Melilotus altissimus*
Plane, London *Platanus* × *hispanica*
Polypody *Polypodium* sp.
Reed, Common *Phragmites australis*
Rocket, Eastern *Sisymbrium orientale*
Spleenwort, Black *Asplenium adiantum-nigrum*
Spleenwort, Maidenhair *Asplenium trichomanes*
Toadflax, Ivy-leaved *Cymbalaria muralis*
Trefoil, Lesser *Trifolium dubium*
Trefoil, Slender *Trifolium micranthum*
Wall-rue *Asplenium ruta-muraria*

## WOODGATE VALLEY WALK

### Description

A walk around the 'border country' where Birmingham and Worcestershire meet.

Woodgate Valley, Bromwich Bluebell Wood and Bartley Green Reservoir each make their own special contribution to this route. Old farmland criss-crossed with hedgerows, flower–filled woodland, and exposed shoreline punctuated by water birds, provide ever–changing views in this remarkable corner of Birmingham. The proximity of the M5 motorway and the inclusion of some short stretches of street emphasise the intimate link between town and country, and serve as a reminder of how easily all of the natural features could have been lost. Not only has this not happened, but the valley is now a country park with a modern visitor centre, financed and run by Birmingham City Council.

**Distance and walking time** Approximately 4 miles. The walk takes about 2½–3 hours at a gentle pace.
**Starting point** Woodgate Valley Visitor Centre/car park (OS grid reference: SO994829).
**Parking** There is ample parking at the Visitor Centre in Clapgate Lane.
**Getting there by public transport** National Express bus route 23 and Travel West Midlands 103 and 103A operate from Birmingham City Centre and stop near the entrance to the Visitor Centre.
**Access/conditions** The route is gently undulating, but can be very muddy and wet where it passes through long grass.
**Facilities and further information** There are refreshment and toilet facilities in the Visitor Centre as well as helpful and knowledgeable staff, and a wide range of leaflets and brochures available providing information about Woodgate Valley and other local attractions.

### THE WALK

→ **From the car park ❶ walk on to Clapgate Lane.**

→ **Turn right and walk up to the island. Bear right for a short distance and cross the road into Lye Close Lane.**

→ **Turn left into Lye Avenue, then right into Parkfield.**

→ **At the end of the cul-de-sac ❷ follow the track which runs directly beneath the line of the pylons, and pick your way across the meadows running parallel with the nearby motorway.**

→ **At the fork of the path continue right below the pylons towards a footbridge crossing the motorway.**

→ **Just before the footbridge, turn left directly after the wooden bench. Go past a 5-bar metal gate ❸ and continue along the track into Clent Way passing maisonettes on both sides into Kitwell Lane.**

The Worcestershire countryside is reluctant to relinquish its grip on the woods and fields – housing, industry and schools nibble at, but never around here completely devour, this arm of the shire which reaches deep into the heart of the city. One of the farms in the area was called Wilderness Farm which may indicate the remoteness of the area in bygone days. There were plenty of other farms in the vicinity, including Stonehouse, Nonsuch and Four Dwellings. Walking into Lye Close Lane it can be seen how thoughtful planning allowed the old hedges to remain despite houses being built behind, making it easy to picture the country lane it once was. Once off the road and onto the path the conifers of the motorway embankment and the planting of alder, willow and other trees form a belt of woodland. The fields are managed in a way which enables them to retain their abundance of wild flowers.

▲ Woodgate Valley Country Park

Great Burnet, Field Scabious, Betony, Sneezewort and Lady's-mantle mingle with the more familiar thistles, clovers and knapweeds to provide colour all spring and summer through. The hedgerows are more striking in autumn, as the soft golden sunlight burnishes their changing leaves, the rose hips, haws and brilliantly-coloured Guelder-rose berries, while plump blackberries glisten with dew.

Walking across old hedge lines, a flood of wild roses pours out of the hedgerow in one place and, in another, Rosebay Willowherb – a plant typical of bare sites in the city – blazes brightly against the green foliage. Elsewhere the angular flower-heads of Sharp-flowered Rush show where this plant enjoys the slightly acid conditions found here.

→ **Turn right into Kitwell Lane and then left into Balmoral Road.**
→ **Turn right at the telephone box opposite Kyles Way ❹ and follow the path with the iron railings on the right.**
→ **Towards the end of the iron railings climb the stile and enter the wood ❺.**

On the corner of Balmoral Road there is a beautiful stand of Tufted Hair-grass, its

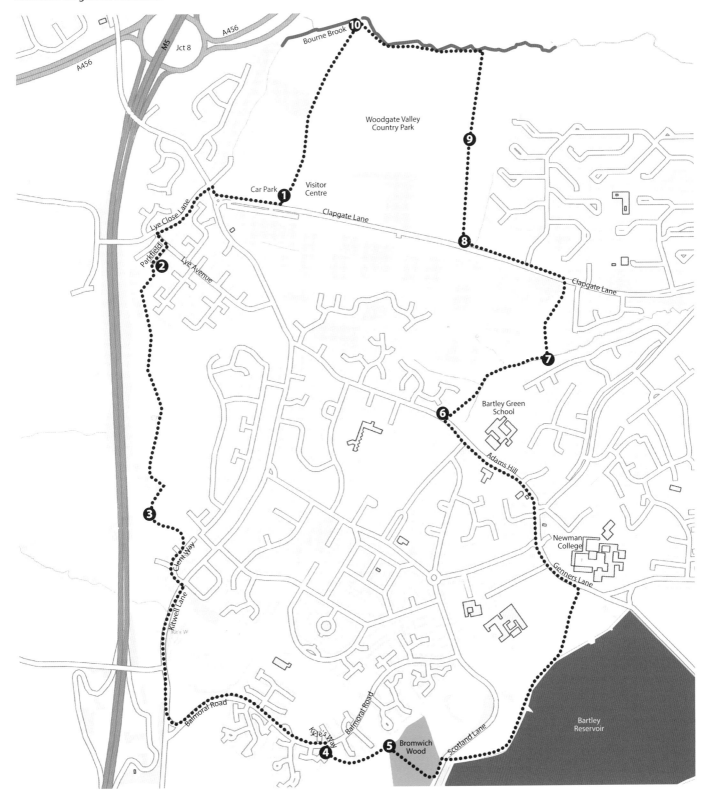

▲ Bluebells in Bromwich Wood

tall and delicate panicles (flower-heads) shimmering in the slightest breeze, the whole bank a pale-straw colour. This is normally a grass of damp pastures where it forms conspicuous tufts.

Prior to reaching the dark line of the trees of Bromwich Wood, good views may be had of Bartley Reservoir.

The atmosphere changes very quickly as the cool darkness of the enfolding wood is reached. This ten-acre fragment is all that remains of a once much larger piece of ancient woodland, and it is home to a number of species which could not live anywhere else in the vicinity. In spring and early summer it is a riot of colour with Bluebell, Greater Stitchwort, Yellow Archangel, Lesser Celandine and Wood Anemone. Above all of these, the Oak, Rowan, Wild Cherry, Silver Birch and Alder form the canopy typical of a lowland English wood, a habitat becoming all too uncommon now.

→ **Make any way through the wood towards the reservoir, cross Scotland Lane and walk along the shore with the water on the right. Follow the path around the boat club and turn left into Genners Lane opposite Newman College.**

→ **Cross the road and continue into Adams Hill passing Bartley Green School.**

→ **Take the path on the right ❻ back into Woodgate Valley Country Park.**

Bleak and exposed in winter and with relatively bare edges, the water of Bartley Reservoir attracts a wide variety of waterfowl, gulls and waders.

The boat-house marks a brief return to buildings as Bartley Green is traversed. The brilliant scarlet of the cherry tree in the street by the school is reflected in the berries and foliage of some more Guelder-rose planted alongside the path.

→ **Take the left fork ❼, pass through a small copse and turn left at Clapgate Lane.**

→ **Cross over and walk along the grass verge with the wooden fence boundary and young plantation woodland on your right, passing the bus shelter, until you reach the wide metal gate ❽.**

→ **Follow the path across the meadow from the mound and cross a plank bridge ❾. Continue until you are able to turn left on to a wider path.**

→ **Continue along this track until you reach a point where the tracks cross near to the footbridge crossing the Bourn Brook.**

→ **Turn left ❿ and follow the double-fenced path to return to the Visitor Centre and Car Park.**

Once over the stile the Woodgate Valley proper is reached again. It is the largest area of grassland in Birmingham and offers a gentle landscape of meadows, trees and hedges, lying in rural tranquillity on either side of the Bourn Brook. This shallow stream loiters and meanders along the valley to a rendezvous with the River Rea. A Horse-chestnut and a Turkey Oak (the latter is easily recognised by the long hairs at every leaf junction) stand on a small mound at the side of the path. This mound, together with others in line with it across the valley, is the remains of a spoil heap left from the building of the Lapal Canal tunnel between 1793 and 1798. At 3,795 yards in length it was one of the longest canal tunnels in the country.

Meadows filled with buttercups and Yellow-rattle disguise the resident Kestrel's living larder, which is filled with mice, voles and shrews.

The meadows in this part of Woodgate Valley are particularly worthy of exploration, especially the permanently moist and damp areas where Meadowsweet grows alongside Common Marsh-bedstraw, Ragged-Robin,

Marsh-marigold, Marsh Thistle, Fox-and-cubs and Tormentil – each has its turn as the seasons advance. In September and October there are hundreds of Devil's-bit Scabious flowers. Such rich corners have almost completely disappeared from many parts of the countryside and yet here is one in Birmingham. The Woodgate Valley could offer nothing more fitting to mark the end of a walk which, without ever getting away from the 'town', weaves a mellow countryside tapestry.

### Species mentioned in the text

Alder *Alnus glutinosa*
Anemone, Wood *Anemone nemorosa*
Archangel, Yellow *Lamiastrum galeobdolon* subsp. *montanum*
Betony *Betonica officinalis*
Birch, Silver *Betula pendula*
Blackthorn *Prunus spinosa*
Bluebell *Hyacinthoides non-scripta*
Burnet, Great *Sanguisorba officinalis*
Celandine, Lesser *Ficaria verna*
Cherry, Wild *Prunus avium*
Cowslip *Primula veris*
Fox-and-cubs *Pilosella aurantiaca*
Guelder-rose *Viburnum opulus*
Hair-grass, Tufted *Deschampsia cespitosa*
Hazel *Corylus avellana*
Horse-chestnut *Aesculus hippocastanum*
Lady's-mantle *Alchemilla* sp.
Marsh-bedstraw, Common *Galium palustre*
Marsh-marigold *Caltha palustris*
Meadowsweet *Filipendula ulmaria*
Oak, Pedunculate *Quercus robur*
Oak, Turkey *Quercus cerris*
Ragged-Robin *Silene flos-cuculi*
Rowan *Sorbus aucuparia*
Rush, Sharp-flowered *Juncus acutiflorus*
Scabious, Devil's-bit *Succisa pratensis*
Scabious, Field *Knautia arvensis*
Sneezewort *Achillea ptarmica*
Stitchwort, Greater *Stellaria holostea*
Thistle, Marsh *Cirsium palustre*
Tormentil *Potentilla erecta*
Willowherb, Rosebay *Chamerion angustifolium*
Yellow-rattle *Rhinanthus minor*

▲ Horse-grazed meadows

# Section 2 · Finding wild flowers with contributions from several authors

This section presents an overview of the best botanical features of Birmingham and the Black Country. It starts with a brief description of our two largest sites, Sutton Park and the Sandwell Valley and continues with overviews of each of the five metropolitan districts.

## SUTTON PARK (by Peter Coxhead)

Some 900 hectares (2,200 acres) in area, Sutton Park is one of the largest urban parks in Europe, situated as it is only 11km (7 miles)

from the centre of Birmingham. The bulk of the Park was already a Site of Special Scientific Interest (SSSI) when National Nature Reserve status was added in March 1997. In recognition of its long history of human use, and the quality of the remaining evidence of that use, large parts of the Park were declared a Scheduled Ancient Monument in March 2002.

Most of the Park is formed of what are traditionally called 'Bunter Pebble Beds': a mixture of pebbles, often quite large, embedded in a sandstone matrix. The beds are thought to have been created by a large river flowing from south to north in early

Triassic times (around 240 million years ago). When the ice last withdrew from the area of the Park (around 130 thousand years ago), the melting of the glaciers left deposits of sand with some boulder clay. The result is a generally free-draining, somewhat acid soil, but with waterlogging where there is more clay (Geological information largely follows Toghill, 2000).

▲ Heathland at Sutton Park

Only a very small area of the Park has ever been cultivated, but it has been subject to sustained human use, which, along with its geology, is a key factor in understanding its major habitats and the plant communities they support (historical information follows *Sutton Park National Nature Reserve*, an undated booklet published by Birmingham City Council). Little is known in detail about the period before the Roman occupation. Flint tools and a number of 'burnt mounds' have been found, showing that there was a human presence, initially of nomadic hunter-gatherers. A Roman road runs through the Park, built not long after the invasion began in AD 43. The ground surface underneath this suggests that the land was previously covered with heath or light woodland.

By the early 12th century, the Park was part of Sutton Chase, a large forested area extending from almost the centre of modern Birmingham out to Shenstone. What is now Sutton Park was used as a deer park, complete with an outer boundary and inner divisions. The banks and ditches used to create the enclosures are still visible; along with the Roman road, this is one of the reasons for parts of Sutton Park being given Scheduled Ancient Monument status. The preservation of the Park to the present day is the result of a Royal Charter in 1528 which allowed Bishop Vesey to enclose part of Sutton Chase for the benefit of the people of Sutton Coldfield. They were allowed to hunt there and use the park to graze their animals. The presence of cattle and other livestock is evidenced by the construction of further banks and ditches which kept them out of some areas, producing a habitat of grazed heathland and light woodland with smaller areas of denser woodland. Four artificial fish pools were constructed between the early 1400s and 1730. One of these is Little Bracebridge, a shallow pool where fish may have been raised or placed for fattening, and which is now at the centre of very important wetland habitat. The remaining pools were constructed to power water mills.

The traditional use of the Park, in which grazing maintained open heathland, ended in the early 19th century when recreational use increased; at one time there were two race courses, and the first of two golf courses was started in 1880. The extension of the railway to Sutton Coldfield in 1862 increased visitor numbers, and extensive entertainment facilities were constructed.

Three major habitats can be distinguished in the Park: woodland; open grassland, heath and mire; and streams and pools. The woodland has long been extensively managed to produce timber and other useful products. Holly is likely to have been used for winter fodder for both deer and cattle; there is also evidence of

coppicing (not all within the original woodland boundaries). The outcome is that the woodland in Sutton Park is not an especially notable habitat. There are few very old trees, and markers of ancient woodland – tree species such as Small-leaved Lime or herbs such as Dog's Mercury are either absent or rare. Birch is the pioneer species (both Silver Birch and Downy Birch); oaks follow (both Sessile Oak and Pedunculate Oak); and where trees have not been managed for long periods, extensive stands of Holly develop. Bracken spreads in drier, more open areas of woodland. There are a few areas of very wet woodland, where species such as Opposite-leaved Golden-saxifrage flourish. Evidence of management in the form of deliberately planted alien species can be found throughout the Park; some of these have then spread naturally, including hybrid oaks and various conifers.

Sutton Park was used extensively for grazing for much of its known history (including its use as a deer park in this category). A variety of animals have been recorded, goats and donkeys as well as cattle, sheep and horses. This activity created extensive open areas which form acid grassland, dry heath, wet heath and mires ('bogs'), depending on the drainage situation, base status and fertility levels. When grazing diminished through the reduction in commoner's rights, changes in agricultural practices and increased recreational use, these open areas were invaded by trees, typically beginning with the ever-present birches. Loss of heath through tree invasion remains the most serious threat to the wildlife value of the Park. Although efforts have been made to check this loss – by deliberate clearance, by trying to raise the numbers of grazing cattle to the south of the railway line and by introducing grazing by Exmoor ponies to the north of the railway line – long term success is far from guaranteed.

Among the less common plants in the Midlands, the dry heath supports Heather, Bell Heather – now apparently very scarce in the Park – Cowberry, and Western Gorse in addition to the ubiquitous Gorse. The wet heath supports plants such as Cowberry and Cross-leaved Heath. Grass-of-Parnassus occurs in a single small strip of lower-lying land beside a stream. It is now well-removed from any other populations, the nearest being in Derbyshire. The floristic jewels of Sutton Park are to be found in its mires. These support plants now exceedingly rare in lowland areas of Britain, such as Common Butterwort, Round-leaved Sundew, Marsh Lousewort, Marsh Pennywort, Bog Pimpernel, Marsh Violet, Marsh Arrowgrass and Few-flowered Spike-rush.

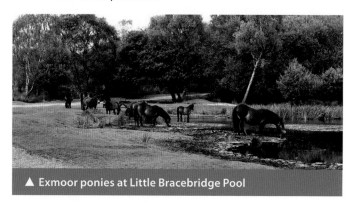

▲ Exmoor ponies at Little Bracebridge Pool

The streams in the Park are natural and appear to have suffered few attempts to alter their courses or 'improve' their flow. They primarily arise within the Park, although during heavy rain drainage overflows, sometimes carrying pollution, enter from the north-west. In contrast to the streams, all the pools within the Park are man-made. The earliest, such as Bracebridge and the associated Little Bracebridge, are believed to have been constructed to raise and contain fish. Later pools provided water-power for a variety of purposes, such as blacksmithing at Longmoor Pool. The margins of pools and slow-flowing streams overlap to some degree with mires as habitats and support interesting plants such as Blinks, Bogbean, Small Water-pepper, Greater Spearwort and Yellow Iris, as well as the alien Sweet-flag. Of interest growing in the water will be found a number of members of the Pondweed Family (including Bog Pondweed, Blunt-leaved Pondweed, Curled Pondweed and Fennel Pondweed) and a Bladderwort (probably *Utricularia australis*).

It is difficult to overestimate the botanical significance of Sutton Park in relation to the English midlands. Apart from its areas of heathland and woodland, its relatively small areas of wetland form the main refuge for species associated with old habitats in the conurbation. It is our only habitat in B&BC for a huge number of such species, many of which are mentioned above but which also includes Dioecious Sedge, Tawny Sedge, Smooth-stalked Sedge, Flea Sedge, Whorl-grass, Fen Bedstraw, Round-leaved Crowfoot, Lesser Skullcap, Knotted Pearlwort and Cranberry. It is probably the only habitat for several more such as White Sedge and Marsh Violet which may have been recently lost elsewhere in our area. Many other species otherwise very uncommon in the conurbation, such as Green-ribbed Sedge, and Hare's-tail Cottongrass are found here. It may also be the best botanical site in the Warwickshire vice-county (vc. 38), where it is the sole site for many of the above species, for others such as Lesser Tussock-sedge, Star Sedge and Meadow Thistle and for

species of other habitats such as Autumnal Water-starwort and Cowberry. Even some of the common species of Sutton Park such as Pill Sedge, Heath Rush and Mat-grass are otherwise quite rare in vc. 38. Sutton Park also stands out as a highly significant site if the other surrounding vice-counties of Staffordshire, Worcestershire and Shropshire are included in the comparison and many of the species unique to Sutton Park in our area now occur mainly in upland areas to the north and west of the conurbation.

The flora of the Park has been well documented over the years, with Floras of Sutton Park being published in 1876, 1971 and 1991. The steady increase in the total number of taxa listed as present (for example from 461 in 1876 to 505 in 1991), conceals dramatic changes. Only 55% of the species have been recorded as present in all three Floras, and 22% of the species once recorded as present were thought to be lost in 1994 (Coxhead 1994) although some have since been re-found. Some of these losses have very obvious causes. In the late 19th century, when Bagnall began recording, Sutton Park was bordered by agricultural land rather than being entirely surrounded by housing as at present. The construction of a railway line in the same period also added a number of species close to it which have since disappeared. Thus it is not surprising that the highest losses have been among plants associated with agriculture and disturbed ground, e.g. Wild-oat, Corncockle or Corn Marigold, and among casuals, aliens or garden escapes, e.g. Hemp or Dusky Crane's-bill. No species characteristic of heathland are yet known to have been lost.

▲ Bracebridge Pool

## SANDWELL VALLEY (by John Shrimpton and Mike Poulton)

'The Valley' as it is locally known, lies close to the centre of the conurbation, immediately south of the M5/M6 Motorway junction. It is fed by the river Tame and a number of springs.

During the Middle Ages the hamlet of *Broomwich Heath* grew up between an Anglo-Saxon church where All Saints or Old Church now stands and the Lyndon spring, indicating that the primeval woodland had largely been replaced by Gorse, Broom, Heather and heath. Habitation had spread a mile or so when important coal deposits were found, and the name West Broomwich Heath eventually became West Bromwich.

The Lyne Purl probably originally flowed through primeval woodland down into the hollow recorded on 18th century maps as

Chambers Wood which was later to become better known as Sot's Hole, celebrating the activities of the landlord of a nearby Victorian pub called The Bear and Ragged Staff. It then flowed along the woodland which now skirts the edge of Dartmouth Golf Course to Forge Mill and into the river Tame.

By the stream flowing through Sot's Hole, mounds of burnt stones have been discovered, possibly the remains of Bronze Age saunas and dating back to 1500 to 1000BC. A Small-leaved Lime tree growing in Sot's Hole could possibly be a descendant of the tree which gave the spring flowing through the hollow its name Lyne Purl or Lyndon, in Saxon or medieval times.

In the 18th century the land was purchased by The Earl of Dartmouth who built Churchfields Hall as the rectory to Old Church, Sot's Hole becoming part of the rectory garden. During

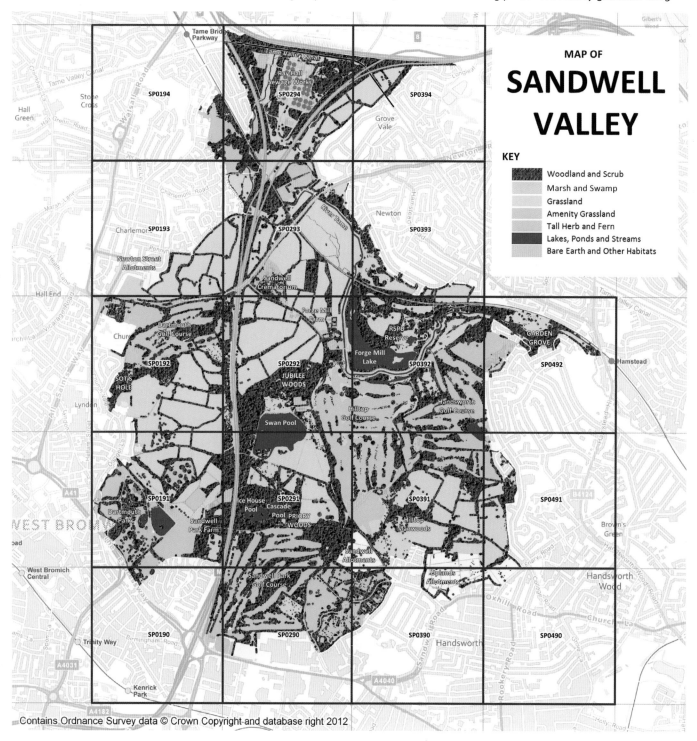

Contains Ordnance Survey data © Crown Copyright and database right 2012

this time many ornamental plants and trees were planted, so we find Sycamore and False-acacia naturalised here, also Japanese Knotweed, a pernicious weed proving almost impossible to eradicate.

Stone implements and axe heads have been found near the Sandwell Spring indicating the presence of Stone Age people some 9000 years ago. It was the site of a hermitage and later a Benedictine Priory which was sold off to yeomen farmers during the dissolution of the monasteries in the 16th century.

Later, the Earl of Dartmouth built Sandwell Hall beside the spring and on the site of the priory. An estate of ornamental gardens, a 'ha-ha' (a ditch used to keep out animals), an ice-house, a deer park and a large lake were laid out. One of the earls showed a great interest in trees and a number of exotic and unusual species were introduced to the estate. Specimen trees such as Lucombe Oak, Sweet Chestnut, Fern-leaved Beech, False-acacia, Garden Privet, Rhododendron and Swamp Cypress survive to this day, but in recent years secondary woodland has sprung up and today the Valley is possibly more densely wooded than it has been at any point in its history.

During the 19th century rich seams of coal were discovered in the area and mining operations began. The coal seams would have been laid down in the Carboniferous Period 350 million years ago. The vegetation would have consisted of Giant Clubmosses, Giant Horsetails and Tree Ferns. The diminutive relatives of the latter two still flourish in the Valley today. There were two pits in the Valley, the Sandwell and Jubilee Collieries. The Jubilee Colliery was quite close to Sandwell Hall. It financed the Earl's coffers but spoilt his environment, so he moved away. The lake was drained, the deer were destroyed and finally the Hall was demolished. The farms remained and most of the land was still farmed.

In 1947 the Earl of Dartmouth sold the estate to the council. It became somewhat run down, the M5 motorway was built across it and there were plans to turn the area into a sewage farm and build on parts of it. These plans were rejected and now part of the Valley is established as a Country Park and the first urban RSPB reserve in Britain is located around parts of Forge Mill Lake. Other parts have been designated as Local Nature Reserves (LNRs), Sites of Interest for Nature Conservation (SINCs) and Sites of Local Interest for Nature Conservation (SLINCs).

Sandwell Valley is totally surrounded by the vast urban sprawl of Birmingham, Sandwell and Walsall and no part of it can be regarded as natural. There has been a great deal of tree planting over the last 40 years; the woodlands of Sot's Hole have been extended over adjoining fields. The area of water has increased, Swan Pool being enlarged, Forge Mill Lake created as a balancing lake for the river Tame and four pools created on the site of the lake to Sandwell Hall. The River Tame, once considered one of the

most polluted rivers in the country, flows between high artificial banks, its course much altered by man. In recent times its water quality has markedly improved and nowadays throughout its course through the Valley, long, fan-like trails of Fennel Pondweed sway with every movement of the current. In spring and early summer its banks are transformed into a flowery haze of yellow and white from thousands of Wild Turnip and Cow Parsley flowers. These are succeeded in their turn by Russian Comfrey, Hemlock, Hogweed, Wild Angelica, Indian Balsam and a multitude of other herbs and grasses as the seasons unfold.

The Valley's hedgerows are well-maintained and in places new ones have been planted, additionally some are believed to be very old if not ancient because of the variety of woody species contained within. This is particularly apparent near to the boundary with Walsall where Pedunculate Oak, Ash, Wych Elm, English Elm, Elder, Hazel, Sycamore, Goat Willow, Dog-rose, Field Maple and Hawthorn are all found within the same hedge line and some of the trees have become so large that in places the hedge has become a narrow strip of woodland.

Orchids, Cowslips and Primroses, which had virtually disappeared a few years ago, have returned, and during spring an impressive display of native Bluebells can be seen in Sot's Hole. Broad-leaved Helleborine has long been known at Priory Wood, a short distance from the remains of the Benedictine Priory and in the surrounding woodland Wood-sedge, Wood Anemone, Dog's Mercury, Wood Dock, Hairy-brome, False Brome, Pendulous Sedge and Giant Fescue can all be found.

Despite the increasing domination of woodland, grassland is still an important part of Sandwell Valley and is the preferred habitat for many species. In wet meadows near Swan Pool, where Skylarks can still be heard and seen during the summer months, stands of Great Burnet and Wild Angelica flourish amidst more familiar Hogweed, Soft-rush, Reed Canary-grass and Tufted Hair-grass. Fragments of heathland containing Heath Bedstraw, Mat-grass, Sheep's Sorrel and Sheep's-fescue can still be found near Hill Top golf course and on the rising ground towards the Gun Emplacements.

Lower down on the Birmingham side the fields have been much improved and are relatively species-poor and dominated mainly by grasses. The Sandwell side fares little better and much of its grassland has been given over for amenity use or grazing. In one meadow a short distance from the Priory ruin – (aptly known as the wildflower meadow), Fox-and-cubs, Cowslip, Fritillary and in excess of 250 Common Spotted-orchid can all be seen, and in recent years heather-strewing has successfully been carried out in the scrub-cleared area beneath the pylons. Crown Vetch and Chicory are now thoroughly naturalised in the grounds of the RSPB on the grassy banks sloping down to the marsh, having originally been part of an acid grassland mix sown during the early days of the reserve.

Arable fields in the north-west of the Valley once contained a diverse weed flora which included Field Pansy, Common Poppy, Long-headed Poppy, Bugloss, Common Hemp-nettle and unusual species such as Large-flowered Hemp-nettle and Thorn-apple, but since ploughing of the land ceased, when the farmer from Hill House Farm retired, many of the arable weeds have become very scarce.

On the borders of Sandwell and Birmingham and reputed to be the largest allotment site in Europe, is the sprawling 13 hectares (32 acres) and over 400 plots of Uplands Allotment Gardens. This busy site, subjected to regular soil disturbance from the many plot-holders, has encouraged a wide-range of weeds associated with cultivation and disturbance. They include Shaggy-soldier and Gallant-soldier, relative newcomers to Sandwell Valley, Common Poppy, Long-headed Poppy, Field Woundwort, Scarlet Pimpernel,

▲ Cascade Pool

Black-bindweed, Fat-hen, Red Dead-nettle, Red Goosefoot, Many-seeded Goosefoot, Common Field-speedwell and Green Field-speedwell to name but a few.

One of the Valley's main attributes is its abundant supply of clean water from springs and streams which link up many of the Valley's pools and ponds. Forge Mill Lake, the largest water-body in Sandwell, was built in the 1980s to control flooding of the River Tame and Swan Pool was originally a mill pond before being enlarged to take the extra water being pumped out of the nearby mine. After closure of the mine it became a leisure facility used for windsurfing and other water pursuits. Other pools are allegedly water-filled bomb craters from World War 2 and the pool beneath the pylon stands on a wartime testing ground for locally-made tanks.

Not surprisingly, with all this water around, the Valley can boast a substantial aquatic flora, some more welcome than others. Featured in the Valley's pools are Nuttall's Waterweed, Curly Waterweed, Rigid Hornwort, Fan-leaved Water-crowfoot, Amphibious Bistort, Arrowhead, Flowering-rush, Water-cress, Fool's-water-cress, Yellow Water-lily, Fringed Water-lily, Greater Spearwort, Common Duckweed, Fat Duckweed, Ivy-leaved Duckweed and in recent years the pernicious Floating Pennywort.

Great Horsetail, which may well have been deliberately introduced into the Earl's Estate, is now thoroughly naturalised in many places on the Sandwell side where moisture-retaining soils occur. Large colonies can be seen in the water-saturated ground on the bank of Cascade Pool growing alongside Butterbur, whose spikes of reddish-pink flowers produced in late-winter are followed by enormous shade-casting rhubarb-like leaves. The shores of Swan Pool are transformed during June and July with drifts of purple-flowered Southern Marsh-orchid intermingling with the showy blooms of Yellow Iris.

Bee Orchids can regularly be seen on the gently-sloping banks of Forge Mill Lake and Twiggy Mullein, a native plant of the south-west of England occasionally reappears from the banks of the tiny North Island after periodical scrub clearance has been carried out. The secluded Ray Hall Sewage Works, located towards the northern end of Sandwell Valley, is possibly the most reliable Bee Orchid site in Sandwell and also provides a refuge for two other notable plants, Grass Vetchling and Blue Fleabane.

Local botanists and members of Sandwell Valley Naturalists Club have scoured every part of the Valley and to date the floral species recorded exceed 700, representing 95 plant families. Located right in the heart of Birmingham and the Black Country there can be no doubt whatsoever that Sandwell Valley is a botanical hotspot and provides a lung for the surrounding urban area. It is up to us all to preserve and keep it this way.

▲ Sandwell Valley Naturalists

## BIRMINGHAM (by Nicola Farrin, Stefan Bodnar and the editors)

The city of Birmingham forms the south-eastern half of B&BC. As elsewhere in the West Midlands, its flora is largely determined and shaped by man's activities. Relict areas exist, including some largely natural river corridors such as the southern River Cole, fragmented semi-natural ancient woodlands such as Bromwich Wood and the "jewel in the crown", Sutton Park, often regarded as one of the finest remaining examples of a medieval compartmented Deer Park in Britain. These areas, though influenced by man's activities over many centuries, are floristically very rich, and botanically a visit to Sutton Park is a must for any plant lover. The site has been exceptionally well recorded, initially by Bagnall in the 19th century, and latterly by the Sutton Coldfield Natural History Society.

The heathland at Sutton Park is particularly important and rare, and its flora, along with the flora of the park's other notable habitats (such as its wetlands and ancient woodlands), is described in the first part of this section. Outside of Sutton Park, other fragmented heathlands exist, most notably those on rock outcrops associated with the Lickey Hills, to the south of the City at Rednal and Rubery. These heathlands are of a different character to those of Sutton Park. At Rednal Hill, Heather and Bilberry predominate, but areas of acid grassland can also be found, with Wavy Hair-grass, Heath Bedstraw, Wood Sage and (at one of its last locations in B&BC) Common Cow-wheat.

Remnant agricultural landscapes exist on the periphery of the urban area, particularly to the south and east of the City. Some of these areas are now 'Country Parks' – Woodgate Valley, Sheldon, the flood meadows at Pype Hayes Park and the Hilltop area (which forms a substantial part of the Sandwell Valley described above). Where elements of traditional management exist, these areas can be botanically rich and are typified by neutral grasslands and hedgerows, though there are few good examples of high quality ancient hedgerows remaining, an example being one within Rectory Park, Sutton Coldfield where many shrub species have been recorded including Field Maple, Hazel, Birch, Hawthorn, Oak, Ash, Holly, Guelder-rose, and English and Wych Elm.

Historically, Woodgate Valley was a patchwork of farms, with Bourn Brook meandering along the valley bottom. Arable and dairy farming were the dominant land uses, and the fields next to the brook often flooded in winter, creating water meadows. The establishment of the Country Park in 1984 safeguarded the core of this historic agricultural landscape, including species-rich meadows, mature hedges, wetland, small ponds and the brook itself. The Valley's former farm fields and meadows support a diverse flora, notable species including Meadow Vetchling, Devil's-bit Scabious, Bird's-foot-trefoil, Tormentil, Perforate St John's-wort and Glaucous Sedge. Closer to the brook, remnants of the low-lying, marshy former water meadows can still be found, where damp-loving species including Cuckooflower, Common Sedge, Pale Sedge, Great Burnet, Wild Angelica, Water Figwort, Southern Marsh-orchid and Common Marsh-bedstraw have been recorded. Damp grassland in the Pinewoods area adjacent to the east side of the M5 Motorway includes Betony, Devil's-bit Scabious and the only known extant B&BC record for Saw-wort. An ancient hedgerow, dating back to the 13th century, exists at the western boundary of the Country Park, along Watery Lane. The associated hedge bank is extremely diverse and includes Wood Melick, Red Campion, Dog's Mercury, Lesser Celandine and Bluebell.

On the western edge of the City, the fields and hedgerows at Quinton Meadows were, until fairly recently, part of an agricultural tenancy. Now this area has been encompassed within Woodgate Valley Country Park. The old meadows of the two main fields support a diverse range of meadow grasses and herbs, more notable species include Common Centaury, Meadow Vetchling and Common Spotted-orchid. The ancient hedgerows around and between the two fields are notable for their mature standard Pedunculate Oaks as well as both Midland Hawthorn and Common Hawthorn and Crab Apple. In damper grassland to the south of the business park, Grass Vetchling and Red Bartsia may be found.

As well as these remnant agricultural landscapes, a few ancient semi-natural woodlands have survived as further examples of encapsulated countryside. On the eastern boundary of the City, on a north facing scarp slope above the River Tame, are the ancient woodlands of Springhill Wood and Parkhall Wood. Wych Elm and Small-leaved Lime are present in the canopy layer, and the ground flora is perhaps one of the most diverse of semi-natural woodlands in the City, including Broad-leaved Helleborine, Wood-sorrel, Bluebell, Dog's Mercury and Yellow Archangel.

▲ Ancient woodland at Parkhall

A scattering of smaller areas of ancient semi-natural woodlands can be found elsewhere across the City – Stocks Wood (Bournville) is another wood with Wood Anemone, as are Cutler's Rough (Bartley Green), Jones Wood (Walmley), Cocks Moors Woods (Brandwood) and Balaam's Wood (Frankley). The latter is particularly rich with Moschatel, Wood Anemone, Large Bitter-cress, both Opposite-leaved and Alternate-leaved Golden-saxifrage and Wood Horsetail.

At Bromwich Wood, on the west side of Bartley Reservoir, Pedunculate Oak dominates in the canopy, although at some locations, Wild Cherry is abundant. The ground flora, although dominated by Bluebell, includes a selection of other ancient woodland indicator species including Woodruff, Wood-sedge, Wood-sorrel, Wood Speedwell, Opposite-leaved Golden-saxifrage, Wood Melick and old records for Wood Horsetail. Two further species of interest – Common Valerian and Large Bitter-cress – can be found along the ditch along the eastern boundary. This lovely little wood is quite similar to Park and Ashen Coppices in Wolverhampton.

Pitts Wood in Quinton is a tiny isolated island of ancient semi-natural woodland entirely surrounded by housing and is all that is left today of what was, at some time in the past, a vast forest linking up with Warley Woods to the north. Bluebells still carpet the woodland floor in some quantity and other ancient woodland plants such as Moschatel, Yellow Pimpernel, Wood Millet and Yellow Archangel survive despite an ever-increasing encroachment

by Bramble and Holly and non-native introductions such as Cherry Laurel and Snowberry.

While the majority of the City's rivers and streams have been heavily engineered and reflect the urbanised landscape through which they flow, an interesting selection of flora can be found where these watercourses have managed to retain a more natural character. In the south of the City, the River Rea and a number of its smaller tributaries – Bourn Brook, Merritt's Brook and Chinn Brook – include stretches with natural banks and in-channel features such as pools and riffles. There are remnants of an ancient woodland flora along many of these streams, with plants such as Wood Anemone extending north into the city centre as far as Balsall Heath. The aquatic flora is not rich, but although little was recorded in the Warwickshire Flora of 1971, now there is much Stream Water-crowfoot, Fennel Pondweed and Curled Pondweed, suggesting improving water quality.

Fox Hollies Park SLINC in Acocks Green lies in the gently sloping valley of the Westley Brook and contained within its grounds are areas of spring-flushed grassland which give rise to a surprisingly interesting and diverse flora for a City park. Lesser Spearwort, Common Sedge, Oval Sedge, Bristle Club-rush, Betony, Cuckooflower and Sneezewort share this permanently damp habitat along with colonies of the attractive Greater Spearwort, in one of its few Birmingham sites.

In the north of the City, Plants Brook rises in Sutton Park and flows through Newhall Valley Country Park, Pype Hayes Park and Plants Brook Reservoirs before entering the River Tame south of Castle Vale. Species-rich damp meadow flanks the canalised brook through Pype Hayes Park, with a good diversity of wet grassland species including Great Burnet, Meadowsweet, Cuckooflower, Ragged-Robin, Brown Sedge, Lesser Pond-sedge, Greater Tussock-sedge and Marsh-marigold.

North of Sutton Coldfield, parts of Hill Hook LNR are wet Alder woodland (Alder carr) and colonising the woodland stream and marsh are Marsh-marigold, Great Horsetail, Lesser Pond-sedge, Pendulous Sedge and Remote Sedge along with noteworthy species such as Large Bitter-cress and Opposite-leaved Golden-saxifrage. The drier parts of the woodland contain fine stands of Red Currant, Bluebell and Wood Anemone. The large pool which originally provided water to Hill Hook Corn Mill is home to Brooklime, Water Mint and a number of species more reminiscent of the Sutton Park pools such as Bogbean, Marsh Cinquefoil, Lesser Bulrush and the uncommon Greater Tussock-sedge.

▲ The mill pool at Hill Hook

The City's two main rivers – the Cole and the Tame – also include sections where the watercourse has retained a more natural course, resulting in a range of typical floodplain habitats. The River Cole enters Birmingham from Solihull at Shirley and exits back into Solihull at Kitt's Green. Much of its length is incorporated into Shire and Kingfisher Country Parks and includes many pleasant woodlands and floodplain grasslands. The River Tame, with sources in Willenhall and Oldbury, enters N Birmingham in the Sandwell Valley. Flowing parallel with the M6 Motorway it passes along with the Tame Valley Canal beneath junction 6 (Gravelly Hill or 'Spaghetti Junction'). Both rivers support a simple submerged aquatic flora, typically dominated by Fennel Pondweed but also with Stream Water-crowfoot quite frequent. Within the unimproved floodplain grassland adjacent to the River Tame at Parkhall, some of the more uncommon species include Bog Stitchwort, Sneezewort and Betony.

▲ The River Cole at the Ackers

Amongst the City's wetland sites, Edgbaston Pool SSSI stands out for the diverse semi-natural community it supports. The predominant reedswamp species is the Lesser Bulrush, with various admixtures of the commoner Bulrush and quite a large stand of Common Reed at the northern end. Sweet-flag can be found amongst the emergent vegetation surrounding the pool, and the fen community on the eastern shore includes Skullcap, Water Horsetail and a small stand of Cyperus Sedge amongst other reedswamp sedges. There is a small area of Yellow Loosestrife, also Common Marsh-bedstraw and scattered plants of Narrow Buckler-fern. There is also a fine stand of Wood Club-rush, first recorded here by Miss D.A. Cadbury in 1935 and still present, and unusually extensive pure stands of Remote Sedge under Willow carr on the western shore. There is extensive Alder carr south of the pool, with the remains of an Opposite-leaved Golden-saxifrage and Greater Tussock-sedge field layer, but it is also notable for the huge stands of American Skunk-cabbage and far too much Indian Balsam.

Also well worth a visit for its wetland flora is Moseley Bog Local Nature Reserve. Although wet and dry woodland now cover much of the site, its name derives from the "bog" which formed in the late 19th century following the draining of a holding pool (the Great Pool) which supplied the nearby Sarehole Mill. Moseley Bog has a range of old woodland species plus Wood Horsetail and until recently Royal Fern and Marsh Cinquefoil, which might be the last survivors of the flora of Moseley Common, which extended over much of SP0982 and SP0981 up to the early 19th century and then had an incredible range of species of base-deficient mires

including Fir and Stag's-horn Clubmosses, Petty Whin and White Beak-sedge, all now sadly extinct in the conurbation and well beyond.

A range of designed and 'accidental' landscapes and habitats complete the diverse mosaic within Birmingham. Planned areas include formal and informal Parks and gardens within the City including modern innovations such as green/brown roofs. The BVSC building in Digbeth was recently (2008) retrofitted with a brown roof designed to reflect the characteristics of the brownfield sites within Eastside and the wider city centre. Species that can be encountered on the brown roof include Corncockle, Wild Mignonette, Kidney Vetch, Wild Carrot, Great Mullein and Viper's-bugloss (these are not included in the distribution maps!).

The current (2000s) regeneration of Birmingham's Eastside through a multi-billion pound investment is transforming the neglected area east of the city centre into a network of high quality public and private sector buildings, public squares, spaces and streets. As a result of compulsory purchase orders many of the old industrial buildings have gone or will soon disappear to make way for the new buildings of the 21st century. The inevitable, temporary creation of post-industrial brownfield land brought about by demolition work has resulted in colonisation by a diverse and interesting flora. Four species, whose country of origin is thousands of miles from Birmingham, are particularly common, Butterfly-bush from China, Eastern Rocket from Eastern Europe, Canadian Goldenrod from North America and a relatively recent arrival to Birmingham, Guernsey Fleabane from sub-tropical South America. Of the four, by far the most successful coloniser is Butterfly-bush, whose fine, wind-blown seeds have not only led to the plant's establishment on every available piece of vacant land but also vast stretches of the brickwork mortar of the arches which carry the city's rail network through Eastside. Such is its resilience that a plant has put down roots in to the top of one of the crushed car blocks forming the entrance to the car park in Heath Mill Lane.

Where land is left undeveloped for any length of time, early colonisers of recently disturbed sites are succeeded by perennials and woody species, leading, in time, to the formation of woodland. A good example of where this has happened can be seen from below looking up towards the elevated section of railway known as the 'railway viaduct to nowhere', straddling the Eastside from Bordesley Station to the north of Great Barr Street. Along its top a woodland corridor comprising Birch, Willow and Butterfly-bush sits high above the surrounding buildings and remains virtually

River Tame by the M6 at Gravelly Hill (by Sue Nicholls)

unaffected by the changes taking place at street level below. The classic Staffordshire blue bricks and special mortars used in the construction of the railway arches have also been exploited by a number of our native ferns. Where suitable shaded and damp conditions in the brickwork occurs, Hart's-tongue, Black Spleenwort, Maidenhair Spleenwort and Wall-rue have made their home.

Accidental landscapes in Birmingham include the transport corridors of rail, road and canal and post-industrial land. Botanically, the last-mentioned of these can be particularly interesting, especially in the early phases of colonisation, where the new, unusual and recombinant communities can be floristically quite diverse. The stressed conditions of these sites including nutrient, water, and mineral stress can provide unusual and relatively unique habitat forms and species mixtures. Many of these areas are by their very nature not accessible by the public and in light of this, these sites are excluded from detailed description, although there are places on the main Birmingham to London route, just out of New Street station, where you can see naturalised thickets of the showy garden plant Spanish Broom and a bank of the coastal sand-dune plant Lyme-grass from the trains! The Ackers is a partly public site which combines the river Cole with a whole range of wet and dry transportation corridors plus made and original ground. Species include Silver Hair-grass, Pyramidal Orchid, Bee Orchid, Betony and Hare's-foot Clover.

In reviewing the flora of Birmingham, note should be made that the process is a dynamic one. Considerable areas are undergoing relatively rapid successional processes, colonisation/invasion by 'new' species that will alter and shape these areas in future years, and many areas are being altered by changing land use and redevelopment/infill. The spread of invasive weed species is a feature that is part of this process and the spread of Japanese Knotweed and Indian Balsam in Birmingham in recent years are well documented.

The prevalence of less problematic species such as Canadian Fleabane, Guernsey Fleabane and Prickly Lettuce, which can be found across virtually all former housing and post industrial sites in Birmingham is another facet of this change. The use of rock salt as a de-icing material has created a spread of halophytes (salt-tolerant plants) such as Buck's-horn Plantain and Danish Scurvygrass that are now obvious in grass verges on most major roads. Species increasing on sites within Birmingham include Montbretia and Bladder-senna on former garden/housing sites and the various species of the genus *Cotoneaster* which are now being recorded frequently within woodlands, the origin thought to be primarily due to roosting birds dispersing their seeds.

Minworth Sewage Works, a site naturally not open to the public but nevertheless of considerable botanical interest, spreads over three monads (square kilometres) east of the centre. It is a repository of a wide range of native and alien opportunist species; there are vast expanses of old sludge beds, allowing nitrogen-lovers such as Hemlock and Red Goosefoot, not to mention Tomato which arrives as seed in the sewage, to flourish. In 2006 the banks of tipped material had many plants of the Cotton Thistle, Wild Mignonette and Cape-gooseberry, but doubtless the flora will change from year to year.

A relatively recent phenomenon has been the deliberate planting of wildflowers, both as individual plants and seeds and as mixtures. Used as a landscape and biodiversity enhancement on many sites, the presence of species such as Viper's-bugloss, Corncockle and Fritillary when encountered in Birmingham are all likely to be signs of this. Some mixtures have mimicked 'natural' meadows quite well, and two sites – Queslett Landfill (not accessible to public) and Plantsbrook Local Nature Reserve

– both have excellent examples of diverse created wildflower meadows.

## DUDLEY (by Mike Poulton and Ian Trueman)

Dudley forms the south-western part of the conurbation and, compared with other parts, is notably hilly. Right by the town centre, Dudley Castle stands prominently on Castle Hill, which is the most southerly of the four limestone hills in Dudley, Hurst/Turls Hill, Sedgley Beacon and the Wrens Nest being the other three. In quiet places within the confines of the zoo, patches of Deadly Nightshade occur in one of its few reliable Black Country haunts. It is particularly abundant on the Castle ruins themselves, where Black Spleenwort, Wall-rue, Maidenhair Spleenwort, Ploughman's-spikenard and Wall Lettuce also grow. Nearby, Castle Mill Woods is comprised mainly of Ash, Sycamore and Beech and was replanted extensively in the early 1800s to soften a scarred and industry-ravaged landscape. A feeling of naturalness and tranquillity has once more returned and beneath the tree canopy, shade-loving woodland species such as Enchanter's-nightshade and Dog's Mercury thrive, and the fronds of Male-fern and Broad Buckler-fern drape over moss-covered rocks.

To the north of Castle Hill, the Wren's Nest is one of the most notable geological locations in the British Isles and was declared a National Nature Reserve in 1956. A mantle of green vegetation now cloaks the limestone slopes, hiding many of the scars and upheavals inflicted by the extensive quarrying that took place here during the Industrial Revolution and today it is a refuge for many special plants and animals. Ferns cover the shaded sides of tree-lined quarries seeking out moisture in damp cracks, and mosses cover the boulders littering the quarry floors. In places Traveller's-joy drapes over Hazel, Dogwood, Wayfaring Tree (which may be entirely introduced) and Hawthorn and in the thin soils covering the rock some of the Black Country's scarcest plants flourish. Small Scabious, Fairy Flax and Common Milkwort share the fossil-littered quarry slopes with Hoary Plantain, Quaking-grass and Bee Orchid and in April and May the creamy-pink flower spikes of the root parasite, Toothwort push through the soil-surface around the base of hazel and other shrubs, sometimes in their hundreds. Common Gromwell, Hairy Violet and Autumn Gentian still cling on precariously in what is believed to be their only Black Country site and recently Pyramidal Orchid has been recorded from the Quarry.

▲ **Landmark fossiliferous limestone at the Wren's Nest**

Located on the boundary with Wolverhampton, Sedgley Beacon at 230 metres above sea-level is one of the highest hills in Dudley. Beacon Hill is best viewed from the abandoned quarry accessible from the Wolverhampton Road, where a considerable extent of limestone grassland occurs with Upright Brome dominant, and much Greater Knapweed, Hawkweed Oxtongue, Field Scabious, and lesser amounts of Quaking-grass, Carline Thistle and Common Milkwort. From the top of Beacon Hill the views of the conurbation to the east are spectacular and, in the days of massive steel production, the entire landscape was lit at night by many furnace fires.

South of Dudley centre two splendid wardened nature reserves, Saltwells Local Nature Reserve and Buckpool and Fens Pools Local Nature Reserve, occupy significant parts of the predominantly industrial landscape and combine portions of post-industrial Dudley with much more ancient features. Saltwells LNR includes Saltwells Wood, Doulton's Claypit, the Gorse-covered Netherton Hill to the north, also Cinder Bank and Dragonfly Pool reclaimed from open-cast mining. Saltwells was designated as the first Local Nature Reserve in the West Midlands Metropolitan County in 1981 and is one of the largest urban nature reserves in the country. Up to the 1930s the claypit was used for clay extraction for sanitary ware by the Royal Doulton Company. The abandoned workings today demonstrate the best exposure of the Productive Coal Measures in the South Staffordshire Coalfield and are notified as a geological Site of Special Scientific Interest. Trees and shrubs now cloak the sides and the bottom of the pit and a diverse flora has developed. Southern Marsh-orchid and Common Spotted-orchid flourish along with their hybrids, Hard Rush, Common Yellow-sedge and Field, Water, Marsh and Shore Horsetails. Spreading along the path by the pool in the claypit is the Spreading Mouse-ear-hawkweed. There are stands of Western Gorse on the flanks of the claypit.

Saltwells Wood stands at the heart of the reserve and at 40 hectares (100 acres) in size is the largest area of woodland in the borough. Contained within this (in parts) ancient woodland is a diverse woodland flora which includes, particularly along the valley of the Black Brook, Ramsons, Wood Anemone, Wood-sedge, Wood Speedwell, Yellow Archangel, two very old specimens of Small-leaved Lime and possibly the finest display of Bluebells in the borough. There are also modestly species-rich old grasslands with Yellow-rattle, Red Bartsia and populations of Marsh-orchids.

Following the Black Brook down past the Saltwells themselves, it passes through a pleasant Alder wood with Marsh-marigold into Mushroom Green and then into the Stour. Upstream from this point the River Stour forms the boundary, not only between Cradley and Cradley Heath, but also between Sandwell and Dudley. The densely-wooded river banks provide a sheltered corridor enabling plants and animals to penetrate deep into the heart of the urbanised areas. For much of its journey through the Black Country the river bank is densely colonised by Indian Balsam and thickets of Japanese Knotweed, but here and there patches of Bluebell, Greater Stitchwort, Red Campion, Wood Anemone and Opposite-leaved Golden-saxifrage can be seen.

Growing in the narrow ribbon of compacted, bare soil along the path edges within the confines of Homer Hill Recreation Gardens in Cradley is a small colony of what is arguably one of the most significant UK native species so far found in Birmingham and the Black Country. Since its discovery in 2003, Jersey Cudweed, belonging to the large Asteraceae family has fluctuated in quantity from 60+ plants in 2003 to as few as three in 2009. A former Red Data Book species, recent evidence suggests this annual may now be increasing in Britain but until very recently this small area of parkland in Dudley has been its only known Birmingham

▲ Jersey Cudweed at Homer Hill colonising a rockery

and Black Country location. Its recent colonisation of a rockery in the park owes much to its protection by Dudley Council and the Friends of Homer Hill Park. The site also contains much Common Whitlowgrass and Bird's-foot. A huge stand of Common Broomrape appeared nearby in 2012, on the site of a demolished school.

Downstream from the junction with the Black Brook, the Stour Valley is a most interesting mixture of industrial land, public access and private woodlands. The wooded parts have some old dingle woodlands with one site for Thin-spiked Wood-sedge. At Stambermill there are small fields, with Heather, Heath-grass, Dyer's Greenweed and Tormentil.

Little more than 1km (0.6 miles) west from Saltwells LNR, across the corner of the Merryhill Shopping Centre and the remains of the Round Oak Steelworks, is Buckpool and Fens Pools Nature Reserve, which, largely reclaimed from the spoil left over from coal and iron industries, refuse tips and disused canals, is astonishingly rich in wildlife. Most of the Fens Pools which includes Fens, Middle and Grove and numerous smaller pools dotted throughout the area have SAC and SSSI designation mainly for the exceptional amphibian populations which live here. As well as Smooth Newt, Common Frog and Common Toad the area immediately surrounding Fens Pool has one of the highest Great-crested Newt counts recorded for Britain. Additionally, well over two hundred species of ferns and flowering plants

▲ Middle Pool at Fens Pools

are documented, some of them nationally or locally scarce. Noteworthy species include White Mullein, Adder's-tongue, Royal Fern, Tall Mouse-ear Hawkweed, Purple Willow, Field Mouse-ear, Southern Marsh-orchid and in the near past, Shining Pondweed, Loose Silky-bent, Orange Foxtail, and Purple Small-reed, although it is believed that the last three of these are now extinct in Birmingham and the Black Country.

The Stourbridge Canal which once served the area is now disused and terminates in the stretch known as Wide Waters within the LNR. A continuous band of emergent vegetation has established throughout its length and throughout the summer, Branched Bur-reed, Reed Sweet-grass, Yellow Iris and Bulrush provide cover and shelter and establish a wildlife corridor linking-up Fens pools with The Leys and Buckpool Dingle (which contains Wood Club-rush). The surface of the canal between Cressett Lane Bridge and the dilapidated railway bridge which once carried freight along the Kingswinford Railway line has in recent times been colonised by the aggressive alien aquatic Floating Pennywort.

West of the railway bridge the canal returns to open water once more and the arm running north-west which abruptly comes to an end after a hundred and fifty metres or so is all that now remains of the Stourbridge Extension which once served local collieries and brickworks. A large colony of Water-soldier is now thoroughly naturalised in this clear undisturbed section of canal. Dudley has many other canal-side locations which bring together aquatic floras and post-industrial landscapes such as the site of the Green-flowered Helleborine and Tall Fleabane associated with a neglected canal dry dock in the Stour Valley at Wollaston, Stourbridge.

Across Pensnett High Street from the Fens Pools reserve (and accessible via a railway tunnel with Dwarf Elder by the entrance) is Barrow Hill LNR. Based around the rock faces and spoil banks and open grassland (and lovely views!) associated with the long-abandoned quarry in a massive outcrop of dolerite, it has a rich flora of mostly base-loving plants including Silver Hair-grass, Early Hair-grass, Kidney Vetch, Deadly Nightshade, Harebell, Carline Thistle (which quite recently clothed large areas of scree-like quarry spoil but is much scarcer now), Greater Knapweed, Dropwort (probably spreading from a neighbouring churchyard), Dyer's Greenweed, (which lost a lot of its territory in the construction of the nearby hospital), Burnet-saxifrage, Knotted Clover and Narrow-leaved Bitter-cress (known at the site since at least 1801).

Flanking the quarry area and extending into the private farmland of Cooper's Bank is a complex of old meadows and pastures, with Yellow-rattle, Betony, Lesser Spearwort and the

**Cooper's Bank from Barrow Hill**
(by Sue Nicholls)

native subspecies of Salad Burnet. Across an old railway track is Tansey Green, until recently a clay pit and now offering new habitats which are being colonised by many of the Barrow Hill speciality plants. Pools there have been landscaped and hold extensive (presumed introduced) reedswamps which include thriving stands of Blunt-flowered Rush, which is otherwise almost unknown in B&BC, and Grey Club-rush as well as the commoner Common Club-rush.

Dudley also has a series of excellent sites around its countryside periphery to the west and south. Next to Wolverhampton, Alder Coppice on the Penn Brook is (despite its name) a good bluebell wood, if rather hemmed in by housing. Cotwall End Valley LNR includes a lovely, tranquil (except for unofficial motorcycle scrambling use) woodland dingle with the usual old woodland indicator species including superb displays of Bluebell and Ramsons, Moschatel, Early Dog-violet and Violet Helleborine, and an intriguing acid patch with Heather and Bog-mosses. It also includes steep fields, natural springs and spoil banks with Pale Sedge, Devil's-bit Scabious, Marsh-orchids and Grass Vetchling.

South of Stourbridge, farmland at Iverley has had some interesting weed records such as Green Nightshade and Corn Marigold. The remains of Pedmore Common and the heathland of Stourbridge Golfcourse have recent records of plants scarce in the midlands as a whole such as Heath Dog-violet and Upright Chickweed as well as a good range of other heathland species uncommon in B&BC such as Heather, Pill Sedge, Bird's-foot and Bilberry.

Part of Wychbury Hill is also in B&BC. It has some interesting grassland containing Harebell and Heath Bedstraw and also some old woodland. Only half a kilometre north and completely surrounded by housing is Ham Dingle, a particularly fine deciduous woodland with a varied ancient woodland flora including Hard-fern, Thin-spiked Wood-sedge, Great Horsetail and Great Wood-rush. In the same green wedge is Lutley Gutter with Moschatel, Large Bitter-cress and Toothwort.

The fringe of countryside continues south of Halesowen and culminates in one of the great treasures of the conurbation, Illey. The Illey area would be a very fine piece of ancient countryside, wherever it was, and it is contiguous with a similarly high interest landscape in current Worcestershire and with the Woodgate Valley in Birmingham across the M5. The main features of biodiversity interest are the high percentage of ancient woodland, with many beautiful dingles (locally called gutters), and a pastoral history with numerous permanent grasslands including a good proportion which are species rich and some of which are designated as an SSSI. The grasslands vary in base status and wetness and Sneezewort, Velvet Bent, Hairy Lady's-mantle, Marsh-marigold, Spring-sedge, Carnation Sedge, Dyer's Greenweed, Rough Hawkbit, Adder's-tongue, Burnet-saxifrage, Tormentil, Great Burnet, Betony and Devil's-bit Scabious can all be found, as can Bog Pondweed and Marsh Speedwell, associated with field ponds. The woodlands support Moschatel , Wood Anemone, Large Bitter-cress, Opposite-leaved Golden-saxifrage, Great Horsetail, Woodruff, Water Avens and Hybrid Avens, Wood Barley, Toothwort, Yellow Archangel, Wood Melick, Sanicle, Wood Speedwell and Early Dog-violet.

A kilometre north across the A456 is the Leasowes. It is a 57-hectare public park set in a much larger open space, containing the remains of a landscape garden designed by the poet William Shenstone in the 18th century and created from farmland. It forms a diverse landscape of wooded valleys, open grassland, lakes and streams and is listed as Grade 1 on the English Heritage 'Register of Parks and Gardens of Special Historic Interest in England'. It also retains a great deal of nature conservation interest, with a range

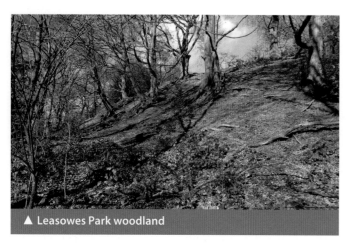

▲ Leasowes Park woodland

of essentially unimproved grasslands, old woodlands and pools, suggesting a remnant of an ecological landscape similar to that of Illey, with such species as Hairy Lady's-mantle, Wood Anemone, Quaking-grass, Large Bitter-cress, Opposite-leaved Golden-saxifrage, Heath-grass, Broad-leaved Helleborine, Great Horsetail, Eyebright, Field Scabious, Bitter Vetch, Burnet-saxifrage, Tormentil, Betony, Devil's-bit Scabious and Wood Speedwell.

Dudley also includes many exceptionally interesting, often very large, post-industrial sites such as the Hawne Colliery site near Halesowen, the hinterland of the Crooked House public house at Gornal Wood and the moulding sand quarry in Holloway Street in Gornal.

**Parkhead viaduct** (by Anne Daly)

## SANDWELL (by Mike Poulton)

Sandwell, in the centre of the conurbation, is unique in having no boundary with the adjoining countryside and also in supporting important links between the river, canal and other transport corridors of the other four B&BC districts which surround it. South of the junction between the M5 and M6 motorways, Sandwell Valley Country Park is by far the largest area of open space in Sandwell stretching beyond its boundary into Birmingham and linking the countryside areas of Walsall and Halesowen across the conurbation. This site has been given its own entry previously in this section.

At the northernmost tip of Sandwell, north of the M6 motorway and west of Dartmouth High School, Rough Hawkbit, Fairy Flax, Glaucous Sedge and Yellow-wort appear in the lime rich soils of Dartmouth Meadow along with Bee Orchids, whose numbers in recent years have dramatically declined since they were first discovered there in the 1990s.

Gorse Farm Wood, situated on the boundary of Sandwell and Birmingham in the east is an oasis of semi-ancient deciduous woodland, cut off and virtually surrounded by the urban sprawl of Great Barr and Hamstead. Remarkably, in wet woodland towards its southern end, a large colony of Wood Horsetail survives. In recent years, steps to remove encroaching scrub and prevent drying out have been rewarded with a notable increase in numbers of plants.

Created entirely by the hand of man, the Galton Valley corridor in Smethwick displays the history of transport in Birmingham and the Black Country of the last 350 years. Spanning a width of about 800m it includes the original old turnpike road, a modern dual carriageway, two canals and a main line railway all running parallel with each other. The largest man made earthworks in the world at the time were made during the construction of the 453ft Birmingham Level canal in the 1820s in a deeper cutting, running parallel to the older 491ft summit level. Despite all its past upheavals, however, remnants of a flora characteristic of the heathland which once occurred all around this area can still be found along the steep sided banks of the Birmingham Canal to the north of Tollhouse Way, and during the spring its banks are transformed into a blaze of golden yellow by Gorse blossom, followed later in the year by patches of Heather, Wavy Hair-grass and other acid grassland species, with fairly recent records for Cowberry, Star Sedge and Lemon-scented Fern.

The Birmingham Canal continues westwards through Oldbury, running beneath an arm of the summit level canal known as the Titford branch which climbs steadily via a series of locks through Tat Bank and Langley, towards its highest point at Titford Pool, now in the shadows of the elevated section of motorway near junction 2 of the M5. Titford Pool, originally constructed as a reservoir to supply water to the Birmingham Old Main Line, was once a hive of industrial activity, and a means by which locally mined and quarried coal, clay and Rowley Rag (a hard, igneous rock) were transported to Birmingham and beyond. Nowadays it is a haven for wildfowl and a tranquil place to walk. On the bend of the canal to the west of the Wolverhampton Road, along the landward side of the canal towpath growing mixed in with nettles, there is a colony of the medicinal herb Motherwort, a plant which was once used to treat conditions related to childbirth. It has been known here for at least 25 years and is found nowhere else in Birmingham and the Black Country outside cultivation.

Along the route of the Titford Canal in Langley there was a railway branch line known as the Langley Loop which once connected the Birmingham to Worcester line at Langley Green with nearby works in Oldbury. Today it is barely discernable and densely overgrown but in the few remaining open areas between Birch, Willow and Butterfly-bush scrub which have colonised the old route, patches of Common Toadflax and the much scarcer Pale Toadflax grow side by side in the old track bed ballast. Swarms of the hybrid between the two species, displaying characteristics of both parents on the same plant, have arisen due to this close encounter.

In the near distance the Rowley Hills command panoramic views of an urbanised landscape. They include the highest point in Birmingham and the Black Country at 271 metres. Extensively quarried in the past and still so in parts up to the present day, they retain fragments of the hillside flora that must have been at one time commonplace in these parts. Bitter-vetch, Ramsons, Wood Horsetail and Bluebell still cling on in unimproved meadowland to the west of Oakham Road, and where extensive landscaping on top of landfill was carried out, to the south of Bury Hill Park and Darby's Hill Quarry, a mosaic of white, blue and yellow from patches of Oxeye Daisies, Tufted Vetch, Bird's-foot-trefoil and

▲ Pre-1970s photograph of Blue Rock Quarry

▲ Blue Rock Quarry after landfill

Meadow Vetchling transforms the banks during the summer months. On steep, water-stressed slopes overlooking the rear of houses in Wallace Road and Ivy House Road species favouring dry, sunny locations have colonised. Mouse-ear-hawkweed, Burnet-saxifrage, Narrow-leaved Meadow-grass, Silver Hair-grass and Fern-grass share this harsh habitat with a recent discovery, Tall Mouse-ear-hawkweed, in one of its two known sites in Birmingham and the Black Country. Another relatively recent arrival, Great Lettuce, grows intermingled with colonies of majestic purple Foxglove on grassed-over quarry sides and a large specimen of Hooker's Hebe has found shelter from the wind on the side of one of the quarry slopes and is Birmingham and the Black Country's only record for this shrub outside gardens. To the north-west the former Darby's Hill Quarry which was extensively landscaped after landfill, has an interesting hillside flora which includes Common Restharrow. Nearby on the top of the steep sided quarry bank, overlooking City Road, a colony of Wood Horsetail creeps between tall grasses and shrubs in an uncharacteristic open situation.

To the south-west, the Rowley Hills slope down to Warren's Hall Park on the Sandwell and Dudley border. Cob's Engine House dominates this picturesque site and the extensive Netherton Canal tunnel begins its mammoth 2,767m journey beneath Rowley Hills. Pleasant walks along the canal and around the pools reward the visitor with an interesting marginal aquatic flora with Gypsywort, Skullcap, Yellow Iris and Clustered Dock, just few of the many species to be found here.

On the lower slopes of the Rowley Hills, to the east of Brickhouse Road, Rowley Regis, a diverse and interesting flora has survived which includes the diminutive Early Hair-grass on its few remaining areas of bare, sandy exposures. Elsewhere, on

sunny, well-drained, grassy slopes, patches of Burnet-saxifrage and Wild Onion intermingle with Yellow Oat-grass and Musk-mallow. Southern Marsh-orchid, Ragged-Robin, Greater Bird's-foot-trefoil and Great Horsetail flourish among Sharp-flowered Rush and Jointed Rush in spring-flushed areas near the bottom of the bank.

The grounds of Haden Hill House and Park slope gently down to the valley of the River Stour forming the border with Sandwell and Dudley. Within the 30 hectares (74 acres) of its landscaped estate are many mature trees, some dating back to the 1870s. A rich, native ground flora flourishes below them, and during the spring patches of Goldilocks Buttercup, Wood Anemone, Ramsons and Bluebells clothe the wooded banks. Near the main entrance of the estate in Halesowen Road, high up among the branches of two Lime trees, clumps of parasitic Mistletoe have been known for many years and are clearly visible during winter and early spring when the trees are devoid of leaves. Extensive patches of pale yellow-flowered Tuberous Comfrey appear in late spring on bare banks between shrubs near the lower pool in its only known Birmingham and the Black Country site.

Glimpses of Sandwells' fast disappearing industrial past can still be found in places but many foundries and factories have now gone. Post-industrial land is quickly redeveloped for factory units or housing, but in the brief interim period before development a specialised urban flora appears for just long enough to enable the seed bank to be replenished. Rarely are such areas left undisturbed. One such site between Burnt Tree Island and the Birmingham Canal has Bee Orchids, Perennial Wall-rocket, Common Cudweed, Blue Fleabane, Rum Cherry, Large-flowered Evening-primrose, Hoary Mustard and Rose Campion among others in its virtually soil-less substrate of ash, foundry sand and building rubble. Nearby, the derelict railway which once linked Dudley with Walsall and Birmingham crosses the Birmingham Canal and throughout its length secondary woodland comprising Birch, Ash, Willow and Butterfly-bush have largely obscured the track-bed to form 'urban woodland'. In the few areas not yet colonised by trees and shrubs, patches of Common Toadflax and Perforate St John's-wort persist. At the point where the bridge carrying the old track bed crosses Sedgley Road East, near Coneygre Leisure Centre, two enormous Fig trees sprawl down the southern side of the embankment, draping over the bridge brickwork and nearby advertising hoardings.

▲ Unique community on spoil near Burnt Tree Island

The railway walkway to the south of Tipton Leisure Centre supports a number of our showiest wild flowers such as Field Scabious, Musk-mallow, Great Willowherb and Common Bird's-foot-trefoil along with a non-native perennial, Yellow Flax (see Neophytes section).

In the later part of the 18th century and well into the 20th century Tipton was one of the most important industrial areas in the Midlands. With over 21km (13 miles) of intricate waterway it soon became known as the Venice of the Midlands enabling

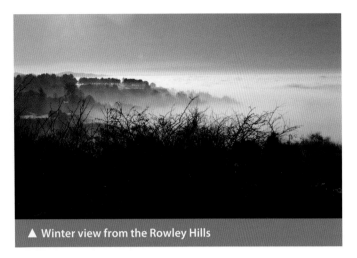

▲ Winter view from the Rowley Hills

finished products to be efficiently transported anywhere in the country. The canals of Tipton today provide a more tranquil setting and have become wildlife corridors linking up to all parts of the conurbation. In places colonies of Yellow Water-lily have spread across the surface of the water providing cover for large Carp and other course fish and a marginal flora which includes Branched and Unbranched Bur-reeds, Yellow Iris, Reedmace and Reed Canary-grass has colonised the margins throughout the system. Water Dock is worth a special mention. Our tallest native dock, it is a plant of freshwater margins and marshes but in Birmingham and the Black Country it is overwhelmingly a plant of canal margins.

From Tipton the Birmingham Canal runs parallel with the main line railway linking Birmingham and Wolverhampton, passing over Dudley Port aqueduct and continuing along an embankment overlooking Sheepwash Urban Park. Sheepwash Urban Park is today a complex of wetland, scrub, young woodland and grassland but has not always been so. Reclaimed and landscaped from a clay pit after landfill, a foundry site, sewage farm and allotments, much of the area has now been designated LNR status and contains pools, grassland, the River Tame and planted woodland. The flora is varied and wide ranging as befits the different habitats present on the site.

To the south of Hydes Road, the large extent of open space surrounding Mill Pool has a diverse and interesting flora and fauna which includes Agrimony and Hedge Bedstraw. Also worthy of mention is Warley Woods which is a park landscaped by Repton and contains some of the largest Beech trees surviving in Sandwell, remnant ancient woodland, Mat-grass and Heath-grass surviving in the lawns and other interesting habitats.

## WALSALL (by Simon Phipps)

Walsall borough comprises the north-east quarter of the Black Country. Its western half is densely urban and contains the settlements of Walsall, Willenhall, Darlaston and Bloxwich. In contrast, the eastern towns of Aldridge and Brownhills are set in a more open, rural landscape. As in much of the Black Country, an historic pattern of mining, housing and industrial development lies side-by-side with traditional farming and undisturbed pockets of woodland, grassland and wetland. The tide of urban encroachment has left an often rich scattering of ancient and more recent habitats. Even in the urban west and central parts of the borough, broad wedges of open land separating urban settlement are characteristic. Examples include Rough Wood Chase separating Willenhall and Bloxwich and the Goscote Valley between Bloxwich and Pelsall. As a result of historic settlement patterns, underlying

geology and good fortune, the borough contains a diverse and important botanical heritage.

In a Birmingham and Black Country context, Walsall borough's finest and most diverse botanical sites are its wetlands. The borough's canals are particularly botanically rich, perhaps because of lower levels of canal boat use resulting from the lack of direct access to the wider UK canal network and their closeness to the canal feeder reservoir at Chasewater.

The Cannock Extension Canal, north of Pelsall, is important in a European context for its population of Floating Water-plantain. This rare plant has been recorded in other parts of the local canal network, mainly in the Pelsall Brownhills area. The Cannock Extension Canal, while mostly outside the borough, is also home to Shining and Perfoliate Pondweeds as well as good populations of Flowering-rush and Arrowhead. These latter two species are widely distributed in Walsall's canal network and can be found in the Walsall Canal within a stone's throw of Walsall town centre.

The Daw End Branch Canal connecting Brownhills and the Rushall area is typical of the botanical diversity of many of the borough's canals. In open water, Spiked Water-milfoil, Curled Pondweed, Perfoliate Pondweed and Common Water-starwort are found. Marginal habitats contain a range of sedges including Lesser and Greater Pond-sedges, and Cyperus Sedge.

The canals also contain some problematic invasive non-native plants. Water Fern is common, and a major infestation of the canal system by Floating Pennywort started in Hollybank Basin, Short Heath probably from a garden 'throw-out'.

Walsall borough contains few large water bodies or substantial rivers. However, Lady Pool, in Rushall, contains the largest reed

▲ Marsh-orchids at Clayhanger SSSI

bed in Birmingham and the Black Country, while Sneyd Reservoir in Bloxwich and Ward's Pool in Moxley both contain a diverse aquatic flora. At Park Lime Pits in Rushall and Walsall Power Station Pool in Beechdale, Lesser Bulrush is found. The Hoar Brook in Walsall Arboretum is a pleasant lowland stream and the Ford Brook provides ecological links through the centre of the borough and into the town centre.

Many of Walsall's best wetland sites contain a mosaic of habitats often formed by mining subsidence and impeded drainage caused by mining, industrial development or the construction of canals, railways or roads. Some of the borough's most species-rich wetlands occur at Clayhanger and Jockey Fields SSSIs. Both sites are private although public footpaths allow limited access.

Clayhanger SSSI, between Pelsall and Brownhills, displays a range of wetland habitats from open water, through fen and marsh communities as well as wet and dry grasslands. In some pools there are stands of Common Club-rush and the much rarer Sea Club-rush. In the fen areas Mare's-tail, Tubular Water-dropwort and Pink Water-speedwell are found. In marshy grassland habitats rushes dominate but Common Sedge and Oval Sedge can be locally abundant and there are considerable areas of Water-purslane. Meadow Thistle is also found on the site.

Jockey Fields SSSI in Walsall Wood is a complex of low-lying fields containing wet grassland, fen and marsh. The site is semi-natural and not the result of major human changes to the landform. The wetter areas contain Bottle Sedge, Greater Bird's-foot-trefoil and Marsh Thistle, although Lesser Pond-sedge and Bulrush are dominant. Other notable plants include: Brown Sedge, Wood Horsetail, Marsh Arrowgrass and Pink Water-speedwell.

Wood Farm and Oily Goughs are fully accessible and form adjacent parts of Rough Wood Chase Local Nature Reserve in the M6 Motorway corridor. This land has probably survived development and agricultural improvement because it was low-lying, wet and cut off from neighbouring land by canals. Like the two SSSIs mentioned above, it comprises a mosaic of wetlands and drier habitats. In the ponds and ditches, Lesser Marshwort, Marsh Pennywort, Fringed Water-lily, Fan-leaved Water-crowfoot and Grey Club-rush are found. The grasslands contain a variety of wet and dry-loving species, including Ragged-Robin, Common Restharrow, Yellow Bartsia, Great Burnet and Common Skullcap.

Another outstanding complex of small pools and marshy grassland is found on private farmland at King's Hayes near Shire Oak. Here a wealth of uncommon wetlands plants have been recorded including Whorl-grass, Intermediate Water-starwort, Common Yellow-sedge, Meadow Thistle, Bristle Club-rush, Ivy-leaved Crowfoot, Narrow-fruited Water-cress and Marsh Arrowgrass. This site probably reflects the flora of rough, damp grazing land over much of the Black Country prior to the middle of the 20th century. Related and equally botanically diverse wetlands and pastures occur west of Brownhills Common and in the fringes of Pelsall Common.

Mill Lane Local Nature Reserve in the Ryecroft area is a much more recent site. This publicly accessible patchwork of wetlands, grasslands and scrub developed on former railway land where the presence of both limestone ballast and colliery spoil left wet and dry as well as both base-poor and base-rich conditions. In the wetter grasslands the only known population of Corky-fruited Water-dropwort in B&BC occurs. Other plants found in the wetter areas include Water Horsetail and the locally rare Bottle Sedge.

All these wetland sites contain patches of drier neutral grasslands characterised by such species as: Common Knapweed, Crested Dog's-tail, Southern Marsh-orchid, Oxeye Daisy and Common Bird's-foot-trefoil. Quaking-grass and Yellow-rattle are

▲ Pond at Mill Lane LNR

also sometimes found. Some sites, including Clayhanger SSSI and King's Hayes fields and Mill Lane Local Nature Reserve also contain areas of acidic grassland containing such species as Harebell, Heath-grass, Wavy Hair-grass, Mat-grass and Sheep's Sorrel. On Clayhanger Common south of Brownhills, an unimproved neutral grassland has been created on a former landfill site. Kidney Vetch, Yellow-rattle and Salad Burnet can all be seen.

Due to underlying geology, there are few calcareous grasslands within Walsall Borough. The one exception is the Park Lime Pits area of Rushall where Wenlock limestone outcrops. Park Lime Pits Local Nature Reserve is a flooded former limestone quarry surrounded by grassland, scrub and woodland habitats. This site and surrounding fields contain plants of limestone grassland including Thyme-leaved Sandwort, Quaking-grass, Fairy Flax, Burnet-saxifrage, Hoary Plantain, Cowslip and Hoary Ragwort.

Much of the Black Country's once extensive heathland survives over the sandstones which underlie the eastern edge of the borough. Extensive areas of wet and dry heath set in a mosaic of acidic grassland, Bracken and scrub are found at Brownhills Common and Pelsall North Common. Dry heath on these sites is typically dominated by Heather with Bell Heather, Bilberry, Cowberry and Western Gorse. In between these shrubby species, grasses such as Purple Moor-grass, Mat-grass and Wavy Hair-grass are found. These grasses become dominant as the heathy habitat grades into acidic grassland. In the damper areas plants such as Cross-leaved Heath, Common Cottongrass, Heath Wood-rush and Heath Rush flourish. Sedges such as Common Sedge, Carnation Sedge and Oval Sedge are also found, together with cushions of

▲ Brownhills Common

Bog-mosses. Bog-moss species include *Sphagnum fimbriatum*, *S. palustre* and *S. squarrosum*.

Heathland is not confined to the Brownhills/Pelsall areas. Barr Beacon in the south-eastern corner of the borough is the most notable example, although this site contains more acidic grassland than heath. It is only 2 km (1.2 miles) away from Sutton Park where the largest tract of heathland in the area is found. The Barr Beacon site contains both Silver and Early Hair-grass as well as Harebell. Heathland is being restored on this site which provides panoramic views over Walsall and the Black Country.

The best secondary heathland is found on the earthworks of the disused Walsall to Lichfield railway line north of Brownhills town centre where the floristic diversity rivals that of much longer established healthland sites. Shire Oak Park Local Nature Reserve contains fragments of heathland and its flora includes Silver and Early Hair-grass as well as Hare's-foot Clover. Even a post-industrial site such as Mill Lane Local Nature Reserve contains a small area of wet heathland and there is another small area on coal spoil west of Brownhills Common which is currently the only known site for Heath Milkwort in the conurbation.

Wet heathlands may grade into base-poor mire habitats which have always been scarce in the borough. The main surviving example at Stubbers Green has largely been lost due to lack of management and encroachment of willow scrub. Species formerly recorded include: Round-leaved Sundew, Common Cottongrass, Marsh Arrowgrass, Bog Pondweed and Narrow Buckler-fern. Another tiny, intriguing mire exists on Clayhanger Common adjacent to the Daw End branch canal. Lesser Skullcap was known there until the 1980s and the flora still includes Bog Pimpernel, Star Sedge, Cross-leaved Heath, Meadow Thistle and one of only two known populations of Heath Spotted-orchid in the conurbation. Another curious site exists on the edge of Anchor Meadow playing fields in Aldridge where a wetland containing Common Cottongrass developed on disused railway sidings.

Walsall borough has a few ancient woodlands which are mainly publicly accessible. The woodlands centred on the Hayhead Wood/ Cuckoos Nook and the Dingle complex between Walsall and Aldridge are amongst the finest. These woods contain areas of both Oak/Bracken/Bramble and Ash/Field Maple/Dog's Mercury woodlands depending on the underlying geology. The Dingle is also a geological SSSI designated for its Barr limestone visible in an old limestone quarry but is botanically very rich. The ground flora of this Ash/Field Maple/Dog's Mercury woodland is dominated in the spring by Ramsons and Dog's Mercury but Wood Anemone,

▲ Hayhead Wood

Scaly Male-fern, Woodruff, Wood Melick, Sanicle and Early Dog-violet are also found. Field Maple occurs as a native rather than introduced species. The tree canopy is dominated by Ash, Sycamore and Beech with two specimens of Large-leaved Lime.

The adjacent Cuckoo's Nook, in contrast, contains predominantly Oak/Bracken/Bramble woodland. Here Bluebell dominates but other species are also found such as Wood Anemone and False Brome. The tree canopy is dominated by Pedunculate Oak while Hazel and Holly occupy the shrub layer. Both Cuckoo's Nook and Hayhead Wood contain patches of wet woodland, where Alder provides the tree canopy and both Marsh-marigold and Large Bitter-cress occur amongst the ground flora.

Rough Wood in Short Heath is part of Rough Wood Chase Local Nature Reserve but is separated from most of the wider site by the M6 motorway. This ancient woodland site is an Oak/Bracken/ Bramble woodland and Pedunculate Oak dominates the tree canopy. The ground flora is somewhat impoverished but Bluebell occurs while Plicate Sweet-grass and Marsh Violet are found in the wetter areas. Alder Buckthorn occurs as an occasional shrub.

The privately owned Castlebank Plantation at Shire Oak is sited on the ramparts of an iron-age hill fort. This site is again an Oak/Bracken/Bramble woodland dominated by Pedunculate Oak and more ornamental species. The ground flora includes: Wood Anemone, Wood-sedge, Wood-sorrel and Wood Meadow-grass.

No account of Walsall's woodlands would be complete without reference to the parkland surrounding Great Barr Hall in the Pheasey area. Here a mixture of ancient and plantation woodlands surround the lakeside site of the now ruined Great Barr Hall, a mansion built in the Strawberry Hill gothic style in 1777. The Duckery is a small Oak/Bramble/Bracken woodland with a ground flora dominated by Bluebell but also includes Moschatel, Hairy-brome and Yellow Archangel. Wet woodland areas include: Marsh-marigold, Large Bitter-cress and Wood Club-rush while more open wetlands contain Hoary Willowherb and Common Valerian. The dryer areas are dominated by Pedunculate Oak and Sycamore while Alder dominates the wetter areas. The largely plantation woodlands surrounding the hall contain a variety of native and ornamental trees and the ground flora in many areas is dominated by Bluebell. The only publicly accessible part of these woodlands is Merrion's Wood Local Nature Reserve. This Local Nature Reserve has an ancient woodland core but also includes plantation areas associated with the landscaping of the Great Barr Park. The tree canopy is dominated by Oak while the ground flora is dominated by Bluebell but Remote Sedge, Opposite-leaved Golden-saxifrage, Pignut and Wood Millet are also found.

Over the last 30 years there has been considerable tree planting carried out in Walsall borough comprising a wide range of tree and shrub species. Some of these plantations have persisted but few, if any, have a woodland ground flora.

The flora of old woodlands persists in some of the hedgerows which remain, particularly in the Barr Beacon area of Walsall and the countryside east of Aldridge. Dog's Mercury and Bluebell are often frequent while Wood Anemone, Enchanter's-nightshade, Bluebell, Wood Melick and Wood Sage can be found in the more diverse hedgerows, amongst the more ubiquitous coarse grasses, brambles and stinging nettles. In one hedgerow in Skip Lane, Walsall, the locally rare Crosswort has been recorded. Spindle and Black Bryony are amongst the more uncommon hedgerow shrubs.

Many of the sites mentioned in this account of Walsall's flora are encapsulated countryside which has survived urbanisation. Some of Walsall Borough's most important sites occur on former mineral and industrial sites which have developed a distinctive flora usually without any deliberate human help. At Moorcroft Wood Local Nature Reserve in Moxley, large blocks of slag give rise to a distinctive flora including unusual lichens, Fern-grass, Squirreltail Fescue, Rat's-tail Fescue, and Polypody. A distinctive flora has also developed amongst the base-rich furnace slag of the former iron works at Pelsall North Common. Common Bird's-foot-trefoil and Lesser Hawkbit are abundant while many other rare and uncommon plants in Birmingham and the Black Country also flourish including: Flattened Meadow-grass, Common Whitlowgrass, Chives, Blue Fleabane, Garden Asparagus, Wild Onion, Little Mouse-ear, Buck's-horn Plantain, Eyebright and large populations of Southern Marsh-orchid, Common Spotted-orchid and their hybrids. Even on currently working quarry sites, rare and uncommon plants can be found. On a working quarry in Walsall Wood, Bithynian Vetch was recently recorded while on the shaded embankments of former industrial land in the west of the borough the Collared Earthstar fungus is recorded.

Even in the town centres unexpected plants can sometimes be seen. In Walsall town centre usually growing in gaps in paving, Whitlowgrass, Black Nightshade and Pellitory-of-the-wall are found. Black Horehound and Lesser Swine-cress are occasionally found on disturbed ground at the rear of the footpath. Prickly Lettuce and the salt-tolerant Danish Scurvygrass are common along road verges and are relative newcomers to the area.

Industrial premises, Willenhall (by Sue Nicholls)

## WOLVERHAMPTON (by Ian Trueman and Peter Millett)

The City of Wolverhampton forms the north-western part of the conurbation. It includes the settlements of Penn, Tettenhall, Wednesfield and Bilston as well as the city centre itself. The open spaces of the western half of Wolverhampton retain memories of the Middle Ages. To the south in particular there are remnants of medieval field systems with species-rich hedges and Bluebell woodlands at Park and Ashen Coppice. Further old woodlands occur to the north at Northycote Farm and fragments to the west on the Tettenhall Ridge. They vary from Oak/Bracken/Bramble woodlands to Ash/Field Maple/Dog's Mercury woodlands to Alder woodlands. At Park and Ashen Coppices, the canopy is Pedunculate Oak, Ash and Alder without any Sycamore and there is an understorey mainly of Hazel with a little Crab Apple. In spring, in addition to huge stands of Bluebell, you can see many of the ancient woodland plant species which are present in more rural woodlands, such as Yellow Archangel, Moschatel, Wood Anemone, Wood-sedge, Greater Stitchwort and Wood Melick. At Northycote Farm there is a good stretch of Alder woodland in the valley bottom, still with some Pedunculate Oak and Ash, and with

▲ Park Wood

an understorey which includes Bird Cherry and tracts of flushed ground with Opposite-leaved Golden-saxifrage and Large Bitter-cress. Across the stream (in Staffordshire!) there are two stands of Wood Club-rush.

In the eastern half of Wolverhampton, especially in the south-east around Bilston, a special flora has colonised the colliery tips, blast furnace spoil and canals which were part of the Industrial Revolution. Indicator species include Common Toadflax, Bladder Campion, Hare's-foot Clover, Red Bartsia, Blue Fleabane, Flattened Meadow-grass, Fern-grass and Bee Orchid. There are few good examples of this type of landscape left; even the furnace slag ramparts to the Bilston steelworks have had soil bulldozed over them. One such remnant at Ladymoor Pool includes an interesting Hard Rush marsh where Marsh Arrowgrass and four species of Bog-moss have been recorded, and huge blocks of very old blast furnace slag with Silver Hair-grass, Biting Stonecrop, Ivy-leaved Toadflax and Oxford Ragwort. Another, considerably reclaimed, is at Stow Lawn and another, with created hay meadows, coal spoil and a clay pit, is at Ettingshall Park (now known as Spring Vale). Peascroft Wood is an unusually mature wood planted on a coal spoil heap in Bilston at the beginning of the 20th century although apart from Lesser Celandine the only old woodland species present have been deliberately introduced. There is a remnant of brickyards at Hawkswell Drive, with two pools, one inside an

▲ Furnace slag at Ladymoor Pool (1980s)

electricity substation enclosure and the other in the open space of a new housing development. They have Slender Tufted-sedge and Tubular Water-dropwort but the public one has been badly trampled by anglers.

Wednesfield in north-east Wolverhampton has the remains of a large post-industrial site at Bowman's Harbour, where reclamation in the 1990s destroyed an area of ridge and furrow with Wood Small-reed but has created an extensive wetland with a huge population of Southern Marsh-orchids, Common Spotted-orchid, Pink Water-speedwell, Oval Sedge and False Fox-sedge and in drier places Flattened Meadow-grass and Bristly Oxtongue.

Wolverhampton also has a range of created hay meadows, the first created in 1983. Many, such as those at Bushbury Hill (1984), Pendeford Mill Nature Reserve (1985) and Northycote Farm (2007, part) were made with hay from the same field on the Shropshire Stiperstones Ridge at Pennerley Meadows SSSI, and plants such as Oxeye Daisy, Yellow-rattle, Cowslips and Quaking-grass have been successfully transferred. Another hay-strewn meadow created at the far end of Kitchen Lane (1993) has Green-winged Orchid, Common Spotted-orchid and Common Twayblade and many Cowslips. The hay was from Eades Meadow NNR in Worcestershire. Two further species-rich meadows made with a seed mixture on a post-mining and quarrying site in 1986, are at Springvale (Ettingshall Park), where Dyer's Greenweed and Great Burnet may be seen.

▲ Green-winged Orchids at Kitchen Lane

Scattered around the city are also examples of tree plantations into which the ground flora of ancient woodlands has been introduced; examples may be seen at Dunstall Hill, Neachells Lane public open space and along the canal north of Highfields Road, where Bluebells, Primrose, Ramsons, Greater Stitchwort, Wood Speedwell and other old woodland species have been successfully introduced.

Up the hill from Bilston to Sedgley is the Gorge, a significant limestone outcrop and quarry, largely wooded with much native Dogwood and a fragmentary semi-natural limestone grassland flora with Quaking-grass, Hoary Plantain, and Burnet-saxifrage.

The canal network includes the relatively clean Wyrley and Essington Canal coming down through Wednesfield from Chasewater to meet the Birmingham Canal, which descends via locks to the Staffs-Worcester Canal by the Racecourse. The flora does not quite approach the flora in the Walsall canals but the Wyrley and Essington is quite rich with much Yellow Water-lily, many stands of Flowering-rush and the occasional spike of Common Broomrape along the towpath. Along the Birmingham Canal there are currently some remnants of an old, industrial "Black Country" flora with such plants as Wormwood, Beaked Hawk's-beard, Russell Lupin, Eastern Rocket and Hare's-foot Clover. Good examples currently (2010) occur where the two canals meet at Horseley Fields, along the branch to Ladymoor and Loxdale,

by the flight of locks just north of the City centre, and in the vicinity of the Science Park (where some are being conserved and include another population of Southern Marsh-orchid and an old population of Common Broomrape).

One of the old features of Wolverhampton's city centre, relics of its earlier connection with the wool trade, are the folds or passages, which have Pellitory-of-the-wall in at least one place.

Derelict factory (now demolished)
Bowmans Harbour, Wednesfield
(by Anne Daly)

In 1998 a wide corridor along the dismantled railway line through Tettenhall station, running parallel with the Staffs-Worcester canal and the Smestow Brook, became the Smestow Valley Local Nature Reserve. The station and line have now lost most of their railway flora and are rather shady but there is much Butterbur, occasional patches of Collared Earthstar fungus, also Ramsons and Pendulous Sedge are colonising. There is an interesting siding at Dunstall Bridge in which a dense Hawthorn wood has developed, also an abandoned sand quarry at Windmill Hill which operates as a no-access bird sanctuary, with Hornbeam and mixed deciduous plantations, and a hay meadow created in 1983.

The LNR links a series of secondary woods, tall-herb stands, rough grass and semi-improved pastures along the track and parallel with the Staffs-Worcester canal where Common Club-rush may be seen. In the canal bank edge at Compton there is a stand of Tor-grass, possibly the only place it may be found in the conurbation. The canal links with the Birmingham canal and hence with the town centre. Close to the junction of the two canals, the best semi-natural grassland in Wolverhampton is within the boundary of the racecourse and has Glaucous Sedge, Great Burnet and Pignut. Canal, stream valley, wooded line, sidings and associated remnants of an agricultural landscape together form a habitat-rich complex noted particularly for its bird populations and linking the old habitats of the west with one another and with the industrial east.

# Section 3 • Neophytes (and where to see them) by Mike Poulton

In the world of plants 'Neophytes' is the name given to non-native plants for which there is no evidence of introduction into the UK before 1500AD. This date reflects the discovery of the Americas in 1492, since when we have received many New World species. Other introduced plants do not normally persist in the wild and are known as casuals, but in fact the process of establishment in a new country has many stages. Most neophytes remain confined to secondary habitats, but some are capable of invading old woodlands and other valuable wildlife sites.

Of the 1449 species, hybrids and recorded subspecies currently established in Birmingham and the Black Country, 555 are considered to be neophytes in Britain (Preston *et al.* 2002). They include many of the popular garden annuals, perennials, shrubs and trees, some of which are now thoroughly naturalised in the British Isles, but also those plants whose introduction causes harm to human health, economic harm or environmental harm. Twenty-five of these are now listed in Schedule 9, Part 2, of the Wildlife and Countryside Act 1981. It is against the law to plant or otherwise cause to grow these in the wild.

In view of the unfamiliarity and complex taxonomy of many neophytes, both English and Latin names are given at the first mention in this chapter. Further information about the origin and distribution of the plants named is given in chapter 8.

Without doubt, the least desirable of the problematic neophytes listed in Schedule 9, and by far the commonest in our area, is Japanese Knotweed *Fallopia japonica*. This pernicious weed tolerates a wide range of soil types and the invasive rhizomes penetrate tarmac and concrete surfaces, damaging roads and paving and even the foundations of buildings. Dense and impenetrable thickets occur along railway and canal banks, on waste ground, in old cemeteries, golf courses, neglected gardens and areas of dereliction throughout the whole conurbation except for the countryside areas of Walsall and Sutton Coldfield and some peripheral areas.

An industry has formed for, and countless thousands of man-hours are annually dedicated to, the eradication of this one species alone. Some confusion in identification may arise with Giant Knotweed *Fallopia sachalinensis* and the hybrid *F. japonica* × *F. sachalinensis*. Confirmed records of the hybrid

▲ *Impatiens glandulifera* along the River Stour, Cradley

have only been reported from sites along south Birmingham river corridors, with one isolated colony growing in wet woodland adjacent to Birmingham Botanical Gardens from where it possibly originated. Isolated Giant Knotweed colonies have been located in Walsall, Sandwell, Dudley and Birmingham, but records are relatively few and widely scattered.

Indian Balsam *Impatiens glandulifera* is a dominating annual, reviled by many because of its invasiveness. Urban colonisation is principally along the banks of our major river corridors, where a continuous monoculture of Indian Balsam clothes many hundreds of metres of riverbank during the summer months, and winter dieback exposes the banks to erosion when the river is in spate. Once established, eradication is virtually impossible as copious seed production guarantees annual re-colonisation.

Flowering is continuous from mid-summer well into autumn, with the pinky-purple, sickly-sweet flowers providing a rich source of nectar for pollinating insects. Concerted efforts by groups of volunteers carrying out annual "balsam bashing" events at some of our local wildlife sites have had only moderate impact on population control.

The sap of Giant Hogweed *Heracleum mantegazzianum* contains toxic chemicals which cause phytophotodermatitis in

▲ *Fallopia japonica*

▲ *Heracleum mantegazzianum*, River Stour, Stourbridge

humans, a reaction which makes skin hypersensitive to ultraviolet light, resulting in blistering and, in extreme cases where the sap comes in contact with eyes, blindness.

Introduced in Victorian times when seeds were taken to Kew Gardens, it is now widely distributed throughout the conurbation in richly fertile, moist to damp soils. Isolated plants occasionally appear in most unlikely situations such as roadsides and shrub borders, but once identified are usually eradicated before attaining their full growth potential. One colony which contained many thousands of plants and created a spectacular display with its enormous flat-topped umbrella-like clusters of flowers, with some plants reaching well over three metres in height, is now covered by the new Queen Elizabeth Hospital in Edgbaston.

Butterfly-bush *Buddleja davidii*, which is not listed in Schedule 9 but perhaps ought to be, became a popular garden shrub in the 20th century with its spikes of lilac, white or purple nectar-filled flowers attracting some of our most colourful butterflies and moths. Nowadays, it has become a pernicious urban weed, perhaps second only to Japanese Knotweed in its invasiveness. A ubiquitous coloniser of old buildings and bridges, the penetrating roots can be particularly damaging, drying out mortar, causing cracks and moving brickwork. The small, winged seeds, prolifically produced, lodge into brickwork mortar high up on buildings where substantial bushes can form. It is particularly abundant on old railway-track ballast and in brickwork mortar associated with railway architecture. Wasteland left abandoned for two years or more is particularly susceptible to colonisation, and on such sites 'Buddleja woodland' is not uncommon.

During our recording period Butterfly-bush has turned up in some unexpected places. Two that particularly stand out are on the bodywork of the preserved Great Western Steam Locomotive No. 2885 residing at Moor Street Station, and from the top of one of the crushed car-blocks forming the entrance to a car park along Heath Mill Lane in Digbeth.

A number of highly invasive, aquatic plants, some of them listed in Schedule 9, have in recent years impacted negatively on our ponds and water-courses, and discovering a pond or entire section of canal totally covered by one of these is by no means unusual. When infestations are severe it can have a detrimental affect on other aquatic pond life, reducing sunlight penetration and altering the whole ecology of the water-body.

Water Fern *Azolla filiculoides*, possibly one of the most prolific invasive neophytes, appears erratically in our ponds and canals.

▲ 'Buddleja woodland' – Birmingham Eastside, 2012

▲ *Azolla filiculoides* – Walsall Canal, 2011

It can be an elusive plant in some years, apparently disappearing from sites where it was once prolific; in other years it may cover the entire surface of a pond or length of canal. It originates from tropical South America, and prolonged cold winter weather significantly impacts on its survival prospects from one year to the next; however, a few submerged buds protected from the extremes of weather in a sheltered spot can lead to rapid re-colonisation. During autumn 2011 its explosive invasiveness could be seen to great effect along a 600-metre section of the Walsall Canal between Rushall Locks at Longwood Junction and Park Hall Locks at Five Ways Bridge in Walsall, where the whole water-surface was turned greenish-purple by millions of individual plants.

Least Duckweed *Lemna minuta* is a relatively recent arrival and is the smallest duckweed found in Britain. A noxious weed with an ever-expanding distribution it is now well-established in some of Birmingham and the Black Country's ponds and canals. Often mixed in with Common Duckweed it is easily transferred from one water-body to another on the feet of birds and once introduced colonisation across the water-surface can be rapid, severe infestations resulting in the exclusion of sunlight penetration which may have a negative effect on other aquatic life.

Floating Pennywort *Hydrocotyle ranunculoides* is an invasive aquatic which has impacted alarmingly on water-bodies during the past ten years. Some of our ponds, ditches and canals have been subjected to colonisation by this aggressive aquatic which received no mention in Stace's *New Flora of the British Isles*, published in 1991. In the second edition, published in 1997, Stace refers to Floating Pennywort as "introduced, naturalised in rivers, canals and ponds, first recorded 1990 from several places in SE England and apparently rapidly spreading". The first recordings in our area occurred in 2004, from a duck pond to the rear of Park Farm buildings in Sandwell Valley and in a ditch near the River Rea in Northfield. In subsequent years parts of the Wyrley & Essington and Stourbridge Extension Canals were badly infested. Once established in a water body, Floating Pennywort runners rapidly reach out across the surface, out-competing and smothering all in its path. Within a few weeks a single individual can cover several metres in every direction, rooting from each node. In deeper water, submerged oxygenating plants are used as support as the runners continue to grow, until a shallow area enables more roots to be put down. In this way small bodies of water are rapidly colonised with most growth occurring in the late summer, when it typically forms extensive floating

▲ *Hydrocotyle ranunculoides* – Stourbridge Extension Canal, taken from Cressett Lane Bridge, 2008

▲ *Hydrocotyle ranunculoides* – Sandwell Valley, 2008

▲ *Hydrocotyle ranunculoides* – Sandwell Valley, 2010

parts of the Stourbridge Extension Canal where in September 2008, in the section between Cressett Lane Bridge and the old railway bridge at Brockmoor, the entire water-surface for approximately 300m was covered.

Three years later, in September 2011, only small patches remained near Cressett Lane Bridge. A possible explanation for its decline could be the prolonged cold spell experienced during the winter of 2010/11, when temperatures plummeted to minus 14°C and daytime temperatures remained below 0°C for many consecutive days, freezing the canal to a great depth. In 2008 Floating Pennywort in the duck pond near Park Farm buildings in Sandwell Valley was so extensive that leaves were rising as much as 25cm from the surface of the water. In 2009 Chemical treatment was carried out at considerable cost, resulting in what was believed at the time to be a total success.

No Floating Pennywort was to be seen in the following year but in August 2011 an inspection through binoculars revealed that plants were once more spreading out into the water from two of the banks. It was apparent that small fragments had survived under the main canopy of leaves, shaded from the herbicide, and re-colonisation was once again underway.

Only time will tell what long-term impact Floating Pennywort may have on the aquatic ecosystem in Birmingham and the Black Country.

Infestations of another pernicious aquatic invader, New Zealand Pigmyweed *Crassula helmsii* were found in a few well-separated locations during early days of recording for the Flora. Since then, new sites for this invasive, semi-terrestrial, aquatic succulent have been discovered regularly, and it appears that very little can be done to prevent further spread. Favouring gently shelving, shallow ponds colonisation is rapid, both within the water and along the shoreline.

Our largest and most devastating infestation is in the scrape at RSPB Sandwell Valley, where a monoculture of New Zealand Pigmyweed has displaced everything else that once grew here. Repeated attempts at eradicating it have so far met with little success. Another large infestation can be seen in the Local Nature Reserve at Fibbersley, Walsall, where New Zealand Pigmyweed has colonised the muddy margins and shallows of one of the woodland ponds. Even more significantly, it is thoroughly naturalised at Little Bracebridge Pool in the National Nature Reserve at Sutton Park, a home to some of Birmingham and the Black Country's most uncommon native plants. Some infestations are almost certainly the result of deliberate introductions, as up until quite recently plants were readily available from aquarists

▲ *Crassula helmsii* – RSPB Sandwell Valley, 2010

mats of vegetation. New infestations are reported annually, but interestingly, at some of the sites a reverse trend has taken place, and following rapid initial colonisation gradual decline has followed. In a pond near the golf course on Rowley Hills, where it was first discovered in 2007, the entire water surface became covered with Floating Pennywort, but four years later none was to be found.

As far as can be established no physical removal or chemical treatment had taken place at the site and the pond had not dried out during this time. The plant also appears to be declining in and garden centres. Additionally, fragments are easily spread from one pond to another on the feet of wildfowl; transference on boots or wellingtons could also be a contributory factor.

Parrot's-feather *Myriophyllum aquaticum* is regarded in some parts of Britain as an aggressive invader of ponds. However, to date it has had no significant impact on water bodies in Birmingham and the Black Country with only a few widely scattered records reported from ponds and canals.

Three submerged aquatics which appear in the Schedule 9 list are found in the conurbation. Canadian Waterweed *Elodea canadensis* was at one time one of our commonest submerged aquatics, but from the outset of the recording campaign it became apparent that Nuttall's Waterweed *Elodea nuttallii* is now the dominant submerged aquatic alien plant in our region, particularly in the canal system where it has largely displaced Canadian Waterweed. Nowadays, Canadian Waterweed is still occasionally found in canals, but tends to favour smaller water bodies such as field ponds in the absence of the more competitive Nuttall's Waterweed. Curly Waterweed *Lagarosiphon major* is a favoured oxygenator plant supplied by aquarists and garden centres. Once established in garden ponds growth is rapid, resulting in unwanted plants often being discarded into a nearby canal or pond where rooting takes place from the smallest fragment. Few records for Curly Waterweed have been reported, but this hardy submerged aquatic, which is capable of surviving our coldest winters, could easily be mistaken for a robust form of Nuttall's Waterweed and may go unnoticed.

in sunny aspects on quarry slopes and drought-liable banks, but generally display no pronounced invasive tendencies here. Other listed Cotoneaster species occur in our area infrequently or not at all.

Rhododendron *Rhododendron ponticum*, Cherry Laurel *Prunus laurocerasus* and Snowberry *Symphoricarpos albus* are perhaps the least desirable of the ornamental shrubs used in planting schemes for parks and large estates. All three are now an established part of our alien flora on account of their invasive tendencies and have infiltrated woodland either as persistent plantings or as self-sown plants. Of the three, only Rhododendron is included in Schedule 9, but a case could easily be put forward for the other two. In particular, Snowberry, a very persistent and extensively suckering shrub, is frequently encountered on waste ground and in abandoned gardens, and also in woodland where it can form extensive patches in relatively shaded conditions. Easily transferred in soil from one site to another by root fragments, it has been recorded in well over half of the 1km squares in Birmingham and the Black Country. No seedlings have been reported for this or Chenault's Coralberry *Symphoricarpos* × *chenaultii,* which occasionally persists in neglected shrubberies and gardens.

Japanese Rose *Rosa rugosa* is regarded as invasive in some parts of the country, and in Birmingham and the Black Country this attractive plant can form large stands in neglected public open spaces or occasionally in isolation on waste ground where it is possibly spontaneous.

▲ *Lagarosiphon major*

▲ *Rosa rugosa*

Cotoneasters are regularly utilised by landscape planners for hedging and covering banks and road verges. In recent times some species of Cotoneaster have become highly invasive in sensitive habitats, resulting in their inclusion in Schedule 9. Self-sown plants, usually occurring through birds eating the berries, have become naturalised in wide-ranging habitats such as woodland, quarry slopes and on walls and waste ground. Of those currently listed as invasive species there appears to be some confusion between Hollyberry Cotoneaster *Cotoneaster bullatus* and Bullate Cotoneaster *Cotoneaster rehderi*. By far the more frequent of the two in our area is Bullate Cotoneaster which often invades secondary woodland, where it becomes naturalised from repeated bird-sowings. Hollyberry Cotoneaster which is Schedule 9 listed occurs only infrequently in similar habitats. Wall Cotoneaster *Cotoneaster horizontalis* and Himalayan Cotoneaster *Cotoneaster simonsii* are typically found

Its liking for permanently moist brickwork mortar at the edge of canals is interesting, as it appears to be increasing in this habitat.

Of the other neophytes regarded as invasive in parts of Britain and listed on Schedule 9, Three-cornered Garlic *Allium triquetrum*, Few-flowered Garlic *Allium paradoxum*, Yellow Archangel *Lamiastrum galeobdolon* subsp. *argentatum* and Montbretia *Crocosmia* × *crocosmiiflora* are all found in our area. The non-native Yellow Archangel, which is distinguished from the native Yellow Archangel by displaying white blotches on the leaves, is the most frequent of these and infiltrates woodland where it could have a detrimental affect on native woodland species. Montbretia is a persistent garden throw-out, sometimes forming large patches on grassy banks, waste ground and in woodland. Three-cornered Garlic seldom persists with us for long and may not be fully hardy except in very sheltered sites, but Few-flowered

Garlic, which has so far been recorded only rarely, may become invasive and is well capable of establishing itself in sites of nature conservation value. A few plants have recently been discovered in wet woodland in Sot's Hole, Sandwell Valley, where it may be increasing.

Many other neophytes are so well-established in Birmingham and the Black Country and elsewhere in Britain that they are now an accepted part of our flora.

Sycamore *Acer pseudoplatanus* is far and away our commonest alien tree, tolerant of most soil types and avoiding only those that are waterlogged or very acidic. Infiltrating former oak and birch woodlands, it successfully out-competes native trees and shrubs, often forming almost pure sycamore woodland. In some years seed-set is prolific, with seedlings appearing in gardens, paving cracks and at the foot of walls and buildings where they grow rapidly when allowed.

The closely related Norway Maple *Acer platanoides* is a widely planted street and park tree which increasingly appears self-sown in the urban area. Spontaneous seeding of Turkey Oak *Quercus cerris* does occasionally take place in secondary woodland and on post-industrial sites, but most trees in our area were originally planted.

Two fruit-bearing exotics are occasionally met with in the urban area, Fig *Ficus carica* and Grape-vine *Vitis vinifera*. A few apparently self-sown, substantial sized specimens of both are reported from river corridors, canal and railway embankments and on neglected waste ground. Two impressive fig trees can easily be seen growing on the embankment of the derelict railway line either side of the bridge at the western end of Sedgley Road East in Tipton, and are believed to be self-sown.

False-acacia *Robinia pseudoacacia* was in past times a frequent woodland planting. It suckers profusely and the prickly suckers eventually replace the original trunk. Italian Alder *Alnus cordata* and Grey Alder *Alnus incana* are often planted and both are fully hardy in Britain, thriving in drier soils than those favoured by our native Alder, and it is not uncommon to encounter young self-sown plants of Italian Alder on waste ground in the apparent absence of any nearby mature specimen. Garden Privet *Ligustrum ovalifolium* has in recent times lost popularity as a garden hedging shrub and is rarely planted these days. Overgrown remnants of former privet hedgerows often persist as a reminder of old garden boundaries on derelict land and post-housing sites.

Plants of the Rosaceae family are frequently naturalised in Birmingham and the Black Country deriving from bird-sowings and original plantings. The most commonly encountered are Willow-leaved Cotoneaster *Cotoneaster salicifolius,* Franchet's Cotoneaster *Cotoneaster franchettii* and Firethorn, more familiar to gardeners as Pyracantha *Pyracantha* sp. Others include Medlar *Mespilus germanica,* which is almost certainly originally from garden stock but looks convincingly 'wild' on Motorway Mound near Park Farm in the Sandwell Valley, where it has now formed an extensive thicket.

Russian-vine *Fallopia baldschuanica* is the Mile-a-minute Vine to gardeners, and is frequently planted to soften the outline of old garden sheds, garages and garden fences. Once established, its rampant growth quickly extends from its intended purpose onto adjacent land, clambering over and up nearby shrubs and trees; and so far-reaching can be the spread that in some instances difficulty arises in determining whether plants are spontaneous in origin.

A spectacular example of the rampant growth of Russian-vine can be seen along the towpath of the Stourbridge Town Arm, where trees and shrubs on the side of the canal have been totally covered by the vine; on a still fine day in mid-October

▲ *Acer platanoides*

▲ *Ficus carica* – **Sedgley Road East**

▲ *Fallopia baldschuanica* – **Stourbridge Town Arm**

immediately preceding leaf fall, the waterside takes on a bright crimson hue that is reflected in the water.

Oxford Ragwort *Senecio squalidus* is a short-lived perennial, thriving in nutrient-poor, well-drained soil and base-rich ballast in a wide range of habitats; it shows a preference for canal towpaths, railway corridors and post-industrial land. Frequent to locally common throughout the Black Country, Oxford Ragwort significantly decreases towards the north-east of the conurbation, and in parts of Birmingham it is apparently absent.

The natural colonisation of old boulders of furnace slag around Moorcroft Pool near Bilston implies some similarity

▲ *Senecio squalidus* on old boulders of furnace slag near Moorcroft Pool, 2011

▲ *Senecio inaequidens*

between this habitat and the volcanic rocks of Southern Europe from where this species originates.

Narrow-leaved Ragwort *Senecio inaequidens* is readily distinguished from Oxford Ragwort by having linear leaves that are not conspicuously toothed or deeply-lobed. A potentially invasive composite from South Africa and a relative newcomer to this area, it has yet to explode into exponential growth. Sites for this plant include a canal towpath, neglected waste ground, cracks and crumbling mortar around the base of industrial buildings and along roadside verges and dual carriageways. The first discovery in 2004 was from canal towpath vegetation and brickwork mortar at the base of a nearby wall along the Walsall Canal in Moxley; since then more plants have been found nearby, growing with shrubs along the central reservation of the Black Country New Road (A41) where its seeds are easily transported in the slip-stream of numerous vehicles. Its spread along this road is now apparent in Great Bridge, approximately 3km to the south, where colonisation of the roadside verge and nearby car park is underway.

Our largest colony is along verges of the approach road and up against buildings and in neglected waste ground at Albion Business Park, Spring Road, Smethwick, where it is thoroughly naturalised. In 2011 one plant was detected on the edge of the hard shoulder of the M5 motorway just inside Sandwell Valley and its further spread along this motorway seems inevitable. With a long and continuous flowering period extending well into autumn, it is late in the year when Narrow-leaved Ragwort becomes particularly noticeable as the surrounding vegetation begins to die back.

Of the thirteen sites so far found all but one are in the Black Country, with only a single plant recorded from Birmingham.

In the relatively competition-free environment brought about by regular applications of contact herbicides, a number of alien plants whose countries of origin in some instances are thousands of miles away find pavements, paths and road verges much to their liking. American Willowherb *Epilobium ciliatum*, Canadian Fleabane *Conyza canadensis*, Eastern Rocket *Sisymbrium orientale* and the rapidly increasing Guernsey Fleabane *Conyza sumatrensis* from South America share this transient habitat with the ubiquitous Pineappleweed *Matricaria discoidea* and some of our popular hardy and half-hardy garden plants such as Sweet Alison *Lobularia maritima*, Snapdragon *Antirrhinum majus*, Garden Lobelia *Lobelia erinus*, Pot Marigold *Calendula officinalis*, Soft Lady's-mantle *Alchemilla mollis*, Californian Poppy *Eschscholzia californica* and Atlas Poppy *Papaver atlanticum*. The popular garden annual or short-lived perennial Argentinian Vervain *Verbena bonariensis* has in recent times escaped from its garden environs and plants increasingly appear in paving cracks and garden paths.

Some of the more unusual neophytes have been recorded from roadside verges and pavement edges. Many-podded Hedge Mustard *Sisymbrium polyceratium* was discovered in paving cracks outside terrace houses in Carlyle Road in Lozells, and Honeywort *Cerinthe major* colonised cracks of a garden path in Sutton Coldfield. A specimen of Hairy Canary Clover *Dorycnium hirsutum* was recorded growing at the foot of a garden wall along the pavement in Jayshaw Avenue, Great Barr and attained a metre in height before it was eventually sprayed with weedkiller, and a spreading patch of Yellow Flax *Linum flavum* agg. discovered among Perforate St John's-wort at the side of a path leading from a derelict railway line to the local Asda store in Tipton in 2001 was still there in the summer of 2011 despite being somewhat reduced in size. Belonging to a difficult group of closely allied plants this find was confirmed by Eric Clement, an

▲ *Verbena bonariensis*

▲ *Campanula portenschlagiana*

▲ *Linum flavum* agg.

authority on alien plants as the first record for Britain outside of a garden.

Two small, yellow-flowered Oxalises are thoroughly established in garden paths and paving throughout the conurbation but seldom stray away from habitation; Procumbent Yellow-sorrel *Oxalis corniculata,* whose seeds are ejected explosively from the capsules enabling it to spread into garden paths and flower borders, is the more widespread of the two. Originating from New Zealand and Tasmania, Least Yellow-sorrel *Oxalis exilis* is smaller in all its parts and is often overlooked in garden paths and short-mown grassland. Once established in the latter habitat, it is relatively unaffected by mower blades and becomes quite persistent.

Young self-sown Garden Lavender *Lavandula angustifolia* plants are often encountered in paving usually not far from a mature specimen in a nearby garden and Water Bent *Polypogon*

*viridis* appears to be increasing in dry as well as wet situations, and is usually found at the foot of walls delimiting roadside pavements. This grass is particularly frequent in paving cracks along roads in Handsworth. Other alien grasses appear from time to time in the pavement environment; Canary-grass *Phalaris canariensis,* Cockspur *Echinochloa crus-galli,* Yellow Bristle-grass *Setaria pumila* and Greater Quaking-grass *Briza maxima* are the most frequent but none persist for more than a season or two.

Urban brickwork mortar provides an alternative habitat for those plants that naturally grow from rock crevices and slopes. The more floriferous species are largely encouraged, the virtue being their showy, long-flowering blooms which brighten up otherwise drab walls. Ivy-leaved Toadflax *Cymbalaria muralis* is almost exclusively a wall specialist and is virtually unknown in natural habitats in this country. Throughout the summer months its small and prolifically produced lilac flowers adorn walls and bridges throughout the conurbation. Yellow Corydalis *Pseudofumaria lutea* is a long-flowering coloniser of roadside walls, paths and paving cracks and is well-naturalised and widely distributed; it frequently shares walls with Trailing Bellflower *Campanula poscharskiana,* which has slate-blue, long-lasting, star-like flowers, or the similar Adria Bellflower *Campanula portenschlagiana,* whose violet-blue flowers are not so deeply cut. Once established, both of the two bellflowers often become locally abundant, colonising walls and garden paving.

Red Valerian *Centranthus ruber* is another attractive and long flowering garden escape which typically frequents walls and dry banks where the deep red, pink or sometimes white flowers provide a cheery sight.

Former housing and industrial sites provide a most productive habitat for neophytes. Land recently cleared of housing invariably contains many garden relics which have recovered from the upheaval, growing alongside a wide range of native and alien annuals whose seeds have been exposed by disturbance or have blown in. Hardy perennial geraniums of garden origin often

▲ *Geranium endressii*

▲ *Lathyrus latifolius* – land at Burnt Tree

▲ *Lupinus* × *regalis*

▲ *Lupinus arboreus*

appear on these sites usually as survivors from original garden plantings. The one most frequently encountered is French Crane's-bill *Geranium endressii* a showy, pink-flowered perennial which rapidly out-competes surrounding vegetation. Once established it spreads steadily to form large, persistent patches. A reliable site for this plant is at the back of the gardens along the southern side of St Brades Close, Tividale, on the Rowley Hills, where an outstanding example of its colonising capabilities can be seen. Extensive patches are thoroughly established for 20–30m along both sides of the path.

Druce's Crane's-bill *Geranium* × *oxonianum* (*G. endressii* × *G. versicolor*) which can be confused with French Crane's-bill, has slightly smaller, pale-pink and deep-pink flowers appearing on the plant at the same time. Rock Crane's-bill *Geranium macrorrhizum* with deeply divided aromatic leaves and reddish-purple or pinky-white flowers is an attractive, patch-forming perennial which often outgrows its intended garden situation. Once established outside of gardens, if left undisturbed, plants can persist for many years. Purple Crane's-bill *Geranium* × *magnificum* is a sterile hybrid with abundant, stalked glands and large, purplish-violet flowers somewhat resembling a more compact Meadow Crane's-bill. Discarded from gardens, plants occasionally persist for a year or two before encroachment from more vigorous vegetation brings about their demise.

Honesty *Lunaria annua* is a showy late spring and early summer-flowering biennial that is well naturalised in many hedgerows and waste places and, although predominantly pink flowered, an attractive, white flowered variant is occasionally found.

A small colony of Motherwort *Leonurus cardiaca,* discovered over twenty years ago growing among nettles and other coarse perennials along the canal towpath at Titford Pool, is still thriving despite regularly being cut back to ground level. Only two other casual records have been reported for this plant, which has a long history of use as a 'herb' in traditional medicine in parts of Europe, Asia and North America.

Neophytes belonging to the pea family bring splashes of bright colour to urban waste sites. Crown Vetch *Securigera varia,* though scarce in Birmingham and the Black Country, consistently appears in quantity in rough grassland on the RSPB Reserve in Sandwell Valley, where it is thoroughly established, having first been introduced in an acid grassland mix sown in the early 1980s just after the conception of the Reserve. Russell Lupin *Lupinus* × *regalis,* whose flowers outside of gardens are usually a shade of blue, and Broad-leaved Everlasting-pea *Lathyrus latifolius* with flowers in shades of pink through to pure white are widely

naturalised. Young plants of Laburnum *Laburnum anagyroides* frequently appear on waste ground and on post-housing sites but seldom reach maturity in such habitats.

Tree Lupin *Lupinus arboreus*, Sainfoin *Onobrychis viciifolia*, Lucerne *Medicago sativa* subsp. *sativa* and Goat's-rue *Galega officinalis* all have showy flowers and sometimes appear in great quantity on recently abandoned sites but often do not persist for more than a season or two.

A very interesting Black Country site where an array of neophytes can be seen growing alongside some of our scarcer native plants is on the large area of brownfield land near the

▲ *Silene* **coronaria** – land at Burnt Tree

▲ Early spring bulbs – St Michael and All Angels, Tettenhall

▲ *Crocus tommasinianus*

canal and derelict railway at Burnt Tree in Sandwell. Naturalised here are Large-flowered Evening-primrose *Oenothera glazioviana*, Rose Campion *Silene coronaria,* Perennial Wall-rocket *Diplotaxis tenuifolia,* Bastard Cabbage *Rapistrum rugosum,* Hoary Mustard *Hirschfeldia incana* and Rum Cherry *Prunus serotina* to name but a few.

Records for the exotic looking Thorn-apple *Datura stramonium* have appeared only infrequently during the survey period, but in the 1980s, when road widening was taking place along the A4123 in Oldbury, hundreds of plants appeared simultaneously all along the grass verge on the western side of the dual carriageway. Long-buried seed brought to the surface during excavation work and a prolonged warm spell inducing a mass-germination was believed to have been the explanation for this unusual phenomenon. Recent road works in the same area have so far produced nothing. Another historical site for this plant, is a former potato field in Sandwell Valley which has been left to grass over since the late 1990s; a revival has recently been seen here when a number of plants appeared in the disturbed soil around newly erected post holes, which were dug out for the erection of a fence along the edge of the field.

Churchyards are frequented by a wide range of neophytes and vary enormously in size and management they receive. Older, unused areas are often left neglected and abandoned, becoming densely overgrown with bramble, ivy, ash and sycamore. Snowdrop *Galanthus nivalis*, crocuses, daffodils and Garden Grape-hyacinth *Muscari armeniacum* originally planted on graves are the most successful colonisers of churchyards but occasionally lesser-known species naturalise in the grassland away from the graves. Green Snowdrop *Galanthus woronowii*, Greater Snowdrop *Galanthus elwesii*, Balkan Anemone *Anemone blanda,* Glory-of-the-snow *Scilla forbesii* and Dog's-tooth-violet *Erythronium dens-canis* have all been found in Birmingham and Black Country churchyards.

Birmingham has its share of interesting churchyards and an early spring stroll through the grounds of the parish church of St Peter, Harborne, will reward the visitor with fine displays of Common Snowdrop, Early Crocus, Spring Crocus and Primrose *Primula vulgaris*, which are followed by masses of Ramsons and Cow Parsley. On one grave, and escaping from it into the surrounding grassland, is our only known site for Greater Snowdrop *Galanthus elwesii* which must have been originally planted many years ago if the inscription on the gravestone is anything to go by.

For sheer diversity of species a walk through St Mary's Churchyard on Hampstead Road, Handsworth can be highly

recommended. Within its grounds no less than 152 species of flowering plants were recorded from two visits carried out in the spring and summer of 2008.

St Michael and All Angels in Tettenhall, Wolverhampton, is well worth an early spring visit, not only for its venerable Yews, but also for its outstanding floral displays.

During February and March parts of this cemetery turn into a haze of white, purple and pink from the thousands of Common Snowdrop *Galanthus nivalis*, Early Crocus *Crocus tommasinianus* and cultivars of Spring Crocus *Crocus vernus* such as 'Pickwick', 'Remembrance', 'King of the Whites' and 'Little Dorrit' which have naturalised throughout the grassland.

With the increasing day-length many types of naturalised daffodils ensure a continuous display of colour throughout the spring months. Two alien succulents – Reflexed Stonecrop *Sedum rupestre* and White Stonecrop *Sedum album* – are often planted on graves and frequently spread onto surrounding graves and along the edges of nearby paths.

Parks, gardens, urban amenity areas and public open spaces provide habitats for some of the more conspicuously flowered neophytes such as Large Bindweed *Calystegia silvatica*, Green Alkanet *Pentaglottis sempervirens*, Dotted Loosestrife *Lysimachia punctata*, Russian Comfrey *Symphytum × uplandicum,* Purple Toadflax *Linaria purpurea,* Snow-in-summer *Cerastium tomentosum* and the hybrid bluebell *Hyacinthoides × massartiana* as well as those whose flowers are less obvious such as Lesser Swine-cress *Lepidium didymum* which is a frequent coloniser of well-trodden paths and tracks.

Neophytes frequenting managed grassland are relatively few and tend to be low-growing plants which are unaffected by regular mowing. Slender Speedwell *Veronica filiformis* has spread from site to site by fragmented vegetative shoots transferred on the blades of mowing machines, and is widespread in lawns and amenity grassland, often creating a blue haze throughout the sward in early summer between cuts. Fox-and-cubs *Pilosella aurantiaca* regularly appears in garden lawns, producing its distinctive orange-brown to brick red flowers when cuts are infrequent. Leptinella *Cotula squalida* is thoroughly naturalised in regularly mown grassland in Lodge Hill Cemetery, Selly Oak, and also in the front lawn of a garden in Bearwood and Matted Pratia *Pratia pedunculata* still persists in a garden lawn in Darbys Hill Road, Tividale, where it has been known for over twenty years.

The marginal habitats of canals and ponds provide a suitable habitat for some of our more attractive neophytes.

Unlike the invasive Indian Balsam, Orange Balsam *Impatiens capensis*, does not currently impact negatively in Birmingham and the Black Country. Plants are increasingly met with in the emergent vegetation along the water's edge of canals and sometimes ponds. With attractive orange flowers flecked with yellow-brown, surprisingly, Orange Balsam was not recorded in the 1970s editions of the Floras for both Staffordshire (Edees 1972) and Warwickshire (Cadbury *et al.* 1971), suggesting a marked increase in our area. Small Balsam *Impatiens parviflora* has never really established itself in the Black Country with most of the modern records coming from Birmingham. To judge by 'A Computer Mapped Flora of Warwickshire' by Cadbury *et al.* (1971), it would appear that this species was seen far more often then than it is today.

Fringecups *Tellima grandiflora* is a garden escape which has become naturalised and is almost certainly increasing. Favouring damp soils and tolerant of shade, it occurs along woodland streams and in wet woodland and is generally well distributed throughout the conurbation where conditions are favourable. In such habitats plants are found with native Cuckooflower, Marsh-marigold and Opposite-leaved Golden-saxifrage.

Beggarticks *Bidens frondosa* is a frequent component of water-saturated brickwork mortar along canal edges throughout the network, typically sharing this waterside habitat with native species such as Skullcap, Clustered Dock, False Fox-sedge, Hemlock Water-dropwort and Water Dock. Because it is a late flowerer, young plants may have in the past been misidentified as the native Trifid Bur-marigold, which favours muddy margins and fluctuating water levels of ponds and pools but also occurs by canals. Sweet-flag *Acorus calamus* is one of our less invasive aquatic aliens, occasionally encountered in the reedswamp fringes of ponds and canals. A relatively shy flowerer with aromatic leaves which in places are transversely wrinkled, it is almost always believed to be an original introduction. Two sites where plants flower reliably are in the shallows of Little Bracebridge Pool in Sutton Park and around the margins of Edgbaston Pool in Birmingham.

Fringed Water-lily *Nymphoides peltata* is an attractive, floating-leaved exotic often recorded from canals and ponds. A favourite planting in garden ponds because of its small, floating leaves and attractive fringed, yellow flowers, its invasive tendencies are underestimated. Occasionally discarded from garden ponds or more often deliberately introduced in pond creation schemes, once established its spread across the whole water surface can be rapid.

To conclude this section on neophytes reference must be made to the swampy woodland next to Winterbourne Botanic Gardens which is home to one of the more spectacular exotic neophytes found in Britain. In late March and early April, hundreds of enormous, foul-smelling, yellow spathes of American Skunk-cabbage *Lysichiton americanus* fill the woodland. These are followed in early summer by enormous cabbage-like leaves attaining almost 2 metres in height. Despite attempts in the past to eradicate this plant from the woodland it is still thriving.

▲ *Lysichiton americanus* – Edgbaston Woods, 2006

# Section 4 • A register of the designated nature conservation sites

This section lists the main sites which have been recognised as having nature conservation value in each of the local authorities of the conurbation, and gives extremely brief details of their botanical and habitat interest. Since the same system is used to recognise sites of geological interest, these have also been included in the account. Many sites have both biological and geological interest, but "**G**" is used to indicate where a site is designated for purely geological features. In the text "ancient woodland (NE inventory)" means "an area of ancient semi-natural woodland as recorded on the ancient woodland inventory by Natural England" and "plantation on an ancient woodland site (NE inventory) means "an area of woodland planted on an ancient woodland site as recorded on the ancient woodland inventory by Natural England".

The main designation which is recognised in national legislation is the **Site of Special Scientific Interest (SSSI)**. The SSSIs are Britain's best biological and geological sites and there are over 4000 in England, 23 in the West Midlands county and (currently) 17 in B&BC. Some SSSIs have special international status, notably **Special Areas of Conservation (SACs)** which are sites strictly protected under the European Commission Habitats Directive. Two of our B&BC sites have this status. All are briefly described in our register.

In all parts of Britain there are at least one and usually two tiers of non-statutory biological and geological Local Sites. These are described by DEFRA as "sites of substantive nature conservation value".

Although they do not have any statutory status, many are equal in quality to the representative sample of sites that make up the series of statutory SSSIs. In B&BC they are recognised in the planning process and there are two tiers: **Sites of Importance for Nature Conservation (SINCs)** which are recognised as having B&BC importance and **Sites of Local Importance for Nature Conservation (SLINCs)**, recognised as having importance within the Borough or City. In B&BC there are over 200 SINCs covering more than 2,000ha and over 400 SLINCs covering more than 4,000ha. All the SINCs are listed in this register, but not the SLINCs except where they link with the SINCs.

The **National Nature Reserves (NNRs)** represent many of the finest wildlife and geological sites in the country. They are declared by Natural England (and its predecessors) as a selection of the very best parts of our SSSIs. B&BC possesses two NNRs: The Wren's Nest in Dudley and Sutton Park in Birmingham. These are dealt with within the register.

The **Local Nature Reserve (LNR)** is a statutory designation made by a local authority to offer people special opportunities to learn about, study and enjoy nature. In B&BC they may be SSSIs, SINCs, SLINCs, or combinations of these (or even none). All so far declared are listed in the register either directly or within the SSSI or SINC entry.

In the register NNRs, LNRs and SSSIs are specifically identified, all other sites are SINCs. Many of the sites listed are privately owned and are not open to the public. It is the responsibility of the visitor to make sure that access is allowed before attempting to visit any of these sites. The grid reference given for each site is for a central location. Site areas are given in hectares (ha). Where a site has been divided into subsidiary sites, the entries for the latter follow the former.

▲ Rowley Hills

## BIRMINGHAM

### 1. Hill Hook
SK105003
An old mill pool with rich marginal aquatic vegetation plus species-rich wet alder woodland. Area 5.01ha. Forms part of **Hill Hook LNR**, Area 5.65ha, designated 1992.

▲ Dingle at Hill Hook

### 2. Sutton Park NNR & SSSI
SP098974
The largest and richest tract of wild, unenclosed country in B&BC and vc. Warwickshire, with areas of heath, wetland and ancient woodland (NE inventory). Also of interest for the remnant outcrops of Triassic sandstones and conglomerates. Area 877.38ha, designated 1954.

### 3. Moor Hall Golf Course
SP127978
A golf course designated primarily for its ornithological interest, but includes some botanically interesting acid grassland. Privately owned, not publicly accessible. Area 37.89ha.

### 4. Wheatmoor Wood and Wheatmoor Plantation
SP139981
Two ancient semi-natural woodlands (NE inventory) at Whitehouse Common. Privately owned, not publicly accessible. Area 3.05ha.

### 5. Lindridge Pool and Langley Mill
SP150969
Two former mill pools with associated reedswamp, marginal vegetation and partly ancient semi-natural wet woodland (NE inventory). Privately owned. Area 8.95ha.

### 6. Home Wood
SP133955
Ancient semi-natural broad-leaved woodland (NE inventory). Area 4.35ha.

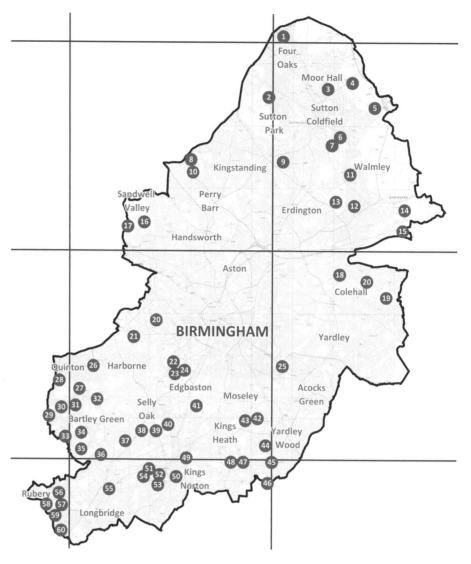

### 7. Newhall Valley
SP129951
Remnant farmland comprising a section of Plants Brook, adjacent wet grasslands and ancient semi-natural woodland (NE inventory). Area 9.45ha.

### 8. Land at Queslett
SP060944
A former sand and gravel extraction site now landfilled and capped, with subsequent habitat creation. Site is linked to wider SLINC. Part of site is not publicly accessible. Area 4.65ha.

### 9. Oakwood Spinney
SP105943
Ancient semi-natural broad-leaved woodland (NE inventory). Area 1.33ha.

### 10. Perry Beeches Nature Reserve
SP061938
Former farmland plus predominantly broad-leaved plantation and secondary woodland within school grounds. Site linked to wider SLINC. Area 4.64ha.

### 11. Jones's Wood
SP138937
Ancient semi-natural woodland (NE inventory). Area 2.52ha.

### 12. Plants Brook Reservoirs
SP140922
Old reservoirs along the line of the Plants Brook with adjoining areas of scrub, plantation and meadow. Declared **Plants Brook Reservoirs LNR** in 1992. Area 10.6ha.

### 13. Pype Hayes Park (Plants Brook Watercourse)
SP131924
Old meadowland, some damp, plus a little woodland by Plants Brook and within Pype Hayes Park. Area 12.95ha.

### 14. Minworth Sewage Works
SP165920
Bare sludge, open water, tall herb, sallow scrub and willow carr; also grassland alongside the River Tame. Primarily ornithological interest. Privately owned, not publicly accessible. Area 136.23ha.

### 15. Park Hall
SP164910
Section of the River Tame flood plain, remnant farmland, ancient semi-natural woodlands (NE inventory). Also archaeological interest. Wildlife Trust for Birmingham and the Black Country Nature Reserve. Area 44.21ha.

▲ Meanders Pool at Park Hall

### 16. Sandwell Valley
SP037914
Former farmland comprised of grassland and meadow with mature boundary hedgerows, plus area of woodland which pre-dates 1794 and may be ancient. Associated with Sandwell Valley Country Park. Area 56.53ha.

### 17. Sandwell Valley – Forge Lane Middle Wood
SP029912
Ancient semi-natural woodland (NE inventory). Forms part of wider **Sandwell Valley SINC & LNR**. Area 2.05ha.

### 18. Hodge Hill Common
SP133889
An historic village common with extensive acid grassland. Area 7.46ha.

### 19. Project Kingfisher LNR
See Cole Valley and Colehall Farm Sewage Works below.

### 20. Cole Valley and Colehall Farm Sewage Works
SP157877
Section of the River Cole corridor with improved and unimproved grassland, wetland, scrub and ruderal communities. Area 55.7ha. Site forms part of **Project Kingfisher LNR**, which extends into Solihull, 52.23ha, designated 2004 and also has UK Man and the Biosphere recognition.

### 21. Edgbaston Reservoir LNR
SP043867
Canal feeder reservoir with narrow fringes

of parkland woodland; predominantly ornithological interest. Designated as LNR in 2011. Area 29.7ha.

### 22. Harborne Walkway
SP032859
Disused railway line with cuttings, embankments and a matrix of woodland, scrub, tall herb and grassland communities with some artificial ponds. Area 6.06ha.

### 23. The Vale, Edgbaston
SP053847
Parkland in the grounds of Birmingham University Halls of Residence with a man-made lake of ornithological interest. Area 4.12ha.

### 24. Edgbaston Pool SSSI
SP054841
Long-established lake with extensive fen, swamp and woodland communities including Alder carr. Restricted access via Winterbourne Garden. Area 15.92ha, designated 1973.

### 25. Edgbaston Park Golf Course
SP057843
Improved but base-poor grassland surrounded by planted shelterbelts and scattered clumps of trees. The course of Chad Brook is open in the north. Part of a British Trust for Ornithology-registered site. Site adjoins/forms part of wider Edgbaston Pool SSSI. Private golf course, not publicly accessible. Area 39.4ha.

### 26. The Ackers
SP105845
Complex, partly post-industrial area with River Cole, tributaries, a former mill race, active railway lines and the Grand Union Canal. Area 8.94ha.

▲ The Ackers

### 27. Woodgate Valley
SP005834
An extensive area of former farmland formerly connected to the ancient

▲ Medieval bank and ditch at Woodgate Valley

Worcestershire countryside, now managed as Woodgate Valley Country Park with areas of horse-grazed grassland, meadows (several species-rich) managed for hay, species-rich hedgerows, plantations, scrub with ponds and wetland. Based on the valley of the Bourn Brook together with other small watercourses. Site forms part of wider Woodgate Valley SINC & SLINC. Five specific further areas have been designated as SINCs and are described below. Area 90.37ha.

### 28. Quinton Meadows LNR
SO995838
Two sloping and partly damp unimproved meadows of rough grassland with invading scrub with species-rich old hedgerows. Designated as LNR in 2011. Area 3.41ha.

### 29. Woodgate Valley – Pinewood Area
SO990821
Several sloping species-rich meadows with old boundary hedgerows, flanking the M5 motorway. Area 15.18ha.

### 30. Broadhidley Wood
SO996825
Woodland which is partly an area of ancient semi-natural woodland (NE inventory). Area 1.49ha.

### 31. Woodgate Valley – Juggins Wood
SP003826
Broad-leaved woodland with an old boundary bank. Woodland pre-dates 1830s and may be ancient. Area 0.68ha.

### 32. Woodgate Valley – Stonehouse Brook
SP014829
Grassland scrub and plantation associated with the Stonehouse Brook. Area 0.78ha.

### 33. Bromwich Wood
SO998811
Oak-dominated ancient semi-natural broad-leaved woodland (NE inventory) with a fine bluebell-dominated flora. Area 3.16ha. Site forms part of **Bromwich Wood LNR**, 3.56ha, designated 1991.

### 34. Bartley Reservoir
SP006813
A large concrete-sided impounding reservoir designated primarily for its ornithological interest. Area 47.36ha.

### 35. Cutler's Rough
SP006805
Ancient semi-natural broad-leaved woodland (NE inventory). Privately-owned. Area 2.27ha.

### 36. Merritt's Brook
SP012800
Brook corridor with a variety of habitats. Area 0.74ha.

### 37. Manor Farm Park
SP028809
Section of Griffin's Brook with landscaped pools, remnants of former meadows, plus woodlands which partly pre-date 1830s and may be ancient. Area 7.49ha.

### 38. Grounds of Woodbrooke, Bournville
SP036814
Plantation broad-leaved woodland adjoining a man-made lake fed by a modified watercourse in the grounds of Woodbrooke College and formerly the home of George Cadbury. Privately owned, may not be publicly accessible. Area 1.36ha.

### 39. Stocks Wood
SP045816
Broad-leaved woodland which pre-dates 1830s and may be ancient. Privately owned, may not be publicly accessible. Area 1.44ha.

### 40. Elm Road Pool
SP049817
A flooded clay pit surrounded by grassland, scrub and woodland and noted for its large population of breeding amphibians. Privately owned, not publicly accessible. Area 1.47ha.

### 41. Holder's Wood
SP063826
Plantation on an ancient woodland site (NE inventory) in the valley of the River Rea. Area 4.34ha.

### 42. Moseley Bog
SP093820
Mixed broad-leaved woodland with mire communities developing on the floor of a former mill pond. Formerly an SSSI. There are archaeological and literary interests. Area 3.66ha. Forms part of **Moseley Bog LNR**, Area 11.2ha, designated 1991.

▲ Moseley Bog

### 43. Moseley Golf Course, woodland and pool
SP087819
Ancient semi-natural woodland (NE inventory) fringing Coldbath Pool. Ornithological interest. Private golf course, not publicly accessible. Area 4.96ha.

### 44. The Dingles
SP097807
A mostly unmodified section of the River Cole and Chinn Brook with woodland, grassland (former meadow), hedgerows and some veteran trees. Area 9.87ha. Site forms part of Shire Country Park.

### 45. Trittiford Pool and adjoining land
SP099800
A stretch of the River Cole with a former mill pond and adjacent areas of grassland and secondary woodland. The pool is noted for good numbers of foraging bats. Site forms part of Shire Country Park. Area 12.44ha.

### 46. Priory Pool and adjoining land, Yardley Wood
SP098790
Several small former farm fields, a small amount of heathland and a stream-fed mill pool. Site is a Warwickshire Wildlife Trust nature reserve. Area 6.9ha.

### 47. Cocks Moors Wood
SP086799
Area of Chinn Brook and tributary including ponds, grassland, secondary woodland and mature hedgerows. Area 7.71ha.

### 48. Cocks Moors Woods (Ancient Woodland)
SP080799
In part ancient semi-natural woodland (NE inventory). Area 2.93ha.

### 49. Lifford Reservoir and adjoining land
SP058801
A reservoir and adjacent areas of broad-leaved woodland. Area 6.94ha.

### 50. King's Norton Playing Fields
SP053792
Part of the River Rea, a tributary stream and a canal feeder running through King's Norton Park with adjacent areas of woodland and grassland. Area 4.77ha.

### 51. King's Norton LNR
See Merecroft Pool, Wychall Lane and Wychall Reservoir SINCs.

### 52. Land north of Wychall Lane, King's Norton
SP043791
A section of the River Rea in a semi-natural state, fringed by a narrow strip of grassland with hedgerows and trees. Site forms part of **Kings Norton LNR**. Area 3.7ha.

### 53. Merecroft Pool and meadowland, King's Norton
SP044788
A pool linked to River Rea via a small watercourse and adjacent old pastures with hedgerows. Area 6.57ha. Site forms part of **Kings Norton LNR**, 18.79ha, designated 2005.

### 54. Wychall Reservoir
SP037792
Former canal feeder-reservoir and associated watercourse with open water, reedswamp, wet woodland and marshy grassland. Site forms part of **Kings Norton LNR.** Area 11.63ha.

### 55. Mill Lane, Northfield
SP020786
A short length of the River Rea with adjacent scrub, woodland and grassland. Area 4.07ha.

### 56. Balaam's Wood
SO995784
An area of ancient semi-natural

▲ Balaam's Wood

woodland on the River Rea (NE inventory). Area 3.07ha. Site forms part of **Balaam's Wood LNR**, 5.92ha, designated 2008.

### 57. Rubery Hill Woods
SO997777
Ancient semi-natural woodland (NE inventory). Area 4.45ha.

### 58. Rubery Hill
SO990777
Formerly partly quarried, with remnant heathland and acid grassland and colonising scrub/woodland. The quarry represents the most northerly outcrop of the Lickey Quartzite Formation of the Ordovician Period. Area 6.97ha.

### 59. Rubery Cutting and Leach Green Quarries
SO993774
G. Particularly important in interpretation of the sedimentary and volcanic history of the region from the Cambrian to the early Silurian periods. Designated **LNR** 1991. Area 0.62ha.

### 60. Land at Rednal Hill
SO996766
The most northerly section of the Lickey Hills Country Park with remnant heathland and acid grassland with colonising scrub/woodland. Area 4.08ha.

## DUDLEY

### 1. Alder Coppice
SO911949
An ancient mixed broad-leaved semi-natural woodland site (NE inventory). Of note for an almost complete absence of sycamore. Area 8.77 ha

### 2. Beacon Hill Quarry
SO919949
Former limestone quarry with a significant limestone grassland flora. This is the largest remaining exposure of a once extensive

outcrop of the Silurian Sedgley (Brown) Limestone. Part of wider SLINC. Area 3.55ha.

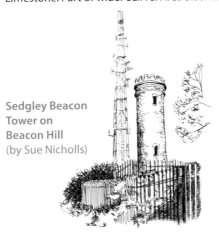

Sedgley Beacon Tower on Beacon Hill (by Sue Nicholls)

### 3. Sedgley Hall Farm Park and Western Escarpment
SO915943
A complex mosaic of habitats including woodland, neutral, calcareous and wet grassland and watercourses. Parts of woodland pre-date 1830s and may be ancient. Twin streams expose beds of alternating clay and mudstone with harder sandstone and conglomerate of the Salop Formation of the Carboniferous Period. Area 19ha.

### 4. Hurst Hill Wood
SO928937
A former quarry in the Wenlock limestone of the Silurian Period, colonised by secondary woodland enclosing fragment of valuable calcareous grassland. There is almost a complete succession through the nodular member of richly fossiliferous limestones and a number of mine entrances. Area 4.65ha.

### 5. Coseley Canal Cutting
SO943936
G. Exposures on the eastern embankment show siltstone and ironstone with fossil plant remains. The tunnel here has numerous flowstone stalactites. Area 1.53ha.

### 6. Dingle View Outcrop
SO912929
G. A small path-side outcrop providing the only exposure of Calcareous Conglomerate in the Cotwall End Valley complex. Area 0.03ha.

### 7. Cotwall End LNR
SO911925
A large mosaic of habitats including ancient woodland (NE Inventory), wet woodland along Bobs Brook, lowland

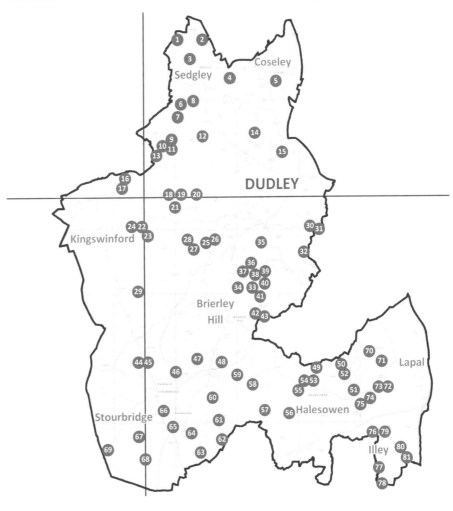

heathland, acid flushes, unimproved and marshy meadows, ponds, scrub and hedgerow. Limestones and sandstones of the Silurian and Devonian periods form a pronounced ridge to the north and east of the valley. Conglomerates and sandstones of the Upper Carboniferous Period produce a tiered hill to the west of the valley whilst softer deposits of coals and clays form the valley floor. Area 51.54ha.

### 8. Moden Hill
SO916930
Forms northern part of Cotwall End LNR. Small site with attractive wetland and unimproved grassland habitats. The fields show a marked break in slope and the soil contains fragments of the Aymestry Limestone Formation of the Silurian Period. Area 4.51ha.

### 9. Turner's Hill SSSI
SO909918
**G.** An important sequence of strata of late Silurian age which are rarely so well exposed in Britain. Area 1.56ha., designated 1968.

### 10. Cotwall End South
SO906916
Large area of dense scrub and mature trees adjoining the Cotwall End LNR. Area 2.73ha.

▲ Cotwall End

### 11. Ellowes Road
SO909915
**G.** The stream section shows grey shale and sandstones with red sandy marls. Site is very close to the Western Boundary Fault complex so minor faults are visible. Area 0.23ha.

### 12. Ruiton Quarry (Holloway Street)
SO919919
The site of former, extensive quarries in the Downton Castle Formation, (known locally as the Gornal Grit) of the Upper Silurian period. Although quarried here as

a refractory material the stone was used in many buildings of the Dudley area. Open water and a watercourse are colonised by woodland, scrub, grassland, ruderal, swamp and marshy habitats. Area 7.93ha.

### 13. Brick Kiln Lane
SO904913
Semi-improved pasture, unmodified watercourses and associated strips of woodland and hedgerows, part of a larger site extending into Staffordshire. Almost links with Turner's Hill and Cotwall End SINCs. Area 7.12ha.

### 14. Wren's Nest NNR & SSSI
SO936920
One of the most notable geological locations in the British Isles, of exceptional paleontological importance particularly for rocks of Wenlock age, it has yielded both macro-and micro-fossils of superb preservation, great variety and in great abundance since the beginning of the 19th century and remains an outstanding source of material for students of Silurian marine faunas. It also includes an excellent limestone flora in its quarries, grasslands and woodlands plus a wide range of other habitats. Area 34.03ha, NNR designated 1956. Much of the accessible part of the site forms **Wren's Nest LNR** (SO940923). Area 19.32ha, designated 1994.

*Ripple beds exposure, Wren's Nest (by Neville Walters)*

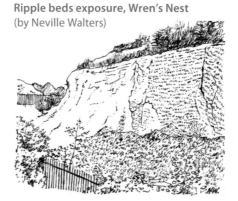

▲ Wren's Nest

### 15. Castle Hill
SO945914
**G.** An outcrop of Wenlock Group limestone related to Wren's Nest SSSI/NNR and Hurst Hill; primarily designated for the exposed reef, extensive vertical exposures and mine entrances. Habitats include plantation and secondary broad-leaved woodland with some areas potentially ancient. Area 31.22ha.

### 16. Oak Farm
SO894906
Former site of mines and quarries with associated railway lines now abandoned and colonised by scrub/woodland with remnant pastures and hedgerows and an unmodified tree-lined watercourse. The quarry has wide exposures of the Etruria Formation and contains sedimentological features and abundant carbonised plant remains. Area 36.31ha.

### 17. Oak Lane Quarry
SO893903
Species-rich pasture on edge of clay quarry located in the Oak Farm Wedge, much now probably lost to quarry expansion. Contains an extensive outcrop of Etruria Formation of the Carboniferous Period exhibiting sedimentary features and palaeosols. Area 3.57ha.

### 18. Smithy Lane
SO908901
Former colliery spoil heap colonised by mosaic of scrub, acidic and marshy grassland. Area 10.63ha.

### 19. Chase Road Pond
SO911901
Pond supporting diverse flora and amphibian populations situated within unimproved pasture. Area 0.5ha.

### 20. Barrow Hill and Cooper's Bank
SO917901
Quarry and other post-industrial sites, woodland including ancient semi-natural

▲ Barrow Hill

woodland (NE inventory) and farmland including species-rich grassland and wetland. Barrow Hill is a small dome of dolerite intruded into the Etruria Marl, extensively quarried in the 19th century for use as road stone. Area 50.1ha. Includes **Barrow Hill LNR**, (SO915898), 38.86ha, designated 2005. Links to larger SLINC.

### 21. Tansey Green Claypit Ashbeds
SO910897
**G.** Shows the only known example in the Black Country of surface volcanic activity. The quarry face contains many volcanic ash deposits that have yielded primitive 3-D conifer remains in life position. A proposed SSSI. Area 1.52ha. Linked to wider SLINC.

### 22. Ketley Claypit SSSI
SO899891
**G.** An outstanding section through the upper part of the Etruria Formation of the Carboniferous Period, showing the junction with the overlying Halesowen Formation. Area 1.57ha, designated 1990.

### 23. Ketley Quarry
SO899890
Section of Dawley Brook with strip of semi-natural broad-leaved woodland. The Junction zone between Halesowen and Etruria Formations of the Upper Coal Measures of the Carboniferous Period is exposed. Area 0.61ha. Links to larger SLINC.

### 24. Ketley Quarry West
SO898891
Section of Dawley Brook lined with strip of semi-natural broad-leaved woodland. Area 1.6ha. Site links to larger Ketley Quarry SINC/SLINC area.

### 25. Fens Pools SSSI and SAC
SO920886
Designated for its amphibian interest; an extensive post-industrial site with canal

Holly Hall, Fens Pools (by Sue Nicholls)

feeder pools. Area 38.42ha, designated 1989. Much of the site forms part of **Buckpool and Fens Pools LNR.** Area 63.07ha. Designated 1983.

### 26. Fens Pools – the Plateau
SO923887
A former industrial area colonised by a mosaic of scrub, grassland, marshy grassland and open water. Area 5.81ha.

### 27. Fens Pools – Sunmed Slope
SO916884
An area of furnace slag colonised by unusual pioneer plant community of base-loving species. The site is underlain by Etruria Marl and Middle Coal Measures of the Carboniferous period. Area 0.71ha.

▲ Middle Pool, Fens Pool (also showing Sunmed slope behind pool)

### 28. Fens Pools – North of Middle Pool
SO914887
An area of spoil colonised by mosaic of scrub, grassland, marshy grassland and small pools. Possible geological interest. Area 0.73ha.

### 29. Buckpool and The Leys
SO898871
A stream valley highly modified by mining and tipping of spoil. Habitats include relict woodland (this pre-dates 1822 and may be ancient), scrub, marshy grassland, acidic grassland, open water and watercourses. Also an excellent site for teaching many aspects of geology. Rocks of many different formations are evident and sedimentary and structural features can also be seen. Area 19.56ha. Much of the site forms part of **Buckpool and Fens Pools LNR** 63.07ha, designated 1983.

### 30. New Rowley Road
SO954891
**G.** Planted broad-leaved woodland in former quarry which is the only accessible place within the Rowley Hills where the Dolerite (igneous) contact with the Etruria

Formation country rock can be seen. Area 0.31ha.

### 31. Warrens Hall Woodland (Tansley Hill)
SO957890
Remnants of a group of fields now part-grazed and colonised by scrub/woodland with a watercourse forming eastern boundary of site. Adjoins Warren's Hall Farm SINC in Sandwell. Area 1.83ha.

### 32. Bumble Hole LNR
SO951882
Canal junction, pools, grassland, scrub, woodland and post-industrial habitats with a diverse range of species. Area 9.52ha, designated 1996. See also **Warrens Hall LNR** in the Sandwell list, with which this site is contiguous.

▲ Bumble Hole and Warrens Hall Park

### 33. Saltwells LNR
SO935872
Includes Saltwells Wood, Cinder Bank, Netherton Hill, Mushroom Green, Doulton Claypit and Brewin's Canal Section.

### 34. Saltwells Wood
SO931872
The first LNR declared in the West Midlands, it includes ancient semi-natural woodland, plantation, pasture, meadow, streams, pools, wetland, quarry, bell-pit and colliery sites and is managed as a wardened nature reserve. It incorporates the **Doulton's Clay Pit SSSI.** Area 42.27ha, designated **LNR** 1981.

### 35. Cinder Bank
SO938886
Reclaimed coal mine site with a rich habitat mosaic. Area 18.33ha, designated **LNR** 1981.

### 36. Netherton Hill
SO935879
The largest area of open space in the borough in which a wide number of habitats are represented including one of the largest expanses of Gorse in the West Midlands. Area 19.13ha, designated 1981.

### 37. Dragonfly Pools and Butterfly Meadow
SO932877

Former opencast mine capped and landscaped with created habitats including 'wildflower' grassland, plantation woodland, scrub and open water with section of Black Brook. A small ravine cut by a tributary drainage channel exposes Lower Coal Measure sandstones and shales with prominent plant fossils. Area 8.37ha.

### 38. Brewin's Canal Section SSSI
SO936876

**G.** Exhibits the contact between rocks from the Carboniferous and Silurian periods and provides an invaluable insight into the development of coal deposits in the English Midlands. Area 1.25ha, designated 1955.

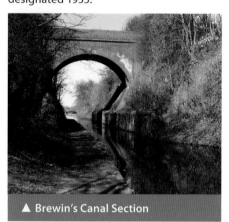

▲ Brewin's Canal Section

### 39. Lodge Farm Reservoir Bank
SO937876

A belt of semi-natural broad-leaved woodland/scrub. Links to larger SLINC. Area 0.16ha.

### 40. Knowle Hill
SO938874

Acid grassland with scattered scrub occupying steep bank of canal. Linked to larger SLINC. Area 0.52ha.

### 41. Doulton's Clay Pit SSSI
SO937871

**G.** The best site in the Midlands for a sequence of Coal measures of Carboniferous age. Coal seams, iron stones, clays, siltstones and sandstones magnificently displayed. Claypit also includes diverse wetland vegetation and amphibian populations. Area 3.06ha.

### 42. Mushroom Green
SO936864

Willow carr and reedswamp linking the River Stour corridor to Saltwells Wood. Area 9.51ha.

### 43. Griff Chains and Mousesweet
SO939863

An area of scrub and acidic grassland on made ground on site of former colliery with Mousesweet Brook forming a southern boundary. Linked to wider SLINC. Area 2.59ha.

### 44. Old Wharf Road
SO899849

**G.** An extension of Old Town Gasworks site (see below) with an interglacial terrace, comprising sand and gravel which was deposited by the River Stour when it flowed on a different course and level, exposed behind the factory. Area 0.09ha.

### 45. Old Town Gasworks
SO901849

**G.** Former gas works now developed as housing. The only known exposure in the Black Country of interglacial sand and gravels from the Devensian Stage of the Quaternary Period overlying Triassic Wildmoor Sandstone. Area 0.42ha.

### 46. Stambermill
SO910846

Semi-natural grassland partly colonised by woodland and scrub occupying a slope above the River Stour. Area 2.26ha.

### 47. Freehold Farm
SO917850

Group of semi-improved neutral grassland fields, remnant hedgerows and a former mined area. Area 2.16ha.

### 48. Meers Coppice
SO925849

A small area of former valley coppice, possibly associated with charcoal burning, now forming a semi-natural broad-leaved woodland that pre-dates 1822 and may be ancient. Area 3.26ha.

### 49. Hawne Colliery
SO956847

A large, privately owned former colliery site with a network of hummocks and hollows and spoil, colonised by woodland, scrub, neutral grassland, acidic grassland, ephemeral pioneer vegetation and some small areas of wetland with much bare ground. Area 7.66ha.

### 50. River Stour Valley – Furnace Hill to Corngreaves Road
SO964848

Stretch of River Stour valley with adjacent strips of broad-leaved woodland. Linked to wider SLINC. Area 5.08ha.

### 51. River Stour Valley – Earls Way to Furnace Hill
SO968840

Stretch of River Stour with adjacent area of broad-leaved woodland. Linked to wider SLINC. Area 4.09ha.

### 52. Furnace Coppice
SO965845

Ancient semi-natural woodland (NE inventory) occupying a steep western slope in the Stour Valley. Area 1.87ha.

### 53. Bellevale Woodland
SO955843

Secondary broad-leaved woodland and scrub with diverse canopy along small stream. Part of wider SLINC. Area 1.26ha.

### Lutley Gutter
SO9584

A steep-sided wooded stream valley supporting good woodland flora linked with ancient countryside landscape to the south in Worcestershire. Three sections are designated as SINCs:

### 54. Lutley Gutter, Bellevale
SO952843
Area 1.11ha.

### 55. Lutley Gutter, Lutley Mill Road
SO950840
Area 1.8ha.

### 56. Lutley Gutter South
SO947833

Here a series of stream sections provide a virtually complete succession through the lower Halesowen Formation of the Carboniferous Period. Area 10.57ha. Links to wider SLINC.

### 57. Foxcote Meadows
SO939834

A mosaic of diverse grasslands, probably of some age, within an historic field pattern with hedgerows and small ponds. Area 3.76ha.

### 58. The Hayes
SO935842

A large area of scrub/woodland with small areas of remnant diverse marshy grassland on a former colliery site. Much lost to succession and tipping. The site provides panoramic views of the area's topography and landscape demonstrating the relationship between different rock types. Area 10.91ha. Links to wider SLINC.

### 59. Hayes Cutting
SO930844

**G.** The road cutting exposes the junction

between Coal measures of the Carboniferous Period and the underlying rocks of the Silurian Period. Area 0.11ha.

### 60. Ludgbridge Brook
SO922838

**G.** A unique outcrop of the basement conglomerate of the Lower productive coal-measures is exposed. Linked to wider SLINC. Area 0.52ha.

### 61. Wollescote Dingle
SO924831

A broad-leaved 'dingle' woodland following the course of the Lugbridge Brook. Pre-dating the 1830s it may be ancient. The site includes a major geomorphological feature in the form of a two stage waterfall. In the adjacent banks is seen a small series of thin coals belonging to the Carboniferous Halesowen Formation. Adjacent to wider SLINC. Area 3.3ha.

### 62. Hodgehole Dingle
SO925825

Ancient semi-natural dingle woodland (NE inventory) with steep valley sides associated with a small watercourse. Halesowen Formation sandstones and shales are present in the sides of the stream. Adjacent fields contain abundant red clay and red sandstone fragments characteristic of the Alveley Member of the Salop Formation. Area 1.19ha.

### 63. Wychbury Hill
SO917820

**G.** With a small but important exposure of red and purple Clent breccias of the Permian Period in the banks above the path. Area 0.18ha.

### 64. Ham Dingle
SO915827

Deeply-incised broad-leaved dingle woodland along the valley sides of two watercourses. Ancient semi-natural woodland (NE inventory). The stream and adjacent road cuttings encompass strata belonging to the Triassic, Permian and Upper Carboniferous periods which are juxtaposed as a result of faults related to the edge of the South Staffordshire Coalfield. Area 4.67ha.

### 65. Stourbridge Junction South Railway Cutting
SO909829

**G.** Shows the boundary between the dark brown Bromsgrove Sandstone Formation, and the underlying softer red/brown Wildmoor Sandstone Formation of the Carboniferous Period. Area 1.19ha.

### 66. Glasshouse Hill
SO906834

**G.** A roadside cutting above the junction between the Bromsgrove and underlying Wildmoor Sandstone formations. Area 0.01ha.

### 67. Pedmore Common
SO898826

A former common, now a golf course south of Stourbridge with remnant areas of heathland and acid grassland and woodland plantings. Area 18.42ha.

### 68. Ounty John Wood
SO900819

Strip of mature woodland with mature plantings of Beech occupying formerly quarried slope. Area 1.54ha.

### 69. Norton Covert
SO888822

A former sand and gravel pit colonised by woodland with some mature plantation of broad-leaved and coniferous trees. Fluvioglacial sand and gravel deposits from the Devensian Stage of the Quaternary Period are exposed. The 'hummocky' topography is thought to represent the dumping of glacial outwash materials in banks by rivers flowing to the south of the limit of the glacial ice front. Area 5.52ha.

### 70. Coombeswood North
SO973852

Birch woodland and base-poor grassland with important geological exposures, including a conglomerate with unusually large boulder-size quartzite pebbles indicative of extreme climatic and/or tectonic activity at the onset of the 'red-bed' phase of the Upper Carboniferous Period. Area 6.05ha. Links to wider SLINC.

### 71. Coombeswood South
SO977849

Woodland partly pre-dating 1830s which may be ancient, surrounded by areas of acidic, neutral and marshy grassland. The site exposes the Junction zone of the Russells Hall Fault between the Etruria and Halesowen geological Formations. Area 6.24ha. Links to wider SLINC.

### 72. The Leasowes
SO979841

Sections of former parkland landscape created by William Shenstone in the 18th century, now a Grade 1 listed historic landscape and partly a golf club. Includes strips of ancient woodland along the edges of watercourses, pools, and grassland, some base-poor. Area 27.35ha.

▲ The Leasowes

Forms part of a wider SINC & SLINC and includes two further specifically identified SINC sites:

### 73. The Leasowes – Crown Tip
SO976841

Former refuse tip, colonised by matrix of scrub, grassland and tall herb. Area 2.25ha.

### 74. Leasowes Canal Embankment
SO973836

Formerly developed land colonised by scrub, base-poor grassland and ruderal vegetation with boundary hedgerows. Area 0.31ha.

### 75. Bromsgrove Road Cutting, Tenterfields SSSI
SO971836

**G.** The best available exposure of the Basal Sandstone Member of the Halesowen Formation of the Carboniferous Period. It provides important evidence to help the environmental interpretation of Britain during the Upper Carboniferous Period. Area 0.18ha, designated 1990. **Tenterfields LNR,** SO971836, was designated in 1995 with an area of 0.48ha.

### 76. Manor Abbey Woodland
SO974827

Woodland along a watercourse, which pre-dates 1830s and may be ancient, with adjacent species-rich neutral grassland. Area 1.51ha. Linked to wider Illey Brook SLINC.

### 77. Illey Brook
SO976816

Includes areas of species-rich woodland following the course of Illey Brook. The brook and its tributaries provide a series of exposures of most of the Halesowen Formation of the Carboniferous Period. Area 4.84ha. Several associated areas in this ancient countryside landscape are SINCs.

### 78. Illey Pastures SSSI
SO977811
One of the richest grassland floras in B&BC. Area 3.91ha, designated 1989.

▲ Illey Pastures

### 79. Tributary of Illey Brook
SO978827
Small unmodified tree-lined watercourse supporting rich woodland flora. Area 1.09ha.

### 80. Cooper's Wood and Lyclose Meadow
SO984821
A small ancient woodland occupying the shallow valley slopes of a small watercourse together with a species-rich meadow. Area 3.34ha.

### 81. Illey Meadows and Kitswell Dingle
SO985819
A series of species-rich neutral meadows and a strip of species-rich woodland following a watercourse towards the embankments of the M5 motorway. Area 3.27ha.

## SANDWELL

### 1. Wood Green Road
SO997964
Receptor site for arrested pioneer vegetation with a calcareous influence which was translocated from an adjacent post-industrial site lost to development. Area 0.19ha.

### 2. Basin Sidings, Wednesbury
SO977946
Former railway and canal basin sidings, colonised by species-rich grassland, scrub and ruderal vegetation with areas of open water. Also received translocated grassland habitat from a site nearby. Area 0.79ha.

### 3. Shaw Street
SO986936
A filled-in section of former canal colonised by neutral grassland, wet grassland and scrub. Area 2.13ha.

### 4. Ray Hall Sewage Works
SP028946
Within an active sewage works, a secluded area of former sewage beds with a diverse range of terrestrial and aquatic habitats. Area 4.48ha.

### 5. Hill Farm Bridge Fields
SP033951
A series of meadows supporting valuable species-rich grassland including a lime-loving flora in parts with good quality hedgerows and scattered scrub. Forms link to larger SLINC. Area 14.17ha.

### 6. Wilderness Wood
SP040951
Woodland formerly managed as an Oak/Hazel coppice with some areas of wet woodland, pond and meadow. Woodland pre-dates 1830s and may be ancient. Forms link with larger SLINC. Area 0.7ha.

### 7. Holly Wood and pasture
SP053945
Mixed deciduous woodland which pre-

dates 1830s and may be ancient, plus adjacent species-rich pasture. Area 8.54ha. Part designated **Holly Wood LNR** in 2000, area 5.04ha.

### 8. Eastwood Road
SP046936
A diverse range of habitats including scrub, unimproved grassland and wet woodland which pre-dates 1830s and may be ancient. Area 6.19ha. Designated as **Gorse Farm Wood LNR** in 1995, area 6.2ha.

### 9. Land at Beaconview Road
SP021939
An area of former farmland linked to the River Tame and railway line, N of Sandwell Valley, with a diverse range of habitats. Area 11.71ha.

### 10. Sandwell Valley SINCs and LNRs
SP0392
The main area of the Sandwell Valley was designated as an LNR in 1991 with an area of 105.22ha. Other declared SINCs and LNRs within Sandwell Valley are:

### 11. Sandwell Hall, Site and grounds
SP019912
Landscaped woodlands, grasslands and hedgerows with artificially created

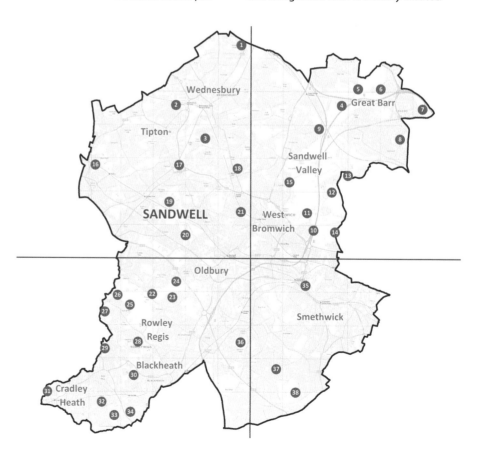

waterbodies. Part of **Priory Woods LNR**. Area 8.19ha.

### 12. Park Farm, Priory Woods and Swan Pool
SP025920
Landscaped woodlands, grasslands and hedgerows with artificially created waterbodies. Designated **LNR** 1991 with an area of 21.6ha.

### 13. Forge Mill Lake LNR
SP030925
Open water, grassland, scrub, hedgerows and floodplain. Designated in 1991 with an area of 63ha.

### 14. Sandwell Park Golf Course Woodland
SP026908
Ancient semi-natural woodland (NE inventory) plus associated grassland and scrub. Area 2.28ha. A private site and linked to SLINC site (area 5.17 ha).

### 15. Sots Hole
SP012923
A brook valley with former mill pool, dry and wet woodland which is partly ancient woodland (NE inventory), marshy grassland and watercourse. Area 4.43ha. Comprises part of **Sot's Hole and Bluebell Woods LNR**, designated in 1996 with an area of 5.5ha.

### 16. Princes End Triangle (also known as Bloomfield Triangle)
SO952928
Former railway junction near to Tipton with tipped limestone colonised by lime-loving flora. Also similar vegetation from an adjacent hollow used for dumping was translocated onto the site. Area 2.17ha.

### 17. Great Bridge Canal Basins
SO978928
A short section of Walsall Canal, River Tame, disused canal basins and adjacent land supporting terrestrial and aquatic habitats. Area 1.47ha.

### 18. Ridgeacre Branch Canal
SO996927
A stretch of canal and associated corridor with diverse vegetation associated with the Sandwell Valley. Area 4.88ha.

### 19. Sheepwash LNR
SO975917
A major contaminated land and landfill landscape reclamation scheme in the 1980s, it has a diversity of created pools, neutral grassland and plantation

▲ Sheepwash Local Nature Reserve

woodland blocks alongside the course of the River Tame. Designated as LNR in 2000. Area 39.42ha.

### 20. Gower Branch Canal
SO980907
A section of canal corridor linking the two levels of Birmingham Main Line Canal with a good assemblage of submerged, floating and emergent vegetation. Area 3.75ha.

### 21. Snow Hill to Wolverhampton Railway – Guns Lane to Dartmouth Street
SO997914
**G.** Sandstones of the Salop Formation of the Carboniferous Period are exposed in the rail cutting, now part of the Metro route. Area 0.47ha.

### 22. Rowley Hills SLINC and SINCs
SO972889
Parts of the Rowley Hills open space containing former quarries in the Dolerite intrusion. The Dolerite was extensively quarried in the 19th century for use as road stone. A scenic landscape with remaining rock faces and extensive grasslands. Includes the following two SINCs:

### 23. Land north of Ivy House Road
SO976889
Area of species-rich grassland developed on water-stressed quarry spoil. Area 1.73ha.

### 24. Land at Edale (Blue Rock Quarry)
SO977892
Former quarry with pond and broad-leaved woodland. Examples of columnar jointing and nodular exfoliation (onion weathering) in the dolerite make the site ideal for teaching igneous geology. These dolerites were intruded in a molten state into strata of the Coal Measures and Etruria Marls late in the Carboniferous period and cooled at depth forming the hard

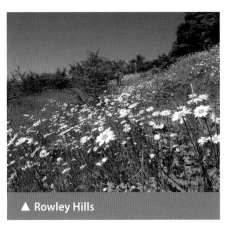

▲ Rowley Hills

crystalline rock that is locally known as the 'Rowley Rag'. Accessible to public. Area 4.26ha.

### 25. Dudley Golf Course
SO962888
Open hillside with base-poor and neutral grassland and the former Rough Hill Quarry cliff face with relic Dolerite exposures exhibiting typical weathering and exfoliation features and columnar jointing associated with an igneous intrusion. Area 0.84ha.

### 26. Warrens Hall Farm
SO958889
A series of old pastures divided by hedges with additional areas of open water, wetlands, scrub, tall herb and woodland. Area 34.79ha.

### 27. Warrens Hall LNR
SO955884
Pools, canals, grassland, scrub, woodland and post-industrial habitats with a diverse range of species, across the Dudley Road from Warrens Hall Farm. Designated in 1996, area 16.8ha. See also Bumble Hole LNR in the Dudley list, with which this site is contiguous.

### 28. Sheepfold Close/Brickhouse Road LNR
SO965874
Partly quarried, includes wetland and wet and dry, species-rich grassland and marsh. Area 6.2ha.

### 29. Darby's End Disused Railway
SO955873
**G.** Shows a small exposure of the once common Etruria marl of the Carboniferous Period. Area 0.06ha. Connected to larger SLINC.

### 30. Waterfall Lane
SO964865
A former colliery site, now partially landscaped but with semi-natural habitats

including scrub, marshy grassland and open water. Area 5.41ha.

### 31. Mousesweet Brook
SO937860
River valley landscape with broad-leaved woodland, some of it wet, grassland and tall herb vegetation adjoining the larger Mushroom Green LNR in Dudley. Area 5.19ha. Part designated as **Mousesweet Brook LNR in 1995**, area 4.37ha.

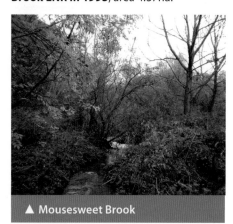
▲ Mousesweet Brook

### 32. Codsall Coppice
SO954857
Ancient semi-natural woodland (NE inventory). Area 2.5ha. Designated as **Codsall Coppice LNR** in 2000.

### 33. Haden Hill Park
SO958853
A park managed for wildlife with habitats including woodlands pre-dating the 1830s which may be ancient, grassland and open water. Part of a wider SLINC. Area 15.26ha.

### 34. Land south of High Haden LNR
SO963854
A wooded hillside forming a valuable landscape feature. Area 6.06ha.

### 35. Galton Valley
SP017892
The embankments and cuttings associated with the canal corridors of both levels of

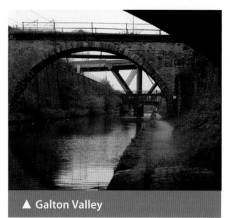
▲ Galton Valley

the Birmingham Canal immediately adjacent to the main Wolverhampton–Birmingham railway line. Habitats include woodland, scrub, acidic and neutral grassland and small patches of heathland. Heritage significance. Glaciofluvial sands of the Anglian Stage of the Quaternary Period are exposed. Area 14.37ha. Part of wider SLINC.

### 36. Barnford Hill Park
SO997875
**G.** An old gravel quarry now within the park shows the best of a small number of outcrops in Sandwell of the calcareous conglomerate within the Enville Member of the Salopian Formation of the Carboniferous Period. It bears an interesting flora. Area 1.34ha.

### 37. Thimblemill Brook
SP008867
A well-wooded stretch of the brook, supporting a good range of flora (with some introductions) and fauna. Area 2.93ha.

### 38. Warley Woods
SP014860
A park and golf course incorporating a surviving Repton landscape with planted deciduous woodland, grassland (some acid) and elements of ancient semi-natural woodland (NE inventory), with a recently-tipped area of open-mosaic landscape. Area 13.37ha.

## WALSALL

### 1. Brownhills Common (partly SSSI)
SK040063
An aggregate of four sites comprising a large patchwork of dry heath, acid grassland, marshy acidic grassland, damp heath, flush communities, an area of ancient semi-natural woodland (NE inventory), a series of unimproved pastures, a variety of permanent and temporary pools and areas of coal mine spoil. Much of the heath is now Birch woodland. The entire area N of the Chester Road became part of the **Chasewater and the Southern Staffordshire Coalfields Heaths SSSI** in 2010. Area 102.37ha.

### 2. Walsall to Lichfield Railway Line
SK049062
Two parallel, steep, flat-topped embankments separated by the flat former track bed supporting heathland, grassland, scrub and wetland communities. Area 5.35ha.

### 3. Clayhanger Common
SK045052
A matrix of heathland, marshy acidic grassland, ponds and scrub with many botanical quality indicator species. Part of a wider area of open land designated as a SLINC. Area 2.11ha.

### 4. Pelsall North Common
SK014045
Significant areas of lowland heathland, both wet and dry, with small amounts of base-poor mire are combined with base-rich furnace slag which roughly marks the location of the former Pelsall Iron Works. There are two canals (one of which is the Cannock Extension Canal SAC), several ponds and a variety of marginal agricultural habitats. Area 46.64ha. 42.7ha were designated as **Pelsall North Common LNR** in 1990.

▲ Canal at Pelsall North Common

### 5. Cannock Extension Canal SSSI and SAC
SK019045
Botanically the richest known waterway of its type in Staffordshire and the West Midlands, and high within the national canal network series. Only a small part is within B&BC. Area 2.09ha, designated in 1993.

### 6. Clayhanger SSSI
SK034045
Open water, wetland and unimproved wet grassland habitats, also with interesting post-industrial features. Botanical quality outstanding for B&BC. Area 27.21ha, designated 1986.

### 7. Grange Farm Wood
SK039036
Mixed broad-leaved woodland with a field layer associated with acid soil, dominated by mature oak. Area 2.99ha.

### 8. Jockey Fields SSSI
SK041030
An exceptional range of semi-natural

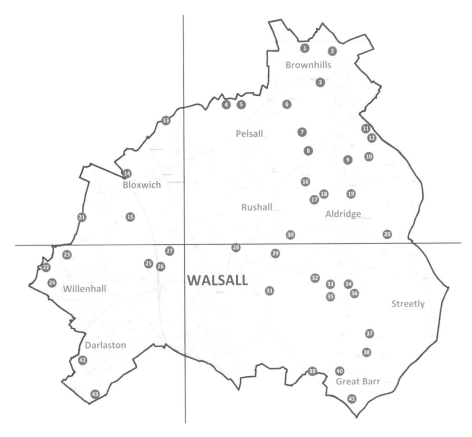

## 15. Rough Wood Chase
SJ982009
An exceptionally species-rich habitat complex straddling the M6 corridor with ancient semi-natural woodland, wet woodland, acidic grassland, heath, marsh, a series of pools, canal margins and post-industrial habitats. Area 68.35ha. Forms the core of **Rough Wood Chase LNR,** designated 2003, covering 98.28ha and including Sneyd Reservoir (q.v.).

▲ Rough Wood Chase

vegetation types including well-grazed damp pasture, neglected grassland, fen and mire with a network of well-vegetated ditches. Area 17.92ha, designated 1994.

## 9. King's Hayes Fields
SK054027
Botanically rich, unimproved, damp and dry neutral and base-poor horse-grazed pastures. Area 7.29ha.

## 10. Lazy Hill Wood
SK061028
Botanically rich broad-leaved woodland, adjacent pasture and a pond. Area 1.98ha.

## 11. Shire Oak Park
SK060037
Formerly a sand and gravel quarry, it

▲ Shire Oak Park

has now succeeded to lowland heathland, with grassland, woodland and ponds. Displays the variability of the Kidderminster Formation of Triassic age together with the contact with glacial sands and gravel. Designated as **Shire Oak Park LNR** in 1993. Area 24.45ha.

## 12. Castlebank Plantation
SK062034
A mixed woodland plantation dating from mid 19th century. The site is a hillfort thought to be of Late Bronze Age and early Iron Age. A private house guards the site. Area 5.09ha.

## 13. Newtown Pool
SJ994040
A large pool surrounded by an area of broad-leaved and wet woodland and an area of semi-natural grassland. Area 3.14ha.

## 14. Sneyd Reservoir
SJ981023
A disused 19th century canal feeder reservoir, with a complex of woodland, grassland, open water swamp and wetland. In places the ground water quality is very good and the reservoir is noted for its assemblage of freshwater macro-invertebrates. Site forms part of **Rough Wood Chase LNR.** Area 9.14ha.

## 16. Swan Pool and The Swag SSSI
SK040019
The reedbeds associated with these pools once held the largest roost for swallows and other hirundines in the West Midlands County. Area 6.05ha, designated 1986.

## 17. Stubber's Green
SK044015
An area of semi-improved pasture with a varying water regime associated with species-rich dry and marshy grassland and ephemeral pools divided by the Anchor Brook. Ornithological interest. Area 8.5ha.

## 18. Stubber's Green Bog SSSI
SK046016
A very unusual shallow pool with fringing base-poor valley mire and swamp communities within a post-industrial setting. Currently partly drained and heavily scrubbed-over. Area 2.78ha, designated in 1978.

## 19. Leigh's Wood
SK055016
Partly ancient semi-natural woodland (NE inventory) with an associated pond. Area 4.3ha.

## 20. Branton Hill Quarry
SK067003
**G.** One of the best and most extensive outcrops of Kidderminster Formation rocks

of Triassic age in Walsall. The occurrence of glacio-fluvial channel deposits adds further interest. Area 3.8ha.

### 21. Perry Hall Bridge
SJ966009
A matrix of grassland, scrub and tall herb with two pools supporting significant amphibian populations and botanical diversity. Area 1.8ha.

### 22. Waddens Brook
SO954995
A diverse habitat mosaic with marshy grassland areas and acidic colliery spoil, with scrub, grassland and wetland habitats, with both standing and running open water. Area 18.52ha. 12.66ha were designated in 1997 as **Fibbersley LNR**.

### 23. Fibbersley
SO961997
A former clay extraction site, now a mosaic of scrub, horse-grazed neutral grassland, marshy grassland and acidic grassland with a number of ponds. Area 13.86ha. Part of larger complex of sites including Wadden's Brook (q.v.) where 12.66ha were designated in 1997 as **Fibbersley LNR**.

▲ Fibbersley

### 24. Willenhall Memorial Park
SO956988
A relict field pond of 'very high conservation value' and adjacent coal spoil mounds with mature planted woodland and small areas of grassland sited in a formal public park. Supports important amphibian populations. Area 2.09ha.

### 25. Poplar Avenue Pond
SO988994
A good range of aquatic and marginal plant species. Assessed as 'very high'

▲ Poplar Avenue Pond

using Pond Action's Pond Conservation Assessment. Area 0.75ha.

### 26. Pouk Hill Quarry
SO992993
**G.** The only Black Country site to see Dolerite intrusive into the Lower Coal Measures. Area 1.93ha.

### 27. Walsall Power Station Pool
SO995998
A post-industrial site colonised by species-rich neutral grassland and scrub, with a number of created ponds supporting an introduced but interesting flora. Area 1.62ha.

### 28. Mill Lane
SP017999
An area of former railway sidings subject to a land reclamation project in 1990s with a diverse range of soil types and associated vegetation representing grassland on base-rich and base-poor soils, heathland, reedswamp, open water, scrub and plantation woodland. Area 11.06ha. 8.27ha were designated as **Mill Lane LNR** in 2007.

### 29. Park Lime Pits
SP030997
Centred on a disused limestone quarry, with two large pools, wet hollows, calcareous, neutral and wet grassland,

▲ Park Lime Pits

hawthorn thickets, small wooded areas and farmland with conservation arable field margins. Area 50.34ha. 9.39ha were designated in 1991 as **Park Lime Pits LNR**.

### 30. Daw End Quarry and Railway Cutting SSSI
SK035003
**G.** Provides one of the best exposures available in Britain of Wenlock Shale (Coalbrookdale Formation) and the overlying Silurian Wenlock Limestone. Area 8.06ha, designated 1986.

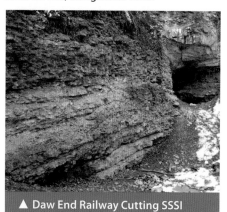
▲ Daw End Railway Cutting SSSI

### 31. Walsall Arboretum Extension
SP028985
A narrow stream corridor encompassing a diverse strip of rough grassland, scrub, drainage ditches and wet hollows. The eastern half was part of the former Grange Golf Course, which is now being developed as a Country Park. Area 5.57ha.

### 32. Hay Head Wood
SP043989
Broad-leaved woodland (part ancient semi-natural woodland in the NE inventory), calcareous grassland, scrub, grassland, marsh and a pond which is the remnant of an old canal. Area 10.75ha. 6.78ha were designated as **Hay Head Wood LNR** in 1993.

### 33. Hay Head Quarry SSSI
SP048987
**G.** The type locality for the Barr Limestone Formation comprising a lens of rock at the base of the Coalbrookdale Formation laid down during the middle of the Silurian Period. An outstanding source of material for students of Silurian marine faunas. Area 5.52ha, designated in 1986. Adjacent to Cuckoo's Nook and the Dingle SINC (q.v.).

### 34. Cuckoo's Nook and The Dingle
SP054987
Some of the site is ancient semi-natural

woodland with an associated rich flora, with some post-industrial features and geological interest including the Silurian limestone of Hay Head Quarry geological SSSI. Area 10.09ha. **Cuckoo's Nook and The Dingle LNR** was designated in 2002 and includes 12.99ha.

### 35. Three Crowns Pasture
SP048983
Two grazed species-rich pastures (calcareous, neutral and marshy), associated hedgerows with a diverse field layer and an overgrown unmetalled trackway. Area 3.83ha.

### 36. Birch Wood
SP056984
Ancient semi-natural broad-leaved woodland (NE inventory) with some standing open water and adjacent grassland. Area 3.55ha.

### 37. Barr Beacon
SP061971
Unimproved acidic grassland interspersed with scrub and areas of heathland restoration with a rich *Cladonia* lichen flora. The highest topographical feature on the eastern side of the Black Country, comprising sediments of the Triassic Period capped by the hard conglomerate of the Kidderminster Formation which together give rise to the prominent north-south trending ridge. Area 25.05ha. **Barr Beacon LNR**, extended to 31.33ha, was declared in 2008.

### 38. Pinfold Lane Quarry
SP060965
The quarry is colonised by broad-leaved woodland with pasture grassland adjacent. The only accessible site to see the junction of the Hopwas Breccia and conglomerate of the Kidderminster Formation of the Triassic Period. Area 4.92ha. 2.05ha were designated as part of **Barr Beacon LNR** (q.v.) declared in 2008.

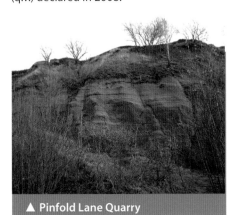
▲ Pinfold Lane Quarry

### 39. Merrion's Wood
SP042959
Part of Great Barr Park (Grade II landscape, believed to be a Repton design), an attractive mature broad-leaved woodland (ancient semi-natural woodland in the NE inventory), also a pool. Area 7.03ha.

▲ Merrion's Wood

### 40. The Duckery
SP051959
An ancient semi-natural woodland site (NE inventory), where dry and wet woodland are associated with a small stream. Also part of Great Barr Park (Grade II landscape, believed to be a Repton design). Area 4.07ha.

### 41. St Margaret's Hospital Grounds
SP055950
A partly formally landscaped mosaic of man-made pools and plantation woodlands which also encompasses an NE inventory ancient woodland (Gilbert's Wood). Also part of Great Barr Park (Grade II landscape, believed to be a Repton design). Area 15.85ha.

### 42. Ward's Pool
SO966963
A pool formed within a former clay pit surrounded by neutral grassland with areas of scrub and boundary hedgerows. Area 2.83ha.

### 43. Moorcroft Wood
SO970952
A post-industrial site with 100 year old

▲ Blast furnace slag at Moxley Pool, Moorcroft Wood

plantation woodland, furnace slag and pools, designated as **Moorcroft Wood LNR** in 1996. Area 12.21ha.

## WOLVERHAMPTON

### 1. Moseley Hall
SJ931037
Mature semi-natural and amenity woodland along course of Waterhead Brook and large former mill pond. Parts of woodland pre-date 1816 and may be ancient. Area 14.03ha.

### 2. Northycote Farm Parkland
SJ932034
Part of wider Northycote Farm SINC/SLINC. Mature parkland, recent planted woodland, hedgerows and a strip of diverse semi-natural woodland pre-dating 1830s which may be ancient. Area 17.38ha.

▲ The dingle, Northycote Farm

### 3. Northycote Farm Coppice
SJ932029
A small broad-leaved coppice woodland pre-dating 1816 which may be ancient. Part of Northycote Farm Country Park. Area 0.44ha.

### 4. Rakegate Wood
SJ911023
An area of broad-leaved woodland that pre-dates 1816 and may be ancient. There is also a small pond feature. Area 0.46ha.

### 5. Barnhurst Bridge Railway Cutting, Pendeford Ave
SJ894018
**G.** The bridge at Pendeford Avenue/Barnhurst Road affords views of the sandstones of the Bromsgrove Sandstone Formation of the Triassic Period. Area 0.38ha.

### 6. Smestow Valley LNR
SO891998
A wide corridor centred around the

**13. Smestow Brook, Compton**
SO877985
Watercourse with woodland, scrub and grassland. Area 4.55ha.

**14. Windmill Wood (or Peasley's Wood)**
SO872983
A former quarry with a stand of Hornbeam, created meadows and a sandstone rock exposure. Cliff faces present sections parallel to and perpendicular to the depositional dip of the sandstones of the Wildmoor Sandstone Formation of the Triassic Period. Glacial sands and gravels of the Devensian Stage of the Quaternary Period are also present. Area 3.76ha.

**15. The Rock, Tettenhall Road**
SJ889001
**G.** Thomas Telford's well known road cutting ascends the ridge at Tettenhall and exposes the junction between the sandstones of the Wildmoor and Bromsgrove Sandstone Formations of the Triassic Period. Area 0.17ha.

**16. The Rock, Old Hill**
SJ889000
**G.** A road cutting with a number of small exposures of sandstones of the Wildmoor Sandstone Formation of the Triassic Period. Area 0.03ha.

**17. Tettenhall Wood**
SO886996
Beech and Sycamore-dominated woodland, an ancient woodland site (NE inventory). Area 3.72ha.

**18. Beechcroft Wood**
SO879995
A belt of mature planted woodland dominated by beech. Area 1.06ha.

**19. Mount Hotel Woodland**
SO875988
Mature Beech/Ash/Hornbeam plantation with a native Bluebell-dominated field layer. Area 2.11ha.

**20. Wightwick Court Woodland**
SO872987
Beech-dominated woodland plantation on an ancient woodland site (NE inventory). Area 1.22ha.

**21. Wightwick Bank**
SO870984
**G.** A road cutting exposes the junction zone between sandstones of the Bromsgrove and Wildmoor Sandstone Formations of the Triassic Period. Area 0.08ha.

former railway, the Staffs & Worcs canal and the Smestow Brook, with adjacent pockets of woodland and meadows. 51.01ha were declared as Smestow Valley LNR in 1998. Noted for its bird life, it includes several SINC sites including much of the railway corridor, also:

**7. Hawthorn Wood**
SJ897005
A wooded siding with glades and an embankment down to a canal. Area 3.11ha.

**8. Dunstall Park Racecourse**
SJ902009
An area of mixed semi-natural habitat including a semi-improved meadow. SINC not open to the public. Area 4.85ha.

**9. Oxley North: The Holdings**
SJ903012
A mosaic of habitats forming an exceptionally diverse area adjacent to Smestow Valley LNR. Area 4.4ha.

**10. Smestow Valley – Compton Park**
SO886991
Abandoned farmland with plantations, a large created meadow and old hedgerows. Area 2.02ha.

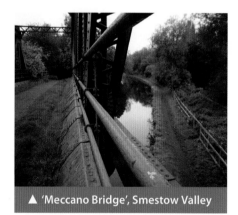

▲ 'Meccano Bridge', Smestow Valley

**11. Staffs and Worcs Canal**
SO888994
Area 8.8ha.

**12. Wightwick Wedge**
SO877983
Large area of meadowland with some uncommon species, hedgerow, scrub and a small stream and pond. The area of former workings includes enigmatic channel features within the Wildmoor Sandstone bedrock not seen elsewhere in Wolverhampton. The remnant quarry face and immediate relic workings have glaciofluvial and Till deposits in contact with the Wildmoor Sandstone. Area 13.9ha.

### 22. Wightwick Manor
SO868984
A matrix of pools, grassland and woodland with some unusual species recorded. Fine collection of glacial erratics displayed. National Trust site. Area 2.37ha.

### 23. Stafford Road Cutting
SJ913002
**G.** The site shows a laterally extensive outcrop of sandstone of the Bromsgrove Sandstone Formation of Triassic age with overlying glacio-fluvial sands and gravel. Area 0.22ha.

### 24. Finchfield Hill Cutting
SO884986
**G.** The outcrop is noteworthy for the atypical lithofacies present in the Wildmoor Sandstone Formation of the Triassic Period. Area 0.05ha.

### 25. Merridale School Bog
SO903981
Bog and pond habitats created in school grounds in 1983, supporting an unusual introduced flora. Area 0.18ha.

### 26. Coppice Road Wood
SO886974
A small fragment of mature woodland dominated by Birch, Ash and Pedunculate Oak, adjoined on three sides by houses and gardens. Area 1.14ha.

### 27. Waddens Brook
SO955996
A strip of land following the course of Waddens Brook adjoining a Walsall SINC site. Much lost to industrial development. Area 19.16ha.

### 28. Brook Point Pool
SO952995
An area of open water and emergent and marginal vegetation with some scrub, supporting good amphibian populations. Area 0.97ha.

### 29. Monmore Green Disused Railway
SO929979
A length of disused railway line stretching south-east from the city centre and colonised by grassland, tall herb and scrub with some wetland areas. Area 4.38ha.

### 30. Penn Hall School Wood
SO891955
Mature broad-leaved woodland dominated by Beech and Sycamore. Area 1.09ha.

### 31. Colton Hills
SO908957
A mosaic of scrub, tall herb and grassland on former quarry and arable land. Area 3.86ha.

### 32. Park Coppice
SO910957
A block of ancient semi-natural woodland (NE inventory). Area 4.13ha.

### 33. Ashen Coppice
SO913952
Ancient semi-natural woodland (NE inventory). Area 4.61ha.

### 34. Park Hill
SO919957
A former quarry site, it is the only outcrop in Wolverhampton of the Ludlow Series i.e. Elton, Aymestry Limestone and Whitcliffe Formations of Silurian age. Heavily colonised by scrub it still (2010) contains remnant patches of calcareous grassland. Area 1.18ha.

### 35. Springvale Park
SO924954
Post-industrial site with colliery spoil tipped into an abandoned clay pit. Additional created woodland and meadows. Clay pit shows exposures of the Lower Coal measures of the Carboniferous Period. Area 4.13ha.

▲ Created meadows, Springvale Park

▲ Springvale Park

## The Gorge
Two features have Biological and Geological features of interest and SINC status:

### 36. The Gorge, Cinder Hill
SO927941
A former limestone quarry colonised by woodland but with a small portion of calcareous grassland and some rock exposures (see below).

### 37. Gorge Road Cutting
SO928940
**G.** Together with Cinder Hill it is the only outcrop in Wolverhampton of Wenlock Formation rocks of the Silurian Period. Area 0.05ha.

▲ The Gorge

### 38. Ladymoor Pool
SO943951
Botanically rich post-industrial site with mine spoil, furnace slag, marsh, tipped areas, canal margin and pool. The large and sculptural blocks of furnace slag representing some of the best examples in Wolverhampton and are evocative of the area's industrial heritage. Area 6.36ha.

### 39. Peascroft Wood
SO950970
Broad-leaved woodland planted in the early 20th century on coal spoil mounds, with one of only a handful of former pit shafts visible in the heart of the Thick Coal district. Area 3.8ha.

▲ Peascroft Wood

# Section 5 • References

Anon. (undated) *Sutton Park National Nature Reserve*. Birmingham City Council.

Bagnall, J.E. (1876) *Notes on Sutton Park: Its Flowering Plants, Ferns, and Mosses*, read at a general meeting of the Birmingham Natural History and Microscopical Society, held December 6th, 1876. (A version with updated scientific names is online at http://www.spnh.scnhs.org.uk/Bagnall_SP.pdf.)

Coxhead, P. (1994) Changes in the Vascular Plant Flora of Sutton Park. *Proceedings of the Birmingham Natural History Society* 27(1), pp.2–12.

Cadbury, D.A., Hawkes, J.G. & Readett, R.C. (1971) *A Computer-mapped Flora – A Study of the County of Warwickshire*. Academic Press, London.

Edees, E.S. (1972) *Flora of Staffordshire*. David & Charles, Newton Abbot.

Fowkes, H.H. & Coxhead, P. (eds) (1998) *A Natural History of Sutton Park – Part 1: The Vascular Plants*. 2nd revised edition. Sutton Coldfield Natural History Society.

Readett, R.C. (1971) A Flora of Sutton Park. *Proceedings of the Birmingham Natural History Society* 22, pp. 1–88; also published as a separate reprint.

Preston, C.D., Pearman, D.A. & Dines, T.D. (2002) *New Atlas of the British & Irish Flora*. Oxford University Press, Oxford.

Toghill, P. (2000) *The Geology of Britain: an introduction*. Swan Hill Press, Shrewsbury.

**Bumble Hole and Warrens Hall** (by Anne Daly)

## Chapter 3

# Background to the Flora

edited by Peter Jarvis

◀ Wren's Nest, Dudley

## GENERAL INTRODUCTION

Because plants and plant communities depend on and reflect their environment, and respond to changes in it, it is instructive to examine the environmental and historical background to Birmingham and the Black Country (B&BC). This chapter considers three aspects of this. (1) The physical background – **geology** and **climate** have together effected the region's **relief** (topography) and **drainage**, which in turn have influenced its **hydrology** (changes in water quality reflecting changes in agricultural, industrial and domestic activities). (2) All of these, together with

**soil**, have affected the distribution of plants, largely by providing a suite of different **habitats** which, in turn, support a more-or-less distinctive set of plant communities and **vegetation** types. (3) Over the millennia both the physical landscape and its vegetative cover have been modified or completely altered by climatic change and **human activity**. The region's flora clearly reflects the environmental conditions of its various pasts as well as its present.

In interpreting the text, the figures included in Chapter 3 should be supplemented by referring to the main map at the beginning of the book.

# Section 1 • Geology and geodiversity by Alan Cutler

## INTRODUCTION

Geodiversity is the geological variety of rocks, minerals, fossils and landscape together with the natural processes which form them. Geodiversity embraces both the natural and historic environments and increasingly is being seen as the link between the landscape, people and their culture: the variety of phenomena and processes that creates the landscape and soils and provides the framework for life on earth.

Geology is, of course, the foundation of the natural world and although not always seen, it is the underlying geology that influences the shape of the landscape, the habitats and the ecosystems. Every English landscape, whether hilly or flat, owes its character to geodiversity. The processes of weathering, erosion and sedimentation (geomorphology) act upon the landform to give the mountains, hills and valleys that we see today. Through its influence upon landform, elevation, drainage and soils, geodiversity underpins biodiversity. In fact biodiversity (the

variety of life on earth) relies on geology for diversity of habitat and the ecosystem, and soil is the link between them.

For its size, B&BC has some of the most diverse geology in the world (Figure 3.1). The underlying bedrock (solid) formations include rocks from the Ordovician, Silurian, Carboniferous, Permian and Triassic Periods (Table 3.1). The present-day shape of the landscape is mainly the result of erosion by ice and water during the Ice Age, which left most of the area with a blanket of superficial sands, gravels and sandy clays lying on top of the bedrock formations. The Ice Age, technically known as the Quaternary (Pleistocene Period), was not just one episode of severe glacial climatic conditions but several oscillations from cold glacial to warm interglacial. In B&BC the glacial deposits are assigned to either the Devensian Stage (110,000–10,000 years ago) or the Anglian Stage (478,000–424,000 years ago). The ice sheets of the last phase of glaciation, the Devensian, which peaked around 20,000 years ago, reached as far south as Wolverhampton and Walsall.

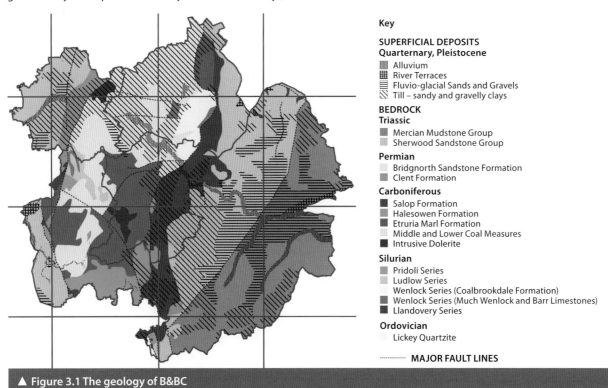

Key

**SUPERFICIAL DEPOSITS**
**Quarternary, Pleistocene**
- Alluvium
- River Terraces
- Fluvio-glacial Sands and Gravels
- Till – sandy and gravelly clays

**BEDROCK**
**Triassic**
- Mercian Mudstone Group
- Sherwood Sandstone Group

**Permian**
- Bridgnorth Sandstone Formation
- Clent Formation

**Carboniferous**
- Salop Formation
- Halesowen Formation
- Etruria Marl Formation
- Middle and Lower Coal Measures
- Intrusive Dolerite

**Silurian**
- Pridoli Series
- Ludlow Series
- Wenlock Series (Coalbrookdale Formation)
- Wenlock Series (Much Wenlock and Barr Limestones)
- Llandovery Series

**Ordovician**
- Lickey Quartzite

---------- **MAJOR FAULT LINES**

▲ **Figure 3.1 The geology of B&BC**

## Table 3.1 Geological timeline

| Geological Period | Formation (or other subdivision) | Indicative age of deposits (Million years) | Environment | Landscape examples |
|---|---|---|---|---|
| **Quaternary, Pleistocene** | Peat | | Glacial, periglacial and tundra conditions. | Sutton Park |
| | Alluvium | | | River valleys |
| (Devensian and Anglian stages) | Head | 0.01–0.45 | | Rowley Hills |
| | River Terraces | | Intermediate interglacial warm periods. | Countryside north, east and west of Wolverhampton |
| | Fluvio-glacial Sands and Gravels | | | Sandwell Valley River Valleys Stourbridge–Wallheath |
| | Till – sandy and gravelly clays | | | North Birmingham Stourbridge–Wolverhampton |
| | | | | North Wolverhampton Smethwick–Harborne South Birmingham |
| **Triassic** (Mercia Mudstone Group) | Includes the Arden Sandstone | 220–240 | Arid, low rainfall, windblown material deposited in temporary lakes. Used extensively for brick making. High evaporation rates. | Eastern Birmingham |
| (Sherwood Sandstone Group) | Bromsgrove | 240 | Arid hot windswept deserts, rare storms, seasonal rainfall. Harder sandstones much used as building stones throughout the area. | Tettenhall Ridge Edgbaston to Sutton Coldfield |
| | Wildmoor | 245 | Principal source for moulding sands. | Smestow Valley, Stourbridge, Hockley, Ladywood |
| | Kidderminster | 250 | Pebble beds give rise to prominent hills and ridges. Pebbles crushed for gravel. | Bushbury to Cannock Chase Wollaston Ridge Barr Beacon |
| | Hopwas Breccia | 255 | | Barr Beacon (Pinfold Lane) |
| **Permian** | Bridgnorth Sandstone | 260 | Aeolian deposited sand dunes. Most arid period in Midlands geological record. | Cooknell Hill, Wordsley |
| | Clent | 280 | Scree fan material, torrent deposited. | Small outcrops in Wolverhampton, Stourbridge and Sandwell |
| **Carboniferous (Upper)** Upper Coal Measures – Stephanian ? – Westphalian Series (D) | {Enville* {Keele* *Now grouped together as Salop Formation | 300 | Semi-arid desert basin, seasonal rainfall. Soft sandstones used for building sand. Calcareous conglomerates used for gravels. Harder sandstones used as local building stone. | Elevated landscape in the south of the area around Oldbury, Halesowen and Wollescote. Hills around Frankley and Romsley |
| Westphalian D | Halesowen | | | |
| Intrusive Dolerite | | 310 | Crustal stretching and volcanic activity. The hardest rocks of the area. | Rowley Hills, Barrow Hill, Wednesfield sill, Pouk Hill |
| Bolsovian | Etruria (Marl) | 310 | Well-drained floodplain. Clays used for brick making. | Central Black Country Pensnett |
| Middle and Lower Coal Measures – (Duckmantian and Langsettian) | (Undivided) | 318 | Tropical forests and delta swamps. Source of principal productive coal seams, ironstones and fireclays. | Central Black Country Plateau |
| **Silurian** Pridoli series | | 416 | The highly inclined limestones form conspicuous steep-sided wooded hills. They give rise to well drained calcareous habitats. Limestone quarried for flux in iron industry. Also used as a building stone. The Much Wenlock Limestone at Dudley records a mid-continental shelf, shallow marine environment, with a rich tropical fauna and global climate warmer than today. By contrast the land was almost all desert as land plants were only just evolving. | Gornal, Netherton |
| Ludlow series | | | | Sedgley Beacon |
| Wenlock series | Wenlock & Coalbrookdale | | | Hurst Hill Wrens Nest Hill Castle Hill, Dudley Hayhead, The Dingle, Walsall |
| Llandovery series | Rubery Formation | 439 | | Road cutting and old Leachgreen quarry at Rubery |
| **Ordovician** | Lickey Quartzite | 490 | The oldest rocks of B&BC forming pronounced topography of SW Birmingham. Rocks extensively quarried for roadstone. | Rubery Hill |

The geology of B&BC divides into three distinct parts which are also reflected in both the topography and historical and cultural influences. The central core area comprises the southern part of the South Staffordshire Coalfield (also known as the Black Country or Dudley Coalfield) which extends from Rubery through Halesowen and the Black Country to North Wolverhampton and Walsall. The coalfield is flanked on the east and west by younger rocks mostly belonging to Triassic age formations with some Permian and late Carboniferous outcrops.

## THE COALFIELD

Structurally the coalfield is an uplifted block comprising rocks mostly of Carboniferous age (318–300 million years old) collectively known as the Coal Measures. The Black Country is distinguished as being structurally more complex than Birmingham. The east and west sides of the coalfield are delineated by major faults which displace the rocks either side by hundreds of metres. Within the coalfield there are two major fold axes (lines of disturbance) which affect the surrounding topography. The most prominent is the NNW–SSE trending, discontinuous ridge of hills known as the Lickey-Sedgley Ridge, which approximates to the main watershed of England (see sections 2, 3 and 4 in this Chapter). West of this axis, the landscape is undulating with marked ridges and narrow, deeply incised river valleys which drain to the River Severn. East of the axis the country is relatively flat as far as the eastern boundary fault, with the broad floodplain of the River Tame and tributaries which drain via the Trent to the North Sea.

The centre section of the ridge, the Rowley Hills, is composed of dolerite, an alkaline igneous rock intruded into the Coal Measures about 300 million years ago as a result of crustal stretching and thinning. The dolerite is an extremely hard rock, much prized as a road dressing, forming at Turners Hill, Rowley, the highest point of the area. The dolerite gives rise to the elevated landscape of the hills with its mostly thin neutral soils.

To the north-west of the Rowley Hills, older, highly inclined, limestone rocks of Silurian Age (424 million years old) form the well-known steep-sided features of Castle Hill and Wren's Nest Hill at Dudley and the high ground of Hurst Hill and Sedgley Beacon. The limestones were originally dug for agricultural lime or lime mortar, but output soared from the 17th century onwards to provide a flux for the developing iron industry of the Black Country. The Silurian rocks at Dudley are renowned worldwide for the exceptionally well-preserved invertebrate fossil fauna, which still inspires research today. These Silurian hills are important for their calcareous habitats.

The oldest rocks within B&BC are found at the south-eastern end of the axis, where they form the high ground at Rubery extending towards the Lickey Hills just outside our region. Here Ordovician-age Lickey quartzites (formerly classified as of Cambrian age) form the core of the elevated ground, with early Silurian Rubery Formation sandstones and mudstones.

The coalfield is traversed by a second fold, the Netherton axis, which extends from Wollescote, east of Stourbridge, through Netherton to Walsall. The fold again brings Silurian age rocks to the surface, notably at Walsall where the largest expanse of limestones and calcareous mudstones is to be found.

The Coal Measures rocks present a diverse range of rock types, ranging from clays and mudstones to coal seams, bands of ironstones and sandstones. Some of the sandstones are quite hard and can give rise to marked features such as Hodge Hill, Wollescote. Some of the sandstones in the higher part of the sequence are fairly calcareous and include one or two thin limestones which encourage occurrences of lime-loving plants. The mudstones and sandstones of the Coal Measures have yielded a diverse fossil flora which has received attention from Kidston (1914, 1923–25) and Crookall (1955).

Complicating the soil types and habitats in the older industrialised part of the Black Country is a layer of colliery waste which is found evenly spread over most of the terrain.

## THE TRIASSIC COUNTRY

East and west of the coalfield the rocks are all much younger, recording a very long desert phase ranging from Late Carboniferous formations (about 300 million years old), through late Permian age (250–290 million years old), to formations belonging to the Sherwood Sandstone Group and Mercia Mudstone Group respectively of Early and Middle Triassic age.

The Sherwood Sandstone Group (240–250 million years old) is subdivided into Kidderminster, Wildmoor and Bromsgrove Formations, comprising pebbly and cross-bedded sandstones with occasional thin mudstones. The Triassic sediments infilled ancient rift valleys east and west of the coalfield, forming wide desert basins. Today, the group gives rise to gently rolling country interspersed by long, usually well-wooded ridges and hilly areas, where pebble beds, sometimes calcareous, predominate, such as the Wollaston to Wolverhampton ridges and Barr Beacon. The Triassic rocks include important aquifers and where free of superficial drift deposits, give rise to fertile, easily worked soils. Also characteristic of the Triassic sediments is well-drained heathland. Locally the Bromsgrove Formation, used as a building stone for churches and walls, forms the high ground of Birmingham City centre and the Tettenhall Ridge, Wolverhampton.

The Sherwood Sandstone Group is succeeded by softer red mudstones (marls) of the Mercia Mudstone Group (220–240 million years old), which underlies the eastern half of Birmingham in a broad strip from West Heath to Sutton Coldfield, forming the western part of the 'Knowle basin'. It is relatively low-lying and separates the higher ground of the Warwickshire coalfield in the east and the eastern edge of the South Staffordshire (Black Country) coalfield to the west.

This is a gently rolling landscape with the only topographic features arising from thin, intermittent sandstone horizons within the mudstones known as 'skerries', of which the Arden Sandstone is the most developed. Once important for brick manufacture, the Mercia Mudstones form poorly drained claylands.

## SUPERFICIAL DEPOSITS

All the bedrock formations have been modified by the action of ice, frost and melt water processes during various phases of the Ice Age to give the present-day landform. Deposits found in the north and west of the area are generally assigned to the later Devensian Stage, those in the east to the earlier Anglian Stage. The receding ice left behind large sheets of till (sandy or gravelly clays), giving rise to heavy, poorly drained soils with consequent effects on the botany.

Fluvio-glacial sands and gravels were deposited by meltwater streams. Sometimes the streams would have been under or within the ice sheets or glaciers. In other cases they are the product of outwash flooding during the seasonal thaw and form sheet-like spreads or river terrace deposits away from the ice front. They are generally free-draining, giving lighter soils and are important sources of aggregates (sand and gravel).

# Section 2 • Climate by David J. Mitchell

## INTRODUCTION

The altitudinal range within the B&BC region is from 50m (164 ft) above sea level in the Stour Valley to 271m (876 ft) at Turners Hill on the border of Dudley and Rowley Regis. Although localised microclimate variations occur, the watershed between the west-flowing streams of the River Severn basin and the east-flowing streams of the River Trent basin (Figure 3.2) probably has the most significant natural effect on climate.

This is a part of the main watershed in England, with western climatic influences occurring on the western flanks and more 'continental' influences on the eastern flanks. Although most of the region lies in the 'continental' zone, the climate of the dominant

ridge and the western flanks will most likely present different habitats for plants.

Smith (1976) divided England and Wales into agroclimatic regions, obtained by subdividing the country into relatively homogeneous land use types with respect to climate and soils. In addition to fundamental climatic parameters such as air temperature and rainfall, monthly variations in soil temperature, potential transpiration, sunshine, radiation and illumination are also available. These additional climatic factors are, in many cases, more relevant to predicting site- and season-specific crop growth than spontaneous plant growth. Most of B&BC lies in Agroclimatic Region 20 (Table 3.2).

Summit of Turners Hill –
highest point in B&BC
(by Neville Walters)

### Table 3.2 Summary of selected climatic parameters for Agroclimatic Region 20 (Smith 1976)

| Climatic parameters | | Values for mean altitude |
|---|---|---|
| Altitude: average height | | 121m |
| Mean annual precipitation | | 695mm |
| Mean annual potential transpiration | | 494mm |
| Mean annual potential transpiration during the growing season | | 457mm |
| Effective transpiration during the growing season | | 366mm |
| Maximum soil moisture deficit median values | | 95mm |
| Mean air temperature | January | 2.7°C |
| | July | 16.0°C |
| Mean soil temperature at 30cm depth | January | 3.2°C |
| | July | 17.1°C |
| Day length | January | 9.6 h |
| | July | 17.8 h |
| Solar radiation | January | 60mWh$^{-1}$ cm$^{-2}$ |
| | July | 430mWh$^{-1}$ cm$^{-2}$ |
| Illumination | January | 65 kilolux h |
| | July | 525 kilolux h |
| Sunshine (average hours per day) | January | 1.3 h |
| | July | 5.3 h |
| Growing season: days above 6°C | | 241 days |
| | | 29 March to 25 November |
| Grazing season | | 217 days |
| | | 6 April to 9 November |
| Degree days above 10°C May to October | | 745 |
| Winter degree days below 0°C | | 160 |

## ALTITUDINAL CONTROLS

Altitudinal controls on climatic parameters have been well documented (Smith, 1976; Taylor, 1976): a summary of their general lapse rates (changes with altitude) are given in Table 3.3. With only a modest range in altitude in the region, some of the individual rates of change in the parameters are small, and may not influence many plants but, if all the parameters are taken collectively, the altitudinal influence may be more significant. Except for rainfall and wind speed, the parameters all decrease with altitude and have an adverse effect on plant growth.

In some cases these lapse rates cannot be used directly because of the urbanisation of the region. The presence of

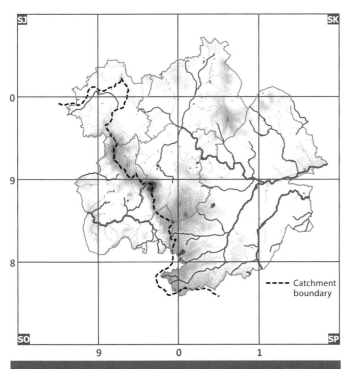

▲ Figure 3.2 River systems, showing the main watershed between the Severn and the Trent basins

Catchment boundary

artificial surfaces, heat energy and pollution in urban areas can establish distinct microclimates, influencing a number of climatic parameters (see comments below on the urban heat island).

**Table 3.3 Altitudinal variation of climatic parameters, from Taylor (1976) and Smith (1976)**

| Climatic parameter | Season | Direction of change | Approximate rate of change per 100m rise in altitude |
|---|---|---|---|
| Rainfall | | Increase | 100 mm per year |
| Mean temperature | | Decrease | 0.6°C |
| Maximum temperature | | Decrease | 0.7°C |
| Minimum temperature | | Decrease | 0.5°C |
| Wind | | Increase | 20–30% |
| Sunshine | January | Decrease | 0.11 hday$^{-1}$ |
| | July | Decrease | 0.21 hday$^{-1}$ |
| Soil temperatures | January | Decrease | 0.25°C |
| (at 30 cm depth) | July | Decrease | 0.85°C |
| Accumulated temperature | May–Oct | Decrease | 100–110 |
| (degree days above 10°C) | | | |
| Solar radiation | January | Decrease | 1.7 mWh$^{-1}$ cm$^{-2}$ |
| | July | Decrease | 6.9 mWh$^{-1}$ cm$^{-2}$ |
| Potential transpiration | Winter | Decrease | 10 mm |
| | Summer | Decrease | 17.5 mm |
| Soil moisture deficit | | Decrease | 20–25 mm |
| Growing season | | Decrease | 20–25 days |
| (days when temperature at 30 cm depth is above 6°C) | | | |

## PRECIPITATION

### Rainfall

West–east variations in climate can be identified using data from three long-term climatic stations: Shawbury (72m above sea level, SJ545224) in Shropshire, west of the region; Edgbaston (163 m, SP055845) in the centre of the urban area of Birmingham; and Elmdon (Birmingham Airport) (94 m, SP170835) on the eastern boundary. Variation in mean monthly rainfall at these stations is shown in Figure 3.3.

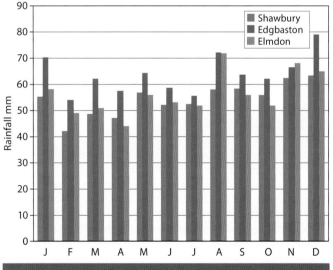

▲ Figure 3.3 Mean monthly rainfall 1961–1990 at Shawbury, Edgbaston and Elmdon climatological stations

Average rainfall at Shawbury is less than Edgbaston throughout the year. Although the majority of the rain-bearing winds come from the west, Shawbury is in the rain shadow of the Cambrian Mountains. Rising from the Severn valley, westerly-dominated rainfall increases again on the western slopes, mainly in winter, reaching a maximum on the main watershed, the Sedgely-Dudley-Quinton ridge. Although Edgbaston is just in the lee, rainstorms are often carried over the ridge. In summer, average rainfall in the region is controlled by the relief and the semi-continental influences of Central England, resulting in increased convectional rainfall. Eastwards, rainfall decreases again at Elmdon, except in August when semi-continental influences are similar to those at Edgbaston.

Using mean annual precipitation (1941–70) for rainfall stations in both the Severn and Trent Catchments (Environment Agency 2008), a positive association between precipitation and altitude can be found for both catchments (Figure 3.4).

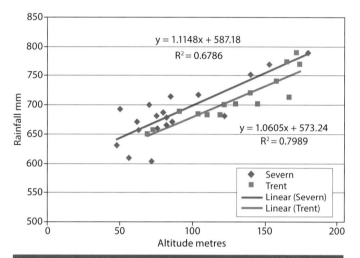

▲ Figure 3.4 Relationship between rainfall and altitude in the Severn and Trent Basins

Separate regression lines calculated from data for the Severn and Trent stations identify the following differences between the western Severn flank and the eastern Trent flank of the watershed:

(a) The base rainfall (theoretical rainfall at sea level) in the Severn is greater than in the Trent.

(b) The rate of increase with height, i.e. the slope of the regression lines, is steeper in the Severn. Although the westerly rain-bearing winds have crossed the Cambrian Mountains, the relatively rapid rise in altitude from the Severn valley to the watershed ridge leads to increased precipitation, leaving the Trent catchment a partial rain shadow area.

(c) The correlation confidence is better for the Severn stations because of the dominance of the westerly origins of rainfall, compared with the more continental influences in the Trent catchment, which result in more convectional storms that are statistically more variable. The increase in precipitation with altitude in the Severn catchment is 111mm per 100m compared with 106mm per 100m in the Trent Catchment.

A number of isohyet maps (showing lines of equal rainfall) of mean annual precipitation have been published (Saward, 1950; Meteorological Office, 1990). Although these maps identify the general rainfall pattern in the region and in particular show the highest level of precipitation along the watershed ridge, they are not at a sufficient scale for comparison on a 1km grid scale. Therefore, using the mean relief of each 1km grid square (monad)

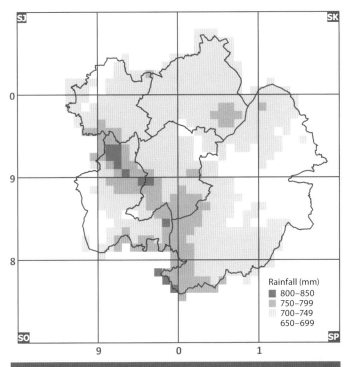

**▲ Figure 3.5 Average annual rainfall in each monad, using the regression analysis in Figure 3.4**

and the regression equations for the Severn and Trent catchments, precipitation values have been calculated on a 1km grid square resolution (Figure 3.5). Where a monad straddles the watershed, the mean value between the Severn and Trent calculation has been used.

The rainfall distribution on the 1 km grid distinguishes highest precipitation (750–850 mm) on the main watershed and lowest rainfall (less than 700 mm) in the Tame/Rea, Smestow/Stour and Penk river valleys.

Matthews (1972) in a study of Midland weather stations, found a relationship between rainfall intensity and synoptic (regionally generalised) type. At Elmdon, 83.3% of the rainfall came from cyclonic westerlies but the heaviest rainfall intensity was from thunderstorms with an occurrence of only 1.2% (Table 3.4).

**Table 3.4 Variation of precipitation intensities (mm h⁻¹) with synoptic type at Elmdon for 1956 and 1960, simplified from Matthews (1972)**

| Synoptic type | Mean rainfall intensities mm h$^{-1}$ | % frequency of each category |
|---|---|---|
| Cyclonic | 1.2 | 83.3 |
| Polar Maritime from NW | 1.6 | 13.9 |
| Polar Continental from NE | 0.5 | 1.3 |
| Arctic from N | 0.5 | 0.5 |
| Thunderstorms | 7.4 | 1.2 |

**Fog**

Pollution from combustion in the urban areas of B&BC modifies the thermal properties of the atmosphere by reducing sunlight and providing condensation nuclei (Mitchell and Searle 2004). Pollutants are composed of suspended particulates such as carbon, and industrial and domestic gases such as sulphur dioxide, carbon monoxide, hydrocarbons, nitrogen oxides and ozone.

Pollutants mainly concentrate in stable atmospheric conditions as a result of calm conditions, minimal vertical turbulence, high relative humidity, vertical temperature inversions and localised proximity to factories or dense housing. Although particulates reduce incoming insolation (a measure of solar radiation energy) and sunshine, they absorb radiation, leading to warming of urban air. Furthermore, particulates provide condensation nuclei leading to increases in the frequency of urban fogs.

Unsworth *et al.* (1979) examine the frequency of fog in the Midlands by comparing Edgbaston Climatological Station with rural stations at Newport (Shropshire) and Sutton Bonington (Nottinghamshire), showing the effects of the Clean Air Act 1956.

**Table 3.5 Mean annual incidences of fog before and after the Clean Air Act (1956) (after Unsworth, 1979)**

| Site | Winter fog frequency (days/year) | |
|---|---|---|
| | 1936–55 | 1956–75 |
| Sutton Bonington | 30.0 | 17.2 |
| Newport | 14.6 | 11.4 |
| Birmingham (Edgbaston) | 31.3 | 21.4 |

More fogs occurred at Edgbaston than at Newport because of the urban influence at the former site. Extra fogs decreased from a peak 40 per year in 1941 to about 5 per year in 1970 due to the improvement in air quality. Although smoke concentration from coal combustion continued to fall, fogs have tended to start increasing again, attributable to the increase in particulate matter from diesel exhausts (Mitchell and Searle, 2004).

## TEMPERATURE

The variation between urban and rural stations is clearly shown by the differences in minimum temperatures, with Shawbury and Elmdon almost identical, and Edgbaston in the centre of the urban conurbation 1–2°C warmer throughout the year, with the greatest difference in winter (Figure 3.6). Although all three stations have similar maximum temperatures in summer, in early and later

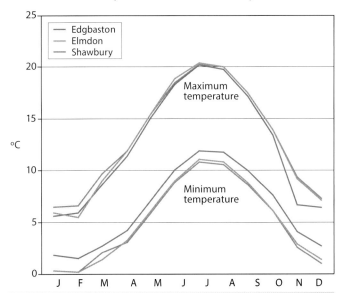

**▲ Figure 3.6 Mean monthly maximum and minimum temperatures for Edgbaston, Elmdon and Shawbury**

periods of the year the rural stations have higher maximum temperature with Edgbaston 1–2°C cooler.

From the Agroclimatic Region 20, using the mean January and July air temperatures at an average height of 121m and standard lapse rate 0.6°C/100 m, January and July temperature maps have been generated at a 1 km resolution using the mean height of each monad (Figures 3.7 and 3.8).

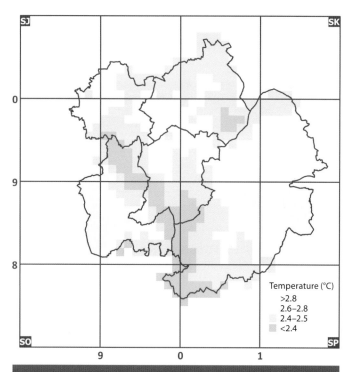

Temperature (°C)
>2.8
2.6–2.8
2.4–2.5
<2.4

▲ Figure 3.7 Mean January temperatures

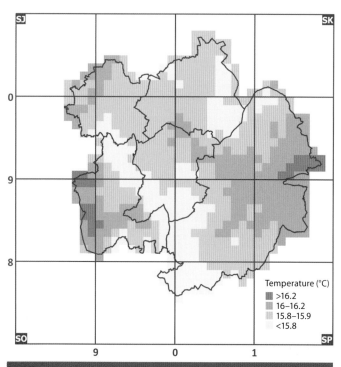

Temperature (°C)
>16.2
16–16.2
15.8–15.9
<15.8

▲ Figure 3.8 Estimated mean July temperatures (not corrected for heat island effects, see Figure 3.9)

## The urban heat island effect

Urban areas develop their own microclimate, particularly in temperature modification, which is known as the urban heat island effect. Howard (1833) was the first scientist to observe that city temperatures were mostly higher than rural ones. The urban heat island effect varies according to meteorological conditions and urban characteristics. Moving from a rural area, the boundary with the urban area causes a steep temperature gradient which can be as much as 4°C km$^{-1}$. The suburban and commercial districts tend to have a relatively constant temperature varying according to the proximity of parks and lakes (cooler) and increased density of buildings (warmer). The greatest intensity of the heat island is found in the city centre dominated by tall buildings and high-density development. During stable synoptic conditions, such as high pressure, the heat island intensity varies diurnally with a maximum a few hours after sunset and minimum at midday. Intensity of the heat island effect is related to the population size of the city, and even small settlements with populations of 1000 generate a heat island (Oke, 1973).

Oke hypothesised seven possible 'causes' for the canopy-layer heat island, the relative impact of which varies with seasons, urban land use and urban structure:

1. Increased counter-radiation due to absorption of outgoing long-wave radiation and re-emission by polluted urban atmosphere
2. Decreased net long-wave radiation loss from 'canyons' due to a reduction in their sky view factor by buildings
3. Greater short-wave radiation absorption due to the effect of 'canyon' geometry on the albedo
4. Greater daytime heat storage due to the thermal properties of urban materials and nocturnal release
5. Anthropogenic heat from building sides
6. Decreased evaporation due to the removal of vegetation and surface 'waterproofing' of the city
7. Decreased loss of sensible heat due to the reduction of wind speed in the canopy.

Chandler (1967), measuring night-time temperatures in Leicester during stable synoptic conditions in August 1966, found that local urban form was more relevant than city size in determining urban temperature anomalies on calm, clear nights. Differences in heat island intensities for similar housing densities were the same for Leicester, 8km (5 miles) across, and London, 40km (25 miles) across. With minimal combustion during August he considered that the heat island was mainly generated by thermal and wind effects of buildings, especially their high thermal capacity, surface area and group geometry. The thermal lag of urban materials and the trapping of warm air between buildings increased the temperatures in the densest urban zones by up to 5°C.

Using maximum and minimum air temperature data for Edgbaston, an urban station, and Elmdon, a rural station, for the period 1965–74, Unwin (1980), compared mean (Table 3.6), seasonal and synoptic variations between the two stations. He concluded that a nocturnal minimum heat island effect is a regular feature in Birmingham, especially in spring and autumn in stable anticyclonic conditions, with urban temperature as much as 5°C greater than those in rural areas. Although not so prominent, he found that urban day-time temperatures were colder than in rural areas, especially in spring and summer. Using the data he calculated the frequency of each of four heat island types (Table 3.7).

**Table 3.6 Mean temperatures in °C for Edgbaston and Elmdon 1965–74 (Unwin, 1980)**

|  | Edgbaston (urban) | Elmdon (rural) | Difference $T_{(urban-rural)}$ |
|---|---|---|---|
| Mean | 9.49 | 9.22 | 0.27 |
| Mean maximum | 12.41 | 12.90 | -0.49 |
| Mean minimum | 6.56 | 5.54 | 1.02 |

**Table 3.7 Temperature differences between urban and rural areas for each heat island type (Unwin, 1980)**

| Type | Higher daytime temperature | Higher nocturnal temperature | No of recordings in Birmingham | % |
|---|---|---|---|---|
| 1 | Rural | Urban | 1964 | 54 |
| 2 | Urban | Urban | 507 | 14 |
| 3 | Rural | Rural | 1054 | 29 |
| 4 | Urban | Rural | 123 | 3 |

Most studies of the heat island effect have been carried out for individual city units, many of which are located in valley lowlands. In the case of B&BC there are a number of separate urban centres within the conurbation; historically these settlements developed from small isolated centres, which have now amalgamated into a mixed urban area with large tracts of open space. Theoretically each of the historical nucleated settlements has its own heat island. Furthermore, unlike in many of the major cities, some of these centres are located on higher plateaux, so air temperatures are reduced due to the altitudinal lapse rate.

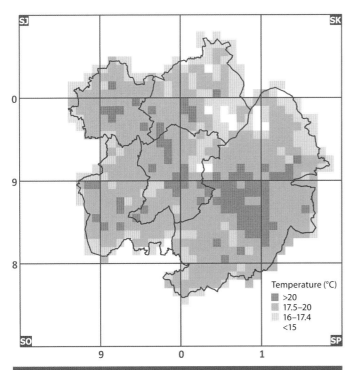

▲ **Figure 3.9 Mean July temperatures corrected for heat island effect**

Johnson (1985) took temperature readings along a 20km route from the centre of Birmingham south-west to Holy Cross (Worcestershire) and used thermograph records from Elmdon Airport and Edgbaston. The urban area had smaller heating and cooling rates of increase, diminishing towards the city centre with a steep gradient in the rate at the urban boundary. The greatest differences occurred at sunrise and sunset, with rural sites heating rapidly after sunrise, causing the urban heat island to decay. Two causes are associated with the urban cooling rate: an increased upward heat flux to the air from heat stored in urban surfaces by day, and a difference in long-wave radiation due to reduction in sky-view factors associated with the dense geometrical configuration of the city buildings.

To evaluate the potential areal influence of the heat island effect the air temperature map for July (Figure 3.8) has been re-generated to take into account the combined residential and non-residential density in each monad scaled up to a maximum of 5°C for the most dense zones (Figure 3.9). The resulting map shows an extensive area of central Birmingham and the numerous small centres of the surrounding urban settlements dominating the temperatures, drowning out the relief effects occurring in Figure 3.8. This urban warmth leads to earlier budding and flowering of flowers and trees in urban areas, with, generally, a longer growing season.

### Frosts

The Midlands are subjected to frost due to radiational cooling and drainage of cold air, especially on dry sandy soils. Frost can occur as late as May and as early as September, leading to a short frost-free period. Shawbury, in a frost pocket, can experience as many as 123 ground frosts and 62 air frosts a year, while for Elmdon the averages are 109 and 50 respectively (Kings and Giles, 1997). Excluding the winters of 2008, 2009 and 2010 there has been a recent trend of warmer, wetter winters with reduced incidence of frost. As a result some plant species can continue to grow and flower throughout the year. Furthermore, urban areas are less prone to frosts than rural areas. The increased warmth of urban areas due to the heat island effect notably reduces the occurrence of frosts. In rural areas prominent 'frost pockets' occur but the converse can occur within urban areas where 'frost-free pockets' can be found due to the heat island effect.

### POTENTIAL TRANSPIRATION[1]

The concept of and equations for potential transpiration were introduced by Penman (1948) as the water transpired by a complete cover of short green grass, which has an ample supply of soil moisture. Using the mean annual potential transpiration at an average height of 121m from Agroclimatic Region 20 and the standard lapse rate of 13.73mm /100m, a Potential Transpiration Map (Figure 3.10) has been generated at 1km resolution using the mean height of each monad. The measurement estimates the amount of transpiration possible if moisture is available, but if there is a moisture deficit, transpiration decreases, becoming actual transpiration, which is difficult to measure.

As expected, the greatest potential transpiration is in the valleys. These wetter river lowlands will also have a tendency

---

[1] Transpiration is the evaporation of water into the atmosphere from the leaves and stems of plants.

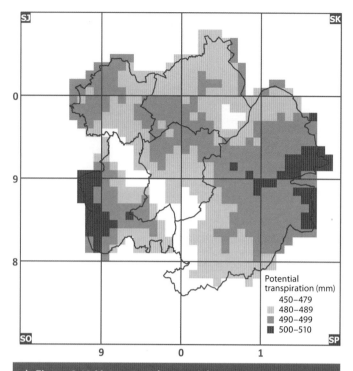

▲ Figure 3.10 Mean annual potential transpiration

to maintain soil moisture levels longer than the drier higher watershed. Furthermore, parts of the watershed are composed of limestone rocks which have reduced soil moisture levels.

## CLIMATIC TRENDS

There have been major changes in the vegetation since the last Ice Age, known as the Smestow Advance, which decayed from a line across the region approximately 10,000 years ago. At present we are in the Sub-Atlantic period, characterised by a natural vegetation of deciduous woodland. Shifts in bioclimates normally take a long time, but the current problem of anthropogenic-enhanced global warming may cause an acceleration in botanical changes. The flora has been surveyed in a snapshot of any changes taking place, so it is useful to examine current climatic trends and to consider some of the implications on species.

Using data from historical sources and from University of Birmingham weather stations, Giles and Kings (1996) derived rainfall and temperature series for Birmingham from 1790 to 2000. Using this published data, a mean decadal rainfall amount (i.e. the annual rainfall averaged over ten years) was plotted against the mid-decadal point (Figure 3.11).

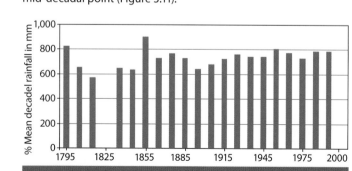

▲ Figure 3.11 Mean decadal rainfall based on data from Giles and Kings (1996)

Although the two wettest decades were from 1791 to 1800 and from 1851 to 1860, the trend since 1900 shows a gradual increase in annual rainfall. Percentages of total annual rainfall occurring in winter (December, January and February) and summer (June, July and August) were also plotted using the same data set (Figure 3.12).

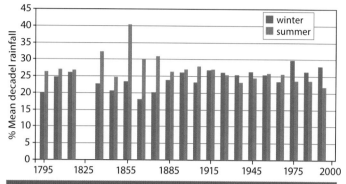

▲ Figure 3.12 Percentage of total annual rainfall occurring in winter and summer based on data from Giles and Kings (1996)

The results show that up to 1900 percentage summer decadal rainfall was always greater than percentage winter rainfall, with noticeable variability in values which may have been related to cold dry winters and summer convectional storms. Since 1900, percentage winter rainfall has been greater than summer values except for two decades, 1951–1960 and 1961–1970, when values were similar. This trend supports the national pattern of wetter, warmer winters associated with features of climate change in Britain. It is also noticeable that the last three decades of the data (1971–2000) have the largest percentages of winter rainfall. Years with average rainfall will not normally affect plant growth, but exceptionally wet or dry years may influence species. Above-average rainfall in spring and early summer may result in rapid growth of some species, crowding out others, while below-average rainfall in a similar period can result in moisture stress, allowing other species to flourish. This latter condition can be accentuated during spring and early summer droughts, particularly in the eastern Tame-Rea lowlands. During the "one-in-a-thousand years" drought of 1975–76, the eastern part of the region had a high drought intensity index similar to that for south-east England (Doornkamp et al., 1980).

Mean decadal January and July temperatures were also plotted to show trends (Figures 3.13 and 3.14). Mean January temperatures show a definite warming trend, while mean summer temperatures show no significant changes over the 200 years of data. Mean

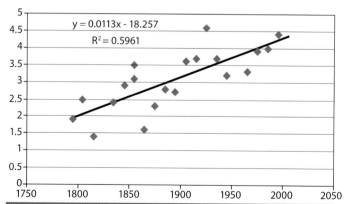

▲ Figure 3.13 Mean decadal January temperatures based on data from Giles and Kings (1996)

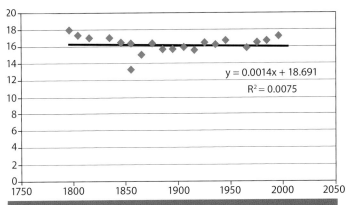

▲ **Figure 3.14 Mean decadal July temperatures based on data from Giles and Kings (1996)**

$$y = 0.0014x + 18.691$$
$$R^2 = 0.0075$$

January temperatures have increased from a minimum 1.4°C (1811–1820) to maxima of 4.6°C (1921–30) and 4.4°C (1991–2000), while summer temperatures are unaltered, possibly due to the masking effects of the influence of increased urbanisation in the conurbation and changes to the industrial landscape.

The results from species monitoring can be directly affected by the climate, particularly temperature. Variations in temperature can affect the occurrence, density and phenology (including flowering dates) of species, so monitoring the same monad on different occasions (year or season) may produce different results. In addition to these year-to-year or season-to-season changes, species variation may respond to climatic change.

The Central England Temperatures series (Manley, 1974; Parker and Horton, 2005) is the longest continuous temperature record in existence, beginning in 1659. This series enables the recent monitoring period to be placed into context and also enables the identification of climatic trends. In the twelve-year period, the earliest years (2000 and 2001) were near average. In the middle period (January 2002 to August 2008), 71 months out of 80 months were noticeably warmer than the long-term average. This period included 2006, which had the highest annual mean temperature of 10.82°C, making it the warmest year of the 348-year series, and the mean July temperature of 19.7 °C in the same year was the hottest in the series. The later years, from September 2008, were noticeably cooler, with three successive cold winters. These different climatic periods could have an impact on the survival of perennial species. In the warm periods species would have survived and continued to grow through the year while, in contrast, consecutive severe winters would have had a deleterious effect on some species.

Warm temperatures can be correlated with hours of sunshine, which have been recorded in Central England since 1929. The sunniest summer since that date was in 2003. Warming in Central England in the 20th century has resulted in lengthening the thermal growing season by about one month, mainly as a result of the early onset of spring. In the same period annual sunshine hours have increased from 1400 to 1500 hours.

The collection of phenological observations in the past were regarded as of interest but not as having scientific value, but in recent years phenological trends have been used as a measure of climatic change, especially the first flowering dates of target species. Correlation between phenological records, especially early flowering dates and temperature records, has been used to assess changes (Tooke and Battey, 2010). Using Central England Temperatures and dates of first flowering of 385 plant species, Fitter and Fitter (2002) found that dates on average were 4.5 days earlier than in the previous four decades, but that little had changed before 1960. Comparing the 58-year British phenological network (Royal Meteorological Society) with Central England Temperatures, Sparks *et al.* (2000) suggested flowering advances of 2–10 days per 1°C rise in temperature. Again using Central England Temperatures, a longer statistical analysis was made by Amano *et al.* (2010). They used records for 405 plant species over a 250-year period and found that flowering advanced 5 days for every degree rise in temperature; they furthermore found that this rise correlated with the mean temperatures from February to March. This research supports the effect of warmer spring temperatures. Fitter and Fitter (2002) concluded that these responses did not apply to all species. They consider that annuals are more likely to flower early than congeneric perennials, and insect-pollinated species earlier than wind-pollinated species. A more local phenological study was carried out by Anne Phillips in Walsall from 1976 to 2009 (cited by Sparks, 2009). She found 58.8% of the events showed a significant response to warmer temperatures, and that 76.4% significantly related to the temperatures of the three preceding months. All events, which included other taxonomic groups than plants, showed on average 8 days' advancement per 1°C rise in temperature. It is important to remember that many flowering plants respond to day length, which is unaltered, unlike temperature trends.

# Section 3 • Relief, drainage and soils by John Gerrard

## INTRODUCTION

As noted in Section 1, relief, drainage and soil development have been determined largely by the nature of the rocks as acted upon by erosion and deposition over a long period of time. Landforms and topography are the result of the interaction between what can be called the driving and resisting forces in the landscape. The driving forces are the processes by which energy is exerted on the earth materials, and include both surface processes, such as weathering and erosion, and sub-surface geological processes. The resisting forces are the surface materials, with their strengths and weaknesses determined by highly variable physical and chemical properties. The landscape reflects this interaction, as may be seen by looking either southwards and westwards from Barr Beacon, or eastwards from Turners Hill, although obscured by the built-up conurbation. In the following account, the description and analysis of relief and drainage occasionally strays outside the strict delineation of the region under consideration: the physical landscape rarely follows arbitrary human boundaries.

## DRAINAGE CHARACTERISTICS

The drainage systems rise on the main watershed of England and have cut into the plateau-like surface of much of the West Midlands. This watershed separates the Trent and Severn drainage basins (section 3.1 and 3.2; Figure 3.2 page 95), and follows the Sedgley-Northfield Ridge and Clent-Lickey Hills. It also separates the comparatively gently sloping area leading to the River Tame in the east from the steep slopes of the Upper Stour Valley to the west. The ridge and watershed can be seen clearly on the map of maximum altitude, stretching from north-west to south-east in the west of the region (Figure 3.15).

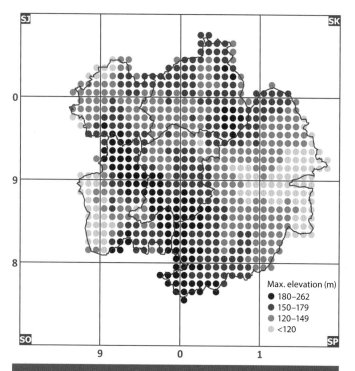

▲ Figure 3.15 Distribution of maximum elevation

The drainage pattern of the River Tame dominates the area which is clearly divided into two main components, separated by a comparatively large area with few rivers and streams. The main part of the system flows south and east through the Wolverhampton and Walsall area. The Birmingham area is dominated by the tributaries of the Rivers Rea and Cole, although the Cole joins the Tame after joining the River Blythe, outside our region. The many drainage systems are clearly visible in the pattern of river alluvium shown on the map of geology (Figure 3.1 page 92).

Drainage density is generally low, especially in the Upper Tame area. One way of assessing drainage density is to measure the number of stream courses in each monad as represented on Ordnance Survey 1:50,000 maps (Gerrard 1996a). Large areas of the region possess no or few stream courses: over 20% of the monads possess no stream courses and 40% possess only one stream. Less than 2% possesses four or more stream courses. This paucity of stream courses means that the degree of dissection is slight, reflected in the relief characteristics.

## RELIEF CHARACTERISTICS

The main relief units described here follow closely the subdivision and terminology of Warwick (1950). In places the boundaries between units are somewhat arbitrary and generalised, but the subdivision does represent the relief units of the area quite clearly and are visually evident from the Barr Beacon and Turners Hill vantage points. The statistics used in this account are again derived from the analysis of monads.

Three main relief elements occur in the landscape and generally trend approximately north to south or north-west to south-east, decreasing in elevation from west to east. The Sedgley-Northfield Ridge and Clent-Lickey Hills in the west mostly have elevations above 200m. In the centre of the region is a general plateau-like area, with elevations ranging from 150m to 200m, dissected by the River Tame and its tributaries. In the east the Lower Tame Valley widens, with elevations of 100m to 150m. The central plateau has been divided into two by the incision of the River Rea and its tributaries. This pattern can be seen in the map of maximum elevation (Figure 3.15).

The Sedgley-Northfield Ridge, as noted, separates the Trent and Severn drainage systems. Its highest point is 271m at Turners Hill. The Ridge varies in elevation from 180m to 271m, with a mean maximum elevation of 241m. The link between geology and topography is clear. The Ridge is mostly composed of Silurian limestones and shales intruded with the hard dolerite noted in the geodiversity section. Turners Hill is formed of this dolerite. The prominence of Rowley Hill has also been influenced by dolerite. South of Quinton, the Ridge narrows at Frankley Beeches, then broadens out and becomes dissected by the River Rea.

The Clent-Lickey Ridge, only a small part of which lies in our region, is nevertheless an important physical feature. As Britain's climate is dominated mostly by westerly depressions, the Ridge tends to form a climatic barrier. The upper tributaries of the River Rea also rise on its eastern flanks. The Ridge contains the highest land in the area, 316m at Walton Hill. Because of the way the Ridge has been dissected by the river systems, in terms of mean maximum elevation (231m) it does not appear as high as the Sedgley-Northfield Ridge, but this is misleading and it ranges in height from 165m to 316m. In this respect the map of mean elevation (Figure 3.16) is more revealing.

The Upper Tame Valley, the boundaries of which are not as clear as for some of the other units, is essentially the area between Wolverhampton and Walsall centres. It possesses an average maximum elevation of 150m with a modal group of 135m. It is a very uniform area as indicated by the very high percentage

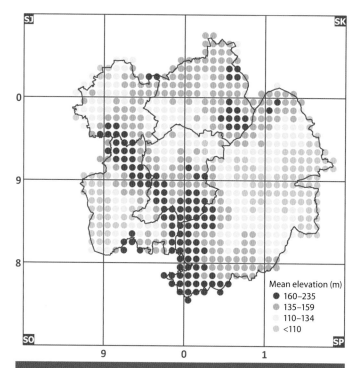

▲ Figure 3.16 Distribution of mean elevation

(41%) of values in the modal elevation group. The area has been dissected by the major upper tributaries of the River Tame into a landscape of low hills and ridges. Many of these hills and ridges are capped with glacial deposits, and many of the towns of the Black Country, such as Wednesbury and Darlaston, are situated on such hills.

Much of the City of Birmingham is built on what has been called the West Bromwich-Harborne Plateau. Although largely obscured by buildings, the edge of the Plateau can be seen by the drop from Birmingham City Centre to Digbeth, where the lower land of the River Rea's former floodplain is reached. Even if it is difficult to visualise it as a plateau, the elevation data show that its name is well deserved. The average maximum elevation is 177m, with 45% of the monad values within the modal group of 150m. The Solihull Plateau, largely outside the region, is an extension of the West Bromwich-Harborne Plateau, but separated from it by the Rivers Rea and Cole. The northern edge of the Solihull Plateau is dissected by the River Cole and its tributaries and is largely covered by the southern suburbs of Birmingham. It possesses a slightly lower maximum elevation than the West Bromwich-Harborne Plateau, with mean maximum elevation of 145m.

The plateau-like topography is also found in the north of the region with a small part of the South Cannock Plateau and the Sutton Plateau. The small area of the South Cannock Plateau occurs in the north-west of the region, with most of the land between 120m and 180m in elevation. Its western edge is drained by the River Penk north to the River Trent and to the south by the tributaries of the Upper Tame. Much of the Sutton Plateau is similar in elevation to the West Bromwich-Harborne Plateau. In an evolutionary sense it is probably part of the same geomorphological surface. It is almost impossible to separate it from the West Bromwich-Harborne Plateau in terms of maximum elevation with a value of 175m. Its southern edge slopes towards the Middle and Upper Tame Valley. There is a conspicuous north-south ridge on its western edge stretching from Shire Oak to Queslett, with the high point of Barr Beacon composed of Triassic pebble beds.

The Middle Tame valley is separated from the Upper Tame by a narrow valley between West Bromwich and Great Barr. Until the Rivers Rea, Tame and Cole were controlled, the floodplains were often inundated. The Middle Tame Valley area is generally at a maximum elevation of 120m, occasionally rising to just over 165m.

## RELIEF ANALYSIS

A general description of topography provides only a simplistic picture of the region. Individual habitats, including soil types, are more closely related to angles, aspect and position on specific slopes. To this effect a number of topographic indicators have been derived, again based on analysis of monads (Gerrard, 1996b). The indices calculated were maximum slope angles, relative relief and ruggedness. Maximum slope angle in a monad is defined as the minimum contour spacing. A contour spacing of 1mm represents an average slope of 13.5° and 2mm represents 6.75° on a 1:50,000 Ordnance Survey map. Relative relief represents the difference between maximum and minimum elevation in a monad, and ruggedness is defined as the number of contours crossing the four edges of the monad. Although these indices can be criticised by being somewhat subjective, they are consistent and so do provide a way to compare and contrast the characteristics of the main relief units.

## Maximum slope angle

The values quoted here are bound to be minimum values of maximum steepness as there will probably be areas of steeper slopes not identified at this scale and contour interval. As there is usually, but not always, a relationship between elevation and slope angle, the west of the region tends to be dominated by steep slopes, with gentler slopes to the east and in the main valley basins. However, there are smaller areas of steep slopes related to localised incision by streams. The boundaries between plateaux and river systems are also marked by steeper slopes. A frequency distribution of angles shows a clear bimodality, which reflects general level plateau areas and incised valley slopes. Average values of maximum slope angles are therefore meaningless. Slightly over 25% of the monads possess moderate steep slopes (greater than 6.75°) while approximately 25% possess extremely gentle slopes. The Clent-Lickey Ridge possesses the highest maximum slope angles. The Sedgley-Northfield Ridge also possesses a high proportion of steep slopes. The majority of the topographic units possess intermediate slope angle values with some high but, in general, comparatively low maximum slope angles. The units with the lowest slope angles are the Upper, Middle and Lower Tame and the Rea and Cole valleys.

## Relative relief

The pattern of relative relief is much simpler than that of maximum slope angles and can be visualised by comparing the distribution of maximum elevation (Figure 3.15) with that of minimum elevation (Figure 3.17). There is a concentration of high values in the west and of low values in the major river valleys and in the east. The Sedgley-Northfield Ridge possesses the highest average values. Most topographic units possess intermediate relative relief, with areas around the Lower Tame Valley possessing the lowest values. The West Bromwich-Harborne Plateau appears as more dissected than the other plateaux, such as the South

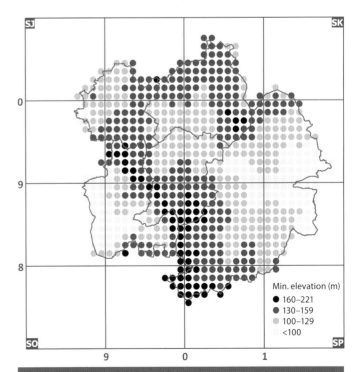

▲ **Figure 3.17 Distribution of minimum elevation**

Cannock and Sutton Plateaux. This probably represents the level of incision achieved by the Rivers Rea and Cole.

**Ruggedness**

There is a similar pattern with ruggedness, with high ruggedness values in the west and low values in the central and eastern areas. However, apart from the Sedgley-Northfield and Clent-Lickey Ridges, there is less differentiation over the rest of the region, although there are subtle differences between the plateaux, with the West Bromwich-Harborne Plateau again being more rugged than the others.

## SOILS

The classic equation for soil formation involves the five factors of climate, biota (organisms), topography (relief), parent material and time. However, many soil scientists have recently argued that a sixth soil factor, human activity, should be added. Although human activity will affect the five original factors, the presence of a sixth factor emphasises the role that human activity has in modifying existing soils and even creating new ones.

All soils in urban areas are affected by human intervention (Bullock and Gregory, 1991). At one extreme are anthropomorphic soils where the main soil-forming factor is human influence, while at the other extreme are natural soils that have been used by humans but have received inputs of contaminated dust or precipitation, an example of which would be salt spray from roads. Processes in such soils differ greatly from those in rural areas. Contaminant loads can be quite high, and parent materials are diverse and often of extreme chemical composition (Rossiter, 2007). Soils from technical materials, such as industrial wastes, often experience rapid weathering, unlike natural soils. The importance of soils in urban areas was recognised by the establishment of an International Union of Soil Sciences working group 'Soils of Urban, Industrial, Traffic and Mining areas' in 1998.

Ideally soils should reflect, in some measure, underlying parent materials and topography. Loamy and clayey floodplain soils are evident in our region, but many of these will have been artificially drained and have had the properties altered. The pattern follows closely the geological diversity discussed in Section 3.1. The majority of soils are slightly acid and loamy, apart from sandy (often podzolised) soils in areas such as Sutton Park, and patches of more alkaline soils associated with the small limestone outcrops.

However, as indicated, this is a largely unrealistic pattern. The relatively new World Resource Base for Soil Resources has introduced a new Reference Soil Group, Technosols. The central concept is the dominance of soil properties and factors by technical human activity as shown by the substantial presence of artefacts, materials created or modified by gardens, industrial or other activity, a nearly continuous impermeable geomembrane, called a liner, or technical hard rock, such as pavements and roads. The generally high prevalence of hard surfaces in built-up areas demonstrates why this classification is significant for B&BC. Even apparently significant areas of amenity grassland would have had their soil properties affected by drainage, fertiliser applications, and input from solid particulate matter and rain water. In the soil classification scheme, mentioned above, qualifiers have been introduced to indicate some of these effects, such as 'Densic' for soils with strong compaction.

This all means that, although there are undoubted relationships between flora and soil types and properties, these are very difficult to establish at a one-kilometre scale, and therefore only very general statements can be made. However, it also emphasises that standard soil surveys are probably inappropriate for urban areas. Parent material has been changed, topburden and soils have been transported from one area to another, topography and drainage have been modified, and even the local climate altered. Urban areas are diverse, exhibit rapid change and defy simple analysis.

# Section 4 · Hydrology and water quality by David J.Mitchell

## INTRODUCTION

The hydrology of the river basins is important for the aquatic and wetland species along the stream courses and for moisture levels in the valley bottoms. Furthermore, local water quality conditions may restrict or enhance certain species. The water balance, which compares inputs and outputs, may be estimated using the following simplified equation: Precipitation = Runoff + Evapotranspiration. Using the data from rainfall (Figure 3.5, page 97) and potential transpiration (Figure 3.10, page 100) gives an approximation of runoff with a square kilometre resolution for the region (Figure 3.18). Within the river basins there are other controls which either decrease or increase runoff. Different rock types affect permeability: for example, the Coal Measures of the Black Country are impervious, while the limestones and sandstones are permeable. Within the built-up area the effects of the geological substrates are nullified by the extent of artificial surfaces and the network of storm drains.

As shown in Figure 3.2 (page 95) the main watershed of England crosses the region (see also sections 3.1 and 3.3). To the west of this divide the main rivers are Smestow Brook and the River Stour, which drain into the River Severn and hence to the Bristol Channel. To the east the main rivers are the Tame, Cole, Rea and Penk, which join the River Trent, and drain into the Humber Estuary. The water balance map (Figure 3.18) shows that the greatest runoff (the excess of rainfall over potential transpiration) occurs on the divide and the Walsall plateau.

## WATER QUALITY

The poor water quality of the rivers of B&BC has been problematic because of the location of residential and industrial areas within the catchments. In most cases in Great Britain industrial towns are located in the lower courses of rivers so that high quality water available from headwaters of the catchments can contribute to the cleansing of the lower courses. But the situation in B&BC is reversed, with residential and, more seriously, industrial areas located in the headwaters, so that high quality flow is unavailable to neutralise polluted water-courses.

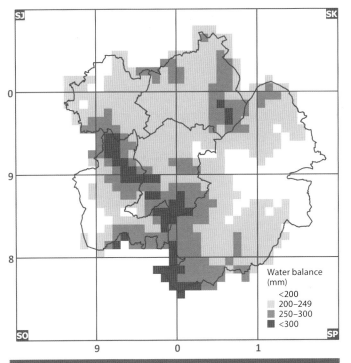

▲ Figure 3.18 Water balance of Birmingham and the Black Country

**Legend:**
Water balance (mm)
- <200
- 200–249
- 250–300
- <300

## River Tame

Before the Industrial Revolution, the River Tame was unpolluted, providing a clean water supply for small scattered hamlets. Later, water was used for washing products and water mills associated with an agricultural community were built, but it was still a high quality trout stream. In the 19th century the conditions of the River Tame and its tributaries declined rapidly with the expansion of coal mining, industrial processes and the unsanitary conditions of residential areas. Continual decline in water quality in the 20th century made the Upper Tame possibly the most polluted system in Britain. From the mid-20th century the Trent River Authority and later the National Rivers Authority and Environment Agency invested in improving the water quality because of increasing demands on the River Trent for water supply. New sewage treatment works were established and purification lakes were built at Lea Marston in the 1980s, which enabled water quality to improve downstream.

Although coal mining has ceased and heavy industries have declined, the Upper Tame still remains highly polluted, but it may no longer be the most polluted in the region. Besides new industries and waste disposal sites, the remnants of the Industrial Revolution such as spoilheaps continue to cause pollution especially when they are disturbed for urban development. Two tributaries join the River Tame near Bescot, a key flow- and quality-monitoring site. The main river, which rises in the Wolverhampton area, is affected by heavy metals from past mining and sewage effluent from Willenhall Sewage Treatment Plant. The Oldbury tributary receives contaminated ground water from a former chemical tip near its source and sewage effluent from Oldbury Sewage Treatment Works, and its tributary, Tipton Brook, discharges further sewage effluent. Flowing through the industrial centre of Walsall, Ford Brook receives sewage effluent from Goscote Sewage Treatment Plant and seepage from an abandoned copper refinery, as well as from clay extraction and brick and tile production. Indicating the vulnerability of the area, a major pollution incident occurred in July 1995 (Picken, 1995). Following

six weeks of hot, dry weather, a series of intense thunderstorms on 10th July washed large volumes of contaminated water into the River Tame. This storm event instantly reduced the dissolved oxygen, causing fish deaths in the Lower Tame and River Trent. Dissolved oxygen fell from 25% saturation to zero at the water quality monitoring station at Lea Marston. The sources of pollution were overflowing sewage systems, runoff from contaminated land, and scouring anoxic sediments (sediments depleted of oxygen) entrained within the river gravels.

## River Stour

Although the River Stour has its source in the Clent Hills, the upper course passes through our urban area. The river has a low natural flow, but receives sewage effluent. During heavy rainfall there is a marked deterioration of water quality due to discharge from storm sewage and contaminated surfaces. In the Cradley and Lye areas, storm discharges still contain high levels of non-ferrous metals, particularly zinc. The source is unknown, but it probably originates from past land disposal of zinc-galvanising waste. There has been recent improvement in water quality, particularly in the Halesowen area of the river, but downstream river quality deteriorates mainly due to the poor quality of the Mousesweet Brook (Environment Agency, 1997).

Smestow Brook, the main tributary of the Stour, rises in Wolverhampton. Although Wolverhampton's main sewage treatment works at Barnhurst is in the Penk Catchment, the works discharge into an adjacent canal which can overflow into Smestow Brook during storm events. This storm effluent from the canal and pollution from Penn Brook together lower the water quality of the Smestow downstream to the confluence with the Stour.

## Water quality monitoring

Since 1988, General Quality Assessment (GQA) has been measured by the Environment Agency on a monthly basis at routine

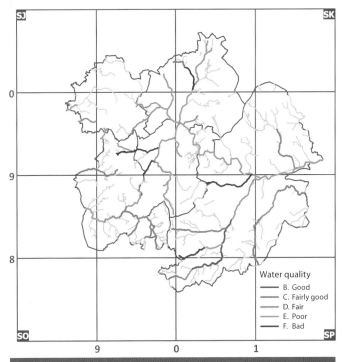

**Water quality**
- B. Good
- C. Fairly good
- D. Fair
- E. Poor
- F. Bad

▲ Figure 3.19 Chemical quality of rivers of B&BC in 1996 adapted from Environment Agency (1998a, 1998b)

**Table 3.8 General Quality Assessment grading for rivers and canals (Environment Agency 1998a, 1998b)**

| Water quality | Grade | Dissolved oxygen (% saturation) 10th percentile | Bio-chemical Oxygen Demand mg/l 90th percentile | Ammonia mgN/l |
|---|---|---|---|---|
| Very Good | A | 80 | 2.5 | 0.25 |
| Good | B | 70 | 4 | 0.6 |
| Fairly Good | C | 60 | 6 | 1.3 |
| Fair | D | 50 | 8 | 2.5 |
| Poor | E | 20 | 15 | 9.0 |
| Bad | F | <20 | >15 | >9 |

sampling points on rivers and canals. The chemical assessment is based on Dissolved Oxygen (DO), Biochemical Oxygen Demand (BOD) and ammonia, so that stretches are classified into six bands (Table 3.8) (Environment Agency, 1998a, 1998b). The grade of a stretch is calculated over three consecutive years from 36 samples. Using these criteria, analysis of the main streams in the region in 1996 has been plotted (Figure 3.19). Results for 1990, 1994 and 1996 for the whole Tame area of the West Midlands show significant improvements in the chemical quality of the Tame, but poor results still remain in some of the headwater streams (Table 3.9).

**Table 3.9 Percentage changes in river water quality in the Tame area according to the General Quality Assessment scheme 1990–1996 (Environment Agency 1998a, 1998b)**

| Water quality | Grade | 1990 % | 1994 % | 1996 % |
|---|---|---|---|---|
| Very Good | A | 0 | 0 | 0 |
| Good | B | 0 | 15 | 22 |
| Fairly Good | C | 10 | 24 | 26 |
| Fair | D | 38 | 18.5 | 12 |
| Poor | E | 34 | 34 | 33.5 |
| Bad | F | 18 | 8.5 | 6.5 |

# Section 5 • Habitats and vegetation by Peter J. Jarvis

## INTRODUCTION

The habitats of B&BC are greatly affected by a wide range of environmental conditions and pressures associated with their urban context, and for this very reason host a number of interesting and often uncommon plant species and communities.

Habitats are mappable arenas within which communities and the physical environment interact in a characteristic and distinctive manner, and are definable in terms of both spatial boundary and the environmental characteristics of the space within that boundary. Habitat is therefore linked with vegetation, which in turn is linked with flora. Habitats often contain a characteristic flora, and the flora of a habitat – given issues of dispersal – depends on the vegetation and physical and chemical characteristics of that habitat, modified by any human activity. Habitat, vegetation and flora are all inextricably linked with land use.

Because a particular habitat is often visually characterised by a particular kind of plant community, many habitat types are described by vegetation type – in general terms, for example, deciduous woodland and tall herb; with more taxonomic implication, for example, heathland, which implies an ericaceous flora as well as a physiognomy (outward morphological appearance) which is that of low shrub; or floristically precise, for instance reedswamp. Other habitat types use a key physical feature such as water – river, canal and pond, for instance, and there are a variety of particularly urban habitats associated with Oliver Gilbert's technological landscape and often associated with buildings, transport and a suite of so-called wasteland sites (urban commons or brownfield sites) (Gilbert, 1989).

Urban landscapes are generally more fragmented and fine-grained than rural areas: habitat parcels tend to be smaller, more densely packed into the landscape, and more varied (Young and Jarvis, 2001a, 2001b). This is important: in examining 22 plant species in parts of Birmingham, Bastin and Thomas (1999) found a significant positive association between the density of habitat patches available and the proportion of these patches that were occupied. Species occupancy tended to increase with, among other things, habitat patch age, patch area and similarity of neighbouring habitats.

Habitat boundaries are not always clear-cut, though they are often more distinct in the built environment where land parcels are precisely delineated with often contrasting adjoining land uses. Ecotones are vegetational transition zones between more distinct habitats and will not only contain some species found in each of the adjacent habitats but may also possess organisms found only within that ecotone.

Many sites change from one habitat type to another as succession and other dynamic vegetation processes take place. Given time and a lack of interference, for instance, an abandoned building site may be colonised by pioneer species which through processes generated by the vegetation itself develop into a tall herb community into which scrub species appear, in turn succeeded by young then mature trees: woodland within a few decades. Most such sites do not survive so long in urban areas, but as existing sites are built upon, for example, new ones are created. Analogous with the idea of a metapopulation, a meta-habitat will in effect have been created – a spatially ever-changing mosaic of a particular habitat type, the non-contiguous components interacting in some way, for example as source and reception sites for pollen (Young and Jarvis, 2001b).

A list of habitats in the built environment will therefore include sites of great antiquity in the landscape – ancient woodlands whose origins lie before 1600, for example – and ones which are ephemeral. Older sites may have a convergent flora that is generally predictable (but which of course will still contain surprises). Younger, especially post-industrial sites at early successional stages, generally contain a less predictable and sometimes unique collection of species. This may be partly because of quasi-random dispersal processes, partly because of often stressful or disturbed environmental conditions, which can lead to a more diverse and varied flora, and partly because of the arrival and establishment of often introduced ornamental species from gardens and gardenesque landscapes. These are ecological recombinations, defined as novel plant associations 'that have been induced or created by people deliberately, inadvertently or indirectly. They are generally made up of various mixes of indigenous or exotic species, but they may also involve associations of indigenous species alone, never before seen in nature' (Meurk, 2010: 198).

Island biogeography theory suggests that, very crudely, increasing the area of a habitat island by an order of magnitude will more or less double the number of species (MacArthur and Wilson, 1967), so site size is important. Small sites (less than the usual survey threshold of 0.5 ha) can nevertheless be ecologically important habitats, not only in themselves but, in particular, by increasing the overall density of green habitat and providing or increasing linkage.

Other aspects of island biogeography theory include linkage, so that habitat corridors might allow more rapid movement of species between otherwise separate sites (though Angold et al. (2006) suggest that such corridors are not important for plants), and isolation, so that the further a habitat is from a similar habitat the less the likelihood of colonisation and the more impoverished the flora. Flora is likely to be most diverse and richest in large metahabitats and in sites that comprise a number of adjoining habitats, for example Sutton Park.

Ancient semi-natural woodland is considered here as a single distinct habitat type, but within any such a woodland there are likely to be a number of floristically important sub-habitats; for example, an old Hazel coppice or an open glade would present different environmental conditions to an area dominated by mature Oak. Microhabitats, too, will contain distinctive floras. Scale, then, is another consideration when looking at habitats, vegetation and flora.

Habitats and vegetation in urban areas are subjected to anthropogenic pressures, encouragements and constraints that should make them amenable to classification along an axis from artificial to semi-natural. Hemeroby, an index of human impact, is defined by Kowarik (1990) as 'the sum of the effects of past and present human activities on the current site conditions or vegetation, which prevent the development to a final stage'. The original use of this concept in an urban context was as a simple heavy/light + frequent/infrequent matrix, associated with trampling and in particular relating to level of soil compaction with consequent effects on vegetation. This has been extended to relate to the general level of human impact and consequent degree of 'naturalness': oligohemeroby (semi-natural, e.g. lightly managed woodland), mesohemeroby (e.g. heathland), euhemeroby (e.g. managed grassland) and polyhemeroby (e.g. pioneer vegetation on railway ballast and rubbish dumps) (Hill, Roy and Thompson, 2002; Ziarnek, 2007).

Because vegetation and habitat are closely related it might be expected that the UK's National Vegetation Classification (NVC) – commissioned by the then Nature Conservancy Council in 1975 to produce a comprehensive classification and description of the country's plant communities (jncc.defra.gov.uk/page-4259) – would show a correspondence with habitat classification. As with the NVC, however, habitat classifications are generally based on the countryside, and are often unhelpful when considered in an urban context (Rodwell, 2000; links to summaries of all NVC habitats are at en.wikipedia.org/wiki/ British_National_ Vegetation_Classification).

A review of habitat mapping in urban areas in connection with planning and nature conservation is provided by Jarvis (2010), and problems associated with relating land classification to habitat types in the region's built environment are considered by Owen et al. (2006). The habitat types and descriptions in this chapter are based on the national habitats of principal importance, together with a handful of locally distinctive habitats, as identified in the Biodiversity Action Plan for B&BC (2000; www.wildlifetrust. org.uk/urbanwt/ecorecord/bap/index.html), but other habitat classifications (particularly that used in Phase 1 surveys) have been incorporated, particularly in the case of the built-up environment. Equivalence of habitat types is shown in Table 3.10.

## Table 3.10 Equivalence of urban habitat in UK BAP and Phase 1 surveys

| Habitats of national (N) and local (L) importance (UK BAP; Biodiversity Action Plan for Birmingham and the Black Country) | Habitats identified in Phase 1 Survey (NCC/EN/NE) |
|---|---|
| WOODLAND<br>Ancient semi-natural woodland (N)<br>Wet woodland (N)<br>Wood pasture and parkland (N) | WOODLAND (A1)<br>Semi-natural and broad-leaved (including earth banks J2.8)<br><br>Parkland and scattered trees (A3) |
| | SCRUB (A2) |
| HEATHLAND<br><br>Lowland heathland (N) | HEATHLAND<br>Dry dwarf shrub heath (D1)<br>Wet dry dwarf shrub heath (D2)<br>Dry heath/acid grassland mosaic (D5)<br>Wet heath/acid grassland mosaic (D6) |
| GRASSLAND<br>Lowland meadow (N)<br>Lowland calcareous grassland (N)<br>Lowland dry acid grassland (N)<br>Purple moor-grass and rush pastures (N)<br>Floodplain grazing marsh (N) | GRASSLAND and MARSH<br><br>Calcareous grassland (B3)<br>Acid grassland (B1)<br><br><br>Marsh/marshy grassland (B5)<br>Neutral grassland (B2)<br>Improved (B4)<br>Poor semi-improved (B6)<br>Amenity (J1.2) |
| WETLAND<br>Mesotrophic lakes (N)<br>Eutrophic standing waters (N)<br>Ponds (N)<br>Reedbed (N)<br><br><br>Lowland fens (N)<br>Lowland raised bog (N)<br>Rivers (N)<br>Canals (L) | WETLAND<br>Standing water (G1)<br><br><br>Swamp (F1)<br>Marginal vegetation (F2.1)<br>Inundation (F2.2)<br><br><br>Running water (G2) |
| FARMLAND<br>Arable field margins (N)<br>Hedgerows (N) | FARMLAND<br><br>Hedges: intact (J2.1); defunct (J22.); with trees (J2.3) |
| BUILT<br>Gardens (L)<br>Parks and public open space (L)<br>Allotments (L)<br>Inland rock outcrops (N)<br>Open mosaic on previously developed land (N) | BUILT<br>Introduced shrub (J1.4)<br><br><br><br>Ephemeral/short perennial (J1.3)<br>Tall herb – ruderal (C3.1)<br>Tall herb – non-ruderal (C3.2)<br>Wall (J2.5)<br>Buildings (J3.6)<br>Bare ground (J4) |

The habitat statement for urban areas in the 1994 UK Biodiversity Action Plan distinguishes, not particularly usefully, between four categories of greenspace.

- Remnants of ancient natural systems, e.g. ancient woodlands, wetland and freshwater
- Pre-industrial rural landscape remnants, e.g. meadow, heathland and marsh
- Managed greenspace, e.g. parks, amenity grassland and private gardens
- Naturally seeded urban or industrial sites, e.g. demolition sites, disused railway lines or unexploited industrial land

However, using the B&BC BAP classification, 21 nationally significant habitats are found in the area covered by this flora, to which can be added a further five habitats of regional (local) importance. In very broad terms 2005 data from EcoRecord (the Biological Record Centre for B&BC, which collects and manages information relating to the wildlife, wildlife sites and habitats of the area) indicated that 22,705ha of B&BC are built up, a figure representing 36% of the total area; gardens comprise 17,566ha (28%); and open space 22,175ha (36%).

## WOODLAND

▲ Park Coppice, Wolverhampton

The distribution of woodland in the region is shown in Fig. 3.20. Some 422 woodland sites were noted in the 1982–83 West Midlands County Council survey of habitats larger than 0.5ha in size, covering a total of 994.6ha. Birmingham had 173 such sites, totalling 480.7ha, Dudley 83 (225ha), Sandwell 50 (61.6ha), Walsall 77 (163.9ha) and Wolverhampton 39 (63.4ha). In 1977 the Forestry Commission's National Inventory of Woodland and Trees (published in 2002; see www.forestry.gov.uk/pdf/westmidlands.pdf/$FILE/westmidlands.pdf) had identified 311 woods larger than 2ha in size in the former West Midlands county.

There seems to have been an increase in woodland and scrub cover by around 800ha between 1977 and 1983 in the West Midlands county region (Pisolkar, 2005). Studies specifically in Walsall and in the Sandwell Valley add detail suggesting that the area of woodland and scrub had approximately doubled in 20 years. In Walsall there was a change from 163.9ha to 307.9ha between 1983 and 2001, in the Sandwell Valley an increase from 40.5ha in 1977 to 107.7ha in 2004. Increases were net: in Walsall, for example, 5.4ha of woodland were also lost between the surveys.

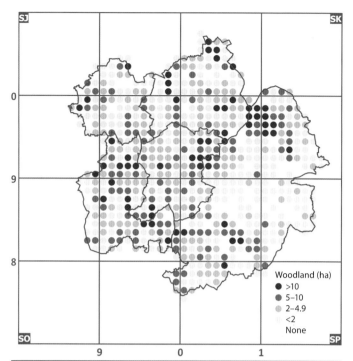

▲ Figure 3.20 Distribution of woodland in B&BC

Many of the gains in the region were the results of plantings by the Black Country Urban Forest partnership between 1995 and 2000, in which some 629 sites of varying sizes were planted with a variety of broad-leaved trees, covering around 360ha.

Ancient semi-natural broad-leaved woodlands are those which have been continuously treed since 1600. This does not imply that any tree is necessarily that old, nor that the woodland has not been subjected to sympathetic management such as coppicing. These are habitats of intrinsic historical interest, but they are also vital for the conservation of genetic material and as a source for restocking neighbouring woodlands. They are often mixed Oak woodlands, and invasive trees such as Sycamore are not unusual. In NVC terms these woodlands are either (Pedunculate) Oak – Bracken – Bramble woodlands (NVC actually using the Latin names, viz. *Quercus robur – Pteridium aquilinum – Rubus fruticosus*), designated W10, or Oak – Birch – Wavy Hair-grass (W16) on drier, more acid soils. Such woods often contain ground flora species which are very slow colonisers

▲ Woodland on acid soil at Saltwells LNR

and are therefore useful pointers as ancient woodland indicators – Dog's Mercury, Wood Anemone, Wood Millet and Wood Horsetail, for instance. Our understanding of the status of these woods has improved: an assessment in 1999 suggested 79 such sites covering 301 ha, but by 2010 some 89 ancient woodland sites had provisionally been identified in B&BC, covering a total area of 318 ha. Clusters of small sites are particularly associated with the urban fringe: in the south-west of the region around Lye, Halesowen, Bartley Green and Longbridge; around Sutton Coldfield in the north-east; and at Park Hall Wood in east Birmingham. In 1990, Sandwell also had 3.2ha of ancient replanted woodland, where the original tree cover had been cleared then replanted, Walsall had 1.6ha and Wolverhampton 1.2ha.

Secondary woodland is the term given to woodlands that have grown since 1600, often having done so on neglected ground that had previously been used for other purposes. A number of secondary woodlands have developed through natural colonisation and succession, though many are recent, and they are often transient features in the landscape.

Plantation woodlands have been planted for commercial or, in this region, more generally for amenity use, typically using saplings, and since the last decade of the last century particularly associated with the Black Country Urban Forestry Unit.

The commonest Oak woodlands in B&BC are classified as lowland oak woodland, dominated by Pedunculate Oak, though this species also commonly hybridizes with Sessile Oak. Mixed oakwood will include mature specimens of other species, particularly Sycamore, Ash and Birch; Hazel, Holly and Rowan are common understorey species; and the ground vegetation and flora also vary considerably depending, for instance, on soil type, hydrology and aspect.

In Walsall good examples of secondary oak woodland are at Rough Wood, Coppice Lane Wood and Cuckoo's Nook. Oak woodland, too, is the kind of habitat generally planted up by the Black Country Urban Forestry Unit during the 1980s and 1990s, although other tree species were often also prominent. Mixed woodland has also developed on disused land – industrial sites, railway embankments and the like, often still dominated by wind-dispersed early-succession tree species such as Willows, Birch, Ash and in particular Sycamore, and bird-dispersed species such as Hawthorn, Elder and occasionally Cotoneaster, rather than Oak.

Pockets of beechwood (W14) or oak-beech woodland are associated with (under) plantings of Beech, for example at Saltwells Local Nature Reserve. Beech woodlands, especially the older ones, may possess distinctive ground floras and a varied shrub and tree layer, particularly where shade does not supress growth. These layers can include Rowan, Holly, Hawthorn, Elder, Field Maple, Sycamore and Sweet Chestnut.

Associated with steep slopes and base-rich soils, a small amount of so-called upland ash woodland (W8 Ash – Field Maple – Dog's Mercury community) is found in the region, for example at Park Lime Pits and Cuckoo's Nook and The Dingle in Walsall. Good examples in Dudley are at Saltwells and on disused limestone quarry workings at Wren's Nest and Castle Hill. Ash often co-mixes with Oak and other deciduous tree species, typified by Field Maple and Hazel, and is subject to invasion by Sycamore.

As its name indicates wet woodland is found on permanently or seasonally moist soils, with Alder, Willows and Birch characteristic dominants. Some Alder-dominated woodland belongs to the W7 Alder – Ash – Yellow Pimpernel NVC community, but the W6 Alder – Common Nettle community may be found on nutrient-rich soils where Nettle, Cleavers and Elder become common species associates. Such woodlands often border flowing water, floodplains and pool edges, and they can create mosaics of distinct vegetation in damper parts of dry woodland. Habitat boundaries are often not clear, for example wet woodland merging into dry wood with a transition zone or ecotone measuring tens of metres. Also, as soil builds up and dries out, succession may lead to a change in vegetation and habitat type. The ground flora is variable, and in places has become dominated by introduced species, for example American Skunk-cabbage at Edgbaston Pool, and the ubiquitous and iniquitous Indian Balsam in many woodland riverside edges in the region. Cuckoo's Nook is again an important site, and Sneyd Reservoir is another Walsall example. Wet woods along river corridors include those along the Stour, Mousesweet Brook, and the northern part of Sandwell Valley. Coopers Wood, Newhall Valley and Sutton Park are good examples in Birmingham. The presence of Greater Tussock-sedge under Alder at Edgbaston Pool and Sutton Park, and stands of Downy Birch over Purple Moor-grass and Sphagnum moss, also at Sutton Park, suggests that other wet woodland NVC communities may be present in B&BC, but as yet not described.

Wood pasture and parkland represent a mosaic of habitats, often associated with former woodland grazing sites and deer parks, and not to be confused with ornamental urban parks. Parts of Sutton Park, Northycote Farm and the Great Barr Hall area are examples, with a mixture of mature (sometimes veteran) trees and open grass, scrub or heath.

▲ Tree planting at Peascroft Wood by the Bilston Conservation Association in 1981

▲ Alder woodland at Northycote Farm, Wolverhampton

## SCRUB

Urban scrub is generally a habitat and vegetation type associated with succession: Bramble and young Hawthorn, Goat Willow, Sycamore, Ash, Birch and other young trees mingling with grasses and tall herbs, often on land previously under stone, bricks, mortar or concrete (analogous with primary succession) or formerly gardens (secondary succession). Also characteristic is the presence of a wide range of shrub and small trees belonging to the non-native genus *Cotoneaster* whose origins lie in escapes from gardens and other ornamental plantings. A further feature is scrub dominated by another introduced plant, *Buddleia davidii* (Butterfly-bush), which can become dominant very rapidly on sites that are disturbed or cleared of housing or industry.

This successional stage usually arrives from five to ten years after clearing (though *Buddleia* often appears within the first couple of years) and under undisturbed conditions will slowly change into young woodland after a dozen to twenty years. Grassland and heathland will also develop into scrub if management ceases, with Hawthorn and Bramble common on the former, Birch on the latter.

## HEATHLAND

The open landscapes of lowland heathland (mostly referable to the NVC H9 Heather – Wavy Hair-grass community) represent a group of dwarf shrub habitats, characterised by ericaceous species (Heather, Bell Heather, Cross-leaved Heath and Bilberry) and Western Gorse. These landscapes are separable both floristically – according to such physical features as soil acidity and moisture (for example Cross-leaved Heath associated with wet heath, Bell Heather on dry) – and physiognomically, whether because of the presence of patches of other vegetation types or because of successional age. Heathland therefore often contains mosaics of heath, grass, Bracken, Bramble, scrub and young colonising trees, initially often Birch. An anthropogenic habitat, grazed and/ or (more commonly) burned it requires management to avoid succession leading to woodland. Fire burns off most of the above-ground vegetation, leaving roots to resprout or seed to germinate on the bare ground. Heathland structure therefore also reflects age since previous burning, and the ericaceous component grows through young, intermediate and mature stages.

▲ Cross-leaved Heath

The regional importance of the 250ha of heathland of B&BC (180ha dry heath, 70 wet) is that, while classed as lowland, and while possessing many of the floristic characteristics of the more typical lowland heaths of southern England, they also have characteristics of both the western wet heaths of Shropshire and the Welsh Borders and the upland wet heaths of the Peak District further north and further west into Wales.

Much of the heathland in the region (Figure 3.21) seems to be the remnant of ancient heaths associated with the farming that preceded industrialisation and urbanisation. That they were formerly much more widespread is suggested by the number of times the word 'heath' is found in place names in both B&BC (see Chapter 4.2). Heathland also developed on base-poor or acidity-generating industrial spoil, particularly coal spoil: examples are found adjacent to pre-existing old heath at Pelsall North Common and Brownhills Common.

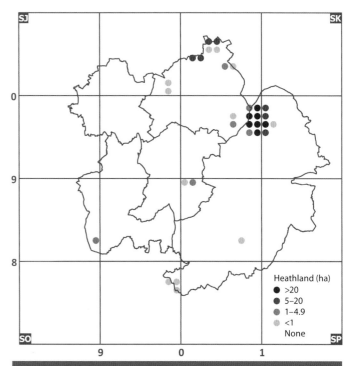

▲ **Figure 3.21 Distribution of heathland in B&BC**

The most extensive areas of heathland in this region are within Sutton Park and at Pelsall North Common, Brownhills Common and Shire Oak Park, the last three sites being in Walsall and connecting with South Staffordshire heathland. Parts of Dudley, Sandwell, and the Lickey Hills in South Birmingham have smaller sites. Another area lies along the Galton Valley in Smethwick, and there are patches of heath along some railway cuttings in South Birmingham. Most sites (totalling around 180ha) are entirely or predominantly dry heaths, but there are about 70ha of wet heathland, for example at Pelsall North Common (4.5ha) and Holland Park (4ha) (all Walsall), and Sutton Park. Heathland is being newly created in parts of Walsall, for example at Barr Beacon, and Dudley, and a restoration programme at Sutton Park began in 2003.

## GRASSLAND

Just over 13,000ha of grassland were recorded in the early 1980s, 20% of the total area of B&BC (Pisolkar, 2005). This included improved grassland, but excluded such amenity grasslands as playing fields, public parks and roadside verges. Thirty years later it is clear that much of this grassland has been lost, and very few areas have been added. Most grasslands in the region are associated with the mesotrophic grasslands (MG1 etc.) of the NVC, associated with chemically neutral soils, but small areas of calcareous and acid grasslands are also evident.

In the urban context lowland pastures are represented by grassland grazed by horses and other livestock, together with lowland meadow – cut for hay and grazed for part of the year – and areas of reconstructed species-rich hay meadow. Some of the more species-rich of these can be allocated to the NVC MG5 Crested Dog's-tail – Common Knapweed community, but the MG6 Perennial Rye-grass – Crested Dog's-tail community is more common.

Appropriate management is crucial for the survival of such meadows, which are generally no more than 3ha in extent, and often isolated or found in small clusters. Recently created meadows, like their traditionally managed rural source sites, need to be cut in July or August and the thatch removed (failure of which leads to a return to a more species-poor neutral grassland); post-cut grazing in autumn, however, is rarely evident. As well as a number of orchid species, arrays of fine-leaved grasses such as fescues and Crested Dog's-tail are complemented by a rich herb flora that frequently includes Common Knapweed, Great Burnet, Yellow-rattle, Cowslip and Bird's-foot-trefoil. Examples are at Northycote Farm (Wolverhampton), Park Lime Pits and Clayhanger (Walsall), Cotwall End, Bumble Hole, Leasowes Park and Illey Pastures SSSI (Dudley), along parts of the River Cole and Woodgate Valley Country Park (Birmingham), and in a few places in the Sandwell Valley.

Unmanaged lowland calcareous grasslands are found in just a few locations – Wrens Nest NNR and Sedgley Beacon (both Dudley) and parts of Rushall in Walsall – associated with limestone workings (quarries, railway cuttings) or outcrops. The total area is only 11ha (1980s figures). The base-rich soils of such sites support a rich mixture of grasses and herbs such as Quaking-grass, Small Scabious and Common Milkwort. With rock at or close to the surface of this habitat, succession does not necessarily lead into scrub, though small shrub species such as Hawthorn are found in the slightly deeper soils of troughs and crevices, even on steep slopes, and the coarse grass Upright Brome is sometimes dominant in the absence of grazing.

Some 560ha of lowland acid grassland are found on some dry sandy soils and over both superficial and solid geology-derived gravel or pebble deposits, for example in parts of Barr Beacon and Sutton Park. With 223ha, Dudley has the greatest area. These

figures, however, date from the 1980s and cover is now almost certainly lower. The dominant species are grasses, most often Common Bent and the fine-leaved fescues, with only a limited flora of such species as Tormentil, Heath Bedstraw, Sheep's Sorrel and Early Hair-grass.

Purple Moor-grass and rush pastures are found in some northern parts of the region – Brownhills Common, Pelsall North Common, Clayhanger and Black Cock Farm (all Walsall) and in Sutton Park – over acidic, poorly drained soils, and often interspersed in a mosaic pattern with wet heath, grassland, scrub and swamp.

Floodplain grazing marshes are associated with flooded pasture or meadows where standing fresh water is found for some or all of the year, and often with associated ditches. Some are grazed; a few are cut for hay or silage. In the region, this habitat is found on clay soils in river valleys that are regularly flooded, for example at Jockey Meadows (Walsall) and Park Hall Nature Reserve (Birmingham). Remnants of old floodplain grazing marshes can also be seen in amenity grasslands along some Birmingham streams, sometimes little managed except for occasional mowing, or otherwise difficult to detect under frequent mowing regimes. An interesting example has also developed on poorly drained post-industrial land, parts having been used for landfill, at Bowmans Harbour in Wolverhampton. In total, marshy grassland covered 91ha when last assessed in the early 1980s. A variety of vegetation may be present depending on the fertility and base status of the soil, but the larger rushes and Tufted Hair-grass are typically abundant, sometimes with sedges or such species as Greater Burnet and Southern Marsh-orchid.

Improved and semi-improved neutral grasslands are all important habitats in terms of area, covering just over 12,260ha in the 1980s (of which 8,230 was improved grassland), but now rather less as a consequence of building development, planting and succession. An estimated 1044ha of grassland was lost to development between 1983 and 2001, representing 8.4% of the total. Wolverhampton lost the greatest proportion with a 17% loss (219ha); Birmingham showed the greatest loss by area – 322ha, or 6.6%. Similarly, analysis of aerial photographs taken of a 480.8ha sample area in the Sandwell Valley showed an increase in cover of scrub and wood from 40.5ha in 1977 to 107ha in 2004. This increase included a small amount of tree planting but was mostly due to succession, and took place at the expense of grassland. Such grasslands tend to be more species-poor than the other grassland habitats described here, and have a preponderance of species that can withstand the stresses of trampling or grazing. They are generally heavily managed, and include grazed pasture,

▲ Calcareous grassland and scrub, Sedgley Beacon

▲ Secondary grazing on open-cast at Saltwells LNR

verges and central reservations, the last two often containing Danish Scurvygrass along the edges where de-icing salt has been used on the roads (Scott and Davison, 1982; Scott, 1985). Many of these grasslands form as patches on post-industrial sites, with MG1 False Oat-grass communities on richer soils and various kinds of Common Bent/Red Fescue-dominated grassland on drier, nutrient-poor or contaminated sites. This type of vegetation is a very important component of the open mosaic habitats BAP priority habitat.

Amenity grasslands, similar to the above but predominantly associated with playing fields, golf courses and municipal open space, are sown, heavily and frequently mown (with clippings taken off-site) and sometimes subjected to herbicidal applications. Trample-resistant species such as Perennial Rye-grass are favoured both by sowing and subsequent usage. Chemically sprayed and disturbed margins often support quite rich floras of the annual 'weedy' species which are described later.

## WETLAND AND OPEN WATER HABITATS

Lakes, reservoirs, pools and ponds are all important lentic (standing or relatively still water) habitats which are generally shallow and mesotrophic (with moderate concentrations of nutrients, particularly inorganic nitrogen and available phosphorus). Such mesotrophic wetlands include open water with submerged, free-floating or floating leaved plants. Examples include Edgbaston Pool (Birmingham), Swan Pool (Sandwell) and Fens Pool (Dudley). Large reservoirs such as at Bartley Green and Edgbaston in Birmingham are generally unimportant for plant life.

Other kinds of mesotrophic wetland are the slowly moving waters of ditches and canals. Created during the late 18th and first half of the 19th centuries for haulage of raw materials, canals were superseded by the railways and many fell into disuse. Recent repair and conservation efforts have returned many canals to recreational and some commercial use, with consequent improvements as habitats for plants and wildlife. Some 220 km of canal remain in the region: good examples of this habitat are evident along the Wyrley and Essington Canal, Rushall Canal, Birmingham Main Line Canal and the Dudley Canal. Canal vegetation tends to be cleared to allow boat passage and there are only small stretches of submerged and emergent vegetation in the water. The highest proportion of canal-containing vegetation in Birmingham in a 2004 survey was 6.2% in the 6km stretch of the Worcester and Birmingham Canal between Gas Street Basin and Wasthill Tunnel.

With higher natural concentrations of nutrients or as a consequence of artificial enrichment, some lakes and reservoirs are more accurately classed as eutrophic standing waters: these productive waters are subjected to algal blooms in summer, the water turning green, lowering light penetration and in turn the rate of underwater photosynthesis. As a result, such waters are typically devoid of aquatic plants, and even marginal vegetation is often grazed out by Canada Geese. Many public parks contain eutrophic lakes, for instance West Park (Wolverhampton) and Grove Park (Birmingham).

A pond, as defined by Pond Conservation (2002), is an area of between 2m$^2$ and 2ha that holds water for at least four consecutive months of the year. The sheer number of garden ponds makes this, cumulatively, an important habitat, though individually varying in size and floristic content (Wyatt, 1998). Little is known of them because of the difficulty of organising systematic surveys, though a sample of 37 ponds in north-western England indicated that there was a highly significant correlation between garden pond density and species richness (Gledhill et al., 2008). More significant

are the 1,052 non-garden ponds identified in the region, up to 2ha in area, of which around 5% meet criteria as national priority habitats, for instance containing Red Data Book or UK BAP species, species protected under the Wildlife and Countryside Act Schedules 5 and 8, or Habitats Directive Annex II species. Good examples are located around Park Lime Pits and Clayhanger (Walsall), Fens Pools (Dudley) and Elm Road Pool (Birmingham). A few, especially in Walsall, are extremely clean and nutrient-poor, and harbour species such as Lesser Marshwort, uncommon even in the surrounding countryside. Many of the smaller ponds and pools, however, continue to be lost to development and natural succession. Comparing 1982 data with 2001 data for Walsall, for example, shows a loss of 22ha or nearly 40% of such waterbodies (34% in terms of area), though offset by the creation of 53 new pools (12.45ha).

▲ Pond created at Merridale School, Wolverhampton

Reedbeds and other kinds of marginal vegetation are areas of swamp where water is at or above ground level for most or all of the year, generally bordering mesotrophic waters such as lakes or canals. Such vegetation is often dominated by tall monocotyledonous species, in particular Common Reed or Bulrush, either species forming near-monospecific stands, with Reed Sweet-grass, Common Club-rush and Branched Bur-reed also found along canals.

Boundaries with open water or on the landward side may be sharp but this habitat can also merge with adjoining wet grassland or wet woodland. True reedbed is a very fragmented and localised habitat in the region, being found for example in parts of the Blackbrook Valley (Dudley), and at Lady Pool (Walsall) and Edgbaston Pool (Birmingham).

Lowland fens are only to be found within Sutton Park, especially around Little Bracebridge Pool and Longmoor Pool. With water derived from underlying Triassic sandstone these waters are less base-rich than fens usually are, but plants such as Marsh Pennywort, Bogbean, Marsh Cinquefoil, Common Butterwort, Marsh Valerian and Grass-of-Parnassus testify to the floristic importance of this habitat.

Waterlogged and acidic lowland raised bog, which develops on Sphagnum moss and peat, is present only in a severely degraded and probably secondary form at Stubbers Green Bog (Walsall), the site having been badly damaged during the 1980s, and subjected to successional Birch colonisation.

Rivers and streams are lotic (moving water) habitats that vary in width, speed of flow and nutrient chemistry (including the level and nature of pollution). Larger streams may themselves incorporate pools, shingle bars, sand banks and other sub-habitats. The aquatic flora is typically poor, including not only species of highly eutrophic waters such as Fennel Pondweed, but also Stream Water-crowfoot. Rivers also commonly have marginal and terrestrial bankside (riparian) vegetation, and often serve as important habitat corridors, though they are also routes along which invasive species such as Indian Balsam disperse. There are over 800 km of rivers and streams in B&BC. Many sections have been highly modified, for example by straightening, culverting and vegetation clearance, but remnant sections have retained many natural features, for example parts of the Cole and Rea at Hall Green and Kings Norton, respectively, in South Birmingham, and the Stour on the Dudley-Sandwell boundary at Haden Hill.

▲ Smestow Brook, Tettenhall

## FARMLAND

Areas of encapsulated arable and improved pasture are found within B&BC, as well as around the fringes of the conurbation. Arable field margins (a BAP priority habitat) are sited on the outer margins of the field, commonly up to 2m in width (and occasionally wider), and consisting of a herb-grass mix that sometimes includes now-rare 'arable weeds' such as Cornflower. A good example of this habitat is at Lime Pits Farm in Rushall (Walsall), managed for many years after 1993 under the Government's Countryside Stewardship scheme, with recent records for the rare Corn Buttercup.

▲ Common Poppy and Wild Radish in a bean field, Kingswinford

Farmland hedgerows (often in fact a hedge-ditch-verge complex) vary in length, integrity, connectedness, tree content and age, the last being particularly important as the older the hedge the greater the number of woody species likely to be present. Hedgerow complexes are particularly associated with the urban fringe, for example in Woodgate Valley Country Park and the Sedgley area, eastern Walsall and northern Wolverhampton; or in sizeable green wedges such as the Sandwell Valley Country Park. Old hedges can still sometimes occur further into the built-up area, for example along canals. In other densely populated areas tiny fragments can still survive, especially along old roads and boundaries. Their age and value have often not been recognised, however, and they have been destroyed.

## BUILT ENVIRONMENT

This category is a very varied one. It includes sets of both residential and industrial/commercial habitats which in places overlap, for example the ornamental landscapes associated with houses, institutions such as schools and hospitals, churchyards, and areas of shrub bordering many larger supermarkets and car parks. Post-industrial sites represent often important habitats where, for example, heavy metals remaining in the soil can permit or indeed promote some unusual plant species. Lime-rich building rubble is another distinct substrate which can lead to distinct plant assemblages shortly after demolition. The built environment also includes transport corridors, in particular railways (tracks and ballast, embankments and cuttings, marshalling yards), roads and canals. Some of these habitats have already been described, for example roadside verges as an improved grassland habitat.

▲ Disused railway line, Bescot Triangle SLINC

Gardens cover an estimated 17,566ha within B&BC, over 28% of the region's area. Not all of this area is vegetation or water: extrapolating results from a sample of 500 houses in Birmingham and Sandwell covering a range of property types, for example, almost 60% of front gardens were over 80% paved. While they vary in size and character and therefore in value to wild plants and wildlife, gardens often form sizeable contiguous areas, together providing an important series of habitat patches or metahabitat (Davies et al., 2009). Gardens often link with areas of semi-natural vegetation, enhancing the green landscape of the built environment. With increasing interest in wildlife gardening and a less critical approach to adventitious flora many gardens are today valuable botanical oases. This habitat is described more fully in section 3.6.

In many ways an extension of the traditional vegetable and, to an extent, flower garden the allotment is another important land use where some interesting plant species have appeared and are tolerated. Following a report into allotments (HMSO, 1969) which advocated their development into more 'family-oriented' ornamental landscapes, some Birmingham sites in particular were, at least briefly, re-landscaped in such a manner during the 1970s. Analogous to allotments are community gardens, often created on formerly derelict land or waste ground, which have sprung up in the region since the 1980s.

Many allotment sites – formalised by a series of Allotments Acts from 1887 onwards – have been open land for many years. They developed in Birmingham from the 'guinea gardens' of the Victorian period, the Edgbaston Guinea Gardens adjacent to the Botanic Gardens being the sole survivor. Some contain remnants of semi-natural habitat. The 276 allotment sites recorded for the region cover 428ha and while, like gardens, they vary in size and degree of cultivation they provide additional habitat for a range of species, particularly those associated with disturbed ground (ruderals), and their flora bears close similarity to that of arable field margins. Some species which are becoming increasingly scarce in field margins due to the widespread use of selective herbicides are still quite frequent in our allotments, for example Field Woundwort.

A survey of the flora of the allotments at Bordesley Green in 2008 found 174 spontaneously growing plant species. The botanical significance of allotments is accentuated where they adjoin other important habitats, in particular where they have been disused for some time; this is the case with the 3.7ha site at Pereira Road in South Birmingham, which has become an RSPB reserve with wetland and woodland edge habitat, and which adjoins the Harborne Walkway, a disused railway track lined with deciduous trees and occasional pools.

All of the major towns and cities in the region possess a number of formally designed and landscaped municipal parks and similar areas of public open space. Birmingham claims to have over two hundred parks, the largest being the 72ha Cannon Hill Park, which includes a 2ha young planted woodland and a wildflower meadow. The strict management regimes required to sustain wildflower meadows make it difficult for parks departments to maintain this kind of habitat, and not all persist; the meadow created in the 40ha Pype Hayes Park, for example, has not persisted, although the ward's millennium woodland has fared better. Walsall Arboretum is 32ha of wooded walks as well as more open grassland, ornamental planting and a number of lakes. The 17ha West Park in Wolverhampton, however, is perhaps more typical of this land use: while it has a sizeable (3.24 ha) lake the grounds include only amenity grassland, ornamental bedding and a variety of mature trees; a small conservation area planted with young trees in around 1990 has developed into dense scrub.

Municipal ornamental plantings are also integrated with some roadside verges and central reservations (e.g. the Wolverhampton Ring Road), town squares and pedestrianised areas and, while heavily managed, from time to time nevertheless support 'weedy' species.

Cemeteries and in particular churchyards are in some ways hybrid habitat types, part that mixture of mown grass and often scattered trees that characterises parkland habitat, part tall herb and scrub, especially in older and less-managed churchyards. A few incorporate patches of semi-natural vegetation. Gravestones are analogues of stone walling that can be important for often species-rich lichen and moss communities, and lichens in

**Graveyard, Pensnett** (by Sue Nicholls)

particular can be used as indicators of changes in atmospheric pollution.

Inland rock outcrops have generally been exposed through human activity, for example as quarries, leading to an acidic substrate, such as at Pinfold Lane Quarry and Shire Oak Park, both in Walsall, or a calcareous substrate, as at Wrens Nest, Dudley. These sites have been colonised by lichens, bryophytes, ferns and a variety of grasses and herbs.

Open mosaic habitats on previously developed land include some very interesting habitats on post-industrial sites where, for example, industrial waste or slag-derived heavy metals in the soil have encouraged a number of plant rarities; they also includes the dynamic habitat associated with the first half dozen or so years following building demolition. Plants are generally stress-tolerators associated with nutrient-poor or very dry soils but the flora might also comprise or include ruderals (disturbance-tolerating plants) and competitive species (those best able to acquire and use resources such as soil nutrients and water, enabling them to out-compete less aggressive species), since former gardens often provide disturbed but nutrient-rich

▲ Vegetation on an industrial spoil tip, to the north of Coneygre Business Park, Burnt Tree

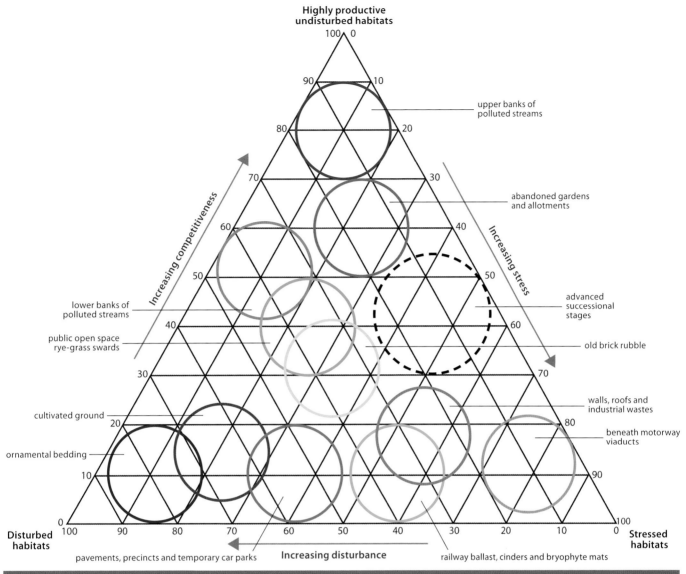

**▲ Figure 3.22 Relationships between habitats associated with stressed, disturbed and highly productive undisturbed habitats in towns (after Gilbert 1989 and Grime 1979). Axes show percentages of stress and disturbance and competitiveness.**

substrates. The mortar-rich substrates of many former buildings can encourage calcicolous (lime-loving) plants. Such sites often have a high percentage of bare substrate in their earliest years, and impermeable building material or soil compaction frequently leads to impaired drainage and the establishment, for a few years at least, of small pools or seasonally flooded areas. Vegetation is usually a mixture of native and non-native, annual and perennial herbs and grasses, nutrient-rich sites in particular turning into tall herb communities later colonised by shrubby species and small trees, particularly Sycamore, Goat Willow and Silver Birch (Hodge and Harmer, 1986).

The relationship between some stressful, disturbed and productive habitats is summarised in Figure 3.22.

Tall herb vegetation, therefore, often develops as part of the succession found on 'wasteland', especially where there is a nutrient-rich substrate, and is commonly associated with NVC OV24 Common Nettle – Cleavers, OV26 Great Willowherb and OV27 Rosebay Willowherb communities. Left to itself tall herb vegetation will generally develop into scrub and woodland, but it may also be seen alongside railways and some roadsides where periodic management such as cutting prevents trees from colonising. The flora is characterised by tall perennial or biennial

dicotyledonous species, usually over 25 cm in height, with willowherbs and Common Nettle being typical, often intermixed with rank grass and in places invasives such as Japanese Knotweed.

Buildings and walls are also significant habitats for some plants, particularly where old brick is involved. An old wall will have different kinds of vegetation and species depending on substrate (different kinds of brick or stone), where one is looking (top, vertical face, base) and aspect. Similarly, at this kind of scale, plants growing in the damper detritus accumulated at the base of a wall will differ from those growing in pavement cracks, and differ again from the vegetation of the gutter (Jarvis and Woodhouse, 1994). Darlington (1981) has estimated that there is typically around 1ha of vertical wall in every 10ha of urban habitat. Walls are not only associated with buildings or property edges – brick or stone walls formed 55% of the banks of a 2004 sample of nearly 48km of canal. When bricks become broken and where mortar has begun to crumble a number of higher plants, whose seeds have been brought in by wind or birds, can establish themselves. These range from small annuals to woody colonisers such as Butterfly-bush (greatly in evidence in a number of railway stations) and Ash. A bryophyte flora is associated with many of these sites: old slate and asbestos roofs, for instance, are often partly covered by lichen and moss as well as algae. The OV39 Maidenhair Spleenwort – Wall-rue NVC community is widely represented in B&BC on canal and railway bridges built using hard blue brick and (often) lime mortar.

Railway land and more recently the Midlands Metro corridor offer a number of valuable plant habitats, although these are often not sufficiently well surveyed owing to access problems. Apart from rock exposures and shallow-soiled cuttings and embankments, the ballast on which the tracks are set, typically constructed from coarse limestone gravel, can be particularly valuable. Often managed by rather drastic but intermittent herbicide regimes, on active lines a flora of lime-loving annual and short-lived perennial herbs can develop, which can persist and diversify for quite a long time when the line is abandoned.

The urban flora is also enhanced by a number of marginal or transitional habitats, often very limited in extent, but offering a refuge from the constant disturbance which can limit colonisation. These habitats include the junction between garden walls and pavements, around the bases of lamp posts and telegraph posts and amongst the exposed roots of street trees, miscellaneous heaps of unwanted soil, rubble and junk generously deposited in the margins of both waste land and semi-natural habitats (Wheater, 2010). Here many species can produce at least a few seeds, sufficient to perpetuate their presence until more amenable habitats materialise. Similar opportunities are offered by imperfectly sealed surfaces: cracks in concrete, between pavement slabs and paver bricks support the seedlings of garden escapes, drought-tolerance specialists and refugees from semi-natural habitats alike. Immediately by roads the added filter of de-icing salt encourages a salt-tolerant flora, characterised by Danish Scurvygrass and Buck's-horn Plantain since the 1990s, but more recently adding several other species such as Reflexed Saltmarsh-grass, Lesser Sea-spurrey and Narrow-leaved Pepperwort.

# Section 6 • The garden habitat by Christopher Young

Gardens are one of the most widespread, most familiar, yet one of the least known of the habitats found in B&BC. Although general features can be seen (see below) each individual garden has its own distinctive character as a result of household landscaping choices and planting practices, individual household history, local historical factors, e.g. agricultural/industrial activity, and cultural traditions (Marco et al., 2010; Quigley, 2010). Additionally, and importantly, they are subject to complex and ad hoc direct management or neglect, both often within the same garden, and both often to extreme degrees. This management affects the species that persist there and their potential for colonising other gardens and the wider urban landscape. Therefore, on a small scale, what happens in gardens reflects the kinds of changes happening in the wider urban landscape, with a constant turnover of species, extreme management and managed/forced successional changes.

Despite the problems of looking into the characteristics of every garden to get a perspective on their exact characteristics, recent studies have attempted to do just this. Using a series of national datasets Davies et al. (2009) estimated that 22.7 million households (87% of the total number of households) in the UK had access to a garden of some kind: this equates to a total area of 432,924ha at an average size of 190m². Within B&BC this translates as 17,566ha or over 28% of the area of the region – a significant amount by any measure.

Even though gardens are predominantly private spaces, meaning that the precise characteristics of each are unknown, the most obvious tree and shrub components are often visible beyond their immediate boundaries. The influence of these private spaces extends beyond their physical boundaries, resulting in an aesthetic impact since neighbouring gardens tend to develop similarities in the types of species that are both planted and which can then persist. The result of this can often be distinctive local garden patterns with their own neighbourhood styles (Zmyslony and Gagnon, 2000), and it is this totality of garden resource that lies at the heart of their importance. Management of individual gardens for their biodiversity value in general is increasingly part of the public consciousness, with many gardeners not only using reduced chemical inputs but also actively adding wildlife-friendly features to encourage wildlife into their gardens. As a result, one of the most important roles of gardens is in providing additional resources and therefore added value where they abut or are near to other greenspaces, extending the influence of these sites beyond the constraints of their physical and administrative boundaries (Davies et al., 2009; Goddard et al., 2010).

Even when the caveat of individual variation is recognised, taken in their totality it is still possible to identify a distinctive set of characteristics that can be applied to the garden habitat as a whole:

- Gardens are often extremely species rich and, particularly when looked at in their totality, contain a diversity of plants that is unmatched in semi-natural habitats (Smith et al., 2006; Gaston and Gaston, 2010)
- They provide a reservoir of common and exotic species for movement outside the confines of the garden and into adjacent areas, in the process acting as seed foci (Trueman and Young, 2012)
- They are forcibly managed for extended periods of time, leading to localised environmental extremes of temperature, moisture, vegetation coverage and vegetation absence which may be at odds with seasonal conditions
- Exaggerated and extreme temporal variability (especially short-term) are commonplace within individual gardens
- Early stages of succession are maintained or else garden areas or species are restricted to particular stages of succession due to intervention
- There is a distinctive shifting mosaic working at a very fine scale creating a constantly varying range of colonisation opportunities for many different species
- Individual gardens which may be abandoned and reverting to a naturalistic appearance are cheek-by-jowl with highly manicured ultra-controlled environments. This metahabitat of small patches of distinctly different character together forms a larger, but connected area that is greater in influence than any one individual garden

In all gardens there is an intrinsic diversity of plant species caused by both the planting and deliberate propagation of particular species (native and introduced). Alternatively, individual gardens may provide just the right conditions for the establishment of incoming plants and the development of natural communities, thereby extending the species' urban living zone beyond the borders of the remaining semi-natural habitats and encapsulated countryside. This intricate mix of species of different origins was demonstrated in the study by Smith *et al.* (2006), who showed that gardens contained on average 45% natives, irrespective of garden size, although doubling garden size led to an increase in species richness of 25%. In terms of relative contributions annuals comprised around 11%, biennials and perennials 63%, shrubs 18% and trees 8%. Although 55% were alien species, shrubs were disproportionately represented within this total.

An additional factor that helps to shape this diversity is a social grouping among neighbours and gardeners that provides a network of plant donations and exchanges (Marco *et al.*, 2010). These are often species that propagate easily, and so this network has the potential to contribute significantly to the diversity of both native and non-native species in gardens. Such easily propagated exchanges also have the potential to escape and establish populations in the wider urban landscape, and this therefore may play a key role in the invasion processes of all plants, though of ornamental and new exotic plants in particular.

Garden type and age have a distinct influence on the availability of habitats and niches and provides a distinct structural complexity that compares favourably with all other habitats. For example, a study in north-west Wolverhampton (Young and Jarvis, 2001) demonstrated that by far the most structurally diverse habitats are the mature residential garden areas, with newer residential areas tending to lack the more specialised garden components such as mature trees, dead wood and water features. The net result of this lessened complexity is a lower species niche potential in newer areas, a fact that is worth bearing in mind when looking at the expansion of new developments in general and evolving residential areas in particular.

A notable feature of recent years across all urban areas, including B&BC, has been the conversion of large rear gardens in suburban areas into several smaller dwellings. These valuable mature habitats, some of which may have been slowly evolving their diversity of niches and species over considerable periods of time, are then lost and are impossible to replace. Habitats of similar age, diversity and history in the wider countryside would be protected, yet in urban areas these are considered to be 'fair game' for development. As early as the 1980s the infilling of gardens for development and the commensurate loss of greenspace was recognised as a significant feature in the region (Whitehead and Larkham, 1991), yet despite this recognition this process has been occurring incrementally and continuing largely unhindered to the present day (Pauliet *et al.*, 2005), chipping away at one of our most valuable urban resources.

▲ **Landscape with gardens**

# Section 7 • The history of human occupation by Margaret Kingsbury

▲ **Birmingham from the Dome of St. Philip's Church in 1821 by Samuel Lines Senior © Birmingham Museums Trust (part image).** The view is painted looking south-west from the Church of England cathedral with Colmore Row to the right. The immediate foreground shows what were probably the last fields within the town and Christ Church (now demolished) beyond them. Down Temple Street on the left, are smoking chimneys of the houses and workshops of the developing industrial areas. Open countryside is very close and the distant range of hills is probably the Lickeys.

Since the end of the latest ice age about 10,000 years ago there have been many alterations to the landscape of the area which is now B&BC – natural environmental changes, particularly in climate, and those originating from human activities. The most significant change has been the extent of the area taken up by human occupation, reducing the amount and fundamentally changing the nature of the space available for vegetation. This expansion was linked to and reliant on the growth of trade, particularly after the Norman Conquest, and did not develop in isolation. It was interrelated with activities elsewhere, and there is evidence for this from an early date.

Information about earlier times comes from archaeological, palaeo-ecological and geophysical investigations. Written evidence becomes available in the Anglo-Saxon period (5th to 11th centuries AD), when charters and other documents give clues to what the landscape was like, and gradually increases after the Domesday Record of 1086.

## BEFORE THE NORMAN CONQUEST

The last ice sheet did not cover the whole of our area (see section 1). When the ice retreated tundra vegetation spread, dominated by mosses, lichens, sedges, grasses and dwarf shrubs – particularly those of the heather family. As the temperature continued to rise other herbaceous plants re-colonised the Midlands, followed by the return of trees. The predominant tree species varied over time, responding to climatic fluctuations. Animals also returned, followed shortly after by humans, attracted by fresh water and food resources. The land bridge connecting Britain with Europe was cut through about 6000BC, preventing further natural migration of plants from the Continent.

Before about 8000BC the evidence shows variations in climate including a return to 'arctic conditions' sometime between 11,000 and 10,000BC followed by a period of gradually increasing warmth (Lamb 1995). Evidence for colder temperatures than today was found in a layer of peat during the construction of the Wholesale Markets in Birmingham city centre. It showed remains of beetles at about 9000BC which are now found in mountainous regions of Britain and Scandinavia (Hodder 2004). By about 4500BC most of Britain was covered with 'wildwood' – natural woodland unaffected by early farming or later civilisation (Rackham 2003). None of this remains today but most of the same tree species can still be found such as Oak, Birch and Hazel. Owing to the nature of the terrain B&BC may not have been densely wooded, especially in places where there was only a thin soil layer such as the pebbly tracts of land east and west of the coalfields.

The earliest evidences of human presence are stone tools: some probably from the **Palaeolithic** (500,000–8500BC)[2] made from local quartzite pebbles, but most from the **Mesolithic** (8500–4000BC) made from flint pebbles, most of which are found in the glacial drift deposits and the gravel of river terraces in the area. The finds are usually close to a water source, some in small clusters, but there are several sites where large numbers of worked flint pieces have been discovered. At Wishaw Hall Farm there were 1,400 and at Sandwell Priory over 800 were found (Hodder 2004). In the Borough of Dudley there is an important site in the Stour Valley where upwards of 20,000 flints have been retrieved in an area of three fields surrounding a pond. All these sites suggest meeting places visited periodically by **hunter-gatherer** groups. At this early date they were unlikely to have made permanent camps but would range in small groups over wide areas, which would have allowed the environment to recover from their exploitation (Fagan 2004). However, the flint tools in the Stour valley differ from those found elsewhere in this area; the majority are made from black flint (from chalk deposits) which is not local in origin. The source is not known but they would have been brought in by the visiting groups, suggesting that some form of trade or exchange of goods was already in operation at that time (Hemingway, pers. comm.). Those found locally in the glacial drift are brownish in colour and not of such good quality, but the numbers found showing signs of use indicate that they had value over the local quartzite pebbles (Hodder 2004).

In our area the earliest dated evidence for human occupation, 8500BC and 8400BC, has been found in Banbury Street, in Birmingham's Eastside, near the River Rea. In the lower level two flint tools were found, and pollen analysis shows that the vegetation was mainly Pine and Birch, with some sedges and moss, i.e. a typical early post-glacial flora. In the later upper layer the vegetation included Alder, Hazel, Pine, sedges and mosses. There was also a consistent layer of pine charcoal which might indicate deliberate burning to create clearings, possibly to encourage new grass for grazing. (www.birmingham.gov.uk/archaeology; Score and Higgins, 2011).

In the **Neolithic** (4000–2400BC), in addition to tools made from local materials, some polished stone axes have been found in various locations in Birmingham and in the Stour Valley. These have been traced to Langdale in the Lake District, North Wales, Cornwall and Leicestershire. Flint from eastern or southern England of better quality than local deposits has also been found. This shows that countrywide communications were in existence at that time (Hodder, 2004; Hemingway, pers. comm.). This period is usually associated with the beginning of farming and the necessary clearance of woodland but here, as elsewhere in the country, the major clearance of woodland did not take place until the Bronze Age (Hodder, pers. comm.). However, there is evidence for the presence of Neolithic farmers in the Stour valley (Hemingway, pers. comm.), the more sheltered valley situation perhaps being an advantage.

From about 8000BC the climate became warmer, and by the **Bronze Age** (2400–700BC) the weather was generally warm and dry, but evidence shows that climate variations were greater than before (Lamb, 1995). Farming developed here during this period and with it changes to the landscape, resulting in a reduction of tree cover and evidence for soil erosion. Signs of landscape use have been found, referred to as 'burnt mounds', with radiocarbon dates between 1700–1000BC. These are collections of heat-shattered stones and charcoal found mostly along stream and river banks, and are thought to be the debris from producing steam for bathing or from boiling water for cooking. At least forty have been found in Birmingham (Hodder, 2004). Many in the Black Country could have been destroyed by later industrial activities. Fieldwalking on agricultural land in the south of the Borough of Dudley has revealed scatters of cracked stone over most areas, including wet parts such as Uffmoor Wood (Hemingway, pers. comm.), just beyond the boundary.

An increase in the population of the West Midlands was likely during this period, as happened elsewhere in the country. There is known to have been extensive travel and trade during the Bronze Age, and there are ridgeways through this region linking with others in the surrounding countryside (perhaps the continued use of tracks already in use in the Neolithic period).

There are few remains from the **Iron Age** (700BC–43AD): known hill forts at Castle Old Fort in Brownhills and at Wychbury Hill near Dudley, and two farms found on the line of the M6 Toll motorway in Sutton Coldfield. There must have been many farms. There was a change in climate from the late Bronze Age, which became cooler and wetter, and which continued into the Iron Age. This caused a drop in the mean temperature of 2°C which shortened the growing season by up to five weeks (Lamb, 1981), followed by a very wet period between 800 and 400BC (Lamb, 1995). A climate change of this nature for a prolonged period would affect human interaction with the landscape. More pastoral activity and a reduction in crop cultivation was likely as cereals would be more difficult to grow in the cooler, wetter conditions (Hooke, 2006). Increased grazing would result in a further loss of tree cover, although during the worst of the period a reduction in the population was likely. Between about 400 and 200BC there was some improvement in the weather followed by a return to colder conditions (Cunliffe, 2004).

The climate was more favourable during the period 43–410AD when the **Romans** occupied Britain (Lamb, 1995). They arrived in our region in about 47AD and within a few years a fort had been built, located adjacent to the old Queen Elizabeth Hospital in Edgbaston, Birmingham. It was for military purposes and there were several Roman roads linking it with other places locally and beyond. It was vacated in around 200AD.

Evidence for the Roman Occupation elsewhere in the area is shown by pottery finds such as those at Parson's Hill, Kings Norton, and at a possible farm site found during redevelopment in the Birmingham Bull Ring. Kiln sites have been found at Perry Barr and Sutton Coldfield. Clay is found in the Birmingham area but the proximity of a reliable source of wood for fuel was probably more important. Both sites are close to areas of woodland known to have been coppiced after the Norman Conquest, and perhaps also in Roman times (Hodder, 2004). A large rural site at Longdales Road, Kings Norton (close to the Roman Icknield Street), and dated to the 2nd to 4th centuries, had enclosures larger than one would expect for a farmstead, suggesting the possibility of a centre for storage and supply of animals, and perhaps also crops, or a roadside market. There is similar evidence for large enclosures in Sutton Coldfield on the site of the M6 Toll motorway. The sites were on marginal land and the large enclosures suggest a specialisation in livestock. Large areas of grazing would be required, implying that the surrounding landscape would have been grassland or wood pasture and possibly also heathland

---

[2]  The pre-historic period, when documentary evidence is not available, has been divided into periods identified by the predominant material people used for tools and weapons. The approximate time periods used here are: Palaeolithic (Old Stone Age) 500,000–8500BC; Mesolithic (Middle Stone Age) 8500–4000BC; Neolithic (New Stone Age) 4000–2400BC, the qualifying word changing as the style of the tools changed; Bronze Age 2400–700BC; Iron Age 700BC–43AD. From Roman times more is known about people's way of life and this classification is no longer appropriate.

(Hodder, 2004). These remains suggest larger-scale farming activity, but elsewhere many of the farmers would have been the indigenous people, present since the Iron Age, farming a smaller area of land. The evidence suggests the possibility of many farmsteads not more than about 1km (0.6 mile) apart (Hodder, 2004). Roman pottery finds less than a mile apart in the Borough of Dudley support this view (Hemingway, pers. comm.). There is no suggestion of nucleated village settlements.

Recent **archaeological investigations** of a former river channel of the Tame at Perry Barr provide palynological (pollen-analytical) support for the changes of the landscape noted above. It covers the period from the Late Neolithic (2890–2745BC) to the Late Romano-British period (240–420AD) which included the Bronze and Iron Ages (Tetlow et al., 2009).

**Pollen analysis** involves the extraction and identification of pollen deposited in peat and other organic material, in this case organic-rich silt. The pollen can be dated, giving a relative date by its position in the sample or an absolute date by radiocarbon dating. Pollen samples dominated by tree species suggest woodland; samples dominated by grassland and weed species suggest an open landscape.

In the late Neolithic (2890–2745BC) there was dense woodland with Alder carr (wet woodland) established on the floodplain, possibly expanding to replace Pine owing to increasing wetness, shown by the presence of alluvial deposits. This wetting is not thought to be the result of human action. Drier soils beyond the floodplain were dominated by Lime, Oak and Hazel, but few herbs were present indicating shady undisturbed habitats. Spores of Polypody were found, a frequent epiphyte in Lime-Oak woodland (epiphytes are plants growing in crevices on the surface of trees). There was also evidence of grasses and sedges, probably suggesting areas of wetter grass and sedge fen.

During the Bronze Age (from about 2130–1500BC) the loss of Lime woodland to agriculture is suggested by an increase in the amounts of pollen in the samples of grasses, Ribwort Plantain, Dandelions, Common Knapweed, Fat-hen and members of the Pink family such as Chickweed and Corn Spurrey. These species are typical of cultivated and meadow-like environments and are often associated with human activities, but may also have been growing naturally on the drier parts of the floodplain. Heather and Bracken were also present, possibly indicating grassy heath habitats on the drier land. By about 1500BC (coinciding with dates for the burnt mounds) there is more reduction in tree cover and further increases in grasses and sedges.

Between 900BC and the beginning of the first millennium BC, pollen values in the samples are extremely low and no meaningful conclusions about vegetation can be drawn. Pollen includes Alder, Hazel, Heather, Dandelions, Cornflowers, the Pink family, Goosefoot, Fat-hen, Bracken and Polypody. These are considered

▲ River Tame

to be indications that renewed soil erosion had taken place which would have been exacerbated by the earlier woodland clearance.

By 240–420AD pollen levels increase and point to an open treeless landscape in both wet and dry areas, but there may have been woodland at a distance. Cornflower is present – a common arable weed – so some cereal cultivation is likely. However, the upper part of the sequence is dominated by grasses (45%), possibly including wetland grasses, and high levels of Dandelions, indicating a short grassy sward and suggesting animal grazing as the main land use. Remains of dung beetles also indicate grazing animals.

This analysis shows how the landscape changed in one locality over a long period, and species with wind-dispersed pollen such as Ribwort Plantain and most of the tree species would have arrived from quite a wide area. Archaeological investigations of a burnt mound from the Bronze Age on Griffins Brook at Cob Lane, Bournville, Birmingham, revealed environmental evidence indicating forest clearance and soil erosion just before the burnt mound was established (radiocarbon date 1270BC). Beetle remains show that the mound lay in open woodland and that there were grazing animals, indicating the possibility of woodland management or clearance. Similar evidence has been found at other sites. This suggests that woodland management and cattle grazing may have been a more general practice (Hodder, 2004).

**Heathland** is a 'cultural' landscape, i.e. it is man-made, and evidence suggests that it was present in our region in the Bronze Age. It is formed by the reduction of tree cover followed by overgrazing and/or burning, and is maintained largely by grazing pressure. The soil (typically light and well-drained) is exposed to leaching of minerals making the upper levels grey-coloured and results in lowered fertility and raised acidity – a typical heath soil type known as podzol. This is an ideal habitat for the spread of species that characterise heathland vegetation, notably members of the Heather family, together with Gorse, Bracken, Broom and certain trees (particularly Birch species). Heathland provides useful if not very productive grazing land, and the various plants had other uses such as bedding, thatching and fuel. But heathland reverts to woodland unless it is managed (Rackham, 2003). Results of archaeological investigations at Tameside, Perry Barr, suggest that heathland developed here in the Bronze Age as a result of human activity, though its extent at that time is unknown, and it has been present to a greater or lesser degree ever since. It is still present in Sutton Park, on Barr Beacon, on Brownhills Common and on the Lickey Hills (see section 5). That it was originally a common part of our landscape is clearly indicated by place names such as Heath Town, Short Heath, High Heath, Small Heath, West Heath and other locations. (See also William Yates's maps of Staffordshire (Yates, 1775; Phillips, 1984) and Warwickshire (Yates, 1789) and also Chapter 4 section 2).

What happened after the Romans departed and whether the local population was depleted is not clear. The Roman influence may have initiated changes but farming would still have been the occupation for most of the population. Scrub and trees would have regenerated anywhere no longer farmed or used for human activities. Pollen analyses from archaeological investigations at the Roman fort in Birmingham certainly suggest this (Hodder, 2004). How general this was elsewhere in this area after 410AD is not known, but there is also evidence for an abandoned field system in Sutton Coldfield (Hodder, 1992). However, signs of human activity and woodland clearance are noted again at about 600AD, after which there was more reduction of woodland and an increase in open land.

In these early times timber was the main building material. The construction of the Bronze Age camp discovered in 2010 at Pedmore, near Stourbridge in the Borough of Dudley, the Iron Age forts and the Roman fort all required large amounts, supplied from

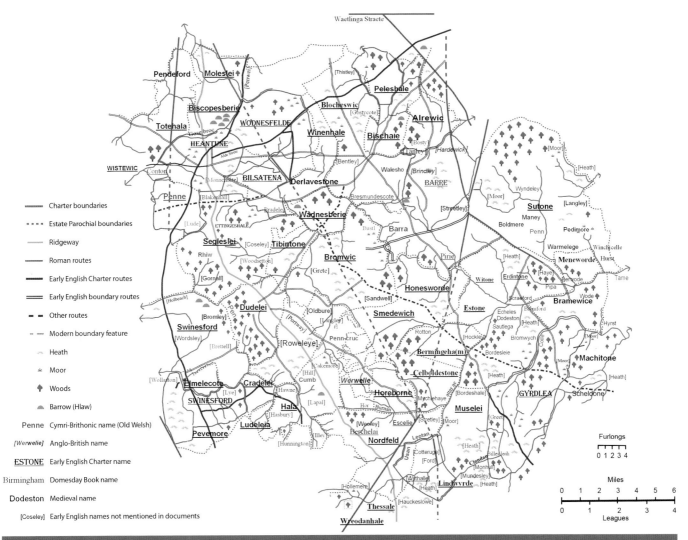

▲ Figure 3.23 Early English Birmingham and the Black Country. A map produced by John Hemingway (pers. comm.), shows the landscape at the time of the Norman Conquest (1066AD) as a result of his research from the end of the Roman period. The names shown are the Early English (Anglo-Saxon) estate names found in charters (Duignan, 1912; Mawer and Stenton, 1927; Gover *et al.*, 1936). Most are recognisable as place names in use today, and many of them are also listed in the Domesday Book of 1086. However, there are also names of British (Celtic) origin which are mostly topographical, such as Barr and Penn; river names like the Cole (Colle), Rea (atter ae) and Tame; and there are a few place names. This shows that Celts were present when the Anglo-Saxons arrived, but over time the latter became dominant. There were routeways passing through the area and the landscape was relatively open. Woodland areas are indicated; and also areas of heath and of moor.

local resources. It was also needed for the dwellings of the local people, for everyday domestic items and tools, and also for fuel. Human interaction with the landscape had changed this area from woodland in the Neolithic period to one of more open grassland and heathland by Roman times. Confirmation that heathland pre-dates the Romans is shown by the fact that the base of the Roman road through Sutton Park rests on podzol (Hodder, 2004).

Fewer pottery remains have been found in the **post-Roman/ Anglo-Saxon** period than in the Roman period but this does not mean there were fewer people. Wooden platters and bowls and horn drinking vessels, which would decay and leave no evidence, were often used instead of pottery (Hemingway, pers. comm.). The climate was wetter and colder from the 3rd to the 9th century, and in 536AD there was an environmental catastrophe thought to be a massive volcanic eruption, the location so far unidentified, which adversely affected conditions in the northern hemisphere for 15 years. Evidence from Irish bog oaks show narrow tree ring growth at that time, indicating cold summers (Lamb, 1995). Periods of disease and famine followed. The population estimated to be

about four million at the end of the Roman Period was greatly reduced (possibly by half) (Wood, 2010). Similar conditions must have existed in B&BC.

## AFTER THE NORMAN CONQUEST

According to the Domesday Book record of 1086, the amount of woodland cover in England (including wood-pasture) was 15% (Rackham, 2003). The population of England at that date has been estimated to be 1.7 million (Broadberry *et al.*, 2011), so there were only likely to be a few thousand people in B&BC, perhaps no more than two to three thousand [3].

From about 1000 to 1300 the climate was warm and more settled (the Medieval Warm Period) and the population rose

---

[3]  Population – Before the ten-yearly national census introduced in 1801 all population figures are estimates which are continually being updated in the light of new evidence.

to about 4.75 million nationally. There had been no urban development in the Anglo-Saxon period, but now settlements started to grow (Rowlands, 1987) and evidence shows increasing commercial activity. Charters were granted for weekly markets and annual fairs and, as these had to be paid for, the amount of trade must have justified the expense. The chief trades were tanning and leatherwork; wood and metal working; textiles; manufacture of tools, and domestic items made of horn and bone. In Birmingham, pottery and tiles were also made (Hodder, 2004). From at least the 13th century local supplies of iron ore, charcoal and coal were used in the metal trade (Rowlands, 1987); and water power, already introduced by the Anglo-Saxons for corn grinding (Jones, 1963), was used in the fulling process in the textile trade. Water was also important in the leather and tanning trades. In addition, pewter and brass goods were manufactured, both requiring raw materials from beyond the region. The period after 1066 showed a good deal of economic activity in England, involving much travel and trade in which merchants and traders from this area participated. There are records of long-distance journeys: London, Lincoln, Nottingham, Southampton and Bristol were among the destinations mentioned, as well as continental contacts. By the 16th century locally made pewter (a rapidly expanding industry) was being sold in London, and by 1600 local merchants were successfully challenging the monopoly of the London iron market (Rowlands, 1987).

▲ Ruins of Dudley Castle

However, **farming** would have been the main occupation, and in some of the larger settlements farming may have been carried out within the town, as was the case in Birmingham. The settlements were surrounded by fields for arable crops and were linked by a network of roads and tracks (Rowlands, 1987). Domestic animals were pastured on grassland or heath commons and there were also likely to be areas of wood pasture, land managed for woodland products and grazing (Hodder, 2004).

Additional resources of all kinds would have been needed to cater for the growing population, and more land required for dwellings and farming. Timber remained the chief building material, and wood and charcoal were needed as a heat source for domestic and trade use. The population was not large but the amount of timber used must have been considerable. Grazing land would be required for the animals used for transporting goods: trains of pack horses were the most usual means, but carts drawn either by horses or oxen were in use from an early date. The Severn and, later, the Trent were also used. In spite of the overland journey to reach them, carriage charges were cheaper and goods could be

carried in bulk. Grazing also would be required for the Welsh cattle trade passing through the area, starting in the 15th century, some for the local markets, and others to destinations further east and south like London (Rowlands, 1987).

Much domestic and industrial waste would have ended up in the nearest watercourse, contaminating the water with noxious substances, particularly from the leather trade; the fulling process in textile manufacture used fuller's earth, human urine and soap to remove grease from the cloth which then needed rinsing; and water from the dyeing process would have been hot. The presence of fisheries, however, suggests that water pollution was not especially great. Dry waste from other trades, such as cinders and slag from the forges, would simply have been dumped on any convenient piece of ground. However, at this time, bearing in mind the relatively small population, most of the damage to the landscape caused by human activity would probably have been quite local.

However, by 1350 **tree cover** had been reduced from 15% nationally in 1086 to possibly as little as 7% (Rackham, 2003), and a similar state of affairs in our region was likely. The biggest single use of timber in the Middle Ages was for building. It was used for decoration as well as for structural support in the larger houses of the wealthy (Rackham, 2003). Wood was also required for many reasons in both domestic and trade situations such as heat, furniture, tools and carts. In the 13th century coal was already being used in the Black Country and the Birmingham area and may point to a shortage of wood for fuel. In the Black Country it was used in both domestic and industrial situations (Rowlands, 1987). In Birmingham industrial use was more likely, but coal found on local medieval moated manor house sites also suggests its domestic use as a status symbol (Hodder, 2004). The medieval records for Pensnett Chase in the Manor of Dudley show that the amount of woodland recorded in the Domesday Book had been 'grossly depleted' by 1273. It was land held in common, and those with common rights used it for grazing which would check the re-growth of trees. A licence issued for common pasture dated 1348 excluded goats which, as browsers, prefer saplings to grass (Hemingway, 2009). There must have been other areas of land held in common used for grazing, and the numbers of grazing animals would have increased to cater for the growing population. This would have contributed to the reduction of tree cover in the Middle Ages.

Having arrived in England in 1348, the **Black Death** reached the Midlands in 1349, but was preceded by a 'devastatingly sudden' change in the weather from about 1313, heralding variable climate and periods of bad harvests and famine (notably the summer of 1315) which continued into the 15th century (Lamb, 1995). Immediately prior to the Black Death the national population estimate was 4.81 million, but this was reduced to an estimated 1.9 million by 1450 (Broadberry et al., 2011) resulting in many social changes, particularly in agricultural customs. Payment of feudal dues 'in kind' gradually ceased, to be replaced by waged labour, and land tenure practices changed. The enclosure by 'private agreement' of formerly open land began, and by the end of the 15th century many villages had a mixture of enclosed and open land (Rowlands, 1987). The overall effect on the landscape was an increase in land devoted to animal pasture rather than arable, stock rearing being easier to manage with the reduced availability of labour. Grazing would require more land than arable crops and would have resulted in reduced tree growth (Hemingway pers. comm.). Continued grazing pressure could have led to the development of heathland (Rackham, 2003).

It was not until the end of the 16th century that the population of England regained the highest level suggested for the Middle

Ages – an estimated 4.27 million (Broadberry et al., 2011). Towns were not yet densely inhabited and there is mention of orchards, tenter grounds (where weavers washed and stretched their fabrics on tenter frames), gardens and waste ground, leaving plenty of odd corners where wild plants could thrive. However, spaces were beginning to fill up (Rowlands, 1987). By the 17th century houses still had timber frames, but these were no longer visible and far less timber was needed (Rackham, 2003). Roof tiles and bricks made from local materials were increasingly used (Rowlands, 1987).

## THE DEVELOPMENT OF INDUSTRY

In the 16th century, possibly by as early as 1507, a diversion to Shrewsbury and the Welsh Marches was made near Stonebridge (just east of the National Exhibition Centre) from the main London to Chester route, bringing it through Birmingham and along the ridge between the Stour and the Tame (Pelham, 1950). By 1600 it was one of the main West Midlands routes and would have been advantageous to trade.

From the late 16th and throughout the 17th century, trade that had developed during the Middle Ages continued to expand, resulting in greater use of local resources and more encroachment into the natural environment. The bulk of these resources were in the **Black Country** which lies over the southern part of the South Staffordshire Coalfield. It was the abundance of **coal** that was of supreme importance. There were nine coal seams of various qualities. The 'Thick Coal' seam, often referred to as the 10 yard or thirty foot coal, was "the richest and thickest coal seam in the whole country" (Wise and Johnson, 1950). There was also **ironstone** of various grades used for different types of metal work. There were good quality deposits, among them those at Rushall and Walsall, but "for the most part the ores were not of high grade (25%–40% iron) and only suitable for the nail trade" (Wise and Johnson, 1950). However, it was an important trade including the export market[4]. There were other rocks and minerals of value in the various trades and manufacturing industries: clay, limestone, Coal Measure Sandstone, Etruria Marl (from which the blue bricks were made in the 19th century), and sand and gravel. **Water** was also an important resource. The Tame, Stour, Rea and Cole and their tributaries provided power for the water mills and for other

---

[4] Estimates in 1799 gave the number of nailers in the region as 35–40,000, consuming about 10,000 tons of iron p.a. (Nash, 1799). Many of the towns and villages in this area are mentioned.

▲ **Sarehole water mill and mill pond, by the River Cole**

trades requiring water, for example leather and textile processing. **Birmingham** did not share the variety of mineral wealth with which the Black Country was provided but benefited from the proximity of these resources in its industrial development. However, it had good deposits of clay, sand, sandstone, pebbles and gravel which were put to good use (Hodder, 2004).

Although there were deposits of iron here, it was also imported. Records show that Birmingham, King's Norton, West Bromwich and Wolverhampton were importing iron from Spain[5] as early as the mid 16th century (Royal Commission on Historical Manuscripts, 1974); and in the 17th and 18th centuries the Midlands metal workers "consumed a large proportion of the iron manufactured in England" (Awty, 1957: 71). Iron was also imported from Sweden, and later from Russia and North America. It was usually imported as pig iron. **Metal working** was important and developed rapidly: nail making[6]; lockmaking; agricultural implements; blades for domestic and military use; and the metal parts for the harnesses for draft animals and riding horses. Domestic items made from brass and copper were also manufactured. **Harnesses and saddles** (an associated trade) were another important developing trade (Rowlands, 1987).

In the mid-16th century there was a further extension of the use of **water power** to improve the production of iron in both the smelting and the refining processes. The ironstone was smelted using charcoal in a small clay bloomery which had an output of only a few kilos. New furnaces built of stone were introduced from the Kent and Sussex iron producing area (The Weald), and the output increased to about one ton per furnace (Rowlands, 1987). The first was built at West Bromwich in 1561/2 (Hooke, 2006). There were also larger and heavier 'tilt hammers' at the forges for refining the smelted iron (pig iron). The Wealden Iron Research Group (www.wealdeniron.org.uk) indicates that it was the new hammers that had driven the need to improve the blast furnace. Water power was required for both, and the forges – requiring greater water power than the furnaces – relocated to larger streams. This resulted in a separation of the two processes previously carried out on the same site. The forges were more numerous than the furnaces because refining required more intensive work than the smelting process (Hemingway, pers. comm.). Charcoal still had to be used for smelting but the forges could use coal. In the 16th century, water power was also brought into use for blade grinding, and in the 17th century for slitting bar iron into rods for the nail trade. By this time there were many water mills on both rivers and streams.

During the latter half of the 16th century, iron manufacture began to move closer to Birmingham along the Tame valley so supplies for the Birmingham smithies could avoid the expense of the long haul from Cannock Chase, which was their source of supply at that time. By about 1600 there is evidence that there were several other iron works on the Tame, which in this part of its course had sufficient volume to provide a steady flow. There were woods at Perry Manor that could provide the fuel and wooded country south of Birmingham when local supplies gave out (Pelham, 1950).

The increased use of water power leading to the creation of additional mill ponds and the separation of the different processes of the various trades resulted not only in increased take-up of land but also in much more movement of goods and materials about the area. However, the effort must have been justified by an

---

[5] Possibly steel for the blade industry.
[6] The term nail included a variety of fastening devices: sprigs, brads, tack, spikes, sheath nails, clouts, dog-eared frost nails, rose, sparrables and others (Rowlands, 1987).

increase in the production of the finished goods and therefore in financial returns.

Not only was the manufacturing industry expanding: so were the towns, and retail and wholesale markets began to emerge. By 1650 every market town and some of the larger villages had permanent retail shops. A large range of goods was available, some manufactured in England and others imported from abroad, but generally sold only in small quantities (Rowland, 1987). Wholesale marketing with links between local centres and the London market stimulated trade, and merchandise was reaching a wider market. By the late 17th century "an increasing emphasis on creating as well as supplying demand encouraged innovation . . . and new customers were sought out" (Rowlands, 1987). The spur was the growth of the population and of consumer demand in England and Europe; the opening up of the West Indies and mainland America, which was dependent on the slave trade; plus the increased availability of a new range of raw materials which were not obtainable locally but depended on national and international trading contacts. The small consumer bought more but cheaper goods, and a whole range of merchandise became available that could be classed as extras which were good to have but not basic necessities. These included the 'toys', the small decorative items such as buttons, buckles and enamel boxes for which Birmingham was famous, which were first noted in 1710. The main centre of production was Birmingham, but they were also made at Wednesbury and (famously in the case of enamels) at Bilston (Rowlands, 1987).

## Charcoal shortage

At the beginning of the 17th century there were rumours that charcoal was becoming scarce owing to a shortage of wood. Coal was already being used in many of the forges for refining, but at that date there was no alternative to charcoal for smelting the ironstone because the sulphur content in coal made the pig iron brittle. The iron industry was one of the heaviest users of wood where, on average, four pounds of wood were required to produce one pound of charcoal (Diamond, 2005). Glass-makers (originally from Lorraine) were in competition with the iron manufacturers because of their need for large quantities of wood – not charcoal (Hooke, 2006) – for their furnaces. Those at Eccleshall and some from Cannock moved to the Stour valley, attracted both by the coal (as an alternative source of fuel) and the high quality refractory clay at Amblecote and Lye (Rowlands, 1987). The leather trade had grown in importance and oak bark was required for the tanning process. Walsall, noted for saddlery, obtained supplies from the Wyre Forest (Hooke, 2006), which implies that the woodlands here were not sufficient for local needs.[7]

B&BC may never have been self-sufficient in charcoal as records show that it was imported from various locations beyond the area. The iron workers at Dudley and Halesowen obtained it from the Wyre Forest as early as the 12th and 13th centuries (Hooke, 2006); it was brought from Arden (east of Birmingham) in the 17th century to furnaces and forges on the Tame and Rea because fuel was scarce (Jones, 1963); and the accounts for the Halesowen forge in the early 18th century show that it was then being obtained from Kingsbury and Lapworth (north-east and south-east of Birmingham respectively) and Glazeley (near Bridgnorth) (Wise and Johnson, 1950). This could mean that there never had been sufficient woodland locally to provide the charcoal required, or

that the heavy use of timber during the Middle Ages had depleted the available supplies.

Charcoal is produced from coppiced trees and in theory should have been a renewable resource if woods were managed with care, as they are known to have been in the Stour Valley (Hemingway, pers. comm.). Well-managed woodlands could supply surprising amounts of timber and underwood products. **Timber** refers to trees scattered within woods and allowed to grow until more than 2 feet in girth, and used for beams and planks. Sometimes trees in hedges were used for timber. Timber trees were usually replaced by seedlings. **Underwood** is the product of woodland management to provide rods, poles and logs used for specialised purposes, especially in large quantities for fuel. The two terms are not interchangeable, timber for example being used in building construction and wood for fires (Rackham, 2003). Best management practices may not always have been used, however. Jones (1963) records that shortages of charcoal and water were causing smiths to migrate downstream even before the end of the 14th century. Pelham (1950) quoting Salzmann (1923) mentions that the early smiths, likely to be itinerant workers, cleared the woods as they went; this does not sound like good management, but at that date the amount of iron being processed may not have been large. Some blast furnaces needed to move from previous production sites owing to lack of fuel. Wednesbury, one of the early metal-producing sites, seems to have been denuded of woodland by the end of the 16th century (Hackwood (1902) cited in Pelham (1950)). In the 17th century the speed of run-off along the Tame increased because woods were cut down and affected the water flow, causing increased ponding of the river above the new mill weirs (Jones, 1963).

The possibility of converting coal to coke as an alternative to charcoal to smelt iron was first attempted in the 17th century (by Dud Dudley) because of the supposed impending shortage of charcoal. Nevertheless, Rackham writes that the ironmasters would have protected their supplies and had their works close to woodland because of the cost and difficulty of transporting charcoal. However, as noted above, charcoal was imported by some producers in this region, perhaps ensuring their supplies because local sources were insufficient. Rackham says that the real reason why manufacturers began to explore the possible use of coal for smelting iron was because the labour costs of coal were cheaper (Rackham, 2003).

## Landscape comments

From the Middle Ages the increase in the population and developments in technology resulted in increased manufacturing, trade and transport, with the inevitable spread of housing, farmland and industrial sites over the landscape. Grazing land was required for farm animals and also for the thousands of horses that were used for transport over the centuries. From the early 18th century B&BC became increasingly dependent on external sources for food supplies. Rowlands (1987) records that the parishes surrounding the area had been supplying a wide range of vegetables to town markets. Fruit came from Pershore and Evesham. Water-borne pollution did not appear to have had a detrimental effect on fish stocks. Riverside fisheries were noted in the 17th century (Rowlands, 1987), but no mention is made of serious water pollution and its effect on fish stocks until the 1860s. There would also have been increasing amounts of waste from mining and quarrying, and slag and cinder heaps from the metal trades, but these activities had yet to reach their highest levels.

However, although the population is known to have increased rapidly during the latter part of the 18th century, especially in

---

[7] Oak bark was always used – no other would do (Rackham, 2003) and Hooke (2006) records that 25 tonnes of bark were required to tan 100 hides.

Birmingham, even by 1800 the population would still have been perhaps no more than 300,000 people. This would have limited the damage to the landscape, leaving plenty of open space between the towns and villages, and the mining and industrial activity, where spontaneous vegetation could grow.

## THE INDUSTRIAL REVOLUTION

By the beginning of the 18th century industrialisation in the Black Country was only just beginning to have a greater impact on the landscape: farming continued, but a curate noted in 1717, "Today we reaped the coalpit field". During the century "common fields and pastures gradually became a patchwork of closes, cottages, gardens, pits and works" ( Rowlands, 1987).

In order for the iron industry to expand further several improvements were required. The first was an increase in the supply of coal. In the 17th century coal was still mined chiefly from the outcrops and shallow pits (bell pits). Reaching the deeper seams for better quality coal was prevented by flooding, and a replacement for the horse gins then in use was needed. There was also a hope of improving smelting and refining techniques so that coal could be used instead of charcoal. Thirdly, an improvement was required in the transport system.

Information about the mechanisation of industry during the 18th and 19th centuries is well known and available elsewhere. The advances were made by local people and also by those attracted to the area because of the developing industries. Progress began with the invention and installation of the first steam pump in 1711 (by Thomas Newcomen) which improved mine drainage. The use of coal to replace charcoal for smelting and refining the iron ore followed, the various stages being completed during the first decades of the 19th century. These improvements enabled the iron industry to progress at a faster rate.

Horse-drawn road transport had become inadequate and a better system of carrying bulk goods was needed. The suggestion to construct **canals** was proposed early in the 18th century, but the first was not completed until 1769. The network gradually expanded over the following decades to provide both local transport and links to the national canals. Canal construction continued until the 1850s, and they continued to be used for transport into the 20th century. By the middle of the 19th century the mining and industrial areas of the Black Country had the densest network of canals for any given area of comparable size in Britain (Johnson and Wise, 1950), and included many branch canals to connect collieries and industrial works to the main canals (Hadfield (1966) cited in Rowlands, 1987). There were also railway tracks for wagons drawn by horses or stationary engines with winches, connecting the coalfields to canal wharfs or to industrial sites (Rowlands, 1987). The canals were advantageous for loose bulky materials such as coal, clay, sand and gravel. Birmingham developed its own canal system, and the Birmingham Canal became the busiest in the kingdom with 300 tons of goods going daily to London, increasing to over 3 million gross tonnage by 1838: most of this was coal (Rowlands, 1987). The journey took four days. There was great competition for industrial sites on or near to the main canals (Johnson and Wise, 1950; Rowlands, 1987).

The canals were an added imposition on the landscape. They were not an unmixed blessing, and some businesses relying on water power were put out of action by them. Drainage was altered: some streams were diverted or absorbed, and mill pools and leats cut off, some streams becoming 'foul ditches'. Surface subsidence due to shallow mining occurred causing 'swag

pools' to develop, and quarrying resulted in some sites being abandoned (Jones, 1963).

However, after 60 years the volume of traffic was causing congestion and the potential of steam **railways** was being discussed. Rail transport became possible from the late 1830s, providing further improvement in the carriage of goods. From the 1840s a confused system of railway lines was added to the maze of roads and canals, and often ran parallel to them along the low-lying valleys of the Tame and Rea. As with the canals, industries also followed the railways. More durable road surfaces were developed from the 18th century, including Tarmac of Ettingshall in the 19th century using furnace slag and tar. In the early years of the 20th century lorries and commercial vans were added to the means of carrying goods and materials, although horse-drawn transport continued for a time (Johnson and Wise, 1950; Rowlands, 1987; Collins, 1998).

## TRANSITION IN THE 19TH CENTURY AND ITS EFFECTS ON THE LANDSCAPE

At the beginning of the 19th century, with a population of possibly no more than 200,000–300,000, the whole area could still be described as predominantly rural. Intensive industry was only just beginning but was gathering speed. **Birmingham** was the largest town, centred on the Bull Ring. In 1086 it had been one of the smallest settlements listed in the Domesday Book, but the tax returns for 1327 show it as the third largest town in Warwickshire (Leather, 2001). It continued to expand over the centuries into a busy industrial and market centre. At the beginning of the 19th century it had fully emerged as the leading industrial and commercial focus of the region (Wise and Thorpe, 1950). In the **Black Country** district, there were several large centres of population, for example Dudley and Wolverhampton, and many smaller towns and villages.

The invention of James Watt's steam engine for pumping and rotary power in 1783 meant that forges and furnaces need no longer be confined to watercourses, and the larger industries in the Black Country began to move to the coalfields where iron ore, and sometimes other minerals such as sand and clay, were all available on one site. Steam power was costly and only economical if kept in use for 24 hours a day and seven days a week (Rowlands, 1987), so the smaller firms continued to use water power and traditional production methods (Wise and Thorpe, 1950). The drainage problem was not solved completely as it was not cost-effective to install the pumps below a certain depth. Steam power was used in Birmingham as larger factories gradually developed from the mid-19th century, but was not suitable for use in most of the workshops of the small traders which at that time comprised the majority of its workforce (Chinn 1994).

The difference in the development of Birmingham and the Black Country is mainly related to their geology and the nature of their resources. The **Black Country's** riches had to be extracted from the ground, and processing these before the 19th century relied on water power, which necessitated the movement of raw materials and goods about the area. Development of the heavy industries was haphazard. Villages and farms were still in existence but mine shafts were being sunk, blast furnaces constructed, quarries dug and new canal basins cut, with tramways and tracks sprawling across the fields. No thought was given to planning, which led to the waste of many millions of tons of coal which could have been extracted (Johnson and Wise, 1950). The population increased rapidly as people seeking work flocked into the district. Houses appeared along the roads, and in clusters among the pit banks and slag heaps (Rowlands, 1987). As with industry, there was no planning and towns and villages grew, spreading out from the old centres (Jones, 1963).

Only the larger industrial businesses had moved to the coalfield. Elsewhere, industry continued as before, some still along rivers and streams. Beyond the limits of the coalfield extractive industries of a different kind were leaving their mark on the landscape: clay and Etruria Marl for glass-making and bricks, and sand and gravel for building. So the towns and villages beyond the mining area spread as their industries expanded, also at the expense of the countryside.

The only extractive minerals in the **Birmingham** area were clay, sand and gravel. Other raw materials, which included coal and iron from the Black Country, had to be brought in by road until canals were built. The area did not suffer the same upheavals as the Black Country because of the lack of rocks and minerals that made the Industrial Revolution possible. Manufacturing was centred mainly in Birmingham, and the Rea and its tributary streams supplied water for the trades and power for mills. The population increased, with people migrating to the town in search of the opportunities offered by the rapidly expanding industries and were accommodated within the town. Houses were crowded into back yards and any other available space. Villages were scattered in the surrounding countryside and Sutton Coldfield was the only other town. The surrounding area was patchily covered by farmland, woodland and large areas of heath such as Birmingham Heath (now Winson Green), Moseley Common (now Moseley Bog Nature Reserve), and Sutton Park (formerly part of the much larger Sutton Chase).

Coal had been used since the Middle Ages, but from the early 19th century the amount used increased[8]. Sulphur in the soot from the many steam engine chimneys and also from domestic fires, both as dust and dissolved as 'acid rain', would have been detrimental to the vegetation, especially in the immediate area of the industrial works, and would also be carried by wind and rain over a wider area. The extent of the damage cannot now be ascertained. Lichens are particularly sensitive to atmospheric pollution, and signs of their decline were noted nationally at the end of the 18th century, and from that time acid rain began to spread to rural areas (Rackham, 2003). In 1840, industry was still developing in our region and only about 15% of the coalfield was in use. By 1885, 46% of it had already become disused. This proportion increased as the extractive industries declined and, by 1900, 65% had been abandoned (Quigley, 2010). The amount of damage may therefore have been limited and not concentrated in one area for a long period. However, although gas and electricity were brought into use in the latter part of the century, some industries continued to use coal for power in the 20th century. With the increases in the population and therefore in housing, home heating, industry and transport, atmospheric pollution during the 20th century may have been worse than in the 19th century until the Clean Air Act of 1956. The accumulation of exhaust gases from the increasing use of motor vehicles has added to the pollution problem. However, since the 1980s many different forms of lichen have started to reappear, signifying a reduction in acid rain (Rackham, 2003).

Before the advent of modern drainage systems, watercourses were the usual recipients of industrial waste and sewage. As the population and industry increased from the 18th century, the Tame, its tributaries and the canals were no exception. The canals

became prime sites for industry because of their transport value. Industries grew in size, and as new ones were introduced the range as well as amounts of noxious waste products increased, and included human sewage. Major pollution incidents in the 1860s and 1870s destroyed fisheries in the Tame, and by 1945 the river was so polluted it could not sustain any life at all. The 'Sustainable Management of Urban River Flood Plains Project' (Birmingham City Council, 2007) reported that pollutants in the ground were also flushed into the streams, rivers, canals and reservoirs by rain, destroying many natural aquatic habitats. Legislation to remedy the situation was not implemented until after World War II.

Rowlands (1987), however, comments that although the Tame was heavily polluted with sewage the soil on the banks was enriched (whether by flooding or deliberate application was not stated) and enabled local gardeners to grow flowers and flower roots for the townspeople, especially gillyflowers (Carnations and Pinks) which were clove-scented. On the other hand, this enrichment led to the simplification of semi-natural water-margin communities, which became replaced by smaller numbers of competitive species. This change is still apparent along almost all our streams and rivers, and must have been even worse in the days of unregulated waste disposal.

Many plant species, with some surprising plant associations in unexpected situations, have nevertheless managed to survive the landscape upheavals in the Black Country. Attempts to repair the damage caused by mining and industry were made as early as 1815 by the Earl of Dudley, who planted the abandoned limestone quarries at Dudley and the Wren's Nest with Beech, Sycamore, Ash and Alder. Similarly, much of the woodland at Saltwells Local Nature Reserve was planted at a similar date (possibly as early as 1790) to clothe and reclaim a landscape scarred by coal mining. Local authorities later created parks on former coal mining sites, for example East Park in Wolverhampton. Between 1904 and 1924 the Midland Reafforesting Association planted about 650 acres (260ha) of trees on pit waste, furnace slag and sand pits, but as the wooded areas became established only a poor ground flora developed (Rees and Skelding, 1950), and this is still true today. However, many of the best places for native plants found today are the derelict sites that have not received any cosmetic treatment and have been left to recover naturally. Examples include Ladymoor Pool on the Dudley/Wolverhampton border; the subsidence pools which have conserved a pre-industrial

▲ **Beech at Saltwells Wood, possibly planted as post-industrial reclamation in the 1790s**

---

[8] "By 1830… Britain was consuming coal with an annual energy output equivalent to 15 million acres of forest, about three times the size of Wales." (Matt Ridley, cited in The Economist 23 October 2010: 89)

landscape at Clayhanger and other sites in Walsall; and many of the most interesting nature reserves of Dudley and Sandwell.

For the first few decades of the 19th century, many areas of farmland in the Black Country were scattered between the industrial sites. Farming was still not intensive, and many plants could survive in the permanent pastures and along the edges of fields. Much of this farmland still included the remnants of coppice and woodlands that had been such an important part of the medieval village economy, and some persist to this day. Undeveloped areas alongside the roads, canals and railways added further new habitats, and the distribution and spread of countless plant species are directly correlated with these transport systems. Canals have been present in the landscape since quite early in the development of industry, long before the railways, and offered room for plants both in and by the water. This means that the associated flora can have some antiquity and interest, although the submerged aquatic flora must have changed a great deal in response to variation in intensity of use. Busy canals are often too opaque and disturbed for a submerged flora to survive, and abandoned canals can rapidly become overgrown with species-poor swamp (Rees and Skelding, 1950). As more land was brought into use and abandoned in its turn the picture continually changed, and there are frequent references to 'derelict' land. When land is left unattended nature begins to take over, but these abandoned sites would have had piles of cinders, slag or pit waste on them. Which plant species colonised and how long it took would depend on various factors, including the nature of the industrial waste. The piles of pit waste would be from underground and would not have had a seed bank, so growth of plants would not be immediate. Heaps of hot slag and cinders accumulated on many industrial sites, and coal spoil tips and even underground seams were capable of spontaneous combustion and could burn for years. Smoke and flames were still issuing out of the ground in the post-industrial area close to the Crooked House pub in Dudley in the 1980s. When sites were abandoned the surface would cool down quite quickly, but what was below would remain hot for perhaps 20–30 years. Weathering and the accumulation of wind-blown dust and soil were needed to provide a reasonable substrate for seeds to germinate. Shallow-rooted vegetation could then become established, but the subterranean heat would delay the growth of deeper rooted vegetation such as trees. However, as the whole of the available area was never in use at any one time, there must have been many places where wild plants could survive.

▲ 'Crooked House' pub, Dudley

By 1860 it was already being forecast that the **South Staffordshire Coalfield** would be exhausted in about 40 years. Drainage was a continuing problem at depth, which led to the closure of some mines. Pig iron production had reached its peak in 1865, and iron ore was already being imported from north Staffordshire, Northamptonshire and elsewhere (Johnson and Wise, 1950). There was also increased competition from steel-making districts. The ore in the Black Country was not suitable for steel production as it was not phosphorous-free haematite ore (Rowlands, 1987). By the 1880s half the mining land in the Black Country had become disused and the prospect of the exhaustion of local resources had to be faced (Quigley, 2010). However, gas and electricity were being introduced as alternative power sources; raw materials were imported from elsewhere; and a skilled workforce was available. The ability to innovate was demonstrated as industry in the whole area, Birmingham as well as the Black Country, adapted and diversified.

## INDUSTRIAL AND RESIDENTIAL EXPANSION FROM 1800

In spite of the upheavals caused by mining and manufacturing dating from the late 18th century and the different types of industries that followed in the 19th century, the greatest human environmental impact in the region has been the population growth and the spread of housing in the 20th century from the inter-war years up to the present. In the early years of the 19th century in the **Black Country** industry was spreading over the landscape and houses were built around the mines and industrial works and on open ground. In **Birmingham**, where industry was still town based, expansion was outwards for both residential and industrial accommodation. As industry expanded during the 19th century, the houses built to accommodate the influx of workers were of shoddy construction, with no adequate services or sanitation, and no thought given to planning.

Heavy industry was based mainly in the Black Country but some also developed in Birmingham. However, the basis of industry until the 1860s in all urban centres was the dwelling of the small craftsman with his workshop in his home or adjacent to it. Small industries persist to the present day. In the latter part of the 19th century, there was a change to larger factory-style premises which in **Birmingham** moved to undeveloped land by the canals and railways, the floodplain of the Tame and Birmingham Heath. Industry also started to move further out, influenced by the transport links, and locations included villages which until the 1860s had retained their rural character. Residential accommodation developed around and between the industrial areas. Industries and housing continued to spread in all directions from the town centre. In the **Black Country** industry had already spread over the landscape, and the towns and villages spread further out towards each other. But the end result was the same: farms, heathland and woodland areas gradually disappeared, although in the Black Country the more patchy expansion often led to small areas of countryside becoming surrounded and isolated, and some of those still persist. Similar examples are not found in the Birmingham area owing to the different nature of their development. In the Black Country, former derelict mining has also sometimes been redeveloped for housing (Quigley, 2010).

As more people became able to afford better quality housing there was an emerging view that conditions for the poor should also be improved, but it was not until the latter part of the 19th century that action was initiated to implement these ideas

(Rowlands, 1987). Larger houses of better quality began to replace the slums of the labouring classes. These new suburban houses had water and drainage facilities and their own, often sizeable, gardens. More land was required per dwelling and for the first time residential accommodation was not part of the industrial complexes. Development continued after the Second World War and high rise blocks of flats made their appearance, particularly in the 1960s.

The result of these changes has been a massive reduction in the proportion of open land in B&BC, especially since the 1930s. The conurbation has been transformed from clusters of towns and villages to a much more uniform urban landscape. Redevelopment included the use of the World War II bombed sites, many for new industries or the extension of older ones. Industry has also continued to use land, although there have been changes, particularly in the 1980s when some huge iconic industries, such as Bilston Steel, collapsed. The land vacated by these industries has been re-used for housing, shopping and leisure centres, trading estates, and new enterprises. The redevelopment of such 'brownfield' sites and the pressure to develop remaining open pockets of inner city land have attracted criticism from urban ecologists, who value them for their wildlife and their potential to transform the lives of city dwellers for the better, but redevelopment is set to continue into the 21st century.

## CONCLUSIONS

It was not until the introduction of the ten-yearly National Census in 1801 that it was possible to establish reasonably accurate population figures. Overall the population has increased since the Middle Ages, in spite of periods of disease and famine. In the latter part of the 18th century, the attraction of employment prospects in the growing industries led to a rapid increase in the population, followed by even greater increases during the 19th century.

The total population of England in 1801 was 8.3 million. At that time B&BC included parts of the counties of Staffordshire, Warwickshire and Worcestershire. The combined total population for these counties was 586,676 (about 7% of the national total): Staffordshire's share of this was 239,153 and a good many people were likely to have lived in the Black Country; of Warwickshire's total of 208,190, some 60,822 lived in Birmingham (all other suburbs now included within the City boundary are excluded from this figure); and Worcestershire's total of 139,333 included Dudley and parts of what are now within the City of Birmingham (Office of National Statistics). The total population in this area was unlikely to have been above 300,000.

In the course of 12,000 years the landscape of B&BC has changed: from tundra, followed by woodland; then tree cover was reduced when farming began and heathlands developed.

### Table 3.11 Birmingham and Black Country time line

| 500,000–8,500BC Palaeolithic Period | 8,500–4,000BC Mesolithic Period | 4,000–2,400BC Neolithic Period | 2,400–700BC Bronze Age | 700BC–43AD Iron Age | 43–410AD Roman Period | 410–1066AD Anglo-Saxons |
|---|---|---|---|---|---|---|
| • Retreat of ice sheet about 10,000BC<br>• Return of tundra plants, including heather, followed by trees and animals<br>• Local quartzite pebbles used for stone tools | • Climate improves<br>• Hunter-gatherers: Earliest dated evidence of humans 8,500BC in Birmingham<br>• Flint tools found<br>• 'Wildwood' developed and covered most of Britain by 4,500BC | • Farming in Stour Valley<br>• Polished stone axes from other parts of the country found here | • Main period of farming growth: loss of tree cover; heathland development<br>• Burnt Mounds<br>• Evidence of soil erosion<br>• Bronze Age camp found in 2010AD in Borough of Dudley<br>• Late Bronze Age: climate deteriorates | • Little evidence – hill forts and two farms<br>• Weather continues to deteriorate<br>• Crop growing difficult, leading to more animal grazing | • Roman fort built and occupied until 200AD<br>• Evidence of Roman pottery and kilns, and large-scale farming<br>• Most local British people would be farmers on small farms; there is no evidence for villages | • Environmental catastrophe in 536AD<br>• Few obvious remains of their presence but most place names today have Old English (Anglo-Saxon) origins and are listed in the Domesday Book (1086)<br>• Celtic names: most are topographical referring to rivers and landscape features; there are a few place names, indicating the |

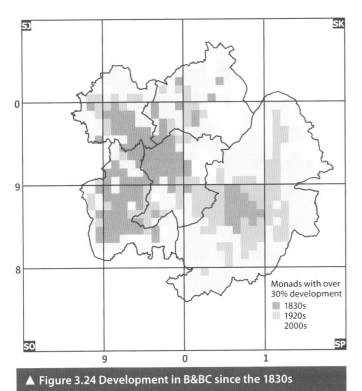

Monads with over 30% development
- 1830s
- 1920s
- 2000s

▲ Figure 3.24 Development in B&BC since the 1830s

For the first few millennia the population would have been small, and industries were small-scale until the Industrial Revolution. Since the Black Death in 1349, in a little less than 700 years, the population has made an overall increase from no more than a few thousand people to just over 2 million today, spread over the same area of 624 square kilometres (Figure 3.24). Industry and commerce played a large part in this, but it is the growth of housing associated with it which now dominates the landscape. However, industry has changed and considerable areas have been abandoned, and a variety of post-industrial vegetation has developed which in many ways characterises our local botany.

Despite and because of these developments, in both Birmingham and in the Black Country there remain a surprising number of open spaces where a variety of wild plants still grow, and semi-natural vegetation is encouraged or tolerated: sites designated as nature reserves, urban parks and country parks; remnants of agricultural land and woodland areas; former industrial sites and derelict land; and gardens and allotments. However, the planned increase in housing is likely to mean that some of these open spaces will continue to disappear.

| 1066 – Norman Conquest: Middle Ages | Growth of Industry 16th–17th centuries | Industrial Revolution 18th–19th centuries | 20th century | 21st century |
|---|---|---|---|---|
| • 1086 Domesday Book: Today's local place names listed; tree cover nationally only 15%<br><br>• Improved climate; population increase: towns and villages developed; trade and travel nationally and with London and Europe<br><br>• Water power used in textile industry 13th century<br><br>• Early 14th century – climate deteriorated again<br><br>• 1349 – Black Death: population greatly reduced; long period of recovery<br><br>• Further reduction in tree cover to 7% by 1350<br><br>• Changes in agricultural customs; more cattle farming<br><br>• Welsh cattle trade from 15th century | • From late 16th century trade expanded; greater use of local resources, most in the Black Country; coal of particular importance; local deposits of iron ore, but also imported<br><br>• Improvements in industrial technology: water power used in metal trades from 16th century; early small-scale smelting gradually replaced in 16th century by new, large stone-built blast furnaces and larger, water-operated forge hammers introduced from the Kent/Sussex iron-producing area<br><br>• From mid-16th century, iron manufacturing sites set up closer to Birmingham for ease of transport of raw materials<br><br>• New technology resulted in separation of industrial processes and more movement of goods about the area<br><br>• Evidence for degradation of landscape<br><br>• Population increased and towns expanded; retail and wholesale markets developed | • Early 18th century– first attempt to solve mine drainage to improve coal supplies. First steam engine 1711 (Newcomen)<br><br>• Use of coke introduced; search for method of using coal in iron manufacture to replace charcoal<br><br>• Dramatic increase in the population from mid-18th century continuing in 19th century, resulting in extensive housing development<br><br>• Transport – canals from late 18th century; railways from late 1830s<br><br>• Steam engines gave independence from water power; Watt's engine for pumping and rotary power (1783); industry expanded; increased coal use – atmospheric pollution; increased industrial activity – water pollution; reduction of semi-natural vegetation<br><br>• Attempts to rectify damage to landscape by creating woodlands from early 1800s; Exhaustion of local raw materials from 1860 | • Changes in industrial pattern – larger factory units developed<br><br>• Population and housing continued to increase<br><br>• Expansion of housing and industry continued after WWII<br><br>• Larger industries began to decline from 1970s but adapted and changed<br><br>• Growth of trading estates and leisure centres | • At the beginning of this century a surprising number of open spaces still remain, but are likely to be reduced by the need to provide more housing |

# Section 7 • References

## GEOLOGY AND GEODIVERSITY

Crookall, R. (1955) Fossil plants of the Carboniferous rocks of Great Britain. Second section, part 4. *Memoirs – Geological Survey of Great Britain, Palaeontology*. HMSO, London.

Kidston, R. (1914) On the fossil flora of the Staffordshire Coalfields, Part III. The fossil flora of the Westphalian series of the South Staffordshire Coalfield. *Transactions – Royal Society of Edinburgh*, 50: 73–190.

Kidston, R. (1923–25) The fossil plants of the Carboniferous rocks of Great Britain, *Memoirs –Geological Survey of Great Britain*, 2. HMSO, London.

Powell, J.H., Glover, BW & Waters, C.N. (2000) Geology of the Birmingham area. *Memoir of the British Geological Survey*, Sheet 168.

Whitehead, T.H. & Eastwood, T. (1947) Dudley and Bridgnorth. *Memoir of the Geological Survey of Great Britain,* Sheet 167.

## CLIMATE

Amano, T., Smithers, R.J., Sparks, T.H. & Sutherland, W.J. (2010) A 250-year index of first flowering dates and its response to temperature changes. *Proceedings – Royal Society, B,* 277 (1693): 2451–2457.

Chandler, T.J. (1965) *The climate of London*. Hutchinson, London.

Chandler, T. J. (1967) Night-time temperatures in relation to Leicester's urban form. *Meteorological Magazine*, 96: 244–250.

Doornkamp, J.C., Gregory, K.J. & Burn, A.S. (1980) *Atlas of drought in Britain 1975–76*. Institute of British Geographers, London.

Environment Agency (2008) *Midlands Region hydrometric report and catalogue 2007*. Environment Agency, Bristol.

Fitter, A.H. & Fitter, R.S.R. (2002) Rapid changes in flowering time in British plants. *Science*, 296: 1689–1691.

Giles, B.D. & Kings, J. (1996) Birmingham weather through two centuries. In: A.J. Gerrard and T.R. Slater (eds) *Managing a conurbation: Birmingham and its region*. Brewin Books, Studley: 101–114.

Howard, L. (1833) *The climate of London deduced from meteorological observations made in the metropolis and at various places around it*. Harvey and Dalton, London.

Johnson, D. B. (1985) Urban modification of diurnal temperature cycles in Birmingham, UK. *Journal of Climatology*, 5: 221–225.

Jones, P.D. & Lister, D.H. (2009) The urban heat island in Central London and urban-related warming trends in Central London since 1900. *Weather*, 64: 323–327.

Kings, J. & Giles, B.D. (1997) The Midlands. In: D. Wheeler and J. Mayes (eds), *Regional climates of the British Isles*. Routledge, London: 111–130.

Manley, G. (1974) Central England temperatures: monthly means 1659–1973. *Quarterly Journal – Royal Meteorological Society,*100: 389–405.

Matthews, R.P. (1972) Variation of precipitation intensity with synoptic type over the Midlands. *Weather*, 27: 63–72.

Meteorological Office (1990) *The Climate of Great Britain: The Midlands. Climatological Memorandum 132*. HMSO, London.

Mitchell, D.J. & Searle, D.E. (2004) Urban pollution stone weathering in the Black Country In: D.J. Mitchell and D.E Searle (eds) *Stone deterioration in polluted urban environments*. Science Publishers, Plymouth: 23–42.

Oke, T.R. (1973) City size and their urban heat island. *Atmospheric Environment*, 7: 769–79.

Parker, D.E. & Horton, E.B. (2005) Uncertainties in Central England temperature 1878–2003 and some improvements in the maximum and minimum series. *International Journal of Climatology*, 12: 1173–1188.

Penman, H.L. (1948) Natural evaporation from open water, bare soil and grass. *Proceedings – Royal Society, A*, 193: 120–45.

Saward, B. (1950) Climate. In: R.H. Kinvig, J.G. Smith & M.J. Wise (eds), *Birmingham and its regional setting*. British Association for the Advancement of Science, Birmingham: 47–50.

Smith, L.P. (1976) The agroclimate of England and Wales. *MAFF Technical Bulletin*, 35. HMSO, London.

Sparks, T.H. (2009) Climate change and adaptation in the West Midlands. *West Midland Biodiversity Partnership*, Seminar 25.

Sparks, T.H., Jeffree, E.P. & Jeffree, C.E. (2000) An examination of the relationship between flowering times and temperature at the national scale using long-term phenological records from the UK. *International Journal of Biometeorology*, 4: 82–87.

Taylor, J.A. (1976) Upland climates. In Chandler T.J. and Gregory S. (eds). *The climate of the British Isles*. Longmans, London: 264–283.

Tooke, F. & Battey, N.H. (2010) Temperate flowering phenology. *Journal of Experimental Botany*, 61: 2853–2862.

Unsworth, M.H., Shakespeare, N.W., Milner, A.E. & Ganendra T.S. (1979) The frequency of fog in the Midlands of England. *Weather*, 34: 72–77.

Unwin, D.J. (1980) The synoptic climatology of Birmingham's urban heat island, 1965–74. *Weather*, 35: 43–50.

## RELIEF AND DRAINAGE

Bullock, P & Gregory, P.J. (eds) (1991) *Soils in the urban environment*. Blackwell Scientific, Oxford.

Gerrard, J. (1996a) The physical framework of the West Midlands conurbation. In: A.J. Gerrard & T.R. Slater (eds) *Managing a conurbation: Birmingham and its region*. Brewin Books, Studley: 3–12.

Gerrard. J. (1996b). Planning and slopes. In: A.J. Gerrard & T.R. Slater (eds) *Managing a conurbation: Birmingham and its region*. Brewin Books, Studley: 59–74.

Rossiter, D.G. (2007) Classification of urban and industrial soils in the World Reference Base for Soil Resources. *Journal of Soils and Sediments*, 7: 96–100.

Warwick, G.T. (1950) Relief and physiographic regions. In: R.H. Kinvig, J.G. Smith & M.J. Wise (eds), *Birmingham and its regional setting*. British Association for the Advancement of Science, Birmingham: 3–15.

## HYDROLOGY AND WATER QUALITY

Environment Agency (1997) River Stour third annual review January 1996 – December 1996. Midlands Region Environment Agency.

Environment Agency (1998a) West Midlands – Tame consultation report. LEAP, West Midlands Environment Agency.

Environment Agency (1998b) West Midlands – Stour consultation report. LEAP, West Midlands Environment Agency.

Harkness, N. (1982) The River Tame – a short history of water pollution and control within an industrial river basin. *Water Science & Technology*, 14: 153–165.

Picken, A. (1995) *Low dissolved oxygen incident on the River Tame and River Trent on 10th July 1995*. West Midlands Local Authority.

## HABITATS AND VEGETATION

Angold, P.G & nine others (2006) Biodiversity of urban habitat patches. *Science of the Total Environment*, 360: 196–204.

Bastin, L. & Thomas, C.D. (1999) The distribution of plant species in urban vegetation fragments. *Landscape Ecology*, 14: 493–507.

Darlington, A. (1981) *Ecology of walls*. Heinemann, London.

Davies, Z.G., Fuller, R.A., Loram, A., Irvine, K.N., Sims, V. & Gaston, K.J. (2009) A national scale inventory of resource provision for biodiversity within domestic gardens. *Biological Conservation*, 142: 761–771.

Gilbert, O.L. (1989) *The ecology of urban habitats*. Chapman and Hall, London.

Gledhill, D.G., James, P. & Davies, D.H. (2008) Pond density as a determinant of aquatic species richness in an urban landscape. *Landscape Ecology*, 23: 1219–1230

Grime, J.P. (1979) *Plant strategies and vegetation processes*. John Wiley, Chichester.

Hill, M., Roy, D.B. & Thompson, K. (2002) Hemeroby, urbanity and ruderality: bioindicators of disturbance and human impact. *Journal of Applied Ecology*, 39: 708–720.

HMSO (1969) *The Thorpe report: Departmental Committee of Inquiry into Allotments*. Ministry of Land and Natural Resources, London.

Hodge, S.J. & Harmer, R. (1996) Woody colonization on unmanaged urban and ex-industrial sites. *Forestry*, 69: 245–261.

Jarvis, P.J. (2010) Urban habitat type mapping. In: I. Douglas, D. Goode, M. Houck and R. Wand (eds), *The Routledge handbook of urban ecology* (Routledge, Abingdon): 478–487.

Jarvis, P.J. & Woodhouse, H.L. (1994) Mural ecology: lichen and moss associations of walls in Moseley, Birmingham. *Proceedings – Birmingham Natural History Society*, 27: 23–35.

Kowarik, I. (1990) Some responses of flora and vegetation to urbanization in Central Europe. In: H. Sukopp, S. Hejny & I. Kowarik (eds), *Urban ecology: plants and plant communities in urban environments*. SPB Academic Publishing, Amsterdam: 45–74.

MacArthur, R.H. & Wilson, E.O. (1967) *The theory of island biogeography*. Princeton University Press, Princeton.

Meurk, C.D. (2010) Recombinant ecology of urban areas: characterisation, context and creativity. In: I. Douglas, D. Goode, M. Houck & R. Wand (eds), *The Routledge handbook of urban ecology*. Routledge, Abingdon: 198–220.

Owen, S.M., MacKenzie, A.R., Bunce, R.G.H., Stewart, H.E., Donovan, R.G., Stark, G. & Hewitt, C.N. (2006) Urban land classification and its uncertainties using principal component analyses: a case study for the UK West Midlands. *Landscape and Urban Planning*, 78: 311–321.

Pisolkar, E. (2005) *The endless village revisited technical report*. Wildlife Trust for Birmingham & the Black Country.

Pond Conservation (2002) *A guide to monitoring the ecological quality of ponds and canals using PSYM*. Environment Agency, West Midlands.

Rodwell, J.S. (ed.) (2000) *British plant communities. Volume 5. Maritime communities and vegetation of open habitat*. Cambridge University Press, Cambridge.

Scott, N.E. (1985) The updated distribution of maritime species on British roadsides. *Watsonia*, 15: 381–386.

Scott, N.E. & Davison, A.W. (1982) De-icing salt and the invasion of road verges by maritime plants. *Watsonia*, 14: 41–52.

Wheater, C.P. (2010) Walls and paved surfaces: urban complexes with limited water and nutrients. In: I. Douglas, D. Goode, M. Houck & R. Wand (eds), *The Routledge handbook of urban ecology*. Routledge, Abingdon: 239–251.

Williams, D., Young, C.H., Hooper, I.D. & Jarvis, P.J. (2009) Urban small sites – landscape ecology and contribution to urban green space. In: R.D.J. Catchpole, R. Smithers, P. Baarda & A. Eycott (eds), *Ecological networks: science and practice*. International Association of Landscape Ecology, Edinburgh: 197–200.

Wyatt, N. (1998) *The Birmingham Pond Survey*. Wildlife Trust for Birmingham & the Black Country.

Young, C.H. & Jarvis, P.J. (2001a) Measuring urban habitat fragmentation: an example from the Black Country. *Landscape Ecology*, 16: 643–658.

Young, C.H. & Jarvis, P.J. (2001b) Assessing the structural heterogeneity of urban areas: an example from the Black Country. *Urban Ecosystems*, 5: 49–69.

Ziarnek, M. (2007) Human impact on plant communities in urban area assessed with hemeroby grades. *Polish Journal of Ecology*, 55: 161–168.

## THE GARDEN HABITAT

Davies, Z.G., Fuller, R.A., Loram, A., Irvine, K.N., Sims, V. & Gaston, K.J. (2009) A national scale inventory of resource provision for biodiversity within domestic gardens. *Biological Conservation*, 142: 761–771.

Goddard, M.A., Dougill, A.J. & Benton, T.G. (2010) Scaling up from gardens: biodiversity conservation in urban environments. *Trends in Ecology and Evolution*, 25: 90–98.

Marco, A., Barthelemy, C., Dutoit, T. & Bertaudière-Montes, V. (2010) Bridging human and natural sciences for a better understanding of urban floral patterns: the role of planting practices in Mediterranean gardens. *Ecology and Society*, 15: 2 (www. ecologyandsociety.org/vol15/iss2/art2/)

Pauliet, S., Ennos, R. & Golding, Y. (2005) Modelling the environmental impacts of urban land use and land cover change – a study in Merseyside, UK. *Landscape and Urban Planning*, 71: 295–310.

Quigley, P. (2010) Recycled landscape: The legacy of 250 years in the Black Country. Second report. An analysis of the Black Country historic landscape characterisation (Black Country Archaeology Service) (ads.ahds.ac.uk/catalogue/adsdata/arch-939-1/dissemination/pdf/RecycledLandscape.pdf)

Smith, R.M., Thompson, K., Hodgson, J.G., Warren, P.H. & Gaston, K.J. (2006) Urban domestic gardens (IX): Composition and richness of the vascular plant flora, and implications for native biodiversity. *Biological Conservation*, 129: 312–322.

Smith, R.M., Thompson, K., Warren, P.H. & Gaston, K.J. (2010) Urban domestic gardens (XIII): Composition of the bryophyte and lichen floras, and determinants of species richness *Biological Conservation*, 143: 873–882.

Trueman, I. & Young, C. (2012) Ecological value of urban environments. In: Booth, C., Hammond, F., Lammond J. & Proverbs, D. (eds) *Solutions for Climate Change Challenges of the Built Environment*. Blackwell, Oxford: 99–112.

Whitehead, J.W.R. & Larkham, P.J. (1991) Housebuilding in the back garden: reshaping suburban townscapes in the Midlands and South East England. *Area*, 23: 57–65.

Young, C.H. & Jarvis, P.J. (2001) Assessing the structural heterogeneity of urban areas: an example from the Black Country (UK). *Urban Ecosystems*, 5: 49–69.

Zmyslony, J. & Gagnon, D. (2000) Path analysis of spatial predictors of front-yard landscape in an anthropogenic environment. *Landscape Ecology*, 15: 357–371.

## THE HISTORY OF HUMAN OCCUPATION

Awty, B.G. (1957) Charcoal ironmasters in Cheshire and North Staffordshire, 1600–1785. *Transactions of the Historical Society of Lancashire and Cheshire*, 109: 71–124.

Birmingham City Council (2007) *Sustainable management of urban river floodplains* (http://www.birmingham.gov.uk/cs/Satellite?c= Page&childpagename=Development%2FPageLayout&cid= 1 223092715125&pagename=BCC%2FCommon%2FWrapper %2FWrapper)

Broadberry, S., Campbell, B.M.S. & van Leeuwen, B. (2011) English medieval population: reconciling time series and cross-sectional evidence (www2.lse.ac.uk/economicHistory/pdf/Broadberry/population.pdf)

Chinn, C. (1994) *Birmingham: The great working city*. Birmingham City Council, Birmingham: 37.

Collins, P. (1998) Slag options – a history of Tarmac's Ettingshall site. In: R.W.D. Fenn (ed.) Tarmac papers: The archives and history initiative of Tarmac plc, vol 3: 165–191 (Wolverhampton Archives and Local Studies: LS/L624/3) (blackcountryhistory.org/collections/getrecord/GB149_LS_L624_3/)

Cunliffe, B. (2004) *Iron Age Britain* (second edition). B.T. Batsford/English Heritage, London.

Diamond, J. (2005): *Collapse – How Societies Choose to Fail or Succeed*. Viking, New York.

Duignan, W.H. (1912, reprinted 2009) *Notes on Staffordshire place-names*. BiblioLife, Charleston, SC.

Fagan, B. (2004) *The long summer – How climate changed civilisation*. Basic Books, New York.

Gover, J.E.B., Mawer, A., Stenton, F.M., Houghton, F.T.S. & Smith, A.H. (1936) *The place-names of Warwickshire*. Cambridge University Press, Cambridge.

Hackwood, F.W. (1902; reprinted 2002) *Wednesbury ancient and modern*. Brewin Books, Studley.

Hadfield, C. (1966) *The canals of the West Midlands*. David & Charles, Newton Abbot.

Hemingway, J. (2009) *An illustrated chronicle of Dudley town and manor*. MFH Publishing, Dudley.

Hodder, M.A. (1992) Continuity and discontinuity in the landscape: Roman to medieval in Sutton Chase. *Medieval Archaeology*, 36: 178–182.

Hodder, M. (2004) *Birmingham: The hidden history*. History Press, Stroud.

Hooke, D. (2006) *England's landscape: The West Midlands*. Collins, London.

Johnson, B.L.C. & Wise, M.J. (1950) The Black Country 1800–1950. In: R.H. Kinvig, J.G. Smith & M.J. Wise (eds), *Birmingham and its regional setting*. British Association for the Advancement of Science, Birmingham: 229–248.

Jones, J.M. (1963) Local rivers as sources of power. *Proceedings – Birmingham Natural History and Philosophical Society*, 20: 22–36.

Lamb, H.H. (1981) Climate from 1000BC to 1000AD. In: M. Jones & G. Dimbleby (eds) *The environment of Man: The Iron Age to the Anglo-Saxon period*. British Archaeological Reports British Series, Oxford, 87: 53–65.

Lamb, H.H. (1995) *Climate, history and the modern world*. 2nd edition. Routledge, Abingdon.

Leather, P. (2001) *A brief history of Birmingham*. Brewin Books, Studley.

Mawer, A. & Stenton F.M. (1927) *The place-names of Worcestershire*. Cambridge University Press, Cambridge.

Nash, T. (1799) Collections for a History of Worcestershire. Cited in Wise, M.J. & Johnson, B.L.C. (1950) The changing regional pattern during the eighteenth century. In: R.H. Kinvig, J.G. Smith & M.J. Wise (eds), *Birmingham and its regional setting*. British Association for the Advancement of Science, Birmingham: 161–168.

Pelham, R.A. (1950) The growth of settlement and industry c.1100–c.1700. In: R.H. Kinvig, J.G. Smith & M.J. Wise (eds), *Birmingham and its regional setting*. British Association for the Advancement of Science, Birmingham: 135–158.

Phillips, A.D.M. (ed.) (1984) Map of the county of Stafford, 1775, by William Yates. *Staffordshire Record Society*, 4th series, 12.

Rackham, O. (2003) *The illustrated history of the countryside*. Weidenfeld & Nicolson, London.

Rowlands, M.B. (1987) *The West Midlands from AD 1000*. Longman, London.

Quigley, P. (2010) Recycled landscape: The legacy of 250 years in the Black Country. Second report. An analysis of the Black Country historic landscape characterisation (Black Country Archaeology Service) (ads.ahds.ac.uk/catalogue/adsdata/arch-939-1/dissemination/pdf/RecycledLandscape.pdf)

Rees, W.J. & Skelding, A.D. (1950) Vegetation. In: R.H. Kinvig, J.G. Smith & M.J. Wise (eds), *Birmingham and its regional setting*. British Association for the Advancement of Science, Birmingham: 65–76.

Royal Commission on Historical Manuscripts (1974) 'Paper of John Smythe of Bristol, Merchant 1538–1550', cited in Rowlands (op. cit.), London: 142.

Salzman, L.F. (1923) *English industries of the Middle Ages*, cited by R.A. Pelham (1950) The growth of settlement and industry c.1100–c.1700. In: R.H. Kinvig, J.G. Smith & M.J. Wise (eds), *Birmingham and its regional setting*. British Association for the Advancement of Science, Birmingham: 135–158.

Score, V. & Higgins, T. (2011) Early prehistoric clearance in Birmingham? Excavations at Banbury Street. *Transactions – Birmingham and Warwickshire Archaeological Society*, 114: 1–12.

Tetlow, E., Geary, B. & Halsted, J. (2009) Palaeoenvironmental evidence for Holocene landscape change and human activity at Tameside, Aldridge Road, Perry Barr, Birmingham. *Transactions – Birmingham and Warwickshire Archaeological Society*, 112: 1–11.

Wise, M.J. & Johnson, B.L.C. (1950) The changing regional pattern during the eighteenth century. In: R.H. Kinvig, J.G. Smith & M.J. Wise (eds), *Birmingham and its regional setting*. British Association for the Advancement of Science, Birmingham: 161–168.

Wise, M.J & Thorpe, P.O. (1950). The growth of Birmingham 1800–1950. In: R.H. Kinvig, J.G. Smith & M.J. Wise (eds), *Birmingham and its regional setting*. British Association for the Advancement of Science, Birmingham: 213–228.

Wood, M. (2010) *The story of England*. London; Penguin Books.

www.birmingham.gov.uk/archaeology

www.wealdeniron.org.uk

Yates, W. (1775) *A map of the county of Stafford from an actual survey begun in 1769 and finished in 1775*. See: Phillips, A.D.M. (ed.) (1984).

Yates, W. (1789) *A map of Warwickshire drawn from an actual survey taken in the years 1787–1788–1789*.

Chapter 4

# Exploring the Flora records

by Ian Trueman

◀ Wyrley & Essington Canal, Heath Town, Wolverhampton

# Section 1 • Describing the urban landscape

## NUMBERS OF PLANT RECORDS

The vascular plant Atlas (Chapter 8) contains information about the locations of 1,820 species, interspecific hybrids and well-defined subspecies (i.e. 1,820 '**taxa**') in Birmingham and the Black Country (B&BC). 83 other taxa are also mentioned, mostly trees, which are considered to be always planted and which have been recorded once or a few times from parks, gardens, in streets, etc.

142 of the 1,820 are only present as pre-1995 records and have not been included in the following analysis although all are described in the Atlas. However these old records should not be assumed to be a complete list of taxa previously recorded in the conurbation since the focus of the present survey has been very much on the period 1995–2008, with some further significant records accepted from the period 2009–2012.

The 1995–2012 database consists of over 240,000 individual records. A few of the more critical groups include quite a large number of undifferentiated records. Therefore, for the purposes of the analysis, 25 groups of species have been treated as aggregates (groups of similar species used for recording where identification of the segregates is difficult). These are:

*Aconitum napellus* agg. (2 or more segregates); *Amaranthus* spp. (5); *Aphanes arvensis* agg. (2); *Arctium minus s.l.* (3); *Arenaria serpyllifolia s.l.* (2); *Aster* spp. (4); *Beta vulgaris s.l.* (3); *Dryopteris affinis s.l.* (2); *Erophila* spp. (2); *Euphrasia* spp. (1); *Fuchsia magellanica*/'Riccartonii' (2); *Galium palustre s.l.* (2); *Hieracium* spp. (14); *Narcissus* spp. (4); *Nasturtium officinale* agg. (3); *Philadelphus* spp. (3+); *Polygonum aviculare* plus *Polygonum arenastrum*; *Polypodium vulgare* agg. (2); *Rubus* subgenus *Rubus* (32); *Sagina apetala* plus *Sagina filicaulis*; *Sorbus aria* agg. (2); *Sorbus intermedia* agg. (1); *Sorbus latifolia* agg. (2); *Taraxacum* spp. (55) and *Veronica hederifolia s.l.* (2)

The following species are represented in the database by two or more constituent subspecies and/or varieties which have been consistently recorded: *Euphorbia amygdaloides* (2 subsp.); *Festuca rubra* (3); *Ficaria verna* (2); *Lamiastrum galeobdolon* (2); *Lotus corniculatus* (2); *Medicago sativa* (2); *Populus nigra* (2) and *Vicia sativa* (3). Also 121 interspecific hybrids have been included in the analysis. Many other subspecies and varieties have not been consistently recorded and have therefore not been included in the analysis except as records for the 'parent' species.

After these consolidations and amendments, the database available for analysis includes 1,449 taxa and the analysis described in the present chapter is based on the distribution of these. The BSBI *New Atlas of the British and Irish Flora* (Preston *et al.*, 2002) dealt with 4,111 taxa, of which 2,412 are described in the book and a further 942 on CD-ROM, giving a total of 3,354 taxa described, excluding the main microspecies aggregates of *Rubus* subgenus *Rubus*, *Hieracium* and *Taraxacum*.

This number of 3,354 must be largely comparable with the 1,449 taxa dealt with in the present analysis although, as is suggested above, we have not included a number of critical

▲ Queen Elizabeth Hospital, Selly Oak

species and subspecies included in the BSBI New Atlas. Ignoring that, our 1,449 taxa represent over 43% of the flora of Britain and Ireland in an area of little more than 2% of the total land mass (under 625 square kilometres spread over 715 one kilometre squares and 15 ten-kilometre squares). This quite substantial proportion is all the more remarkable considering the complete lack of coastal and upland habitats in B&BC.

## THE BALANCE BETWEEN NATIVE AND INTRODUCED TAXA

Preston et al. (2002) adopted a classification of plants present in the wild as naturalised populations into **native taxa**, which are present without human intervention, whether intentional or unintentional, and **introduced taxa**, introduced at least indirectly by humans. Introduced taxa, following Thellung (1918/19), are divided into **archaeophytes**, plants which became naturalised before 1500 when the New World was discovered, and **neophytes** for which there is no evidence of naturalised populations until after 1500. **Casuals** are plants which are encountered as spontaneous introductions but which fail to persist, with a period of persistence of approximately five years being the usual dividing line.

A crude comparison is made with the Preston et al. (2002) data in Table 4.1, using a slightly simplified classification and the total numbers presented in the BSBI Atlas book and CD-ROM combined. The 'Others' category in Table 4.1 includes taxa of uncertain origin ("native or alien" in Preston et al. 2002) and hybrids between native and introduced species. Values in brackets are percentages of the row total, either for Britain and Ireland or for B&BC. The third row of data shows each of the origin groups which are present in B&BC as a percentage of the British and Irish total.

### Table 4.1 Comparison of species numbers and origins with the British and Irish flora as a whole

|  | Native taxa | Archaeo-phytes | Neo-phytes | Casuals | Others | Total |
|---|---|---|---|---|---|---|
| Britain and Ireland | 1,571 (46.8%) | 158 (4.7%) | 1,305 (38.9%) | 252 (7.5%) | 68 (2.0%) | 3,354 |
| B&BC | 693 (47.8%) | 105 (7.2%) | 555 (38.3%) | 63 (4.3%) | 33 (2.3%) | 1,449 |
| B&BC as a % of Britain and Ireland | 44.1 | 66.5 | 42.5 | 25.0 | 48.5 | 43.2 |

The low showing of casuals in B&BC in relation to the national Atlas was expected, since many are rare, chance occurrences and the time slice for the national Atlas is much wider. It should however also be remembered that many of the taxa categorised as neophytes nationally (and even a few of the natives) have only a casual occurrence in B&BC.

There is a relatively high number of archaeophytes in B&BC, which was again expected, since they are plants typically associated with human activity. Analysis elsewhere (Botham et al., 2009) has suggested that archaeophytes are re-establishing themselves in the countryside and that the urban bias in their distribution is diminishing. B&BC clearly still offers a considerable refuge to these taxa.

Our data do not suggest that the conurbation has a substantially greater proportion of neophytes compared with natives than Britain and Ireland as a whole, an interesting result

when considering that many or most neophytes are likely to have naturalised from use, cultivation or as contaminants of goods, humans and vehicles in urban areas.

Table 4.1 also shows that the conurbation does not have a substantially lesser proportion of native taxa than Britain and Ireland and demonstrates that native taxa constitute the largest origins group. This predominance of native taxa is confirmed and reinforced in Table 4.2 which sums the number of one kilometre square (henceforth referred to as '**monad**') records achieved by all taxa in each of the different origin types to give a total number of monad records for each type. These numbers are expressed as percentages of the whole in the second row, and are divided by the number of taxa in the relevant group as presented in Table 4.1 to give number of records per taxon in row three.

Almost 70% of monad records are represented by native taxa; neophytes have a much smaller overall percentage and not much greater than that for archaeophytes. There is a much lower average number of monad records per neophyte than per native plant taxa. The average number of records per taxon is highest of all for the archaeophytes. They constitute a small proportion of the taxa but many are clearly very widely distributed in the conurbation.

It should however be remembered that many taxa occur more than once in a monad so that these proportions are only valid in relation to distribution, not abundance.

### Table 4.2 The contribution of taxa from the different origin types to the database

|  | Native taxa | Archaeo-phytes | Neo-phytes | Casuals | Others | Total |
|---|---|---|---|---|---|---|
| Total no. of monad records | 89,433 | 15,861 | 21,561 | 596 | 910 | 128,361 |
| % of monad records | 69.7 | 12.4 | 16.8 | 0.5 | 0.7 | 100.1 |
| No. of records per taxon | 129.1 | 151.1 | 38.8 | 9.5 | 27.6 | 88.6 |

A further uncertainty arises from the fact that the categories of origin applied to plant distribution in Britain and Ireland are only of limited relevance within a single part such as B&BC. Many taxa native in Britain are only present in B&BC as introductions and many taxa present casually in B&BC are permanently established elsewhere in the UK. Many native taxa are considered by our recorders to be entirely or almost entirely introduced into B&BC. Some of these types of introduction may be considered for removal from the list of native taxa in B&BC. Criteria which might be used to decide how to accomplish this include:

- **Species which although native in some parts of the UK, appear to be entirely garden escapes in B&BC** (e.g. Meconopsis cambrica) **or apparently always planted** (e.g. Salix pentandra). Osmunda regalis has also been included in this group since it is considered extinct as a native in B&BC. All these taxa can be justifiably removed from the 'locally native' list in B&BC. The complete list removed on these grounds is given in Table 4.3
- **Species which are native elsewhere in Britain, appearing apparently spontaneously in secondary habitats in B&BC.** Four of this group are well-naturalised: Cochlearia danica, Puccinellia distans and Spergularia marina by roadsides and Brachypodium pinnatum at one canalside site. Others are probably essentially casual at present: Atriplex littoralis,

*Fumaria capreolata, Geranium columbinum, Hypericum hirsutum, Hypochaeris glabra, Lepidium heterophyllum, Myriophyllum alterniflorum, Oenanthe pimpinelloides, Oxyria digyna, Pimpinella major, Polypogon monspeliensis, Potentilla argentea, Rumex maritimus, Thymus polytrichus,* and *Vicia bithynica*. Since their appearance in our area seems to be essentially spontaneous they have not been removed from the 'locally native' group.

- **Species with an apparently native distribution locally, which are also widely planted and escaping from cultivation or spontaneously increasing in recently created habitats** These include *Acer campestre, Rhinanthus minor, Carex pendula* and, beloved of landscape architects, *Viburnum opulus*; possibly also *Ranunculus lingua*. (A similar phenomenon is represented by *Plantago coronopus*, which has had its original distribution supplemented by its spontaneous spread along salted roads). These taxa have generally been left in the 'locally native' list but they clearly represent an over-recording of 'native' taxa.

**Table 4.3 List of native taxa considered to be entirely naturalised from cultivation in B&BC**

| | |
|---|---|
| *Alchemilla alpina* | *Lythrum salicaria* |
| *Allium schoenoprasum* | *Malva arborea* |
| *Allium sphaerocephalon* | *Meconopsis cambrica* |
| *Anacamptis morio* | *Mentha pulegium* |
| *Apium graveolens* | *Mentha suaveolens* |
| *Aquilegia vulgaris* | *Muscari neglectum* |
| *Arabis hirsuta* | *Myosotis sylvatica* |
| *Armeria maritima* | *Nymphoides peltata* |
| *Buxus sempervirens* | *Ononis spinosa* |
| *Campanula glomerata* | *Origanum vulgare* |
| *Campanula trachelium* | *Osmunda regalis* |
| *Carpinus betulus* | *Pinus sylvestris* |
| *Clinopodium ascendens* | *Polemonium caeruleum* |
| *Convallaria majalis* | *Polygonatum multiflorum* |
| *Crepis biennis* | *Potentilla fruticosa* |
| *Cynoglossum officinale* | *Primula elatior* |
| *Cyperus longus* | *P. × polyantha* |
| *Dianthus deltoides* | *Rosa spinosissima* |
| *Fagus sylvatica* | *Ruscus aculeatus* |
| *Festuca rubra* ssp. *commutata* | *Salix pentandra* |
| *Filipendula vulgaris* | *Salvia verbenaca* |
| *Fritillaria meleagris* | *Sedum forsterianum* |
| *Geranium sanguineum* | *Sedum rosea* |
| *Geranium sylvaticum* | *Sedum telephium* |
| *Hedera hibernica* 'Hibernica' | *Silene uniflora* |
| *Helleborus foetidus* | *Stratiotes aloides* |
| *Hippophae rhamnoides* | *Symphytum tuberosum* |
| *Hordeum secalinum* | *Thalictrum minus* |
| *Hypericum androsaemum* | *Tilia × vulgaris* |
| *Iris foetidissima* | *Verbascum lychnitis* |
| *Juniperus communis* | *Verbascum nigrum* |
| *Lepidium latifolium* | *Verbascum virgatum* |
| *Leymus arenarius* | *Veronica spicata* |
| *Ligustrum vulgare* | *Viburnum lantana* |
| *Linum bienne* | |

If the proportion of native taxa in the B&BC Flora is recalculated without the 69 taxa in Table 4.3, the total number of locally native taxa is reduced to 624 and 43.1% of the B&BC flora, representing 39.7% of the native taxa of the British and Irish flora. This does represent a somewhat reduced proportion compared with the British and Irish flora as a whole. The taxa thought to be native in B&BC are however much more widely distributed. Calculations

similar to those used in Table 4.2 show that they constitute 67.7% of monad records and 139.3 monad records per taxon. The introduced natives form 2.0% of monad records and have on average 36.4 monad records per taxon, figures more resembling those for neophytes than those for natives.

## DISTRIBUTION OF MONAD RECORDS

The distribution of the 1995–2012 EcoRecord database of vascular plant records across the one km squares (monads) of B&BC is shown in Figure 4.1. The figure shows considerable variation in overall numbers from monad to monad. The low minimum (100 common species) may have meant that certain monads were not as thoroughly surveyed as others, especially where within-period site survey data previously existed for a monad. Also some small fragments of monads in the periphery have not reached 100 records. Some of the highest scoring monads are in nature reserves (Saltwells (SO9387), Woodgate Valley (SP0083), Sandwell Valley (e.g. SP0291), Barrow Hill (SO9189)) where the flora is very well known.

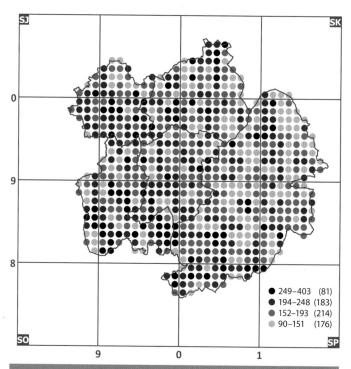

▲ **Figure 4.1 Number of taxa recorded in each monad in B&BC 1995–2012**

Nevertheless, Figure 4.1 does suggest that some areas of B&BC are particularly rich in vascular plant diversity. There is a slight tendency for these richer areas to be concentrated in the periphery of B&BC.

Figure 4.2 shows the distribution of the 1995–2012 monad records for taxa considered to be native in the UK expressed as a percentage of the total number of taxa in order to minimise variation due to unevenness of recording. Because of the general tendency for native taxa to be more abundant in the vegetation, peripheral monads with only small areas will naturally tend to have high proportions of native taxa. For this reason, all monads with less than 25% of their area within B&BC have been omitted in the figure. Despite this, native taxa appear to be more strongly associated with the periphery than taxa as a whole.

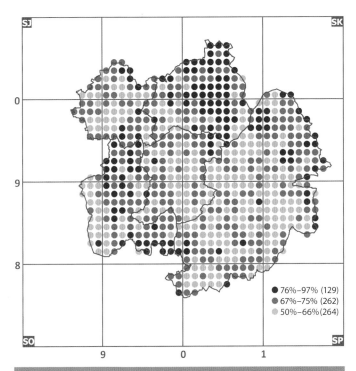

▲ **Figure 4.2 Distribution of taxa native in the UK, expressed as a percentage of the total number of taxa** (monads with <25% of their area within B&BC have been omitted)

76%–97% (129)
67%–75% (262)
50%–66% (264)

Figure 4.2 shows that there is a remarkably wide variation in percentage of native taxa between the monads, with the low 50s percentage native taxa in some areas (SP0886, SP1199) and the high 90s in others (SO9581, SP0996). This is quite a profound range and much of the discussion in the present chapter centres on this variation.

To an extent the proportion of native taxa appears to be correlated with the degree of survival of pre-industrial habitats in the different areas, although it also reflects the greater penetration of the urban core by archaeophytes and neophytes. Areas particularly rich in native taxa and poor in introduced taxa are found in Sutton Park, Halesowen in South Dudley (extending into Birmingham in the Woodgate Valley) and much of Walsall. Areas poor in native taxa and richer in introduced taxa characterise a central core of the conurbation, centred in Birmingham and narrowing but persisting towards the north west across Sandwell to Wolverhampton centre and beyond.

There are however many exceptions to this interpretation. Much of the western fringe of Dudley appears to be proportionally quite poor in natives. This is mostly a densely residential part of the conurbation, with the edge of the green belt coinciding with the Borough boundary. Some parts of the south-east boundary of Birmingham, where it abuts built-up areas of Solihull, are also proportionally rather poor in locally native taxa and rich in introduced ones.

More centrally in the conurbation, a major focus of monads proportionally rich in native taxa is associated with the Walsall countryside and extends further south into the Sandwell Valley. Other major incursions of proportionally native-species-rich monads mark Sutton Park and Pype Hayes (SP1292 etc.) in Birmingham and a broad band in central Dudley, extending north along the boundary between Wolverhampton and Walsall. The latter group may in part represent recovery from old industry as much as the survival of pre-industrial habitats. There are also some less-marked increases in the proportion of native taxa in parts of suburban

south Birmingham, at least in parts associated with the river valleys, especially the River Cole. There is another increase north and east of Birmingham city centre (which is at *circa* SP070870), along the canal/river corridor to Gravelly Hill and beyond.

Archaeophytes, the plants anciently introduced into Britain, have been shown in Tables 4.1 and 4.2 to be relatively abundant in B&BC. Figure 4.3 shows the distribution of archaeophytes in B&BC, expressed as a percentage of the total number of taxa in a monad. Again, peripheral monads with less than 25% within B&BC have been omitted.

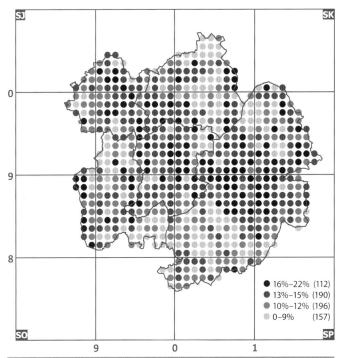

▲ **Figure 4.3 Distribution of archaeophytes in B&BC, expressed as a percentage of the total number of taxa** (monads with <25% within B&BC omitted)

16%–22% (112)
13%–15% (190)
10%–12% (196)
0–9%     (157)

Figure 4.3 is naturally to some extent a mirror image of Figure 4.2 but the **correlation coefficient**[1] between the actual numbers of natives and the actual number of archaeophytes in monads (-0.65 all native; -0.59 locally native), does suggest that the archaeophytes do to some extent replace the native taxa in the more central regions of the conurbation.

It should however be remembered (Table 4.1) that we are dealing with a much smaller group of taxa than the natives and that we are representing distribution at the monad level as presence or absence rather than by measuring abundance.

There are some interesting differences between residential suburban areas. Those of south Birmingham seem to be proportionally poor in archaeophytes; this is less true in western Dudley (Stourbridge and Kingswinford) or north-east Birmingham (Sutton).

Figure 4.4 is a similar map of percentages of the more recently introduced taxa, the neophytes.

---

[1] A number between +1 and -1 calculated to show how two variables depend on one another. A value close to zero suggests that there is no relationship between the two variables. A value close to +1 means that high values of one variable generally go with high values of the other and low values of one generally go with low values of the other. A value close to -1 means that high values of one variable always go with low values of the other.

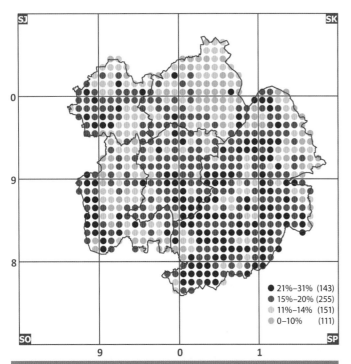

▲ **Figure 4.4 Distribution of neophytes in B&BC, expressed as a percentage of the total number of taxa** (monads with <25% area within B&BC omitted)

Figure 4.4 suggests that neophytes are even more strongly a mirror image of percentages of native taxa (correlation coefficient actual number of natives : neophytes =-0.90 all native, -0.90 locally native) but that their frequency is not closely parallel with that of the archaeophytes (correlation coefficient actual numbers of neophytes : archaeophytes = +0.22). Archaeophytes are associated both with arable and intensely urban areas. Neophytes, on the other hand, are likely to be preferentially associated only with heavily populated areas. Not surprisingly, since many of them are garden escapes, they are proportionally as common or commoner in the suburbs than in industrial areas. Furthermore, neophytes are often imperfectly naturalised and may be dependent on frequent local re-introduction from gardens. Also street maintenance may be more intensive in residential areas compared with industrial areas, again negatively affecting persistence. In the eastern countryside fringes of Walsall and Birmingham, where there is still considerable arable land, archaeophytes have a particularly high percentage and neophytes a particularly low percentage.

The survival of rural habitats in south-west Birmingham and west Wolverhampton in particular has not prevented the development of a neophyte flora there, since these are overwhelmingly residential areas. Possibly for the same reason Sutton Park, Sandwell Valley and the countryside south of Halesowen appear more closely 'besieged' by neophytes than by archaeophytes. This appears to be less true in the native-species-rich areas of central Dudley and north Walsall. This is likely to be a reflection of their industrial rather than residential history.

## TWINSPAN ANALYSIS OF THE MONAD FLORA DATA

TWINSPAN (Hill 1979; Hill & Šmilauer 2005) is a computer program which can be used to compare the one km squares (monads) with one another on the basis of the taxa recorded in each, although

it was originally designed to compare much smaller samples of vegetation. The complete set of 1449 independently recorded taxa has been used in a TWINSPAN analysis.

TWINSPAN analyses the data using a computer program (DECORANA, Hill & Gauch, 1980) which assesses similarity between two botanical samples (monads in the present case) according to the taxa they have in common and also according to the taxa which they lack in common but which are present in other samples. On this basis it identifies the strongest numerical trend in differences between monads and divides them into two groups at the average position on the trend. The two groups are then analysed separately in the same way and each divided similarly into two groups. The process is repeated further and the entire set of monads is thus divided into successively smaller groups which are internally more and more similar. The divisions are achieved mathematically but the results are generally open to ecological interpretation, for example monads rich in wetland sites may be on one side of a division and monads with only dry sites on the other, since the relevant taxa differ considerably.

Interpretation can be carried out by examining lists of taxa that are associated with each group. Those taxa commoner in one group in its division from another are known as its **preferential species**, and the preferential species with the strongest association with that side, defined mathematically, are called **indicator species.**

Clear divisions rarely occur in nature, and particularly between monads, so that at least some indicator and preferential species (and the ecological situations they represent) which characterise one group will still be found in a few monads on the other side in a division. Furthermore the differences are specific to a particular division. Just because a species is characteristic of a group does not mean that it is entirely absent from other groups. The same species can even appear as an indicator in several contrasting parts of the analysis.

TWINSPAN also conducts a parallel comparison between species according to the monads in which they occur and the classical output is a table which combines these two analyses. However in view of the large size of the present analysis we have concentrated on division of the monads and represent the groups which are formed in tree-like diagrams or **dendrograms**, showing the successive divisions and the indicator species associated with each division.

Ideally comparisons should be made between samples completely equivalent in area. Test analyses suggested that the ecological nature of the divisions was surprisingly similar whether all 715 monads recorded were used, or just the 530 entire monads, or at various intermediate levels of cut-off, but that the size of equivalent groups did tend to vary according to the cut-off. Also where monads represented by particularly small portions were included they tended to ally themselves with the least species-rich groups of whole monads. The use of all the monads in which at least 25% of the area is present in B&BC was found to be an acceptable compromise. This involved the analysis of 1,447 taxa in 655 monads.

The characteristics of the taxa used in interpreting the TWINSPAN output are set out in Chapter 8 of the present work based on the personal experience of the recorders in B&BC, together with observations by Grime *et al.* (2007), Hill *et al.* (1999), Hill *et al.* (2004), Preston *et al.* (2002) and Sinker *et al.* (1985).

### Primary TWINSPAN divisions

These are shown in the dendrogram which forms Figure 4.5. The groups are labelled using binary notation, with the group to the

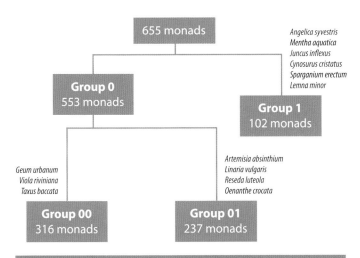

Angelica syvestris
Mentha aquatica
Juncus inflexus
Cynosurus cristatus
Sparganium erectum
Lemna minor

Artemisia absinthium
Linaria vulgaris
Reseda luteola
Oenanthe crocata

▲ **Figure 4.5 Dendrogram showing the primary divisions of a TWINSPAN analysis of monads in B&BC** (monads with <25% area within B&BC omitted). Species shown are indicators for the relevant side of a division

left of a division labelled 0 and the group to the right of the same division labelled 1, with the number of digits used for the label of a group showing the level of division. Thus the whole set is divided into Groups 0 and 1 and Group 0 is divided into 00 and 01.

In later diagrams, Group 00 is divided into 000 and 001, Group 01 into 010 and 011, Group 1 into 10 and 11, Group 10 into 100 and 101.

The first division cuts off a relatively small group of 102 monads to form Group 1. Only the division of the larger Group 0 is shown in Figure 4.5, cutting off a group of 237 monads as Group 01 from the 316 which forms Group 00.

The numbers of monads and the average number of plant taxa per monad for these three groups are shown in Table 4.4, which shows that Group 1 monads are more species-rich than Group 0 monads and the **standard errors**[2] suggest that the difference is statistically significant.

**Table 4.4 Numbers of monads and numbers of taxa per monad in the three main TWINSPAN groups**

| | | No. monads in group | Average no. taxa per monad | Standard Error (SE) of average |
|---|---|---|---|---|
| Group 0 | | 553 (84%) | 179.9 | 1.92 |
| | Group 00 | 316 (48%) | 179.4 | 2.57 |
| | Group 01 | 237 (36%) | 180.5 | 2.88 |
| Group 1 | | 102 (16%) | 232.8 | 6.33 |

The six indicator species for the division are all associated with Group 1. All are native species both in B&BC and in UK. All save one suggest wetland, and two of those, *Lemna minor* and *Sparganium erectum*, are extremely common species of almost any relatively permanent, fairly or very nutrient-rich waters. *Angelica sylvestris*, *Mentha aquatica* and *Juncus inflexus* suggest the presence of

2   A number calculated to estimate how the average value for a sample may be expected to differ by chance from the true value for the whole population sampled. In the present study, when comparing two means, if the difference between two averages is greater than twice the SE of one plus twice the SE of the other, then the two estimated averages can be accepted as significantly different with a 95% probability.

modestly base-rich, nutrient-intermediate, fairly long-established wetland and *Cynosurus cristatus* suggests relatively long-established grassland.

Including the above, a total of 132 taxa are preferential for Group 1. The majority of these are wetland and open water plants, but the character of other preferential species extends the range of semi-natural habitats which must be commoner in this group to include grassland (e.g. *Achillea ptarmica*, *Betonica officinalis*, *Carex flacca*, *Knautia arvensis*, *Leontodon hispidus*, *Odontites verna*, *Rhinanthus minor*, *Succisa pratensis*), heathland (e.g. *Aira praecox*, *Calluna vulgaris*, *Carex nigra*, *Deschampsia flexuosa*, *Festuca ovina*, *Galium saxatile*, *Potentilla erecta*) and old woodland (e.g. *Bromopsis ramosa*, *Caltha palustris*, *Lamiastrum galeobdolon* subsp. *montanum*, *Melica uniflora*, *Mercurialis perennis*). The list also includes a large number of plants strongly associated with canals in B&BC (e.g. *Alisma lanceolata*, *Alisma plantago-aquatica*, *Bidens frondosa*, *Berula erecta*, *Carex otrubae*, *Lycopus europaeus*, *Oenanthe crocata*, *Potamogeton crispus*, *P. natans*, *P. pectinatus*, *P. perfoliatus*, *Scutellaria galericulata*, *Sparganium emersum*). The presence of several submerged aquatic plants in this canal plant list suggests that it includes the richest stretches, with better quality water and little boat traffic, which can support such species.

Since they are associated with Group 1, it follows that wetland, open water and other long-established semi-natural habitats must be less common in the 553 monads forming Group 0, but no indicators were found for Group 0. Seventeen taxa are preferential for Group 0 and are listed in Table 4.5. Only one is native in UK, and five are archaeophytes. Almost all are plants associated with residential areas. The ten marked with * are garden escapes rarely found far from gardens and the rest are annual weeds of cultivation, except for *Vulpia myuros*, which is frequent in bare ground in both residential and industrial areas and *Geranium pusillum*, which grows in the margins of lawns, road verges and other slightly disturbed situations.

**Table 4.5 Preferential taxa associated with Group 0 in the TWINSPAN analysis.** Species marked with * are garden escapes, rarely found far from gardens in B&BC

| | |
|---|---|
| *Antirrhinum major* | *Oenothera glazioviana* |
| *Centranthus ruber* | *Oxalis corniculata* |
| Euphorbia peplus | *Papaver somniferum* |
| Geranium pusillum | *Pseudofumaria lutea* |
| Lamium amplexicaule | Urtica urens |
| Lepidium didymum | Veronica agrestis |
| *Linaria purpurea* | *Viola × wittrockiana* |
| *Lobularia maritima* | Vulpia myuros |
| *Meconopsis cambrica* | |

The first TWINSPAN division appears to represent trends towards the presence of a variety of water-rich habitats and also towards the presence of a wide ecological range of longer-established, semi-natural habitats in Group 1 monads, with the implication that particularly open water and wetland, but also other semi-natural habitats, are relatively scarce in Group 0 monads. The 'residential' preferentials for Group 0 point to the widespread nature of residential situations in Group 0 monads and a lack of, or a limited extent of, residential land in at least some of the Group 1 monads.

The next division of Group 0 cuts off a second relatively small group to form Group 01. The indicators for this group are *Artemisia absinthium*, *Linaria vulgaris*, and *Reseda luteola*, perennial species associated with post-industrial sites in B&BC and *Oenanthe crocata*, a species associated with canal margins, suggests that the canal flora is not exclusively associated with Group 1 monads.

The juxtaposition of post-industrial and canal habitat types in the Group 01 monads is likely to partly reflect the fact that the canals originally served industry and the persistence of this association in the flora. The preferentials almost all fit this pattern also, and are listed in Table 4.6 as an interesting grouping of taxa characteristic of industrial B&BC. Only *Alnus incana* and *Rosa rugosa* seem in any way out of place, and may reflect naturalisation of these species from areas planted to tidy up waste spots in industrial areas.

**Table 4.6 Preferential taxa associated with Group 01 in the TWINSPAN analysis.** Species marked with * are associated with canals

| | |
|---|---|
| *Alisma lanceolata | *Potamogeton pectinatus |
| *A. plantago-aquatica | *Ranunculus sceleratus |
| Alnus incana | Resesa lutea |
| Artemisia absinthium | Reseda luteola |
| *Butomus umbellatus | Rosa rugosa |
| *Carex otrubae | *Rumex conglomeratus |
| Centaurium erythraea | *Rumex hydrolapathum |
| Conium maculatum | *Salix viminalis |
| Daucus carota | *Scutellaria galericulata |
| *Glyceria maxima | Silene latifolia |
| Hypericum perforatum | Silene vulgaris |
| Linaria vulgaris | Sisymbrium orientale |
| Lupinus x regalis | *Sparganium emersum |
| *Lycopus europaeus | *Sparganium erectum |
| Malva moschata | Trifolium arvense |
| Melilotus albus | Trifolium campestre |
| Melilotus officinalis | Trifolium hybridum |
| Odontites vernus | *Typha latifolia |
| *Oenanthe crocata | Vicia cracca |
| *Persicaria amphibia | Vulpia bromoides |

Table 4.6 demonstrates that industrial areas are not devoid of botanical diversity and that the canals, on which the early development of industry was based, form a strong feature. The only *Potamogeton* in the list is the relatively pollution-tolerant *P. pectinatus*, suggesting a distinction in water quality from the canal stretches of Group 1.

There are three indicators for the largest group, Group 00. *Geum urbanum*, which, although essentially a woodland species, is now widely distributed in gardens, allotments and other recently disturbed areas in B&BC. *Viola riviniana*, which, although found in old woodland is also an abundant (often tolerated) garden weed. *Taxus baccata*, which is widely planted, especially in the suburbs, and appears even more widely as seedlings and saplings from spread in bird droppings etc. The preferentials for Group 00 are a combination of:

• Species becoming established from gardens in residential areas (*Alchemilla mollis, Aquilegia vulgaris, Campanula persicifolia, Campanula trachelium, Erysimum cheiri, Meconopsis cambrica, Melissa officinalis, Narcissus* agg., *Nigella damascena, Oxalis corniculata, Pilosella aurantiaca, Pseudofumaria lutea, Sedum album, Silene coronaria, Spiraea* spp., *Veronica hederacea*).
• Plants of shady greenspace (*Allium ursinum, Arum maculatum, Brachypodium sylvaticum, Circaea lutetiana, Conopodium majus, Dryopteris dilatata, Filipendula ulmaria, Glechoma hederacea, Hyacinthoides non-scripta, Mercurialis perennis, Rumex*

*sanguineus, Schedonorus giganteus, Stellaria holostea, Veronica beccabunga*).
• Species spanning residential and greenspace habitats (*Carex pendula, Ficaria verna* subsp. *fertilis, Geum urbanum, Luzula campestris, Hyacinthoides × massartiana, Myosotis sylvatica, Veronica filiformis, Veronica serpyllifolia, Viola riviniana*).
• A selection of mostly alien tree taxa (*Castanea sativa, Chamaecyparis lawsoniana, Fagus sylvatica, Prunus domestica, Prunus laurocerasus, Pinus sylvestris, Rhododendron ponticum, Taxus baccata, Ulmus glabra, Ulmus procera, × Cuprocyparis leylandii*).

*Poa humilis* is also a preferential for Group 00. It is a grass which, although not always well-separated from *Poa pratensis*, was often observed in roadside situations in the survey.

Group 00 appears to represent suburban B&BC, or at least areas with less industrial and canal habitat than Group 01 monads, with fewer wetland sites and other old habitats than Group 1 and with more evidence of gardens and other habitats characteristic of residential areas. The prevalence of woodland species (including some such as *Allium ursinum* and *Mercurialis perennis* showing some affinity with ancient woodlands) when compared with Group 01 monads may reflect a survival of some pre-industrial habitats in areas only relatively recently taken for residential purposes or others where old woodlands have been conserved. These woodland preferentials associated with Group 00 suggest that long-established habitats are not entirely confined to Group 1 monads.

In summary the botanical records have allowed the division of the monads into three groups according to their predominant land uses. In only 36% of monads (Group 01) is association with industry shown to be a predominant feature of the flora; hence this might be described as the **Industrial** group of monads. In 16% of monads (Group 1) the predominant feature is the natural environment (including the best of the canals). The preferentials suggest that Group 1 could be described as the **Rich Semi-natural** group, although the strong bias towards open water and wetland taxa in the list of indicators and preferentials for Group 1 suggests that there might be other non-wetland natural habitats outside Group 1.

The floras of the remaining 48% of monads forming Group 00 is by definition not predominantly Industrial nor predominantly Rich Semi-natural, and the principal feature seems to be the presence of residential property. Group 00 could be described as the **Suburban** group of monads.

The distribution of the three TWINSPAN groups of monads across B&BC is shown in Figure 4.6 and forms an interesting description of the conurbation which should be studied in relation to a more detailed map of B&BC such as that found at the beginning of this book.

Not unexpectedly the Group 00 Suburban monads tend to be in the periphery of the conurbation and the Group 01 Industrial monads form a central core, which is more substantial in the Black Country than in Birmingham. The distribution of the Group 1 Rich Semi-natural monads is quite complex, but the group is clearly much more widespread in the Black Country than in Birmingham and is concentrated in the south-west and the north-east of the conurbation.

Most of the commercial centres of B&BC and the major and long-established manufacturing areas have been included in the Industrial group 01. The Industrial group is a particular feature of the central parts of the Black Country boroughs, extending relatively narrowly into Birmingham, with a strong west-east strand along canal and railway transport corridors and the River

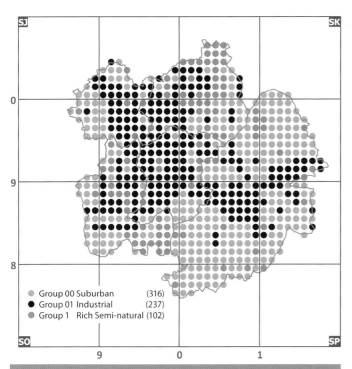

SJ / SK

0

9

8

● Group 00 Suburban (316)
● Group 01 Industrial (237)
● Group 1 Rich Semi-natural (102)

SO / SP

9    0    1

▲ Figure 4.6 Division of the B&BC monads into three TWINSPAN groups

Tame and with weaker lateral branches north-west towards Perry Barr along the M6 and south towards Acocks Green. The greatest expanse of industry-dominated monads is in west and central Sandwell, relieved to some extent by the island formed around the Sheepwash Urban Park and its attendant canal (SO9791 & SO9792) and of course by the Sandwell Valley in the north-east.

The Industrial area extends strongly into Dudley, Wolverhampton and west Walsall, to some extent delimiting the legendary Black Country of the Industrial Revolution. In this area there is also a pervasive intermingling of monads with floras dominated by Industrial and Rich Semi-natural land use, suggesting that the industrial core of B&BC has its own quota of 'trapped countryside' and also possesses habitat-rich post-industrial areas, many associated with the canal system and with the aftermath of the old industries such as mining.

Key areas delimited by the Group 1 Rich Semi-natural monads are the core monads of Sutton Park and the Sandwell Valley, the ancient countryside of south Dudley and Halesowen and parts of north and central Walsall away from the Black Country towns of Willenhall and Darlaston and the Bloxwich-Rushall industrial cluster. In Walsall even the town centre (SP0198) is almost surrounded by Rich Semi-natural monads, influenced particularly by the botanically rich canals of the area despite the presence of industrial and residential areas in the relevant monads.

Walsall is relatively well provided with countryside compared with the rest of B&BC and Figure 4.6 suggests that one is rarely far from rich habitats there. However some of the Walsall countryside east of Aldridge has been included in the Suburban Group 00 and even in Industrial Group 01. Many of these monads have more farmland than residential or industrial areas. However, from our records the farmland is improved and mostly quite poor in plants of semi-natural habitats and fairly rich in the arable weeds which are also often frequent in suburban gardens and allotments. The busy A452 also passes through, allowing colonisation by plants such as *Artemisia absinthium* and *Reseda luteola* which are more associated with industrial areas. Further south, to the east of Barr

Beacon and along the borders with Birmingham, there are more areas with countryside which are included in the Suburban group. Much of this landscape was once heathland; the field pattern reflects enclosure rather than long-established farmland and the predominant land-use is intensive arable.

In the centre of this 'suburban arable' belt, Barr Beacon (SP0697) has been anomalously included in the Industrial group, despite its large expanses of acid grassland and re-created heathland. These habitats are relatively poor in vascular plant species and the heathland component seems therefore to have been numerically overwhelmed in the analysis by the flora associated with the busy B4154 road. This problem was also encountered in the TWINSPAN analysis of the Staffordshire Flora (Lawley 2011), where the excellent heathland of Highgate Common (SO8389, SO8390) fails to stand out. In contrast, in the present analysis the heathlands of Brownhills Common (SK0405 etc.) and Pelsall North Common (SK0104 etc.) are grouped in the Rich Semi-natural group, but those monads include also unimproved farmland, post-industrial sites and often botanically rich canals. A few other monads with little residential land and with much open space relatively poor in plant species and without old habitats have been classified with either the Industrial or Suburban groups.

In Wolverhampton the Industrial zone of monads follows the canal/railway corridor from Bilston to Oxley and spreads east along the Wyrley and Essington canal to Wednesfield. The few, scattered, Rich Semi-natural monads reflect rich post-industrial areas, rich sections of canal scattered in the industrial corridor and remnants of ancient woodland. The border with Walsall, quite well provided with canals and open spaces, is also represented in the Rich Semi-natural group. Almost the entire western half of Wolverhampton is within Group 00, reflecting the different heritages of the two halves of the city (see Chapter 2).

Dudley is dominated by its Rich Semi-natural south-eastern fringe and the rich central mix of Industrial and Rich Semi-natural monads. The Suburban monads tend to lie in the periphery of these areas. As in Walsall, in the west and south-west periphery of Dudley, a few of the Suburban monads include extensive areas of relatively species-poor arable farmland. As with Barr Beacon in Walsall, heathland indicator species clustered south of Stourbridge centre seem to have had little impact on the analysis at this level.

The Rich Semi-natural monads of Halesowen extend into south Birmingham in the Woodgate Valley. Sutton Park presents a solid (but tightly constricted) group of Rich Semi-natural monads in north Birmingham. Much of Birmingham is however dominated by Suburban monads, punctuated by a few Rich Semi-natural monads mainly in the Cole Valley in the south and Plantsbrook in the east. North Birmingham is particularly dominated by Suburban monads which extend around Sutton Park, even including some of the western fringes of Sutton Park itself, where the vegetation is largely dense, relatively species-poor woodland, combined with residential areas outside the Park.

It is also interesting to compare Figure 4.6 with the coincidence maps for the relative distributions of native species, archaeophytes and neophytes. (Figures 4.2–4.4). The Rich semi-natural areas in the TWINSPAN map coincide with high proportions of native species, the Industrial areas with high proportions of archaeophytes and the Suburban areas mostly with high proportions of neophytes.

## Further TWINSPAN divisions

A further division of the two larger TWINSPAN groups is shown in Figure. 4.7. Numbers of monads and numbers of taxa per monad are shown in Table 4.7. The distribution of the groups is mapped in Figure 4.8.

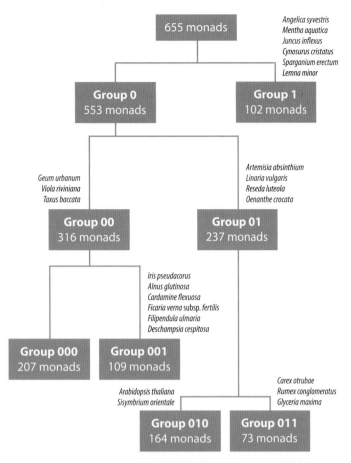

Angelica syvestris
Mentha aquatica
Juncus inflexus
Cynosurus cristatus
Sparganium erectum
Lemna minor

655 monads

Group 0
553 monads

Group 1
102 monads

Geum urbanum
Viola riviniana
Taxus baccata

Artemisia absinthium
Linaria vulgaris
Reseda luteola
Oenanthe crocata

Group 00
316 monads

Group 01
237 monads

Iris pseudacorus
Alnus glutinosa
Cardamine flexuosa
Ficaria verna subsp. fertilis
Filipendula ulmaria
Deschampsia cespitosa

Group 000
207 monads

Group 001
109 monads

Carex otrubae
Rumex conglomeratus
Glyceria maxima

Arabidopsis thaliana
Sisymbrium orientale

Group 010
164 monads

Group 011
73 monads

▲ Figure 4.7 Dendrogram showing further divisions of the major TWINSPAN groups of monads in B&BC (monads with <25% area within B&BC omitted). Species shown are indicators for the relevant side of a division

Table 4.7 Numbers of monads and numbers of taxa per monad in the secondary TWINSPAN groups shown in Figure 4.7

|  | No. monads in group | Average no. taxa per monad | Standard Error of average |
|---|---|---|---|
| Group 000 | 207 | 167.8 | 2.83 |
| Group 001 | 109 | 201.3 | 4.47 |
| Group 010 | 164 | 185.2 | 3.70 |
| Group 011 | 73 | 169.8 | 4.06 |
| Group 1 | 102 | 232.8 | 6.33 |

The Suburban Group 00 is divided into Groups 000 and 001. Group 001 monads are, on average, more species-rich than Group 000 monads (Table 4.7). There are no indicator species for Group 000 and only 13 preferential species. All but two are a selection of weeds of cultivation and weakly escaping garden plants. The two exceptions are *Plantago coronopus*, which is now common along road margins and *Sisymbrium orientale*, which is commonest in post-industrial areas but is becoming much more widespread in residential areas along roads.

Group 000 appears to consist of those monads in the conurbation which have the least affinity with semi-natural habitats. The monads are most frequently characterised by the absence of species of such habitats and/or the presence of features associated with housing, roads and/or other forms of disturbance

by humans. They are significantly poorer in species than Group 001 monads and could be described as the **Habitat-poor Suburbs** despite the inclusion of some (predominantly arable) farmland monads. Thus Group 000 seems to represent areas dominated by housing and/or cultivation with little species-rich greenspace.

The six indicator taxa for Group 001 (Figure 4.7) suggest shade and damp soils (for example alder carr) and also seem to represent a transition with the Rich Semi-natural Group 1. The large number (68) of preferentials for Group 001 are mostly plants of relatively mature habitats, include some such as *Anemone nemorosa*, *Bromus ramosus*, *Lamiastrum galeobdolon* subsp. *montanum*, *Melica uniflora*, and *Schedonorus giganteus* which suggests the presence of old woodlands with ecological interest. Group 001 monads could be described as the **Habitat-rich Suburbs**.

Figure 4.7 also shows a first division of the Industrial group (Group 01). A smaller group of 73 monads is cut off to form Group 011. The three indicators for Group 011 are all common canal margin plants and the 28 preferentials are also all aquatics and water-margin plants associated with the canals in our area. This suggests that the group encompasses Industrial monads transitional with the canal facies of the Rich Semi-natural group which might be named the **Industrial/Open-water** group. The indicators for Group 010 are the annual weed of cultivation *Arabidopsis thaliana* and the annual colonist of waste places *Sisymbrium orientale*, together with 25 preferentials which are almost all weeds of and colonists from gardens. This suggests that Group 010 has a botanical affinity with the Suburban group and that the name **Industrial/Suburban** group would be appropriate.

Rather unexpectedly, the Industrial/Suburban monads are on average richer in species than the Industrial/Open-water group monads (Table 4.7). Possibly in some areas the relative species poverty of the Industrial/Open-water monads reflects the fact that some of them have reached the minimum species score on the basis of canal-oriented surveys and may be under-recorded away from the canals (see also further discussion in axiophytes analysis below).

The Industrial/Suburban monads, however, are even more clearly richer in species than the Habitat-poor Suburban monads of Group 000 (Table 4.7). The presence of industry seems to give more opportunities for plant diversity than are available in purely residential areas.

The spatial distribution of the monads in the five TWINSPAN groups is shown in Figure 4.8.

Group 000 and Group 001 (Figures 4.7 and 4.8) show some interesting contrasts between the districts. The Habitat-poor Suburbs (Group 000) are quite uncommon in Walsall, reinforcing the impression of the borough as relatively rich in countryside areas. Incongruously, in Walsall the greatest concentrations of Habitat-poor Suburban monads is in the periphery of the conurbation east of Aldridge, where, along with a few monads misclassified as Industrial/Suburban monads, they actually describe areas of improved agriculture.

In Wolverhampton the Habitat-rich Suburban group is again common, but with clusters of Habitat-poor Suburbs monads particularly in the south-west in Blakenhall and parts of Penn.

In Dudley the Habitat-poor Suburban monads are mainly in the west and south-west periphery and to some extent reflect intensive farming as well as intensively residential areas. The tendency for clusters of heathland species to occur in the Stourbridge area still does not appear to affect the classification of the relevant monads which are uniformly part of the Habitat-poor Suburban group. There are also a few of these Habitat-poor Suburban monads in south-east and east Dudley.

Areas classified with the Suburban group in Sandwell are mostly of the Habitat-poor type, although there is a scatter of

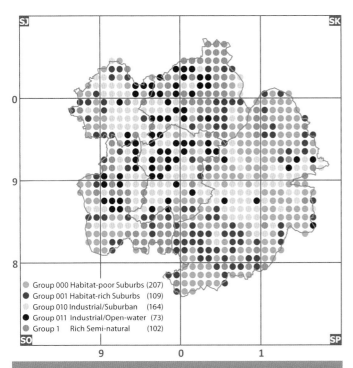

Group 000 Habitat-poor Suburbs (207)
Group 001 Habitat-rich Suburbs (109)
Group 010 Industrial/Suburban (164)
Group 011 Industrial/Open-water (73)
Group 1 Rich Semi-natural (102)

▲ Figure 4.8 Division of the B&BC monads into five TWINSPAN groups

Habitat-rich Suburban monads in the peripheries of the Rowley Hills and the Sandwell Valley.

Habitat-rich Suburban monads predominate in south Birmingham except in the Northfield area and reinforce the few Rich Semi-natural monads of the Cole Valley. There is a similar grouping of Rich Semi-natural and Habitat-rich Suburban monads in the Plantsbrook corridor of east Birmingham. The greatest concentration of Habitat-poor Suburban monads in the whole of B&BC extends eastwards from Handsworth (SP0390), northwards on both flanks of Sutton Park and southwards towards Birmingham Airport.

The distribution of the two segregates of the Industrial group is also shown in Figure 4.8. The Industrial/Open-water monads are a particular feature of the Black Country canals and in many places form links with the Rich Semi-natural monads, which are themselves often places where the canal flora is particularly rich. Industrial/Open water monads are relatively rare in Birmingham, despite the widespread distribution of canals there. This is probably a reflection of the effects on botanical diversity of the greater intensity of boat use and canalside development in Birmingham compared with the Black Country.

There are 102 monads in Group 1 (Rich Semi-natural), which can usefully be divided into three TWINSPAN segregates. These divisions are shown in Figure 4.9. Numbers of monads and numbers of taxa per monad are shown in Table 4.8.

The first division splits off twelve monads to form Group 11, with *Nardus stricta* and *Hydrocotyle vulgaris* as indicators, plants associated with semi-natural heaths and mires. The preferentials include many other plants of wet and dry heaths and some of rather more mesotrophic mires and wet grassland.

A further division of the remaining, larger, Group 10 gives a larger Group 100 with the pondweed *Potamogeton pectinatus*, a plant almost ubiquitous in any canal capable of sustaining submerged aquatic plants, as sole indicator. The indicators for Group 101 are all woodland plants, and all except *Arum maculatum* are plants confined to old woodlands.

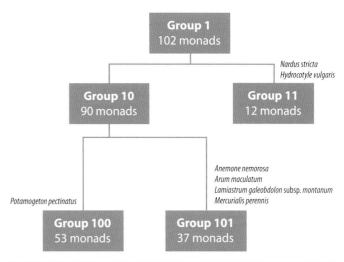

▲ Figure 4.9 Dendrogram showing further divisions of Group 1 of a TWINSPAN analysis of monads in B&BC (monads with <25% area within B&BC omitted). Species shown are indicators for the relevant side of a division

Table 4.8 Numbers of monads and numbers of taxa in the three groups of monads within TWINSPAN Group 1

| | No. monads in group | Average no. taxa per monad | Standard Error of average |
|---|---|---|---|
| Group 100 | 53 | 223.7 | 7.75 |
| Group 101 | 37 | 252.5 | 12.35 |
| Group 11 | 12 | 212.3 | 12.34 |

These divisions clearly sort the Rich Semi-natural group of monads into a **Heath & Mire** Group 11, an **Open-water Semi-natural** Group 100, and a **Wooded Semi-natural** Group 101. In Figure 4.10, the distribution of these three groups is shown across the conurbation.

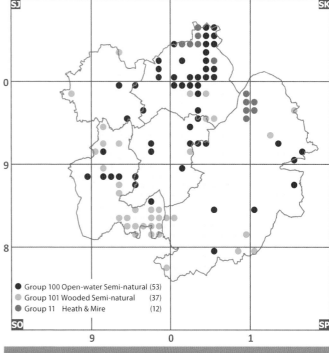

Group 100 Open-water Semi-natural (53)
Group 101 Wooded Semi-natural (37)
Group 11 Heath & Mire (12)

▲ Figure 4.10 Division of Group 1 monads into three sub-groups

The Heath & Mire group probably represents the most distinctive group of monads in the conurbation and forms a central core of six monads in Sutton Park. In the analysis scattered monads in north Walsall are associated with the Sutton Park monads. The key features in these Walsall monads appear to be the heaths of Brownhills (SK0306, SK0305) and Pelsall North Common (SK0104 and SK0204), but also the intriguing botanically rich mires and wet grasslands present in those monads and at Clayhanger (SK0304) and King's Hayes Fields (SK0502). Some small but equally distinctive dry heathland areas in south Dudley and Birmingham have been excluded from this group, presumably because of the small number of vascular plant taxa characterising the dry heath vegetation type.

The Wooded Semi-natural group is much more widespread across the conurbation, being found in every district. Not all these squares possess great areas of obviously ancient woodland although many do. There is a particularly striking cluster in and around Halesowen in south-east Dudley which also include outstanding grasslands.

The Open water Semi-natural group demonstrates the importance of the canal system for botanical diversity in B&BC and also that although this type is concentrated in Walsall, there are 'hot spots' in every district, usually associated with canals, but sometimes, as in the Sandwell Valley, marking the presence of lakes valuable for botanical diversity.

The overall distribution of the seven TWINSPAN groups described above is shown in Figure 4.11, and the main features of this classification of the monads of the conurbation is described in Table 4.9.

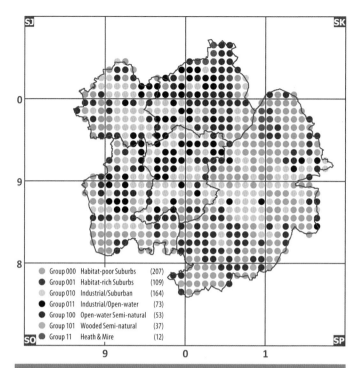

Group 000  Habitat-poor Suburbs  (207)
Group 001  Habitat-rich Suburbs  (109)
Group 010  Industrial/Suburban  (164)
Group 011  Industrial/Open-water  (73)
Group 100  Open-water Semi-natural  (53)
Group 101  Wooded Semi-natural  (37)
Group 11  Heath & Mire  (12)

▲ Figure 4.11 Division of the B&BC monads into seven TWINSPAN groups

| Name | | TWINSPAN groups | No. monads | No. spp. per monad | Description of groups of monads |
|---|---|---|---|---|---|
| Suburban | ● Habitat-poor | 000 | 207 | 168 | Residential and intensive agricultural land use predominates, markedly semi-natural habitats lacking. |
| | ● Habitat-rich | 001 | 109 | 201 | Residential and intensive agricultural land use predominates, semi-natural habitats, especially old woodlands, present. |
| Industrial | ○ Industrial/Suburban | 010 | 164 | 185 | Industry a predominant feature in the flora, species-rich open water habitats absent. |
| | ● Industrial/Open-water | 011 | 73 | 170 | Industry a predominant feature in the flora, moderately species-rich open water habitats (usually canals) present. |
| Rich Semi-natural | ● Heath & Mire | 11 | 12 | 212 | Significant amounts of rich semi-natural vegetation present, typically with a species-rich flora of wet and dry heaths and often of more mesotrophic mires and wet grassland. |
| | ● Open-water Semi-natural | 100 | 53 | 224 | Significant amounts of rich semi-natural vegetation present, characteristically species-rich open water flora (typically canal flora). |
| | ● Wooded Semi-natural | 101 | 37 | 253 | Significant amounts of rich semi-natural vegetation present, typically species-rich woodland flora. |

Table 4.9 The principal botanical/ecological divisions of B&BC at the monad level

## AXIOPHYTE ANALYSIS

The BSBI axiophyte project (http://www.bsbi.org.uk/axiophytes. html) defines axiophytes as "the 40% or so of species that arouse interest and praise from botanists when they are seen…They are indicators of habitat that is considered important for conservation, such as ancient woodlands, clear water and species-rich meadows." Lockton (2011) writes that they are "the species that we want, because they are the ones that grow in the habitats that we want to protect".

Lists of axiophytes provide a powerful technique for determining conservation priorities. Sites with many axiophytes are usually of greater conservation importance than those with

fewer. The present section explores whether it is possible to characterise monads in B&BC by the number of axiophytes they contain.

Defining particular species as axiophytes can be largely achieved by first drawing up a list of habitats of conservation importance. The axiophytes are those species which are:
- 90% restricted to these conservation habitats
- recorded in fewer than 25% of tetrads in the county.

Also species that have only ever been recorded in one or two sites in a county are often just chance occurrences, having little ecological (or statistical) significance, so records of very rare species should be considered for omission.

Many vice-counties now have lists of axiophytes. In practice they differ considerably from county to county since many of the more ecologically constrained species are confined to particular parts of the country. Often there is insufficient information to define the first criterion quantitatively. It may also be difficult to define 'site' rigorously.

B&BC has parts in three vice-counties, only one of which (vc. 39, Staffordshire) has currently (2012) published a list of axiophytes. It may be viewed on the BSBI website. That list must necessarily apply to the whole of the Staffordshire vice-county, one which extends more than 60 km north from B&BC and includes substantial semi-natural areas including parts of the Peak District. Similarly B&BC only includes small portions of the Warwickshire

and Worcestershire vice-counties. For this reason and also because of the especially urbanised nature of B&BC it has been thought necessary to put forward a list of axiophytes specific to B&BC.

## Axiophytes associated with natural and semi-natural habitats in B&BC

Many habitats widely considered to be of nature conservation importance in B&BC are the remnants of the natural and semi-natural communities which are thought to have characterised the landscape before it was urbanised and in some cases before it was populated by human beings at all. They are the plants which characterise the remaining old woodlands, wetlands,

**Table 4.10 List of 192 mappable axiophyte species and five associated hybrids in B&BC which are strongly associated with natural and semi-natural sites**

| Name | No. of monads | Name | No. of monads | Name | No. of monads | Name | No. of monads |
|---|---|---|---|---|---|---|---|
| Achillea ptarmica | 40 | Catabrosa aquatica | 1 | Juncus bulbosus | 10 | Potentilla erecta | 87 |
| Adoxa moschatellina | 12 | Ceratocapnos claviculata | 6 | Juncus squarrosus | 27 | Potentilla sterilis | 51 |
| Agrimonia eupatoria | 25 | Chaerophyllum temulum | 32 | Lamiastrum galeobdolon | | Pulicaria dysenterica | 37 |
| Agrostis canina | 30 | Chrysosplenium oppositifolium | 47 | subsp. montanum | 91 | Quercus petraea | 84 |
| Agrostis vinealis | 7 | Cirsium dissectum | 6 | Lathraea squamaria | 6 | Ranunculus aquatilis s.l. | 40 |
| Ajuga reptans | 42 | Cirsium palustre | 112 | Lathyrus linifolius | 10 | Ranunculus auricomus | 9 |
| Alchemilla filicaulis | | Comarum palustre | 16 | Lathyrus nissolia | 12 | Ranunculus circinatus | 9 |
| subsp. vestita | 33 | Dactylorhiza fuchsii | 39 | Leontodon hispidus | 65 | Ranunculus flammula | 45 |
| Allium ursinum | 133 | Dactylorhiza maculata | 2 | Lotus pedunculatus | 116 | Ranunculus hederaceus | 9 |
| Anacamptis pyramidalis | 8 | Dactylorhiza praetermissa | 48 | Luronium natans | 6 | Ranunculus omiophyllus | 2 |
| Anagallis tenella | 3 | Dactylorhiza × grandis | 10 | Luzula multiflora | 28 | Rhamnus cathartica | 5 |
| Anemone nemorosa | 93 | Danthonia decumbens | 25 | Luzula pilosa | 5 | Rhinanthus minor agg. | 62 |
| Angelica sylvestris | 164 | Deschampsia flexuosa | 155 | Lysimachia nemorum | 23 | Sagina nodosa | 3 |
| Apium inundatum | 3 | Drosera rotundifolia | 2 | Lysimachia vulgaris | 20 | Salix aurita | 10 |
| Athyrium filix-femina | 103 | Dryopteris affinis s.l. | 28 | Lythrum portula | 6 | Salix aurita hybrids | 8 |
| Betonica officinalis | 53 | Dryopteris carthusiana | 34 | Malus sylvestris sens.str. | 65 | Sanguisorba officinalis | 91 |
| Blechnum spicant | 12 | Eleocharis palustris | 68 | Melampyrum pratense | 1 | Sanicula europaea | 12 |
| Brachypodium sylvaticum | 156 | Eleocharis quinqueflora | 2 | Melica uniflora | 64 | Scabiosa columbaria | 4 |
| Briza media | 27 | Eleogiton fluitans | 1 | Mentha arvensis | 20 | Schedonorus giganteus | 124 |
| Bromopsis erecta | 13 | Empetrum nigrum agg. | 2 | Menyanthes trifoliata | 13 | Scirpus sylvaticus | 5 |
| Bromopsis ramosa | 104 | Epilobium palustre | 41 | Mercurialis perennis | 173 | Scutellaria minor | 1 |
| Calluna vulgaris | 64 | Epipactis helleborine | 21 | Milium effusum | 55 | Senecio aquaticus | 45 |
| Caltha palustris | 79 | Equisetum fluviatile | 56 | Moehringia trinervia | 32 | Senecio sylvaticus | 7 |
| Campanula rotundifolia | 32 | Equisetum palustre | 39 | Molinia caerulea | 34 | Silaum silaus | 6 |
| Cardamine amara | 28 | Equisetum sylvaticum | 21 | Montia fontana | 4 | Silene flos-cuculi | 48 |
| Carex acuta | 2 | Equisetum telmateia | 23 | Nardus stricta | 43 | Silene flos-cuculi | 48 |
| Carex acutiformis | 80 | Erica cinerea | 9 | Odontites vernus | 117 | Sorbus torminalis | 7 |
| Carex binervis | 6 | Erica tetralix | 13 | Oenanthe fistulosa | 2 | Spergularia rubra | 10 |
| Carex canescens | 2 | Eriophorum angustifolium | 11 | Ononis repens | 20 | Stachys palustris | 17 |
| Carex caryophyllea | 4 | Eriophorum vaginatum | 6 | Ophioglossum vulgatum | 5 | Stellaria alsine | 44 |
| Carex demissa | 17 | Euphrasia sp. | 13 | Oreopteris limbosperma | 1 | Stellaria holostea | 140 |
| Carex diandra | 2 | Festuca filiformis | 16 | Ornithopus perpusillus | 11 | Succisa pratensis | 45 |
| Carex dioica | 1 | Filipendula ulmaria | 169 | Oxalis acetosella | 51 | Tamus communis | 95 |
| Carex disticha | 8 | Fragaria vesca | 78 | Parnassia palustris | 2 | Teucrium scorodonia | 64 |
| Carex echinata | 7 | Frangula alnus | 34 | Pedicularis palustris | 2 | Thalictrum flavum | 3 |
| Carex hostiana | 2 | Galium album | 36 | Pedicularis sylvatica | 4 | Tilia cordata | 33 |
| Carex hostiana × C. demissa | 1 | Galium odoratum | 34 | Persicaria bistorta | 56 | Torilis japonica | 59 |
| Carex nigra | 66 | Galium palustre s.l. | 88 | Persicaria hydropiper | 47 | Triglochin palustris | 7 |
| Carex pallescens | 5 | Galium saxatile | 65 | Phleum bertolonii | 32 | Ulex gallii | 57 |
| Carex panicea | 23 | Galium uliginosum | 3 | Pimpinella saxifraga | 21 | Vaccinium myrtillus | 25 |
| Carex paniculata | 19 | Genista tinctoria | 7 | Pinguicula vulgaris | 2 | Vaccinium oxycoccos | 3 |
| Carex pilulifera | 12 | Geum rivale | 4 | Plantago media | 21 | Vaccinium vitis-idaea | 8 |
| Carex pseudocyperus | 37 | Geum × intermedium | 1 | Poa nemoralis | 56 | Valeriana dioica | 3 |
| Carex pulicaris | 2 | Glyceria declinata | 49 | Polygala vulgaris | 6 | Valeriana officinalis | 14 |
| Carex remota | 90 | Glyceria notata | 34 | Polystichum aculeatum | 7 | Veronica beccabunga | 158 |
| Carex riparia | 18 | Hydrocotyle vulgaris | 17 | Polystichum setiferum | 29 | Veronica montana | 47 |
| Carex rostrata | 15 | Hypericum pulchrum | 4 | Populus nigra subsp. betulifolia | 26 | Veronica officinalis | 14 |
| Carex strigosa | 2 | Hypericum tetrapterum | 68 | Potamogeton polygonifolius | 4 | Veronica scutellata | 5 |
| Carex sylvatica | 46 | Isolepis setacea | 22 | Potentilla anglica | 6 | Viola palustris | 4 |
| Carlina vulgaris | 2 | Juncus acutiflorus | 76 | Potentilla × mixta | 24 | Viola reichenbachiana | 30 |

grasslands and heaths of the conurbation. Such plants are rare in habitats which have been recently created, unless they have been deliberately introduced in an attempt to mimic semi-natural habitats. Most if not all such species would be widely recognised as indicators of natural and semi-natural habitats in areas beyond B&BC, although of course the actual list includes only those species typical of our own area.

Axiophyte species in B&BC have been selected from a list of candidate species suggested by our field recorders. The monad rather than the tetrad has been used as the unit in selection. In the conurbation most sites have been highly modified by human activity, so borderline species have only been considered for exclusion where it can be shown that more than 25% of records are from sites not scheduled as being of nature conservation value (SINCs or higher). A few species with currently less than three monad records but with three or more known since 1980 have been included, also a few with two records or even one where the species is clearly part of an old, semi-natural assemblage. Four sections within the genus *Taraxacum* have been named in the text of the atlas as axiophytes, namely sect. Erythosperma, sect. Naevosa, sect. Celtica and sect. Spectabilia but since detailed data is only available for the vc. 37 (Worcestershire) part of B&BC, these taxa have not been included in the following analysis.

The current list is shown in Table 4.10, together with the number of recent (1995–2012) monad records for each taxon.

Several taxa which are widely associated with old sites have nevertheless been excluded from this list despite being commonly included in axiophyte lists elsewhere. This is because the records which exist in B&BC are so few as to suggest the possibility that they are all accidental introductions. Species which fall into this category are listed in Table 4.11. The most controversial species in the list are *Gentianella amarella* and *Viola hirta*, which are almost certainly the remnant of vegetation which is of nature conservation importance but exists in a single area little more than five metres across.

## Distribution of axiophytes strongly associated with natural and semi-natural sites

In order to limit the influence of hybridisation in overemphasising particular genotypes in the analysis, for the purposes of comparing monads the hybrid *Dactylorhiza* × *grandis* has been combined with *Dactylorhiza praetermissa* as a single entity, *Geum* × *intermedium* with *Geum rivale*, *Potentilla* × *mixta* with *Potentilla anglica* and *Salix aurita* hybrids with *Salix aurita*.

The list presented in Table 4.10 is biased towards habitats which are rich in plant species. It includes many more woodland and mire species than dry heathland species for example, just because woodlands and mires will include more species than dry heathlands. Nevertheless, considered as a whole, the species in Table 4.10 are very unevenly distributed in B&BC.

### Table 4.12 B&BC Monads with the highest numbers of axiophytes strongly associated with natural and semi-natural sites recorded

| Monad | Axiophytes | Key sites |
|---|---|---|
| SP0998 | 81 | Sutton Park |
| SP0996 | 74 | Sutton Park |
| SO9983 | 65 | Woodgate Valley |
| SP0995 | 65 | Sutton Park |
| SO9387 | 59 | Saltwells |
| SO9781 | 58 | Lower Illey |
| SK0306 | 57 | Brownhills Common |
| SP1097 | 57 | Sutton Park |
| SO9189 | 56 | Barrow Hill |
| SO9192 | 56 | Cotwall End |

### Table 4.11 List of species strongly associated with natural and semi-natural sites in the midlands which have been excluded from the axiophyte list for B&BC

| Name | Monads | Reasons for rejection as an axiophyte |
|---|---|---|
| *Avenula pubescens* | 3 | All are considered to be probably casual records |
| *Campanula patula* | 2 | Both sites probably adventive |
| *Carex laevigata* | 1 | A single plant seen in Sutton Park |
| *Chrysosplenium alternifolium* | 1 | A single validated site at the extreme margin of B&BC |
| *Euphorbia amygdaloides* | 1 | A single validated site of uncertain origin |
| *Gentianella amarella* | 1 | A single very local patch at the Wren's Nest |
| *Hordelymus europaeus* | 1 | A single site at the extreme margins of B&BC |
| *Luzula sylvatica* | 1 | A single site and possibly adventive or introduced |
| *Myosotis secunda* | 1 | Very local at a single site – one other in 1971 |
| *Serratula tinctoria* | 2 | One tiny population at the extreme margins of B&BC |
| *Solidago virgaurea* | 1 | Probably only a single site at the extreme margins of B&BC |
| *Utricularia* sp. | 2 | One population in Sutton Park, now apparently spreading into a neighbouring pool |
| *Viola hirta* | 1 | A single very local patch at the Wren's Nest |

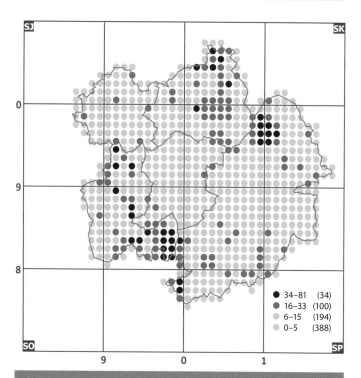

34–81 (34)
16–33 (100)
6–15 (194)
0–5 (388)

▲ Figure 4.12 Distribution of axiophytes strongly associated with natural and semi-natural sites in B&BC

78 monads (11%) have no records of any of the species in Table 4.10 at all and 387 (54%) have five or less. At the other extreme, only 74 monads (10%) have 25 or more recorded. The 'top ten' monads are shown in Table 4.12.

Figure 4.12 shows the distribution of axiophytes across the whole of B&BC, including in the fragments of monads around the periphery of the conurbation.

Figure 4.12 shows clearly that axiophyte diversity varies considerably across the conurbation. The majority of the Rich Semi-natural TWINSPAN group show high axiophyte scores (Figure 4.6, page 141). The map of axiophyte diversity and the distribution of the Rich Semi-natural monads both represent a focusing of the pattern of a high proportion of native species which was first seen in Figure 4.2, (page 137).

Axiophyte diversity, like native species diversity, tends to increase in the periphery, but again this is not the overwhelming feature. The major feature of the distribution has a north-west – south-east trend, with the central one third of the conurbation (the 'urban core') from eastern Birmingham to Wolverhampton showing generally low axiophyte diversity, with considerably higher axiophyte diversity in the upper and lower thirds, passing respectively from Brownhills in Walsall to Castle Vale in Birmingham and from Sedgley in Dudley to King's Norton in Birmingham.

There is also an interrupted strand of higher axiophyte diversity traversing across the central zone, focused on both the Sandwell and the Birmingham portions of the Sandwell Valley and potentially linking the richer upper and lower thirds across the urban core. There is a minor break in this strand in the row of monads in the Sandwell/Walsall boundary and a much broader gap between the Sandwell Valley and Halesowen across Smethwick, with only the Galton Valley (SP0189) and Warley Woods (SP0186 etc.) areas offering wildlife 'stepping stones' across the gap.

Furthermore the coincidence map shows clearly that there are several strong focuses of axiophyte diversity in B&BC. There are two core areas, in Sutton Park and south-east Dudley, where five or more 34+ axiophyte monads are contiguous, a more diffuse but very extensive core area in Walsall and a more narrowly delimited but very strong network in north and central Dudley.

### The **Sutton Park** axiophyte core area

Sutton Park is the strongest focus, SP0998 with 81 axiophytes and SP0996 with 74 axiophytes having the highest axiophyte scores of any in B&BC. Five monads in the Sutton Park group have more than 50 axiophytes, eight monads have more than 30 and every one of the 15 monads (even those with only a small proportion within the Park) has at least 17 axiophytes strongly associated with natural and semi-natural sites. The totals here are probably under-estimated, because Sutton Park abounds in species known nowhere else in the conurbation and therefore hard to justify as axiophytes. The Sutton Park core area is largely embedded in the conurbation and is only weakly connected with the Walsall high axiophyte core area to the west and with the open countryside to the north.

### The **Halesowen Countryside** axiophyte core area

The second core area, in the Halesowen/Illey area of south-east Dudley, is slightly less rich in axiophytes than the Sutton Park core area, with SO9781 (Lower Illey) with 58 axiophytes, SO9883 (Lapal/Leasowes) with 55 and SO9983 (Woodgate Valley) with 65, but the area is even more extensive with a central core of 9 monads

with 34+ axiophytes. However the zone of high axiophyte diversity essentially encompasses the whole of the southern periphery of Dudley from Pedmore in the west to the Leasowes and Combeswood in the north and Lapal and Illey in the east. It extends into Birmingham in the Woodgate Valley.

This core area also links with, and indeed is part of, a large area of high quality "ancient countryside" outside the conurbation to the south in rural Worcestershire including the Clent Hills, which harks back to a social setting where farming practice was traditional, small-scale and more sustainable.

The cluster of high-scoring monads to the south around Rednal represents an extension of this core area and a connection with the Lickey Hills, also in the same area of Worcestershire countryside.

### The **Walsall Countryside** axiophyte core area

The third core area includes much of the Walsall Countryside. It has a particular focus of very high axiophyte diversity in the Brownhills/Clayhanger area of north Walsall, with SK0306 the highest scorer with 57 axiophytes and with an adjacent cluster of monads with 34+ axiophyte, but high-scoring monads extend west to Pelsall North Common, east to King's Hayes Fields (SK0502) and south all the way to the border with Birmingham and Sandwell, encompassing over 30 monads with 16 or more axiophytes. This core area area links northwards across the A5 and the M6 Toll Road with the Chasewater SSSI and Cannock Chase beyond the conurbation, and has only narrow gaps with the Sutton Park core area and with the Sandwell Valley.

### The **Central Dudley** axiophyte network

This is a fourth, more diffuse but very extensive network of high axiophyte diversity centred in central and north Dudley, extending into the Penn Common (or 'Goldthorn') green wedge in Wolverhampton in the north (SO9195) and linking with the Wren's Nest to the east (SO9391, SO9392). Several strands extend southwards and almost link with the Halesowen Countryside axiophyte core area. The network includes very high scoring monads at Saltwells (SO9387), Barrow Hill (SO9189) and Cotwall End (SO9192), in a network of 18 monads all with 15 or more axiophytes. This demonstrates the way that primary habitats have persisted in a network extending across Dudley, thanks in many cases to pioneer creation of urban nature reserves.

### Less intense axiophyte foci and corridors

In **Wolverhampton**, the Smestow Valley LNR, together with the Staffs and Worcs Canal, old woodland on the Tettenhall Ridge (SO8798) and the Racecourse (SJ9000) form a well-marked patch of monads with modestly raised axiophyte scores in the north-west fringes of the conurbation. It is also possible to see that this area extends towards the city centre via the Birmingham Canal and adjacent habitats (SJ9000, SJ9100) and north-eastwards towards rich old woodland at Northycote Farm (SJ9303). The Penn Common (or Goldthorn) green wedge (SO9195) in the south, between Wolverhampton and Dudley, apart from being part of the Central Dudley axiophyte network, has enhanced monad axiophyte scores which extend east as far as Ladymoor Pool in Bilston (SO9495). This may suggest that Ladymoor Pool, which is clearly a post-industrial site, might also be a remnant of primary habitat, or alternatively that certain post-industrial sites have the capacity eventually to accumulate groups of species otherwise largely confined to old sites. There is a third enhanced patch in the east of Wolverhampton in the south Wednesfield/Willenhall area. This too must be essentially post-industrial.

In **Walsall**, apart from the Wednesfield/Willenhall core area described above, there is an interesting patch around Junction 10 on the M6 (SO9998) and a stronger and significant focus near Bloxwich at Rough Wood (SJ9800) and Wood Farm, which connects (northwards) with the countryside in the M6 corridor.

In **Birmingham**, there is no continuous zone of high value monads in the north-eastern and eastern periphery of Sutton/Birmingham, despite the presence of more or less continuous countryside within these peripheral monads. Instead several rather isolated high-scoring nodes are revealed, particularly at Hill Hook (SK1000), Lindridge (SP1596), Parkhall (SP1691), Fordbridge (SP1787), Marston Green (SP1785) and Fox Hollies (SP1282). Plantsbrook (SP1293) and Pype Hayes (SP1392) presents a larger, more internal high quality patch almost connecting with Sutton Park and with the open countryside to the east.

The other striking feature of Birmingham is the presence of a strong network of fairly high-scoring monads throughout south Birmingham which also penetrate quite deeply northwards into central Birmingham. The network is largely but not entirely linked with the presence of river and stream valleys and the existence of old woodland along these streams. Via the Woodgate Valley (SP0083) this network has links with the Halesowen Countryside axiophyte core area.

**Sandwell** lies almost entirely within the conurbation urban core. Beyond the crucial role of the Sandwell Valley in acting as a reservoir and a stepping stone of high botanical diversity connecting the two main countryside areas of the conurbation in Walsall/Sutton Park and Halesowen/Woodgate Valley, high axiophyte areas in Sandwell are rather isolated. There is quite a strong signal from the area including the Sheepwash Urban Park (SO9791) and a weaker one from the canal system at Tipton (SO9592), but the most important seems to be the Rowley Hills area (SO9688), which is not only quite rich in axiophytes but also almost links with the Central Dudley axiophyte network. The Rowley Hills are greatly modified by human activity, particularly quarrying and later landfilling, but the data suggests a significant remnant of primary habitat.

Practically all the axiophyte hotspots in **Dudley** can be associated either with the Halesowen countryside core area or the Central Dudley axiophyte network.

### Axiophytes not strongly associated with natural and semi-natural habitats in B&BC

Groups of indicator species which are not associated with natural or semi-natural vegetation of conservation importance (e.g. fertility indicators) are not included in the above axiophyte list. However in B&BC (and probably everywhere in lowland Britain) nature conservation cannot just confine itself to the preservation of the old, less human-modified areas containing essentially natural or semi-natural sites which are identified above, because of the intensive and long-term human use of the landscape and the needs of people for 'nature' wherever they live.

In addition to the 192 species and five associated hybrids delimited in Table 4.10, a range of other taxa were felt by our recorders to be equally worthy of conservation but which, in B&BC at least, are predominantly associated with artificial or at least relatively recently established sites.

Examples include less common members of the arable weed community, many of which have become uncommon due to the widespread use of selective herbicides in agriculture and horticulture and hence are now considered worthy of conservation. Also, in B&BC, submerged aquatic species are generally found in the patently artificial canal habitat, but several such species are generally useful indicators of clean, mesotrophic or oligotrophic waters in the UK and are widely recognised elsewhere as axiophytes.

One major habitat type, which seems to occur widely in B&BC and which has been characterised recently by Natural England, has now been designated as the UK National Biodiversity Action Plan (UK BAP) priority habitat of 'Open mosaic habitats on previously developed land'. The habitat type is partly defined by the presence of bare, unvegetated areas and a characteristic degree of spatial variation. The published descriptions (probably strongly influenced by Gilbert 1989) focus on the species-rich early successional stages which can develop rapidly after land has been recently cleared. Such sites can have their own beauty, and can maintain remarkably rich populations of invertebrates. Unfortunately such communities are usually transient, disappearing due to development but also as a result of the natural processes of succession, as perennials and eventually woody species appear and much of the original diversity and the invertebrate communities they support are lost. Recently this loss has been accelerated by the extremely rapid colonisation of such sites by *Buddleia davidii* which can generate dense scrub as quickly as in the second year after clearance, although of course it has advantages for butterflies and other nectar feeders. However whilst early successional communities cannot be easily conserved individually without repeated episodes of disturbance, their frequency in the landscape should be assessed and measures taken to conserve this frequency (see further discussion in Post-industrial Sites, section 2 of the present chapter).

Furthermore there are sites which retain these characteristics for a long period of time due, for example, to soil poverty, mineral unbalance or even toxicity (Trueman & Young, 2012). Many of these are of interest as ecological phenomena and can and should be considered for conservation. For all these reasons it was felt necessary to include some of the characteristic species of these habitats in our axiophyte analysis.

A variety of vegetation types are recognised as possible in the open mosaic matrix, notably "(a) annuals, or (b) mosses/liverworts, or (c) lichens, or (d) ruderals, or (e) inundation species, or (f) open grassland, or (g) flower-rich grassland, or (h) heathland." (Riding *et al.* 2010; ADAS Ltd, 2010). Interestingly, many species characteristic of such habitats are native species strongly associated with natural and semi-natural sites and are included in Table 4.10, but others are not. Often the annuals associated with such habitats, such as *Arenaria serpyllifolia*, *Centaurium erythraea*, *Linum catharticum* and *Trifolium arvense*, are defined by Grime *et al.* (2007) as stress-tolerant ruderals (i.e. adapted to a degree of both disturbance and stress) and together with some similar biennials or short-lived perennials are colonists of open situations on skeletal, often drought-liable soils. Their presence for any length of time suggests conditions for very slow colonisation and hence possible generation of the patchworks of vegetation with bare land which characterise the open mosaic habitat. Many of the ruderals (i.e. plants adapted to disturbance) listed in the UK BAP schedule for these open mosaic habitats are also found in arable land and are often too frequent everywhere to be useful as indicators in the monad-level analysis possible using the Flora data.

Table 4.13 is a first list of 58 axiophyte taxa not strongly associated with natural and semi-natural habitats in B&BC but

**Table 4.13 List of 55 axiophyte species, one hybrid and two subspecies which in B&BC are associated with artificial and secondary sites.** Taxa associated with open-mosaic post-industrial sites are marked with an asterisk. The rest are mainly aquatic and wetland plants associated with canals, plus a few species associated with cultivation

| Name | Number of monads | Name | Number of monads | Name | Number of monads |
|---|---|---|---|---|---|
| *Aira caryophyllea | 33 | *Erigeron acris | 45 | Potamogeton pusillus | 7 |
| *Aira praecox | 66 | *Erophila verna s.l. | 79 | *Poterium sanguisorba subsp. sanguisorba | 5 |
| *Anthyllis vulneraria | 44 | *Filago minima | 3 | *Reseda lutea | 110 |
| Apera spica-venti | 3 | *Filago vulgaris | 9 | Sagittaria sagittifolia | 72 |
| *Arenaria serpyllifolia s.l. | 52 | Fumaria muralis | 17 | *Sambucus ebulus | 4 |
| Asplenium adiantum-nigrum | 29 | *Inula conyzae | 9 | *Senecio erucifolius | 34 |
| Asplenium ceterach | 11 | *Linum catharticum | 35 | *Senecio viscosus | 65 |
| Bidens cernua | 9 | *Ophrys apifera | 29 | *Sherardia arvensis | 23 |
| Bidens tripartita | 27 | *Orobanche minor | 4 | *Silene vulgaris | 136 |
| *Blackstonia perfoliata | 4 | *Picris hieracioides | 12 | Stachys arvensis | 23 |
| Butomus umbellatus | 92 | *Pilosella praealta | 3 | *Stellaria pallida | 5 |
| *Calamagrostis epigejos | 16 | *Poa angustifolia | 5 | Thlaspi arvense | 36 |
| *Catapodium rigidum | 40 | *Poa compressa | 26 | *Trifolium arvense | 132 |
| *Centaurea scabiosa | 47 | Potamogeton berchtoldii | 4 | *Trifolium medium | 165 |
| *Centaurium erythraea | 113 | Potamogeton friesii | 4 | *Trifolium micranthum | 25 |
| *Cerastium semidecandrum | 15 | Potamogeton x lintonii (P. crispus × friesii) | 5 | *Trifolium striatum | 9 |
| *Chaenorhinum minus | 22 | Potamogeton lucens | 14 | Veronica catenata | 7 |
| Chenopodium polyspermum | 39 | Potamogeton obtusifolius | 3 | Veronica polita | 15 |
| *Clematis vitalba | 78 | Potamogeton perfoliatus | 46 | *Vicia tetrasperma | 82 |
| *Daucus carota subsp. carota | 141 | | | | |

**Table 4.14 List of species excluded from B&BC axiophyte list for species which are associated with artificial and secondary sites**

| Name | No. of monads | Reasons for rejection as an axiophyte |
|---|---|---|
| Allium vineale | 23 | Appears to be a colonist of rough secondary grassland in B&BC |
| Cardamine impatiens | 2 | Long-persistent at one quarry site, otherwise appears ephemeral |
| Lithospermum officinale | 2 | Very local at the Wren's Nest |
| Parentucellia viscosa | 2 | Long-persistent at one wet grassland site, otherwise appears ephemeral |
| Saxifraga tridactylites | 2 | On railway ballast at one site and close by apparently as an adventive. |

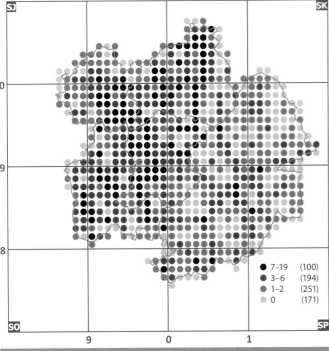

▲ **Figure 4.13 Distribution of axiophytes strongly associated with artificial and secondary sites in B&BC**

which our contributors consider are worthy of conservation and ought to be included in the list of axiophytes for B&BC. It is made up partly of the species in the lists approved nationally for the description of open mosaic habitats on previously developed land (marked with an asterisk), plus similar species considered to be worthy of axiophyte status in B&BC. In addition it includes threatened species of arable present in B&BC and submerged aquatics found entirely or almost entirely in the canal network in B&BC.

The species in Table 4.14 were rejected from Table 4.13 for the stated reasons.

Figure 4.13 shows the distribution of the taxa listed in Table 4.13 in B&BC. *Potamogeton x lintonii* was included in this analysis as a distinct taxon. The distribution of these taxa is less polarised than that of the axiophytes strongly associated with natural and semi-natural sites, with a relatively larger proportion of monads with at least a modest representation. The patterns of distribution shown in Figure 4.13 are obscured by the rather unsatisfactory association of urban mosaic and canal taxa in the list. However, taken together these axiophytes are most common in the Black Country, where their distribution is fairly pervasive away from the periphery of the conurbation and the countryside areas of Walsall and the Sandwell Valley, suggesting a general presence of these interesting taxa and the temporary and more permanent sites which support them. In Birmingham they appear to be associated specifically with the canals and also with eastern parts of central Birmingham.

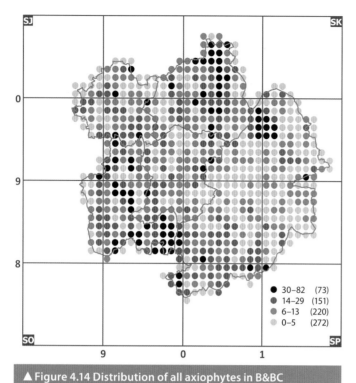

▲ Figure 4.14 Distribution of all axiophytes in B&BC

● 30–82 (73)
● 14–29 (151)
● 6–13 (220)
● 0–5 (272)

All 250 axiophytes (again omitting the five hybrids omitted from Figure 4.12) are mapped in Figure 4.14.

Despite the inclusion of axiophytes strongly associated with artificial and secondary sites, the essential features of the map of axiophytes strongly associated with natural and semi-natural sites (Figure 4.12) and the conservation foci and networks described in connection with Figure 4.12 are maintained, probably because the number of taxa added are not large and the original differentiation was great. Figure 4.14 does however demonstrate that the canal system and open mosaic sites often enhance connections between the conservation foci and also suggests that the characteristics of post-industrial sites in particular in the central part of the Black Country districts are positive for nature conservation.

**Combination of Axiophyte and TWINSPAN analysis**

Bearing in mind the fact that both analyses are based on the same database, a useful description and evaluation of the spontaneous vegetation of B&BC can be arrived at by combining the TWINSPAN group and axiophyte assessment of each monad in a single map. This has been attempted in Figure 4.15, which is a reiteration of the seven TWINSPAN group map shown in Figure 4.11 with the total axiophyte score shown for each monad.

Not unexpectedly the axiophyte scores correlate well with the perceived species-richness and nature conservation value of the TWINSPAN group monads (Table 4.15). On average, the three groups of Rich Semi-natural monads have higher scores than the rest, the Habitat-rich Suburban monads are richer in axiophyte taxa than the Habitat-poor Suburban monads and the Industrial monads are slightly richer in axiophytes than the Habitat-poor Suburban monads.

The Habitat-poor Suburban monads are, as might be expected, mostly very poor in axiophytes. The type is particularly abundant in Birmingham. It marks areas of suburbs in which the main source of spontaneous plants are gardens and minor

roadsides. It is difficult to see how to improve these areas in biodiversity terms except by improving parks, gardens and open spaces by habitat creation and by encouraging wildlife gardening. The Habitat-rich Suburbs, on the other hand, include some monads with very high axiophyte scores equivalent to those in the Rich Semi-natural groups. In some ways these monads are particularly valuable because of their close proximity to human populations where they live in the suburbs.

Both Suburban groups include some monads with atypical axiophyte scores. Some must clearly represent transitions between the two types but others, particularly around the Halesowen and Sutton Park axiophyte foci seem to represent particularly subtle combinations of vegetation which the analysis has found difficult to classify. Some of the low-scoring Habitat-rich Suburban squares are in fact essentially agricultural landscapes, for which it has proved difficult to define more than a very few axiophytes. This complexity and difficulty in classification has also led to several apparently suburban- and agricultural landscape-dominated squares being assigned to the Industrial group, possibly because road verges have been the main source of taxa characteristic of a TWINSPAN group.

Some industrial areas clearly do not lack interesting taxa, although others can be very poor. In general, the Industrial monads are richer in the Black Country, where axiophyte numbers can be comparable with Habitat-rich Suburban and even Rich Semi-natural monads, than in Birmingham, where there are nevertheless relatively rich patches associated e.g. with Digbeth (SP0886), Tyseley (SP1184), Selly Oak (SP0482, SP0483) and Perry Barr (SP0692).

As might be expected, much of the perceived richness in the Industrial group is associated with the axiophytes of artificial and secondary sites (see Figures 4.13 and 4.14). Canals are usually involved in axiophyte-rich Industrial monads, although paradoxically, the Industrial/Suburban group has a wider range of axiophyte scores than the Industrial/Open-water group. Possibly high axiophyte Industrial monads with canals resemble and segregate with the canal-oriented Open Water Rich Semi-natural group, removing high scorers from the Industrial/Open-water group. As a result there are often clusters of open-water Rich Semi-natural monads mixed with Industrial/Open-water monads. Canal improvement might be the easiest way to reinforce these linkages.

Although many of the Industrial/Suburban group monads are quite, or even very, axiophyte-poor, there are a few very high scores, usually where semi-natural features are present alongside industrial features. Paradoxically, some of these Industrial/Suburban monads include (presumably not very characteristic) canals! These are also probably places where management improvement might cause transition into the Rich Semi-natural group although some may be specific foci of biodiversity based entirely on industrial activity.

Despite the relatively low numbers of axiophytes attributed to heathland, the Heath & Mire group of Rich Semi-natural modules are extremely and uniformly rich in axiophytes. The sites which confer this status must themselves be seen as particularly special and worthy of unequivocal protection in the B&BC context. Open-water and Wooded Semi-natural groups are both more variable. There are high scores equivalent to those in the Heath & Mire group, but there are also some with quite low scores. These must contain sufficient habitat and hence sufficient numbers of preferentials to qualify for the TWINSPAN group whilst lacking the axiophyte 'quality indicators'. Whether this represents site degradation or opportunities for site improvement must depend on more detailed local assessments than are possible here.

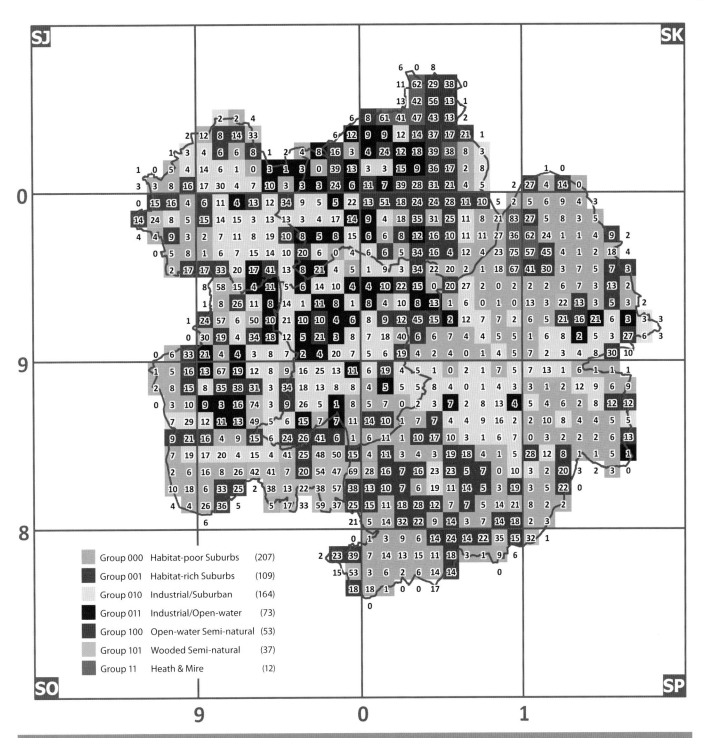

Group 000   Habitat-poor Suburbs      (207)
Group 001   Habitat-rich Suburbs      (109)
Group 010   Industrial/Suburban       (164)
Group 011   Industrial/Open-water      (73)
Group 100   Open-water Semi-natural    (53)
Group 101   Wooded Semi-natural        (37)
Group 11    Heath & Mire               (12)

▲ Figure 4.15 TWINSPAN coincidence map of B&BC showing total axiophyte scores for each monad as numbers

**Table 4.15 Axiophyte scores of the principal botanical/ecological divisions of B&BC at the monad level**

| | Axiophyte scores | | |
|---|---|---|---|
| TWINSPAN Group | Average | Median | Range |
| Habitat-poor Suburban | 5.5 | 4 | 0–27 |
| Habitat-rich Suburban | 17.0 | 15 | 3–45 |
| Industrial/Suburban | 8.4 | 7 | 0–30 |
| Industrial/Open-water | 8.5 | 8 | 1–21 |
| Heath & Mire Rich Semi-natural | 55.9 | 59 | 36–83 |
| Open-water Rich Semi-natural | 26.4 | 24 | 8–56 |
| Wooded Rich Semi-natural | 39.3 | 38 | 13–74 |

# Section 2 • Influences on the urban landscape

## INTRODUCTION

It is obvious that the well-being of diversity is centred on the well-being of individual habitats. The contribution of many of the more ancient and well-defined habitat types such as woodland and mire is self-evident in the previous section and is well expressed in the SSSI and SINC designated sites described in Chapter 2. The present section attempts to characterise the flora and examine the contribution of some of the other influences and habitat types where the contribution is less well understood. These analyses deal briefly with geological influences, canals, railways, roads, post-industrial sites, river corridors, allotments and heaths in the urban context.

### Statistical note

In many of these cases it has been possible to divide the B&BC monads into two types, for example with canals and without canals, or with railways and without railways. It then becomes possible to compare the two types in terms of the differences in frequency of particular taxon. Where a taxon is fairly frequent it is possible to test this difference using the statistical 'chi squared' test. Usually three levels of statistical significance are used. 5% significance is where a significant difference will be recorded which is likely to be correct in 95 cases out of 100. 1% significance is where it is likely to be correct in 99 case out of 100. 0.1% significance is where it is likely to be correct in 999 case out of 1,000.

Where it has been possible to divide the monads into two groups in relation to an environmental variable such as the presence or absence of canals, all taxa with 10 or more records have had chi squared calculated. 802 taxa had 10 or more monad records in the survey. Because there is only a single comparison possible, a version of chi squared with Yates' correction has been used. For the purposes of the comparison only taxa which differentiate at the relatively rigorous 0.1% significance level have been highlighted for discussion.

## THE MAIN GEOLOGY FEATURES

### Superficial deposits

Appreciable superficial deposits, mostly glacial but also river alluvium, cover most of B&BC (Figure 4.16). There are however 213 monads, mainly in a broad band of land running from Dudley in the south-west to Aldridge and Sutton Park in the north-east, with little in the way of superficial deposits. If the 502 monads where superficial deposits are present are compared with the remaining 213, the two types are not significantly different in average numbers of taxa per monad. Only 19 taxa show differentiation significant at the 0.1% level in chi squared tests. *Agrimonia eupatoria*, *Betonica officinalis*, *Carex flacca*, *Cynosurus cristatus*, *Leontodon hispidus*, *Odontites vernus*, *Pilosella officinarum*, and *Trisetum flavescens* are much less frequent in monads with superficial deposits. Possibly this is because they are often found in open grassland on poor, shallow soils which might be expected to be more common where the bedrock is exposed. This may also be true of *Melica uniflora* which

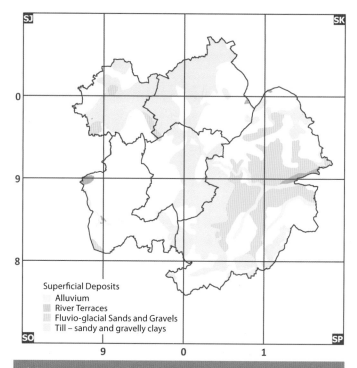

▲ Figure 4.16 Superficial geology of B&BC

*(map legend:)* Superficial Deposits
Alluvium
River Terraces
Fluvio-glacial Sands and Gravels
Till – sandy and gravelly clays

sometimes manages to grow over soft sandstone outcrops in old woodland, but this is not what one associates with the habitat of other old woodland and shade taxa also associated with monads without recorded superficial deposits, *Bromopsis ramosa*, *Lamiastrum galeobdolon* subsp. *montanum* and *Vicia sepium*. The taxa strongly associated with superficial deposits are plants associated with water and with residential areas. The full list is *Bidens frondosa*, *Campanula trachelium*, *Carex acutiformis*, *Galium palustre s.l.*, *Lemna minuta*, *Lupinus × regalis* and *Solidago canadensis*.

### The bedrock strata

The bedrock strata of B&BC shown in Figure 4.17 lie in nearly parallel bands from north to south of the conurbation. The Black Country is dominated by the Coal Measures of the Carboniferous which were the source of its industrial importance. The younger Triassic rocks which characterise the rest of B&BC include the coarser sandstones and conglomerates of the Sherwood Sandstone Group either side of the Carboniferous exposures, with a broad band of finer sandstones, silts and mudstones of the Mercia Mudstone Group occupying the eastern half of Birmingham.

366 monads, more than half, include bedrock strata attributed to the Carboniferous, with some igneous intrusions and some small exposures of older Silurian limestone. Some monads have portions of the younger Triassic formations. The monads where Carboniferous strata are present are significantly richer in taxa (average 191 taxa per monad, SE 3.01) than the other 349 (average 167, SE 3.03) where Triassic rocks occupy the whole surface. This is probably mostly the result of the intensive and complex industrial activity in the Black Country as a result

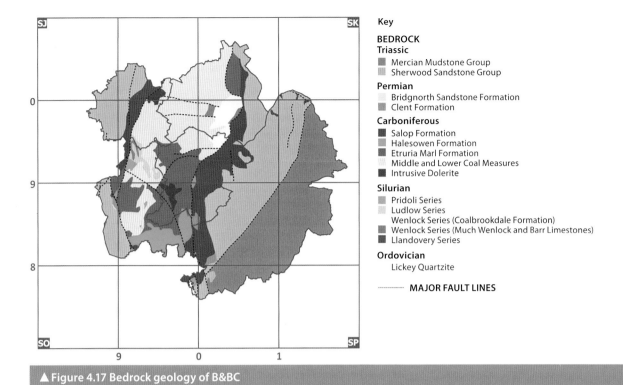

Key

**BEDROCK**
**Triassic**
▪ Mercian Mudstone Group
▨ Sherwood Sandstone Group
**Permian**
░ Bridgnorth Sandstone Formation
▪ Clent Formation
**Carboniferous**
▪ Salop Formation
▪ Halesowen Formation
▪ Etruria Marl Formation
░ Middle and Lower Coal Measures
■ Intrusive Dolerite
**Silurian**
▪ Pridoli Series
▨ Ludlow Series
   Wenlock Series (Coalbrookdale Formation)
▪ Wenlock Series (Much Wenlock and Barr Limestones)
■ Llandovery Series
**Ordovician**
   Lickey Quartzite

········ **MAJOR FAULT LINES**

▲ **Figure 4.17 Bedrock geology of B&BC**

of its mineral wealth. 122 taxa are strongly associated with the Carboniferous (0.1% level). They include a long list of canal plants, a few old woodland taxa and more old grassland taxa, plus a good range of plants from post-industrial sites. 23 taxa strongly negatively associated with these monads (0.1% level) and therefore strongly positively associated with the Triassic exposures are almost entirely plants characteristic of residential areas, but also *Bryonia dioica*, a hedgerow plant probably reflecting the more agricultural past of the relevant monads.

The Sherwood Group, consisting mainly of sandstones and conglomerates is found in 288 monads. Selecting just these monads and comparing them with the remaining 427, the average monad number of taxa is 175 (SE 3.21) for the Sherwood Group compared with 182 (SE 2.93) for all the remaining monads. 22 taxa are strongly associated with the Sherwood Group (0.1% level). This includes a range of heathland taxa: *Festuca filiformis*, *Carex pilulifera*, *Juncus squarrosus*, *Carex paniculata*, *Molinia caerulea* and *Nardus stricta*, reflecting the acid soils which have developed on these substrates in north Walsall and Sutton Park in the eastern exposures and south of Stourbridge in the west. It also includes a list of trees, shrubs and forbs associated with suburban gardens reflecting the residential nature of these areas west and east of the coalfields. 50 taxa are strongly negatively associated with the Sherwood group (0.1% level). These include many of the canal and post-industrial taxa associated with the coalfields, but also those associated with semi-natural grasslands which develop on less base-poor substrates: *Betonica officinalis*, *Centaurea nigra*, *Knautia arvensis*, *Lathyrus pratensis*, *Leontodon hispidus*, *Linum catharticum*, *Odontites vernus*, *Ophrys apifera*, *Pimpinella saxifraga*, *Plantago media* and *Sanguisorba officinalis*.

If all the 241 monads including Mercia Mudstone Group exposures are compared with the rest, the average monad taxa richness is 173 (SE 3.38) compared with 183 (SE 2.79) for all the remaining 474 monads. This is even (slightly) lower than the average of 175 found for the Sherwood Group. Only ten taxa are strongly positively associated with the mudstones at the 0.1%

level and are rather miscellaneous: woodland and hedgerow taxa form the majority: *Allium ursinum*, *Arum maculatum*, *Brachypodium sylvaticum*, *Elymus caninus*, *Mercurialis perennis* and *Tamus communis*, probably reflecting the wide range of monads in this group which are adjacent to the wider countryside beyond the boundaries of B&BC. The list also includes *Ranunculus penicillatus* from the River Tame system, *Sanguisorba officinalis* from the river valley grasslands, *Arctium lappa* which has an easterly distribution in B&BC and *Nigella damascina*. The 20 taxa strongly negatively associated with the Mercia Mudstones (0.1% level) includes some of the plants associated with the heathland, canal and post-industrial sites found predominantly on the other geological strata, also *Erodium cicutarium*, *Raphanus raphanistrum*, and *Pteridium aquilinum*.

## Implications for nature conservation

These simple calculations tend to confirm the perception that there is a strong relationship between flora and geology even in the highly artificial situation which applies within the conurbation. One implication is that a consideration of the geological background ought to be generally applied to evaluating ecological features.

Much of the botanical interest of the conurbation is positively correlated either directly or indirectly with the Carboniferous strata, despite the fact that the botanically richest area of the conurbation, Sutton Park, lies within the area of the Sherwood Group of the Triassic. Sutton Park is probably the main site favouring the heathland taxa on the Sherwood Group, but there is evidence that this can be a more general feature of these strata, and should be taken into account in future heathland creation schemes. Apart from that, the Triassic areas of B&BC are apparently less able to sustain high botanical diversity than the mainly Carboniferous central belt, which suggests that possibly a less exacting set of criteria ought to be applied when assessing the value of biological sites on the Triassic and especially on the Mercia Mudstones.

# CANALS

**Introduction** (by Paul Wilkinson)

▲ Worcester and Birmingham Canal, at Selly Oak

The canal system of Birmingham & Black Country consists of 450 km of canal, opened between 1772 and 1858. The Old Main Line Canal between Tipton and Smethwick is characterised by narrow locks and 18th century brick bridges/structures where the lime mortar creates a niche for the ferns *Asplenium ruta-muraria* and *Asplenium trichomanes* subsp. *quadrivalens*. These structures also provide ideal habitat on the bridges for species such as *Erophila verna* and *Capsella bursa-pastoris* around the lock quadrants. The towpaths have remained for the most part unimproved over the last 200 years, with *Dactylorhiza fuchsii*, *Galium verum*, and *Primula veris* among many wildflowers to be found in the heart of the industrial areas. With disturbance, *Linaria vulgaris* and *Papaver rhoeas* can be common.

The main supply of water to the canal system is from Chasewater Reservoir (SK0307, just outside the northern limit of B&BC), Edgbaston Reservoir (SP0486) and through pumps on the Bradley Arm Canal (SO9595). This water then flows to the Birmingham Canal Navigation (BCN), the canals of Staffordshire, Worcestershire and Warwickshire and finally into rivers. The canals also reflect the period in which they were constructed, such as contour canals with clay lining and mainline canals with brick lining. The canals show a diversity of both recreational use and ecology.

▲ Bradley Arm Canal, Bilston

Wetland species that are commonly represented on the canals of the region are *Glyceria maxima*, *Typha latifolia*, *Sparganium erectum*, *Alisma plantago-aquatica*, *Rumex hydrolapathum*, *Rumex conglomeratus*, *Oenanthe crocata*, *Epilobium hirsutum*, *Lycopus europaeus* and *Scutellaria galericulata*. These species grow commonly where there is opportunity, such as towpath fringe, soft bank, and between brickwork.

Truly aquatic species that are commonly represented include *Potamogeton pectinatus*, *Sparganium emersum* and *Nuphar lutea*. *Potamogeton pectinatus* is represented on all the canals and is dominant on the Bradley Arm canal. *Potamogeton natans* and *Potamogeton crispus* have both appeared to have declined on the BCN although they are both still very common on the Bradley Arm Canal (SO9495 etc.).

Although many species are present on the canal system, the populations generally increase towards the north and south-west of the region, with *Alisma lanceolatum*, *Butomus umbellatus*, *Sagittaria sagittifolia*, *Bidens tripartita*, *Bidens cernua*, *Mentha aquatica*, *Berula erecta* and *Carex acutiformis* all being locally common.

The pondweed community on the canal system can be stable or dynamic depending on external influences. *Potamogeton perfoliatus* is a large and relatively striking pondweed which is reasonably well distributed and can be locally common on parts of the Tame Valley Canal, Dudley No.1 & 2 Canals, Stourbridge Canal, Wyrley & Essington Canal, Daw End Canal and the Rushall Canal. *Potamogeton lucens* is also striking with its large paddle like leaves, but it is more restricted to the northern canals of Walsall. There are records of some very rare pondweeds and hybrids such as *Potamogeton friesii* and *Potamogeton × lintonii* (*P. crispus × P. friesii*). Introduced species such as *Elodea canadensis* and *Lagarosiphon major* have shown a decline after an initial boom period, for the two named, in the first and second halves of the 20th century respectively.

▲ Wyrley and Essington Canal, Bloxwich

The close proximity of the canals to industry and residential areas make it inevitable that species from back gardens will eventually colonise the canal, either through natural processes or deliberate introduction. Species that were once rare and confined to the south-east are now locally common and increasing in some cases, such as *Nymphoides peltata* and *Stratiotes aloides*.

Other non-native species that have established themselves through escaping from gardens include *Mimulus guttattus*, *Heracleum mantegazzianum* and *Myriophyllum aquaticum*. Of the most serious introductions, *Crassula helmsii* is isolated to a few ponds adjacent to the canal system, whilst *Hydrocotyle ranunculoides* is well established on the Wyrley & Essington Canal and in places on the Stourbridge Extension Canal. *Impatiens glandulifera* can dominate large areas, but at present is restricted to isolated patches. Its North American relative, *Impatiens capensis*, is less dominant but widely spread.

With a warming climate and a more unpredictable weather system, it is likely that species once on the edge of their northern boundary will in future have a greater likelihood of colonisation and establishment through milder winters. This includes species such as *Myriophyllum aquaticum*, *Ludwigia* spp. (Water Primrose), possibly even *Pistia stratiotes* (Water Lettuce). English names have been added here for those species not mentioned elsewhere in the Flora.

A notable part of the canal ecology is the presence of *Luronium natans* to the north-east of the region, being recorded on the Cannock Extension Canal SAC (Special Area of Conservation), Wyrley & Essington Canal, Daw End Canal and Rushall Canal. It is recorded as abundant on the Cannock Extension Canal SAC which once extended further into the coal fields of Staffordshire. The distribution and status (declining with distance from the Cannock Extension Canal SAC), colonising the Black Country via the Cannock Extension Canal and Chasewater Reservoir, could indicate that the populations have spread and are spreading from this stronghold. *Luronium natans* has a niche on the northern canal system, benefiting from the occasional disturbance and prevention of succession from other marginal and aquatic macrophytes.

The typical canal assemblage consists of marginal macrophytes of *Typha latifolia*, *Glyceria maxima*, *Sparganium erectum*, *Carex acutiformis*, *Rumex hydrolapathum* and *Oenanthe crocata*. Typical emergent plants include *Schoenoplectus lacustris*, *Butomus umbellatus*, *Sagittaria sagittifolia*, *Hippuris vulgaris*, *Sparganium emersum*, *Alisma plantago-aquatica* and *Alisma lanceolatum*. Submergent plants vary through the sections of the canal, but can consist of *Nuphar lutea* beds, *Potamogeton pectinatus*, *Callitriche* spp., *Ceratophyllum demersum*, *Myriophyllum spicatum*, *Elodea nuttallii*, introduced *Nymphaea* spp., *Potamogeton perfoliatus*, *Potamogeton lucens* and *Ranunculus* subgenus Batrachium (Water-crowfoots). Some sections also have floating plants including *Lemna minor*, *L. minuta*, *L. trisulca* and (old records) *Spirodela polyrhiza*, *Azolla filiculoides* and the liverwort *Riccia fluitans*. *Riccia fluitans* can be very common on the Wyrley & Essington Canal.

Several sections also suffer from filamentous algal blooms, and very rarely, *Cyanophyta* (Bluegreens or Bluegreen Algae) can occur although they are more frequent on the reservoirs and are often destroyed through the discharge of water to the canal system.

## Characterisation of the canal flora from analysing the Flora data

The distribution of extant canals in B&BC is shown in Figure 4.18. The system is clearly highly continuous and even the apparent hiatus between the Dudley canals and the rest is connected under the watershed via the Dudley and Netherton Tunnels, both of which are close to 3km long.

From the figure, the canal system is also clearly very extensive in the conurbation and the monads of B&BC can be divided into 214 (30%) which include measurable areas of canal and 501 (70%) which do not.

If the flora associated with these two sets of monads is compared, there are marked differences (Table 4.16).

The canal-containing monads are richer in taxa, both in terms of total numbers of records and in terms of average number of

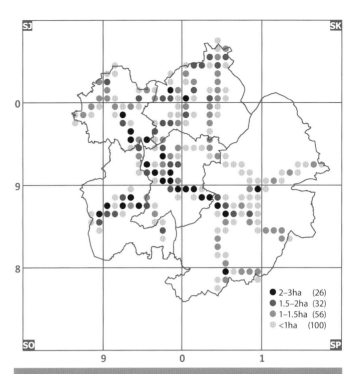

▲ Figure 4.18 Areas of extant canal in the monads of B&BC

Table 4.16 Balance of Flora records between monads with extant canals and monads without extant canals

| | Number of monads | Total monad records | Average records per monad ±standard error (SE) |
|---|---|---|---|
| Monads containing extant canals | 214 | 43,268 | 202±2.58 |
| Monads without extant canals | 501 | 85,093 | 170±3.64 |
| Totals | 715 | 128,361 | 180±2.18 |

▲ Dudley No. 2 Canal, Selly Oak Branch, looking north to Dog Lane Bridge

records per monad. This suggests that the canal system has a large influence on the flora of the conurbation.

Many of the taxa more frequent in the non-canal monads are garden escapes and other plants of residential areas and some are old woodland species. Most of the taxa more frequent in the canal monads are plants associated with open water, water margins and wetlands, plus almost as many plants which are characteristic of essentially dry post-industrial sites. This combination probably reflects the fundamental connection between the canal system and the development of industry in the conurbation and to some extent parallels the second strongest trend in the data described in the TWINSPAN analysis in the present chapter, which was after all based on the same data.

There are only a few water-loving plants which are more frequent in the non-canal monads. They are mostly plants of clean, infertile, relatively base-poor situations (mesotrophic to oligotrophic situations). Species confined to or commonest in Sutton Park figure largely, although the list includes the river plant *Ranunculus penicillatus* and plants associated particularly with ponds and streams, notably *Veronica beccabunga, Lysimachia nummularia, Myriophyllus aquaticum, Ranunculus lingua, Crassula helmsii, Thalictrum flavum,* and *Caltha palustris.* The Sweet-grasses,

*Glyceria fluitans, G. notata,* and *G. declinata* are also negatively associated with the canal corridor although of course *Glyceria maxima* is a characteristic plant of the canal system.

Most water-loving plants are more likely to be encountered in the canal corridor squares, and some are very strongly associated with the canal system. 305 taxa have some statistically significant difference (5% probability in a chi squared test) between their frequencies in the two types of monad, although some of these are too scarce for this analysis to be reliable. 124 reasonably well-distributed taxa showed a highly significant difference (0.1% probability). Of these, only four are more frequent in the non-canal squares. These were *Veronica serpyllifolia, Meconopsis cambrica, Viola riviniana* and *Veronica hederifolia s.l.*, a combination which suggests residential areas.

120 taxa were more frequent in the canal-containing monads, and 61 of them, which are associated with wet conditions and therefore at least potentially associated with the canals and their margins, are listed in Table 4.17.

In Table 4.17 there are few surprises and almost all the herbaceous species are immediately recognisably part of the flora of the B&BC canals. It would only be necessary to add the much scarcer plants which are confined or almost confined to the canals

### Table 4.17 Plants of wet conditions which are significantly more frequent in canal-containing squares

| Taxa | In monads with canals | In monads without canals | Taxa | In monads with canals | In monads without canals |
|---|---|---|---|---|---|
| Alisma lanceolatum | 37.9 | 1.2 | Nymphoides peltata | 11.2 | 2.4 |
| Alisma plantago-aquatica | 40.7 | 11.0 | Oenanthe crocata | 79.0 | 4.4 |
| Alnus cordata | 18.2 | 7.0 | Persicaria amphibia | 45.8 | 23.7 |
| Alnus glutinosa | 75.7 | 54.0 | Petasites hybridus | 18.2 | 8.0 |
| Angelica sylvestris (Ax.) | 33.2 | 18.5 | Phalaris arundinacea | 47.7 | 25.5 |
| Apium nodiflorum | 36.9 | 18.9 | Populus tremula | 32.7 | 19.5 |
| Azolla filiculoides | 10.7 | 1.8 | Potamogeton crispus | 24.3 | 3.4 |
| Berula erecta | 25.7 | 3.8 | Potamogeton lucens (Ax.) | 6.5 | 0.0 |
| Bidens frondosa | 30.4 | 1.0 | Potamogeton natans | 23.4 | 4.6 |
| Bidens tripartita (Ax.) | 10.3 | 1.2 | Potamogeton pectinatus | 52.3 | 4.8 |
| Butomus umbellatus (Ax.) | 37.4 | 2.4 | Potamogeton perfoliatus (Ax.) | 21.0 | 0.2 |
| Carex acutiformis (Ax.) | 21.0 | 7.0 | Pulicaria dysenterica (Ax.) | 10.3 | 3.0 |
| Carex otrubae | 60.7 | 6.6 | Ranunculus sceleratus | 32.2 | 12.0 |
| Carex pseudocyperus (Ax.) | 10.3 | 3.0 | Rorippa amphibia | 21.0 | 4.0 |
| Ceratophyllum demersum | 13.6 | 4.8 | Rorippa palustris | 14.0 | 5.2 |
| Elodea canadensis | 8.9 | 3.0 | Rumex conglomeratus | 64.0 | 15.1 |
| Elodea nuttallii | 25.7 | 6.0 | Rumex hydrolapathum | 79.0 | 4.0 |
| Eupatorium cannabinum | 18.7 | 5.2 | Sagittaria sagittifolia (Ax.) | 33.6 | 0.0 |
| Galium palustre s.l. | 19.2 | 9.4 | Salix alba | 30.4 | 17.7 |
| Glyceria maxima | 74.3 | 14.5 | Salix cinerea | 67.8 | 46.4 |
| Hippuris vulgaris | 10.3 | 2.0 | Salix viminalis | 37.9 | 20.1 |
| Hydrocotyle ranunculoides | 5.6 | 0.8 | Schoenoplectus lacustris | 15.4 | 3.4 |
| Impatiens capensis | 12.1 | 0.6 | Scrophularia auriculata | 22.0 | 10.4 |
| Iris pseudacorus | 65.0 | 30.9 | Scutellaria galericulata | 66.8 | 2.8 |
| Juncus inflexus | 57.0 | 36.7 | Sparganium emersum | 35.5 | 1.4 |
| Juncus tenuis | 8.4 | 2.0 | Sparganium erectum | 54.7 | 16.9 |
| Lemna minor | 56.5 | 23.7 | Typha latifolia | 64.5 | 24.1 |
| Lemna minuta | 24.3 | 6.0 | | | |
| Lemna trisulca | 22.4 | 3.6 | | | |
| Lycopus europaeus | 88.8 | 16.1 | **Key** | | |
| Mentha aquatica | 36.9 | 16.3 | (Ax.) – species is a B&BC Axiophyte | | |
| Myriophyllum spicatum | 25.2 | 1.6 | Non-invasive species | | |
| Nuphar lutea | 24.8 | 3.0 | Invasive species | | |
| Nymphaea alba | 17.3 | 5.8 | ■ Reedswamp and marginal aquatic species | | |
| | | | ■ Free-floating, floating-leaved and submerged aquatic species | | |

for this to constitute a characteristic B&BC canal flora list. These additional species are *Callitriche platycarpa*, *Lemna gibba*, *Luronium natans*, *Potamogeton friesii*, *P. lintonii* (*P. crispus* × *P. friesii*), and *P. pusillus*.

The least satisfactory species in the list are *Juncus inflexus* and *Ranunculus sceleratus*, which although clearly associated with the canal corridor and sometimes present by canals are scarcely confined to the canal habitat. Both may be present in this list because of their association with post-industrial land rather than with canals. This association may also account for the presence of *Juncus tenuis* on the list, a neophyte which seems to be spreading moderately fast in B&BC but not particularly immediately by canals according to our records.

On the other hand it is tempting to add *Phragmites australis* and *Zannichellia palustris* which are significantly associated with the canal corridor monads but only at the 1% level and also *Carex rostrata* and *Lagarosiphon major* which occur in canals but are not statistically associated with the canal corridor monads relative to the rest. There are, of course, other species such as *Epilobium hirsutum* which are frequent in canal margins but which are equally common on other waterside situations not associated with canals, so our lists should not be seen as a comprehensive description of the canal flora.

Also, although several wetland trees appear in Table 4.17, some are most often planted and others are probably too common to be usefully associated with the canal flora.

The list of 59 taxa which were significantly more frequent in canal corridor monads but are NOT associated with wet habitats is dominated by 43 taxa which are found most commonly in post-industrial and industrial land. Elsewhere in this chapter they have been listed either as preferentials for the Industrial TWINSPAN group or (below) for monads including railways or previously developed land. These have been used to help characterise the flora of post-industrial land in a subsequent section (see Table 4.20 page 165). It is most likely that the relationship mainly reflects the history of the canal corridor as a focus of industry. Also the canals themselves do include habitats, particularly the towpaths, which are managed in a similar way to, and have some of the character of, industrial sites.

13 of these taxa were not included in our other assessments of the post-industrial flora and are possibly plants preferentially associated with the canal towpath and other dry associated habitats rather than with post-industrial land as a whole. They are *Alnus incana*, *Arctium minus s.l.*, *Carex spicata*, *Cornus sanguinea*, *Galega officinalis*, *Helminthotheca echioides*, *Melilotus altissima*, *Poterium sanguisorba* (Ax.), *Senecio erucifolius*, *Sonchus arvensis*, *Torilis japonica* (Ax.), *Ulex europaeus* and *Viburnum opulus*.

There are also three spleenworts on the list, *Asplenium adiantum-nigrum*, *A. scolopendrium* and *A. trichomanes*, which are associated with canal bridges.

## Assessing canal quality

The wetland taxa identified in Table 4.17 have been divided into marginal, aquatic and invasive taxa as in the table and coincidence maps constructed showing the numbers of each type in each monad of the conurbation. *Callitriche platycarpa*, *Lemna gibba*, *Luronium natans*, *Potamogeton friesii*, *P.* × *lintonii*, and *P. pusillus* have been added to these lists and *Juncus tenuis*, *Ranunculus sceleratus* and *Juncus inflexus* have been removed for the reasons discussed above.

The coincidence maps are shown in Figures 4.19–4.22. The circle within each monad is coloured in relation to the number of the particular group of wetland plants present. In addition, the

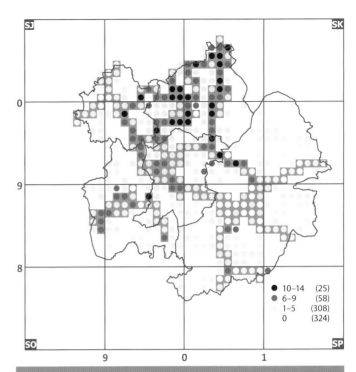

▲ **Figure 4.19 Coincidence map of canal free-floating, floating-leaved and submerged aquatic taxa in the B&BC monads.** Monads which include canals are outlined in grey

monads forming the canal corridor are marked in each figure as grey squares surrounding the circles.

The 20 species and one interspecific hybrid included in Figure 4.19 are: *Callitriche platycarpa*, *Ceratophyllum demersum*, *Hippuris vulgaris*, *Lemna gibba*, *L. minor*, *L. trisulca*, *Luronium natans* (Ax.), *Myriophyllum spicatum*, *Nuphar lutea*, *Nymphaea alba*, *Persicaria amphibia*, *Potamogeton crispus*, *P.* × *lintonii* (Ax.), *P. friesii* (Ax.), *P. lucens* (Ax.), *P. natans*, *P. pectinatus*, *P. perfoliatus* (Ax.), *P. pusillus* (Ax.), *Sagittaria sagittifolia* (Ax.) and *Sparganium emersum*. ((Ax.) = axiophyte).

There are some moderately high scoring monads away from the canal corridor, notably associated with Sutton Park, the eastern fringe of Birmingham, south Birmingham and central Dudley and largely attributable to ponds and lakes. However almost all of the highest scores are particularly associated with the Walsall canals, probably due to the high quality of the water derived from Chasewater and also to the less intensive use of these canals compared with others. The Dudley canals also score highly. The Wolverhampton and Sandwell canals are clearly less rich in submerged and floating aquatics, apart from the Bradley Arm (almost unused and with its own water supply) and places where the Wyrley and Essington and the Walsall Canals penetrate. Birmingham canals are generally much poorer. It should however be noted that there are hotspots with high scores throughout the canal system, suggesting that by analysing the factors which control these high scores, higher diversity could be achieved much more widely.

In Figure 4.20, taxa associated with the canal margins are mapped.

The 28 species and species aggregates included in Figure 4.20 are: *Alisma lanceolatum*, *A. plantago-aquatica*, *Angelica sylvestris* (Ax.), *Apium nodiflorum*, *Berula erecta*, *Bidens tripartita* (Ax.), *Butomus umbellatus* (Ax.), *Carex acutiformis* (Ax.), *C. otrubae*, *C. pseudocyperus* Ax.), *Eupatorium cannabinum*, *Galium palustre s.l.* (Ax.), *Glyceria maxima*, *Iris pseudacorus*, *Juncus inflexus*,

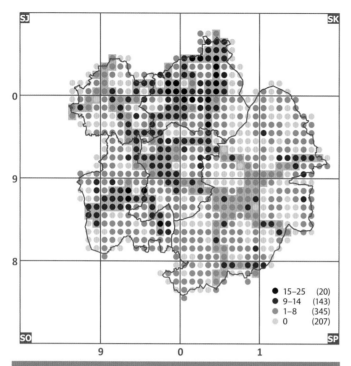

▲ **Figure 4.20 Coincidence map of canal reedswamp and marginal aquatic species in the B&BC monads.** Monads which include canals are outlined in grey

Legend:
- 15–25 (20)
- 9–14 (143)
- 1–8 (345)
- 0 (207)

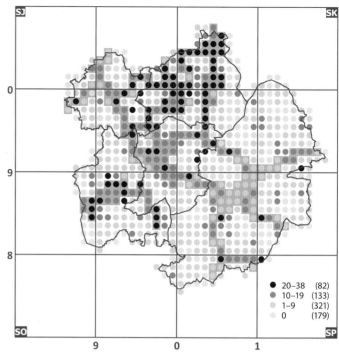

▲ **Figure 4.21 Coincidence map of canal aquatic and marginal species in the B&BC monads.** Monads which include canals are outlined in grey

Legend:
- 20–38 (82)
- 10–19 (133)
- 1–9 (321)
- 0 (179)

*Lycopus europaeus, Mentha aquatica, Oenanthe crocata, Phalaris arundinacea, Pulicaria dysenterica* (Ax.), *Rorippa amphibia, Rumex conglomeratus, R. hydrolapathum, Schoenoplectus lacustris, Scrophularia auriculata, Scutellaria galericulata, Sparganium erectum, Typha latifolia.*((Ax.) = axiophyte.)

Again, the highest scoring monads are largely confined to Dudley and (especially) Walsall. These species are perhaps less likely to be influenced by water quality than the submerged and floating-leaved aquatics, suggesting that degree of use (and probably the amount of recent canalside development) might be the largest influence. Intermediate scores are more widely spread than is the case with the submerged and floating-leaved aquatics and most Sandwell canals achieve this status. Again, Birmingham's canals score poorly, although higher scores in the periphery of Birmingham again suggest that much more could be achieved with appropriate management.

In Figure 4.21 the aquatic and marginal canal species from Figsures 4.19 and 4.20 are combined, to give an overall picture of the botanical status of the canal corridor in B&BC. The pre-eminence of the Walsall canals is further confirmed.

Figure 4.22 maps the distribution of six officially invasive alien species, plus two more species: *Bidens frondosa*, which has largely

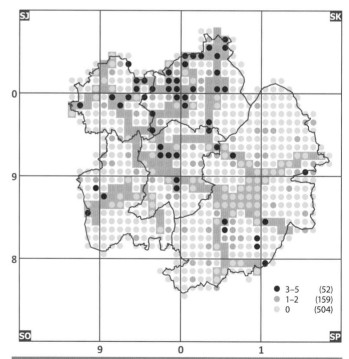

▲ **Figure 4.22 Coincidence map of canal invasive alien aquatic species in the B&BC monads.** Monads which include canals are outlined in grey

Legend:
- 3–5 (52)
- 1–2 (159)
- 0 (504)

▲ **Grand Union Canal traverses the Ackers, Birmingham**

replaced the native *Bidens* species in the conurbation after first being noticed in Birmingham (SP0987) in 1952, also *Impatiens capensis*, which has a similarly wide range in B&BC but has not so far proved to be as invasive as *Impatiens glandulifera*. *I. glandulifera* does not show a strong association with the canal system. The eight mapped species are: *Azolla filiculoides*, *Bidens frondosa*, *Elodea canadensis*, *E. nuttallii*, *Hydrocotyle ranunculoides*, *Impatiens capensis*, *Lemna minuta*, *Nymphoides peltata*.

Figure 4.22 shows that these species are widespread in B&BC and that, unfortunately, they are particularly prevalent in Walsall, the district with the richest canal flora.

## Implications for nature conservation

The data analysis suggests that the canal corridor, although it has only been present in B&BC in the last 200 years or so, is one of the richest botanical features of the conurbation. It carries not only the vast majority of the distribution of a wide array of water-loving species but also acts as a major focus of the species associated with post-industrial situations. It should also not be forgotten that it constitutes an ecological corridor probably more reliably and more multi-dimensionally continuous than any other in the conurbation and offering links to a particularly wide range of non-aquatic as well as the more obviously linked aquatic species.

On the other hand, canals are uniquely easy to survey because the towpath gives ready access to both the entire water column and the fringe habitats, without any privacy problems and few accessibility problems. For these reasons the habitat is likely to be better surveyed than most others.

Walsall, and to a slightly lesser extent Dudley, sustain the greatest concentrations of canal botanical diversity. Thorough investigation of the reasons for this fact and how to protect their canals from loss and from the build-up of invasive species must be a high priority.

▲ Walsall Canal

Most of the best sections of the canal network in Wolverhampton and Sandwell (and even to some extent in Birmingham) are where it is penetrated by the Walsall canals. These are probably the areas where it would be most easy to undertake measures to maintain and extend the current diversity. Western Sandwell in particular would benefit as a whole if it were possible to pay more attention to sustaining and enhancing the flora in its pervasive canal network. Because the Sandwell network is a major link between the canals of the other districts, attention there could also benefit the conurbation as a whole.

▲ Wyrley and Essington Canal, Heath Town

Birmingham's canals are the least botanically rich. There are however sufficient botanical hotspots to suggest that Birmingham also has considerable potential for improvement. Central Birmingham seems the least rich area and currently must constitute one of the main barriers to ecological continuity in the canal system. Canalside development in central Birmingham and elsewhere has frequently had a sanitising effect on the associated vegetation which must have contributed to this poverty. It is worth remarking that other canalside developments, such as the one at Bowman's Harbour in Heath Town Wolverhampton, have been able to maintain botanical interest.

## RAILWAYS

The railways were essentially made in the 19th century. Even in the first Ordnance Survey maps of the region, which were published in the 1830s, railways are almost absent. They have, nevertheless, been consistently (if rather brutally) managed ever since their development and have to a considerable extent developed a characteristic flora. Species which have been considered particularly strongly associated with the railways in Brirain have included *Diplotaxis muralis*, *Reseda lutea*, *Senecio squalidus* and *Vulpia myuros*. (Sargent 1984). Others (e.g. Sinker *et al.*) have commented on the association of *Chaenorhinum minus* with limestone railway ballast.

▲ Langley Green Station – looking south

Unfortunately, as has been remarked previously, for safety reasons, our access to railways for the Flora survey has been greatly restricted compared with our access to canals and has been largely confined to recording disused lines and sidings and railway stations and to making observations from adjacent properties. We have not even been able to check early 1990s records for *Cynodon dactylon* and *Carex arenaria* from railway sidings in Wolverhampton, nor have we been able to monitor adequately fragments of heathland in the Galton Valley.

Figure 4.23 shows the distribution of railways across B&BC. A comparison with Figure 4.18 shows immediately the close correlation of canal and railway corridors in B&BC, due presumably to the fact that both transport systems developed to supply the same industrial heartlands.

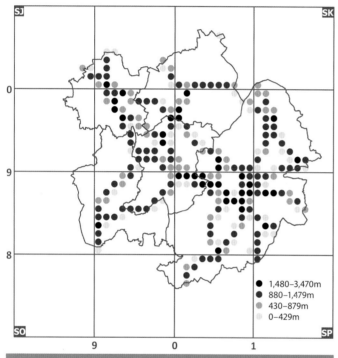

| | | 1,480–3,470m |
| | | 880–1,479m |
| | | 430–879m |
| | | 0–429m |

▲ Figure 4.23 Distribution of areas of extant railway track and verge in B&BC

Table 4.18 Balance of Flora records between monads with extant railways and monads without extant railways

| | Number of monads | Total monad records | Average records per monad ±standard error (SE) |
| --- | --- | --- | --- |
| Monads containing extant railways | 254 | 47,995 | 189±3.12 |
| Monads without extant railways | 461 | 80,366 | 174±2.88 |
| Totals | 715 | 128,361 | 180±2.18 |

An analysis was undertaken in which monads including railway tracks and verges were compared with monads which did not. The results of a simple comparison are shown in Table 4.18.

These data suggest that the railway monads are slightly, but significantly richer than the non-railway monads, but not to the same extent as are the canal corridor monads, despite the

considerable overlap between the two habitat types. It should however be noted that railways have been less well surveyed.

In chi squared tests, 188 taxa showed some statistically significant difference (5% probability) between their frequencies in the railway-containing and non-railway monads. 54 of these showed a highly significant difference (0.1% probability). Of these 54, five are more frequent in the non-railway squares. These are *Glyceria notata* and four old woodland taxa: *Melica uniflora*, *Lamiastrum galeobdolon* subsp. *montanum*, *Bromopsis ramosa* and *Mercurialis perennis*.

The taxa positively associated with railway monads include the commonest canal submerged aquatic species (*Potamogeton pectinatus*) and five of the most frequent canal marginal species (*Glyceria maxima*, *Lycopus europaeus*, *Oenanthe crocata*, *Rumex hydrolapathum* and *Scutellaria galericulata*), reinforcing the concept of a strong correlation between the presence of canals and of railways in monads in B&BC. It includes four fern taxa associated with the 'blue brick' bridges over both canals and railways: *Asplenium adiantum-nigrum*, *Asplenium ruta-muraria*, *Asplenium scolopendrium* and *Asplenium trichomanes* subsp. *quadrivalens*.

The other species positively associated with railway monads are mostly species of dry, post-industrial sites and correlate closely with the list of canal monad species not associated with wet conditions. In a later section they have been used in forming Table 4.20 characterising the flora of post-industrial sites.

In particular, the railway list includes *Reseda lutea*, *Senecio squalidus*, *S. viscosus*, *Verbascum thapsus* and *Vulpia myuros*, species commonly associated with railways, although not *Diplotaxis muralis*, which was mentioned as a railway plant by Sargent (1984), but in B&BC has more records from non-railway monads and a distribution not differing significantly between railway and non-railway monads. Similarly *Chaenorhinum minus*, although it has records from disused railway lines, is not statistically associated with extant railway monads. *Reseda lutea*, *Senecio squalidus*, *S. viscosus*, *Verbascum thapsus* and *Vulpia myuros* are also associated with other post-industrial monads and are included in Table 4.20. *Mycelis muralis*, associated with shady walls and *Papaver rhoeas*, associated with cultivation, were also strongly associated with railways but not with other industrial and post-industrial habitats.

*Fallopia japonica* was strongly associated with both canal and railway monads. There is also quite a long list of other invasive or potentially invasive alien taxa which are strongly associated with railways but not canal habitats: *Aster* spp., *Buddleja davidii*, *Hedera hibernica* 'Hibernica', *Heracleum mantegazzianum* and *Lathyrus grandiflorus*, but not *Rosa rugosa*, which was positively

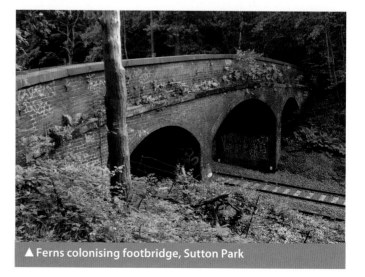

▲ Ferns colonising footbridge, Sutton Park

associated only with canal monads. This suggests that the railways may be a more important reservoir for quite a few of these less welcome taxa.

## Implications for nature conservation

The nature conservation interest of railway land is probably mainly in terms of its early successional vegetation which is ideally maintained by the existing management involving occasional scrub removal and intermittent use of herbicides. However, there seems to be a need for Network Rail to be aware of and to monitor and protect very uncommon species and unusual habitats which exist within or adjacent to the network. There also seems to be a need for Network Rail to intensify its approach to the control of invasive alien plants on railway land.

## ROADS

▲ A section of the A458 Hagley Road West

It is difficult to assess the importance of roads in the botany and ecology of B&BC because they are so ubiquitous. The conurbation includes the junction of two major UK motorways: the M5 and M6, which meet in SP0294. 78 monads include sections of motorways, 637 lack them. If motorway-including squares are compared with non-motorway squares as has been done above for canals and railways, the former are slightly less species-rich, but the difference is not significant. Only 63 spp show differences in frequency at the 5% level in a chi squared analysis. These are mostly garden escapes and ruderals associated with the suburbs in B&BC, and are less common in the motorway squares. Only *Viola riviniana*, of these species rarer in motorway squares, was significantly rarer at the 0.1% level. No plants were strongly positively associated with motorways. The surveying of motorways is even more difficult than survey of railways, which probably limits the value which can be attached to these results.

A similar comparison of the major ('A'-classification) trunk roads gave more interesting results. 481 monads contain sections of A roads, 234 lack them. On average, the major roads squares were rather more species-rich than the rest, with an average score of 183.6 taxa (SE = 2.60) against 171.1 (SE = 3.94) for the monads without A roads. In chi squared tests, 126 taxa showed a difference significant at the 5% level, but only 15 at the 0.1% level. Of those, *Stellaria holostea* and *Viola reichenbachiana* were less common by roads.

The taxa commoner in squares including major roads are listed in Table 4.19.

| Table 4.19 Taxa strongly associated with monads containing portions of major (A) roads | | |
|---|---|---|
| | **% frequency** | |
| **Taxa** | **In monads with major roads** | **In monads without major roads** |
| *Buddleja davidii* | 74.2 | 50.4 |
| *Cochlearia danica* | 38.0 | 15.8 |
| *Erodium cicutarium* | 20.0 | 9.4 |
| *Fumaria officinalis* | 33.9 | 17.1 |
| *Linaria vulgaris* | 49.5 | 28.2 |
| *Malva sylvestris* | 58.0 | 38.5 |
| *Melilotus officinalis* | 28.1 | 14.1 |
| *Papaver dubium* | 54.3 | 33.8 |
| *Platanus × hispanica* | 17.9 | 7.3 |
| *Reseda lutea* | 19.1 | 7.7 |
| *Scutellaria galericulata* | 26.0 | 13.7 |
| *Senecio squalidus* | 71.9 | 47.4 |
| *Sisymbrium orientale* | 32.2 | 15.0 |
| *Vulpia myuros* | 36.2 | 20.1 |

Some of the plants listed in Table 4.19 would be expected. *Platanus × hispanica* is most often planted by roadsides and the spread of *Cochlearia danica* by major roads in response to gritting with salt is another well-known phenomenon. Surprisingly *Plantago coronopus*, a plant usually found in association with *Cochlearia danica* by salted roads, showed no strong statistical association with 'A' road monads. *Malva sylvestris* is another plant which is often conspicuous by roadsides. All but one of the other taxa in the list are a further subset of the plants of dry, post-industrial sites which are so strongly associated with canals and railways. The odd plant out, *Scutellaria galericulata*, is commonest in the edges of canals in B&BC. It reinforces the suspicion that in common with the canals and railways, the major roads are still associated with the old centres of industry in the conurbation.

## Implications for nature conservation

Vast areas of land in B&BC are managed as road verge, road banks and central reservations. A large part of this is developing an increasingly diverse halophyte community right at the edges of the roads. This is taking place completely spontaneously (apart from the actual application of salt!). This process appears to be

▲ Newton Road, Sandwell with *Cochlearia danica*

unstoppable and at least generates some cheerful flowerings in spring, probably with value for invertebrates when little else is flowering. Apart from this, and although contributing some characteristic diversity associated with mowing and herbicide use on the margins of grass verges, roads in B&BC do not appear to display notably high levels of biodiversity. This is a pity because they represent a great deal of corridor habitat, connecting existing valuable sites and penetrating almost all parts of the conurbation. More imaginative management of some appropriate stretches, for example by introducing species by strewing hay from rich sites, or just by allowing spring flowering before cutting commences, should be contemplated, especially where important connections between rich areas can be demonstrated. Attempts to establish and successfully manage hay meadow floras along the Black Country Route (A454) have been quite successful.

Diversity is likely to be maximised in stressed habitats which do not become dominated by a few competitive species. Poor soils, low in the major plant nutrients and steep slopes subject to leaching and water stress are likely to support good levels of diversity if appropriately managed.

## THE POST-INDUSTRIAL SITES

Beaver (1946) reported on derelict land in the Black Country, and described it as "land which has been so damaged by extractive or other industrial processes or by any form of urban development that in default of special action it is unlikely to be effectively used again within a reasonable time and may be a public nuisance in the meanwhile." The Black Country was known for its industrial pollution and dereliction by the early 19th century. Derelict land was estimated to cover 5670 ha by 1903 (Wallwork 1974). The A4123 between Wolverhampton and Birmingham was driven through it in the 1920s and much was reclaimed for housing and industrial use in the 20s and 30s. In 1946, Beaver identified 3763.6 ha in the Black Country and ascribed much of it to coal spoil, coalfield subsidence and blast furnace spoil.

By 1950 only 2428 ha of derelict land were said to remain (Rees and Skelding, 1950) and 1100 ha by 1971, with major concentrations south-west of Dudley and north-west of Walsall (Wallwork 1974). The activities of the West Midlands County Council in the early 1980s and the Black Country Development Corporation from 1987–1998 used much European money to reclaim more for housing, roads and industry, so that today it is difficult to find good examples or even examples where natural reclamation by succession has taken place.

Rees and Skelding (1950) described the vegetation associated with derelict land in the Black Country. They described the colonisation of Coal Measures shales on the site of opencast and bell pit workings near Brownhills as commencing with *Deschampsia flexuosa*, "assisted to a lesser extent by *Galium saxatile* and *Empetrum nigrum*," (the latter now very rare in B&BC and possibly extinct in the Brownhills area) "with an orderly succession to open Oak/Birch woodlands". Intermediate stages involved the dominance of *Molinia caerulea* with *Deschampsia flexuosa*, *Erica tetralix* and *Calluna vulgaris*, or *Nardus stricta* with *Deschampsia flexuosa* and *Juncus squarrosus*. Today much of this succession appears to have proceeded to Birch or Oak/Birch woodland or has been redeveloped or is in the Chasewater area which is now outside the boundaries of B&BC. On Brownhills Common itself some mined areas may have reverted to *Calluna vulgaris – Erica cinerea* heath or Birch scrub, often with a field layer of *Molinia caerulea*, such as probably existed on the Common before mining took place. Nevertheless small examples of coal

mine spoil tips still exist in the Black Country, for example west of Brownhills Common and also scattered across Clayhanger SSSI and Clayhanger Common, mostly as grassland with much bare ground with *Deschampsia flexuosa*, *Nardus stricta*, *Festuca ovina*, *Festuca rubra* agg., *Agrostis capillaris*, *Cynosurus cristatus* and *Danthonia decumbens*, with scattered *Calluna vulgaris*, *Galium saxatile*, *Rumex acetosella s.l.*, *Hypochaeris radicata*, *Pilosella officinarum*, *Potentilla erecta* and (at only one site) *Polygala serpyllifolia*. There are further mounds of burnt coal spoil along the canal at Rough Wood.

Much of the coal spoil further south from north Walsall is less acid. Rees and Skelding described "large tracts of flat Coal Measures spoil north of the Dudley – Wren's Nest ridge" as "rapidly becoming colonised with various grasses and weeds, together with Elder and Hawthorn scrub". There are still traces of this landscape left, either somewhat or little reclaimed and treated as tumbledown horse pasture, or incorporated into amenity land. They are usually dominated by *Agrostis capillaris – Festuca rubra* grasslands with copious amounts of annual and perennial ruderals such as *Artemisia absinthium*, *Centaurium erythraea* and *Linaria vulgaris*, probably representing the original colonists. There are scattered examples in Bilston and Coseley, and east to Willenhall. There are similar post-colliery areas in Dudley, for example at Saltwells LNR (SO8386) and Hawne (SO9684).

There are actual coal spoil heaps at Spring Vale (SO9295) and near the Grapes in Bilston (SO9597). At Peascroft Wood in Bilston (also SO9597) a coal spoil tip was planted with *Acer pseudoplatanus*, *Alnus glutinosa* and other trees in 1905 by an early derelict land reclamation group, the Midlands Reafforesting Association and is now a SINC.

▲ Peascroft Wood, Bilston

Rees and Skelding also refer to vast areas in the Black Country which had been turned into reedswamp as a result of coal mining subsidence. There is still a scatter of small pools across the relevant areas of the Black Country, some of which, such as the one which forms the core of Clayhanger SSSI, have developed into rich plant communities, but practically no large continuous areas remain.

Furnace spoil is a third category. It is still found abundantly as a material used to construct walls, but otherwise has almost disappeared from the landscape. The great Bilston Steelworks (SO9495), which covered almost a whole square kilometre, closed in the 1970s. Following opencast mining of coal and landfill on the site there is little left to see except for a few remnants of peripheral ramparts along Ladymoor Road which had *Aira caryophyllea*, *Anthyllis vulneraria*, *Catapodium rigidum*, *Erigeron acer*, *Erodium cicutarium*, *Poa compressa*, *Potentilla recta* and *Silene vulgaris* although little remains of this in 2012. Close by, there are small

▲ Furnace slag at Moorcroft Wood

heaps of solid furnace slag at Ladymoor Pool in Bilston (SO9495) which appear to derive from earlier phases of the industrial revolution, although they were exposed by the removal of finer material from the site in the 20th century. Another similar major exposure of solid furnace slag may be found lining the pools at Moorcroft Wood in Moxley (SO9795).

Typical vascular plant species found on this solid slag material include *Aira caryophyllea*, *Aira praecox*, *Cardamine hirsuta*, *Cymbalaria muralis*, *Festuca ovina*, *Festuca rubra*, *Hieracium* sect. Vulgata, *Pilosella officinarum*, *Sedum acre*, *Senecio squalidus* and *Vulpia bromoides*. There are also quite rich bryophyte and lichen assemblages which are mentioned in the relevant chapters. Rees (1955) also recorded *Arenaria serpyllifolia*, *Artemisia absinthium*, *Inula conyzae*, *Linaria vulgaris*, *Reseda luteola*, *Sedum anglicum*, *Silene vulgaris* and *Trifolium campestre* on furnace slag.

Even fine spoil from the iron and steel industry is now rare in the landscape. The Round Oak Steelworks in Brierley Hill closed in 1982. Much of the remains disappeared under the Merry Hill Shopping Centre and the adjacent Waterfront Development in the late 1980s and early 1990s but there are some examples of (mostly fine) spoil associated with the Fens Pools LNR, particularly south of Middle Pool (SO9188) and east of Fens Pool itself (SO9288), including *Arenaria serpyllifolia*, *Cerastium semidecandrum*, *Hieracium* cf. *scotostictum*, *Pilosella praealta*, *Taraxacum* cf. sect. Erythrosperma, *Verbascum lychnitis* and, in the 1980s, *Apera interrupta*.

There were also huge ironworks on Pelsall North Common (SK0104) which finally closed in 1892, although the buildings were finally demolished in the 1920s and machinery ('The Cracker') was brought in in the 1940s and 50s to reduce and remove spoil for railway ballast. Some landfill was incorporated into the site in the 1950s. Currently there are extensive areas of fine spoil with quite a rich flora including *Arenaria serpyllifolia*, *Dactylorhiza praetermissa*, *Linum catharticum* and *Euphrasia nemorosa*, and a small area of coarser slag, apparently mixed with coal spoil, with the remains of a colonising flora including *Cerastium semidecandrum* and *Taraxacum* cf. sect. Erythrosperma and with invasions of *Calluna vulgaris* and *Nardus stricta* from the semi-natural heathland which persists nearby on the Common.

Rees (1955) described the colonisation of dolerite spoil near Springfield, Rowley Regis. The pioneers were *Dactylis glomerata*, *Festuca ovina* and *Senecio squalidus*; with *Fraxinus excelsior*, *Salix caprea*, *Rubus fruticosus* agg., *Achillea millefolium*, *Agrostis capillaris*, *Artemisia absinthium*, *Cirsium arvense*, *Hieracium* spp., *Pilosella officinarum*, *Hypochaeris radicata*, *Lapsana communis*, *Linaria*

*vulgaris*, *Lotus corniculatus*, *Rumex acetosella*, *Tussilago farfara* and other common species appearing later.

There is also a scattering of rather more miscellaneous post-industrial sites. Many sites appear when industrial or commercial or even housing complexes are demolished or become derelict and may only exist briefly, developing early successional communities, mainly of annual plants, such as those described by Gilbert (1989), sometimes alongside a range of garden plants which persist or regenerate from seed. Such sites are commoner in the Black Country than in Birmingham but can occur anywhere and are discussed further in the Neophytes section of Chapter 2 and above in the description of 'Open mosaic habitats on previously developed land' in section 4.1.

A fine example was noticed on a demolition lot in central Birmingham by Moor Street Queensway (SP0786) in 2011. The flora included *Anthyllis vulneraria*, *Hyssopus officinalis*, *Poterium sanguisorba* subsp. *balearicum*, *Salvia verbenaca*, *Filago vulgaris* and *Lotus tenuis*. Following the 1939–45 war, the bombed sites of Birmingham were surveyed (Burges & Andrews (1947) and the pre-eminence of *Chamaerion angustifolium* and *Senecio squalidus* noted. Interesting records included *Anthemis cotula*, *Cynosuris echinatus*, *Mercurialis annua* (first record for vc. 38), *Silene baccifera*, and *Sisymbrium orientale*. *Buddleia davidii* and *Impatiens glandulifera* were also noted, also *Fallopia japonica*, which "appears in the most unlikely places, shooting up from under solid flagstones, or forming thickets growing out of heaped-up rubble." Comparing the list with similar ones for London made at that time, the absence of *Conyza canadensis*, *Galinsoga parviflora*, *Solanum nigrum* and *Lactuca virosa* was noted for Birmingham and the presence of *Leucanthemum vulgare*, *Artemisia absinthium*, *Solidago canadensis*, and *Betula pubescens*.

Where problems for reuse are severe, 'early successional' communities may persist for many years, although they usually develop perennial and eventually woody vegetation and lose much of their botanical interest. Where site problems are particularly severe and inimicable for all but the most stress-tolerant plants, colonisation by vegetation can be very slow, unusual and possibly cyclical. The tips north-east of the Coneygre Industrial Estate at Burnt Tree in Sandwell (SO9591) consist of material which appears to include both furnace spoil and casting sand and is extremely dry. The flora includes *Arenaria serpyllifolia* subsp. *serpyllifolia*, *Diplotaxis tenuifolia*, *Erigeron acris*, *Filago vulgaris*, *Geranium* × *magnificum*, *Hippophaea rhamnoides*, *Hirschfeldia incana*, *Silene coronaria*, *Ophrys apifera*, *Poa compressa* and *Prunus serotina*. There are huge stands of *Silene coronaria*

▲ Tips at Coneygre, Burnt Tree

and parts of the site have intriguing combinations of native and introduced species reminiscent of the similarly defined 'recombinant' communities described in Barker (2000).

A large area of post-industrial, post-railway and post-housing land between the Black Country Route (the A463) and the Bradley Arm Canal in Bilston (SO9595, SO9596) was vacant for several years in the first decade of the 21st century and developed a rich flora of over 150 species including *Cephalaria gigantea*, *Erigeron acris*, *Geranium sanguineum*, *Pastinacea sativa*, *Reseda alba*, *Saponaria officinalis*, *Symphoricarpos × chenaultii*, *Trifolium arvense* and *Verbascum speciosum*.

The Foster, Rastrick & Co Ironworks site in Stourbridge (SO8984) has a complex of scrub and bare areas along both sides of the Stour in two vice counties and is rich in plant species. *Epipactis phyllanthes* was recorded there in 2004 and 2005 and *Erigeron annuus* in 2011 and 2012.

▲ Foster, Rastrick & Co site, Stourbridge

Some post-industrial sites include species-rich wetland vegetation. The furnace slag heaps at Ladymoor Pool (SO9495) are surrounded by a mysterious marsh dominated by *Juncus inflexus* and at least in the recent past containing *Achillea ptarmica*, *Briza media*, *Carex demissa*, *C. nigra*, *C. muricata* subsp. *pairae*, *Dactylorhiza praetermissa*, *Pulicaria dysenterica*, *Triglochin palustris* and no less than four species of *Sphagnum*. Nevertheless it is species of dry soils which most widely characterise interesting post-industrial sites, either in the brief period between site clearance and the development of a continuous vegetation or more long-term on skeletal, impoverished, mineralogically unbalanced and often physically stressed soils.

It is possible to adopt a similar approach to the one used in the canal, railway and road sections in order to arrive at a generic list of taxa associated with post-industrial sites. Figure 4.24 shows the monad distribution of areas of previously developed land (i.e. vacant and derelict land) from the National Landuse Database NLUD (2006).

These data have been used to divide B&BC into monads *with* and monads *without* previously developed land and compare the floras associated with the two categories using chi-squared statistics.

The flora of the 446 monads with previously developed land is slightly richer in plant taxa than the 269 without. The results parallel those for canals and railways, further demonstrating the physical correlation between canals, railways and post-industrial land. 12 old woodland, hedgerow and wetland taxa are significantly (0.1% level) less common in the previously developed monads, whilst 15 canal aquatics and 48 taxa of dry situations are

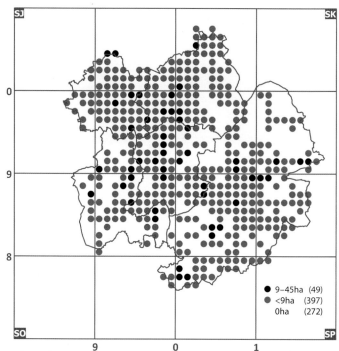

▲ Figure 4.24 Previously developed land in B&BC from the National Landuse Database NLUD (2006)

significantly (0.1% level) commoner in the monads with previously developed land.

In Table 4.20 the preferential taxa for the Industrial TWINSPAN group and those dry habitat taxa strongly positively associated with canal monads, railway monads and previously developed land have been combined to create a characteristic list of taxa associated with monads with an industrial history. Not surprisingly, since they derive from the same data set, all the TWINSPAN preferentials were listed for at least one of canal, rail or previously developed land lists and are given in red in Table 4.20.

Species listed for only one of the above habitats and which are not TWINSPAN preferentials have been omitted from the table. There is an implication that those taxa are associated with a specific habitat rather than being characteristic of post-industrial sites as a whole. Several have been mentioned in the canal or railway section. Others are *Conyza canadensis*, *Lathyrus latifolius*, *Malva sylvestris*, *Oenothera glazioviana*, *Papaver dubium*, *Platanus × hispanica*, *Raphanus raphanistrum* and *Sorbus intermedia* agg., which are taxa mostly associated with road margins or generally with disturbance.

In addition, the spleenworts *Asplenium adiantum-nigrum* (Ax.), *Asplenium ruta-muraria*, *Asplenium scolopendrium*, and *Asplenium trichomanes* subsp. *quadrivalens* were listed both for canals and railways, but have been omitted from Table 4.20 since they are specifically associated with the brickwork of old railway and canal bridges.

## Implications for nature conservation

The taxa characteristic of dry post-industrial sites listed in Table 4.20 includes nine axiophytes, suggesting that there is nature conservation value associated with this habitat type. However there is a much wider range of axiophytes found on post-industrial sites.

The list of axiophytes not strongly associated with natural and semi-natural habitats in B&BC which is given in section one of the present chapter (see Table 4.13, page 149) includes 29 taxa

**Table 4.20 Taxa strongly associated with dry soils in the post-industrial landscape of B&BC.** (Preferentials for the Industrial TWINSPAN group are given in red, indicator taxa in bold red. (Ax.) = B&BC axiophyte. Invasive introduced taxa are also indicated.)

| | |
|---|---|
| *Arenaria serpyllifolia s. l.*(Ax.) | *Melilotus officinalis* |
| *Armoracia rusticana* | *Odontites vernus* (Ax.) |
| **Artemisia absinthium** | *Reseda lutea* (Ax.) |
| *Buddleja davidii* (invasive) | **Reseda luteola** |
| *Centaurium erythraea* (Ax.) | *Rosa rugosa* (invasive) |
| *Clematis vitalba* (Ax.) | *Senecio inaequidens* (potly. invasive) |
| *Conium maculatum* | *Senecio squalidus* |
| *Convolvulus arvensis* | *Senecio viscosus* |
| *Cytisus scoparius* | *Silene latifolia* |
| *Daucus carota* subsp. *carota* (Ax.) | *Silene vulgaris* (Ax.) |
| *Diplotaxis tenuifolia* | *Sisymbrium altissimum* |
| *Dipsacus fullonum* | *Sisymbrium orientale* |
| *Erigeron acris* (Ax.) | *Solidago canadensis* |
| *Fallopia japonica* (invasive) | *Tanacetum vulgare* |
| *Foeniculum vulgare* | *Tragopogon pratensis* |
| *Hieracium* spp. (all records) | *Trifolium arvense* (Ax.) |
| *Hirschfeldia incana* | *Trifolium campestre* |
| *Hypericum perforatum* | *Trifolium hybridum* |
| *Lepidium draba* | *Tussilago farfara* |
| **Linaria vulgaris** | *Verbascum thapsus* |
| *Lupinus* × *regalis* | *Vicia cracca* |
| *Malva moschata* | *Vicia hirsuta* |
| *Medicago sativa* subsp. *sativa* | *Vulpia bromoides* |
| *Melilotus albus* | *Vulpia myuros* |

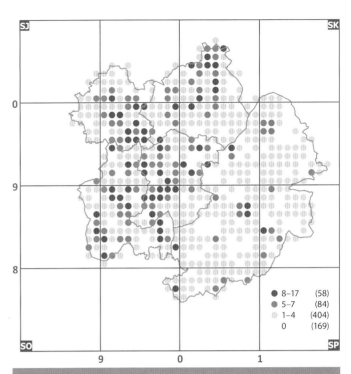

▲ **Figure 4.25 Coincidence map of axiophytes characteristic of stressed post-industrial situations**

which are also found on post-industrial sites but which did not appear in Table 4.20 probably because they also occur on other drought-stressed sites or because they are very uncommon. These are *Aira caryophyllea, Aira praecox, Anthyllis vulneraria, Blackstonia perfoliata, Calamagrostis epigeios, Catapodium rigidum, Centaurea scabiosa, Cerastium semidecandrum, Chaenorhinum minus, Erophila verna s.l., Filago minima, Filago vulgaris, Inula conyzae, Linum catharticum, Ophrys apifera, Orobanche minor, Picris hieracioides, Pilosella praealta, Poa angustifolia, Poa compressa, Poterium sanguisorba* subsp. *sanguisorba, Sambucus ebulus, Senecio erucifolius, Sherardia arvensis, Stellaria pallida, Trifolium medium, Trifolium micranthum, Trifolium striatum* and *Vicia tetrasperma.*

There are a further six axiophytes strongly associated with natural and semi-natural sites which are also recorded on post-industrial sites. These are *Anacamptis pyramidalis, Carlina vulgaris, Deschampsia flexuosa, Odontites vernus, Ornithopus perpusillus,* and *Spergularia rubra.*

Figure 4.25 is a coincidence map of this overall total of all these 44 axiophytes found on post-industrial sites.

Heathland areas in North Walsall and Sutton Park, also on Rubery Hill (SO9978) have high scores since many of the taxa will also occupy similar heathland soils. Otherwise Figure 4.25 demonstrates that these axiophytes are widespread at modest concentrations throughout the conurbation, suggesting that post-industrial and related drought-stressed sites may contribute considerably to nature conservation in B&BC. However high scores are strongly associated with the industrial heartlands of the Black Country, although there are also some 'hot spots' in Birmingham, especially in the old industrial areas east of Birmingham city centre. It is in these areas that post-industrial sites could make a positive contribution to nature conservation.

Apart from the need for plant species conservation implied in axiophyte designation, post-industrial sites have a value as habitats, particularly for invertebrates, as was remarked in discussing open mosaic habitats on previously developed land in section 4.1. Examples which have achieved some age without losing their interest can be conserved and some are already designated as SINCs or even SSSIs. Others are likely to be relatively short-lived and cannot be easily conserved since the natural processes of succession lead to their loss as tree cover develops. Nevertheless, wherever possible such sites should be allowed to go through these species-rich early stages without excessive landscaping and their existence should be logged so that it is possible to monitor their frequency in the landscape rather than trying to conserve individual sites. Gilbert (1989) made some suggestions about short-term conservation of early successional sites, such as calling them 'urban commons' and landscaping and maintaining their margins to demonstrate that they are not neglected. Such approaches have

▲ **Post-industrial landscape near Crooked House, Dudley 1981**

been applied to some extent in Sheffield. One developing problem with such an approach is the increasing frequency of *Buddleja davidii*, which can find such sites and cover them in single-species scrub within two years of their creation.

## THE ALLOTMENTS

Allotments were surveyed as part of the general monad recording scheme wherever possible, but in addition a specific botanical survey of the spontaneous flora of allotment gardens took place in 2008 at the end of the Flora survey. Lists of allotments were kindly provided by the Local Authority allotment officers and a selection made to give a reasonably even distribution of 56 sites across B&BC (see Figure 4.26). In some Local Authority areas there are substantial numbers of allotments which have essentially independent status. Where records of their secretaries were not held by the Local Authority allotment officers it has only been possible to include a few in the survey.

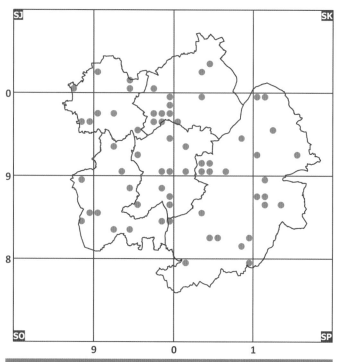

▲ Figure 4.26 Map showing locations of allotments surveyed for the present study

Typically an 80–100 plot allotment took three hours to survey. The aim was to examine every individual plot by walking all the paths and between-plot baulks of the site, and to produce a single cumulative list of plant taxa. Those taxa which had been deliberately planted as crops or for ornament were not recorded. Where other vegetation types were present, such as unused mown or unmown grassland, streams, woodland, areas maintained for wildlife, hedges etc these were also included in the survey. In a few cases where portions of the allotment site had been taken over and divided off for other use – for example as a bird reserve in one case – these portions were not included in the survey.

### Site size

476 taxa (species, interspecific hybrids, and in a few cases subspecies, varieties and cultivars) were encountered on the

▲ Allotments in an industrial part of Sandwell

▲ Allotments at Uplands, Sandwell

allotment sites, representing 32.9% of the taxa present in B&BC and 14.2% of the whole flora of the Britain and Ireland (see Table 4.1, page 135). The average number of plant taxa per allotment site was 111.8. This is a very respectable number for a limited area with a single land use, and illustrates that allotments are making a significant contribution to local plant biodiversity.

None of the allotments visited was species-poor, a few were particularly species-rich, but the smallest number of taxa per allotment in the survey was 67 and the largest 174. The smallest allotments, consisting of between 6 and 20 plots, had an average of 91.0 taxa per allotment. This number increased slightly as the number of plots increases, so that the group with more than 101 plots had an average number of taxa of 139.3.

There was however a great deal of variation between allotments of a similar size. The largest sites were not always the most species-rich: the combined Uplands and Friary Road sites (SP0390, SP0391, SP0490 and SP0491) with over 400 plots was the largest site and did have the highest number with 174 taxa, but the smaller Bordesley Green site (SP1187, SP1186 & SP1087) with 120 (potentially 200) plots had the same number of taxa and the much smaller Wheelers Lane site (SP0881) with 67 plots had 172 taxa.

### Site land use

The amount of land at a site which is not being currently used for allotments appears to have some influence on the overall number of taxa. Sites were divided qualitatively into three categories: with

**Table 4.21 Relationship between species diversity and proportion of unused land**

| Unused land | Number of taxa | | |
| --- | --- | --- | --- |
| | minimum | average | maximum |
| Little | 68 | 108.3 | 141 |
| Moderate | 67 | 110.1 | 174 |
| Substantial | 112 | 141.1 | 174 |

little, moderate, or substantial proportions of unused land. Range and average numbers of taxa in each are shown in Table 4.21.

Table 4.21 suggests that the highest levels of species richness can occur with only moderate levels of unused land, but also that sites with substantial amounts of unused land are likely to have high species richness. This is usually because such sites have remnants of other, often semi-natural habitats such as wetlands, canal banks or woodlands.

The presence of unused plots does not seem greatly to increase diversity. Unused plots appeared soon to lose the high diversity associated with cultivation and become dominated by a limited range of coarse grasses, tall herbs and brambles. Where they are kept mown they have slightly higher levels of plant diversity.

## Native and introduced taxa

Numbers of taxa encountered in the allotment survey associated with type of origin are summarised in Table 4.22. The categories in the table are the same as those used in Preston *et al.* (2002) and defined in the first part of the present chapter.

From Table 4.22, there is no reduction in the proportion of native plants compared with B&BC as a whole. 25 of these fall into the category of native plants entirely introduced in B&BC which are listed in Table 4.3 on page 136, which still leaves 218 or 45.8%. As might be expected, the commonest allotments native plants are ruderals. *Chenopodium album, Poa annua, Sonchus oleraceus, Stellaria media* and *Taraxacum* sp. were recorded at every site. *Solanum nigrum* was perhaps the most interesting native commonly present, being recorded as a weed of cultivation at 37 sites.

19 native axiophytes were recorded; almost all single records in remnant semi-natural habitats or as the result of deliberate introduction in seed mixtures, although *Equisetum palustre* occurred as an abundant weed of cultivation on one site.

Three native axiophytes associated with cultivation were occasionally recorded. *Fumaria muralis* on five sites is probably largely an allotment plant in B&BC and *Vicia tetrasperma* was found on ten allotment sites but occurs in 82 monads in B&BC as a whole. *Sherardia arvensis* was recorded at a single site but is much commoner away from allotments in open grassland.

Allotments do not appear to be a major refuge for neophytes, where they are relatively poorly represented compared with the B&BC flora as a whole. Some nationally uncommon neophytes, such as *Malva parviflora* and *Lysimachia ciliata*, were recorded. A few neophyte taxa are now common weeds of cultivation in allotments: *Calystegia silvatica, Epilobium ciliatum* and *Veronica persica* were present in all or almost all the sample and *Lepidium didymum* at 33 sites. *Galinsoga quadriradiata* (25 sites) and *G. parviflora* (16 sites), both from South America, were recorded as particularly rampant at some sites and may be developing into invasive species.

▲ *Galinsoga* climbing Runner Bean poles

Nationally casual taxa are also only modestly represented in the allotments compared with B&BC as a whole. *Coriandrum sativum, Lepidium sativum, Limnanthes douglasii, Raphanus sativus* and *Trigonella foenum-graecum* are short-lived remnants of cultivation and probably many more cultivated vegetables have a marginally casual presence in allotments. However *Malva verticillata* and *Nicandra physalodes*, also garden plants, are starting to spread on one or two individual sites such as Wheelers lane and Amos Lane and may be in the process of becoming established neophytes.

Table 4.22 shows very clearly that in relation to both the British and Irish flora and the B&BC flora, the main area of richness in the allotment flora is in archaeophytes, which have proportionally more abundance in the allotment sample. This is not really surprising since these are the plants which have spread anciently around the world with agriculture and cultivation. Many of these taxa are pernicious weeds and not very welcome guests in the allotments! However since the advent of selective weed killers

**Table 4.22 Numbers of vascular plant species and interspecific hybrids in a survey of 56 allotments in B&BC compared with those in B&BC as a whole and with those in the Atlas of the British and Irish Flora**

| Type of plant | Allotment survey (% in brackets) | B&BC Flora survey | % B&BC Flora in allotments | Atlas of the British and Irish Flora | % British & Irish flora in allotments |
| --- | --- | --- | --- | --- | --- |
| Natives | 243 (51.1) | 693 (47.8) | 35.1 | 1571 (46.8) | 15.5 |
| Archaeophytes | 66 (13.9) | 105 (7.2) | 62.9 | 158 (4.7) | 41.8 |
| Neophytes | 152 (31.9) | 555 (38.3) | 27.4 | 1305 (38.9) | 11.6 |
| Casuals | 14 (3.0) | 63 (4.3) | 22.2 | 252 (7.5) | 5.6 |
| Others | 1 (0.2) | 33 (2.3) | 3.0 | 68 (2.0) | 1.5 |
| Total taxa | 476 | 1449 | 32.9 | 3354 | 14.2 |

**Table 4.23 The 66 archaeophyte taxa recorded in the allotment survey, arranged in order of frequency** (Ax.) = B&BC axiophyte

| Name | Frequency | Name | Frequency | Name | Frequency |
|---|---|---|---|---|---|
| Euphorbia helioscopia | 56 | Geranium dissectum | 29 | Erysimum cheiri | 7 |
| Euphorbia peplus | 56 | Artemisia vulgaris | 27 | Reseda luteola | 4 |
| Capsella bursa-pastoris | 54 | Fumaria officinalis | 27 | Salix viminalis | 4 |
| Lamium purpureum | 53 | Viola arvensis | 26 | Euphorbia lathyris | 4 |
| Veronica agrestis | 51 | Tripleurospermum inodorum | 25 | Veronica hederifolia s.l. | 4 |
| Papaver somniferum | 50 | Vicia sativa subsp. segetalis | 25 | Alopecurus myosuroides | 3 |
| Fallopia convolvulus | 49 | Matricaria chamomilla | 24 | Artemisia absinthium | 3 |
| Lamium album | 47 | Raphanus raphanistrum | 23 | Saponaria officinalis | 3 |
| Urtica urens | 43 | Sinapis arvensis | 23 | Asparagus officinalis | 2 |
| Tanacetum parthenium | 42 | Avena fatua | 16 | Centaurea cyanus | 2 |
| Agrostis gigantea | 41 | Prunus domestica | 16 | Conium maculatum | 2 |
| Myosotis arvensis | 41 | Chenopodium polyspermum (Ax.) | 14 | Castanea sativa | 1 |
| Anisantha sterilis | 39 | Foeniculum vulgare | 14 | Diplotaxis tenuifolia | 1 |
| Sisymbrium officinalis | 38 | Aegopodium podagraria | 12 | Glebionis segetum | 1 |
| Lamium amplexicaule | 37 | Spergula arvensis | 12 | Inula helenium | 1 |
| Lactuca serriola | 34 | Mentha spicata | 11 | Malva neglecta | 1 |
| Papaver rhoeas | 34 | Salix fragilis | 11 | Mercurialis annua | 1 |
| Malva sylvestris | 33 | Anchusa arvensis | 10 | Misopates orontium | 1 |
| Papaver dubium | 31 | Erysimum cheiranthoides | 10 | Onopordum acanthium | 1 |
| Hordeum murinum | 30 | Stachys arvensis (Ax.) | 9 | Helminthotheca echioides | 1 |
| Lamium hybridum | 30 | Thlaspi arvense (Ax.) | 9 | Polygonum arenastrum | 1 |
| Armoracia rusticana | 29 | Vulpia myurus | 9 | Silene latifolia | 1 |

a large number of (especially annual) weeds of cultivation have become very scarce and threatened in the countryside and the allotments still appear to provide a refuge for some of these.

Table 4.23 is a complete list of the 66 archaeophyte taxa recorded in the allotment survey, arranged in order of their frequency. Some of these taxa, such as *Papaver somniferum*, *Armoracia rusticana*, *Tanacetum parthenium*, *Prunus domestica* and *Cheiranthus cheiri*, are obviously still being continuously naturalised from cultivation, and the same is probably true of the two cornfield weeds *Centaurea cyanus* and *Glebionis segetum*, which are both so uncommon now in the wild that they are most likely to have been introduced deliberately in a seed mixture. Others are very common and pernicious weeds: allotments may offer a safe haven to the currently problematic grass weeds of agriculture *Anisantha sterilis* and *Alopecurus myosuroides*.

Allotments are however an important refuge for a range of potentially threatened annual archaeophyte taxa. Several are now quite scarce in Britain, notably *Chenopodium polyspermum*, *Stachys arvensis* (nationally near threatened), *Mercurialis annua* and *Misopates orontium* (nationally vulnerable). A longer list is of plants which are quite hard to find in B&BC outside allotments: *Veronica agrestis*, *Lamium amplexicaule*, *Lamium hybridum*, *Spergula arvensis* (nationally vulnerable), *Erysimum cheiranthoides*, *Thlaspi arvensis*, *Helminthotheca echioides* and even *Avena fatua* and *Urtica urens*. Several of these have been added to the B&BC axiophyte list and are marked in Table 4.23 with (Ax.).

## Implications for nature conservation

The reported survey only covered about 20% of the municipally administered allotments and a tiny proportion of the self-administered allotments in the B&BC area. Nevertheless sites were almost always rich in plant species and a remarkably high proportion of the known vascular plant flora of the conurbation

has been identified in the sample, demonstrating the wildlife importance of allotments. This diversity is large compared with that occurring in typical agricultural arable land partly as a result of the variety of crops grown and the large extent of edge effects because of the small size of plots, but mainly because of the reluctance of allotment plot owners to use selective herbicides.

Most of the significant nature conservation interest was associated with the cultivated land of the allotments and the interest is particularly focused on the ancient weeds of cultivation, the archaeophytes. The greatest decline in species of the different UK Biodiversity Action Plan broad habitats is in species of arable and horticulture (Preston *et al*, 2002a). Our data do however demonstrate that there is at least one part of that broad habitat type in which the archaeophytes are still thriving, i.e. in the allotments of B&BC.

An examination of the ecological indicator species in the allotments flora gave some evidence that remnants of semi-natural vegetation such as hedgerows, streams, wetlands and possibly old grassland species are sometimes contributing to the diversity. This suggests that where such areas are identified the nature conservation value of the allotment would be maximised by appropriate management of such fragments. Nevertheless,

**A Dudley allotment** (by Sue Nicholls)

the present study suggests that the overwhelming nature conservation value of the allotment garden is associated with the cultivated land itself, and is centred on a range of annual arable weeds which are often common in allotment plots and yet seem to be rare outside. The allotment garden is mainly of value as a refuge for uncommon wild flowers **because** it is cultivated not **despite** being cultivated.

## RIVER CORRIDORS

River Tame in the Sandwell Valley
(by Neville Walters)

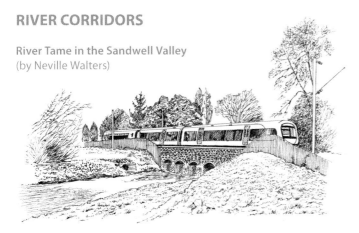

Figure 4.27 shows the distribution of floodzones in B&BC. Clearly the major system is the eastwards flow of the River Tame, but the west-flowing Smestow in Wolverhampton and Stour in Dudley are also significant. The polluted (but improving) nature of these flowing water systems has been described in Chapter 3. In many parts there is a simple submerged aquatic flora in which *Potamogeton pectinatus* is the main constituent, although increasing amounts of *Ranunculus penicillatus* are encountered. However, as the figure suggests, the systems include vast areas of floodplains, most of which are not built up and are managed for amenity. These include some remnants of old dingle woodlands, of which those associated with Bob's Brook in Cotwall End and

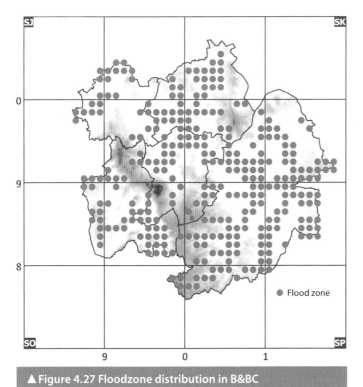

▲ **Figure 4.27 Floodzone distribution in B&BC**

Merritt's Brook in Manor Farm Park, south Birmingham are good examples, but the main land use is grassland, with patchworks of frequently and intermittently-mown swards. Here and there these do include features of old grassland, often marked by the appearance of *Sanguisorba officinalis*, but periodic inundation with fertility-laden waters has tended to suppress diversity.

A simple comparison has been made between monads including rivers and river floodplain as shown in Figure 4.27 and those which do not. The results are summarised in Table 4.24.

| Table 4.24 Balance of Flora records between monads with streams, rivers and floodplains and monads without | | | |
|---|---|---|---|
| | Number of monads | Total monad records | Average records per monad ± SE |
| Monads containing streams, rivers and floodplains | 328 | 62,856 | 192±3.16 |
| Monads without streams, rivers and floodplains | 387 | 65,505 | 169±2.91 |
| Totals | 715 | 128,361 | 180±2.18 |

Table 4.24 illustrates the remarkably high proportion of monads with running water habitats, and the not unexpected fact that monads with such habitats are on average significantly richer in taxa than those without. 159 taxa are significantly different in frequency in the two monad types at the 5% level in chi squared tests, and 43 taxa at the more rigorous 0.1% level.

Very few taxa are commoner in the non-floodzone monads: only five and only at the 5% level. *Viola riviniana*, *Chamaecyparis lawsoniana* and *Platanus × hispanica* suggest the residential areas which are generally not built in the river corridors. *Potamogeton lucens* suggests unpolluted canals and *Erophila verna* suggests shallow, drought-liable soils, neither of which are features one would naturally associate with the damp and rather eutrophic river floodplains. The 43 taxa which are highly significantly commoner in floodzone monads are listed in Table 4.25.

| Table 4.25 Taxa highly significantly commoner in monads with streams, rivers and floodplains than those without in B&BC | |
|---|---|
| *Alisma plantago-aquatica* | *Nasturtium officinale* agg. |
| *Allium ursinum* (Ax.) | *Oenanthe crocata* |
| *Alnus glutinosa* | *Persicaria amphibia* |
| *Angelica sylvestris* (Ax.) | *Persicaria bistorta* |
| *Apium nodiflorum* | *Petasites hybridus* |
| *Arctium minus s.l.* | *Phalaris arundinacea* |
| *Bidens frondosa* | *Phragmites australis* |
| *Carduus crispus* | *Potamogeton crispus* |
| *Carex paniculata* (Ax.) | *Ranunculus aquatilis s.l.* (Ax.) |
| *Centaurea scabiosa* (Ax.) | *Ranunculus penicillatus* |
| *Conium maculatum* | *Ranunculus sceleratus* |
| *Cornus sanguinea* | *Reseda lutea* (Ax.) |
| *Elymus caninus* | *Rumex hydrolapathum* |
| *Filipendula ulmaria* (Ax.) | *Salix alba* |
| *Glyceria maxima* | *Salix fragilis* |
| *Impatiens glandulifera* | *Salix viminalis* |
| *Iris foetidissima* | *Sanguisorba officinalis* (Ax.) |
| *Iris pseudacorus* | *Scrophularia auriculata* |
| *Linaria vulgaris* | *Silene dioica* |
| *Lycopus europaeus* | *Sparganium erectum* |
| *Lythrum salicaria* | *Veronica beccabunga* (Ax.) |
| *Mentha aquatica* | |

The majority of the plants listed in Table 4.25 conform to the damp and fairly fertile nature of the habitat. It is interesting to note that *Potamogeton crispus*, rather than *P. pectinatus*, is strongly associated with the rivers. Presumably the predilection of the latter for the canals outweighs its relative frequency in the rivers. Apart from that species and *Ranunculus penicillatus*, the canals are clearly a much more important reservoir of aquatic plants, despite the fact that rivers occur in more monads (328) than do canals (214). On the other hand the water margin taxa in the list overlap greatly with those of the canals, despite only poor correlation in the distribution of canals and rivers. Some differences in the marginals are *Alisma lanceolatum*, *Rorippa amphibia*, *R. palustris*, *Rumex conglomeratus*, *Schoenoplectus lacustris*, which are only highly significantly commoner in the canal corridors and *Impatiens glandulifera*, *Nasturtium officinale* agg., *Ranunculus aquatilis* s.l., and *Phragmites australis* which are only highly significantly commoner in the river corridors. Among marsh plants, *Carduus crispus*, *Persicaria bistorta* and *Veronica beccabunga* only feature in the river list, as does *Salix fragilis*. The much more particular *Carex paniculata* is also only strongly correlated with river corridors, showing that there are some better riverine sites in B&BC.

A very small number of old wet pasture taxa feature in the river corridor list: really only *Filipendula ulmaria* and *Sanguisorba officinalis*. Both are however axiophytes. The presence of *Linaria vulgaris* and *Reseda lutea*, which are also strongly associated with industrial sites, in the rivers list is rather mysterious, similarly *Centaurea scabiosa* and even *Silene dioica*. Whether these are associated with eroding river banks or with some completely non-aquatic feature of the river corridors is not clear. In Birmingham there is a positive relationship between the Tame valley and the canals and railways, also the Stour Valley is heavily industrialised. It is possible that this has been enough to account for these associations.

▲ River Tame at Newton

### Implications for nature conservation

Although the river corridors have some special features compared with the canals, on the whole the strongly associated taxa are less impressive than those associated with the canals and even the riverine grasslands have only a few (but still a few) key wet pasture taxa associated. Clearly there is still a great deal of improvement possible in the river corridor vegetation, mainly by reducing the amount of nitrogen compounds and other contributors to excessive fertility in river water. The high frequency of trapezoidal engineered banks and a lack of natural features such as riffles and gravel banks which might support aquatics must also contribute to the botanical poverty. There is nevertheless a modest list of rather

▲ River Tame in flood, Castle Vale 1981

miscellaneous axiophytes strongly associated with rivers, mainly demonstrating potential value. Probably *Ranunculus penicillatus* should be added to the list of B&BC axiophytes as an indicator of improving water quality.

## LOWLAND HEATH (by Andy Slater)

Lowland heathland is thought to have once covered extensive tracts of Birmingham and the Black Country, forming a near-continuous link with the heaths of Cannock Chase and the countryside of Warwickshire and Worcestershire. Today only remnant patches remain, found scattered in Sutton Park, on Brownhills Common and in a small handful of other sites across the rest of the area. However, many telling clues exist which show us the extent to which Birmingham and the Black Country was once a wild landscape of heather and gorse.

The botany of the lowland heaths of B&BC is described in Chapter 3. In brief, lowland heathland is a dwarf-shrub habitat which occurs on free-draining acidic soils which have a low nutrient content. This habitat is characterised by heather species such as *Calluna vulgaris* and *Erica cinerea* while other acid-loving plants such as *Ulex gallii* and *Vaccinium myrtillus*, grasses such as *Deschampsia flexuosa* and *Nardus stricta* and mosses such as *Polytrichum formosum* and *Dicranum scoparium*, help contribute to the complexity, ecological diversity and colourfulness of this now rare and threatened habitat. Heathland also provides

▲ Heathland in Sutton Park

a valuable habitat for many of Britain's rarest species such as Nightjar *Caprimulgus europaeus* and many of Britain's reptiles such as Common Lizard *Zootoca vivipara* along with many rare invertebrates.

Heath-type vegetation has existed in Britain for at least the past 14,000 years, with the retreat of the ice sheets giving way to the establishment of tundra-type vegetation, including Heather. As the British climate continued to warm, it is thought that woodland species began to dominate, leaving heath species surviving only in places such as open glades and woodland margins (*Offwell Woodland & Wildlife Trust 2001*).

Pollen records suggest that large scale heathland creation began in Neolithic times, as a result of human activity, as man gradually began clearing woodland areas for purposes such as crop growing. As soil nutrients in these areas became depleted, the no-longer productive land is thought to have been given over to grazing, either by domesticated or wild animals, which may have prevented the re-establishment of woodland. As a result, by the Bronze Age, heathland had become widespread across the UK.

The practice of woodland clearance continued until the 17th century, and while more nutrient-rich ground was typically used for agriculture, heaths, which were unsuitable for more intensive use, were often used as common grazing land, while *Ulex* spp., which produced a quick hot blaze for heating ovens, was commonly used for fuel (Rackham 2000).

In present-day England only one sixth of the heathland present in 1800 now remains (UK BAP 1995). There are a number of reasons for the dramatic decline of the habitat. The 17th century onwards brought the Agricultural Revolution, along with new technology to cultivate land which was previously considered 'nutrient-poor wasteland'. These technological advances, coupled with the series of 'Enclosure Acts' passed primarily between 1760 and 1820, divided and fragmented the previously extensive commons and heaths of Birmingham and the Black Country and converted them into more intensively used privately owned farmland.

Other reasons for the loss of heathland areas include the decline in traditional activities, such as charcoal burning, which had, for centuries, maintained the heathland structure. In many of these areas the heath would have reverted back to woodland. Similarly in the 1950s, the decline of the rabbit population, as a direct result of the Myxomatosis disease, caused heaths which were previously maintained by rabbit grazing, to slowly become dominated by tree species. Urban development has also contributed significantly to the loss of heathland areas.

Although we know where the current day heathland remnants survive in Birmingham and the Black Country, there are also a number of clues that offer us an indication of the 'heathy' past of the area. Modern-day place names are perhaps the most obvious link to the past character of the landscape. Through looking at modern maps of the area it is possible to identify at least 61 places names that allude in some way to the past presence of heathland, although the word might not have been always used to describe heathland as we now know it. Walsall has, for example, a 'Blakenall Heath', a 'Wallington Heath' and a 'Druid's Heath'; Wolverhampton has a 'Heath Town' and a 'Stow Heath'; Dudley contains a 'Wall Heath'; Sandwell, a 'Cradley Heath', 'Hateley Heath' and a 'Blackheath' while Birmingham has a 'King's Heath', a 'Balsall Heath' and a 'Washwood Heath'.

In the Black Country core, the onset of the industrial revolution and subsequent extraction of the vital natural coal and clay resources meant that many of the heathland areas were destroyed much earlier than those of Birmingham.

In cases where heaths and commons survived up until the era of large-scale mapping, they can be seen marked on the

▲ Brownhills Common

historical county maps. The County maps of Warwickshire (1822) and Staffordshire (1775) show large swathes of common (or waste) land encircling Sutton Park, stretching around Birmingham's greenbelt, while the eastern side of Walsall was shown to be covered by a near-continuous band of commons linking the heaths of Cannock Chase to those in Sutton Park. Perhaps more surprising is that a 1775 map shows that the present day High Street, West Bromwich (whose name incidentally means "the little village on the heath of broom" crossed an open area that was then known as 'Bromwich Heath'.

First-hand written evidence exists for some of these former heathland areas, for example, the 1810 Parish Map of Birmingham shows an area marked 'Birmingham Heath' which now covers present-day Soho and Winson Green. Showell's Dictionary of Birmingham (Harman & Showell, 1885) tells us that before 1756 this area was "little better than barren heath, the home of conies and a few beggarly squatters".

Another notable example is Streetly, where charcoal burners had cleared much of the original forest by the 13th century. The land, known as 'Barr Common', was left as heath and marshland which was described in the late 18th century as "a barren sheep walk containing in some large tracts scarcely any other plants than heath, in other places fern, gorse, whortleberries and rushes with grass in small proportion". The common, which would have linked the existing remnant heaths of Barr Beacon with those of Sutton Park, was enclosed in 1795 and was divided and let as farmland (Neath 2005).

These historical features and the current extent of heathland are summarised in Figure 4.28. They are superimposed on extracts from the geological map of the area. Through mapping the former distribution of heathland, we can begin to understand the geological conditions that gave rise to this habitat in Birmingham and the Black Country. The main heathland swathes including Sutton Park are associated with the band of Sandstone bedrock to the east of Barr Beacon, stretching down the western side of Birmingham. Similarly the band of sandstone stretching down the western side of Wolverhampton and Dudley, is associated with heathland areas, such as Pedmore Common, Stourbridge which is still an area of remnant heathland today.

The figure does however demonstrate that the historical presence of heathland in B&BC seems to have been even more closely linked to the presence of free-draining sand and gravel deposits, left behind by the glaciers of the ice age.

Mapping where these historic heaths once lay allows us to identify key areas which could be appropriate for re-creating heathland habitats in order to create and enhance vital habitat links between the currently fragmented heathland remnants that remain today. This could help to safeguard the ecological diversity

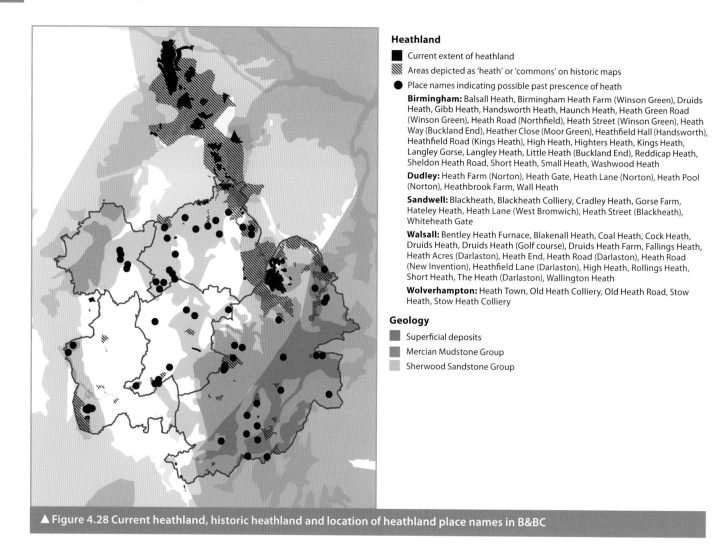

**Heathland**

■ Current extent of heathland

▨ Areas depicted as 'heath' or 'commons' on historic maps

● Place names indicating possible past prescence of heath

**Birmingham:** Balsall Heath, Birmingham Heath Farm (Winson Green), Druids Heath, Gibb Heath, Handsworth Heath, Haunch Heath, Heath Green Road (Winson Green), Heath Road (Northfield), Heath Street (Winson Green), Heath Way (Buckland End), Heather Close (Moor Green), Heathfield Hall (Handsworth), Heathfield Road (Kings Heath), High Heath, Highters Heath, Kings Heath, Langley Gorse, Langley Heath, Little Heath (Buckland End), Reddicap Heath, Sheldon Heath Road, Short Heath, Small Heath, Washwood Heath

**Dudley:** Heath Farm (Norton), Heath Gate, Heath Lane (Norton), Heath Pool (Norton), Heathbrook Farm, Wall Heath

**Sandwell:** Blackheath, Blackheath Colliery, Cradley Heath, Gorse Farm, Hateley Heath, Heath Lane (West Bromwich), Heath Street (Blackheath), Whiteheath Gate

**Walsall:** Bentley Heath Furnace, Blakenall Heath, Coal Heath, Cock Heath, Druids Heath, Druids Heath (Golf course), Druids Heath Farm, Fallings Heath, Heath Acres (Darlaston), Heath End, Heath Road (Darlaston), Heath Road (New Invention), Heathfield Lane (Darlaston), High Heath, Rollings Heath, Short Heath, The Heath (Darlaston), Wallington Heath

**Wolverhampton:** Heath Town, Old Heath Colliery, Old Heath Road, Stow Heath, Stow Heath Colliery

**Geology**

▨ Superficial deposits

▨ Mercian Mudstone Group

▨ Sherwood Sandstone Group

▲ **Figure 4.28 Current heathland, historic heathland and location of heathland place names in B&BC**

of these areas and ensure the survival of heathland habitats for future generations to enjoy.

## Implications for nature conservation

In order to further understand the opportunities for enlarging and re-connecting our existing heathland, mapping the current distribution of taxa associated with heathland has been attempted in Figure 4.29. The taxa chosen are the axiophytes associated with heathland. The 34 taxa are *Agrostis vinealis, Aira praecox, Blechnum spicant, Calluna vulgaris, Campanula rotundifolia, Carex binervis, Carex nigra, Carex pilulifera, Dactylorhiza maculata, Danthonia decumbens, Deschampsia flexuosa, Empetrum nigrum agg., Erica cinerea, Erica tetralix, Festuca filiformis, Galium saxatile, Juncus squarrosus, Luzula multiflora, Melampyrum pratense, Molinia caerulea, Nardus stricta, Oreopteris limbosperma, Ornithopus perpusillus, Pedicularis sylvatica, Potentilla erecta, Salix aurita* and hybrids, *Senecio sylvaticus, Spergularia rubra, Teucrium scorodonia, Ulex gallii, Vaccinium myrtillus, Vaccinium vitis-idaea, Veronica officinalis, Viola palustris.*

Figure 4.29 reveals that concentrations of choice plants associated with heathland and indicating significantly acid soils are still much more widespread in B&BC than are the known examples of heathland. Both major concentrations at Sutton Park and Brownhills Common seem to extend more widely and have been significantly linked by the nurturing of heathland on Barr Beacon. Weaker signals suggest that it might be possible to

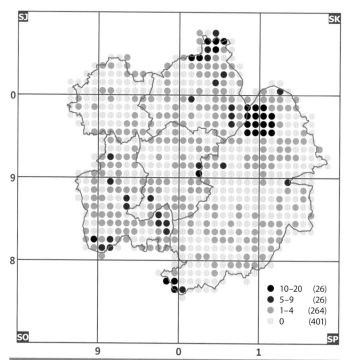

| | |
|---|---|
| ● 10–20 | (26) |
| ● 5–9 | (26) |
| ● 1–4 | (264) |
| ○ 0 | (401) |

▲ **Figure 4.29 Coincidence map of axiophyte taxa associated with wet and dry heathland** establish heathland continuous at the monad level from Brownhills Common to areas well to the south and east of Sutton Park.

Some of the residual commons of Birmingham are still giving a strong signal and the known heathlands of the Rednall area close to the Lickey Hills beyond our boundary have associated high scores spreading into several adjacent monads. Opportunities apparently still exist in the Sandwell Valley, the Rowley Hills, Stourbridge and even Blackheath. There are further, scattered, hotspots, probably mainly post-industrial in origin, across Dudley.

However the high score from Cotwall End (SO9192) emanates from a single, tiny enclave of less than a hectare and much beset by scrub despite the valiant efforts of the Dudley Council Rangers. Many of the other hotspots are similarly minute and often the problem is one of conservation of tiny fragments rather than their extension. Nevertheless, Figure 4.29 is quite encouraging, and suggests that the heaths of B&BC do not necessarily survive only in the names of their original localities.

▲ Red Deer on Brownhills Common

# Section 3 • Implications of the analysis

Lawton *et al.* (2010) summarised five key approaches needed to enhance the resilience and coherence of England's ecological network:

1. Improve the quality of current sites by better habitat management.
2. Increase the size of current wildlife sites.
3. Enhance connections between, or join up, sites, either through physical corridors, or through 'stepping stones'.
4. Create new sites.
5. Reduce the pressures on wildlife by improving the wider environment, including through buffering wildlife sites.

The analysis presented in section 1 of Chapter 4 has enabled us to describe the botanical part of the ecological network of the conurbation and also allows us to consider how to enhance it.

The flora of the B&BC conurbation can scarcely be described as impoverished. Our small area sustains over 40% of the British and Irish flora. Nor is there a preponderance of introduced species here: native species dominate both the overall species list and the lists of total numbers of monad records. Nevertheless, the balance between native and introduced species varies greatly from monad to monad. There are strong concentrations of native species (and/or lacks of introduced species) associated with less populated or otherwise less developed zones and also in some of the older post-industrial areas (see Figure 4.2). If one examines the distribution of the species (mostly natives) which are considered to have the most nature conservation importance, i.e. the axiophytes, the picture presented in Figure 4.2 becomes clearer (see Figures 4.12, 4.14) and it is possible to recognise three principal core areas for our native flora in Sutton Park, the Halesowen area of south-east Dudley and the Walsall countryside, plus an equally strong but more diffuse network in central Dudley.

The Sutton Park core area is particularly remarkable because it constitutes a single, continuous natural landscape and because the flora is significant in a much wider regional and national context. Within the constraints of the present study we have not really been able to do this site justice and there is a strong need for a thorough description and evaluation of all its vegetation in at least National Vegetation Classification terms. Sutton Park also has important

recreational functions in the conurbation and there may be long-term problems in reconciling these with improving the quality of the habitats. From the point of view of the botanist, although the extent of heathland and acid grassland is unsurpassed anywhere else in B&BC, the wetland areas are of most nature conservation importance and greatest fragility. In particular in the past the watercourses of the Park have received emergency disposal of foul water which may be having long-term effects on the wetlands. Sutton Park is also rather isolated, and improving connections with the wider countryside ought to be a priority. The obvious corridor to the south and east along the Plants Brook already includes some fine sites but is rather constricted in its passage across central Sutton Coldfield. The railway corridor might help, also with links with the Staffordshire countryside to the north at Streetly.

The other core areas have a considerable degree of continuity but are largely made up of clusters of distinct habitats, many of which can be quite isolated from one another. The Halesowen Countryside core area has some of the best woodlands and grasslands in the conurbation but is very variously managed: as farmland, as parkland, as golf courses, as SINC sites and even as post-industrial landscape. Recognising it as a whole might allow a wider array of funding to be attracted to conserving what is best in individual sites and enhancing the connections between the different parts. Enhancing the relationship with the rich Worcestershire countryside to the south also needs to be explored, and also the crucial links with both the Woodgate Valley and the botanically rich suburbs of south Birmingham to the west and also the central Dudley network to the north.

A glance at a map of Walsall immediately demonstrates its richness in open spaces. There are fascinating relics of rich heathland, plus unimproved farmland quite distinct from that in South Dudley embedded in some of the last spoil- and subsidence-dominated landscapes in B&BC. All of this contributes to the Walsall Countryside core area, which, as in the Halesowen example, would be enhanced if seen as a single entity and attention paid to internal and external links. Recently Brownhills Common has been linked with Chasewater outside our area in a single SSSI, which demonstrates the coherence of the Walsall Countryside core area with the Staffordshire heaths. Further strengthening of the links across Barr Beacon to bridge the gap between the riches of Walsall and Sutton Coldfield should be high on the agenda of a greener future for Birmingham and the Black Country.

To the south, the Walsall Countryside core area links across the border, through the area where the M5 and M6 motorways join, into the Sandwell Valley. Sandwell Valley, right in the centre of the conurbation, is effectively a botanical core area on its own merits and like Sutton Park has the unusual benefit of continuity. Better coordination between the Sandwell and Birmingham parts and current developments in countryside stewardship should be reinforced to enhance its nature conservation value. South from the Sandwell Valley it is only a few kilometres to the Halesowen Countryside core area. Bridging this gap across Smethwick and Blackheath, possibly by reinforcing the wildlife value of Sandwell Valley and of all the parks, public open spaces and transport systems within a designated zone or 'green corridor' should be a very high priority in improving nature in B&BC. Simultaneously enhancing the existing botanically rich links to the north with the Walsall Countryside core area across the motorway junction would create a broad green corridor right across the centre of the conurbation and contribute to the value and resilience of nature in the conurbation as a whole.

The nature reserves of central Dudley are already a recognised treasure of B&BC and, as is evident in the axiophyte maps, together they form the fourth corridor-like core area from Mushroom Green in the south to Sedgley Beacon in the north, with many strong radiating connections such as those with the Stour Valley, the Rowley Hills, the Wren's Nest and the ancient landscape in the valley of the Penn Brook in Wolverhampton and South Staffordshire. In particular, the central Dudley network links together an axiophyte-rich crescent from South Wolverhampton, through Dudley into South Birmingham, another major feature of the conurbation which seems to need recognition.

The TWINSPAN analysis was based on the entire floras of the individual monads rather than just the species selected as axiophytes and produced the three main TWINSPAN groups shown in Figure 4.6. In 16% of the monads the predominant botanical feature was found to be the natural environment (including the best of the canals). This was described as the Rich Semi-natural Group (TWINSPAN Group 1), which has a very similar distribution to that of the axiophytes associated with natural and semi-natural sites (Figure 4.12) and the list of species preferentially found in these monads included many of those axiophytes.

Figure 4.6 shows that another 36% of monads are associated with industry and the remaining 48% of monads with the presence of residential property (also arable farmland). Both industrial and suburban types are divided by their species complements into richer and poorer versions. The richer monads, typically residential or agricultural areas with significant woodland, or industrial areas with rich canals, should be seen as part of the networks and stepping stones linking the core areas and targeted for enhancement.

The potential value of this approach can be seen particularly in the western half of Sandwell plus neighbouring areas of Wolverhampton, Dudley and Walsall in the final TWINSPAN map (Figures 4.11 and 4.15), where scattered monads of rich semi-natural monads are clearly linked by industrial/open water monads, many of which could be enhanced by canal improvement in order to extend and consolidate the rich semi-natural area. Similarly the existing scatter of rich semi-natural monads both in south Birmingham and in west Wolverhampton are linked into networks by habitat-rich suburban monads which could also be targeted for enhancement.

Both axiophyte and TWINSPAN analyses show a broad central zone in Birmingham of habitat- and mostly species-poor suburban and industrial/suburban monads. This zone narrows to the north and west but stretches as far as central Wolverhampton and occupies as much as one third of the conurbation. A definitive break across this zone could be achieved by the consolidation of the green corridor across the Sandwell Valley between the richer areas to the north-east and south-west of the conurbation which has been advocated above.

Logically the primary objective in enhancing the resilience and coherence of the ecological network of the conurbation as a whole and relieving the botanical poverty of the urban core would be to develop this green corridor between the Halesowen Countryside core area in the south-west and the Walsall Countryside and Sutton Park core areas in the north-east.

A second, and long-recognised, regional objective would be to consolidate and improve the links between the heathlands of Staffordshire, Walsall and Sutton (Anderson Associates, 2006).

A third objective for the conurbation as a whole would be to recognise the existing and potential ecological continuity which exists from South Wolverhampton to South Birmingham, via the Dudley ecological network, the Halesowen Countryside core area, the Woodgate Valley and the river valleys and woodlands of south Birmingham.

Figures 4.13 and 4.15 demonstrate a complex of high axiophyte industrial monads in the Bilston/Darlaston/Wednesbury/Coseley area, plus much of western Sandwell, which link the central Dudley network and the Walsall Countryside core area and also potentially form a second corridor across the habitat-poor central zone of the conurbation. This potential corridor should also be recognised.

There are a series of other important local objectives which are described in section 1, particularly in the axiophyte analysis. It is necessary to recognise, value and defend all the hotspots of botanical diversity such as those shown in Figure 4.15, especially those which form green wedges around the periphery of the conurbation. It would also be possible to use the Flora data to advocate the improvement of parks, gardens and open spaces by habitat creation and by encouraging wildlife gardening in the axiophyte-poor and generally botanically-poor zones.

Section 2 of the present chapter has explored some specific situations and habitats found in the conurbation and has considered the ecological implications of each, which often offer useful information for achieving the objectives summarised above.

The brief survey of the botanical implications of the geology suggests that local geology should be taken into account in evaluating sites and vegetation, both in terms of the objectives and the standards to be set.

The canals are clearly a rich botanical asset to the conurbation, especially in Walsall and Dudley, and offer all kinds of possibilities for improving continuity. The ecological implications in canalside development should always be considered and ameliorated.

The river corridors conserve some interesting botanical features but could become much more significant with further improvement in river structure and water quality. The analysis suggests that *Ranunculus penicillatus* should be added to the list of axiophytes.

The railways and roads are also important linking habitats. The railways are necessarily poorly investigated habitats because of safety implications and a comprehensive project, with the support of the railway authorities, to monitor, improve and manage habitats along the rail network is needed. Some suggestions towards maximising the value of the road system are given in the relevant section.

The post-industrial sites fall into two (overlapping) categories. The early-successional sites perform useful ecological roles but are essentially temporary and are probably best defended by avoiding wholesale landscaping prior to development and by continuing to study their intrinsic and corridor value. The historical sites are often highly significant in terms of botanical diversity and are becoming rare. Like the pre-industrial habitats such as ancient woodlands, these post-industrial sites have heritage value. The process of designating these sites should continue to be a priority.

The allotments of the conurbation are important botanical refuges, particularly for uncommon arable weeds and should be recognised as such. They are also quite rich in native plants, often with fragments of countryside habitats, even in areas otherwise poor in both.

A spatial survey of axiophytes associated with heathland suggests that further opportunities for heathland creation may exist in the conurbation.

The analysis undertaken in the present chapter was entirely limited to the vascular plants, for which we have reasonably satisfactory data. It is possible that similar surveys of some of the other plant groups would give different results, although a comparison between King's Lynn and the East Anglian region as a whole (Stevenson & Hill 2008) demonstrated that the town's bryophyte flora was exceptionally species-rich for the region.

It is also true that although vegetation is fundamental to the life of animals, the nature of the relationships are by no means clear or simple. Considerations of groups such as mammals, birds, fish and all the groups of invertebrates need to be taken into account in maximising the nature conservation value in the conurbation as elsewhere. The present analysis has avoided discussing the value of the ecological network for its principal life-form, i.e. people, but it would be a brave person who claimed that Birmingham and the Black Country would be a better place for people without an ecological network.

Even within the vascular plant profile, some types of plant will have been undervalued by analysis at the monad level and the need to use measures which are widely applicable across the conurbation. This may be particularly true of the extremely limited extent of the limestone exposures. The Wren's Nest and Mons Hill include fragments of limestone countryside seen nowhere else in B&BC. However the fragments are extremely small: an area few metres square holds all the *Gentianella amarella* and *Viola hirta* in B&BC, and is surrounded by most of the *Lithospermum officinale*. There are other worthy, but often tiny and/or scrubbed-over fragments of limestone and other highly calcareous sites in Dudley, Wolverhampton and Walsall. Similarly the value of small features such as ponds has been difficult to assess. Some of them can be very rich but they are often very fragile in the urban context.

Furthermore, some groups such as the Lichens (see Chapter 6) are evidently undergoing rapid and fluctuating change connected with changes in the urban atmosphere involving falls in sulphur dioxide, increases in plant-available nitrogen compounds and fluctuations in rainfall. These changes also affect the bryophytes and are likely to affect the vascular plant flora, especially where the soils or other substrates are thin or less buffered, as is the case in heathland and in many built-up situations. For these reasons, and because of the under-assessed consequences of climate change, the analysis requires a consideration of change which can only really be achieved by repeating the Flora survey in the future!

▲ Species-rich grassland and geological exposures, Rowley Hills, Sandwell

# Section 4 • References

ADAS (UK) Ltd (2010) *Open Mosaic Habitats on Previously Developed Land – Site Identification Guide* Defra Biodiversity Policy Unit, Wolverhampton.

Anderson Associates (2006) Cannock Chase to Sutton Park, biodiversity enchancement area, decision rules. Contract E237, report to Natural England.

Barker, G. (ed.) (2000) *Ecological recombination in urban areas: implications for nature conservation.* Centre for Hydrology and Ecology, Monks Wood.

Beaver, S.H. (1946) *Report on derelict land in the Black Country.* Ministry of Town and Country Planning, London.

Botham, M.S., Rothery, P., Hulme, P.E., Hill, M.O., Preston, C.D. & Roy, D.B. (2009) Do urban areas act as foci for the spread of alien plant species? An assessment of temporal trends in the UK. *Diversity and Distributions*, 15 (2): 338–345.

Burges, R.C.L. & Andrews, C.E.A. (1947) Report of the bombed sites sub-committee. *Proceedings of the Birmingham Natural History and Philosophical Society*, XVIII (part I): 1–12.

Gilbert, O.L. (1989) *The Ecology of Urban Habitats* Chapman & Hall, London.

Grime, J.G., Hodgson, J.C. & Hunt, R. (2007) *Comparative Plant Ecology: A Functional Approach to Common British Species ed 2.* Castlepoint Press.

Harman, T.T. & Showell, W. (1885) *Showell's Dictionary of Birmingham.* Dodo Press.

Hill, M.O. (1979) *TWINSPAN, a FORTRAN program for arranging multivariate data in an ordered two-way table by classification of the individuals and attributes.* Section of Ecology and Systematics, Cornell University, Ithaca, New York.

Hill, M.O. & Gauch, H.G. (1980) Detrended Correspondence Analysis – an improved ordination technique. *Vegetatio*, 42 (1–3): 47–58.

Hill, M.O., Mountford, J.O., Roy, D.B. & Bunce, R.G.H. (1999) *Ellenberg's Indicator Values for British Plants.* Centre for Ecology and Hydrology, Cambridgeshire.

Hill, M.O., Preston, C.D. & Roy, D.B. (2004) *PLANTATT Attributes of British and Irish Plants.* Centre for Ecology & Hydrology, Cambridgeshire.

Hill, M.O. & Šmilauer, P. (2005) *TWINSPAN for WINDOWS v. 2.3 Users Guide.* Centre for Ecology and Hydrology, Huntingdon and University of South Bohemia, České Budějovice.

Lawley, S.D. (2011) Chapter 10 Computer analysis of flora data in Hawksford, J.E., Hopkins, I.J., Cadman, D., Hill, R.N., Lawley, S.D., Leak, A., Radford, E., Reynolds, J.R., Steward, D. & Waller, R. (2011) *The Flora of Staffordshire.* Staffordshire Wildlife Trust. Stafford.

Lawton, J.H., Brotherton, P.N.M., Brown, V.K., Elphick, C., Fitter, A.H., Forshaw, J., Haddow, R.W., Hilborne, S., Leafe, R.N., Mace, G.M., Southgate, M.P., Sutherland, W.J., Tew, T.E., Varley, J., & Wynne,

G.R. (2010) *Making Space for Nature: a review of England's wildlife sites and ecological network.* Report to UK Government Department Defra.

Lockton, A. (2011) Axiophyte research *BSBI Recorder*, 15: 9.

Neath, A (2005) *History of Streetly and Personal accounts and memories.* [online] Available at: http://www.streetly.org/5.html *[Accessed 13th October 2011]*

Offwell Woodland & Wildlife Trust (2001) Lowland Heath – Historical Background. [online] Available at: http://www.countrysideinfo.co.uk/historic.htm [Accessed 13th October 2011]

Preston, C.D., Pearman, D.A. & Dines, T.D. (eds) (2002) *New Atlas of the British and Irish Flora.* Oxford University Press, Oxford.

Preston, C.D., Telfer, M.G., Carey, P.D., Cooper, J.M., Dines, J.M., Hill, M.O., Pearman, D.A., Roy, D.B. & Smart, S.M. (2002a) *The changing Flora of the UK.* Defra Publications, London.

Rackham, O. (2000) *The History of the Countryside.* Weidenfeld & Nicolson, London.

Rees, W.J. (1955) Some preliminary observations on the flora of derelict land. *Proceedings of the Birmingham Natural History and Philosophical Society* XVIII (V): 114–133.

Rees, W.J. & Skelding, A.D. (1950) Vegetation, in Kinvig, R.H., Smith, J.G. & Wise, M.J. (eds) *Birmingham and its regional Setting*: 65–76 British Association, Birmingham.

Riding, A., Critchley, N., Wilson, L. & Parker, J. (2010) *Definition and mapping of open mosaic habitats on previously developed land: Phase 1 Final Report.* Defra Biodiversity Policy Unit, Wolverhampton.

Sargent, C. (1984) *Britain's Railway Vegetation.* Institute of Terrestrial Ecology, Cambridge.

Sinker, C.A., Packham, J.R., Trueman, I.C., Oswald, P.H., Perring, F.H & Prestwood, W.V. (1985) *Ecological Flora of the Shropshire Region.* Shropshire Wildlife Trust, Shrewsbury.

Stevenson, C.R. & Hill, M.O. (2008) Urban myths exploded: results of a bryological survey of King's Lynn (Norfolk, UK). *Journal of Bryology*, 30 (1): 12–22.

Thellung A., (1918/1919) Zur Terminologie der Adventiv- und Ruderalflora. *Allegmeine Botanische Zeitschrift für Systematik, Floristik, Pflanzengeographie.* 24/25: 36–42.

Trueman, I.C., & Young, C.H. (2012) Ecological value of urban habitats, in Booth, C.A., Hammond, F.N., Lamond, J.E. & Proverbs, D.G. (eds) *Solutions to climate change challenges in the built environment.* Wiley-Blackwell, Chichester.

UK Biodiversity Action Plan (1995) *Habitat Action Plan: Lowland Heathland.* [online] Available at: http://webarchive.nationalarchives.gov.uk/20110303145213/http://ukbap.org.uk/ukplans.aspx?ID=15 *[Accessed 13th October 2011]*

Wallwork, K.L. (1974) *Derelict Land.* David & Charles, Newton Abbot.

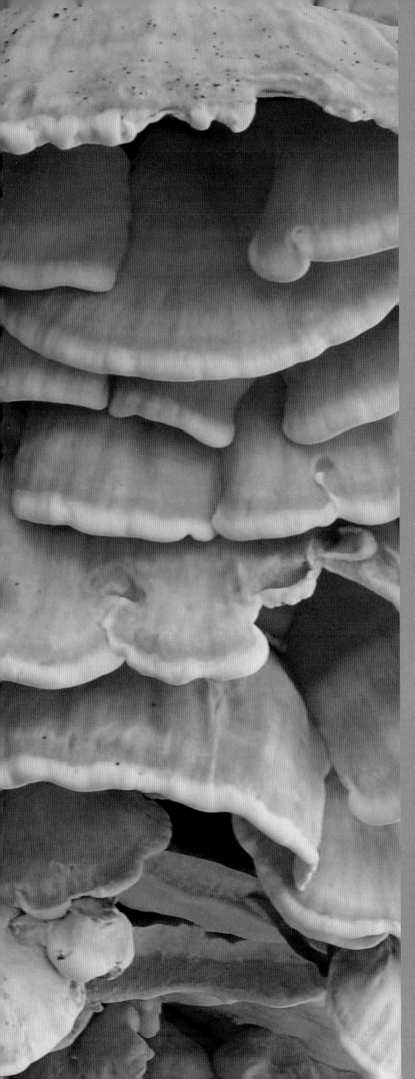

Chapter 5

# Fungi

by D.J. Antrobus and W.T. Moodie

◀ *Laetiporus sulphureus*

## Introduction

In 1965, the Warwickshire Fungus Survey began a survey of the fungi of Vice County 38, including parts of Birmingham within vc. 38. The intention was to follow the methods used to produce *A Computer-Mapped Flora. A Study of the County of Warwickshire* (Cadbury, Hawkes and Readett, 1971). The project was organised by staff at the University of Birmingham (Brand, 2006). After initial trials, it was decided not to survey particular 1km squares, because of the difficulties involved in recording fungi.

Fungi are identified by their fruitbodies, but the appearance of fruitbodies is erratic and they often last for short periods, sometimes only a day or two. An experienced surveyor would need to visit a site regularly for at least a year and would need to examine almost every square metre to be sure of recording 90% of even the larger fruitbodies. The smaller fruitbodies would require the inspection of, for example, soil, leaves, stems and wood with a hand lens. The field work in one square and the consequent laboratory work could take several years to ensure that most of the fungi had been recorded. In view of the small number of experienced volunteers available, it was not possible to survey the distribution of even a limited number of species in the Vice County (Clark, 1980). Consequently, records were collected from only a limited number of sites as and when they could be visited. Members of the Survey specialised in different groups of fungi. Voucher material of every species recorded is stored in the herbarium at Warwick museum or in some other herbarium, such as the Royal Botanic Gardens, Kew or the Royal Botanic Garden, Edinburgh.

## Coded sites

In the Birmingham area, the Warwickshire Fungus Survey visited the University of Birmingham campus frequently from 1965 to 2005. This included Edgbaston Nature Reserve, formally designated Edgbaston Pool (SSSI). Sutton Park was visited often and Moseley Bog was also visited, even though this site is in vc. 37 (Worcestershire). In West Bromwich, members of the Sandwell Valley Naturalists' Club recorded fungi over a similar period of time in vc. 39 (Staffordshire). The Warwickshire Fungus Survey also visited the Sandwell Valley.

The Birmingham and Black Country Wildlife Trust was founded in 1980 and later, from 1991, species records were collected and incorporated in the 'EcoRecord' Database, using RECORDER software. The fungus records have been included in the present list. Regular forays were organised by the Walsall Countryside Services Group in the Walsall Area.

Over a number of years, the late Michael Austin, a member of the South Staffordshire Fungus Recording Group, recorded species in the Black Country Area. Most sites are given two-letter codes in the following list of fungi. Some additional sites, with fewer records, are included by site name and grid reference.

### Site Codes

**BA** Balaams Wood & Holly Hill Nature Park. vc. 37 (Worcestershire), SO9978. Records are from EcoRecord.

**BB** Birmingham Botanical Gardens, Westbourne Road, Birmingham, vc. 38 (Warwickshire), SP0485. Records are from D.J. Antrobus.

**BC** Barr Beacon, vc. 39 (Staffordshire), SP0697. Records are from the late M.J. Austin.

**BE** Birmingham Eastside, including Digbeth and part of Bordesley within the squares SP0786 and SP0886, vc. 38 (Warwickshire). Records are from D.J. Antrobus.

**BP** Bantock Park, Wolverhampton, vc. 39 (Staffordshire), SP8997, SP8998. Records are from the late M.J. Austin.

**DY** Dudley Castle and Zoo, vc. 39 (Staffordshire), SO9490. Records are from the late M.J. Austin.

**ED** Edgbaston Nature Reserve, formally designated Edgbaston Pool (SSSI) and the University of Birmingham campus, vc. 38 (Warwickshire). The area lies within the squares SP0584, SP0483, SP0583. Records are from the Warwickshire Fungus Survey.

**GP** Great Barr Pools, vc. 39 (Staffordshire), SP0594. Records are from the late M.J. Austin.

**HA** Halesowen town centre. vc. 37 (Worcester), SO9783. Records are from D.J. Antrobus.

**HH** Hayhead Wood, vc. 39 (Staffordshire), SP0498, SP0599. Records are from W.T. Moodie.

**HW** Handsworth Wood Area and Handsworth Park, vc.39 (Staffordshire), SP0590. Records are from W.T. Moodie.

**LG** Leighswood, Aldridge, vc.39 (Staffordshire), SK0501. Records are from the late M.J. Austin.

**LP** The Leasowes Park, Halesowen, vc. 37 (Worcester), SO9884. Records are from D.J. Antrobus and EcoRecord (N. Williams).

**MG** Martineau Gardens, Priory Road, Birmingham and vicinity, vc. 38 (Warwickshire), SP0684. The main site is designated a Site of Local Importance for Nature Conservation (SLINC). Records are from the Warwickshire Fungus Survey and EcoRecord.

▲ *Flammulina velutipes*

**MO** Moseley Bog Nature Reserve, Birmingham and local area, vc. 37 (Worcester), SP0982 and SP0882. The Bog is an area of damp deciduous woodland. Records are from the Warwickshire Fungus Survey, W.T. Moodie and EcoRecord.

**MR** Merrions Wood and Wilderness Wood, vc. 39 (Staffordshire), SP0495. Records are from W.T.Moodie and EcoRecord.

**MW** Moorcroft Wood, vc.39 (Staffordshire), SO9695 and SO9795. Records are from W.T. Moodie and EcoRecord.

**PD** Pedmore, Stourbridge, vc. 37 (Worcester). The area surveyed lies within the squares SO9183 and SO9182. It includes suburban housing and the wooded area called Ham Dingle. Records are from D.J. Antrobus and EcoRecord.

**PN** Penn and Upper Penn, vc. 39 (Staffordshire), SO8995 and SO8996. Records are from the late M.J. Austin and EcoRecord.

**QU** Quinton, Birmingham, vc. 37 (Worcester), SO9884. A residential area. Records are from D.J. Antrobus.

**RH** Red House Park and vicinity. vc. 39 (Staffordshire), SP0394. Records are from EcoRecord.

**RW** Rough Wood, vc. 39 (Staffordshire), SJ9800. Records are from W.T. Moodie and EcoRecord.

**SM** Smethwick, vc. 39 (Staffordshire), SP0288. Records are from the late M.J. Austin.

**SO** Shire Oak Park, vc. 39 (Staffordshire), SK0305. Records are from W.T. Moodie.

**SP** Sutton Park, mostly vc. 38 (Warwickshire), with a small area of vc. 39 (Staffordshire) west of Ryknild Street, the Roman Road. Records are from Coxhead & Fowkes (1992), the Warwickshire Fungus Survey and others.

**SV** Sandwell Valley, including Sandwell Valley Country Park and the RSPB centre, vc. 39 (Staffordshire). The area covered is the 20 square kilometre rectangle with the diagonal squares SP0190 to SP0494. Records are from Moodie, (2005).

**SW** Saltwells Local Nature Reserve, vc. 39 (Staffordshire), SO9386 and SO9387. Records are from EcoRecord.

**TW** Tettenhall Wood, and College Grounds vc. 37 (Worcestershire), SO8899. Records are from EcoRecord.

**WB** Woodbrooke Quaker Study Centre, Bristol Road, Birmingham, vc. 37 (Worcester), SP036814. Records are from the Warwickshire Fungus Survey.

**WG** Woodgate Valley, vc. 37 (Worcestershire), SP0083. Records are from EcoRecord.

**WK** Wightwick, Wolverhampton, vc. 39 (Staffordshire), SO8798. Records are from the late M.J.Austin.

**WN** Wrens Nest, Bluebell Park and Parkes Hall, vc. 39 (Staffordshire), SO9392. Records are from EcoRecord (N. Williams).

**WW** Warley Woods, vc. 37 (Worcester), and vc. 39 (Staffordshire), SP0185 and SP0186. Records are from the late M.J. Austin and W.T. Moodie.

## Nomenclature standards

The taxonomy of fungi is still changing rapidly. The recent research on fungal DNA indicates that some traditional groupings may be incorrect. New species are described every year and other species are synonymised. Synonymy sometimes results in changes in specific epithet. Therefore the following list is arranged by phylum, class and genus only, because these are relatively stable. Order and family are given for each genus, because these change often and would lead to difficulty in locating species if they were used in the arrangement. Almost every author uses a different taxonomy and so a particular standard must be adopted. Those adopted here are as follows:

- Myxomycota nomenclature is in accordance with *The Myxomycetes of Britain and Ireland* by Ing (1999).
- Basidiomycota nomenclature is in accordance with *Checklist of the British & Irish Basidiomycota* by Legon & Henrici (2005).
- The nomenclature of Ascomycota, Oomycota and other phyla is in accordance with the British Mycological Society Fungal Records Database of the British Isles: *GB Checklist of Fungal Names*, published on their website, February 2007.

## References

Brand, G.M. (2006) How it all began—Personal recollections of the gestation of the Warwickshire Fungus Survey, *Proceedings of the Birmingham Natural History Society*, 28(3), 144.

Cadbury, D.A., Hawkes, J.G. & Readett, R.C. (1971) *A Computer-Mapped Flora. A Study of the County of Warwickshire*. Academic Press, London.

Clark, M.C. (1980) *A Fungus Flora of Warwickshire*. British Mycological Society, London.

Coxhead, P. & Fowkes, H.H. (1992) *A Natural History of Sutton Park Part 2: Fungi, Lichens and Bryophytes*. Sutton Coldfield Natural History Society.

Ing, B. (1999) *The Myxomycetes of Britain and Ireland*. The Richmond Publishing Co. Ltd., Slough.

Legon, N.W. & A. Henrici, A. (2005) *Checklist of the British & Irish Basidiomycota*. Royal Botanic Gardens, Kew.

Moodie, W. (2005) *Fungi of the Sandwell Valley*. Sandwell Valley Naturalists' Club. Also additions to this publication in *The Bulletin of the Sandwell Valley Naturalists' Club*.

## Acknowledgement

Thanks are expressed to Sara Carvalho-Lovell for her assistance with the EcoRecord data.

*Macrolepiota procera*
(by Neville Walters)

# ASCOMYCOTA
## ASCOMYCETES

**Aleuria** Fuckel
PEZIZALES, PYRONEMATACEAE
**aurantia** (Pers.) Fuckel – BA, ED, GP, HW, MO, SP, SV, TW, WN, Hadley's Brickworks (SO9697)

**Allophylaria** (P. Karsten) P. Karsten
HELOTIALES, HELOTIACEAE
**campanuliformis** (Fuckel) Svrcek (=*Pezizella campanuliformis* (Fuckel) Dennis) – ED

**Anthracobia** Boud.
PEZIZALES, PYRONEMATACEAE
**melaloma** (Alb. & Schw.) Boud. – ED

**Apostemidium** P.Karsten
HELOTIALES, VIBRISSEACEAE
**fiscellum** (P. Karsten) P. Karsten – ED

**Arachniotus** J. Schröt.
ONYGENALES, GYMNOASCACEAE
**aureus** (Eidam) J. Schröt. – SV

**Arachnopeziza** Fuckel
HELOTIALES, HYALOSCYPHACEAE
**aranea** (De Not.) Boud. – SP
**aurata** Fuckel – ED
**candidofulva** (Schwein.) Korf – SP

**Ascobolus** Pers.
PEZIZALES, ASCOBOLACEAE
**albidus** P. Crouan & H. Crouan – SP
**denudatus** Fr. – SV
**epimyces** (Cooke) Seaver – ED, SP
**equinus** (O.F. Müll.) P. Karst. – SP
**lignatilis** Alb. & Schw. – ED
**stercorarius** (Bull.) J. Schröt. – SP

**Ascocoryne** Groves & Wilson
HELOTIALES, HELOTIACEAE
**albidum** (Berk.) ined. (=*Endostilbum albidum* (Berk.) D.A. Reid) – GP
**cylichnium** (Tul.) Korf – ED, MO, SP, SV
**sarcoides** (Jacq.) Groves & Wilson – ED, GP, MO, MR, SP, SV

**Ascozonus** (Renny) E.C. Hansen
THELEBOLALES, THELEBOLACEAE
**crouanii** (Sacc.) Boud. – ED

**Aulographum** Lib.
MICROTHYRIALES, AULOGRAPHACEAE
**hederae** Lib. – ED, SP

**Belonidium** Durieu
HELOTIALES, HYALOSCYPHACEAE
**sulphureum** (Pers.) Raitv. (=*Dasyscyphus sulphureus* (Pers.) Massee) – ED, MO, SP, SV

**Betulina** Velen.
HELOTIALES, HYALOSCYPHACEAE
**fuscostipitata** Graddon – ED

**Bisporella** Sacc.
HELOTIALES, HELOTIACEAE
**citrina** (Batsch) Korf & S.E. Carp. – SV, WN

**Botryotinia** Whetzel
HELOTIALES, SCLEROTINIACEAE
**fuckeliana** (de Bary) Whetzel (Anamorph: *Botrytis cinerea* Pers.) – ED, Wigginsmill Road (SO9794)

**Bulgaria** Fr.
HELOTIALES, BULGARIACEAE
**inquinans** (Pers.) Fr. – ED, MR, SP, SV

**Byssonectria** P. Karst.
PEZIZALES, PYRONEMATACEAE
**fusispora** (Berk.) Rogerson & Korf – SP

**Byssostilbe** Petch
HYPOCREALES, CLAVICIPITACEAE
**stilbigera** (Berk. & Broome) Petch (Anamorph: *Blistum ovalisporum* (A.L. Sm.) B. Sutton) – ED

**Calcarisporium** Preuss
INCERTAE SEDIS, INCERTAE SEDIS
**arbuscula** Preuss – WB

**Calloria** Fr.
HELOTIALES, DERMATEACEAE
**neglecta** (Lib.) Hein – ED

**Calosphaeria** Tul. & C. Tul.
CALOSPHAERIALES, CALOSPHAERIACEAE
**wahlenbergii** Nitschke – SP

**Calycellina** Höhnel
HELOTIALES, HYALOSCYPHACEAE
**chlorinella** (Ces.) Dennis – GP
**punctata** (Fr.) Lowen & Dumont – ED, MO, SP, SV
**punctiformis** (Grev.) Höhnel – GP
**spiraeae** (Rob. ex Desm.) Dennis – ED

**Calycina** Nees ex Gray
HELOTIALES, HELOTIACEAE
**herbarum** (Pers.) Gray (=*Hymenoscyphus herbarum* (Pers.) Dennis) – ED, MO, SP, SV

**Camarops** P. Karsten
BOLINIALES, BOLINIACEAE
**lutea** (Alb. & Schw.) Nannf. – ED, SP

**Camposporium** Harkn.
INCERTAE SEDIS, INCERTAE SEDIS
**cambrense** S. Hughes – SP

**Cejpia** Velen.
HELOTIALES, DERMATEACEAE
**hystrix** (De Not.) Baral (=*Belonium hystrix* (De Not.) Höhn.) – SP

**Chaetosphaeria** Tul. & C. Tul.
SORDARIALES, CHAETOSPHAERIACEAE
**callimorpha** (Mont.) Sacc. – ED

**innumera** Tul. & C. Tul. – ED
**myriocarpa** (Fr.) C. Booth – ED

**Cheilymenia** Boud.
PEZIZALES, PYRONEMATACEAE
**fimicola** (De Not. & Bagl.) Dennis – SP
**theleboloides** (Alb. & Schwein.) Boud. – ED

**Chlorociboria** Seaver ex C.S. Ramamurthi, Korf & L.R. Batra
HELOTIALES, DERMATEACEAE
**aeruginascens** (Nyl.) Kanouse ex C.S. Ramamurthi, Korf & L.R. Batra – ED, SP

**Ciboria** Fuckel
HELOTIALES, SCLEROTINIACEAE
**amentacea** (Balb.) Fuckel – PN
**americana** E.J. Durand – SP
**batschiana** (Zopf) N.F. Buchw. – SP
**caucus** (Rebent.) Fuckel – ED

**Ciborinia** Whetzel
HELOTIALES, SCLEROTINIACEAE
**candolleana** (Lév.) Whetzel – ED

**Claviceps** Tul.
HYPOCREALES, CLAVICIPITACEAE
**purpurea** (Fr.) Tul. – ED, LP, SP, SV, Birmingham Eco Park (SP1186)

**Coleroa** (Fr.) Rabenh.
PLEOSPORALES, VENTURIACEAE
**chaetomium** (Kunze) Rabenh. – ED
**robertiani** (Fr.) E. Müller – ED

**Coniochaeta** (Sacc.) Cooke
SORDARIALES, CONIOCHAETACEAE
**ligniaria** (Grev.) Massee – SP

**Coprobia** Boud.
PEZIZALES, PYRONEMATACEAE
**granulata** (Bull.) Boud. – SP, SV

**Coprotus** Korf & Kimbr.
PEZIZALES, INCERTAE SEDIS
**granuliformis** (P. Crouan & H. Crouan) Kimbr. – SP

**Cordyceps** (Fr.) Link
HYPOCREALES, CLAVICIPITACEAE
**militaris** (L.) Link – ED, MO, SP, SV

**Coremiella** Bubák & Willi Krieg.
INCERTAE SEDIS, INCERTAE SEDIS
**cubispora** (Berk. & M.A. Curtis) M.B. Ellis – ED

**Crocicreas** Fr.
HELOTIALES, HELOTIACEAE
**amenti** (Batsch) S. Carp. – ED
**coronatum** (Bull.) S. Carp. – ED, SV
**cyathoideum var. cyathoideum** (Bull.) S. Carp. – ED, SP, SV
**dolosellum** (P. Karst.) S.E. Carp. – SV
**starbaeckii** (Rehm) S. Carp. – ED, SP, SV

**subhyalinum** (Rehm) S. Carp. – ED, GP, SP, SV

**Cryptodiaporthe** Petrak
DIAPORTHALES, VALSACEAE
**vepris** (Delacr.) Petr. (=*Apioporthe vepris* (Delacr.) Wehm.) – ED

**Cudoniella** Sacc.
HELOTIALES, HELOTIACEAE
**acicularis** (Bull.) Schröter – ED, SP
**clavus var. clavus** (Alb. & Schw.) Dennis – ED

**Cylindrium** Bonord.
HYPOCREALES, NECTRIACEAE
**aeruginosum** (Link) Lindau (=*Fusidium aeruginosum* Link) – ED

**Cymadothea** F.A. Wolf
MYCOSPHAERELLALES,
MYCOSPHAERELLACEAE
**trifolii** (Pers.) F.A. Wolf – SP

**Dactylosporium** Harz
INCERTAE SEDIS, INCERTAE SEDIS
**macropus** (Corda) Harz – ED

**Daldinia** Ces. & de Not.
XYLARIALES, XYLARIACEAE
**concentrica** (Bolt.) Ces. & de Not. – BA, ED, MG, MO, PN, SO, SV, WB, WN, Bartley Reservoir (SO9981), Sheepwash Park (SO9791)
**vernicosa** (Schw.) Ces. & de Not. – SO

**Dendryphiella** Bubák & Ranoj.
PLEOSPORALES, PLEOSPORACEAE
**infuscans** (Thüm.) M.B. Ellis – ED

**Dendryphion** Wallr.
PLEOSPORALES, PLEOSPORACEAE
**comosum** Wallr. – ED

**Diaporthe** Nitschke
DIAPORTHALES, VALSACEAE
**eres** Nitschke (=*Phomopsis revellens* (Sacc.) Traverso) – SP, WW
**rostellata** (Fr.) Nitschke (=*Gnomonia rostellata* (Fr.) Bref.) – SP

**Diatrype** Fr.
XYLARIALES, DIATRYPACEAE
**bullata** (Hoffm.) Fr. – SP
**disciformis** (Hoffm.) Fr. – ED, LP, MO, WN
**stigma** (Hoffm.) Fr. – HW, SP, SV

**Diatrypella** (Ces. & de Not.) de Not.
XYLARIALES, DIATRYPACEAE
**favacea** (Fr.) Ces. & de Not. – ED, SV
**quercina** (Pers.) Cooke – ED, SP

**Dictyosporium** Corda
INCERTAE SEDIS, INCERTAE SEDIS
**toruloides** (Corda) Guég. – ED

**Diplpcarpon** F.A. WOLF
HELOTIALES, DERMATEACEAE
**rosae** F.A. Wolf – WN

**Drepanopeziza** (Kleb.) Höhnel
HELOTIALES, DERMATEACEAE
**salicis** (Tul. & C. Tul.) Höhnel – ED

**Echinula** Graddon
HELOTIALES, HYALOSCYPHACEAE
**asteriadiformis** Graddon – SV

**Endophragmiella** B. Sutton
SORDARIALES, LASIOSPHAERIACEAE
**boothii** (M.B. Ellis) S. Hughes – ED

**Endoxyla** Fuckel
BOLINIALES, BOLINIACEAE
**cirrhosa** (Pers.) E. Müller & v. Arx – ED

**Epichloe** (Fr.) Tul. & C. Tul.
CLAVICIPITALES, CLAVICIPITACEAE
**typhina** (Pers.) Tul. & C. Tul. – MO

**Epicoccum** Link
INCERTAE SEDIS, INCERTAE SEDIS
**nigrum** Link – SP

**Erysiphe** Hedw. f. ex DC.
ERYSIPHALES, ERYSIPHACEAE
**alphitoides** (Griffon & Maubl.) U. Braun & S. Takam. (= *Microsphaera alphitoides* Griffon & Maubl.) – ED, MR, RW, SP, SV, WB
**aquilegiae var. ranunculi** (Grev.) R.Y. Zheng & G.Q. Chen – WB
**artemisiae** Grev. – ED, SV
**circaeae** L. Junell – WB
**heraclei** Schleich. ex DC. – LP
**polygoni** DC. – ED, SV
**trifolii var. intermedia** (U. Braun) U. Braun & S. Takam. – ED
**trifolii var. trifolii** Grev. – ED

**Eutypa** Tul. & C. Tul.
XYLARIALES, DIATRYPACEAE
**maura** (Fr.) Sacc. – ED

**Fimaria** Velen.
PEZIZALES, HUMARIACEAE
**hepatica** (Batsch) v. Brummelen – GP

**Fusarium** Link
HYPOCREALES, NECTRIACEAE
**sporotrichioides** Sherb. – SV

**Fusicoccum** Corda
INCERTAE SEDIS, INCERTAE SEDIS
**macrosporum** Sacc. & Briard – WW

**Geoglossum** Pers.
HELOTIALES, GEOGLOSSACEAE
**fallax** Durand – ED, SV
**glutinosum** Pers. – ED
**peckianum** Cooke – SV

**Geopora** Harkn.
PEZIZALES, PYRONEMATACEAE
**arenosa** (Fuckel) S. Ahmad – SP

**Gloniopsis** De Not.
HYSTERIALES, HYSTERIACEAE
**praelonga** (Schwein.) Underw. & Earle – SP

**Gnomonia** Ces. & de Not.
DIAPORTHALES, VALSACEAE
**cerastis** (Riess) Ces. & de Not. – ED

**Gnomoniella** Sacc.
DIAPORTHALES, VALSACEAE
**tubiformis** (Tode) Sacc. – ED

**Graddonidiscus** Raitv. & R. Galán
HELOTIALES, HYALOSCYPHACEAE
**coruscatus** (Graddon) Raitv. & R. Galán (=*Dasyscyphus coruscatus* Graddon) – ED

**Helminthosporium** Link
PLEOSPORALES, PLEOMASSARIACEAE
**velutinum** Link – ED

**Helvella** L.
PEZIZALES, HELVELLACEAE
**crispa** (Scop.) Fr. – SV, WN
**lacunosa** Afz. – ED, Sheepwash Park (SO9791)

▲ *Helvella lacunosa*

*Hyalopeziza* Fuckel
HELOTIALES, HYALOSCYPHACEAE
*ciliata* Fuckel – ED
*millepunctata* (Lib.) Raitv. (=*Unguicularia millepunctata* (Lib.) Dennis) – ED, SP

*Hyaloscypha* Boud.
HELOTIALES, HYALOSCYPHACEAE
*albohyalina* var. *albohyalina*
(P. Karst.) Boud. (= *H. lectissima* (P. Karst.) Raitv.)
– SV
*herbarum* Velen. – SV
*hyalina* (Pers.) Boud. – ED, MO, SP, SV
*leuconica* var. *leuconica* (Cooke) Nannf.
– SP
*paludosa* Dennis – SP

*Hymenoscyphus* Gray
HELOTIALES, HELOTIACEAE
*calyculus* (Sow.) Phill. – ED, SV
*caudatus* (P. Karsten) Dennis – ED, GP, SP, SV
*fagineus* (Pers.) Dennis – ED
*fructigenus* (Bull.) Gray – ED, LP, GP, SV
*imberbis* (Bull.) Dennis – ED, GP, SV
*phyllogenus* (Rehm) O. Kuntze – ED, GP, SP
*repandus* (Phill.) Dennis – ED, SP
*rhodoleucus* (Fr.) Phill. – ED
*rokebyensis* (Svrèek) Matheis – ED
*salicellus* (Fr.) Dennis – MO
*scutula* (Pers.) Phill. – ED, GP, MO, SP, SV
*vernus* (Boud.) Dennis – ED, GP

*Hypocrea* Fr.
HYPOCREALES, HYPOCREACEAE
*pulvinata* Fuckel – ED, SP, SV, WB
*rufa* (Pers.) Fr. – ED, SV
*schweinitzii* (Fr.) Sacc. (Anamorph:
*Trichoderma viride* Pers. *fide* Dingley) – ED

*Hypoderma* De Not.
RHYTISMATALES,
RHYTISMATACEAE
*rubi* (Pers.) DC. – SV

*Hypomyces* (Fr.) Tul.
HYPOCREALES, HYPOCREACEAE
*chrysospermus* Tul. & C. Tul. – LP, SV
*rosellus* (Alb. & Schw.) Tul. – ED

*Hypoxylon* Bull.
XYLARIALES, XYLARIACEAE
*fragiforme* (Scop.) Kickx – ED, LP, SV
*fuscum* (Pers.) Fr. – SP, SV
*howeanum* Peck – SP
*multiforme* (Fr.) Fr. – BA, ED, SP, SV
*nummularium* Bull. – LP, WN
*rubiginosum* (Pers.) Fr. – ED, SP

*Incrucipulum* Baral
HELOTIALES, HYALOSCYPHACEAE
*ciliare* (Schrad.) Baral (=*Dasyscyphus ciliaris*
(Schrad.) Sacc.) – ED, SP
*sulphurellum* (Peck) Baral (=*Dasyscyphus sulphurellus* (Peck) Sacc.) – SV

*Incrupila* Raitv.
HELOTIALES, HYALOSCYPHACEAE
*viridipilosa* Graddon – ED

*Iodophanus* Korf
PEZIZALES, PEZIZACEAE
*carneus* (Pers.) Korf – SP

*Kretzschmaria* Fr.
XYLARIALES, XYLARIACEAE
*deusta* (Hoffm.) P.M.D. Martin (=*Ustulina deusta*
(Hoffm.) Lind) – ED, LP, SV, WB, WN

*Lachnum* Retz.
HELOTIALES, HYALOSCYPHACEAE
*apalum* (Berk. & Broome) Nannf. – SP
*brevipilosum* Baral – ED, MO, SV
*carneolum* (Sacc.) Rehm – ED, GP, SV
*carneolum* var. *longisporum* (Dennis)
Spooner ined. – ED, SV
*castaneicola* (Graddon) R. Galán – SP
*controversum* (Cooke) Rehm – ED
*diminutum* (Roberge ex Desm.) Rehm – ED,
GP, SP
*dumorum* (Roberge ex Desm.) Huhtinen – ED,
SP, SV
*niveum* (R. Hedw.) P. Karst. – ED, SV
*nudipes* (Fuckel) Nannf. – ED
*soppittii* (Massee) Raitv. – ED, SP
*virgineum* (Batsch) P. Karst. – ED, SP, SV

*Lanzia* Sacc.
HELOTIALES, RUTSTROEMIACEAE
*luteovirescens* (Rob. ex Desm.) Dumont & Korf –
ED, GP, SP, SV

*Lasiobelonium* Ellis & Everh.
HELOTIALES, HYALOSCYPHACEAE
*nidulum* (J.C. Schmidt & Kunze) Fr.
(=*Dasyscyphus nidulus* (Schm. & Kunze) Massee)
– ED

*Lasiosphaeria* Ces. & de Not.
SORDARIALES, LASIOSPHAERIACEAE
*ovina* (Pers.) Ces. & De Not. – SP, SV
*spermoides* (Hoffm.) Ces. & de Not. – ED,
SP, WB

*Leotia* Pers.
HELOTIALES, LEOTIACEAE
*lubrica* (Scop.) Pers. – SP

*Lepraria* Ach.
INCERTAE SEDIS, INCERTAE SEDIS
*incana* (L.) Ach. – ED, SV

*Leptosphaeria* Ces. & de Not.
PLEOSPORALES, LEPTOSPHAERIACEAE
*acuta* (Hoffm.) P. Karsten – ED, SV
*doliolum* (Pers.) Ces. & De Not. – SV

*Leptotrochila* P. Karst.
HELOTIALES, DERMATEACEAE
*ranunculi* (Fr.) Schüepp – SV, WB

*Leucoscypha* Boud.
PEZIZALES, PYRONEMATACEAE
*erminea* (E. Bommer & M. Rousseau) Boud. – SP

*Lichenopeltella* Höhn.
MICROTHYRIALES, MICROTHYRIACEAE
*alpestris* (Sacc.) P.M. Kirk & Minter – ED
*nigroannulata* (J. Webster) P.M. Kirk & Minter
– ED

*Melanomma* Nitschke ex Fuckel
PLEOSPORALES, MELANOMMATACEAE
*pulvis-pyrius* (Pers.) Fuckel – SP

*Melanopsammella* Höhn.
SORDARIALES, CHAETOSPHAERIACEAE
*preussii* (W. Gams & Hol.-Jech.) Réblová, M.E. Barr &
Samuels (= *Chaetosphaeria preussii* W. Gams &
Hol.-Jech.) – ED
*vermicularioides* (Sacc. & Roum.) Réblová,
M.E. Barr & Samuels (= *Chaetosphaeria
vermicularioides* (Sacc. & Roum.) W. Gams & Hol.-
Jech. Anamorph: *Chloridium virescens* (Pers.)
W. Gams & Hol.-Jech.) – ED

*Melastiza* Boud.
PEZIZALES, HUMARIACEAE
*chateri* (W.G. Sm.) Boud. – GP

*Menispora* Pers.
CHAETOSPHAERIALES,
CHAETOSPHAERIACEAE
*ciliata* Corda – ED, SV

*Micropodia* Boud.
HELOTIALES, HELOTIACEAE
*pteridina* (Nyl.) Boud. – ED, SP

*Microscypha* Syd. & P. Syd.
HELOTIALES, HYALOSCYPHACEAE
*grisella* (Rehm) Syd. & P. Syd. – SP

*Microsphaera* Lév.
ERYSIPHALES, ERYSIPHACEAE
*alphitoides* Griffon & Maubl. – LP, WB, WN
*sparsa* Howe – WB

*Microthyrium* Desm.
MICROTHYRIALES, MICROTHYRIACEAE
*ciliatum* var. *ciliatum* Gremmen & De Kam
– ED
*microscopicum* Desm. – ED, SP, SV

*Mitrophora* Lev.
PEZIZALES, MORCHELLACEAE
*semilibera* (DC.) Léèv. – WN

*Mitrula* Fr.
HELOTIALES, HELOTIACEAE
*paludosa* Fr. – SP

*Mollisia* (Fr.) P. Karsten
HELOTIALES, DERMATEACEAE
*amenticola* (Sacc.) Rehm – GP, SV

Chapter 5 · Fungi

*caricina* Fautrey – SV
*chionea* Massee & Crossl. – SV
*cinerea* (Batsch) P. Karsten – ED, MO, SP, SV
*juncina* (Pers.) Rehm – ED
*ligni* (Desm.) P. Karsten – ED, SP
*melaleuca* (Fr.) Sacc. – ED, SV
*rehmii* Sacc. – SP

**Mollisina** Höhnel
HELOTIALES, HYALOSCYPHACEAE
*acerina* (Mouton) Höhnel – ED
*rubi* (Rehm) Höhnel – ED, SP, SV

**Mollisiopsis** Rehm
HELOTIALES, DERMATEACEAE
*dennisii* Graddon – SP

**Monilinia** Honey
HELOTIALES, SCLEROTINIACEAE
*fructigena* Honey ex Whetzel – ED

**Morchella** Dill. ex Pers.
PEZIZALES, MORCHELLACEAE
*elata* Fr. – ED, Brades Hall (SO9890),
Highfields School (SO8896), Tamebridge
Industrial Estate (SP0295)
*esculenta* (L.) Pers. – BE, SV, WN
*vulgaris* (Pers.) Boud. – Black Lake Area
(SO9992), Sheepwash Park (SO9792)

**Morenoina** Theiss.
INCERTAE SEDIS, ASTERINACEAE
*pteridicola* J.P. Ellis – ED

**Mycosphaerella** Johanson
MYCOSPHAERELLALES,
MYCOSPHAERELLACEAE
*tulasnei* (Janczewski) Lindau – ED

**Myriosclerotinia** N.F. Buchw.
HELOTIALES, SCLEROTINIACEAE
*curreyana* (Berk. ex Curr.) N.F. Buchw. – SP

**Myrothecium** Tode
HYPOCREALES, INCERTAE SEDIS
*masonii* M.C. Tulloch – ED

**Naemospora** Roth ex Kuntze
INCERTAE SEDIS, INCERTAE SEDIS
*croceola* Sacc. – HW

**Nectria** (Fr.) Fr.
HYPOCREALES, NECTRIACEAE
*cinnabarina* (Tode) Fr. – BA, ED, LP, LW, MO,
MR, MW, PN, SP, SV, WN, Temple Bar Goods
Station (SO9698), Wigginsmill Road (SO9794)
*coccinea* (Pers.) Fr. – ED
*episphaeria* (Tode) Fr. – HW, SV
*peziza* (Tode) Fr. – LP

**Nemania** Gray
XYLARIALES, XYLARIACEAE
*effusa* (Nitschke) Pouzar – ED
*serpens* **var.** *serpens* (Pers.) Gray – ED

**Neobulgaria** Petr.
HELOTIALES, HELOTIACEAE
*pura* **var.** *pura* (Fr.) Petr. – ED

**Niptera** Fr.
HELOTIALES, DERMATEACEAE
*melanophaea* Rehm – ED
*pilosa* (Crossl.) Boud. – ED

**Ombrophila** Fr.
HELOTIALES, HELOTIACEAE
*violacea* (Hedw.) Fr. – ED

**Ophiostoma** Syd. & P. Syd.
OPHIOSTOMATALES,
OPHIOSTOMATACEAE
*ulmi* (Buisman) Nannf. – ED

**Orbilia** Fr.
ORBILIALES, ORBILIACEAE
*alnea* Velen. – ED
*auricolor* (A. Bloxam ex Berk.) Sacc. – ED, MO
*curvatispora* Boud. – ED
*leucostigma* (Fr.) Fr. – SP, SV
*rectispora* (Boud.) Baral – SV
*xanthostigma* (Fr.) Fr. – ED, MO, SP, SV

**Otidea** (Pers.) Bonord.
PEZIZALES, PYRONEMATACEAE
*bufonia* (Pers.) Boud. – SV

**Pachyella** Boud.
PEZIZALES, PEZIZACEAE
*babingtonii* (Berk. & Broome) Boud. – ED

**Paecilomyces** Bainier
EUROTIALES, TRICHOCOMACEAE
*farinosus* (Holmsk.) A.H.S. Br. & G. Sm. – ED, SV

**Penicillium** Link
EUROTIALES, TRICHOCOMACEAE
*brevicompactum* Dierckx – SP
*claviforme* Bainier – ED

**Periconia** Tode
INCERTAE SEDIS, INCERTAE SEDIS
*byssoides* Pers. – ED
*cookei* E.W. Mason & M.B. Ellis – SV
*digitata* (Cooke) Sacc. – ED
*minutissima* Corda – ED

**Pezicula** Tul. & C. Tul.
HELOTIALES, DERMATEACEAE
*amoena* Tul. & C. Tul. – ED
*livida* (Berk. & Broome) Rehm – SP
*myrtillina* P. Karst. – SP
*scoparia* (Cooke) Dennis – SP

**Peziza** Fr.
PEZIZALES, PEZIZACEAE
*badia* Pers. – BA, SP
*cerea* Sowerby – GP, SP
*echinospora* P. Karst. – SP
*limnaea* Maas Geest. – SP

*micropus* Pers. – ED, SP, SV
*petersii* Berk. – ED
*praetervisa* Bres. – SP
*repanda* Pers. – ED, SP, SV, Merecroft Pool
(SP0478)
*varia* (Hedw.) Fr. – MG
*vesiculosa* Bull. – HW, SV

**Pezizella** Fuckel
HELOTIALES, HELOTIACEAE
*alniella* (Nyl.) Dennis – ED, GP
*discreta* (P. Karsten) Dennis – GP
*eriophori* Dennis – SP
*fagi* (Jaap) Matheis – ED
*punctoidea* (P. Karst.) Rehm – SP
*rubescens* Mouton – ED, GP, SP, SV
*turgidella* (P. Karst.) Sacc. – ED

**Phacellium** Bonord.
MYCOSPHAERELLALES,
MYCOSPHAERELLACEAE
*carneum* (Oudem.) U. Braun (=*Isariopsis carnea*
Oudem.) – WB

**Phaeohelotium** Kanouse
HELOTIALES, HELOTIACEAE
*geogenum* (Cooke) Svrèek & Matheis – ED,
MO, SV
*lilacinum* (Bres.) Dennis – ED
*trabinellum* (P. Karst.) Dennis – ED

**Phialina** Höhnel
HELOTIALES, HYALOSCYPHACEAE
*flaveola* (Cooke) Raitv. (= *Hyaloscypha*
*flaveola* (Cooke) Nannf.) – ED
*lachnobrachya* (Desm.) Raitv. – ED, SV
*pseudopuberla* (Graddon) Raitv. – ED, GP, SV

**Phomatospora** Sacc.
XYLARIALES, INCERTAE SEDIS
*dinemasporium* J. Webster – ED

**Phyllachora** Nitschke ex Fuckel
PHYLLACHORALES,
PHYLLACHORACEAE
*graminis* **var.** *graminis* (Pers.) Fuckel – SV
*junci* (Alb. & Schwein.) Fuckel – SP

**Phyllactinia** Lév.
ERYSIPHALES, ERYSIPHACEAE
*guttata* (Wallr.) Lév. – ED
*mali* (Duby) U. Braun – ED

**Plagiostoma** Fuckel
DIAPORTHALES, VALSACEAE
*inclinatum* (Desm.) M.E. Barr – ED

**Plicaria** Fuckel
PEZIZALES, PEZIZACEAE
*carbonaria* Fuckel – ED

**Ploettnera** Henn.
HELOTIALES, DERMATEACEAE
*exigua* (Niessl) Höhn. – ED

*Flora of Birmingham and the Black Country* 183

▲ *Sarcoscypha austriaca*

▲ *Xylaria polymorpha*

***Podosphaera*** Kunze
ERYSIPHALES, ERYSIPHACEAE
***fusca*** (Fr.) U. Braun & Shishkoff – ED

***Polydesmia*** Boud.
HELOTIALES, HYALOSCYPHACEAE
***pruinosa*** (Gerd. ex Berk. & Broome) Boud. – ED, MO, SP, SV

***Proliferodiscus*** J.H. Haines & Dumont
HELOTIALES, HYALOSCYPHACEAE
***pulveraceus*** (Alb. & Schw.) Baral – MO

***Pseudocercospora*** Speg.
MYCOSPHAERELLALES,
MYCOSPHAERELLACEAE
***rubi*** (Sacc.) Deighton – WB

***Pseudolachnea*** Ranoj.
INCERTAE SEDIS, INCERTAE SEDIS
***hispidula*** (Schrad.) B. Sutton – SP

***Pseudopeziza*** Fuckel
HELOTIALES, DERMATEACEAE
***trifolii*** (Biv.) Fuckel – ED, SP

***Psilachnum*** Höhn.
HELOTIALES, HYALOSCYPHACEAE
***chrysostigmum*** (Fr.) Raitv. – ED
***eburneum*** (Roberge) Baral – ED
***inquilinum*** (P. Karst.) Dennis – ED, SP

***Pulvinula*** Boud.
PEZIZALES, PYRONEMATACEAE
***convexella*** (P. Karst.) Pfister – SV

***Pycnostysanus*** Lindau
INCERTAE SEDIS, INCERTAE SEDIS
***azaleae*** (Peck) E.W. Mason – SP

***Pyrenopeziza*** Fuckel
HELOTIALES, DERMATEACEAE
***compressula*** Rehm – SP
***digitalina*** (Phill.)Sacc. – ED
***escharodes*** (Berk. & Br.) Rehm – ED
***lychnidis*** (Sacc.) Rehm – ED
***lycopincola*** (Rehm) Boud. – ED
***mercurialis*** (Fuckel) Boud. – ED
***pastinacae*** (Nannf.) Gremmen – ED
***revincta*** (P. Karsten) Gremmen – ED
***rubi*** (Fr.) Rehm – ED
***urticicola*** (Phill.) Boud. – ED

***Pyronema*** Carus
PEZIZALES, PYRONEMATACEAE
***domesticum*** (Sowerby) Sacc. – ED

***Quaternaria*** Tul. & C. Tul.
XYLARIALES, DIATRYPACEAE
***quaternata*** (Pers.) J. Schröt. – ED

***Ramsbottomia*** W.D. Buckley
PEZIZALES, PYRONEMATACEAE
***asperior*** (Nyl.) Benkert & T. Schumach. – SV

***Ramularia*** Unger
MYCOSPHAERELLALES,
MYCOSPHAERELLACEAE
***purpurascens*** G. Winter – MG

***Rhytisma*** Fr.
RHYTISMATALES, RHYTISMATACEAE
***acerinum*** (Pers.) Fr. – BA, ED, GG, LP, LW, MO, MR, MW, QU, SO, SV, WN

***Rosellinia*** De Not.
XYLARIALES, XYLARIACEAE
***aquila*** (Fr.) De Not. – ED, GG, SV
***thelena*** (Fr.) Rabenh. – SV

***Rutstroemia*** P. Karst.
HELOTIALES, RUTSTROEMIACEAE
***conformata*** (P. Karst.) Nannf. – ED
***firma*** P. Karst. – SP
***fruticeti*** Rehm – ED
***petiolorum*** (Roberge ex Desm.) W.L. White – ED
***sydowiana*** (Rehm) W.L. White – ED, SP, SV

***Sarcoscypha*** (Fr.) Boud.
PEZIZALES, SARCOSCYPHACEAE
***austriaca*** (O. Beck ex Sacc.) Boud. – ED, MG, Park Hall Reserve (SP1590)

***Schizothecium*** Corda
SORDARIALES, LASIOSPHAERIACEAE
***vesticola*** (Berk. & Broome) N. Lundq. – SP

***Sclerotinia*** Fuckel
HELOTIALES, SCLEROTINIACEAE
***sclerotiorum*** (Lib.) de Bary – ED

***Scutellinia*** (Cooke) Lambotte
PEZIZALES, PYRONEMATACEAE
***crinita*** (Bull.) Lambotte – ED
***scutellata*** (L.) Lambotte – ED, MO, SP, SV, WB

***Scutoscypha*** Graddon
HELOTIALES, HYALOSCYPHACEAE
***fagi*** Graddon – SP, MO, SV

***Sordaria*** Ces. & De Not.
SORDARIALES, SORDARIACEAE
***humana*** (Fuckel) G. Winter – SP

***Sphaerosporella*** (Svrèek) Svrèek & Kubicka
PEZIZALES, PYRONEMATACEAE
***brunnea*** (Alb. & Schwein.) Svrcek & Kubicka – ED

***Sphaerotheca*** Lév.
ERYSIPHALES, ERYSIPHACEAE
***epilobii*** (Link) de Bary – WB
***pannosa*** (Wallr.) Lév. – ED
***plantaginis*** (Castagne) L. Junell – WB

***Sporidesmiella*** P.M. Kirk
INCERTAE SEDIS, INCERTAE SEDIS
***hyalosperma* var. *hyalosperma*** (Corda) P.M. Kirk – ED

**Sporormiella** Ellis & Everh.
DOTHIDIALES, SPORMORMIACEAE
**megalospora** (Auersw.) S.I. Ahmed & Cain – WN

**Symplectromyces** Thaxter
LABOULENIALES, LABOULENIACEAE
**vulgaris** (Thaxter) Thaxter – Manor Farm
(SP0280)

**Tapesia** (Pers.) Fuckel
HELOTIALES, DERMATEACEAE
**fusca** (Pers.) Fuckel – ED, SP
**lividofusca** (Fr.) Rehm – SP

**Tarzetta** (Cooke) Lambotte
PEZIZALES, PYRONEMATACEAE
**catinus** (Holmsk.) Korf & J.K. Rogers – SP

**Torula** Pers.
INCERTAE SEDIS, INCERTAE SEDIS
**herbarum** (Pers.) Link – ED, SV

**Trichodelitschia** Munk
PLEOSPORALES, PHAEOTRICHACEAE
**bisporula** (P. Crouan & H. Crouan) N. Lundq. – SP

**Trichodiscus** Kirschst.
HELOTIALES, DERMATEACEAE
**virescentulus** (Mouton) Dennis – ED

**Trichoglossum** Boud.
HELOTIALES, GEOGLOSSACEAE
**hirsutum var. hirsutum** (Pers.) Boud. – LP

**Trichophaea** Boud.
PEZIZALES, PYRONEMATACEAE
**hemisphaerioides** (Mouton) Graddon – SP
**woolhopeia** (Cooke & W. Phillips) Boud. – SP

**Trichothecium** Link
INCERTAE SEDIS, INCERTAE SEDIS
**roseum** (Pers.) Link – SV

**Trochila** Fr.
HELOTIALES, DERMATEACEAE
**ilicina** (Nees) Greenh. & Morgan-Jones – ED, SP, SV
**laurocerasi** (Desm.) Fr. – GP, ED

**Tympanis** Tode
HELOTIALES, HELOTIACEAE
**conspersa** (Fr.) Fr. – SP

**Valsa** Fr.
DIAPORTHALES, VALSACEAE
**abietis** Fr. – SP

**Venturiocistella** Raitv.
HELOTIALES, HYALOSCYPHACEAE
**heterotricha** (Graddon) Baral (= *Trichodiscus heterotrichus* Graddon) – SP

**Verpa** Sw.
PEZIZALES, MORCHELLACEAE
**conica** (O.F. Müll.) Sw. – SV

**Verticillium** Nees
HYPOCREALES, INCERTAE SEDIS
**lecanii** (Zimm.) Viégas – SP

**Volutella** Fr.
HYPOCREALES, NECTRIACEAE
**ciliata** (Alb. & Schwein.) Fr. – ED

**Wettsteinina** Höhn.
PLEOSPORALES, PLEOSPORACEAE
**niesslii** E. Müll. – ED

**Xylaria** Hill ex Schrank
XYLARIALES, XYLARIACEAE
**carpophila** (Pers.) Fr. – ED
**filiformis** (Alb. & Schwein.) Fr. – ED
**hypoxylon** (L.) Grev. – BA, ED, GP, HW, LP, MG, MO, MR, MW, RW, SP, SV, WN, and many other sites
**longipes** Nitschke – LP
**polymorpha** (Pers.) Grev. – ED, LP, MO, MW, RH, SV, WB, WN

## TAPHRINOMYCETES

**Taphrina** Fr.
TAPHRINALES, TAPHRINACEAE
**padi** (Jacz.) Mix – College Farm (SK0300)
**populni** Fr. – Park Street Gardens (SP0786)
**pruni** Tul. – SV, Sheepwash Park (SO9791)
**tosquinetii** (Westend.) Magnus – SP

## BASIDIOMYCOTA
## BASIDIOMYCETES

**Agaricus** L.
AGARICALES, AGARICACEAE
**arvensis** Schaeff. – MG, MR, SV, WN, Yardley (SP1285)

**augustus** Fr. – BB, ED
**bisporus** (J.E. Lange) Imbach – ED, SV
**bitorquis** (Quel) Sacc. – HW
**campestris** L. – ED, PD, PN, SV, Kingstanding (SP0794)
**comtulus** Fr. – ED, PD
**impudicus** (Rea) Pilát – QU
**langei** (F.H. Møller) F.H. Møller – ED, PD
**osecanus** Pilát (=*A. nivescens* (F.H. Møller) F.H. Møller) – ED, QU
**porphyrocephalus** F.H. Møller – SP
**pseudovillaticus** Rauschert (=*A. vaporarius* (Pers.) Cappelli) – ED
**silvaticus** Schaeff. – ED, HH, QU, SP
**silvicola** (Vittad.) Peck – SV
**xanthodermus** Genev. – MW, QU, SV

**Agrocybe** Fayod
AGARICALES, BOLBITIACEAE
**arvalis** (Fr.) Singer – LP
**erebia** (Fr.) Singer – ED
**pediades** (Fr.) Fayod (=*A. semiorbicularis* Bull.) – ED
**praecox** (Pers.) Fayod – ED, PD, SP, SV
**putaminum** (Maire) Singer – LP
**vervacti** (Fr.) Singer – MO

**Amanita** Pers.
AGARICALES, AMANITACEAE
**citrina** (Schaeff.) Pers. – ED, SP
**crocea** (Quel.) Singer – Harborne Road (SP0585)
**excelsa** (Fr.) Bertill. – MO, SV
**fulva** (Schaeff.) Fr. – ED, MR, QU, SO, SP, SV, WB
**muscaria** (L.) Lam. – ED, GP, HW, LG, LP, MO, RH, SO, SP, SV, TW, WB, and many other sites
**pantherina** (DC.) Krombh. – Grand Union Canal (SP1283), Oscott College (SP0994)
**phalloides** (Fr.) Link – ED

▲ *Amanita crocea*

▲ *Armillaria mellea*

▲ *Auricularia auricula-judae*

▲ *Coprinus comatus*

**rubescens** Pers. – BA, ED, GP, MO, MR, PN, QU, RH, SP, SV, SW, TW, and many other sites
**vaginata** (Bull.) Lam. – SP

**Ampulloclitocybe** Redhead
AGARICALES, TRICHOLOMATACEAE
**clavipes** (Pers.) Redhead (=*Clitocybe clavipes* (Pers.) P. Kumm.) – BA, ED, LP, SP

**Antrodia** P. Karst.
POLYPORALES, MERIPILACEAE
**xantha** (Fr.) Ryvarden – SP

**Armillaria** (Fr.) Staude
AGARICALES, TRICHOLOMATACEAE
**gallica** Marxm. & Romagn. – ED, PD, SV
**mellea** (Vahl) P. Kumm. – BA, ED, HW, LP, MO, MW, SP, SV, TW, WN, and many other sites
**ostoyae** (Romagn.) Herink – ED, QU

**Arrhenia** Fr.
AGARICALES, TRICHOLOMATACEAE
**acerosa** (Fr.) Kühner – ED
**retiruga** (Bull.) Redhead – ED, QU

**Athelia** Pers.
POLYPORALES, ATHELIACEAE
**epiphylla** Pers. – SP

**Auricularia** Bull.
AURICULARIALES, AURICULARIACEAE
**auricula-judae** (Bull.) Wettst. – BA, ED, LP, MG, MO, MR, MW, SP, SV, SW, WB, WG, WK, WN, and many other sites
**mesenterica** (Dicks.) Pers. – ED, LP, SV

**Bjerkandera** P. Karst.
PORIALES, CORIOLACEAE
**adusta** (Willd.) P. Karst. – ED, GP, HW, LP, MG, MO, MR, SP, SV, WB, WN

**Bolbitius** Fr.
AGARICALES, BOLBITIACEAE
**reticulatus** (Pers.) Ricken (=*B. aleuriatus* (Fr.) Singer) – ED, SV
**titubans** (Bull.) Fr. (=*B. vitellinus* (Pers.) Fr.) – ED, LP, SP, SV

**Boletus** Fr.
BOLETALES, BOLETACEAE
**appendiculatus** Schaeff. – ED
**badius** (Fr.) Fr. – ED, GP, MO, SP, SV
**chrysenteron** Bull. – BA, ED, GP, HW, LP, MO, SP, SV, WN, Rectory Park (SP1296)
**cisalpinus** (Simonini, H. Ladurner & Peintner) Watling & A.E. Hills – QU
**edulis** Bull. – ED, GP, HW, LP, SP, SV
**fragrans** Vittad. – SP
**impolitus** Fr. – WB, Moat Farm (SK0204)
**luridiformis** Rostk. (=*Boletus erythropus* Pers.) – ED, MO, SP, SV
**porosporus** G. Moreno & Bon – PD
**pruinatus** Fr. & Hök – ED, SP
**pulverulentus** Opat. – BA, HW

**queletii** Schulzer – QU
**rubellus** Krombh. – ED, SV
**subtomentosus** L. – ED, GP, SP, SV

**Bovista** Pers.
AGARICALES, LYCOPERDACEAE
**nigrescens** Pers. – SP
**plumbea** Pers. – QU, SV, WN

**Byssomerulius** Parmasto
STEREALES, MERULIACEAE
**corium** (Pers.) Parmasto – ED, HW, MW, SV

**Calocera** Fr.
DACRYMYCETALES, DACRYMYCETACEAE
**cornea** (Batsch) Fr. – ED, LP, MO, SP, SV, WN
**pallidospathulata** D.A. Reid – ED
**viscosa** (Pers.) Fr. – SP, SW

**Calocybe** Donk
AGARICALES, TRICHOLOMATACEAE
**carnea** (Bull.) Donk – ED, HW
**gambosa** (Fr.) Donk – SV, Hagley Road (SP0486), Cannonhill Park (SP0683)

**Calvatia** Fr.
AGARICALES, LYCOPERDACEAE
**gigantea** (Batsch) Lloyd – ED, HH, SP, SV, WG, Minworth Sewage Works (SP1892), Queen Street Cemetery (SP0097)

**Calyptella** Quél.
AGARICALES, TRICHOLOMATACEAE
**capula** (Holmsk.) Quél. – ED, GP, SP, SV

**Chalciporus** Bataille
BOLETALES, STROBILOMYCETACEAE
**piperatus** (Bull.) Bataille – ED, HW, SP, SV

**Chondrostereum** Pouzar
STEREALES, MERULIACEAE
**purpureum** (Pers.) Pouzar – ED, LG, MG, MW, SP, SV, WG, WN

**Clathrus** Pers.
PHALLALES, CLATHRACEAE
**ruber** Pers. – PD

**Clavaria** Fr.
AGARICALES, CLAVARIACEAE
**argillacea** Pers. – SP
**fragilis** Holmsk. – LP, QU, SV
**fumosa** Pers. – LP

**Clavariadelphus** Donk
CANTHARELLALES, CLAVARIADELPHACEAE
**pistillaris** (L.) Donk – Rubery (SO9978)

**Clavulina** J. Schröt.
CANTHARELLALES, CLAVULINACEAE
**cinerea** (Bull.) J. Schröt. – ED, SP, SV
**coralloides** (L.) J. Schröt. (=*Clavulina cristata* (Holmsk.) J. Schröt.) – ED, SV
**rugosa** (Bull.) J. Schröt. – ED, GP, LP, SP, SV

***Clavulinopsis*** Overeem
CANTHARELLALES, CLAVARIACEAE
***corniculata*** (Fr.) Corner – ED, LP, QU, SV,
Merecroft Pool (SP0478)
***fusiformis*** (Sowerby) Corner – ED
***helvola*** (Pers.) Corner – ED, LP, SP, SV
***laeticolor*** (Berk. & M.A. Curtis) R.H. Petersen – QU
***luteoalba*** (Rea) Corner – LP, QU, RH, SV
***umbrinella*** (Sacc.) Corner – QU

***Clitocybe*** (Fr.) Staude
AGARICALES, TRICHOLOMATACEAE
***americana*** H.E. Bigelow – PD
***brumalis*** (Fr.) Gillet – SP
***diatreta*** (Fr.) P. Kumm. – SP
***fragrans*** (With.) P. Kumm. – ED, GP, PD, SP, SV,
WN
***geotropa*** (Bull.) Quel. – LP, MG, WN
***gibba*** (Pers.) P. Kumm. (=*Clitocybe
infundibuliformis* (Schaeff.) Quél.) – ED, HH, HW,
LP, MR, SV, WG
***metachroa*** (Fr.) P. Kumm. – ED, SP
***nebularis*** (Batsch) P. Kumm. – ED, GP, HW, LP,
PD, QU, RW, SP, SV, WN
***odora*** (Bull.) P. Kumm. – LP, SP, SV
***phyllophila*** (Pers.) P. Kumm. – ED, GP, SP, WN
***rivulosa*** (Pers.) P. Kumm. – PD, SV, WG,
Bustleholme Lane (SP0194)
***vibecina*** (Fr.) Quél. – SP, SV

***Clitopilus*** (Fr. ex Rabenh.) P. Kumm.
AGARICALES, ENTOLOMATACEAE
***prunulus*** (Scop.) P. Kumm. – HW, QU, SP, WB

***Collybia*** (Fr.) Staude
AGARICALES, TRICHOLOMATACEAE
***acervata*** (Fr.) P. Kumm. – SP
***butyracea*** (Bull.) P. Kumm. – BR, ED, GP, LG,
LP, MO, MR, PD, RW, SP, SV, WG, Sheepwash
Park (SO9791)
***cirrhata*** (Pers.) Quél. – LP, SP
***confluens*** (Pers.) P. Kumm. – ED, LP, SO, SP, SV,
WN
***cookei*** (Bres.) J.D. Arnold – ED, SP
***dryophila*** (Bull.) P. Kumm. – ED, HH, MO, PD,
SP, SV, SW, WG
***erythropus*** (Pers.) P. Kumm – ED, MW, SV
***fusipes*** (Bull.) Quél. – ED, MO, RH, SP
***maculata*** (Alb. & Schwein.) P. Kumm. – ED, GP,
MO, SP, SV
***peronata*** (Bolton) P. Kumm. – ED, LP, MO, RH,
SP, SV, TW, WN

*Collybia peronata*
(by Neville Walters)

***Coniophora*** Mérat
BOLETALES, CONIOPHORACEAE
***puteana*** (Schumach.) P. Karst. – BA, MO, HW,
SP, WN

***Conocybe*** Fayod
AGARICALES, BOLBITIACEAE
***apala*** (Fr.) Arnolds (=*Conocybe lactea* (J.E.
Lange) Métrod) – ED, PD
***arrhenii*** (Fr.) Kits van Wav. – PD
***filaris*** (Fr.) Kühner – ED
***juniana*** (Velen.) Hauskn. & Svrèek (=*Conocybe
magnicapitata* P.D. Orton) – ED, PD
***mesospora*** Kühner & Watling – QU
***percincta*** P.D. Orton – ED, SV
***pulchella*** (Velen.) Hauskn. & Svrèek – ED
***siliginea*** (Fr.) Kühner – PD, QU
***striaepes*** (Cooke) S. Lundell – PD
***subovalis*** Kühner & Watling – SV
***tenera*** (Schaeff.) Fayod – ED, SV, WN
***velata*** (Velen.) Watling – QU
***velutipes*** (Velen.) Hauskn. & Svrèek (= *Conocybe
kuehneriana* Singer) – ED

***Coprinus*** Pers.
AGARICALES, COPRINACEAE
***acuminatus*** (Romagn.) P.D. Orton – PD
***atramentarius*** (Bull.) Fr. – ED, HW, LP, MW,
PD, SV, TW, WG, WN, Wigginsmill Road
(SO9794)
***auricomus*** Pat. – LP
***comatus*** (O.F. Müll.) Pers. – BA, ED, GG, GP,
MO, MR, MW, PD, PN, SP, SV, WG, WN, and
many other sites
***congregatus*** (Bull.) Fr. – SV
***disseminatus*** (Pers.) Gray – ED, LP, MO, MW,
PD, QU, SP, SV
***domesticus*** (Bolton) Gray – WB
***impatiens*** (Fr.) Quél. – ED
***jonesii*** Peck (Mis.: *Coprinus lagopides* sensu
auct. Mult.) – ED, SP
***kuehneri*** Uljé & Bas – QU
***lagopus*** (Fr.) Fr. – ED, QU, SP, SV
***leiocephalus*** P.D. Orton – ED, PD, QU
***macrocephalus*** (Berk.) Berk. – Wigginsmill
Road (SO9794)
***micaceus*** (Bull.) Fr. – BA, ED, GP, HH, HW, LP,
MO, MR, MW, QU, SP, SV, SW, TW, WB, WN
***miser*** P. Karst. – ED
***narcoticus*** (Batsch) Fr. – SP
***niveus*** (Pers.) Fr. – SV
***picaceus*** (Bull.) Gray – SV
***plicatilis*** (Curtis) Fr. – ED, PD, PN, SP, SV, WN,
Wigginsmill Road (SO9794)
***radians*** (Desm.) Fr. – ED
***saccharomyces*** P.D. Orton – SP
***silvaticus*** Peck. – ED
***stercoreus*** Fr. – SP
***subdisseminatus*** M. Lange & A.H. Smith – PN
***truncorum*** (Schaeff.) Fr. – ED
***tuberosus*** Quél. – QU

***Cortinarius*** (Pers.) Gray
CORTINARIALES, CORTINARIACEAE

***acutus*** (Pers.) Fr. – SV
***alboviolaceus*** (Pers.) Fr. – SV, SW
***alnetorum*** (Velen.) M.M. Moser – GP
***anomalus*** (Fr.) Fr. – SP
***betuletorum*** M.M. Moser – SV
***bibulus*** Quél. – ED
***brunneus* var. *glandicolor*** (Fr.) H. Lindstr. &
Melot – SP, SV
***casimiri*** (Velen.) Huijsman – ED
***cinnamomeus*** (L.) Gray – SV
***croceoconus*** Fr. – SP
***decipiens*** (Pers.) Fr. – SP
***flexipes*** (Pers.) Fr. – QU, SP
***hemitrichus*** (Pers.) Fr. – ED, SP, SV
***largus* Fr.** – QU
***lucorum*** (Fr.) J.E. Lange – SV
***punctatus*** (Pers.) Fr. – SP
***sanguineus*** (Wulfen) Fr. – SP
***saniosus*** (Fr.) Fr. – PD, SV
***saturninus*** (Fr.) Fr. – ED
***semisanguineus*** (Fr.) Gillet – ED
***subbalaustinus*** Rob. Henry – ED
***trivialis*** J.E. Lange – SV
***uliginosus*** Berk. – ED
***umbrinolens*** P.D. Orton – ED, QU, SP, SV
***uraceus*** Fr. – ED, SP
***vernus*** H. Lindstr. & Melot – QU
***xanthocephalus*** P.D. Orton – ED

***Craterellus*** Pers.
CANTHARELLALES, CRATERELLACEAE
***cornucopioides*** (L.) Pers. – Queen Street
Cemetery (SP0097)

***Crepidotus*** (Fr.) Staude
CORTINARIALES, CREPIDOTACEAE
***carpaticus*** Pilát – MO
***epibryus*** (Fr.) Quél. – SV
***lundellii*** Pilát – PD, SV
***luteolus*** (Lambotte) Sacc. – SV, WN
***mollis*** (Schaeff.) Staude – ED, LP, WB
***variabilis*** (Pers.) P. Kumm. – ED, LG, LP, SP, SV,
WG, WN

***Crinipellis*** Pat.
AGARICALES, TRICHOLOMATACEAE
***scabella*** (Alb. & Schwein.) Murrill (=*Crinipellis
stipitaria* (Fr.) Pat.) – ED

***Crucibulum*** Tul. & C. Tul.
NIDULARIALES, NIDULARIACEAE
***laeve*** (Huds.) Kambly – SM

***Cyathus*** Haller
AGARICALES, NIDULARIACEAE
***olla*** (Batsch) Pers. – SM, SV, Bull Ring Area
(SP0786)
***striatus*** (Huds.) Pers. – SV, Birmingham Canal
(SO9493)

***Cylindrobasidium*** Jülich
STEREALES, HYPHODERMATACEAE
***laeve*** (Pers.) Chamuris (=*Cylindrobasidium
evolvens* (Fr.) Jülich) – ED

▲ *Flammulina velutipes*

▲ *Geastrum triplex*

▲ *Handkea excipuliformis*

▲ *Hericium erinaceus*

**Cyphellostereum** D.A. Reid
POLYPORALES, PODOSCYPHACEAE
*laeve* (Fr.) D.A. Reid – SV

**Cystoderma** Fayod
AGARICALES, AGARICACEAE
*amianthinum* (Scop.) Fayod – ED, SP

**Cystolepiota** Singer
AGARICALES, AGARICACEAE
*hetieri* (Boud.) Singer – SP
*sistrata* (Fr.) Singer – HH, SP, SV

**Dacrymyces** Nees
DACRYMYCETALES, DACRYMYCETACEAE
*stillatus* Nees – ED, HH, LP, MO, MW, SP, SV,
SW, WN

**Daedalea** Pers.
PORIALES, CORIOLACEAE
*quercina* (L.) Pers. – MO

**Daedaleopsis** J. Schröt.
PORIALES, CORIOLACEAE
*confragosa* (Bolton) J. Schröt. – BA, ED, GG,
GP, LP, MO, MR, MW, SO, SP, SV, SW, WB, WG,
Park Hall (SP1590)

**Datronia** Donk
PORIALES, CORIOLACEAE
*mollis* (Sommerf.) Donk – ED, LP, SV

**Delicatula** Fayod
AGARICALES, TRICHOLOMATACEAE
*integrella* (Pers.) Fayod – ED

**Dermoloma** (J.E. Lange) Singer
AGARICALES, TRICHOLOMATACEAE
*cuneifolium* (Fr.) Bon – ED

**Entoloma** (Fr.) P. Kumm.
AGARICALES, ENTOLOMATACEAE
*anatinum* (Lasch) Donk – WN
*clypeatum* (L.) P. Kumm. – SV, WB
*conferendum* (Britzelm.) Noordel. – ED, LP,
QU, SP, WN
*hirtipes* (Schumach.) M.M. Moser – SV, WN
*incanum* (Fr.) Hesler – SV
*infula* (Fr.) Noordel. – ED, QU
*juncinum* (Kühner & Romagn.) Noordel. – ED
*lucidum* (P.D. Orton) M.M. Moser – LP, WN
*minutum* (P. Karst.) Noordel. – ED, SP
*neglectum* (Lasch) Arnolds – SV
*ortonii* Arnolds & Noordel. – ED, LP, SP
*poliopus* **var.** *parvisporigerum* Noordel.
– QU
*politum* (Pers.) Donk – ED, SV
*rhodopolium* (Fr.) P. Kumm. – ED, MO, MW,
PD, SV
*sericatum* (Britzelm.) Sacc. – ED, MO
*sericellum* (Fr.) P. Kumm. – SP
*sericeum* (Bull.) Quél. – ED, GP, HW, LP, SP, SW
*sinuatum* (Pers.) P. Kumm. – SP
*sordidulum* (Kühner & Romagn.) P.D. Orton – ED, PD

*turbidum* (Fr.) Quél. – SP
*vernum* S. Lundell – ED

**Exidia** Fr.
TREMELLALES, EXIDIACEAE
*glandulosa* (Bull.) Fr. – BA, ED, LP
*nucleata* (Schwein.) Burt – ED, MO, SV
*thuretiana* (Lév.) Fr. – ED, MR, MW, SV, WN

**Faerberia** Pouzar
PORIALES, LENTINACEAE
*carbonaria* (Alb. & Schwein.) Pouzar – ED

**Fistulina** Bull.
FISTULINALES, FISTULINACEAE
*hepatica* (Schaeff.) With. – ED, MO, SP, SV

**Flammulaster** Earle
CORTINARIALES, CORTINARIACEAE
*carpophilus* **var.** *subincarnatus* (Joss. &
Kühner) Vellinga – ED

**Flammulina** P. Karst.
AGARICALES, TRICHOLOMATACEAE
*velutipes* (Curtis) Singer – BA, ED, MG, QU, SP,
SV, WN

**Fomes** (Fr.) Fr.
PORIALES, CORIOLACEAE
*fomentarius* (L.) J.J. Kickx – LP

**Galerina** Earle
CORTINARIALES, CORTINARIACEAE
*clavata* (Velen.) Kühner – ED, QU, SV
*hypnorum* (Schrank) Kühner – ED, SP
*laevis* (Pers.) Singer (=*Galerina graminea*
(Velen.) Kühner) – ED, PD
*mniophila* (Lasch) Kühner – ED
*paludosa* (Fr.) Kühner – SP
*pseudomycenopsis* Pilát – ED
*pumila* (Pers.) Singer – QU, SP
*subclavata* Kühner – ED
*vittiformis* (Fr.) Singer – QU

**Ganoderma** P. Karst.
GANODERMATALES,
GANODERMATACEAE
*applanatum* (Pers.) Pat – ED, MW, SP, SV
*australe* (Fr.) Pat. (=*Ganoderma adspersum*
(Schulzer) Donk) – ED, LP, MO, MR, SV, WB
*resinaceum* Boud. – SV

**Geastrum** Pers.
LYCOPERDALES, GEASTRACEAE
*rufescens* Pers. – HH, Whitworth Close,
Darlaston (SO9897)
*schmedelli* Vittad. – St. Mary's Churchyard,
Old Swinford (SO9083)
*triplex* Jungh. – BA, ED, HH, HW, MG, MW,
SV, WB, WN

**Grifola** Gray
PORIALES, CORIOLACEAE
*frondosa* (Dicks.) Gray – ED, GP, SP, SV

**Gymnopilus** P. Karst.
CORTINARIALES, CORTINARIACEAE
**fulgens** (J. Favre & Maire) Singer – SP
**hybridus** (Sowerby) Maire – SP
**junonius** (Fr.) P.D. Orton – ED, LW, MO, MR, SP, SV
**penetrans** (Fr.) Murrill – ED, HH, SP, SV
**sapineus** (Fr.) Maire – ED

**Handkea** Kreisel
LYCOPERDALES, LYCOPERDACEAE
**excipuliformis** (Scop.) Kreisel – BA, ED, HW, RH, SP, SV WG, WN, Sheepwash Park (SO9791)
**utriformis** (Bull.) Pers. – SV, WG, Rowley Hills (SO9789)

**Hebeloma** (Fr.) P. Kumm.
CORTINARIALES, CORTINARIACEAE
**anthracophilum** Maire – SP
**crustuliniforme** (Bull.) Quél. – ED, GP, HW, LP, PD, SP, SV
**leucosarx** P.D. Orton – GP, SP, SV
**mesophaeum** (Pers.) Quél. – ED, MO, PD, SP, SV
**pusillum** J.E. Lange – SV, SW
**sacchariolens** Quél. – ED, GP, QU, SP, SV

**Hemimycena** Singer
AGARICALES, TRICHOLOMATACEAE
**tortuosa** (P.D. Orton) Redhead – ED

**Henningsomyces** Kuntze
SCHIZOPHYLLALES, SCHIZOPHYLLACEAE
**candidus** (Pers.) Kuntze – ED, SV

**Hericium** Pers.
HERICIALES, HERICIACEAE
**erinaceus** (Bull.) Pers. – ED

**Heterobasidion** Bref.
RUSSULALES, BONDARZEWIACEAE
**annosum** (Fr.) Bref. – SP, TW

**Hohenbuehelia** Schulzer
AGARICALES, PLEUROTACEAE
**reniformis** (G. Mey.) Singer – SV

**Hygrocybe** (Fr.) P. Kumm.
AGARICALES, HYGROPHORACEAE
**calyptraeformis** (Berk.) Fayod – LP, MO
**ceracea** (Wulfen) P. Kumm. – LP, SV, WN
**chlorophana** (Fr.) Wünsche – LP, SV
**coccinea** (Schaeff.) P. Kumm. – LP
**colemannia** (A. Bloxam) P.D. Orton & Watling – SV, WN
**conica** (Schaeff.) P. Kumm. – ED, GP, LP, QU, SP, SV, WN
**flavipes** (Britzelm.) Arnolds – LP
**glutinipes** (J.E. Lange) R. Haller Aar. – QU
**helobia** (Arnolds) Bon – SV
**insipida** (J.E. Lange) M.M. Moser – QU, SP, SV
**irrigata** (Pers.) Bon – LP
**laeta** (Pers.) P. Kumm. – LP, SV

**marchii** (Bres.) Singer – SP
**miniata** (Fr.) P. Kumm. – LP, SP, SV
**mucronella** (Fr.) P. Karst. – LP
**pratensis** (Pers.) Murrill – BA, ED, LP, SV, WN
**psittacina** (Schaeff.) P. Kumm. – ED, LP, SP, SV, WN
**punicea** (Fr.) Kumm. – LP
**quieta** (Kühner) Singer – LP, QU, SP, SV
**russocoriacea** (Berk. & T.K. Mill.) P.D. Orton & Watling – LP, PD, WG, WN
**turunda** (Fr.) P. Karst. – LP, SP
**virginea** (Wulfen) P.D. Orton & Watling – BA, ED, LP, PD, QU, SP, SV, WN

**Hygrophoropsis** (J. Schröt.) Maire
BOLETALES, HYGROPHOROPSIDACEAE
**aurantiaca** (Wulfen) Maire – BA, SP, SV, SW

**Hygrophorus** Fr.
AGARICALES, HYGROPHORACEAE
**hypothejus** (Fr.) Fr. – SP

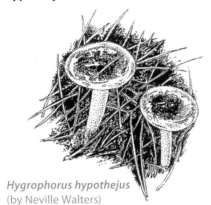

*Hygrophorus hypothejus*
(by Neville Walters)

**Hymenochaete** Lév.
HYMENOCHAETALES, HYMENOCHAETACEAE
**corrugata** (Fr.) Lév. – SP

**Hyphoderma** Wallr.
STEREALES, HYPHODERMATACEAE
**praetermissum** (P. Karst.) J. Erikss. & Å. Strid – ED
**puberum** (Fr.) Wallr. – ED
**setigerum** (Fr.) Donk – ED

**Hyphodontia** J. Erikss.
HYMENOCHAETALES, SCHIZOPORACEAE
**arguta** (Fr.) J. Erikss. – SP
**aspera** (Fr.) J. Erikss. – HW
**sambuci** (Pers.) J. Erikss. – ED, LP, MG, SV

**Hypholoma** (Fr.) P. Kumm.
AGARICALES, STROPHARIACEAE
**capnoides** (Fr.) P. Kumm. – ED
**elongatum** (Pers.) Ricken – ED, SP
**fasciculare** (Huds.) P. Kumm. – BB, ED, GP, HW, LP, MO, MR, MW, QU, SO, SP, SV, WB, WN, and many other sites
**lateritium** (Schaeff.) P. Kumm. (=*Hypholoma sublateritium* (Fr.) Quél.) – ED, SP
**myosotis** (Fr.) M. Lange – ED, SP
**subericaeum** (Fr.) Kühner – SP
**udum** (Pers.) Kühner – SP

**Hypochnicium** J. Erikss.
STEREALES, HYPHODERMATACEAE
**vellereum** (Ellis & Cragin) Parmasto – ED

▲ *Hypholoma fasciculare*

▲ *Lactarius turpis*

▲ *Laetiporus sulphureus*

▲ *Macrolepiota procera*

▲ *Panaeolus semiovatus*

**Inocybe** (Fr.) Fr.
CORTINARIALES, CORTINARIACEAE
**assimilata** Britzelm (=*Inocybe umbrina* Bres.) – Vauxhall (SP0987)
**asterospora** Quél. – ED, SV
**cincinnata** (Fr.) Quél. – ED
**cincinnata var. major** (S. Petersen) Kuyper – SV
**cookei** Bres. – ED
**curvipes** P. Karst. – ED, PD
**erubescens** A. Blytt. (=*Inocybe patouillardii* Bres.) – Quinton Cemetery (SO9885)
**fraudens** (Britzelm.) Sacc. (=*Inocybe pyriodora* (Pers.) P. Kumm.) – HW
**fuscidula** Velen. – HA
**geophylla** (Fr.) P. Kumm. – ED, PD, SV
**geophylla var. lilacina** (Peck) Gillet – SV
**griseolilacina** J.E. Lange – SV
**lacera** (Fr.) P. Kumm. – ED, SP, Saltley Reservoir (SP0988), Vauxhall (SP0987)
**maculata** Boud. – ED
**margaritispora** (Cooke) Sacc. – ED
**napipes** J.E. Lange – SP, SV
**nitidiuscula** (Britzelm.) Sacc. – QU
**petiginosa** (Fr.) Gillet – SP
**rimosa** (Bull.) P. Kumm. – SV
**sindonia** (Fr.) P. Karst. – ED, LG, SP

**Inonotus** P. Karst.
HYMENOCHAETALES, HYMENOCHAETACEAE
**dryadeus** (Pers.) Murrill – RH, MG
**hispidus** (Bull.) P. Karst. – BP, ED, SV, WB, WN
**radiatus** (Sowerby) P. Karst. – BA, ED, SP

**Kuehneromyces** Singer & A.H. Smith
AGARICALES, STROPHARIACEAE
**mutabilis** (Schaeff.) Singer & A.H. Smith – ED, HW, MO, PD, SP, SV, WN

**Laccaria** Berk. & Broome
AGARICALES, TRICHOLOMATACEAE
**amethystina** Cooke – BA, ED, GP, LP, SP, SV, Oscott College (SP0994)
**bicolor** (Maire) P.D. Orton – SP
**fraterna** (Sacc.) Pegler – HW
**laccata** (Scop.) Cooke – ED, GP, HW, LP, MO, QU, SP, SV, SW, WN, and many other sites
**proxima** (Boud.) Pat. – ED, SP
**tortilis** (Bolton) Cooke – ED, MO, SP, SV

**Lachnella** Fr.
AGARICALES, TRICHOLOMATACEAE
**villosa** (Pers.) Donk – ED

**Lacrymaria** Pat.
AGARICALES, COPRINACEAE
**lacrymabunda** (Bull.) Pat. – ED, HW, MO, PD, QU, SP, SV, WG, WN, St. Nicholas Churchyard, Kings Norton (SP0478)

**Lactarius** Pers.
RUSSULALES, RUSSULACEAE
**aurantiacus** (Pers.) Gray – SV

**blennius** (Fr.) Fr. – LP, QU, SP
**camphoratus** (Bull.) Fr. – GP, SP
**chrysorrheus** Fr. – SP
**deterrimus** Gröger – GP, QU
**fulvissimus** Romagn. – QU, SV
**glyciosmus** (Fr.) Fr. – ED, GP, MO, SO, SP, SV
**lacunarum** Hora – QU
**lilacinus** Lasch – Dudley Port (SO9691)
**obscuratus** (Lasch) Fr. – ED
**pubescens** (Fr.) Fr. – ED, HW, SO, SP, SV, Vauxhall (SP0987)
**quietus** (Fr.) Fr. – ED, GP, MO, SP, SV
**rufus** (Scop.) Fr. – ED, SP, SV
**subdulcis** (Pers.) Gray – ED, PD, SP, SV
**tabidus** Fr. – ED, GP, SP, SV
**torminosus** (Schaeff.) Pers. – ED, SV, SW, WG
**turpis** (Weinm.) Fr. – ED, GP, MO, QU, SO, SP, SV, TW
**vietus** (Fr.) Fr. – ED, SP, SV, SW
**volemus** (Fr.) Fr. – SP

**Laetiporus** Murrill
PORIALES, CORIOLACEAE
**sulphureus** (Bull.) Bondartsev & Singer – BA, ED, SP, SV, WW, Billesley Common (SP0880), Brownhills (SK0505)

**Leccinum** Gray
BOLETALES, BOLETACEAE
**duriusculum** (Kalchbr.) Singer – SV
**holopus** (Rostk.) Watling – SP
**roseofractum** Watling – SW
**scabrum** (Bull.) Gray – ED, HW, MO, PD, QU, SP, SV, SW, Vauxhall (SP0987)
**variicolor** Watling – ED, SP, SW
**versipelle** (Fr. & Hök) Snell – MO, SO, SP, SV, Vauxhall (SP0987)

**Lepiota** (Pers.) Gray
AGARICALES, AGARICACEAE
**aspera** (Pers.) Quél. (=*Lepiota friesii* (Lasch) Quél.) – ED, Wigginsmill Road (SO9794)
**boudieri** Bres. – SV, WN
**castanea** Quél. – MW, QU, SP, SV
**cristata** (Bolton) P. Kumm. – ED, GP, HW, LP, MW, PD, QU, SP, SV, SW, WG, WN
**oreadiformis** Velen. – MO
**subalba** P.D. Orton – MW, SP, SV
**subgracilis** Kuhner (=*Lepiota latispora* (Wasser) Bon) – Clayhanger (SK0404)

**Lepista** (Fr.) W.G. Smith
AGARICALES, TRICHOLOMATACEAE
**flaccida** (Sowerby) Pat. – ED, HH, HW, PD, QU, SP, SV, WN, Hawthorn Wood (SJ8900)
**nuda** (Fr.) Cooke – ED, GP, HW, MG, MR, PD, SP, SV, SW, WG, WN, Jenny Lee Centre (SJ9400), Wigginsmill Road (SO9794)
**ovispora** (J.E. Lange) Gulden – SP
**saeva** (Fr.) P.D. Orton – SP, SV, WN, Snow Hill Area (SP0687)
**sordida** (Fr.) Singer – ED, WN

***Leucoagaricus*** (Locq.) Singer
AGARICALES, AGARICACEAE
***leucothites*** (Vittad.) Wasser – ED

***Leucopaxillus*** Boursier
AGARICALES, TRICHOLOMATACEAE
***giganteus*** (Sibth.) Singer – SV

***Lycoperdon*** L.
LYCOPERDALES, LYCOPERDACEAE
***nigrescens*** Pers. – ED, MO, SP, SV
***perlatum*** Pers. – BA, BR, ED, GG, GP, LP, MO, MR, PN, SP, SV, SW, TW, WG, WN, and many other sites
***pyriforme*** Schaeff. – ED, GP, HH, HW, LP, MO, PD, SP, SV

***Lyophyllum*** P. Karst.
AGARICALES, TRICHOLOMATACEAE
***connatum*** (Schumach.) Singer – ED, GP, MO, MW
***decastes*** (Fr.) Singer – ED, PD, SV, WG
***fumosum*** (Pers.) P.D. Orton – ED, SP
***loricatum*** (Fr.) Kalamees – SP

***Macrolepiota*** Singer
AGARICALES, AGARICACEAE
***konradii*** (P.D. Orton) M.M. Moser – ED
***procera*** (Scop.) Singer – LP, PN, SV, Plantsbrook Valley (SP1295)
***rhacodes*** (Vittad.) Singer – ED, HW, MO, MR, MW, SV, Oscott College (SP0994)

***Macrotyphula*** R.H. Petersen
CANTHARELLALES, CLAVARIACEAE
***fistulosa*** (Holmsk.) R.H. Petersen – SV
***fistulosa* var. *contorta*** (Holmsk.) Nannf. & L. Holm – SV
***juncea*** (Fr.) Berthier – ED, SV

***Marasmiellus*** Murrill
AGARICALES, TRICHOLOMATACEAE
***ramealis*** (Bull.) Singer – ED, SP, SV, WN
***vaillantii*** (Pers.) Singer – ED, PD, SP, SV

***Marasmius*** Fr.
AGARICALES, TRICHOLOMATACEAE
***androsaceus*** (L.) Fr. – SP
***epiphylloides*** (Rea) Sacc. & Trotter – ED
***epiphyllus*** (Pers.) Fr. – ED, MO, SV
***graminum*** (Lib.) Berk. & Broome – SP
***oreades*** (Bolton) Fr. – ED, GP, PD, PN, QU, RW, SO, SP, SV, WG, WN, and many other sites
***rotula*** (Scop.) Fr. – ED, MO, SP, SV
***setosus*** (Sowerby) Noordel. – ED

***Megacollybia*** Kotl. & Pouzar
AGARICALES, TRICHOLOMATACEAE
***platyphylla*** (Pers.) Kotl. & Pouzar – ED, SP

***Melanoleuca*** Pat.
AGARICALES, TRICHOLOMATACEAE
***brevipes*** (Bull.) Pat. – ED, SV, WG, WN
***excissa*** (Fr.) Singer – SP

***melaleuca*** (Pers.) Murrill – WG, WN
***polioleuca*** (Fr.) Kühner & Maire – PD, SV

***Melanophyllum*** Velen.
AGARICALES, AGARICACEAE
***haematospermum*** (Bull.) Kreisel (=*Melanophyllum echinatum* (Roth) Singer) – ED, SP

***Melanotus*** Pat.
AGARICALES, STROPHARIACEAE
***horizontalis*** (Bull.) P.D. Orton – SV
***phillipsii*** (Berk. & Broome) Singer – ED, SP, SV

***Meripilus*** P. Karst.
PORIALES, CORIOLACEAE
***giganteus*** (Pers.) P. Karst. – ED, HW, LP, RH, SV, TW

***Merismodes*** Earle
AGARICALES, MARASMIACEAE
***anomala*** (Pers.) Singer – SP

***Micromphale*** Gray
AGARICALES, MARASMIACEAE
***impudicum*** (Fr.) P.D. Orton – BE

***Mutinus*** Fr.
PHALLALES, PHALLACEAE
***caninus*** (Huds.) Fr. – ED, SV

***Mycena*** (Pers.) Roussel
AGARICALES, TRICHOLOMATACEAE
***acicula*** (Schaeff.) P. Kumm. – ED, LP, PD, SV, WN
***aciculata*** (A.H. Smith) Desjardin & E. Horak – ED
***adscendens*** (Lasch) Maas Geest. (=*Mycena tenerrima* (Berk.) Quél.) – ED, MO, SV
***aetites*** (Fr.) Quél. – ED, QU, SV
***arcangeliana*** Bres. – ED, GP, QU, SV, WN
***cinerella*** (P. Karst) P. Karst. – ED, SP, SV
***citrinomarginata*** Gillet – ED
***clavularis*** (Batsch) Sacc. – GP
***epipterygia*** (Scop.) Gray – ED, LP, SP, WN
***filopes*** (Bull.) P. Kumm. – ED, MO, SV, WN
***galericulata*** (Scop.) Gray – ED, GP, HH, LP, MR, MW, PD, RW, SP, SV, SW, WG, WN
***galopus*** (Pers.) P. Kumm. – ED, GP, HW, MO, RW, SP, SV
***galopus* var. *candida*** J.E. Lange – GP
***galopus* var. *nigra*** Rea – ED, SP, SV, WN
***haematopus*** (Pers.) P. Kumm. – ED, MO, SP, WN
***inclinata*** (Fr.) Quél. – ED,GP, MR, SP, SV, WN
***leptocephala*** (Pers.) Gillet – ED, LP, SP, SV, SW, WN
***luteoalba*** (Bolton) Gray – ED, LP, QU, SV, WG, WN
***maculata*** P. Karst. – SV
***metata*** (Fr.) P. Kumm. – SV
***mirata*** (Peck) Sacc. – SV
***olivaceomarginata*** (Massee) Massee – ED, LP, SP, SV, WG
***polyadelpha*** (Lasch) Kühner – SV
***polygramma*** (Bull.) Gray – ED, SV
***pura*** (Pers.) P. Kumm. – ED, LP, PD, SV, WN

***sanguinolenta*** (Alb. & Schwein.) P. Kumm. – ED, MO, SP
***speirea*** (Fr.) Gillet – ED, SP, SV
***stipata*** Maas Geest & Schwöbel (Mis.:=*Mycena alcalina* sensu NCL p.p. & sensu auct.) – ED, GP, MR, SP, SW
***stylobates*** (Pers.) P. Kumm. – ED
***vitilis*** (Fr.) Quél. – ED, SP, SV

***Mycoacia*** Donk
POLYPORALES, MERULIACEAE
***uda*** (Fr.) Donk – HW, SV

***Mycocalia*** J.T. Palmer
NIDULARIALES, NIDULARIACEAE
***denudata*** (Fr. & Nordholm) J.T. Palmer – ED

***Myxomphalia*** Hora
AGARICALES, TRICHOLOMATACEAE
***maura*** (Fr.) Hora – SP

***Naucoria*** (Fr.) P. Kumm.
CORTINARIALES, CORTINARIACEAE
***alnetorum*** (Maire) Kühner & Romagn. – ED
***bohemica*** Velen. – ED
***escharioides*** (Fr.) P. Kumm. – ED, GP, SP
***salicetorum*** D.A. Reid – ED
***salicis*** P.D. Orton – ED, SV
***scolecina*** (Fr.) Quél. – ED, SP
***striatula*** P.D. Orton – ED, GP, SP, SV
***subconspersa*** P.D.Orton – SV

***Nidularia*** Fr. & Nordholm
NIDULARIALES, NIDULARIACEAE
***deformis*** (Willd.) Fr. – SP

***Oxyporus*** (Bourdot & Galzin) Donk
PORIALES, CORIOLACEAE
***populinus*** (Schumach.) Donk – ED

***Panaeolina*** Maire
AGARICALES, COPRINACEAE
***foenisecii*** (Pers.) Maire – ED, HW, PD, QU, SP, SV

***Panaeolus*** (Fr.) Quél.
AGARICALES, STROPHARIACEAE
***acuminatus*** (Schaeff.) Gillet (=*Panaeolus rickenii* Hora) – ED, QU, SP, SV
***fimicola*** (Pers.) Gillet (=*Panaeolus ater* (J.E. Lange) Bon) – ED, PD, QU, SV, WB
***olivaceus*** F.H. Møller – ED
***papilionaceus*** (Bull.) Quél. – SP, SV
***semiovatus*** (Sowerby) S. Lundell – SP, SV, SW

***Panellus*** P. Karst.
AGARICALES, TRICHOLOMATACEAE
***mitis*** (Pers.) Singer – SV
***serotinus*** (Pers.) Kühner – ED, SP, WW

***Paxillus*** Fr.
BOLETALES, PAXILLACEAE
***involutus*** (Batsch) Fr. – ED, GP, HW, LG, MO, MR, MW, QU, SP, SV, and many other sites

▲ *Phallus impudicus* egg

▲ *Pholiota squarrosa*

▲ *Rhodotus palmatus*

**Peniophora** Cooke
STEREALES, PENIOPHORACEAE
**incarnata** (Pers.) P. Karst. – ED, PN, SP, WN
**laeta** (Fr.) Donk – WK
**limitata** (Chaillet) Cooke – ED
**lycii** (Pers.) Höhn. & Litsch – LP, WN
**quercina** (Pers.) Cooke – ED, SP

**Perenniporia** Murrill
POLYPORALES, POLYPORACEAE
**fraxinea** (Bull.) Ryvarden – SV

**Phaeolus** (Pat.) Pat.
POLYPORALES, POLYPORACEAE
**schweinitzii** (Fr.) Pat. – SP

**Phaeomarasmius** Scherff.
CORTINARIALES, CORTINARIACEAE
**erinaceus** (Fr.) Kühner – ED

**Phallus** L.
PHALLALES, PHALLACEAE
**impudicus** L. – ED, GP, HH, LP, MG, MW, SP,
SV, SW, TW, and many other sites

**Phellinus** Quél.
HYMENOCHAETALES,
HYMENOCHAETACEAE
**ferreus** (Pers.) Bourdot & Galzin – ED, SV
**igniarius** (L.) Quél. – ED, MO

**Phlebia** Fr.
STEREALES, MERULIACEAE
**radiata** Fr. – ED, LP, SP, SV, WW
**rufa** (Pers.) M.P. Christ. – ED
**tremellosa** (Schrad.) Burds. & Nakasone – ED, GP,
MO, SP, SV, WN

**Pholiota** (Fr.) P. Kumm.
AGARICALES, STROPHARIACEAE
**adiposa** (Batsch) P. Kumm. – SV
**alnicola** (Fr.) Singer – ED, SP, SV
**aurivella** (Batsch) P. Kumm. – ED
**gummosa** (Lasch) Singer – ED, MW, PD, SP, SV,
WG, WN
**highlandensis** (Peck) Quadr. – BC, ED, SV
**lenta** (Pers.) Singer – GP, SV
**squarrosa** (Weigel) P. Kumm. – ED, HW, MO,
MR, RH, SP, SV, WN, WW

**Piptoporus** P. Karst.
PORIALES, CORIOLACEAE
**betulinus** (Bull.) P. Karst. – BA, ED, GP, LG, LP,
MO, MR, RW, SO, SP, SV, WB, WN, WW, and
many other sites

**Pleurotus** (Fr.) P. Kumm.
PORIALES, LENTINACEAE
**cornucopiae** (Paulet) Rolland – ED, PD,
SP, SV
**dryinus** (Pers.) P. Kumm. – ED, SP, SV, WN
**ostreatus** (Jacq.) P. Kumm. – ED, LP, MO, MR,
SP, SV, WN, WW
**pulmonarius** (Fr.) Quél. – ED, SP

**Pluteus** Fr.
AGARICALES, PLUTEACEAE
**aurantiorugosus** (Trog) Sacc. – MO
**cervinus** (Schaeff.) P. Kumm. – ED, HW, MO, SP,
SV, WN
**chrysophaeus** (Schaeff.) Quél. (=*Pluteus
luteovirens* Rea) – ED, MW
**cinereofuscus** J.E. Lange – HW
**ephebeus** (Fr.) Gillet – ED
**hispidulus** (Fr.) Gillet – ED
**leoninus** (Schaeff.) P. Kumm. – ED
**salicinus** (Pers.) P. Kumm. – ED, HW, QU, SV, WN
**satur** Kühner & Romagn. – ED
**umbrosus** (Pers.) P. Kumm. – ED, MW, SV

**Polyporus** Adans.
PORIALES, POLYPORACEAE
**brumalis** (Pers.) Fr. – ED, SP, SV
**durus** (Timmerm.) Kreisel (=*Polyporus badius*
(Pers.) Schwein.) – SV
**leptocephalus** (Jacq.) Fr. (=*Polyporus varius*
(Pers.) Fr.) – ED, LP, MO, SV, WN
**squamosus** (Huds.) Fr. – ED, LP, MR, MW,
SV, SW, WN, Brownhills Common (SK0306),
Highbury Park (SP0682), Merecroft Pool
(SP0478)
**tuberaster** (Jacq.) Fr. – ED

**Porpoloma** Singer
AGARICALES, TRICHOLOMATACEAE
**metapodium** (Fr.) Singer – ED

**Postia** Fr.
PORIALES, CORIOLACEAE
**balsamea** (Peck) Jülich – ED
**caesia** (Schrad.) P. Karst. – SP, SV
**ptychogaster** (F. Ludw.) Vesterh. – SV

**Psathyrella** (Fr.) Quél.
AGARICALES, COPRINACEAE
**artemisiae** (Pass.) Konrad & Maubl. – ED, SP
**candolleana** (Fr.) Maire – ED, HA, LG, MO,
PD, QU, SP, SV
**conopilus** (Fr.) A. Pearson & Dennis – BB, PD
**corrugis** (Pers.) Konrad & Maubl. (=*Psathyrella
gracilis* (Pers.) Quél.) – ED, GP, PN, SV, WG
**gossypina** (Bull.) A. Pearson & Dennis – SP
**marcesibilis** (Britzelm) Singer – LP
**microrrhiza** (Lasch) Konrad & Maubl. – ED, PD,
SV, WN
**multipedata** (Peck) A.H. Sm. – BE, ED, MO, SV
**pannucioides** (J.E. Lange) M.M. Moser – PD
**pennata** (Fr.) Konrad & Maubl. – SP
**piluliformis** (Bull.) P.D. Orton – ED, LG, LP, SP, SV
**prona** (Fr.) Gillet – PD, SV
**pseudogracilis** (Romagn.) M.M. Moser – ED, PD

**Pseudoclitocybe** (Singer) Singer
AGARICALES, TRICHOLOMATACEAE
**cyathiformis** (Bull.) Singer – ED, MW

**Psilocybe** (Fr.) P. Kumm.
AGARICALES, STROPHARIACEAE
**cyanescens** Wakef. – ED, SV

***montana*** (Pers.) P. Kumm. – ED
***semilanceata*** (Fr.) P. Kumm. – ED, GP, HW, LP, QU, RW, SP, SV, WN, Brownhills Common (SK0306), Cofton Park (SP0076)

***Pterula*** Fr.
AGARICALES, PTERULACEAE
***multifida*** (Chevall.) Fr. – SV

***Radulomyces*** M.P. Christ.
STEREALES, HYPHODERMATACEAE
***confluens*** (Fr.) M.P. Christ. – ED

***Ramaria*** (Fr.) Bonord
GOMPHALES, RAMARIACEAE
***formosa*** (Pers.) Quel. – BA

***Resinomycena*** Redhead & Singer
AGARICALES, TRICHOLOMATACEAE
***saccharifera*** (Berk. & Broome) Redhead – ED, SP

***Resupinatus*** Nees
AGARICALES, TRICHOLOMATACEAE
***applicatus*** (Batsch) Gray – ED, QU
***trichotis*** (Pers.) Singer – ED

***Rhodotus*** Maire
AGARICALES, TRICHOLOMATACEAE
***palmatus*** (Bull.) Maire – BA, SV, TW

***Rickenella*** Raithelh.
AGARICALES, TRICHOLOMATACEAE
***fibula*** (Bull.) Raithelh. – ED, LP, GP, MO, QU, SP, SV, Bustleholme Lane (SP0194), Saltley Reservoir (SP0988), Vauxhall (SP0987)
***swartzii*** (Fr.) Kuyper – ED, LP, QU, SV

***Russula*** Pers.
RUSSULALES, RUSSULACEAE
***aeruginea*** Fr. – SP, SV
***albonigra*** (Krombh.) Fr. – QU
***aquosa*** Leclair – SP
***atropurpurea*** (Krombh.) Britzelm. – ED, GP, LP, MO, RH, RW, SP, SV, WB, WN
***betularum*** Hora – ED, SP, SV
***caerulea*** (Pers.) Fr. – SP
***cicatricata*** Bon – ED
***claroflava*** Grove – ED, MO, QU, SP
***cyanoxantha*** (Schaeff.) Fr. – ED, GP, HW, PN, SP, SV
***densifolia*** Gillet – SP
***emetica*** (Schaeff.) Pers. – SP
***exalbicans*** (Pers.) Melzer & Zvára – SP
***fellea*** (Fr.) Fr. – ED, SP
***foetens*** Pers. – LP
***fragilis*** (Pers.) Fr. – ED, GP, MO, SP, SV
***fragilis* var. *knauthii*** (Singer) Kuyper & Vuure – SP
***gracillima*** Jul. Schäff. – SP
***heterophylla*** (Fr.) Fr. – SP
***ionochlora*** Romagn. – ED
***nigricans*** (Bull.) Fr. – ED, LP, SP, SV, TW
***nitida*** (Pers.) Fr. – ED, SP, SW

***nobilis*** Velen. (=*Russula mairei* Singer) – ED, SP
***ochroleuca*** Pers. – ED, GP, LP, MO, MR, RW, SP, SV
***parazurea*** Jul. Schaeff. – ED, GP, LP, RH, SP, SV
***pseudointegra*** Arnaud & Goris – SV
***puellaris*** Fr. – ED, SP
***sardonia*** Fr. – SP
***silvestris*** (Singer) Reumaux (=*Russula emeticella* (Singer) J. Blum) – ED, SP
***sororia*** Fr. – ED, PD, SP
***velenovskyi*** Melzer & Zvára – ED, HA, QU, SP
***versicolor*** Jul. Schäff. – SP, SV
***vesca*** Fr. – ED, SP, SV
***xerampelina*** (Schaeff.) Fr. – SP

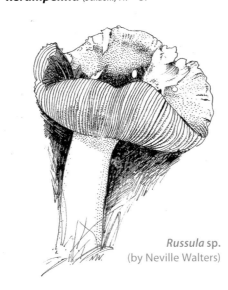

*Russula* sp.
(by Neville Walters)

***Schizophyllum*** Fr.
SCHIZOPHYLLALES, SCHIZOPHYLLACEAE
***commune*** (Fr.) Fr. – ED, LP

***Schizopora*** Velen.
STEREALES, HYPHODERMATACEAE
***paradoxa*** (Schrad.) Donk – ED, MG, SP, SV

***Scleroderma*** Pers.
SCLERODERMATALES, SCLERODERMATACEAE
***bovista*** Fr. – ED, SP, SV
***citrinum*** Pers. – BA, ED, GP, HW, MO, MR, MW, PH, RW, SP, SV, WN
***verrucosum*** (Bull.) Pers. – GP, SV, WB

***Sebacina*** Tul.
TREMELLALES, EXIDIACEAE
***incrustans*** (Pers.) Tul. – SP

***Serpula*** (Pers.) Gray
BOLETALES, CONIOPHORACEAE
***lacrymans*** (Wulfen) J. Schröt. – HW, SV

***Sistotrema*** Fr.
STEREALES, SISTOTREMATACEAE
***sernanderi*** (Litsch.) Donk – ED

***Sparassis*** Fr.
POLYPORALES, SPARASSIDACEAE
***crispa*** (Wulfen) Fr. – SP

***Sphaerobolus*** Tode
SCLERODERMATALES, SPHAEROBOLACEAE
***stellatus*** Tode – ED, GP, SP, SV

***Spongipellis*** Pat.
POLYPORALES, HAPALOPILACEAE
***delectans*** (Peck) Murrill – SV
***spumeus*** (Sowerby) Pat. – ED

***Stereum*** Pers.
STEREALES, STEREACEAE
***gausapatum*** (Fr.) Fr. – ED, LP, RW, SP, SV, WN
***hirsutum*** (Willd.) Gray – ED, GP, HW, LP, MG, MO, MR, PN, RW, SP, SV, WB, WG, WN, WW
***rameale*** (Pers.) Burt – ED
***rugosum*** (Pers.) Fr. – ED, GP, LP, SP, SV
***sanguinolentum*** (Alb. & Schwein.) Fr. – ED, SP
***subtomentosum*** Pouzar – ED

***Strobilurus*** Singer
AGARICALES, MARASMIACEAE
***tenacellus*** (Pers.) Singer – SP, SV

***Stropharia*** (Fr.) Quél.
AGARICALES, STROPHARIACEAE
***aeruginosa*** (Curtis) Quél. – GP, MW, SP, SV, SW, WG, WN
***aurantiaca*** (Cooke) M. Imai – BB, ED, SV
***caerulea*** Kreisel – ED, PD, SP, SV
***coronilla*** (Bull.) Quél. – SV, PD
***pseudocyanea*** (Desm.) Morgan – ED, HW
***semiglobata*** (Batsch) Quél. – ED, SP, SV
***squamosa*** (Pers.) Quél. – ED, HW

***Subulicystidium*** Parmasto
POLYPORALES, HYPHODERMATACEAE
***longisporum*** (Pat.) Parmasto – WB

***Suillus*** Adans.
BOLETALES, BOLETACEAE
***bovinus*** (L.) Roussel – SP
***granulatus*** (L.) Roussel – SP
***grevillei*** (Klotzsch) Singer – GP, PD, SP, SV
***luteus*** (L.) Roussel – ED, PD, SP
***variegatus*** (Sw.) Richon & Roze – SP

***Tephrocybe*** Donk
AGARICALES, TRICHOLOMATACEAE
***ambusta*** (Fr.) Donk – SP
***atrata*** (Fr.) Donk – SP
***palustris*** (Peck) Donk – SP
***tylicolor*** (Fr.) M.M. Moser – ED

***Thanatephorus*** Donk
CERATOBASIDIALES, CERATOBASIDIACEAE
***cucumeris*** (A.B. Frank) Donk – ED

***Thelephora*** Ehrh. ex Willd.
THELEPHORALES, THELEPHORACEAE
***terrestris*** Ehrh. – GP, SP, Saltley Reservoir (SP0988), Vauxhall (SP0987)

***Tomentella*** Pat.
THELEPHORALES, THELEPHORACEAE
***bryophila*** (Pers.) M.J. Larsen – The Spinney (SP0498)

***Trametes*** Fr.
PORIALES, CORIOLACEAE
***gibbosa*** (Pers.) Fr. – ED, LP, MR, MW, SP, SV, WB, WW
***hirsuta*** (Fr.) Pilát – ED, LP, SV
***ochracea*** (Pers.) Gilb. & Ryvarden – SV
***versicolor*** (L.) Pilát – BA, ED, GP, HH, LP, MG, MO, MR, RW, SP, SV, WB, WN, and many other sites

*Trametes versicolor*
(by Neville Walters)

***Tremella*** Pers.
TREMELLALES, TREMELLACEAE
***foliacea*** Pers. – BA, ED
***mesenterica*** Retz. – ED, SV, WK

***Tricholoma*** (Fr.) Staude
AGARICALES, TRICHOLOMATACEAE
***cingulatum*** (Almfelt) Jacobashch – BE, WG, Mill St., Walsall (SP0199)
***columbetta*** (Fr.) P. Kumm. – SV
***fulvum*** (Bull.) Bigeard & H. Guill. – MO, SO, SP, SV
***inamoenum*** (Fr.) Gillet – SP
***saponaceum*** (Fr.) P. Kumm. – SP
***scalpturatum*** (Fr.) Quél. – HW, QU
***sciodes*** (Pers.) C. Martin – ED
***sejunctum*** (Sowerby) Quél. – ED
***terreum*** (Schaeff.) P. Kumm. – GP, SP
***ustale*** (Fr.) P. Kumm. – ED
***ustaloides*** Romagn. – SV

***Tricholomopsis*** Singer
AGARICALES, TRICHOLOMATACEAE
***rutilans*** (Schaeff.) Singer – SP

***Tubaria*** (W.G. Smith) Gillet
CORTINARIALES, CREPIDOTACEAE
***conspersa*** (Pers.) Fayod – ED, SP, SV
***dispersa*** (Pers.) Singer (=*Tubaria autochthona* (Berk. & Broome) Sacc.) – ED, PD, RH, SV
***furfuracea*** (Pers.) Gillet (=*Tubaria hiemalis* Bon) – BA, BB, ED, GP, LP, MG, PD, SP, SV, WN

***Tubulicrinis*** Donk
POLYPORALES, TUBULICRINACEAE
***subulatus*** (Bourdot & Galzin) Donk – WB

***Tylopilus*** P. Karst.
BOLETALES, BOLETACEAE
***felleus*** (Bull.) P. Karst. – SP

***Typhula*** (Pers.) Fr.
CANTHARELLALES, TYPHULACEAE
***erythropus*** (Pers.) Fr. – ED, SV
***micans*** (Pers.) Berthier – GP
***setipes*** (Grev.) Berthier – ED, SV

***Tyromyces*** P. Karst.
PORIALES, CORIOLACEAE
***chioneus*** (Fr.) P. Karst. – LP, SV

***Vascellum*** F. Šmarda
AGARICALES, LYCOPERDACEAE
***pratense*** (Pers.) Kreisel – SV, WN

***Volvariella*** Speg.
AGARICALES, PLUTEACEAE
***bombycina*** (Schaeff.) Singer – ED, SV
***caesiotincta*** P.D. Orton – ED
***gloiocephala*** (DC.) Boekhout & Enderle (=*Volvariella speciosa* (Fr.) Singer) – ED, SV

***Vuilleminia*** Maire
STEREALES, CORTICIACEAE
***comedens*** (Nees) Maire – ED

***Xerula*** Maire emend. Dörfelt
AGARICALES, TRICHOLOMATACEAE
***radicata*** (Relhan.) Dörfelt – ED, SV, WN

## UREDINIOMYCETES

***Coleosporium*** Lév.
UREDINALES, COLEOSPORIACEAE
***tussilaginis*** (Pers.) Kleb. – LP, SV, WN

***Cumminsiella*** Arthur
UREDINALES, PUCCINIACEAE
***mirabilissima*** (Peck) Nannf. – ED

***Gymnosporangium*** R. Hedw.
UREDINALES, PUCCINIACEAE
***cornutum*** F. Kern – SV

***Kuehneola*** Magnus
UREDINALES, PHRAGMIDIACEAE
***uredinis*** (Link) Arthur – SP, WB

***Melampsora*** Castagne
UREDINALES, MELAMPSORACEAE
***caprearum*** Thüm. – SV
***euphorbiae*** (C. Schub.) Castagne – ED
***populnea*** (Pers.) P. Karst. – SV

***Melampsorella*** J. Schröt.
UREDINALES, PUCCINIASTRACEAE
***symphyti*** Bubák – SV

***Melampsoridium*** Kleb.
UREDINALES, PUCCINIASTRACEAE
***betulinum*** (Pers.) Kleb. – SP

***Milesina*** Magnus
UREDINALES, PUCCINIASTRACEAE
***kriegeriana*** (Magnus) Magnus – MG
***scolopendrii*** (Fuckl) D.M. Hend. – MG

***Phragmidium*** Link
UREDINALES, PHRAGMIDIACEAE
***mucronatum*** (Pers.) Schltdl. – SP
***rubi-idaei*** (DC.) P. Karst. – WB
***sanguisorbae*** (DC.) J. Schröt. – SV
***violaceum*** (Schultz) G. Winter – LP, SP, SV, WB

***Puccinia*** Pers.
UREDINALES, PUCCINIACEAE
***behenis*** G.H. Otth – WB
***caricina*** DC. – Pelsall North Common (SK0104)
***circaeae*** Pers. – WB
***cnici*** H. Mart. – ED
***cnici-oleracei*** Desm. – SP
***crepidicola*** Syd. & P. Syd. – ED
***epilobii*** DC. – SP
***galii-verni*** Ces. – SP
***lagenophorae*** Cooke – ED
***malvacearum*** Mont., in Gay – ED
***menthae*** Pers. – SP, SV
***poarum*** E. Nielsen – RH, SV
***punctiformis*** (F. Strauss) Röhl. – SV
***tumida*** Grev. – ED
***urticata var. urticae-vesicariae*** (Kleb.) Zwetko – Belmont Road Lock (SP0887)
***urticata var. urticae-acutae*** (Kleb.) Zwetko – Grand Union Canal (SP0886)

***Pucciniastrum*** G.H. Otth
UREDINALES, PUCCINIASTRACEAE
***circaeae*** (G. Winter.) de Toni – WB
***epilobii*** G.H. Otth – WB

***Triphragmium*** Link
UREDINALES, SPHAEROPHRAGMIACEAE
***filipendulae*** Pass. – SV

***Uromyces*** (Link) Unger
UREDINALES, PUCCINIACEAE
***muscari*** (Duby) L. Graves. – ED
***polygoni-avicularis*** (Pers.) P. Karst. – ED

***Xenodochus*** Schltdl.
UREDINALES, PHRAGMIDIACEAE
***carbonarius*** Schltdl. – SV

## USTILAGINOMYCETES

***Exobasidium*** Woronin
EXOBASIDIALES, EXOBASIDIACEAE
***vaccinii*** (Fuckel) Woronin – SP

***Urocystis*** Rabenh. ex Fuckel
UROCYSTALES, UROCYSTACEAE
***anemones*** (Pers.) G. Winter – SV, SW, WN

***Ustilago*** (Pers.) Roussel
USTILAGINALES, USTILAGINACEAE
***avenae*** (Pers.) Rostr. – ED
***filiformis*** (Schrank) Rostr. – ED
***hypodytes*** (Schitdl.) Fr. – WN

## MYXOMYCOTA
## CERATIOMYXOMYCETES

***Ceratiomyxa*** J. Schröt.
CERATIOMYXALES, CERATIOMYXACEAE
***fruticulosa*** (F. Muell.) T. Macbr. – ED, DY, SP, SV

## MYXOMYCETES

***Amaurochaete*** Rostaf.
STEMONITALES, STEMONITIDACEAE
***tubulina*** (Alb. & Schwein.) T. Macbr. – SM

***Arcyodes*** O.F. Cook
TRICHIALES, ARCYRIACEAE
***incarnata*** (Alb. & Schwein.) O.F. Cook – SV

***Arcyria*** F.H. Wigg.
TRICHIALES, ARCYRIACEAE
***affinis*** Rostaf. – ED, SV
***cinerea*** (Bull.) Pers. – ED, GP, SP, SV
***denudata*** (L.) Wettst. – ED, SM, SP, SV
***ferruginea*** Saut. – ED, SM, SP, SV
***incarnata*** (Pers.) Pers. – DY, ED, GP, SP, SV
***obvelata*** (Oeder) Onsberg – ED, SP, SV
***oerstedtii*** Rostaf. – ED
***pomiformis*** (Leers) Rostaf. – ED, SM, SV

***Badhamia*** Berk.
PHYSARALES, PHYSARACEAE
***macrocarpa*** (Ces.) Rostaf. – SV
***panicea*** (Fr.) Rostaf. – SM, SV
***utricularis*** (Bull.) Berk. – ED, SM, SV

***Brefeldia*** Rostaf.
STEMONITALES, STEMONITIDACEAE
***maxima*** (Fr.) Rostaf. – SM

***Calomyxa*** Nieuwl.
TRICHIALES, DIANEMATACEAE
***metallica*** (Berk.) Nieu. – SM

***Comatricha*** Preuss
STEMONITALES, STEMONITIDACEAE
***nigra*** (Pers.) Schröt. – ED, GP, SP, SV
***pulchella*** (C. Bab.) Rostaf. – ED
***tenerrima*** (M.A. Curtis) G. Lister – SV

***Craterium*** Trentep.
PHYSARALES, PHYSARACEAE
***leucocephalum*** (Pers.) Ditmar – SV
***minutum*** (Leers) Fr. – ED, SP, SV

***Cribraria*** Pers.
LICEALES, CRIBRARIACEAE
***argillacea*** (Pers.) Pers. – GP, SM, SV

***aurantiaca*** Schrad. – ED
***cancellata*** (Batsch) Nann.-Bremek. **var. cancellata** – SV
***rufa*** (Roth) Rostaf. – SP

***Diachea*** Fr.
PHYSARALES, DIDYMIACEAE
***leucopoda*** (Bull.) Rostaf. – SV

***Dictydiaethalium*** Rostaf.
LICEALES, DICTYDIAETHALIACEAE
***plumbeum*** (Schum.) Rostaf. – ED, SP, SV

***Diderma*** Pers.
PHYSARALES, DIDYMIACEAE
***donkii*** Nann.-Bremek. – ED
***effusum*** (Schwein.) Morgan – SP
***hemisphaericum*** (Bull.) Hornem. – ED, SV
***spumarioides*** (Fr.) Fr. – SV

***Didymium*** Schrad.
PHYSARALES, DIDYMIACEAE
***bahiense*** Gottsb. – SM
***clavus*** (Alb. & Schwein.) Rabenh. – SP
***difforme*** (Pers.) Gray – ED, GP, SM, SV
***eximium*** Peck – SP
***melanospermum*** (Pers.) T. Macbr. – SM
***megalosporum*** Berk. & M.A. Curt. – SP
***nigripes*** (Link) Fr. – SP
***squamulosum*** (Alb. & Schwein.) Fr. – ED, SM, SP, SV
***trachysporum*** G. Lister – ED

***Enerthenema*** Bowman
STEMONITALES, STEMONITIDACEAE
***papillatum*** (Pers.) Rostaf. – SV

***Enteridium*** Ehrenb.
LICEALES, LYCOGALACEAE
***lycoperdon*** (Bull.) M.L. Farr – BC, ED, SP, SV

***Fuligo*** Haller
PHYSARALES, PHYSARACEAE
***septica*** (L.) F.H. Wigg. **var. flava** (Pers.) R.E. Fr. – ED
***septica*** (L.) F.H. Wigg. **var. septica** – ED, GP, SP, SV

***Hemitrichia*** Rostaf.
TRICHIALES, TRICHIACEAE
***calyculata*** (Speg.) M.L. Farr – DY, SV
***clavata*** (Pers.) Rostaf. – SV
***intorta*** (Lister) Lister – SV

***Lamproderma*** Rostaf.
STEMONITALES, STEMONITIDACEAE
***arcyrioides*** (Sommerf.) Rostaf. – ED, SV
***columbinum*** (Pers.) Rostaf. – ED
***scintillans*** (Berk. & Broome) Morgan – ED, SM, SP

***Leocarpus*** Link
PHYSARALES, PHYSARACEAE
***fragilis*** (Dicks.) Rostaf. – ED, SP, SV

***Licea*** Schrader
LICEALES, LICEACEAE
***clarkii*** Ing – ED

***Lycogala*** Adans.
LICEALES, LYCOGALACEAE
***epidendrum*** (L.) Fries. – ED, MO, QU, SP, SV
***terrestre*** Fries. – ED

***Metatrichia*** Ing
TRICHIALES, TRICHIACEAE
***floriformis*** (Schwein.) Nann.-Bremek. – ED, SP, SV
***vesparium*** (Batsch) Nann.-Bremek. – SV

***Mucilago*** Battarra
PHYSARALES, DIDYMIACEAE
***crustacea*** F.H. Wigg. **var. crustacea** – MO, SV

***Oligonema*** Rostaf.
TRICHIALES, TRICHIACEAE
***flavidum*** (Peck) Peck – SV

***Paradiacheopsis*** Hertel
STEMONITALES, STEMONITIDACEAE
***fimbriata*** (G. Lister & Cran) Hertel – ED

***Perichaena*** Fr.
TRICHIALES, ARCYNIACEAE
***corticalis*** (Batsch) Rostaf. – SV
***depressa*** Lib. – DY, ED, SM, SV

***Physarum*** Pers.
PHYSARALES, PHYSARACEAE
***bitectum*** G. Lister – ED
***bivalve*** Pers. – ED, SV
***cinereum*** (Batsch) Pers. – ED, SM, SV
***compressum*** Alb. & Schwein. – ED, GP, SM
***contextum*** (Pers.) Pers. – SM
***lateritium*** (Berk. & Ravenel) Morgan – SM
***leucophaeum*** Fr. – ED, SP, SV
***nutans*** Pers – DY, ED, SP, SV
***obscurum*** (Lister) Ing – SM
***psittacinum*** Ditmar – SM, SV
***robustum*** (Lister) Nann.-Bremek. – ED, SV
***rubiginosum*** Fr. – SM
***viride*** (Bull.) Pers. **var. viride** – SP, SV

***Prototrichia*** Rostaf.
TRICHIALES, TRICHIACEAE
***metallica*** (Berk.) Massee – SM, SV

***Stemonitis*** Gled.
STEMONITALES, STEMONITIDACEAE
***axifera*** (Bull.) T. Macbr. – DY, ED
***flavogenita*** E. Jahn – SV
***fusca*** Roth – ED, SM, SP, SV
***herbatica*** Peck – ED
***smithii*** T. Macbr. – DY
***virginiensis*** Rex – SP

***Stemonitopsis*** (Nann.-Bremek.) Nann.-Bremek.
STEMONITALES, STEMONITIDACEAE
***typhina*** (F.H. Wigg.) Nann.-Bremek. – ED, GP, SP, SV

***Symphytocarpus*** Ing & Nann.-Bremek.
STEMONITALES, STEMONITIDACEAE
***amaurochaetoides*** Nann.-Bremek. – SM, SV
***flaccidus*** (Lister) Ing & Nann.-Bremek. – SV

***Trichia*** Haller
TRICHIALES, TRICHIACEAE
***botrytis*** (J.F. Gmel.) Pers. – DY, ED, SM, SP
***contorta*** (Ditmar) Rostaf. **var. *contorta*** – ED, SV
***contorta*** (Ditmar) Rostaf. **var. *karstenii***
(Rostaf.) Ing – DY
***decipiens*** (Pers.) T. Macbr. – DY, ED, SM, SV
***persimilis*** P. Karsten – ED, SP, SV, WB
***scabra*** Rostaf. – DY, ED, SV
***varia*** (Pers.) Pers. – ED, SM, SP, SV

***Tubifera*** J.F. Gmel.
LICEALES, LYCOGALACEAE
***ferruginosa*** (Batsch) J.F. Gmel. – ED, SP

## OOMYCOTA
## OOMYCETES

***Albugo*** (Pers.) Roussel ex Gray
PERONOSPORALES, ALBUGINACEAE
***candida*** (Pers.) Roussel – ED, SV

***Peronospora*** Corda
PERONOSPORALES, PERONOSPORACEAE
***grisea*** (Unger) de Bary – SP
***parasitica*** Tul.{?} – ED

***Plasmopara*** J. Schröt.
PERONOSPORALES, PERONOSPORACEAE
***crustosa*** (Fr.) Jørst. – WB
***pygmaea*** (Unger) J. Schröt. – WB

## PLASMODIOPHOROMYCOTA
## PLASMODIOPHOROMYCETES

***Plasmodiophora*** Woronin
PLASMODIOPHORALES,
PLASMODIOPHORACEAE
***brassicae*** Woron. – ED

## ZYGOMYCOTA
## ZYGOMYCETES

***Spinellus*** Tiegh.
MUCORALES, MUCORACEAE
***fusiger*** (Link) van Tiegh. – ED, SP, SV

***Syzygites*** Ehrenb.
MUCORALES, MUCORACEAE
***megalocarpus*** Ehrenb. – SP

***Umbelopsis*** Amos & H.L. Barnett
MORTIERELLALES, MORTIERELLACEAE
***ramanniana*** (A. Møller) W. Gams – SP

## ANAMORPHIC FUNGI

Anamorphic fungi have been listed as the perfect state under Ascomycetes, but are listed here again as the imperfect state for practical convenience.
***Blistum ovalisporum*** – ED
***Botrytis cinerea*** – ED
***Calcarisporium arbuscula*** – WB
***Camposporium cambrense*** – SP
***Chloridium virescens*** – ED
***Coremiella cubispora*** – ED

***Cylindrium aeruginosum*** – ED
***Dactylosporium macropus*** – ED
***Dendryphiella infuscans*** – ED
***Dendryphion comosum*** – ED
***Dictyosporium toruloides*** – ED
***Endophragmiella boothii*** – ED
***Endostilbum albidum*** – GP
***Epicoccum nigrum*** – SP
***Fusarium sporotrichioides*** – SV
***Fusicoccum macrosporum*** – WW
***Fusidium aeruginosum*** – ED
***Helminthosporium velutinum*** – ED
***Menispora ciliata*** – ED
***Microsphaera alphitoides*** – ED, MR, RW, SP, SV
***Myrothecium masonii*** – ED
***Naemospora croceola*** – HW
***Trichoderma viride*** – ED
***Paecilomyces farinosus*** – ED, GP
***Penicillium brevicompactum*** – SP
***Penicillium claviforme*** – ED
***Periconia byssoides*** – ED
***Periconia cookei*** – SV
***Periconia digitata*** – ED
***Periconia minutissima*** – ED
***Phacellium carneum*** – WB
***Phomopsis revellens*** – WW
***Pseudocercospora rubi*** – WB
***Pseudolachnea hispidula*** – SP
***Pycnostysanus azaleae*** – SP
***Ramularia purpurascens*** – MG
***Sporidesmiella hyalosperma* var. *hyalosperma*** – ED
***Torula herbarum*** – ED
***Trichothecium roseum*** – SV
***Verticillium lecanii*** – SP
***Volutella ciliata*** – ED

Chapter 6

# Lichens

by Peter James

◀ *Evernia prunastre*

▲ *Xanthoria parietina* (×2), a foliose lichen, bearing apothecia, on a willow branch, with the grey foliose lichen *Physcia adscendens* (right)

## Introduction

Lichens are fungi which have a close association, sustained by photosynthesis, with certain selected green algae (Chlorophyta) and/or blue-green (Cyanobacteria) partners which often become so intimately associated that they form identifiable growth forms (**thalli**); a classic example of **symbiosis**. They are most notably conspicuous, often forming complex communities, on barren surfaces, particularly tree-bark (**corticolous**), rock substrates (**saxicolous**), and including a wide variety of man-made surfaces such as worked timber, wooden palings, patios, gravestones, brick, mortar, concrete, asbestos cement etc. Some species consolidate soils (**terricolous**) and are especially distinctive in heathland habitats; others overgrow mosses or rarely (in the British Isles) occur on leaves. Lichens are often very long-living (30 years or more) and slow-growing, many species expanding by only a few millimetres each year. Many different lichen thalli and especially fruiting bodies include a very diverse range of unique substances (many the basis of diagnosis) which may be identified by simple chemical tests or by a range of more sophisticated techniques.

The majority of lichenised fungi belong to a single major group, the Ascomycetes, which characteristically form their spores in special cells called asci, which in turn are typically part of disc-like **apothecia** (e.g. *Lecanora* spp.) or globose **perithecia** (e.g. *Verrucaria* spp.). Lichen fungi (**mycobionts**), although often forming the major part of the thallus, are unable to survive without their respective algal partners (**photobionts**); the latter can however also be free-living. Lichen thalli often achieve a structural complexity which is seldom found in related, non-lichenised taxa. However in some lichen species, especially those on limestone or mortar, the thallus can become totally immersed in its substrate with only the apothecia or perithecia visible. Other species reproduce asexually, producing either powdery granules (**soredia**) or small outgrowths (**isidia**) on their thallii. These contain both mycobiont and photobiont and are shed from the surface to develop into new thallii.

The thallus can be:

- **leprose** – more or less entirely diffuse, powdery and unstructured (e.g. *Lepraria*)
- **crustose** – a crust firmly attached to, or sometimes immersed in, the substrate, the surface often variously cracked but lacking distinct marginal lobes (e.g. *Lecanora*, *Lecidea*)
- **placodioid** – crustose at the centre but with marginal, spreading, often radiating, lobes (e.g. *Lecanora muralis*, *Caloplaca flavescens*)
- **squamulose** – consisting of other numerous, clustered, small (≤1.5 mm), often ±ascending, leaf-like lobes (**squamules**) (e.g. many *Cladonia* species)
- **foliose** – leaf-like, with a spreading, dorsiventral thallus, often with the lower surface only ±loosely attached to the substrate (e.g. *Flavoparmelia* spp., *Xanthoria parietina*)
- **fruticose** – shrub-like, consisting of few to numerous branches which are radially symmetrical in section (e.g. *Usnea*)

In *Cladonia* the thallus is commonly composed of numerous basal squamules from which arise simple or branched, erect outgrowths (**podetia**), which in some species are pointed or may develop apical cups, sometimes bearing red or brown apothecia.

Lichens absorb moisture and associated inorganic nutrients over the entire surface of their thalli thus making them extremely sensitive to the chemical characteristics of both the surrounding air as well as the composition of their immediate substrates. Base-poor siliceous and base-rich calcareous rocks have different, often distinctive, lichen communities. There are also more subtle differences according to the natural base and nutrient status of the bark of different tree species; for example Oak, Beech and Birch have base-poor 'acid' bark whereas Ash, Willow and Sycamore bark is base-rich, resulting in different associated lichen communities. There is a contrast between the lichens of trees in woodland and on isolated trees at field margins. Also, historically, very long-established woodlands (e.g. New Forest, Hampshire) have special 'indicator' species whose particular presence signifies the antiquity of such forests (see James & Davies 2003).

Lichens are particularly sensitive to two major sources of environmental pollution. During the industrial revolution

▲ *Lecanora muralis* (×3), showing apothecia and the placodioid habit of the thallus lobes

increasing atmospheric levels of sulphur dioxide ($SO_2$) were noted, which has had a considerable and largely adverse impact on the abundance and species diversity of the lichen communities affected. Subsequently, post 1970, the levels of $SO_2$ have fallen considerably and the communities are now being replaced by lichens which reflect the increasing concentrations of major agricultural pollutants, principally nitrogen compounds resulting from present day farming methods and, to a lesser extent, car-exhaust gases. This current phase is probably somewhat similar to the environmental situation which existed prior to the industrial expansion in the 19th century.

Hawksworth and Rose (1970) were able to map ten zones of $SO_2$ concentration across Britain by using the presence and abundance of selected lichen species occurring on trees. On their scale B&BC was included in zone 0–2, equivalent to 150µg m$^{-3}$ or more of $SO_2$ which was characterised by a much reduced species diversity and coverage together with the widespread abundance of the $SO_2$-tolerant indicator lichen *Lecanora conizaeoides* on a wide range of different substrates.

Nevertheless Birmingham and the Black Country (B&BC) has never been a true 'lichen desert'. Horizontal branches in favoured situations have always been richer in lichen species and their cover. Also many saxicolous species have been able to persist on base-rich substrates, particularly concrete and mortar, as well as more or less basic gravestones in old churchyards. These are all substrates which are able, to some degree, to neutralise the impact of atmospheric $SO_2$ pollution.

Since 1970 there has been a notable reduction in B&BC of atmospheric $SO_2$ levels, now 20–70µg m$^{-3}$, varying according to wind direction. Consequently many previously $SO_2$-susceptible species have recolonised, while *Lecanora conizaeoides*, which is now mainly restricted to the rough bark of Birch and ancient soft-wood palings and boards, has decreased significantly.

The increase in the number of species recorded since 1970 also partly reflects the intensity of the influence and local concentrations of nitrogen compounds, as well as decreased levels of $SO_2$ pollution. Certain species, e.g. *Xanthoria parietina* and *X. polycarpa* are important indicators of high levels of nitrogen pollutants and are especially common near farms and

▲ *Cladonia macilenta* (×5) characteristic of the ground in heathland, showing pointed podetia, some bearing red apothecia

their out-buildings, together with a greatly increased coverage by algae species not associated in lichen symbioses. A similar extensive local green algae cover can appear, to the detriment of affected lichen communities, after the dispersal of fertiliser on fields at sources often some distance away and affected by the wind direction at the time. Such an event was observed in 2011 on Barr Beacon (SP0697) with a deleterious effect on the lichen communities of some Rowan trees, Hawthorn hedging and old fencing.

Early stages in the development of lichen diversity on particular street trees in the Four Oaks area has also been recently replaced by a dominating cover of green algae not associated with lichen symbiosis, especially in 2012. It appears that the general trend of improvement is still volatile and capable of a rapid reversal.

Lichens are also often consumed by slugs and snails, which particularly prefer the photobiont areas of their thalli. This can be seen in *Lecanora muralis* (Chewing-gum Lichen) where the placodioid thallus often has reduced marginal lobes and an upper surface with a mosaic of white areas due to the exposure of the thallus medulla as a result of persistent mollusc browsing.

2012 was an exceptionally wet and a stressful year for lichen communities. This was reflected in a significant increase in independent algal and bryophyte cover (for example *Grimmia pulvinata* and *Ceratodon purpureus*), especially on walls and older, isolated tree boles in open situations. It was noted that newly established lichen communities in such open sites were also significantly reduced or lost as the result of a big increase in snail and slug activity, due to such weather conditions.

With all these changes currently taking place, these are exciting times for lichenologists! One major feature of considerable interest has been the big increase in the diversity and coverage of lichens colonising trees, particularly their twigs and branches. This recolonisation includes many nutrient-rich indicator species and is in part related to the increase in pollution with nitrogen compounds from farming and car exhausts. There are also recent adverse changes in the abundance and diversity of *Cladonia* species and other lichens characteristic of *Calluna*-rich heathland. These changes reflect the fall of $SO_2$ levels coupled with an increase in the underlying impact of nitrogen pollutants and a corresponding increase in invasive vascular plants.

Other features are also currently adversely affecting lichen biodiversity. For example many of the graveyards which represent the most important saxicolous habitats in B&BC appear to be subjected to a periodical mechanical scrubbing of stones, others are extremely poorly maintained and yet others are treated by regular applications of herbicides distributed indiscriminately over lichens and developing scrub vegetation, killing both.

There is a need to encourage more people to study this beautiful group of organisms, to recognise and conserve existing diverse populations, to continue to monitor change and to make more use of their remarkable value as ongoing environmental indicators.

## The lichen surveys in B&BC

Because there are currently considerable changes in the lichen biodiversity of B&BC, the present account deals only with records made since 2000, although some earlier records from Sutton Park are mentioned in the species entries. Also a large number of records were made by D.C. Lindsay and the Wildlife Trust from Birmingham in the 1980s. Their lists suggest that positive responses to falling $SO_2$ levels had already started in the 1980s. Even some of the $SO_2$-sensitive foliose and fruticose species such as *Flavoparmelia caperata*, *Tuckermanopsis chlorophylla* (which is now possibly decreasing as a result of lowering levels of bark acidification) and *Usnea subfloridana* were recorded, usually on Willow bark and sometimes on fence wood which might have been recently imported into the conurbation. A significantly long list of heathland *Cladonia* species was also recorded, suggesting that their decline is now taking place. Some of the more interesting records have been mentioned in the species entries, but in addition many of the commoner lichens were also recorded then.

The majority of the modern records are derived from 16 recent lichen site or area surveys led by senior members of the British Lichen Society which have been generously contributed to the B&BC Flora project. There are also some notes on some further brief reconnoitres. Each of the sites is described briefly below and the records have been used as the basis of entries for 217 species (plus 4 which are only known from old records). The distribution of the 16 sites surveyed is shown in the following map, plus some un-numbered points for the minor sites.

### Principal surveyors

Peter James (PWJ), Ivan Pedley (IP), Mark Powell (MP), Joy Ricketts (JR) and Rose Golding (RG).

I.C. Trueman (ICT), Eleanor Cohn (EVJC), and Anne Daly (APD) have also assisted with certain of the surveys. Records collected by D.C. Lindsay and the Wildlife Trust surveyors under his direct control are labelled 'DCL' and dated.

### Site Register and general comments on the site lists

In the atlas of lichen species the following sites are given two-letter codes:

### 1. Sutton Park (SP)

- *Surveyed* 2008–2010 by PWJ & MP on a large number of site visits with occasional field assistance given by M. Butler, J. Lloyd, IP, Prof. C. Smith, other members of the British Lichen Society and ICT.
- *Central grid reference* SP097970, although the site extends to more than 900 hectares and includes the whole or parts of 15 monads (kilometre squares). Further location notes are given against many species entries.
- ***156 species recorded***

This is the principal basis of the present B&BC lichen account and has contributed records for over 70% of the entire set of species recorded here, the site being relatively weak only in 'natural' saxicolous habitats. A full discussion of the results will be found in James & Powell (2010). The importance of this site and its long history as a nature reserve has been discussed elsewhere in this book and its function as an oasis for the diversity of lichens in B&BC is very clear.

A lichen list of 27 species was also made by PWJ in the woodland and heathland of the Park in 1977 and a checklist of lichens records from Sutton Park was published by Coxhead & Fowkes (1992) listing 40 species, although of these only 26 had recent (post 1985) records. It is therefore certain that there has been a spectacular increase in the number of species present in the Park, particularly in corticolous species, with the exception of the $SO_2$-tolerant *Lecanora conizaeoides*, abundant in 1977 and rare today. Most of the well-lit branches and twigs in the Park

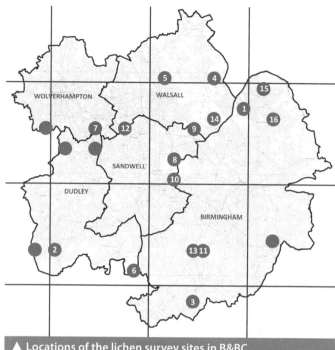

▲ Locations of the lichen survey sites in B&BC

are now colonised, and the now abundant, attractive foliose and fruticose species will be particularly pleasing to the non-specialist and contribute to the already huge aesthetic and scientific value of the natural history of the Park. Particularly interesting is the record for *Usnea flavocardia*, which is considered nationally rare and was previously recorded only from Cornwall, Pembroke and W Scotland. It is also abundantly clear that such changes are by no means complete and are still taking place. With saxicolous species these developments are much more complicated and less extreme, particularly on $SO_2$-buffered calcareous substrates.

These current modifications in lichen cover are not entirely positive. Firstly, the lists reveal the increased influence of nutrient-indicating species, with high frequencies of *Physcia*, *Physconia* and *Xanthoria* species particularly on twigs. Secondly, the terricolous lichens belonging to the genera *Baeomyces*, *Cladonia*, *Peltigera* and *Placynthiella* which are now generally sparse were apparently less so in the past. These species are associated with bare heathland areas, particularly by paths and after burning, which may themselves be becoming scarcer and less long-lasting, ironically with "better" management involving less human disturbance. It is also possible that increased nitrogen inputs into the soils from the atmosphere are allowing a more rapid recovery of the vascular plant cover from disturbance. James & Powell (2010) comment that "the most spectacular heathland-type communities are now to be observed with the aid of a ladder, on the rotting conifer-wood shingle roofs of two small kiosks at the Streetly Gate and Four Oaks entrances to the Park"!

### 2. St Mary's, Old Swinford, Dudley (OS)

- *Surveyed* 19 October 2009 by PWJ, assisted by ICT & APD
- *Central grid reference*: SO907831
- ***54 species recorded***

A very interesting extensive churchyard with many, large, chiefly sandstone, gravestones. Considerable diversity is present as the main rock type has a good and varied lichen community. The abundance of *Melanelixia fuliginosa* subsp. *fuliginosa* is especially interesting. Portions of the outer church wall are heavily shaded, especially near the car park. There is no strong sign of nitrification in the saxicolous flora, but part of the churchyard is immersed in a thicket of herbaceous vegetation with occasional trees (Sycamore, Birch, Oak, Ornamental Cherry etc.) which generally carry a very limited number of nitrophile species The Green algae *Trentepohlia* spp. (orange in colour!) are frequent on trees and gravestones. Also recorded was the fungus *Geastrum schmedelli* Vittad. (= *G.nanum* Pers.)

### 3. St Nicholas, Kings Norton, Birmingham (KN)
- *Surveyed* 8 September 2009 by PWJ assisted by ICT
- *Central grid reference*: SP049789
- **52 species recorded**

The church wall is very shaded. The churchyard is very extensive with *circa* 800 gravestones. There is early evidence of recovery from intense environmental acidification over many years from industrial Birmingham. Probably a very depleted flora then, now being replaced by nitrophyte species (nitrogen needy or tolerant). Acid gravestones are showing a ± healthy development of crustose species (e.g. *Rhizocarpon reductum*, *Buellia* species). *Lecanora conizaeoides* is notably absent indicating the widespread disappearance of that species in current surveys and a good indication of the decreased impact of acidification on lichen communities. Also seen in the graveyard was the fungus *Lacrymaria lacrymabunda* (Bull) Pat. – Weeping Widow! N.B. trees numerous, mainly Horse Chestnut, Yew, Lime, occasional Sycamore and Ornamental Cherry. The trees are very poor in lichen cover, with only a few nitrophilous species on dead twigs of Cherry.

### 4. Aldridge Parish churchyard (AP)
- *Surveyed* 21 September 2009 by PWJ, assisted by ICT
- **37 species recorded**
- *a) main churchyard, central grid reference* SK060006.
Gravestones few, some ±cleaned; overgrown with trees (mostly Yew) & mostly too shaded. Outer wall of churchyard very poor. Few lichens on trees, chiefly on Ornamental Cherry.
- *b) annexe graveyard, central grid reference* SK061007 (mainly additional species).
More grassy than main churchyard, more open, poorly maintained, ±overgrown with grass. No trees.

### 5. Coalpool Cemetery, Walsall (CC)
- *Surveyed* 21 September 2009 by PWJ assisted by ICT
- *Central grid reference*: SK018005
- **35 species recorded**

Very large, poorly maintained. *Evernia prunastre, Hypogymnia physodes, H. tubulosa, Melanelixia subaurifera, Parmelia sulcata, Physcia adscendens, P. tenella,* and *Punctelia subrudecta* are all seen on a single gravestone beneath a Sycamore, demonstrating vividly its nutritional effect on acid substrates beneath its canopy. They were not, or rarely, seen elsewhere in this large cemetery and it was not possible to ascertain whether a similar flora was on branches in the canopy.

### 6. Public footpath E of Black Swan Inn, Illey, Halesowen (IL)
- *Surveyed* 30 July 2010 by PWJ assisted by ICT.
- *Grid references*: SP9881 and SP9882
- **29 species recorded.** From stile at SP982817 to field N of Illey Hall Farm at SP982821; most species are on twigs, often dead twigs. Continuing into SP9882 examining woodland margin, fields, hedgerows (Field Maple and Dog Rose), some Willow (mostly dead), Hazel, Elder (mostly dead or dying).

### 7. Ladymoor Pool Bilston (LP)
- *Surveyed* 22 April 2010 by PWJ assisted by ICT + EVJC
- *Central grid reference*: SO942950
- **19 species recorded**

A relatively small heap of large boulders of very solid furnace slag set in an area of marsh and powdery slag was examined.

### 8. Sandwell Valley Country Park (SV)
- *Surveyed* 19 December 2003 by IP & JR
- *Central grid reference*: SP028926
- **42 species recorded**

Records mostly from SP0292, a few from SP0392.

### 9. St Margaret's, Great Barr, Birmingham (GB)
- *Surveyed* 19 December 2003 by IP
- *Central grid reference* SP049959
- **37 species recorded**

### 10. Handsworth Cemetery, Birmingham (HC)
- *Surveyed* 19 December 2003 by IP
- *Central grid reference*: SP029907
- **42 species recorded**

### 11. Edgbaston Nature Reserve, Birmingham (ER)
- *Surveyed* 17 January 2004 by RG & JR
- *Central grid reference* SP054839
- **29 species recorded**

### 12. Moorcroft Wood, Moxley (MW)
- *Surveyed* 25 May 2010 by PWJ assisted by ICT
- *Central grid reference*: SO970951.
- **33 species recorded**

Partly shaded and well-lit furnace slag mounds around and within one of the shallow water pools surveyed, although access difficult. The woodland trees were largely devoid of lichens although some records were made on fallen branches.

### 13. Birmingham University Campus (BU)
- *Surveyed* 15 September 2009 by IP and OPAL participants
- *Central grid reference*: SP0483
- **53 species recorded**

All the sites are within the 1km square containing the University station: SP0483. They are: a) along a walk line from the Biosciences building N to the canal then E to the athletics track and return to Biosciences; and b) a second walk (with the OPAL group) S to the trees bordering the ring road of the campus overlooking fields to the S. The sandstone records are from the parapet and 'bioroof' experimental plots on the flat roof of one of the older original buildings. *Usnea* sp. observed on Lime bark.

### 14. Barr Beacon Summit (BB)
- *Surveyed* 24 March 2011 by PWJ + ICT and on several subsequent visits in 2011 by PWJ
- **82 species recorded**

A series of distinct habitats was assessed:
(i)   Car park area at *circa* SP06059707: concrete kerbs, roadside stumps and boulders (which have subsequently been removed).
(ii)  Scrub and woodland: Oak, Birch and small area of Pine by reservoir.
(iii) Summit War Memorial: mainly granite, smooth and largely maintained and cleaned – thus poor in lichen cover except in a few recesses overlooked during maintenance – mainly at the perimeter of the monument area.

(iv) Hedgerow along summit track between N and S car parks – Rowan and Hawthorn.

(v) Walls of reservoirs: mixture of mortar, cement, some exposed brickwork, variously shaded and mossy on W side; lichens particularly varied on sheltered E side alongside pathway between N and S car parks.

(vi) *Erica* heathland: two small heathland sites at S end of site at *circa* SP061968. These were created using heather brash from Brownhills Common (SK0406) in 1992 and 1995.

### 15. Four Oaks area (FO)
* *Surveyed* PWJ in 2010 and 2012
* *Grid references*: range within SP1199
* **38 species recorded**

Mainly records from gardens and roadsides and also including stonework at St. James's Church, Mere Green Road.

### 16. Holy Trinity Parish Church, Sutton Coldfield (SPC)
* *Surveyed* PWJ in 2012
* *Central grid reference*: SP121963
* **40 species recorded**

Site would benefit from further visits.

### Other sites briefly visited by PWJ & ICT in 2009 and 2010
* ***St Bartholomew's, Penn* (PC)** (SO894952). Lichens recovering; 7 common crustose species observed.
* ***South Yardley Cemetery* (SY)** (SP125844). Huge site, much managed by applications of weedkillers, short list of 10 common crustose species observed.
* ***All Saints Church Sedgley* (SC)** (SO917937). Much sprayed with herbicide; modest list of 12 species mainly on churchyard wall.

* ***Christ Church, Coseley* (CCC)** (SO947933). Two churchyards; both are maintained with herbicide treatment, having few lichens beyond *Lepraria incana* (7 species altogether).
* ***Stourbridge Cemetery* (STC)** (SO886836). Only 12 species observed although a single large saxicolous colony of *Parmelia saxatilis* was noted.
* ***St Michael & all Angels Church Pelsall, Walsall* (PCW)** (SK020030). Possibly sprayed and/or recently cleaned. Only a very few gravestones with a lichen flora, only 23 species recorded, corticolous lichens absent except for *Xanthoria polycarpa* and *Physcia tenella*, most saxicolous species in the list poorly represented and rare.

Some samples of critical specimens from Sutton Park are housed in Herb. Powell, others, from various sites, in Herb. James.

## References and further reading

Coxhead, P. & Fowkes, H. (eds) (1992) *A Natural History of Sutton Park Part 2: Fungi, Lichens and Bryophytes.* Sutton Coldfield Natural History Society, Sutton Coldfield.

Dobson, F.S. (2005) *Lichens; An illustrated Guide to the British and Irish Species* ed. 5. Richmond Publishing Co. Slough.

Dobson, F.S. (2011) *Lichens; An illustrated Guide to the British and Irish Species* ed. 6. Richmond Publishing Co. Slough.

Purvis, W. (2010) *Lichens.* Natural History Museum, London.

Hawksworth, D.L. & Rose, F. (1970) Qualitative scale for estimating sulphur dioxide air pollution in England and Wales using epiphytic lichens. *Nature* 227: 145–148.

James, P.W. & Davies, L. (2003) Conservation and management. Resurvey of the corticolous lichen flora of Epping Forest. *Essex Naturalist (New Series)* 20: 67–82.

James, P.W., Hawksworth, D.L. & Rose, F. (1977) Lichen Communities in the British Isles: a preliminary prospectus, in Seaward, M.R.D. (ed.) *Lichen Ecology* pp.295–413. London: Academic Press.

James, P.W. & Powell, M. (2010) The Lichens of Sutton Park. *British Lichen Society Bulletin* 107 pp.2–17.

Smith, C.W., Aptroot, A., Coppins, B.J., Fletcher, A., Gilbert, O.L., James, P.W. & Wolseley, P.A. (2009) *The Lichens of Great Britain and Ireland.* British Lichen Society, London.

Wolseley, P.A., James, P.W., Theobald, M.R. & Sutton, M.A. (2006) Detecting changes in epiphytic lichen communities at sites affected by atmospheric ammonia from agricultural sources. *Lichenologist* 38: pp.161–176.

▲ Peter James examining furnace spoil at Moorcroft Wood

## Species entries

Entries are presented alphabetically by genus and then by species for all species positively identified in the present survey in B&BC (plus four old records). The taxonomy follows Smith *et al.* (2009). Most species are illustrated in Dobson (2011). The entry for each species starts with a brief précis of its morphology, ecology and distribution in UK as described in Smith *et al.* (2009) and Dobson (2005), ending with a figure in brackets showing the maximum zone level of $SO_2$ air pollution that can be tolerated by the species as estimated in Dobson (2005) from Hawksworth & Rose (1970), except where there is doubt. A score of 10 indicates "pure" uncontaminated air, and at the other end of the scale a score of 2 records the appearance of the pollution tolerant lichen *Lecanora conizaeoides* on tree bark at winter levels of $SO_2$ declining to about 150µg m⁻³ This scale is not used in Dobson (2011). The remaining remarks record the presence and any other observations about the species at the sixteen main sampled sites, with some further remarks on the other briefly visited sites in B&BC where appropriate.

***Acarospora fuscata*** (Nyl.) Arnold
Crustose; found on hard, siliceous, nutrient-enriched substrates; common throughout UK (3). CC on slate.

***Acarospora rufescens*** (Ach.) Bausch
Crustose; siliceous substrates. SP on brick bridge parapet N of Rowton's Well; BB on granite of War Memorial.

***Acarospora smaragdula*** (Wahlenb.) A. Massal.
Crustose; siliceous rocks and in metal-rich situations. Fairly common throughout UK (5). BU on sandstone.

***Acrocordia salweyi*** (Leight. ex Nyl.) A.L. Sm.
±Immersed, on soft, highly calcareous rocks and old mortar, throughout UK, common in S & W England (5). BB on mortar, SE side of reservoir.

***Agonimia tristicula*** (Nyl.) Zahlbr.
Minutely squamulose, on calcareous soils and dunes and on mosses and lichens in crevices of ±calcareous rocks and walls. BB on shaded mossy mortar on W side of reservoir near roadside.

***Amandinea punctata*** (Hoffm.) Coppins & Scheid.
Crustose; common throughout UK on nutrient-rich or -enriched bark, wood and stone (3). SP frequent on twigs and young bark of oak and other species, on smooth older bark of mature tree trunks and on weathered sawn wood of posts and benches; IL on hawthorn, and wood of a stile; SV on trees in Swan Pool car park and on alders and willows by Swan Pool; ER on a wooden bench; BU on ash bark; BB on hedgerow rowan.

***Arthonia lapidicola*** (Taylor) Branth & Rostr.
Crustose, often partly immersed; calcareous rocks, stones and mortar; frequent in UK (5). SP on iron-stained concrete blocks E of Wyndley Leisure Centre; FO, well developed in metal-enriched run-off of windows, St James's Church.

***Arthonia punctiformis*** Ach.
Immersed in the smooth bark of many tree species (4). SP on hawthorn twigs, N of Longmoor Pool.

***Arthonia radiata*** (Pers.) Ach.
Immersed in the smooth bark of many tree species; widespread and common in UK except in air-polluted areas (7). SP, on oak twigs S of Streetly Gate; IL on young oak and hazel bark; BU on ash bark; BB on oak on W-facing slope.

***Arthonia spadicea*** Leight.
Immersed in very shaded basic bark of tree trunks throughout UK (5). IL in deep shade on smooth bark of oaks.

***Arthopyrenia punctiformis*** A. Massal.
Immersed in smooth bark of twigs and young trees of many species; common in UK except in highly polluted areas (5). SP on young hawthorn bark, S of Longmoor Pool; IL on young oak bark.

***Aspicilia contorta*** (Hoffm.) Kremp.
Crustose; common in UK on hard calcareous rocks, concrete and mortar, tolerant of nutrient-enrichment (4). SV, on concrete kerbs.
**subsp. *contorta***
SP from a concrete dam E of Keeper's Pool and a brick wall E of Wyndley Pool; BB on SE side of reservoir walls.
**subsp. *hoffmanniana*** S.Ekman & Fröberg
SP with subsp. *contorta*; KN, a single thallus; OS a single specimen on calcareous surround of a grave; BU on concrete.

***Bacidia adastra*** Sparrius & Aptroot
Crustose; usually corticolous; typical of the nutrient-enriched zones at the base of trees in parks. SP, base of a birch tree near Toby Carvery; FO on Magnolia.

***Bacidia inundata*** (Fr.) Körb.
Crustose; usually on hard siliceous rock in non-polluted water (6). SP on shaded rock at overflow structure at E end of Powell's Pool.

***Bacidia neosquamulosa*** Aptroot & van Herk
Crustose; sheltered saxicolous and corticolous, ±nutrient-rich sites in urban situations. FO on rockery stones.

***Bacidia saxenii*** Erichsen
Crustose; a common pioneer of a wide range of calcareous or dust-enriched substrates. SP on treated fence posts, Gum Slade.

***Bacidia sulphurella*** Samp.
Crustose, corticolous, typically on tree bases; tolerant of urban conditions in UK. SP on a shaded oak trunk SE of Streetly Gate.

***Bacidia viridifarinosa*** Coppins & P. James
Crustose, on shaded, dry bark of mature deciduous trees and on siliceous or slightly basic rock-faces, old memorials, frequent. SP on sheltered side of boles of old oaks, Gum Slade.

***Baeomyces rufus*** (Huds.) Rebent.
Crustose or minutely squamulose; typically on damp gravelly or peaty acid soils, common in UK (4). SP on sparsely-vegetated soil beside a path W of Keeper's Pool and on a wooden shingle roof at Streetly Gate; MW on furnace slag; BB.

▲ *Baeomyces rufus*, Barr Beacon (×4)

**Belonia nidarosiensis** (Kindt) P.M. Jørg. & Vězda
A powdery crust; on dry, rain-sheltered calcareous rocks and church walls; not uncommon throughout UK (5). SP on shaded limestone of overflow structure E end of Powell's Pool.

**Bilimbia sabuletorum** (Schreb.) Arnold
Crustose; growing typically on mosses on calcareous rocks or walls; common in UK (4). SP on mosses on old mortar on wall by Four Oaks entrance; amongst mosses on mortar on church wall OS; ER on brick walling and mortar; CC on ±basic mortar and also on a bone with *Lecidella stigmatea*; GB; BB on shaded mosses on mortar/cement on W side of reservoir walls; SPC.

**Buellia aethalea** (Ach.) Th. Fr.
Crustose, frequent in UK on siliceous rocks, sometimes in nutrient-rich situations and a pioneer on walls and memorials (5). SP on brick wall at E end of Powell's Pool and sandstone coping stones of parapets of bridges over the railway; OS occasional on hard acid rock substrates; KN widespread on granite with *Rhizocarpon reductum*; AP main churchyard; CC widespread on granite; LP scattered thalli on furnace slag; GB; BU on sandstone; BB on granite War Memorial; SPC; STC; PCW.

**Buellia badia** (Fr.) A. Massal.
Crustose, subsquamulose to squamulose; siliceous rocks, especially roof tiles; uncommon in UK. SP on horizontal coping stones of small bridge parapet approx. 100 metres W of Town Gate.

**Buellia griseovirens** (Turner & Borrer ex Sm.) Almb.
Crustose; common in UK on ±smooth bark (5). Occasional in SP on smooth bark of *Acer*, on old bark of mature oak and on a wooden noticeboard, Bracebridge; FO on ancient oaks, and apple and pear trees.

**Buellia ocellata** (Flot.) Körb.
Crustose; exposed siliceous rocks, pebbles and stonework throughout UK (5). CC and KN in granite communities with *B. aethalea*; PCW.

**Caloplaca arcis** (Poelt & Vězda) Arup
Crustose, minutely lobate at the margin; common on limestone and cement in churchyards and lowland walls throughout Britain. SP on concrete beside Bracebridge Pool and on brick wall at E end of Wyndley Pool; occasional at KN on limestone gravestones and associated mortar; BU on concrete; BB reservoir walls, cement; SPC.

**Caloplaca cerinella** (Nyl.) Flagey
Crustose; in communities on nutrient-rich bark, especially of twigs; scarce or under-recorded (6). Occasional in SP on elder twigs; IL on moribund elder.

**Caloplaca cerinelloides** (Erichsen) Poelt
Crustose; base-rich bark; rare in UK or overlooked. SP on mature trunk of ?*Populus* to S of Wyndley Leisure centre.

**Caloplaca chlorina** (Flot.) H. Oliver
Crustose; damp or shaded siliceous rocks; throughout lowlands (6). SP on sandstone coping-stone of bridge parapet approx. 100 metres W of Town Gate.

**Caloplaca citrina** (Hoffm.) Th. Fr.
Crustose; very common in UK; mainly on manured or calcareous substrates (3). In B&BC recorded at most sites as frequent on basic saxicolous substrates including calcareous gravestones, concrete, mortar and furnace slag. In SP occasional on mortar, and on one occasion on a birch trunk in a wound track. Currently regarded as a complex of species.

**Caloplaca crenulatella** (Nyl.) H. Olivier
Crustose; typically on flat concrete; frequent throughout lowland England & Wales especially in urban areas (4). Occasional in SP, on concrete beside Longmoor & Keeper's Pools and on a brick wall by Wyndley Pool; OS well developed on a horizontal cement gravestone; KN ±frequent on flat, ±base-rich substrates; SV on concrete kerbs; HC; FO, on a concrete patio; SPC.

**Caloplaca dichroa** Arup
Crustose, on limestone rocks, walls; locally abundant in UK. FO, garden walls.

**Caloplaca flavescens** (Huds.) J.R. Laundon
Crustose with a radiating, lobed margin; common throughout the British Isles on calcareous stone but absent from some air-polluted areas (4). OS well developed on a single limestone tablet (back of a seat); KP a single thallus, side of limestone chest tomb; AP annexe; single specimen; BU on concrete; BB on cement of W side of reservoir walls, scattered.

**Caloplaca flavocitrina** (Nyl.) H. Olivier
Crustose; calcareous rocks and base-rich bark; common throughout UK (4). SP occasional, usually on brickwork including mortar, also on large limestone rocks at overflow of Powell's Pool; OS frequent, especially on walls; KN frequent on basic saxicolous substrates; SV on concrete kerbs; AP; GB; BU on concrete; BB on cement of reservoir walls, throughout; FO on a concrete patio; SPC; PCW.

**Caloplaca holocarpa** (Hoffm.) A.E. Wade (Agg.)
Crustose; a pioneer species on calcareous stone, mortar, asbestos cement, rarely on bark; very common throughout the British Isles (2). SP on concrete by Keeper's Pool and on brick wall by Wyndley Pool; occasional at most other sites on basic stones, mortar and concrete kerbs; on furnace slag at LP and on elder twigs at ER; at BU on sandstone. Now regarded as a complex of species. The segregate **Caloplaca oasis** (A. Massal.) Szat. is recorded at BU on concrete, at BB as a single colony on W side of concrete reservoir walls and at FO, on mortar in walls.

**Caloplaca obscurella** (J. Lahm) Th. Fr.
Crustose; typically on nutrient-enriched basic bark; common throughout UK. SP on damp branch, and mature willow trunk, S of Wyndley Leisure Centre.

**Caloplaca saxicola** (Hoffm.) Nordin
Placodioid; calcareous rocks throughout UK (6). Recently recorded from SP by PWJ, there are 2 records from 1980s on walls (SP0279, SP0981) by DCL.

**Caloplaca teicholyta** (Ach.) J. Steiner
Crustose, obscurely placodioid, common on calcareous stone and mortar (4). FO, sterile on outhouse roof (mock asbestos).

▲ *Caloplaca flavescens*, Old Swinford; (left, ×1); with apothecia (right, ×3)

***Candelaria concolor*** (Dicks.) Stein
Minutely foliose or fruticose; mostly on nutrient-rich bark of well-lit wayside trees; local but spreading throughout the British Isles (7). SP on sycamore trunk near Blackroot Bistro.

***Candelariella aurella*** (Hoffm.) Zahlbr.
Crustose, mostly on man-made basic substrates; throughout the British Isles, commoner in urban habitats (2). (Usually sheltered) basic stones, mortar, church walls, often occasional to frequent: SP, OS, KN, AP, CC, ER, BB, SPC and f. ***aurella*** at GB, HC & BU on concrete.

***Candelariella reflexa*** (Nyl.) Lettau
Crustose, with or without minute squamules; on shaded nutrient-enriched bark; common throughout British Isles and spreading (4). SP abundant on nutrient-enriched twigs, branches and tree bases; IL at base of moribund oak; SV on willows and young oak; MW on tree base; BU on sycamore bark.

***Candelariella vitellina*** (Hoffm.) Müll. Arg.
Crustose, subsquamulose; very common in UK on nutrient-enriched siliceous and calcareous rock except in heavily polluted urban areas (3). Occasional in SP on sandstone blocks in walls, and on one instance on a birch trunk in a wound track; frequent at OS on basic gravestones, also church wall pebbles; frequent at KN on sheltered ±base-rich rock and mortar surfaces; AP main churchyard; generally abundant at CC on ±basic stones and mortar; ER on brick walling and mortar, frequent and often fertile at LP on furnace slag; CCC; SPC; recorded as f. ***vitellina*** at HC, GB and BU (on sandstone); SC; STC; PCW.

***Candelariella xanthostigma*** (Pers. ex Ach.) Lettau
Crustose; widely distributed but local in UK on less-shaded trees, and typically not in nutrient-enriched situations. SV on willows and young oak; GB.

***Carbonea vitellinaria*** (Nyl.) Hertel
Thallus inapparent, inhabiting *Candelariella vitellina* on weakly nutrient-enriched acid rocks, widespread. Recorded by DCL in 1981 on concrete wall (SP0277).

***Catillaria chalybeia*** (Borrer) A. Massal.
Thinly crustose; common in UK, mainly on slightly base-rich or nutrient-enriched siliceous rocks (3). Rare in SP on sandstone blocks in walls, and on one instance on a birch trunk in a wound track; KN and CC, on acid gravestones; BB on War Memorial; PCW; GB and BU cited as var. ***chalybeia***.

***Catillaria lenticularis*** (Ach.) Th. Fr.
Thinly crustose; widespread on limestone and highly calcareous building materials. BU on concrete; BB on cement, W side of reservoir.

***Cetraria aculeata*** (Schreb.) Fr.
Thallus forming shrubby tufts of brown, spinulose lobes. Common in heathland (4). BB in small quantity in *Calluna/Erica* heath. There is a 1971 DCL record from Sutton Park, last seen 1988 (Coxhead & Fowkes 1992).

***Chaenotheca ferruginea*** (Turner ex Sm.) Mig.
Crustose, common in UK and tolerant of $SO_2$ pollution, in dry recesses on acid bark (4). Occasional in SP on dry shaded bark of mature tree trunks, mainly oak, in old woodland.

***Chrysothrix flavovirens*** Tønsberg
Leprose; frequent and increasing in the UK on well-lit, rather dry, non-nutrient-enriched wood and bark of mature broad-leaved and coniferous trees. Rare in SP on mature oak trunks; OS in lenticels on birch trunk and on rowan.

***Cladonia chlorophaea*** (Flörke ex Sommerf.) Spreng.
Podetia to 3cm tall, each with a ± regular terminal cup, surface ± granular-sorediate. Common throughout UK on peat, rotting logs and among rocks especially in heathland (4). Occasional in SP on decaying stumps, mature bark and sandy soil; occasional at OS on summits of gravestones; SV on the moss *Hypnum cupressiforme* on willows and young oak, ER in gardens on lignin; MW on furnace spoil; GB; BU; PC; SC. At BB the two chemical races ***Cladonia cryptochlorophaea*** Asah. and ***C. merochlorophaea*** Asah. were distinguished. DCL recorded the chemical race ***novochlorophaea*** Sipman on moss on a wall in SP0891 in 1979.

*Cladonia chlorophaea* (×8)
(by Gemma Edwards)

***Cladonia coniocraea*** (Flörke) Spreng. (Agg.)
Podetia grey-green, to 2cm tall, shortly corticate-squamulose at the base, finely sorediate above, apices pointed or rarely with very narrow cups. Common throughout UK on bases of living or recently dead trees and wood and sometimes on heathy soil (3). Rare in SP on rotting stumps including at the Gum Slade and on shaded wall S of Keeper's Pool; occasional at OS on summits and sides of gravestones; rare at KN on a tree base; ER on a stump; AP annexe, on a mossy path; BB on War Memorial and in the heath; SY.

***Cladonia digitata*** (L.) Hoffm.
Basal squamules usually dominant, densely sorediate and partly orange below; podetia to 1cm tall, pointed or with irregular cups; apothecia rare, red. Throughout UK on rotting wood or peaty soil (6). One sample only at OS on rotting wood. It was also recorded by DCL at Moseley Bog (SP0981, SP0982) in 1979 and 1981.

***Cladonia diversa*** Asperges
(*C. coccifera* (L.) Willd. agg.)
Thallus yellow-green, podetia 1–2cm tall, with ±regular cups, surface granulose, occasionally with red apothecia on their rims. Widespread and common in UK on heathland soil (6). Rare at SP, terricolous on Little Bracebridge Heath; BB in the *Calluna/Erica* heath. Also recorded by DCL in heathland at Rednal Hill (SO9976) in 1971.

***Cladonia fimbriata*** (L.) Fr.
Podetia to 1.5cm tall, with ±regular terminal cups, entirely powdery-sorediate. Common in UK on rotting wood and earth, even in polluted areas (3). Rare at SP, terricolous on Little Bracebridge Heath; FO, rare on rockery stones in gardens.

***Cladonia floerkeana*** (Fr.) Flörke
Podetia to 2cm tall, grey, ± covered with squamules; cups absent, apices frequently

*Cladonia floerkiana* (×12)
(by Gemma Edwards)

with distinctive clusters of red apothecia. Very common in UK on heathland and, more rarely, rotting wood (5). Rare at SP on a shingle roof at Streetly Gate entrance and on heathland SE of Bracebridge Pool; BB in open patches in the *Calluna/Erica* heath.

**Cladonia furcata** (Huds.) Schrad.
Basal squamulose thallus usually absent, podetia to 2.5cm tall, ± tufted, branched, bearing scattered squamules, all apices pointed. Common in the UK in heathland and on other acid soils, with an ecotype (**subsp. subrangiformis** (Sandst.) Abbayes) in open turf on calcareous soils (4). Occasional at SP in heathland SE of Bracebridge Pool; MW on furnace spoil; BB in open patches in the *Calluna/Erica* heath. DCL had many records for this species in our part of vc. 37 in the 1980s.

**Cladonia glauca** Flörke
Podetia to 5cm tall, squamulose at the base, finely sorediate above, simple or antler-shaped towards the apices. Widespread particularly in Scotland and E England on rotting wood and on heathland. SP from a shingle roof, Four Oaks entrance; BB in open patches in the *Calluna/Erica* heath.

**Cladonia humilis** (With.) J.R. Laundon
Podetia to 1cm tall, mostly regularly cup-shaped and entirely finely sorediate. Basal squamules often well-developed. Common throughout UK on dry or sandy, especially recently disturbed soil including suburban gardens (3). Rare at SP, terricolous and at the base of a mature oak outside Streetly Gate; OS well developed on several gravestones; AP main churchyard; MW on furnace spoil; BB on War Memorial; FO, common in neglected gardens on rockery stones; SPC; STC.

**Cladonia macilenta** Hoffm.
Thallus blue-grey, podetia to 2cm tall, simple or becoming branched towards the apices, cups absent, apothecia rare, red. Throughout UK on soil, bark and wood in acid woodlands and heathlands (5). SP on rotting stump, terricolous on Little Bracebridge Heath and shingle roof, Town Gate entrance; BB in the *Calluna/Erica* heath.

**Cladonia ochrochlora** Flörke
Podetia to 4cm tall, simple, mostly with a terminal cup, corticated-squamulose at the base, in part corticated and sorediate above. Common on rotting tree stumps and less often in heathland; throughout UK (6). SP on humus-rich soil of bank of NE end of Blackroot railway bridge; BB in the *Calluna/Erica* heath.

**Cladonia parasitica** (Hoffm.) Hoffm.
Thallus of very small, compacted squamules; podetia to 1cm tall, scattered, contorted-branched. Rather local throughout UK on decaying, decorticated wood especially of oak, also on earth banks, in old woodland (6). SP on lignum of dead oak trunk in the Gum Slade.

**Cladonia pocillum** (Ach.) Grognot
Basal squamules well developed, sometimes dominant; podetia to 1.5cm tall, with regular cups with a coarsely granular surface. Calcicole species, common throughout UK mainly on sandy calcareous soils and old mortar (4). MW on furnace slag; BB on concrete, W side of reservoir.

**Cladonia polydactyla** (Flörke) Spreng.
Podetia to 2cm tall, sometimes branched at the apex, with or without cups, lower part squamulose, becoming finely sorediate above; apothecia red. Throughout UK on rotting wood and soil in woodland and heathland (5). SP at base of birch trunk and on rotting wood at edge of Bracebridge Pool. DCL recorded it on rubble at a derelict brickworks in SP0983 in 1986.

**Cladonia portentosa** (Dufour) Coem.
(*C. impexa* Harm.)
Squamules never present, podetia 4–8cm tall, very richly branched forming rounded, compact, complex clusters. Abundant in heathlands throughout UK. BB in the *Calluna/Erica* heath. DCL recorded it from rubble at a derelict brickworks (SP0983, 1986).

**Cladonia pyxidata** (L.) Hoffm.
Thallus grey-green, podetia to 1.5cm tall, cups widely expanded with a coarsely granular surface. Very common throughout UK on mossy rocks and walls, tree trunks, and fairly dry acid soils (4). CC amongst mosses within grave surrounds; AP annexe graveyard; KN on a single acid gravestone; OS occasional on summits and sides of gravestones; BB in the *Calluna/Erica* heath.

**Cladonia squamosa** (Scop.) Hoffm.
**var. squamosa**
Basal squamules densely matted; podetia to 4cm tall, ±pointed or with deformed, ±perforated, cups. Common on acid soil, peat and rotting wood in UK (6). BB in the *Calluna/Erica* heath. In 1986 DCL recorded it on soil over brick rubble, derelict brickworks (SP0983).

**Cladonia subulata** (L.) F.H. Wigg.
Podetia to 5cm tall; entirely farinose-sorediate, apices pointed or with an antler-shaped, narrow, ill-defined cup. Frequent on dry, sandy heaths in UK (6). BB in the

*Calluna/Erica* heath; DCL recorded it on mossy soil, derelict brickworks (SP0983, 1986).

**Clauzadea monticola** (Ach.) Hafellner & Bellem.
Crustose, often immersed in hard calcareous rocks; widespread throughout UK (4). SP on mortar of wall beside Keeper's Pool; OS occasional on ±calcareous gravestones and similar substrates; KN; AP annexe; BB, mortar, scattered throughout on reservoir walls.

**Cliostomum griffithii** (Sm.) Coppins
Crustose; usually on the dry side of mature trees including conifers, also on wood and walls; abundant throughout UK even in moderately polluted areas (3). SP on young oak, Little Bracebridge Heath.

**Collema crispum** (Huds.) Weber ex F.H. Wigg.
Foliose, gelatinous when wet; throughout UK on calcareous rocks and walls and especially old crumbling mortar (4). OS as a single sample on mortar of church wall.

**Collema tenax** (Sw.) Ach.
Foliose, gelatinous and greatly swollen when wet; common in UK and abundant on base-rich clay, sandy and calcareous soils and mortar (4). SP in basic sandy soil of old gravel pits, E of Keeper's Pool; SPC, fertile between paving stones of ornamental garden.

**Cyrtidula quercus** (A. Massal.) Minks
Immersed in bark of young oak and hazel twigs; common throughout UK (5). Occasional at SP on smooth bark of oak twigs; IL on young oak bark; OS.

**Dimerella pineti** (Ach.) Vězda
Crustose; common in UK on shaded, fairly acid bark especially at tree bases or in crevices or in other habitats (4). Frequent at SP on shaded bark, especially bases of oak trunks; MW on furnace spoil; FO on bark of old pear tree.

**Diploicia canescens** (Dicks.) A. Massal.
Crustose, placodioid, on dry rocks and dry bark in nutrient-rich or calcareous habitats (3). FO on roadside wall.

**Diploschistes scruposus** (Schreb.) Norman
Crustose; widespread throughout UK on siliceous or slightly basic, often nutrient-enriched rocks and walls (5). ER on sandstone walls in the gardens; MW on furnace spoil; BB on cement, W side of reservoir walls; FO on cement-brick wall.

**Diplotomma alboatrum** (Hoffm.) Flot.
Crustose, calcareous rocks and mortar, frequent in UK (5). BB, cement, W side of reservoir walls.

**Evernia prunastri** (L.) Ach.
Foliose, but attached at one point and appearing fruticose; common in UK, especially on well-lit trunks of deciduous trees (5). Occasional at SP, corticolous; SV on trees in the Swan Pool car park and alders and willows fringing Swan Pool; ER on elder twigs and oak branches; CC a single specimen on gravestone below a large sycamore; HC; GB; BU on sycamore bark; BB on oak branches, W-facing slope. DCL recorded it on willow bark at 5 sites in our part of vc. 37 between 1979 and 1985.

**Fellhanera bouteillei** (Desm.) Vězda
Crustose; infrequent throughout UK on twigs and leaves of evergreen trees. Rare at SP on holly leaves near Bracebridge Pool.

**Fellhanera viridisorediata** Aptroot, A.M. Brand & Spier
Crustose; throughout UK, found especially on the bases of native and exotic trees in parks in cities and in many other urban biotopes. Occasional at SP, most occurrences near the base of birch trunks; these trunks were probably visited by urinating dogs; MW on furnace spoil.

**Flavoparmelia caperata** (L.) Hale
Foliose; common in S and W UK mainly on acid-barked broad-leaved trees and now colonising N and E with falling levels of $SO_2$ (6). Now occasional in SP, corticolous; IL high branch of wayside oak; SV wooden railings; HC; GB; BB on oak branches, W-facing slopes; FO on bases of old beech and lime trees. DCL recorded it in 1985 on oak bark at Cadbury College, Kings Norton (SP0478).

**Flavoparmelia soredians** (Nyl.) Hale
Foliose; similar to *F. caperata* and in similar habitats; originally restricted to coastal habitats in UK, now spreading inland and becoming locally common (5). SP on oak branch SE of Streetly Gate; FO, a single specimen on base of an old sycamore and also recorded on oak, Moor Hall Estate.

**Fuscidea cyathoides** (Ach.) V. Wirth & Vězda
Crustose; very common on coarse-grained siliceous rocks in upland UK. OS, a single specimen on granite surround of a grave.

**Fuscidea lightfootii** (Sm.) Coppins & P. James
Crustose; frequent on ±horizontal boughs and twigs, particularly ash and willow, usually in damp areas; frequent especially in W UK (7). Occasional at SP, often in boggy areas, most commonly on willow; IL on willow and moribund elder; ER on a young oak branch.

**Hypocenomyce scalaris** (Ach. ex Lilj.) M. Choisy
Squamulose; common in UK on acid bark, fences and burnt wood, also occasionally on siliceous rock (4). Rare at SP, on base of ancient oak trunk W of Town Gate, also on wood near Four Oaks gate where it was also recorded in 1977; KN single colony on acid stone (poor condition).

**Hypogymnia physodes** (L.) Nyl.
Foliose; very common throughout UK on trees, siliceous rocks and other acid substrates, absent only when mean $SO_2$ levels exceed 100 µg m$^{-3}$ (4). Frequent at SP, corticolous; IL scattered on older tree branches; SV wooden railings and trees in the Swan Pool car park; CC single record on gravestone beneath sycamore; BU on sycamore bark; HC; SPC. It was also quite common much earlier: DLC gives 13 records in our part of vc. 37, 1979–86.

**Hypogymnia tubulosa** (Schaer.) Hav.
Foliose; common throughout UK in situations similar to those for *Hypogymnia physodes*, and often with it, but rarely as frequent, although it is now increasing, especially on roof tops and other elevated situations (5). Frequent at SP, corticolous; ER in canopy litter in main car park; IL scattered on older tree branches; AP main churchyard; CC; HC; BU on sycamore bark; SPC; FO on roof tops, often detatched as the result of storms. DCL recorded it on willow bark in 1980 (SP0982).

**Hypotrachyna revoluta** (Flörke) Hale
Foliose; common in UK on wayside and woodland trees and shrubs, less common on weakly acid rocks and walls (7). Occasional at SP, corticolous; IL on oak.

**Jamesiella anastomosans** (P. James & Vězda) Lücking, Sérus. & Vězda
Crustose; increasing in UK, mostly on smooth, shaded bark, pollution tolerant (5). Frequent at SP, corticolous and on rotting lignum of tree stump.

**Lecania cyrtella** (Ach.) Th. Fr.
Crustose; frequent in UK, mainly on nutrient-rich or enriched bark (6). Occasional at SP on elder twigs.

**Lecania erysibe** (Ach.) Mudd (Agg.)
Crustose; common in UK on nutrient-enriched brick, damp base-rich rocks, asbestos cement and other, often urban habitats (3). Rare at SP, saxicolous, on brick walls; frequent and very variable at OS on gravestones and mortar of church wall; rare – possibly overlooked – at KN, material in ±sorediate form; MW on furnace slag; HC; BU on concrete; BB widespread and variable on reservoir walls; SPC; PCW.

▲ *Cladonia pyxidata*, **Old Swinford** (×3)

▲ *Evernia prunastri*, **Barr Beacon** (×2)

▲ *Flavoparmelia caperata* (×2)

**Lecania naegelii** (Hepp) Diederich & van den Boom
Crustose; on nutrient-rich bark and twigs of trees and shrubs; common in areas not polluted with $SO_2$. Rare in SP on shaded Elder bark, W of Longmoor Pool.

**Lecania rabenhorstii** (Hepp) Arnold
Crustose; throughout UK on base-rich rocks. BU on concrete.

**Lecanora albescens** (Hoffm.) Branth & Rostr.
Crustose; very common in UK on hard calcareous rocks, mortar, concrete, walls etc. (5). In SP occasional on mortar; frequent, especially on mortar of walls; OS; widespread at KN on ±base-rich substrates; common at CC on calcareous substrates; IL on concrete of wall; ER brick walling and mortar; GB; AP Annexe; occasional at LP, with semi-lobed margins, on furnace slag; BU on concrete; BB widespread and common on reservoir walls; FO, ±dominant with *Lecidella scabra* on many roadside mortar-stone walls; SPC; PC; SC; STC; PCW.

**Lecanora campestris** (Schaer.) Hue
Crustose; widespread and very common in UK on mortar, asbestos cement, asphalt paths, mildly basic and nutrient-enriched siliceous rocks and walls and rarely on worked wood (2). Occasional in SP on concrete; frequent at OS on gravestones and surrounds; scattered at KN on ±basic substrates of gravestones; SV on trees in the Swan Pool car park; AP on both plots; three records at CC on ±basic substrates; furnace slag at LP and MW; HC; BU on concrete; BB on War Memorial and reservoir walls; SPC.

**Lecanora carpinea** (L.) Vain.
Crustose; on smooth bark of deciduous trees, exceptionally on stonework; throughout UK (7). Rare in SP, on ash just N of Powell's Pool and NW of Upper Nut Hurst; OS on young sycamore; SV on alders and willows fringing Swan Pool.

**Lecanora chlarotera** Nyl. (Agg.)
Crustose; on bark and wood of deciduous trees and occasionally on worked timber, very common in unpolluted areas of UK (5). Occasional at SP, corticolous; OS on young sycamore; KN a single thallus on smooth bark of cherry; SV on trees in the Swan Pool car park and on alders and willows fringing Swan Pool; IL on oak branches and twigs, and on dog rose; HC; BU on sycamore bark; BB on oak branches and twigs on W-facing slopes and on hedgerow rowan.

**Lecanora compallens** Herk & Aptroot
Crustose; on trunks of wayside and parkland trees, also on timber, probably widespread in UK. Rare in SP, on *Acer* near Toby Carvery.

**Lecanora confusa** Almb.
Crustose; on bark, particularly twigs, also on wood and worked timber; locally abundant in UK in unpolluted areas, especially near the coast (8). Rare in SP, on young sweet chestnut trunk, N of Wyndley Pool; FO on roadside and house palings.

**Lecanora conizaeoides** Nyl. ex Cromb.
Crustose; on a wide range of acidic substrates including bark, wood, siliceous rock, walls, soil, rubberised material, etc. Once the commonest corticolous British lichen in very $SO_2$-polluted areas (2), it is now becoming much more restricted in UK. Rare in SP on birch bark and sawn conifer cladding of outbuilding N of Powell's Pool; SV, wooden railings; AP on trees and gravestones in the main churchyard; HC; GB; BU on sandstone; SPC.

**Lecanora crenulata** (Dicks.) Hook.
Immersed in hard calcareous rocks, walls and mortar, scattered in UK, commonest in SE and E England (5). BB on ±consolidated cement, W side of reservoir walls.

**Lecanora dispersa** (Pers.) Sommerf. (Agg.)
Immersed or a granular crust; on a wide range of natural and man-made calcareous substrates; common throughout UK especially in the lowlands (1). Occasional in SP, saxicolous (mainly concrete) and a feature of highly eutrophicated tree bases visited by dogs; KN scattered on ±basic substrates of gravestones; SV concrete kerbs; CC common and widespread on ±basic substrates; GB; HC; frequent at LP, on furnace slag with very variable development of thalli; BU on concrete; BB on reservoir walls; SC; SPC; PCW.

**Lecanora expallens** Ach.
Crustose; on well-lit or dry bark, wood and worked timber, occasionally on dry vertical rocks, siliceous memorials, walls etc.; very common in UK (2). Occasional at SP, corticolous; OS on cherry; KN well-developed on a single acid gravestone; SV on trees in the Swan Pool car park; HC; BU on sycamore bark; BB on roadside wooden stumps in car park area; SPC.

**Lecanora farinaria** Borrer
Crustose; on wood and on bark of shrubs and trees; rare with a scattered distribution. Rare at SP on weathered plank of wooded roof near Town Gate.

**Lecanora gangaleoides** Nyl.
Crustose; common in UK on hard siliceous rocks, especially near the sea and absent from large parts of central and SE England (6). AP annexe, single specimen.

**Lecanora hagenii** (Ach.) Ach. (Agg.)
Crustose or immersed; a member of the *Lecanora dispersa* group. Common in UK on all substrates, especially on neutral bark, distinctly nitrophyllous. Occasional at SP on elder and willow twigs; OS on ±calcareous surfaces; frequent at KN on ±basic gravestones; scattered records throughout at CC on ±calcareous substrates; LP, two specimens in intermittent rain tracks on furnace slag; SY; SPC; PCW.

**Lecanora jamesii** J.R. Laundon
Crustose, yellow-green sorediate; on smooth bark near the bases of deciduous trees (most frequently willow) growing in damp situations; frequent in W and SW, recently recorded in C and E England and in Scotland (8). Rare in SP at base of a tree near Four Oaks gate; BB on roadside wooden stumps in car park area.

**Lecanora muralis** (Schreb.) Rabenh.
Crustose, lobate at the margin; pollution-resistant and very common on man-made substrates in urban areas (concrete, asbestos cement, asphalt, paving slabs etc.), less so in the uplands where it occurs on nutrient-enriched bird perches (2). Occasional in SP on concrete and walls, often much damaged by browsing molluscs; also present at all other sites, sometimes scarce, sometimes, as at SPC, in ornamental garden, forming almost continuous coverage of paving.

**Lecanora orosthea** (Ach.) Ach.
Crustose; in recesses and below overhangs on dry, siliceous rocks, old walls, occasionally on wood or bark; common in UK (6). Frequent, but often scrappily developed on furnace slag at LP and MW; on gravestones at SY; BB on War Memorial.

**Lecanora persimilis** (Th.Fr.) Nyl.
Crustose; a member of the *Lecanora dispersa* group, apparently common in UK on twigs and small branches of trees and shrubs with neutral bark. SV, alders and willows fringing Swan Pool; HC.

**Lecanora polytropa** (Hoffm.) Rabenh.
Immersed or scattered granules; common throughout UK on siliceous rocks and walls, also on worked timber (5). Rare at SP: on sandstone of wall beside Keeper's Pool and parapet of bridge over railway, also on wooden seating near Town Gate; frequent at OS on acid stones; rare at KN on acid gravestone surrounds; CC on a few acid gravestones and surrounds; LP, a single well-fertile thallus on furnace slag; HC; AP Annexe; BU on sandstone; BB on roadside wooden stumps in car park area and on

War Memorial; FO on boulders in gardens; PC; SY; SC; SPC; CCC; STC; PCW.

### Lecanora pulicaris (Pers.) Ach.
Crustose; on decorticated wood, worked timber and bark of both broad-leaved and coniferous trees; widely distributed in UK but commonest in NE England and Scotland (8). Rare in SP on oak twig SE of Bracebridge Pool; IL, wood of a stile; FO on old palings.

### Lecanora semipallida H. Magn.
Immersed; a member of the *Lecanora dispersa* group and only recently distinguished, thought to be common and widespread in UK on calcareous rocks especially hard limestone. Rare at SP, on concrete structures including wall along SE side of Longmoor Pool; CC; AP annexe; BU on concrete; BB frequent patches on W side of reservoir walls.

### Lecanora soralifera (Suza) Räsänen
Crustose; on siliceous rocks and walls, often in exposed situations, also on wood and worked timber; widely distributed in UK but local; moderately air-pollution tolerant (5). OS, Two specimens seen on upright gravestones; CC, on siliceous boulder in grave surround; BB on War Memorial; FO on acid stones in walls and top of front wall at St James's Church.

### Lecanora sulphurea (Hoffm.) Ach.
Crustose; exposed, somewhat nutrient-rich siliceous rocks and walls; common and widespread in UK (5). KN, a single thallus on acid gravestone; MP on furnace slag; also recorded on walls (especially those made of furnace slag) at SC; PC.

### Lecanora symmicta ( Ach.) Ach.
Crustose; on acid-barked trees, as a pioneer on twigs, on wood and worked timber; widespread and common in UK (7). Occasional in SP, on twigs, especially oak, also on wooden seating; occasional at KN; SV on trees in the Swan Pool car park; IL on smooth bark of oak; BU on ash bark.

### Lecanora varia (Hoffm.) Ach.
Crustose, usually of scattered rounded granules; mostly on wood and worked timber; locally frequent, predominantly in E England and Scotland (7). Rare in SP, on weathered wooden fence near Town Gate; FO on house front palings.

### Lecidea fuscoatra (L.) Ach.
Crustose; on rather smooth, often slightly nutrient-rich siliceous rocks; common throughout UK (5). Rare in SP, on siliceous material within concrete structure near Little Bracebridge Pool.

### Lecidea grisella Flörke
Crustose; in similar habitats and often with *Lecidea fuscoatra,* and even more widespread and common in UK. SP on brick wall at E end of Powell's Pool and beside Wyndley Pool; KN, a single record on surround of gravestone; AP, on sandstone sills beneath four church windows covered with galvanised (zinc-coated) mesh, conf. B. Coppins; BB on War Memorial; FO at St James's Church below windows on S side.

### Lecidea lapicida (Ach.) Ach.
Crustose; on siliceous, often iron-rich rocks; common in N and W of UK. Occasional at OS on acid gravestones and surrounds; KN a single record on surround of gravestone, thallus partially rust-red; AP; SY; BB on War Memorial and adjacent sandstone steps.

### Lecidea lithophila (Ach.) Ach.
Crustose; on exposed siliceous rocks, stones and pebbles, often ones rich in iron; common (5). BB on War Memorial and sandstone steps; MW on furnace slag; SY.

### Lecidella carpathica Körb.
Crustose, apothecia resembling those of *L. stigmatea* but red-brown, not colourless, internally. Throughout UK; uncommon, probably overlooked, on weakly basic, nutrient-enriched, rocks, walls, slate, asbestos cement, worked timber. SPC, on wall of S aisle of church.

### Lecidella elaeochroma (Ach.) M. Choisy
### f. elaeochroma
Crustose; on well-lit smooth-barked twigs and small branches, and wood; very common and increasing in UK, moderately tolerant of air pollution (6). Occasional at SP, corticolous; SV on alders and willows fringing Swan Pool; IL on twigs of oak and dead crack willow; ER on elder twigs and a wooden bench; BU on ash bark; SPC. Also f. soralifera (Erichsen) D. Hawksw. Less frequent, on similar habitats to f. *elaeochroma*. FO on sycamore at edge of garden.

### Lecidella scabra (Taylor) Hertel & Leuckert
Crustose; on siliceous and slightly base-rich rocks, often on walls and memorials, less often on dust-impregnated wood, worked timber or bark; common throughout UK. Occasional at SP on sandstone of mortared walls; frequent at OS on ±calcareous substrates; widespread at KN on ±calcareous substrates; occasional at CC on basic surfaces; MW on furnace slag; GB; HC; AP; BU on sandstone; BB on War Memorial and frequent on reservoir walls; FO common on roadside mortar-stone walls; SY; SPC.

▲ *Lecanora chlarotera* (Agg.) Penn (×4)

▲ *Lecanora polytropa*, Old Swinford (×5)

▲ *Lecidia grisella*, Aldridge Parish Church (×5)

▲ *Melanelixia fuliginosa* subsp. *fuliginosa* on a gravestone, Old Swinford (×1/5)

▲ *Melanelixia fuliginosa* subsp. *glabratula*, Old Swinford (×3)

▲ *Parmelia sulcata* on an oak branch, Penn (×3)

▲ *Parmotrema perlatum*, Barr Beacon (×1.5)

**Lecidella stigmatea** (Ach.) Hertel & Leuckert
Crustose; on weakly calcareous and base-enriched siliceous rocks, cement and mortar; very common throughout UK (3). Occasional at SP on calcareous and base-enriched rocks, cement and concrete; frequent at OS and KN on similar habitats; SV on concrete kerbs; occasional at CC on basic surfaces (also on bone with *Bilimbia sabuletorum*); GB; HC; AP; BU on concrete; BB frequent on reservoir walls; FO, abundant on cement and patio slabs; PC; SY; SPC; PCW.

**Lepraria incana** (L.) Ach.
Leprose; on acid rock, walls, bark and soil sheltered from direct rain; very common, often abundant; throughout UK (2). Frequent in SP, on shaded bark in both ancient and secondary woodland; frequent at OS on sheltered sides of gravestones and on outer church wall; frequent at KN on gravestones and trees (horse-chestnut); on furnace slag at LP and MW; AP on *Acer* sp.; ER; GB; HC; BU on ash bark; BB on War Memorial; SC; SPC; CCC; PCW.

**Lepraria lobificans** Nyl.
Leprose, margins obscurely lobate; on surfaces sheltered from the rain, on bark, wood, siliceous rock, limestone, mortar and soil; widespread and often abundant, especially in the W of UK. Less tolerant of acid substrates than *Lepraria incana* (6). Occasional in SP, on shaded bark S of Streetly Gate; LP on furnace slag; GB.

**Lepraria membranacea** (Dicks.) Vain.
Leprose with marginal lobes; on shaded, vertical, acidic surfaces sheltered from the rain; fairly common in upland Britain (6). MW on furnace slag.

**Lepraria vouauxii** (Hue) R.C. Harris
Leprose or margin slightly delimited; on surfaces sheltered from the rain, on siliceous rocks, limestone, mortar and bark, avoiding the most acid substrates; widespread and frequent in lowland Britain (5). Rare at SP on mortar courses of low walls at NE corner of Powell's Pool; also at LP a single gathering from very sheltered furnace slag, but needs thin layer chromatography to confirm; BB sheltered brickwork, W side of reservoir walls; FO on shaded garden wall.

**Leptogium schraderi** (Ach.) Nyl.
Thallus made up of tufts of cylindrical lobes; on mosses and soil in ±dry, calcareous habitats, particularly in old, mortared walls; locally abundant throughout UK (6). Rare at SP, in mortar course of wall at S side of Keeper's Pool.

**Leptorhaphis maggiana** (A. Massal.) Körb.
Immersed; on hazel and young branches of sweet chestnut; rare in UK. SV.

**Melanelixia fuliginosa** (Fr. ex Duby) O. Blanco, A. Crespo, Divakar, Essl., D. Hawksw. & Lumbsch **subsp. fuliginosa**
Foliose; common in UK on rocks and acid gravestones. Notably abundant at OS on many sandstone gravestones.

**Melanelixia fuliginosa** (Fr. ex Duby) O. Blanco, A. Crespo, Divakar, Essl., D. Hawksw. & Lumbsch **subsp. glabratula** (Lamy) J.R. Laundon
Foliose; mainly on bark of many species of broad-leaved trees but also on siliceous gravestones and basic rocks; common throughout UK (3). Rare at SP, corticolous, E of Bracebridge Pool; rare at OS, on horizontal sycamore branches; HC; BU on sycamore bark. DCL recorded it quite frequently (as *Parmelia glabratula*) from willow bark between 1980 and 1992.

**Melanelixia subaurifera** (Nyl.) O. Blanco, A. Crespo, Divakar, Essl., D. Hawksw. & Lumbsch
Foliose; on smooth bark of neutral to acid-barked trees, especially horizontal branches, less commonly on trunks or rocks; very common in UK (4). Frequent in SP, corticolous; rare at OS on horizontal tree branches (mostly sycamore); frequent at ER and SV; universally common at IL on tree branches; CC on a single gravestone below a sycamore; HC; BB on oak branches, W-facing slopes; SPC. DCL recorded it on willow bark at Wychall Reservoir (SP0379) in 1984.

**Melanohalea elegantula** (Zahlbr.) O. Blanco, A. Crespo, Divakar, Essl., D. Hawksw. & Lumbsch.
Foliose; an open parkland species, mostly on ±nutrient-rich, acid-barked trees, increasing in relatively polluted areas (6). Rare at SP, on oak E of Westwood Coppice.

**Melanohalea exasperata** (De Not.) O. Blanco, A. Crespo, Divakar, Essl., D. Hawksw. & Lumbsch.
Foliose; mostly on well-lit, acid-barked, smooth twigs and branchlets of broad-leaved trees, especially in the W, but decreasing (8). Rare at SP, on an Oak twig S of Streetly Gate and fertile on Oak N of the Donkey sanctuary.

**Melanohalea exasperatula** (Nyl.) O. Blanco, A. Crespo, Divakar, Essl., D. Hawksw. & Lumbsch.
Foliose; mainly on the trunks and branches of nutrient-rich, wayside, broad-leaved trees; widespread, but still only local in England (5). Rare in SP, on oaks S of Streetly Gate and E of Westwood Coppice.

**Micarea denigrata** (Fr.) Hedl.
Crustose, sometimes immersed; usually

on fallen trunks, stumps, worked timber; common and widespread in UK even in polluted areas (4). Rare in SP, on sawn cladding of outbuilding N of Powell's Pool; SV on wooden railings; FO on weathered fencing of neglected garden.

**Micarea erratica** (Körb.) Hertel, Rambold & Pietschm.
Crustose; scattered distribution in UK, often on siliceous pebbles in heathland areas. SP on pebble by roadside near Jamboree Memorial.

**Micarea lignaria** (Ach.) Hedl.
Crustose, sometimes immersed; common and widespread on various acid substrates (5). SV on wooden railings; rare at SP as **var. lignaria** on shingle roof at Streetly Gate.

**Micarea micrococca** (Körb.) Gams ex Coppins
Crustose; common even close to urban centres on acid bark, stumps, debris, soil, etc. SP on holly stems N of Wyndley Pool.

**Ochrolechia parella** (L.) A. Massal.
Crustose; frequent on siliceous rocks, walls, brickwork, rarely on trees (5). FO, young thalli on patio slabs.

**Parmelia saxatilis** (L.) Ach.
Foliose; was abundant throughout UK on acid-barked trees and shrubs and siliceous rocks, memorials, etc., but there is evidence that it is now decreasing and being replaced by *P. sulcata* and *Hypogymnia physodes* (4). Only recorded in the main survey at three sites: rare at SP, corticolous and often poorly developed; on sandstone at BU; at SPC. Also a single colony was observed almost completely covering a 3-dimensional sandstone memorial at STC. DCL also had only a single record, on bark of a dead willow at Wychall Reservoir (SP0379, 1984).

**Parmelia sulcata** Taylor
Foliose; very common and increasing throughout UK on trees and siliceous rocks (4). Frequent, corticolous; at SP, OS, AP, SV, AC, IL, GB, HC, ER, BB, SPC and also on a single gravestone below a sycamore at CC. It was also common in the 1980s: DCL recorded it, generally on tree bark, from 17 sites in our part of vc. 37 between 1973 and 1986.

**Parmotrema perlatum** (Huds.) M. Choisy
Foliose; common in S and W UK in well-lit situations on neutral- to acid-barked trees and siliceous rocks, now colonising more polluted areas (7). Occasional at SP, corticolous; SV on willows and young oak; IL on maple (rare) also on oak; ER on young oak branch; GB; HC; BB on oak branches, W-facing slopes.

**Peltigera didactyla** (With.) J.R. Laundon
Foliose; throughout UK especially on recently disturbed sites (4). MW on furnace spoil. DCL recorded it in 1986 on soil amongst moss, at a derelict brickworks (SP0983).

**Peltigera hymenina** (Ach.) Delise ex Duby
Foliose; common in UK on fairly base-poor soil, mosses, rocks, in lawns etc. (6). SP, terricolous on sandy bank SE of Bracebridge Pool; AP annexe; MW on furnace spoil. DCL recorded it in 1986 at a derelict brickworks site (SP0983).

**Peltigera membranacea** (Ach.) Nyl.
Foliose; common on mossy tree trunks, rocks and ground throughout UK (5). Not recorded in the present survey but seen by DCL in 1986 on soil amongst moss, derelict brickworks (SP0983).

**Pertusaria amara** (Ach.) Nyl.
Crustose; usually on broad-leaved trees, throughout UK (5) but still rare, as are other species of this genus in the Midlands. Recorded only at OS, on sandstone, a single widespreading colony.

**Phaeophyscia nigricans** (Flörke) Moberg
Foliose, habit ±shrubby; mainly on calcareous stonework and asbestos cement, often where nutrient-enriched; scattered in lowland UK, especially in the E (5). SP, on plastic roof tiles of small building at SE corner of Westwood Coppice.

**Phaeophyscia orbicularis** (Neck.) Moberg
Foliose; corticolous and saxicolous; very common throughout UK on nutrient-rich or -enriched substrates (2). Frequent in SP, corticolous and saxicolous; OS on horizontal sycamore branch; SV on trees generally; IL on maple (tree base and lower branches); HC; MW on fallen branches; BU on ash bark; BB on boulders at base of W side of reservoir walls.

**Phlyctis argena** (Spreng.) Flot.
Crustose; on well-lit, deciduous trees; common in UK, pollution tolerant (5). Rare in SP, corticolous, near the Toby Carvery.

**Physcia adscendens** H. Oliver
Foliose; common and increasing throughout UK in response to falling SO₂ levels and rising levels of nitrogenous compounds, on well-lit and nutrient–rich or –enriched substrates including limestone, concrete, tree trunks, branches and twigs (2). Abundant at SP, corticolous, and at OS, KN, CP, CC, IL, SV, GB, HC, ER, MW, CCC , BU, BB, SPC, FO on branches, twigs, occasionally on memorials and sandstone.

**Physcia aipolia** (Ehrh. ex Humb.) Fürnr.
Foliose; common in UK on nutrient-rich or base-rich bark of trees, branches and twigs, possibly spreading (6). Occasional at SP, corticolous; SV on trees in the Swan Pool car park and alders and willows fringing Swan Pool.

**Physcia caesia** (Hoffm.) Fürnr.
Foliose; usually saxicolous on well-lit, basic substrates, common in UK and pollution tolerant (3). Rare in SP, on concrete slab W of the Gum Slade and on tarmac N of Wyndley Pool; SV on concrete kerbs; HC; AP; BU on concrete; BB on concrete kerbs, Oak branches and twigs, War Memorial and on boulders at base of W side of reservoir walls; SPC.

**Physcia dubia** (Hoffm.) Lettau
Foliose, with lip-shaped soralia towards and at the ends of ±ascending lobes. Throughout UK on non-calcareous rocks and building materials in well-lit, nutrient-rich and –enriched situations (4). SPC with *P. caesia* on top of small sandstone memorial beside S aisle.

**Physcia stellaris** (L.) Nyl.
Foliose; branches and twigs of trees, mainly in little-polluted areas of UK (8). SP on oak twig SE of Blackroot Pool.

**Physcia tenella** (Scop.) DC.
Foliose; common and increasing in UK in response to falling SO₂ levels and rising levels of nitrogenous compounds, usually on bark (4). Corticolous, abundant at SP and at almost all other sites visited: OS, KN, AP, IL, SV, GB, HC, ER, PCW, BB, BU, SPC, PCW, FO. Also on a single gravestone below a sycamore at CC.

*Physcia tenella*, Barr Beacon (×6) (by Gemma Edwards)

**Physconia distorta** (With.) J.R. Laundon
Foliose; on basic or nutrient-enriched bark of trees throughout UK (6). Not recorded recently but by DCL in 1980 on willow bark (SP1079).

**Physconia enteroxantha** (Nyl.) Poelt
Foliose; common especially in N UK on well-lit nutrient-rich bark of trees, occasionally on old walls and memorials.

SP on mature willow trunk near Wyndley Leisure Centre.

**Physconia grisea** (Lam.) Poelt
Foliose; on basic, usually dust-impregnated nutrient-enriched bark of tree trunks and frequent on calcareous walls and memorials; common and increasing in lowland UK (3). SV on trees in the Swan Pool car park.

**Placynthiella dasaea** (Stirt.) Tønsberg
Crustose; on dead rotting bark and lignum of pine and gorse, occasionally spreading to soil rich in organic matter, also on well-weathered worked timber; scattered through England, Scotland and Wales. Rare in SP, on upturned root plate of wind-blown tree SE of Bracebridge Pool.

**Placynthiella icmalea** (Ach.) Coppins & P. James
Crustose; in a wide range of acid habitats: dead bark and wood of fallen trees, rotting tops of fence posts, humus-rich soils, a primary colonist of heathland after burning (5). Rare in SP, terricolous in Little Bracebridge Heath and on wooden shingles and wooden seating; BB in the *Calluna/Erica* heath.

**Placynthiella uliginosa** (Schrad.) Coppins & P. James
Crustose; frequent throughout UK on peaty, heathland soils, dead bark and wood of fallen trees and stumps (6). Rare in SP: terricolous on Little Bracebridge Heath and on wooden seating; BB in the *Calluna/Erica* heath. Also recorded in 1979 at Moseley Bog (DCL, SP0981 & SP0982) and in 1983 on soil at a derelict brickworks (DCL, SP0983).

**Placynthium nigrum** (Huds.) Gray
Minutely squamulose, black, with an indigo-blue margin. Widespread in UK, especially on basic stones in churchyards. (4). BB on consolidated mortar; also recorded from Sandwell Valley Country Park (SP029421) by DCL in 1987.

**Platismatia glauca** (L.) W.L. Culb. & C.F. Culb.
Foliose; common throughout UK on trees, rocks and soil especially in leached, acid habitats (6). Rare at SP, S of Streetly Gate on oak branch; SV on wooden railings; ER on young oak branch. DCL had 8 records in the 1970s and 80s in our part of vc. 37 on willow and sycamore bark and wooden railings.

**Polysporina simplex** (Davies) Vězda
Crustose; common throughout England and Wales on acidic or weakly calcareous rocks, especially in churchyards on slate and granite memorials (6). HC.

**Porina aenea** (Wallr.) Zahlbr.
Crustose; on smooth bark, often on trees

with bark with a high pH (sycamore, ash), common in urban areas (8). Rare at SP, near base of sycamore trunk.

**Porina chlorotica** (Ach.) Müll. Arg.
Crustose; on siliceous rocks and stones, often in shade and damp situations; frequent throughout UK, especially N and W (6). KN, deep shade, church wall; LP, a single piece of furnace slag collected in a shaded and damp run-off.

**Porpidia crustulata** (Ach.) Hertel & Knoph
Thinly crustose; mainly on siliceous rock, stonework, pebbles; frequent in lowland and urban areas (5). MW on furnace slag.

**Porpidia macrocarpa** (DC.) Hertel & A.J. Schwab
Crustose, thallus immersed or thin; on siliceous rocks; boulders and pebbles; common, especially in the uplands (5). MW on furnace slag.

**Porpidia soredizodes** (Lamy ex Nyl.) J.R. Laundon
Crustose; siliceous rocks, stonework, pebbles and slate; throughout UK especially in the lowlands (5). Rare at SP, on sandstone coping stones of railway bridge parapet and brick wall beside Wyndley Pool; OS, seen twice on acid gravestones; KN, often in association with *Buellia* species on granite gravestones and surrounds; IL, roof tile at back of farm; GB; AP main churchyard; BU on sandstone; BB on War Memorial; SPC; CCC; STC.

**Porpidia tuberculosa** (Sm.) Hertel & Knoph
Crustose; on siliceous rocks, walls, pebbles; common throughout UK (4). Rare at SP on sandstone coping stones of railway bridge parapet; OS, very frequent on both sheltered and exposed gravestones; KN, often in association with *Buellia* species on granite gravestones and surrounds; CC on granite gravestones and surrounds; GB; HC; AP main churchyard; MW on furnace slag; BU on sandstone; BB on War Memorial; SPC.

**Protoblastenia rupestris** (Scop.) J. Steiner
Crustose; on a wide range of calcareous substrates; common throughout UK (3). Rare at SP on concrete pavers of culvert close to Wydley Leisure Centre; BB single colony in shade, W side of reservoir walls; FO on old mortar of neglected garden wall; SC.

**Pseudevernia furfuracea** (L.) Zopf
Foliose-shrubby, ascendant-pendant, with one or few points of attachment; on exposed, well-lit bark and wood on conifers and acid-barked deciduous trees; widespread in UK, especially N and W (6). Rare in SP on a single hawthorn at SP098970.

**Psilolechia clavulifera** (Nyl.) Coppins
Crustose, granular; on roots, stones and consolidated soil below dry overhangs on banks or on the root systems of fallen trees; rare throughout the British Isles. Rare at SP on peaty soil and dead rootlets of upturned root plate of wind-blown tree SW of Bracebridge Pool.

**Psilolechia leprosa** Coppins & Purvis
Crustose to leprose; on copper-rich rocks, mortar and stonework, below metal grills e.g. on church buildings; frequent in UK (5). GB; HC.

**Psilolechia lucida** (Ach.) M. Choisy
Leprose-granular; often wide-spreading and conspicuous in dry, shady situations on non-calcareous rocks and walls; common in UK (3). Rare at SP on a wall near the Toby Carvery; frequent at OS on church wall and on shaded sides of several upright gravestones; KN on church wall and several gravestones; GB; AP, main churchyard; BB on War Memorial; FO, forming sheets on sheltered brick wall; SC; SPC; STC; PCW.

**Psoroglaena stigonemoides** (Orange) Henssen
Minutely fruticose, densely branched; on shaded bark in humid sites; frequent and widespread, easily overlooked. FO, on branches of magnolia in sheltered garden.

**Punctelia jeckeri** (Roum.) Kalb
Foliose; corticolous on broad-leaved trees; frequent and increasing in UK. Occasional at SP, corticolous; SV, willows and young oak.

**Punctelia subrudecta** (Nyl.) Krog
Foliose; bark of broad-leaved trees, less often on wood, among mosses on siliceous rock, roofing tiles and standing stones; widespread in UK except in Scotland and industrial areas (5). Occasional in SP, corticolous; CC on a single gravestone beneath a sycamore; IL on an older branch of maple; ER on sycamore; GB.

**Ramalina farinacea** (L.) Ach.
Fruticose, shrubby, pendant; in a wide range of situations, most often on nutrient-rich bark; common throughout UK, (5). Occasional at SP, corticolous; SV on willows and young oak; IL on older branches of maple, elder, oak; BU on sycamore bark; BB on oak, W-facing slopes. Also recorded by DCL in the 1980s on willow bark (SP0379 & SP0982).

**Ramalina fastigiata** (Pers.) Ach.
Fruticose, tufted, usually erect; on well-lit, wind-exposed nutrient-rich bark; common in UK but very pollution-sensitive (9). Rare in SP, on oak twig S of Streetly Gate.

**Rhizocarpon petraeum** (Wulfen) A. Massal.
Crustose; on hard siliceous rock close
to mortar, ±base-rich rocks and walls;
common throughout UK (7). Rare in SP on
sandstone in mortared wall beside Keeper's
Pool; LP, a single thallus on furnace slag.

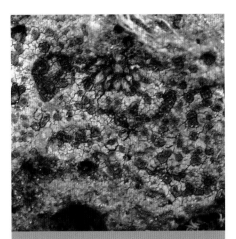

▲ *Rhizocarpon reductum*,
Moorcroft Wood (×5)

**Rhizocarpon reductum** Th. Fr.
Crustose; on siliceous rocks, particularly
gravestones; common throughout UK (6).
Rare at SP on brick wall on N side of
Wyndley Pool; OS occasional on non-
sandstone, acid-rock gravestones;
widespread at KN on granitic gravestones
and surrounds; GB; HC; AP main churchyard;
LP, a few grey-brown, well-fertile thalli on
furnace slag; MW on furnace slag; BU on
sandstone; BB on War Memorial; SPC on
church walls and associated paving stones
of ornamental garden frontage. PCW.

**Rinodina oleae** Bagl.
Crustose; on calcareous, nutrient-rich and
–enriched substrates: rocks, mortar,
concrete, asbestos cement, bark and wood;
pollution tolerant. Rare at SP on brick wall
beside Wyndley Pool and on birch bark in
wound track (recorded in 1990, as *R. gennarii*);
GB; HC; BU on concrete. Widely recorded
by DCL in the 1980s in our part of vc. 37 on
tree bark and decorticated stumps.

**Rinodina sophodes** (Ach.) A. Massal.
Crustose; mainly on twigs of smooth-
barked trees; widespread in UK, especially
in the uplands (8). Rare in SP, found twice
on oak twigs.

**Rinodina teichophila** (Nyl.) Arnold
Crustose; scattered on siliceous to weakly
basic rocks; throughout UK especially in the
lowlands (6). FO, shaded walls of St James's
church; SPC, scattered patches on W-facing,
sheltered sandstone wall of S aisle.

**Sarcogyne regularis** Körb.
Crustose, generally immersed; on calcareous
rocks, walls, asbestos cement, old mortar;
frequent, especially in the lowlands (4).
Rare in SP, on concrete slab W of the Gum
Slade and on mortar; KN, a single record on
calcareous seam of gravestone; BB reservoir
walls, E side, in sheltered recess.

**Scoliciosporum chlorococcum** (Graewe ex
Stenh.) Vězda
Crustose; on shaded damp, ±nutrient-rich
or –enriched bark, less often on siliceous
rock, pollution tolerant and growing with
and replacing *Lecanora conizaeoides*;
very common in UK (2). SP occasional, on
twigs; MW, fertile on tree base; FO on old
magnolias, etc.; SPC. Also with 5 records in
our part of vc. 37 by DCL in 1980s.

**Scoliciosporum sarothamni** (Vain.) Vězda
Crustose; on ±nutrient-rich or –
enriched bark of boles, branches and
twigs; probably widespread in UK but
overlooked. Rare in SP on oak twigs near
the Toby Carvery; KN on dead cherry twig
(fertile).

**Scoliciosporum umbrinum** (Ach.) Arnold
Crustose; basic or siliceous rocks,
memorials, rusty metal work and other
metal-rich substrates, walls, compacted
acid soils, branches, twigs and wood;
widespread in UK and pollution tolerant
(3). KN on a single acid gravestone.

**Stereocaulon nanodes** Tuck.
Squamulose; on sheltered rocks, often in
damp situations, frequent on old lead-
zinc mine spoil heaps, by roads in urban
areas and associated with iron railings in
churchyards; rather frequent throughout
UK (3). Rare in SP: on parapets of 2 bridges
over the railway, on mortar and sandstone.

**Stereocaulon pileatum** Ach.
Squamulose; on damp siliceous rocks,
particularly loose stones, often on mine
spoil heaps and in industrial and urban
areas; rather frequent and increasing
throughout UK. MW on furnace slag. Also
several DCL records in 1980s.

**Strigula jamesii** (Swinscow) R.C. Harris
Crustose, thallus thin ±immersed,
perithecia semi-immersed; on bark. FO,
on aged elder near television station on
Staffordshire border.

**Tephromela atra** (Huds.) Hafellner
Crustose; on siliceous and slightly calcareous
nutrient-rich rock and walls; very common
throughout UK (3). KN, a single record, acid
gravestone; BB on War Memorial; STC.

**Trapelia coarctata** (Turner ex Sm.) M. Choisy
Crustose; on well-lit siliceous rocks,
pebbles and brick walls; very common in
UK (3). Rare at SP on sandstone, including a
pebble lying in heathland SE of Bracebridge
Pool; occasional at OS on ±flat, ±basic
rock surfaces; frequent at KN on acid
gravestones; GB; HC; AP annexe; furnace
slag at LP and MW; BB on War Memorial; FO
very common on old walls; SPC, ±frequent
on sandstone walls of church and
associated paving stones; STC; PCW.

**Trapelia glebulosa** (Sm.) J.R. Laundon
Crustose to subsquamulose; mainly on
siliceous rocks; throughout UK. HC; FO on
wall; SPC, ±frequent on sandstone walls of
church and associated paving stones.

**Trapelia obtegens** (Th. Fr.) Hertel
Crustose; on siliceous rocks and stones;
throughout UK (5). OS, a single specimen
on flat surface of horizontal gravestone;
SPC, ±frequent on sandstone walls of
church and associated paving stones.

**Trapelia placodioides** Coppins & P. James
Crustose; on siliceous rocks, mine spoil and
walls; common especially in the uplands
(6). Rare at SP on sandstone of wall by
Keepers Pool and on tarmac N of Wyndley
Pool; OS, a single, extensive thallus on flat,
horizontal, ±calcareous cement surface;
GB; HC; frequent on furnace slag at LP and
MW; FO, single colony on brick wall; SPC,
±frequent on sandstone walls of church
and associated paving stones.

**Trapeliopsis flexuosa** (Fr.) Coppins & P. James
Crustose; mostly on wood, often abundant;
throughout UK (5). Rare in SP on a
weathered, fallen oak branch, on birch
bark and on wooden roof shingles; SV on
wooden railings.

**Trapeliopsis granulosa** (Hoffm.) Lumbsch
Crustose; usually on acid moorland soils
and decayed wood; common throughout
UK (3). Rare at SP on lignum of large dead
oak trunk in the Gum Slade; MW on furnace
spoil; BB in the *Calluna/Erica* heath.

**Tuckermanopsis chlorophylla** (Willd.) Hale
Foliose; on twigs, branches and trunks of
trees, shrubs and posts; throughout UK (6).
Not seen in present survey but recorded by
DCL from bark of railings in SP0180 in 1981.
Also a record from 1980 for Sutton Park
(Coxhead & Fowkes, 1992).

**Usnea cornuta** Körb.
Fruticose; common mainly on trees in S
and W UK (7). Rare at SP on Oak branches
SE of Streetly Gate.

**Usnea flammea** Stirt.
Fruticose; rock faces, decorticated wood, wayside trees, shrubs and heather stems; widespread and locally frequent in S and W UK, especially near the coast (9). Rare at SP, on branch of oak near Four Oaks Gate.

**Usnea flavocardia** Räsänen
Fruticose; in boggy, undisturbed scrub and Willow carr, rarely on mossy boulders; SW England, Wales and W Scotland. Rare in SP, on dead lower branch of a mature oak N of Wyndley Pool.

**Usnea subfloridana** Stirt.
Fruticose; on trees; common in UK, the most widespread and pollution tolerant *Usnea* (6). Rare in SP on oak branches SE of Streetly Gate; ER on young oak branch; FO, young thalli on roadside lime trees. DCL had records on willow bark in 1979 (SP0379) and 1980 (SP0982) and on bark of railings (SP0180) in 1979.

**Verrucaria baldensis** A. Massal.
Crustose, immersed; on hard limestones, mortar; often abundant, throughout UK (4). Rare in SP on large limestone rocks at overflow of Powell's Pool.

**Verrucaria fuscella** (Turner) Winch & Thornhill
Crustose, not immersed; on calcareous rocks or other rock and brick under calcareous influence; common and widespread in UK (4). KN, often with *V.nigrescens* on ±basic stones and mortar; SPC.

**Verrucaria hochstetteri** Fr. (Agg.)
Crustose, immersed; on calcareous rock; common in UK (3). Rare at SP on mortar of buildings near the Toby Carvery; very common at OS on calcareous substrates; rare at KN on cement, church wall; generally frequent at CC on ±basic substrates and mortar; ER on limestone in rockery, gardens; HC; AP annexe; PCW.

**Verrucaria macrostoma** Dufour ex DC.
Crustose; on limestone, mortar and calcareous sandstone, often on walls; widespread in England and Wales (5). Rare at SP on mortar of buildings near the Toby Carvery; GB; BB reservoir walls; PCW on mortar of S-facing walls.

**Verrucaria muralis** Ach.
Crustose, ±immersed; on limestone, mortar, brick, calcareous soil, pebbles; widespread and frequent in UK (3). Rare at SP on mortar of buildings near the Toby Carvery; GB; HC; BU on concrete; BB reservoir walls; PCW.

**Verrucaria nigrescens** Pers.
Crustose; on well-lit calcareous rock and mortar; very common in UK (2). Rare at SP on mortar of buildings near the Toby Carvery; frequent elsewhere on limestone, concrete, brick walls, furnace slag: OS, KN, AP, CC, SV, GB, HC, ER, MW, BU, BB, SPC, PC, SY, SC, STC, PCW.

**Verrucaria viridula** (Schrad.) Ach.
Crustose, ±immersed; common on calcareous rock, mortar, brick, etc.; throughout UK (3). Mortar of buildings near the Toby Carvery, SP; on mortar, frequent, KN; AP annexe; BB reservoir walls; SPC.

**Xanthoparmelia mougeotii** (Schaer. ex D. Dietr.) Hale
Foliose, with yellow-grey, closely adpressed radiating lobes; convex to ±excavate soralia present. On well-lit siliceous rocks, also roofing tiles, slate, memorials, quartzite chips in churchyards. Widespread and common in uplands, increasing elsewhere (6). SPC on small siliceous rock and also on broken tile on W side of S aisle of church.

**Xanthoria calcicola** Oxner
Foliose; on calcareous, nutrient-rich stonework, brickwork, tiles, monuments, rare on bark and wood, frequent in England and Wales (4). Rare, SP, on wall at E end of Wyndley Pool; FO on old wall with *Xanthoria parietina*. Also records by DCL in 1980s.

**Xanthoria candelaria** (L.) Th. Fr.
Subfruticose; on nutrient-rich substrata such as tops of fence posts and gravestones used as bird perches; widespread and often common throughout UK (5). Trees generally at SV; oak branch, ER; HC. Also recorded by DCL in 1980s.

**Xanthoria elegans** (Link) Th. Fr.
Foliose; well-lit, nutrient-enriched, siliceous and calcareous rocks used as bird perches, also concrete and slate and asbestos cement roofs; throughout UK, local (6). Rare at SP: brick wall beside Wyndley Pool and on concrete wall beside Longmoor Pool; BB three thalli on reservoir walls, N end of W side.

**Xanthoria parietina** (L.) Th. Fr.
Foliose; very common throughout UK on a wide variety of nutrient-rich and –enriched substrates including trees, rocks, walls and roofs (4). Frequent at SP on enriched bark and man-made structures and at all other sites on trees, branches, twigs and sometimes gravestones and concrete.

**Xanthoria polycarpa** (Hoffm.) Th. Fr. ex Rieber
Foliose; common and increasing in the UK on nutrient-enriched, dead and living twigs And fencing (4). SP: occasional, corticolous, locally frequent on twigs and in similar situations at most other sites: OS, KN, CC, SV, GB, HC, ER, BU, BB, SPC, CCC, PCW.

**Xanthoria ucrainica** S.Y. Kondr.
Foliose; on bark of broad-leaved trees, stone and man-made substrates; very common in UK but under-recorded. Occasional, corticolous, in SP; poorly developed on horizontal sycamore branches, OS; dead twigs of cherry, KN; occasional on twigs, IL; BU on ash and lime.

**Xanthoria ulophyllodes** Räsänen
Foliose; in well-lit, humid situations on bark of broad-leaved trees, stone and man-made substrates in churchyards; scattered in England and Scotland. On dead twigs of maple, CC.

# Chapter 7

# Bryophytes
# (mosses, liverworts and hornworts)

by Martin Godfrey

◀ *Hypnum cupressiforme var. cupressiforme*
and *Lophocolea bidentata*

(Sketches by Neville Walters)

## Introduction

The bryophytes (mosses, liverworts and hornworts) are a group of plants which share a common life cycle and reproduce by means of spores. Because they are all more or less small, predominantly green and have no showy flowers they tend to be overlooked; nevertheless they are ubiquitous in both town and country and can form an important part of the flora.

Mosses, and some liverworts, share the 'stem and leaf' morphology of the vascular plants; however other liverworts and all of the hornworts have a '**thallose**' structure. That is to say the main body of the plant is formed from a flat ribbon of green tissue with no trace of leaves (figures 7.1 and 7.2), rather like a miniature seaweed, and care is needed to ensure that these are not confused with the larger lichens, which have a superficially similar structure.

The leafy liverworts are typically rather flattened plants with two rows of leaves, one on either side of the stem, and sometimes a much smaller row of leaves on the underside of the stem (figure 7.3).

Figure 7.3 *Lophocolea bidentata*, a leafy liverwort (×3)

The mosses come in two forms, the **acrocarps** (figure 7.4) – which form short turfs or cushions, and **pleurocarps** (figure 7.5) – which are free branching and form wefts over soil or amongst other vegetation.

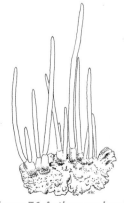

Figure 7.1 *Anthoceros laevis*, a thallose hornwort (×3)

Figure 7.2 *Marchantia polymorpha*, A thallose liverwort. (×1.5)

Figure 7.4 *Bryum capillare*, an acrocarpous moss (×1)

Figure 7.5 *Hypnum cupressiforme*, a pleurocarpous moss (×2)

All three groups produce a **sporophyte**, which consists, in the mosses and liverworts, of a stem with a spore-producing capsule at its tip whilst in the hornworts it is a tubular structure which splits into two valves looking rather like fine blades of grass.

## Classification

At one time the bryophytes were thought to be closely related, by virtue of their common life cycle. Typically, older books will place them in two groups, the *Musci* or mosses, and *Hepaticae* or liverworts, with the *Anthocerotae* or hornworts subsumed into the liverworts.

Recent work, using both morphology and DNA analysis, has radically altered this view; the plants now being divided into three distinct phyla (the level of classification immediately below Kingdom) – the *Anthocerotophyta* (hornworts), *Marchantiophyta* (liverworts) and *Bryophyta* (mosses). This modern classification has also changed the names, and sequence, of groups and species within the bryophytes and it is this sequence which is used here, following the latest checklist (Hill *et al.* 2008). There are no frequently used common names for any member of the group so scientific names are used throughout.

## Ecology

Bryophytes are all around us in the urban and suburban landscape but are rarely noticed. Not only do they grow in parks and gardens and the more "natural" parts of the landscape like woods, field and heaths but many of them are at home in pavement cracks, on walls and in derelict industrial sites.

They are important for several reasons. Many of them are 'pioneer' species which can grow on bare or newly created habitat such as walls, bare ground or bonfire sites. They grow and reproduce rapidly and, as they decay and die, produce a little humus in which higher plants can find a foothold. In less disturbed habitats longer-lived species act as an important source of moisture control. On the ground in woods and grasslands they reduce evaporation and water loss while in mires and bogs *Sphagnum* species can hold large quantities of water and, in the process of producing peat, can sequester huge quantities of carbon dioxide. Finally they are very good indicators of environmental and atmospheric quality as many are very sensitive to pollution. In particular the species which grow on trees, **epiphytes**, tend to be susceptible to air pollution and their presence in this Flora is testament to the reduction in atmospheric sulphur dioxide over the past 40 or so years. On the other hand the individual species of epiphytes are changing in response to the increasing levels of the various nitrogen oxides resulting from increasing levels of road traffic.

## Recording

Probably because of its urban nature our area has, historically, had very little bryophyte recording with the majority of records coming from Sutton Park and those parts of the Lickey Hills which find their way into the Flora region. The most prolific recorder of the 19th century was probably J.E. Bagnall, a selection of whose specimens may be seen in the Lady Peel collection at Tamworth Castle. In the 20th century the only botanist who seems to have made an extensive study of bryophytes in our region was T. Laflin but, sadly, most of his records on the National Biodiversity Network database are not well localised and have very broad date bands. Many other botanists seem to have submitted small numbers of records, perhaps when visiting the area for other purposes or when studying higher plants.

The recording for this flora was introduced late and carried out in just over two years of the project, starting in January 2005, so the information here would probably best be regarded as an annotated checklist and a starting point for further bryological exploration rather than a complete flora of the region. I have included a number of historical records, particularly for those species which seem to be extinct in the region, in the hope of encouraging new bryologists to take up the challenge to re-find them.

In addition to those of the author, most records made for the flora came from James Partridge and Prof Ian Trueman with additional material from Mark Lawley, Alex Lockton and Dr Sarah Whild. Historical material was collated from museum herbaria and the British Bryological Society database held by the NBN.

## Some useful references

**The current Checklist**
Hill, M.O., Blackstock, T.H., Long D.G. & Rothero, G.P. (2008) *A checklist and census catalogue of British and Irish bryophytes.* British Bryological Society.

**Species accounts and standard floras**
Atherton, I., Bosanquet, S. & Lawley, M. (Eds) (2010) *British Mosses and Liverworts – a Field Guide.* British Bryological Society.
Paton, J.A. (1999) *The Liverwort Flora of the British Isles.* Harley Books (now Apollo Books, Denmark).
Smith, A.J.E. (1990) *The liverworts of Britain and Ireland.* Cambridge University Press.
Smith, A.J.E. (2004) *The Moss Flora of Britain and Ireland.* 2nd Edition, Cambridge University Press.

**General**
Porley, R. & Hodgetts, N. (2005) *Mosses and Liverworts.* Collins New Naturalist No 97.
British Bryological Society – www.britishbryologicalsociety.org.uk

▲ *Lunularia cruciata* (×3)

▲ *Marchantia polymorpha* (×3)

▲ *Conocephalum conicum* (×1)

▲ *Fossombronia pusiila* (×2)

▲ *Lophocolea bidentata* (×4)

## ANTHOCEROPHYTA (hornworts)

### ANTHOCEROTOPSIDA

**Phaeoceros laevis** (L.) Prosk.
On more or less permanently wet clay or, occasionally, clay covered rock. Common in the Harborne Botanic Gardens.

There are also a number of poorly localised, undated, records for **Anthoceros punctatus** L. and **A. agrestis** Paton throughout the region. Both are pioneer species of wet bare soil, typically in arable fields.

## MARCHANTIOPHYTA (liverworts)

### MARCHANTIOPSIDA

**Blasia pusilla** L.
To be found on moist non-calcareous ground, more frequently on disturbed sites like paths and ditch sides. Lickey Hills

**Lunularia cruciata** (L.) Lindb.
This a common weed species, found on damp walls, paths and flower pots.

**Marchantia polymorpha** L.
Like *Lunularia cruciata,* which it resembles somewhat, this is a common weed of damp, frequently man-made situations.

**Conocephalum conicum agg.**
Usually on wet soil, rock or walls. In our area a common plant of wet canal brickwork. The two species recently differentiated within the aggregate: *C. conicum* (L.) Dumort. and *C. salebrosum* Szweyk. *et al.* have not been distinguished here.

**Riccia cavernosa** Hoffm.
This is an annual of seasonally flooded areas, typically exposed mud at the edge of reservoirs. There is just one 19th century record for this species at Edgbaston reservoir but it is frequently overlooked and is worth searching for.

**Riccia fluitans** L.
This is a small aquatic plant found floating on the surface of water in ponds and canals. It is of sporadic occurrence but is not uncommon on the less used canals of the region.

### JUNGERMANNIOPSIDA

**Pellia epiphylla** (L.) Corda.
This very common calcifuge can form quite extensive sheets on wet soil or rocks.

**Pellia neesiana** (Gottsche) Limpr.
Less common than *P. epiphylla, P. neesiana*

looks very similar and grows in similar situations on damp substrates. The two species may be told apart only in the presence of female inflorescences. Moseley Bog, Lickey Hills.

**Pellia endiviifolia** (Dicks.) Dumort.
This species of *Pellia* is a calcicole and grows on a wide variety of wet substrates, most commonly on soil.

**Fossombronia pusilla** (L.) Nees
This small plant favours damp, bare, acidic soil such as the floors of quarries, sides of ruts or on bare tracks.

**Aneura pinguis** (L.) Dumort.
Usually found in mires, creeping amongst other bryophytes and low vegetation. Doultons Clay Pit (SO9387).

**Porella platyphylla** (L.) Pfeiff.
This species occurs on lightly shaded and base-rich rocks, walls and around the base of trees. Sutton Park.

**Ptilidium ciliare** (L.) Hampe
Occurs as scattered patches in well-drained acid grassland. Lickey Hills.

**Lepidozia reptans** (L.) Dumort.
Occasional on the bases of deciduous and coniferous trees. Normally found in acidic conditions and rarely, if ever, in basic environments.

**Lophocolea bidentata** (L.) Dumort.
Found throughout in damp grass. Not uncommon on damp, shaded, lawns.

**Lophocolea heterophylla** (Schrad.) Dumort.
Abundant on rotting wood, tree trunks and logs.

**Chiloscyphus polyanthos** (L.) Dumort.
This species is found growing as scattered shoots amongst other vegetation in marshes and flushes.

**Plagiochila asplenioides** (L. emend. Taylor) Dumort.
Occurs in pure patches or mixed with other bryophytes in neutral or calcareous woods or more open grassland. B'ham Botanic Gardens, Harborne.

**Cephalozia bicuspidata** (L.) Dumort.
A calcifuge, at home on moist soils, rotting logs and damp rocks. Barr Beacon, also at Greet Brickworks (SP098838).

**Cephaloziella divaricata** (Sm.) Schiffn.
A plant of acid substrates which are somewhat dryer than is usual for many

leafy liverworts. This minute plant, one of the most common of a difficult genus, is almost certainly under-recorded. Doultons Clay Pit (SO9387).

**Gymnocolea inflata** (Huds.) Dumort.
This species favours wet, acid habitats which are fairly strongly illuminated. One record at B'ham Botanic Gardens, Harborne.

**Lophozia ventricosa** (Dicks.) Dumort.
Very occasional on acid soil and peaty ground.

**Lophozia excisa** (Dicks.) Dumort.
A pioneer species of acid or leached basic substrates. Found on rocks in B'ham Botanic Gardens.Harborne.

**Diplophyllum albicans** (L.) Dumort.
A common calcifuge growing in a variety of habitats, in our area most typically on exposed peaty soil or soil covered rocks. Also found on leached substrates in clay and brick pits.

**Scapania irrigua** (Nees) Nees
A colonist of damp soil in clay and brick pits.

**Calypogeia fissa** (L.) Raddi
Forming small mats on rather acid peat or mineral soil. Occasional, Lickey Hills, Barr Beacon.

**Calypogeia muelleriana** (Schiffn.) Müll. Frib.
In similar habitats to *C. fissa* but will tolerate rather more acid conditions. Lickey Hills.

**Leiocolea turbinata** (Raddi) H. Buch
This plant is a strict calcicole, normally found in moist conditions. Just one record, at Doultons Clay Pit (SO9387), but should be looked for elsewhere around limestone outcrops.

**Jungermannia atrovirens** Dumort.
Usually a species of wet, base-rich habitats, it is found in clay and brick pits in our urban and suburban areas.

**Solenostoma gracillimum** (Sm.) R.M. Schust.
A pioneer species of well-lit, base-poor habitats. B'ham Botanic Gardens, Harborne.

**Solenostoma hyalinum** (Lyell) Mitt.
Occurs most commonly on rocks near water in acid to weakly basic conditions. One record from Ladymoor Pool (SO9495).

## BRYOPHYTA (mosses)

### SPHAGNOPSIDA

**Sphagnum papillosum** Lindb.
A single 19th century record for Sutton Park. This is a species of open bogs on deep, wet peat.

**Sphagnum palustre** L.
This is a plant of quite broad habitat tolerance, being at home in wet woods and grassland as well as marshy conditions. It is shade tolerant and is less acid-demanding than many of the *Sphagna*. Almost certainly under-recorded in our area.

**Sphagnum squarrosum** Crome
This is a plant of swampy mineral-rich ground, in our area most typically growing in wet woods sometimes in the most unpromising urban environments. It is shade tolerant and, where it occurs, can be very abundant. It can be confused with shade forms of the previous species.

**Sphagnum fimbriatum** Wilson
Like *S. squarrosum* this is a species of rather mineral-rich wet woodland where it can form extensive carpets. It is simple to identify and this, combined with its undoubted abundance make it the most commonly recorded *Sphagnum* of the region.

**Sphagnum girgensohnii** Russow
Of broad habitat tolerance this species will occur in wet woodland, flushes and stream and poolsides particularly where the ground has a slight base enrichment. Single record for Ladymoor Pool (SO9495).

**Sphagnum quinquefarium** (Braithw.) Warnst.
Unlike most *Sphagna*, *S. quinquefarium* prefers well-drained ground, usually in woodlands or in sheltered conditions with other vegetation. Single record for Ladymoor Pool (SO9495).

**Sphagnum capillifolium** (Ehrh.) Hedw.
This is the wine red plant most commonly associated with open, deep, peat-rich bogs where it can be very abundant. Sutton Park.

**Sphagnum inundatum** Russow
Despite its name this species is not normally found in water. Instead it is usually associated with swampy ground, damp woodlands and damp heathland; it can tolerate a certain amount of base enrichment. One record, Brownhills Common (SK0306).

**Sphagnum denticulatum** Brid.
A plant of very wet conditions, *S. denticulatum* will often grow submerged in acidic pools where its rather fat shoots and deep green colour make it easy to find. Sutton Park.

**Sphagnum cuspidatum** Ehrh. ex Hoffm.
This species is most often found submerged in very acidic pools where its wispy appearance, with long tapering stems and leaves, give it a very characteristic appearance earning it the nickname of "drowned kitten moss". Sutton Park.

**Sphagnum fallax** (H. Klinggr.) H. Klinggr.
A very common species forming extensive, yellowish ochre, carpets in permanently wet acid conditions such as valley bottoms and by streams and in bogs. Sutton Park.

### POLYTRICHOPSIDA

**Atrichum undulatum** (Hedw.) P. Beauv.
A common, and often abundant, plant of bare soil in damp woodland.

**Pogonatum nanum** (Hedw.) P. Beauv.
A common coloniser of bare disturbed soil on heaths and along paths in woods and by streams. Shade tolerant and demanding of an acid substrate.

**Pogonatum urnigerum** (Hedw.) P. Beauv.
A pioneer species of acid habitats such as dry soil footpaths, crumbling banks and wall tops. A strict calcifuge. Recorded only for the Lickey Hill but should be found elsewhere in suitable habitats.

**Polytrichastrum formosum** (Hedw.) G.L. Sm.
A common species usually found in neutral to acid broadleaf woodland, it is also common under conifers and may extend into heathland. Edgbaston, Lickey Hills.

**Polytrichum commune** Hedw.
Common in a range of damp acid habitats; in our area most frequently in relatively open damp heathland.

**Polytrichum piliferum** Hedw.
A calcifuge pioneer species which can be abundant on dry sandy or peaty soils. Most typical on dry heath but occasional on wall tops.

**Polytrichum juniperinum** Hedw.
A similar species to the last and growing in similar habitats but, if anything, more xerophytic.

## TETRAPHIDOPSIDA

**Tetraphis pellucida** Hedw.
This tiny plant is a strict calcifuge and is most commonly found on well-rotted stumps and logs. It can also colonise damp sandstone.

## BRYOPSIDA

**Encalypta streptocarpa** Hedw.
This species is an obligate calcicole which grows in large patches on limestone exposures. Wren's Nest.

**Funaria hygrometrica** Hedw.
Common throughout and especially associated with old bonfire sites where it can be found fruiting profusely.

**Physcomitrium pyriforme** (Hedw.) Bruch & Schimp.
Occasional on wet mud by small streams and on field margins. It is quite common in cattle–poached fields.

**Aphanorrhegma patens** (Hedw.) Lindb.
Occasional early colonist on wet mud by small streams and reservoir draw-down.

**Schistidium crassipilum** H.H. Blom
Very common on walls, concrete and mortar, especially in full sun.

**Grimmia pulvinata** (Hedw.) Sm.
The grey, hairy, cushions of this species are common everywhere on walls, concrete and mortar.

**Racomitrium aciculare** (Hedw.) Brid.
This is a species of wet, rocky places, and is especially associated with running water. One record for Harborne (SP034854).

**Racomitrium lanuginosum** (Hedw.) Brid.
More commonly associated with bare rocky ground in the uplands, there is one record for Greet Brickworks (SP098838).

**Racomitrium ericoides** (Brid.) Brid.
Normally associated with open, gravelly soil in the north and west. There is one record, on blast furnace spoil, in Dudley (SO922885).

**Fissidens bryoides** Hedw.
Forming small patches on circumneutral soils in shaded situations in woods and on banks. One record for Rough Wood at SJ983009 but is almost certainly under-recorded.

**Fissidens taxifolius** Hedw.
This is the most common species of the genus in our area. It grows on damp clayey soils in woods and on shaded banks. It is probably abundant here as it is pollution tolerant.

**Fissidens adianthoides** Hedw.
One of the larger members of the genus, this species is found occasionally in our area in wet runnels and on wet, basic rocks.

**Fissidens fontanus** (Bach. Pyl.) Steud.
An aquatic species somewhat tolerant of pollution. *F. fontanus* grows just below the surface of canals on concrete and brickwork. It can be quite abundant on locks and bridge footings.

**Pleuridium acuminatum** Lindb.
The records for this plant are rather scattered in our area but it is quite common as a colonist on patches of bare, dry soil in quarries and on banks and heaths.

**Ceratodon purpureus** (Hedw.) Brid.
This plant is common everywhere as a colonist of open, base-poor soils even in the most urban habitats. It is readily recognisable in fruit by its masses of purple setae but when infertile can be quite difficult to identify.

**Dichodontium pellucidum** (Hedw.) Schimp.
A delicate plant normally found colonising sand and fine shingle alongside streams. Here just one record alongside a small stream in B'ham Botanical Gardens, Harborne.

**Dicranoweisia cirrata** (Hedw.) Lindb.
Pollution tolerance means that this epiphytic moss can be found throughout the region on a number of tree species.

**Dicranella schreberiana** (Hedw.) Dixon
Occasional records on disturbed clay soil. The plant favours neutral or slightly calcareous conditions.

**Dicranella crispa** (Hedw.) Schimp.
Scattered records from similar habitats to *D. schreberana*.

**Dicranella varia** (Hedw.) Schimp.
This a common plant, rather similar to *D. heteromalla*, but which prefers neutral or basic soils. One record from B'ham Botanic Gardens, Harborne

**Dicranella cerviculata** (Hedw.) Schimp.
This is most typically a colonist of newly exposed, damp, bare peat. One record from the Lickey Hills. It can be told from *D. heteromalla* growing in similar conditions by the shape of its capsule.

**Dicranella heteromalla** (Hedw.) Schimp.
This is a common and abundant species, perhaps best known as a pioneer of damp, acid soils in woodland. It will also grow on rotting stumps, acid sandstone and will colonise raw peat exposures.

**Dicranum scoparium** Hedw.
This is a very common calcifuge plant most frequently found in grassland in our region but it will also grow on rotten wood and, occasionally, on living trees.

**Campylopus fragilis** (Brid.) Bruch & Schimp.
On peaty soil on heathland. One record from the Lickey Hills.

**Campylopus pyriformis** (Schultz) Brid.
Common on bare acid peaty soil in woods and on heathland and, less commonly, on rotting logs and stumps.

**Campylopus flexuosus** (Hedw.) Brid.
In similar habitats to *C. pyriformis*.

**Campylopus introflexus** (Hedw.) Brid.
This abundant species is a colonist of raw, bare peat and also common on well-rotted logs. It is one of the few common non-native species of bryophyte to be found in Britain. Although first found only in the early 1940s it is now found throughout the British Isles in suitable habitats.

**Leucobryum glaucum** (Hedw.) Ångstr.
Found on the ground in damp woodland and wet heathland this species forms characteristic pale whitish green mounds and balls. One record for Rednall at SO996766.

**Weissia controversa** Hedw.
Perhaps the most widespread member of a very difficult genus this plant is a frequent inhabitant of fairly undisturbed substrates. In our area the plant grows on rock exposures. Wren's Nest.

**Trichostomum brachydontium** Bruch
Most abundant in western and coastal habitats, inland it is a calcicole and in our area grows in patches on limestone. Wren's Nest.

**Gymnostomum aeruginosum** Sm.
This small moss grows in carpets, like green fur, on permanently moist lime-rich substrates such as old walls and in cracks. It is the most common of three rather similar species.

### Pseudocrossidium hornschuchianum (Schultz) R.H. Zander
This inconspicuous plant is quite frequent on well-drained, compacted stony ground. Typically found on the sides of paths and unsurfaced car parks and in abandoned quarries. One record for Harborne Botanic Garden but probably very under-recorded.

### Pseudocrossidium revolutum (Brid.) R.H. Zander
Frequently found on mortar and in the crevices of limestone rocks. Like the previous species small and inconspicuous and likely to be under-recorded. Wren's Nest.

### Bryoerythrophyllum recurvirostrum (Hedw.) P.C. Chen
Found in rather stony more or less calcareous habitats, in local sites most typically on walls and rocky outcrops. It is quite frequent in our area and is noticeable for its rusty red lower stem leaves making it more noticeable than the two previous plants.

### Barbula convoluta Hedw.
A very common plant, this species forms characteristic bright yellow-green patches on disturbed ground such as the edges of paths and on waste ground. It is rather similar to the following species which is somewhat larger.

### Barbula unguiculata Hedw.
Like the previous species this plant is very common throughout on disturbed ground and waste places. It too forms conspicuous yellow green patches but may be distinguished from B. convoluta by its slightly larger size, recurved leaf margins and nerve protruding in a short point from the leaf apex.

### Didymodon rigidulus Hedw.
Common on concrete, old walls and base-rich rock outcrops. It does, however, require some shade.

### Didymodon insulanus (De Not.) M.O. Hill
This moss is easy to recognise with its long narrow leaves curved into a spiral formation. Common on soil, it will also grow on brick walls, concrete and similar man-made substrates.

### Didymodon tophaceus (Brid.) Lisa
This is a species of damp, base-rich habitats such as old walls and rock outcrops which can be told from its many relatives by its blunt leaf tips. Barrow Hill, Dudley.

### Didymodon fallax (Hedw.) R.H. Zander
A short, brownish moss; this species is found on soil by paths and other disturbed ground.

### Didymodon ferrugineus (Schimp. ex Besch.) M.O. Hill
Found on well-drained, bare calcareous soils, such as on the floors of old quarries. Sedgley Beacon Quarry (SO919949).

### Tortula muralis Hedw.
Very common, frequently abundant. On walls, mortar, concrete and similar habitats.

### Tortula truncata (Hedw.) Mitt.
A very common, tiny, ephemeral colonist of bare, disturbed soil in gardens, field margins and similar habitats.

### Phascum cuspidatum Hedw.
A rather common ephemeral colonist of bare soil in disturbed habitats such as gardens, fields and path margins.

### Syntrichia ruralis (Hedw.) F. Weber & D. Mohr
Scattered throughout the region. The natural habitat of this species is rock outcrops and stony ground but in urban habitats is more commonly found on asbestos roofs and at the edges of old tarmac paths and drives.

### Syntrichia montana Nees
Similar to S. ruralis in both appearance and habitat; there is just one recorded site: Acocks Green.

### Syntrichia papillosa (Wilson) Jur.
This small dark green plant is most typically an epiphyte of mature trees; more rarely it grows on rocks. One record at Yardley Wood on rock (SP098809).

### Amblyodon dealbatus (Hedw.) P. Beauv.
A calcicole of wet, open, ground. There is just one record for this species at Sutton Park.

### Leptobryum pyriforme (Hedw.) Wilson
Very common and perhaps most often found as a weed growing in plant pots and in outdoor plant nurseries.

### Zygodon viridissimus (Dicks.) Brid.
An epiphyte found occasionally on mature trees in our region.

### Orthotrichum lyellii Hook. & Taylor
A scarce epiphyte, one record in our region, from Sutton Park.

### Orthotrichum affine Schrad. ex Brid.
An epiphyte found quite commonly on the trunks and branches of sheltered trees.

▲ Grimmia pulvinata (×5)

▲ Campylopus introflexus (×6)

▲ Tortula muralis (×3)

▲ Syntrichia papillosa (×4)

▲ *Ulota bruchii* (×12)

▲ *Bryum pallens* (×4)

▲ *Bryum capillare* (×4)

**Orthotrichum obtusifolium** Brid.
A single 19th century record from Sutton Park. This rare species is probably extinct in our area.

**Orthotrichum diaphanum** Schrad. ex Brid.
An epiphyte which also occurs on old brickwork and concrete. There are occasional records for our area but it is probably overlooked.

**Ulota crispa** (Hedw.) Brid.
A common epiphyte, in our region often found on Elder. Easily confused with the following species.

**Ulota bruchii** Hornsch. ex Brid.
A common epiphyte often found on Elder. Can only be told from *U. crispa* in the field by careful examination of the capsule.

**Philonotis fontana** (Hedw.) Brid.
Prominent in springs and flushes on both soil and rock, it is also occasionally found in other wet habitats such as quarries.

**Bryum pallens** Sw. ex anon.
This moss is frequently pinkish in colour which makes it stand out in its usual habitats of old quarries and similarly where it grows on moist bare soil.

**Bryum capillare** Hedw.
The twisted, often reddish, shoots of this species are common everywhere on walls and more occasionally on trees.

**Bryum pseudotriquetrum** (Hedw.) P. Gaertn. *et al.*
Rather occasional, found on wet soil in marshes and by streams.

**Bryum caespiticium** Hedw.
A common weedy species of waste ground and old walls.

**Bryum argenteum** Hedw.
Abundant weedy species of disturbed, often rather dry habitats such as pavement cracks and old tarmac and gravel. Pollution tolerant and often grows best where there is an abundance of nitrate.

**Bryum dichotomum** Hedw.
A colonist of a variety of unpromising habitats such as compacted soil and old tarmac, often in company with the previous species.

**Bryum ruderale** Crundw. & Nyholm
Occurs on bare compacted ground but is not tolerant of regular disturbance. One record, for Sedgley Beacon Quarry, SO919949.

**Bryum subapiculatum** Hampe
This is a species of sandy heathland where it is tolerant of disturbance. It is difficult to identify in the field and is probably under-recorded.

**Bryum rubens** Mitt.
A plant of disturbed, nutrient-rich, sites such as arable fields and patches of bare soil by roads. It is difficult to identify in the field and is probably under-recorded.

**Rhodobryum roseum** De Not.
Just one 19th century record for Sutton Park. This spectacular species is decreasing nationally and may be extinct in our region.

**Pohlia nutans** (Hedw.) Lindb.
This very common species is a strict calcifuge and may be found in a variety of habitats including old walls and on the ground in industrial sites as well as in more natural situations such as rotting stumps and logs.

**Pohlia melanodon** (Brid.) A.J. Shaw
This easily overlooked species is occasional on wet clay, often in rather shady conditions such as in the long grass at the edge of paths.

**Pohlia wahlenbergii** (F. Weber & D. Mohr) A.L. Andrews
Rather like a larger, paler version of the previous species this too is found in wet conditions on soil on waste ground and by tracks.

**Mnium hornum** Hedw.
This is an extremely common woodland species growing on a variety of substrates including soil, rotting stumps and in rock crevices.

**Rhizomnium punctatum** (Hedw.) T.J. Kop.
A large, common moss usually associated with springs and flushes where it grows on soil and rocks.

**Plagiomnium affine** (Blandow ex Funck) T.J. Kop.
Occurs on the ground in moist woods and grassland. One record for Edgbaston (SP069841).

**Plagiomnium undulatum** (Hedw.) T.J. Kop.
This is a large plant common on soil in damp woodland.

**Aulacomnium palustre** (Hedw.) Schwägr.
This is a plant of acid, boggy habitats where it is frequently associated with *Sphagnum*. Two records; Clayhanger Common (SK044045) and Pelsall Common (SK011046).

**Aulacomnium androgynum** (Hedw.) Schwägr.
Quite a common species of well-decayed damp wood, it is also found on damp sandstone.

**Orthodontium lineare** Schwägr.
This fine-leaved species is somewhat pollution tolerant and can occur in a wide variety of base-poor habitats such as logs, stumps and moist sandstone.

**Fontinalis antipyretica** Hedw.
The long trailing branches of this species are a common sight in canals where it grows on hard substrates, like bridges and locks, just below the surface of the water.

**Climacium dendroides** (Hedw.) F. Weber & D. Mohr
This plant has a curious, tree-like, growth habit and is found in mildly basic grassland. One record for Longmoor Pool, Sutton Park (SP093962).

**Palustriella commutata** (Hedw.) Ochyra
A conspicuous species of springs and flushes; very similar to the following species. Sutton Park.

**Palustriella falcata** (Brid.) Hedenäs
A conspicuous plant of springs and flushes; very similar to the *P commutata* and difficult to separate in the field. Sutton Park.

**Cratoneuron filicinum** (Hedw.) Spruce
Occasional in wet base-rich habitats. Perry (SP075924, in canal); Lickey Hills (SP002752).

**Campylium stellatum** (Hedw.) Lange & C.E.O. Jensen
In wet, base-rich grassland. Longmoor Pool, Sutton Park (SP093962).

**Campyliadelphus chrysophyllus** (Brid.) R.S. Chopra
In short grass in old quarry. Sedgley Beacon Quarry (SO919949).

**Amblystegium serpens** (Hedw.) Schimp.
This tiny plant is very common in a variety of shady habitats including soil, rocks and the base of trees.

**Hygroamblystegium fluviatile** (Hedw.) Loeske
Occasional on stones and rocks in streams and canals. As it is rather small and more or less aquatic it is probably under-recorded.

**Drepanocladus aduncus** (Hedw.) Warnst.
One record, in a pool at Greet Brickworks (SP098838).

**Warnstorfia fluitans** (Hedw.) Loeske
One record, in a pool at Walsall Power Station (SO994997).

**Straminergon stramineum** (Dicks. ex Brid.) Hedenäs
A wetland plant usually found amongst other bryophytes, such as *Sphagnum* species. Sutton Park.

**Hamatocaulis vernicosus** (Mitt.) Hedenäs
There is one 19th century record for this rare and declining species in Sutton Park.

**Scorpidium revolvens** (Sw. ex anon.) Rubers
A species of more or less calcareous flushes. Sutton Park.

**Scorpidium cossonii** (Schimp.) Hedenäs
A rather similar plant to the previous species. One record, Longmoor Pool, Sutton Park (SP093962).

**Calliergon giganteum** (Schimp.) Kindb.
Occasional in wet, muddy base-rich sites. Sutton Park.

**Thuidium tamariscinum** (Hedw.) Schimp.
This conspicuous, feathery moss is common on the ground in deciduous woodland.

**Pseudoscleropodium purum** (Hedw.) M. Fleisch.
Common in many grassland habitats.

**Eurhynchium striatum** (Hedw.) Schimp.
Quite common on the ground in woods growing on basic soils.

**Platyhypnidium riparioides** (Hedw.) Dixon
An aquatic species common in both streams and on the concrete and brickwork of canals.

**Rhynchostegium confertum** (Dicks.) Schimp.
Occasional in damp, shaded places growing in small patches on stones, concrete and bark, particularly bark of Elder.

**Oxyrrhynchium hians** (Hedw.) Loeske
Frequent on neutral or basic soil in woods and under hedges.

**Kindbergia praelonga** (Hedw.) Ochyra
A small, weedy species abundant everywhere on the ground in both damp and dry, shady and open habitats.

**Brachythecium albicans** (Hedw.) Schimp.
Occasional in acid grassland.

**Brachythecium mildeanum** (Schimp.) Schimp.
This is a species of bare, open ground and

▲ *Bryum argenteum* (×3)

▲ *Rhizomnium punctatum* (×4)

▲ *Thuidium tamariscinum* (×2)

▲ *Brachythecium rutabulum* (×1)

▲ *Pleurozium schreberi* (×1.5)

▲ *Plagiothecium undulatum* (×1.5)

is most often encountered at the edges of earth car parks. Frequently confused with the following species it is almost certainly under-recorded. Lickey Hills.

**Brachythecium rutabulum** (Hedw.) Schimp.
Very common everywhere and almost ubiquitous on the ground in all types of woodland.

**Brachythecium rivulare** Schimp.
Rather similar to the previous species it is usually found by water or in flushes.

**Brachytheciastrum velutinum** (Hedw.) Ignatov & Huttunen
Very common as a weed of shady sites, growing over stones and rocks in parks and gardens.

**Homalothecium sericeum** (Hedw.) Schimp.
Usually to be found on exposed rock, especially limestone, it will also grow on similar artificial habitats like mortar and asbestos sheeting. Cannon Hill Park.

**Calliergonella cuspidata** (Hedw.) Loeske
A very common plant of wet, open habitats. Frequently found in wet lawns.

**Hypnum cupressiforme** Hedw. **var. cupressiforme**
Probably the most common moss species in our region, growing on a wide variety of substrates but most often found on tree trunks, branches, walls and rocks.

**Hypnum cupressiforme** Hedw. **var. lacunosum** Brid.
This is a large, calcicole species found on sheltered rock exposures. One record, for Sedgley Beacon Quarry (SO919949).

**Hypnum jutlandicum** Holmen & E. Warncke
Very common amongst heather on heathland.

**Ctenidium molluscum** (Hedw.) Mitt.
Found on rocks and amongst grass in basic habitats.

**Pleurozium schreberi** (Willd. ex Brid.) Mitt.
Common in acid grassland on heaths.

**Rhytidiadelphus squarrosus** (Hedw.) Warnst.
A very common species of moist, nutrient-rich grassland. A common weed of moist shady lawns.

**Plagiothecium latebricola** Schimp.
Occasional on decaying vegetation in damp shady places.

**Plagiothecium denticulatum** (Hedw.) Schimp.
A common species of moist, acid, woodland growing on soil, fallen logs and tree bases.

**Plagiothecium undulatum** (Hedw.) Schimp.
This large and conspicuous species is common on the ground in acid woodland and more occasional on heath.

**Pseudotaxiphyllum elegans** (Brid.) Z. Iwats.
Not dissimilar in appearance to the smaller species of *Plagiothecium*. It is often abundant on earth banks in acid woodland.

**Neckera complanata** (Hedw.) Huebener
Abundant on limestone rock exposures. Wren's Nest (SO934928).

**Homalia trichomanoides** (Hedw.) Brid.
Not dissimilar in appearance to *N. complanata*, it is more normally found growing on trees. Wren's Nest (SO934928).

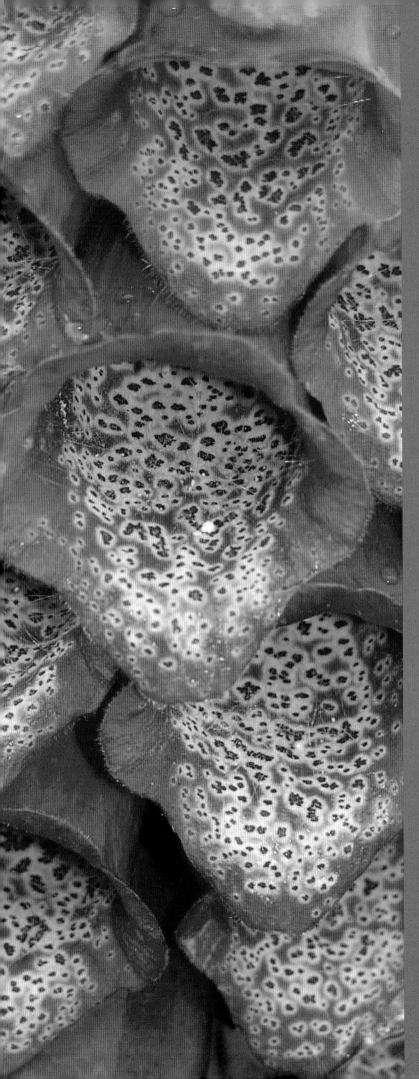

# Chapter 8
# Vascular plants

◀ Foxglove *Digitalis purpurea*

▲ Flora recorders (from the left): Janet Antrobus, David Antrobus, Paul Reade, James Partridge, Ellen Pisolkar, Lucy Bastin, Eleanor Cohn, Ian Trueman, Mike Poulton and Simon Phipps (Birmingham Eastside 2007)

## The recording scheme

The survey area encompasses the modern political boundaries of the cities of Birmingham and Wolverhampton and the Metropolitan Boroughs of Dudley, Sandwell and Walsall, the area for which the Birmingham and Black Country Wildlife Trust and EcoRecord, the local Biological Records Centre, have had responsibility since the 1980s. Together these five metropolitan districts almost exactly delimit the built-up area of the conurbation. The exception is the relatively small built-up areas of Solihull, to the south-east.

The purpose of the present survey was to describe and evaluate the botany of this conurbation as an entity. For national recording purposes the conurbation is divided between three vice-counties: vc. 39 (Staffordshire), vc. 38 (Warwickshire) and vc. 37 (Worcestershire) (see map). Collection and processing of records had therefore previously taken place at three centres, with all the comparisons being with the individual vice-counties. The

existence of the Wildlife Trust and EcoRecord has however given a basis for a direct evaluation of the conurbation as a whole.

The recording project began with a meeting at the University of Wolverhampton in 1997. It was decided to record Birmingham and the Black Country at the monad level, i.e. to produce a list of species for each of the 715 monads (one kilometre squares) in the conurbation. A monad scoresheet was devised to record the presence/absence of 400 species, and more detailed information, including records of habitat, ecology and associated species, for all other plants encountered. The 400 species were those considered to be most frequent in Birmingham and the Black Country on the basis of records then held by EcoRecord. Since these records tended to focus on surveys of recognised wildlife sites, this list perhaps over-represented some species associated with sites having nature conservation interest. It might have been preferable to collect more detailed information about a few of the old habitat indicators such as *Anemone nemorosa* and *Veronica montana*.

Other sources of records have been included in the database. The Wildlife Trust for Birmingham and the Black Country carried out a great deal of survey work of wildlife sites, canals and other habitats in the 1980s and the 1990s. All the biological data from this work was entered onto the RECORDER database by EcoRecord and the plant records formed the basis for the current Flora.

In 1998 a tetrad recording scheme commenced for the whole of vc. 39 (Staffordshire), and an agreement was made with John Hawksford, the BSBI Recorder for vc. 39, to exchange data with the Birmingham and Black Country recording scheme. Similar agreements were made with the BSBI Recorders for vc. 38 Warwickshire, James Partridge and vc. 37 Worcestershire, John Day. We are very grateful for the cooperation shown by the BSBI Recorders. The final exchange with the Staffordshire recording

scheme included records up to 2008 and with Worcestershire with records up to 2007. A new Checklist for the Flora of Warwickshire was published in 2007, and its information has also been incorporated into the Birmingham and Black Country Flora.

Although recorders for the Staffordshire Flora worked to a tetrad recording sheet, they were asked to produce monad lists when working in the Birmingham and Black Country area and most did. Nevertheless, this data and that from the other vice-counties include significant quantities of tetrad records which we are unable to show in our maps. In some cases where this has produced discrepancies, tetrad records have been mentioned in the text.

In view of the potentially rapid speed of change in habitats, especially in a conurbation, and the difficulty in checking old records, it was decided to make January 1995 the starting point

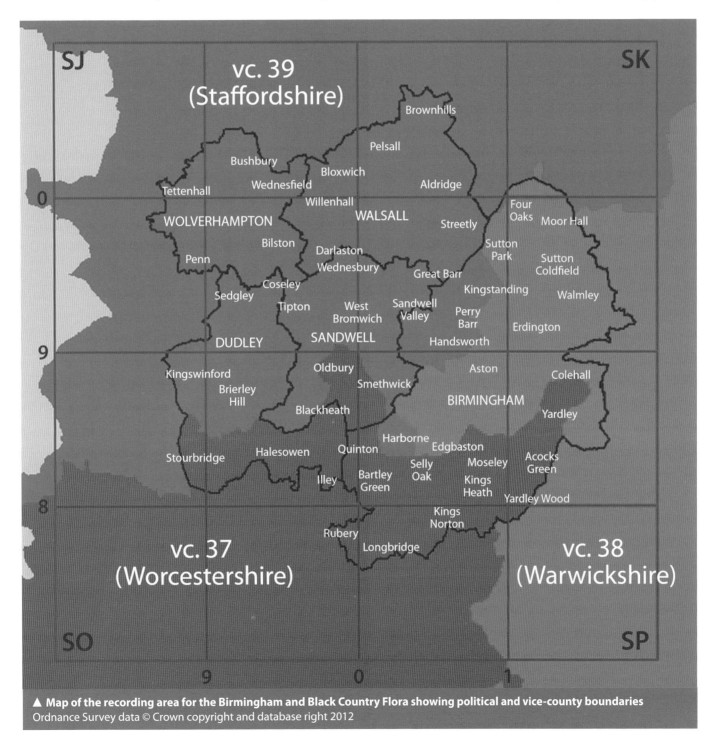

▲ **Map of the recording area for the Birmingham and Black Country Flora showing political and vice-county boundaries**
Ordnance Survey data © Crown copyright and database right 2012

for the Birmingham and Black Country recording scheme. A large number of volunteers contributed records for individual monads in the area between 1998 and 2008, and since then, although no systematic fieldwork has taken place, significant records have continued to be added to the database up to August 2012. Significant earlier records for uncommon species are also mentioned in the text but not mapped.

## Nomenclature used in the text

The systematic order, Latin botanical nomenclature and English names of the taxa follow those used in the third edition of the *New Flora of the British Isles* (Stace, 2010) with the exception of a few aliens not placed in order or not included in that work, which are mainly appended at the end of the entry for the particular genus.

## Distribution maps

Distribution maps are included for almost all species with records from more than five monads and less than 650 monads in the survey area. We would like to gratefully acknowledge Dr Alan Morton and his program **DMAP** which we used in the production of the vascular plant distribution maps. Every map shows the political boundaries of the metropolitan districts of Birmingham, Dudley, Sandwell, Walsall and Wolverhampton downloaded in 2011 from OS OpenData. The map also shows the boundaries of the 10km squares of the Ordnance Survey National Grid. For the sake of clarity, the boundaries of the three vice-counties covered by the survey area are not shown in the individual maps and are shown in the map on page 227.

The dot symbol represents one or more records for the relevant plant in the relevant monad within the main recording period 1995–2008, although significant records added up to August 2012 have been included.

## Structure of species entries

(i) Each entry begins with the **Latin name** in bold italics with the authority in condensed text. Synonymy is limited to significant changes from the second edition of the *New Flora of the British Isles* (Stace 1997).

(ii) The **English name** is given in bold in the second line.

(iii) The **distribution map** normally follows except where its position is altered to economise on space. Taxa with five monad records or less are not mapped, but each record is presented with a locality, 6-figure grid reference, author(s) name(s) and year of record. Taxa with 650 or more monad records are considered ubiquitous and are also not mapped. Attention is drawn to these species by giving the number of monads in bold and in blue.

(iv) The account starts with the **number of monads** for which the taxon was recorded in the recording period. Where the species was listed on the front of the recording card and therefore only 4-figure grid references are available, an asterisk is inserted in front of the monad number.

(v) The taxon is next allocated to its **origin type** following Preston, Pearman and Dines (2002): **native**, or introduced (brought into Britain and Ireland, either intentionally or accidentally,

by humans). Where the origins in Birmingham and the Black Country are considered to differ from the origins in Britain and Ireland, this is commented on. Introduced species are divided into **archaeophytes** (introduced before 1500 AD), **neophytes** (introduced since 1500 AD), and **casuals** (species in which populations fail to persist in the wild for several years and are therefore dependant on constant reintroduction). Again any known differences in origin in Birmingham and the Black Country are mentioned.

(vi) **Axiophytes** are indicated by the abbreviation **Ax**. These are notable species, designated as such by the present authors (see Chapter 4).

(vii) Any **national status**, such as nationally scarce, Red Data List IUCN category, Schedule 9 (invasive) is stated next; all the categories used were abbreviated and may be found in the list of abbreviations.

(viii) The **main text** follows, with brief notes about basic life form, habitats, ecology and distribution. National texts such as Preston, Pearman & Dines (2002), Grime *et al.* (2007), Hill *et al.* (1999), Hill *et al.* (2004), also Sinker *et al.* (1985) were consulted, but the objective was to describe the plant's characteristics in Birmingham and the Black Country. This section is mostly self-explanatory, but typically soil reaction (normally measured by soil pH) is assessed as **base status**: 'base-rich' soils are relatively rich in calcium and other bases, with a pH of 5.5 and above, 'base-poor' soils have few bases available to plants and a pH typically below 4.5. Soil fertility is measured in terms of **nutrient status** (normally measured in terms of the availability to plants in the soil of the plant macronutrients nitrogen, phosphorus and potassium). 'Nutrient-rich' soils are found in gardens, 'improved' agricultural land, some old woodlands and many water margins. 'Nutrient-poor' soils characterise heaths, hill pastures and many old 'unimproved' habitats.

For neophytes, the entry ends with a brief reference to the **geographical origin of the species** in question, based largely on Stace (2010) and Preston *et al.* (2002).

(ix) For many of the species sufficiently frequently encountered in the survey, a list of **typical associated species** has been provided, headed by the abbreviation 'Ass:'. This is a necessarily approximate assessment of those other species, of a similar size and growth form, which are frequently encountered growing in the immediate neighbourhood. Provision was made on the recording card for recorders to list associate species of the less common species in the field, and these data have been used in addition to the personal experience of the authors recording in Birmingham and the Black Country. The list of associates should not be taken as an allocation to a single National Vegetation Classification (Rodwell 1991 *et seq.*) since species which may not necessarily grow together may be associates of the species in question in different circumstances.

(xi) Where a taxon has been subdivided, e.g. where a species has records for one or more subspecies or varieties, these may be described in an addendum at the end of the account. Latin names of any such varieties and subspecies for which there are definite records in B&BC are given in bold italics, with any English names in bold. Latin names of other varieties or subspecies for which there are no definite records in B&BC are given in italics.

(xii) **Cultivars** are described as (e.g.) cultivar 'Herbsfreude' without bold or italics or abbreviation.

## Abbreviations used in the text

### (i) General abbreviations

| | |
|---|---|
| agg. | aggregate |
| Ass | principal associated species |
| Ax. | axiophyte |
| B&BC | Birmingham and the Black Country |
| B'ham | Birmingham |
| BAP | listed in the UK Biodiversity Action Plan |
| BIRA | herbarium of Birmingham Museums and Art Gallery |
| BIRM | herbarium of Birmingham University |
| BSBI | Botanical Society of the British Isles (Botanical Society of Britain and Ireland) |
| conf. | identity confirmed by…. |
| CR | Critically Endangered (IUCN Red Data List category [Cheffings & Farrell 2005]) |
| det. | identity determined by…. |
| E | east |
| EN | Endangered (IUCN Red Data List category [Cheffings & Farrell 2005]) |
| LTR | herbarium of the University of Leicester |
| N | north |
| Nationally Scarce | listed in Stewart *et al.* (1994) as Nationally Scarce |
| NMW | herbarium of the National Museums and Galleries of Wales |
| NT | Near Threatened (IUCN Red Data List category [Cheffings & Farrell 2005]) |
| S | south |
| s.l. | *sensu lato* |
| s.s. | *sensu stricto* |
| Sch. 8 | protected under the Wildlife & Countryside Act (1981) |
| Sch. 9 (invasive) | may not be released or caused to grow in the wild (Schedule 9 of the Wildlife & Countryside Act) |
| Sect. 41 | listed in Section 41 of the NERC Act (2006) – Species of principal importance in England and Wales |
| sp. | species (singular) |
| spp. | species (plural) |
| subsp. | subspecies |
| var. | variety |
| vc. | vice-county |
| VU | Vulnerable (IUCN Red Data List category [Cheffings & Farrell 2005]) |
| W | west |
| W'ton | Wolverhampton |
| Warks BRC | Warwickshire Biological Records Centre |
| WarNaCT | Warwickshire Nature Conservation Trust (now the Warwickshire Wildlife Trust) |
| 125 | At beginning of an entry: number of monads in B&BC where the taxon has been recorded 1995–2012 |
| 675 | At beginning of entry: where number of monad records in a taxon is more than 650 |
| * | A species in the main list on the recording sheet and therefore recorded only at the monad level |
| ** | A species within *Rubus* subgenus *Rubus* considered by Newton & Randall (1988) to be of horticultural origin. |

### (ii) Abbreviations of recorders' names

The following, relatively prolific recorders and referees are represented in the text by the initials specified.

| | |
|---|---|
| AB | Alistair Blackshaw |
| AEEP | the late Else Pickvance |
| AJL | Alex Lockton |
| AJR | A.J. Richards |
| ALP | the late Rev. A.L. Primavesi |
| AMG | A.M. Glaisher |
| APD | Anne Daly |
| AS | Tony Sames |
| AWR | Bert Reid |
| Bagnall | the late J.E. Bagnall |
| BH | the late Brian Hopton |
| BL | Brian Laney |
| BRF | the late Bryan Fowler |
| CBW | Christopher Westall |
| CRP | Chris Parry |
| CW | Craig Wilkinson |
| DH | David Haslam |
| DJA | David Antrobus |
| EJC | Eric Clement |
| EMP | Ellen Pisolkar |
| EVJC | Eleanor Cohn |
| FGB | the late Gordon Bennett |
| HHF | the late Harold Fowkes |
| ICT | Ian Trueman |
| JaH | Jane Hardwick |
| JEH | John Hawksford |
| JJB | Jonathan Bowley |
| JJD | John Day |
| JPM | John Martin |
| JVT | John Tranter |
| JWP | the late James Partridge |
| LG | Les Goodby |
| MES | Mike Smith |
| MHM | Mike Mountford |
| MWP | Mike Poulton |
| PC | Peter Coxhead |
| PLR | Paul Reade |
| PN | Paul Newton |
| PWS | Paul Stephenson |
| Readett | The late R.C. Readett |
| RM | Roger Maskew |
| SAHA | Simon Atkinson |
| SB | Stefan Bodnar |
| SJC | Sue Collingswood |
| SMP | Simon Phipps |
| SPG | the Sutton Park Group |
| SRP | Shirley Price |
| ST | Sue Timms |
| TCH | T.C. Hextell |
| TGCR | Tim Rich |
| TM | Tim Moughtin |
| WAT | Bill Thompson |
| WHH | the late W.H. Hardaker |

Natural England records may have been made by its predecessors Nature Conservancy, Nature Conservancy Council or English Nature.

▲ Mike Poulton and Anne Daly

▲ Ian Trueman, Mike Poulton, James Partridge and Jane Hardwick

## Contributors of records

We are very grateful for the recording work undertaken by so many volunteers over the period of the recording scheme, whether they were working for the Birmingham and Black Country Flora itself, or on site surveys, or for neighbouring recording schemes. As full a list as possible of our recorders is given below. If we have missed anyone we can only offer our apologies.

P.P. Abbott, R. Aberdeen, C. Abrahams, A. Adamou, J. Akers, D.E. Allen, P. Allenby, P. Andrews, C.E.A. Andrews, J. Andrews, P. Anthony, D. Antrobus, J. Antrobus, B.J. Arthur, L. Ashfield, B. Ashley, J. Ashton (†), M. Aspinall, S. Astle, S. Atkinson, S. Ault, M. Austin, H.E.E. Babb, J. Bailey, R. Baker, N. Ball, H. Ball, S. Banfield, E. Barker, F. Barker, G. Barker, S. Barlow, A. Barnell, S. Barnes, S. Barnett, K. Barnett, L. Bastin, G. Beer, M.A. Beilby, P. Bennett, F.G. Bennett (†), R. Berger, C. Berry, N. Betson, J. Bevan, T. Beynon, M.H. Bigwood, R. Billingsley, J. Bingham, S. Bingham, A. Bird, T. Bird, C. Bissaco, A. Black, A. Blackshaw, E. Blackwell, H.H. Bloomer, M. Bloxham, J. Bluck, A.G. Blunt, S. Bodnar, S. Boland, Mrs Bonham, H. Bowler, J. Bowley, J.C. Bowra, J. Box, B. Brand, J. Branscombe, W.T. Bree, B. Bridges, R.C. Broadbent, D. Brookman, D. Broughton, A. Brown, B. Bruce, S. Brueton, P. Bryant, R. Buckland, R.C.L. Burges, M. Burgess, M. Burgoine, P. Burgoine, P. Burkinshaw (†), W. Burnett, S. Burton, R. Busbridge, M. Busby, G. Butler, S. Carvalho, J. Caswell, E. Checkley, R. Christie, M.C. Clark, M. Clark, J.H. Clarke, J. Clayfield, E.J. Clement, J. Clements, K. Clements, E.V.J. Cohn, A. Cole, A. Collinge, R. Collings, S. Collingswood, B.J. Collins, M. Collins, R. Collins, S. Coney, R. Cooper, S. Cooper, P. Copson (†), J. Cornow, A. Coward, J.G. Cox, P. Coxhead, M. Crees, R. Crees, N. Crowley, S. Cunningham, N. Curnow, A.P. Daly, M. Dando, I.M. Dashwood, S. Davey, S. Davies, A. Davis, S. Davison, J.J. Day, I. Denholm, S. Derry, R. Dibble, A. Dimmock, M. Dixon, J. Dorman, A. Douse, M. D'Oyly, C. Driscoll, J. Duckworth, J. Duddlestone, R. Duff, S. Duke, A. Duncan, D. Dupree, R. Dutton, R. Eames, R. Earnshaw, J. Easton, D. Eccleston, J. Edbury, H. Edwards, P. Edwards, C. Evans, G. Evans, L.J. Evans (†), M.E. Evans, T. Fairfield, N. Farrin, A. Faulkner, A. Ferguson, D. Fiddaman, J. Finch, F. Fincher (†), M. Finnemore, C. Flynn, J. Forty (†), H. Fowkes (†), B. Fowler (†), A. Fraser (†), B. Freear, A. Freeman, S. Freeman, R. Fremlin, D. Friday, K. Fry, J. Fryer, J. Fulford, C. Fuller, R. Fuller, R. Fussell, A. Gardner, P.G. Garner, S. Gilks, S. Ginley, A. Glaisher, C. Gleeson, J. Glossop, M. Godfrey, R. Golding, L. Goodby, W. Goodin, C.M. Goodman, J. Gorle, R. Gorman, D.W. Gorrage, R. Gotheridge, R. Gowing, G.H. Green, P.S. Green, M.J. Griffin, H. Griffiths, S.A. Grocott, D. Grundy, J. Gulley (†), R. Hacking, S. Haden, S. Hadley, S. Hancox, J. Hardwick, A. Harlond, A. Harris, P. Harris, D. Harrison, M.E. Hartill, T. Hartland-Smith, D. Haslam, J. Haslett, J. Hawksford, C.J. Hayes, S. Hayhow, D. Haynes, J. Haynes, M. Heap, N. Hewitt, T. Hextell, C.M. Hibbert, B. Hickey, J. Hickman, S. Hicks, B. Hildick, M.J. Hill, D. Hill, P. Hillcox, P. Hills, C. Hinchliffe, S. Hinchliffe, K. Hodge, I. Hodgson, P. Hodgson, C. Hogarth, S. Holland, T. Holland, L. Holloway, L. Holmes, A. Homer, I.J. Hopkins, B. Hopton (†), C. Horne, J. Horton, A. Hotchkiss, S. Houghton, D. Hunt, C. Jackson-Houlston, V. Jacobs, P. James, R. James, S. Jarvis, V. Jasper, M. Jenn, A. Jervis, M. Joachim, C. John, I. Johnson, V. Johnstone, B. Jones, C. Jones, D. Jones, G. Jones, J. Jones, R. Jones, V. Jones, C.R. Jordan, A. Jukes, M. Kay, M. Kearnes, J. Kelcey, A. Ketteridge, J. Kiernan, M. Kingsbury, G. Kitchener, C. Klein, T.D. Knight, R. Knightbridge, P. Knowles, M. Kodaka, R. Labrenz, S.E. Lampard, H. Lancaster, E. Lane, B. Laney, R.V.H. Lansdown, D.R. Larner, M. Latham, S. Lawley, V. Lawrie,

J. Le Page, M. Le Ray, R. Lester, C. Levine, G. Lewis, J. Lewis,
K. Limbrick, J. Little (†), A.J. Lockton, P. Logan, E. Lomas,
H.E. Lowe, S. Lucas, A. Mabbett, M. Mackay, N. MacLean,
J. Maiden, J. Mallin, C. Mansell, P. Marriot, B. Marsh, C. Marsh,
R. Marsh, R.D. Martin, J.P. Martin, L. Martland, R. Maskew,
S. Maslen, D. Mattley, S. May, P. McCormick, J. McGuire,
E. McKay, L. McKevitt, P. Meadows, F. Meeting, R.D. Meikle,
J.W. Meiklejohn, R. Mileto, P. Millett, A. Millward, B. Moodie,
K. Moore, P. Moore, S. Moore, J. Morris, T. Morris, D. Morse,
T. Moughtin, M. Mountford, C. Mulvey, L. Neal, S. Needle,
P. Newton, I. Nicholls, P. Nicholson, G.D. Nickolds, V. Nixon,
A. Normand, B. Normand, R. Nyirenda, D. Oakley, E. O'Donnell,
S. O'Donnell, A. O'Gara, T. Oki, T. Oliver, S. O'Meara, B. Opara,
P. Orwin, C. Osborn, J. Osborne, P. Paddock, G. Palmer,
S. Pancheri, L. Park, J.A. Parris, C.R. Parry, D. Parsons, J. Parsons,
J.W. Partridge (†), R. Payne, G. Peake, A. Pearce, H. Pearce,
T. Pearce, W. Pearson, C. Peglar, M. Perrott, B. Perry, G. Perry,
A. Pervin, O. Pescott, A.M. Pettigrew, J. Phipps, S. Phipps,
R. Pickering, S. Pickles, E. Pickvance (†), T.J. Pickvance, N. Pinder,
G. Pinfield, L. Pinkess (†), E. Pisolkar, J. Pitcher, L. Poulton,
M. Poulton, E. Powell, J. Powell, S. Powell, A. Preece, J. Presland,
W. Prestwood, J. Price, J.E.F. Price, M. Price (†), S.R. Price,
A.L. Primavesi (†), A. Prior, A. Pritchard, B. Pugh, E. Pulford,
A. Purcell, J. Rau, J. Ray, P. Reade, J. Reece, P. Reeve, A. Reeves,
A.W. Reid, L.A. Reid, J.S. Reid, A. Reynolds, T.C.G. Rich,
M. Richardson, E. Richmond, S. Riley, J. Robbins, G. Robinson,
M. Robinson, S. Rogers, F. Rose (†), A. Rostański, B. Rowe,
C. Rowe, S. Rowland, F. Rumsey, A. Sames, S. Sames, M. Scholten,
R. Seadon, P. Seccombe, J. Sells, A. Sestakovs, A. Shepherd,
P. Shirley, J. Shrimpton, N. Sibbett, D. Simkin, H. Simmons,
A. Simons, N. Simpson, A.N.B. Simpson, D. Sinclair, A.D. Skelding
(†), A. Slater, J. Slater, G.C. Slawson, E. Slim, M. Smart, B. Smith,
L. Smith, P. Smith, H.A. Smith, M.E. Smith, L. Southall, R. Speight,
P.D. Stanley, A. Stanneveldt, C. Statham, R. Stebbings,
C. Stenson, K.M. Stephen, P. Stephenson, K. Stevenson,
J. Stokes, A. Strachan, I. Tanner, W.G. Teagle (†), J. Teall,
C. Thomas, W.A. Thompson, S. Thompson, T. Thompson,
C. Thorneycroft, C.R. Thornless, S. Timms, P. Timson, C. Tinstell,
B. Tobin, B. Tokarska-Guzik, S. Tombs, J. Tomlinson, M. Towers,
J. Tranter, C. Tregaskes, I.C. Trueman, J. Turner, A. Underhill (†),
D. Vallance, R. Vann, S. Vincent, C. Walker, D. Walker, N. Walker,
G.J. Walker, D. Wall, M. Waller, E.F. Warburg, J. Warwicker,
A. Wass, C. Waterson, M. Watson, W. Watson, M. Webb,
T. Webster, S. Welch, A. West, G.S. West, K.J. West, C.B. Westall,
B.F. Westcott, V. Weston, B. Westwood, D. Westwood, S. Whild,
F. Whiston, A. Whitbread, D. White, J. White, J. Whittock,
K. Whitton, N. Wilding, C. Wilkinson, K. Wilkinson, P. Wilkinson,
W.H. Wilkinson, N.J. Willby, A. Willets, J. Williams, N. Williams,
A.W. Wills, C. Wilmer, L. Wilson, M. Wilson, S. Wilson, P. Wiltshire,
C. Wishart, D. Withers, J. Wollner, B. Wood, C. Wood, T. Wood,
R. Woodall, G. Woodin, R. Woodward, M. Wooldridge,
J.F. Woolman, T. Worfolk, L. Worledge, J. Woulds, D. Wrench,
N. Wyatt, J. Wynn, C. Young, F. Young, H. Young, M.R. Young,
Betts Ecology, Birmingham City Council Parks Rangers,
Birmingham Natural History Society, BTCV, Centre for Urban
Ecology, Centre of the Earth (B&BC WT), CSa Environmental
Planning, Friends of Balaam's Wood, Halcrow Group, James
Johnson Ecology consultants, King Edward VI School, Natural
England, Pensnett Wildlife Group, Sandwell Valley Naturalists
(SANDNATS), Staffordshire Wildlife Trust, Land Care Associates,
Sutton Park Group, The Wildlife Trust for Birmingham and
The Black Country (B&BC WT), Wardell Armstrong, Warwickshire
Biological Records Centre, Warwickshire Wildlife Trust,
Worcestershire Wildlife Trust.

▲ Ian Trueman

▲ The late James Partridge

▲ Mike Poulton

## References

Amphlett, J. & Rea, C. (1909) *The Botany of Worcestershire*. Cornish Brothers, Birmingham.

Bagnall, J.E. (1876) *Notes on Sutton Park: Its Flowering Plants, Ferns, and Mosses*. Read at a general meeting of the Birmingham Natural History and Microscopical Society, December 6th, Birmingham.

Bagnall, J.E. (1891) *The Flora of Warwickshire*. Gurney & Jackson, London and Cornish Brothers, Birmingham.

Bagnall, J.E. (1901) The Flora of Staffordshire. *Journal of Botany* 39 Supplement.

Burges, R.P. & Andrews, C.E.A. (1947) Report of the Bombed Sites Survey Sub-Committee. *Proceedings of the Birmingham Natural History and Philosophical Society* XVIII (1) pp.1–12.

Cadbury, D.A., Hawkes, J.G. & Readett, R.C. (1971) *A Computer-mapped Flora – A Study of the County of Warwickshire*. Academic Press, London.

Cheffings, C.M. & Farrell, L. (Eds) (2005) *The Vascular Plant Red Data List for Great Britain*. JNCC, Peterborough.

Clement, E.J. & Foster, M.C. (1994) *Alien Plants of the British Isles*. BSBI, London.

Copson, P., Partridge, J.W. & Roberts, J. (2008) *A New Checklist of the Flora of Warwickshire*. Warwickshire Publications, Warwick.

Dudman, A.A. & Richards, A.J. (1997) *Dandelions of Great Britain and Ireland*. BSBI, London.

Edees, E.S. & Newton, A. (1988) *Brambles of the British Isles*. The Ray Society, London.

Edees, E.S. (1972) *Flora of Staffordshire*. David & Charles, Newton Abbot.

Fowkes, H. & Coxhead, P. (1991) *A Natural History of Sutton Park. Part 1: The Vascular Plants*. Sutton Coldfield Natural History Society, Sutton Coldfield.

Gilbert, O.L. (1989) *The Ecology of Urban Habitats*. Chapman & Hall, London.

Graham, G.G. & Primavesi, A.L. (1993) *Roses of Great Britain and Ireland*. BSBI, London.

Grime, J.G., Hodgson, J.C. & Hunt, R. (2007) *Comparative Plant Ecology: A Functional Approach to Common British Species. Ed. 2.* Castlepoint Press.

Hawksford, J.E., Hopkins, I.J., Cadman, D., Hill, R.N., Lawley, S.D., Leak, A., Radford, E., Reynolds, J.R., Steward, D. & Waller, R. (2011) *The Flora of Staffordshire*. Staffordshire Wildlife Trust, England.

Hill, M.O., Preston, C.D. & Roy, D.B. (2004) *PLANTATT Attributes of British and Irish Plants*. Centre for Ecology & Hydrology, Cambridgeshire.

Hill, M.O., Mountford, J.O., Roy, D.B. & Bunce, R.G.H. (1999) *Ellenberg's Indicator Values for British Plants*. Centre for Ecology and Hydrology, Cambridgeshire.

Lansdown, R.V. (2008) *Water-starworts (Callitriche) of Europe*. BSBI, London.

Mabey, R. (1997) *Flora Britannica*. Chatto & Windus, London.

Newton, A. & Randall, R.D. (2004) *Atlas of British and Irish Brambles*. BSBI, London.

Preston, C.D. (1995) *Pondweeds of Great Britain and Ireland*. BSBI Handbook No 8. BSBI, London.

Preston, C.D. & Croft, J.M. (1997) *Aquatic Plants of Britain and Ireland*. Harley Books, Colchester.

Preston, C.D., Pearman, D.A. & Dines, T.D. (2002) *New Atlas of the British & Irish Flora*. Oxford University Press, Oxford.

Readett, R.C. (1971) A Flora of Sutton Park, Warwickshire. *Proceedings of the Birmingham Natural History Society* 22 (1) pp.2–75.

Rich, T.C.G., Houston, L., Robertson, A. & Proctor, M.C.F. (2010) *Whitebeams, Rowans and Service Trees of Britain and Ireland. A Monograph of British and Irish* Sorbus *L.* BSBI in association with National Museum Wales, London.

Rodwell, J.S. (Ed.) (1991 *et seq.) British Plant Communities. Vols. 1–5.* Cambridge University Press, Cambridge.

Sell, P. & Murrell, G. (2006) *Flora of Great Britain and Ireland. Volume 4 Campanulaceae–Asteraceae.* Cambridge University Press, Cambridge.

Sinker, C.A., Packham, J.R., Trueman, I.C., Oswald, P.H., Perring, F.H. & Prestwood, W.V. (1985) *Ecological Flora of the Shropshire Region*. Shropshire Trust for Nature Conservation, Shrewsbury.

Stace, C.A. (1997) *New Flora of the British Isles. Second Edition.* Cambridge University Press, Cambridge.

Stace, C.A. (2010) *New Flora of the British Isles. Third Edition.* Cambridge University Press, Cambridge.

Stewart, A., Pearman, D.A. & Preston, C.D. (1994) *Scarce Plants in Britain*. JNCC, Peterborough.

www.spnh.scnhs.org.uk/vp.html Sutton Park Natural History Society Checklists for Sutton Park.

# PTERIDOPHYTES

## LYCOPHYTES

### 1. LYCOPODIACEAE

***Huperzia selago*** (L.) Bernh. ex Schrank & Mart.
**Fir Clubmoss**
0. Native. Extinct in B&C; lost from most of its lowland sites in UK by 1930. Recorded from a bog on Moseley Common (SP0982) in 1836 by M.A. Beilby and at the same site in 1838 by W. Ick and by E. Lees, when it was already feared to be extinct or nearly so. The extant Moseley Bog is likely to be a fragment of this site.

***Lycopodium clavatum*** L.
**Stag's-horn Clubmoss**
0. Native. Extinct in B&C. This plant of *Calluna* heath and *Nardus* grassland may still have a transient presence not far W of us but seems to have been lost in B&C as early as the more choosy *Huperzia selago*. Last recorded from Sutton Park in 1884 according to Cadbury *et al.* (1971) although Readett (also 1971) gives the last record there as 1841 (S. Freeman). Also recorded from Moseley Common (SP0982, W. Southall, 1843).

### 2. SELAGINELLACEAE

***Selaginella kraussiana*** (Kunze) A. Braun
**Krauss's Clubmoss**
1. Neophyte. A moss-like plant, an escape from cultivation, frost and drought sensitive, rarely found in UK and usually by the sea. In B&C it is in a shaded rockery at B'ham Botanical Gardens, in a depression where a tree-fern is planted (SP049852, JWP, MWP & EVJC, 2007). It is abundant there in glasshouses which are undoubtedly the source. Africa.

## EUSPORANGIATE FERNS

### 4. OPHIOGLOSSACEAE

***Ophioglossum vulgatum*** L.
**Adder's-tongue**
5. Native. Ax. This small, unfern-like fern with a rhizome deep in the soil is easily overlooked but is certainly rare in B&C. It is strongly associated with old grasslands, but also sometimes found in woodland margins and under bracken. Marshy grassland near Willenhall Town FC at Fibbersley (SO957994, AS & A. Simon, 1997, seen again 1999); several places in the ridge and furrow meadow NE of Fens Pool (most recently SO920887, ICT & EVJC, 2007, but long known there); large colony of several 100 plants in grassland to the

rear of Dartmouth High School, although the colony has diminished considerably in recent years (SP0394, MWP, 2000); three plants in an unimproved pasture, Lower Illey (SO977811, WAT, 2002 but known there since at least 1976). It has recently been found for, the first time, in Sutton Park (SP093978, BL, 2010). There are other old records in the Illey area from SO9881 and SO9882 from the 1970s, and from Hay Head Wood in Walsall (SP043990, J. Andrews, 1987) and farmland at Great Barr (SP0395, Sandwell Valley Naturalists' Club, 1992). Ass: *Agrimonia eupatoria, Agrostis capillaris, Centaurea nigra, Cynosurus cristatus, Deschampsia cespitosa, Festuca rubra, Juncus effusus, Lotus corniculatus, Luzula campestris, Pteridium aquilinum, Ranunculus acris*.

***Botrychium lunaria*** (L.) Sw.
**Moonwort**
0. Native. Extinct in B&C? A plant of open situations in old grassland and heaths, it also has a distribution in surrounding counties in lead mine spoil tips and dolerite quarries, so it may yet be refound in B&C. Last seen in rough grassland in Sutton Park (SP0898, SP0998 according to Readett (1971); SP0997, SP0998 according to Cadbury *et al.* (1971)). John Ray had found it in Sutton Park "in great plenty… in a close" in 1662. There are also Victorian records from what became the railway line in Sutton Park. There is a very old record of it from Stourbridge (SO9184, W. Hill, 1792).

## CALAMOPHYTES

### 5. EQUISETACEAE

***Equisetum hyemale*** L.
**Rough Horsetail**
0. Native. Extinct in B&C. A tall rush-like horsetail of woodland and moorland flushes, last recorded in Amphlett & Rea (1909) from Moseley Common bogs (SP0982).

***Equisetum fluviatile*** L.
**Water Horsetail**
*56. Native. Ax. A semi-aquatic and rhizomatous perennial, it can form large single-species stands in still or very slow moving water up to 1.5 m deep in ponds, lakes and reservoirs. It is also often present mixed with many other species in species-rich mire vegetation. Also occasionally in canals, the floodplains of streams and in marshes in quarry bottoms. Common in Sutton Park, it seems most frequent and abundant in old, open habitats on substrates with a low to medium fertility and base status but it can stand higher fertility and some shade and can be

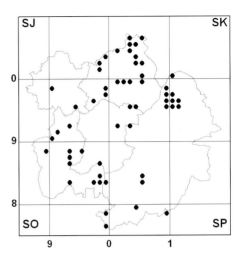

present in recent habitats. Ass: *Alisma plantago-aquatica, Carex acutiformis, Carex pseudocyperus, Carex demissa, Potamogeton natans, Potamogeton polygonifolius*.

***Equisetum × litorale*** Kühlew. ex Rupr.
(*E. fluviatile × E. arvense*)
**Shore Horsetail**

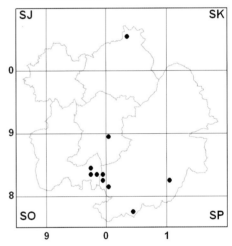

10. Native. Recorded almost entirely in vc. 37 and quite frequently in Halesowen and the Woodgate Valley, possibly overlooked elsewhere. Mainly in wet ground: by canals, at Leasowes, in the Woodgate Valley and by the River Rea, usually where these sites have been disturbed. It may be present without the parent species. Not mentioned in either Edees (1972) or Cadbury *et al.* (1971), but one old record at Hill Hook (SK106004, J. Andrews, 1987), was not refound.

***Equisetum arvense*** L.
**Field Horsetail**
*630. Native. A perennial herb with deep far-ranging rhizomes, common almost throughout B&C. Both a pioneer plant and an ineradicable weed, tolerant of toxins and herbicides, it is perfectly suited to our industrial and urban area with its constantly changing tapestry of waste

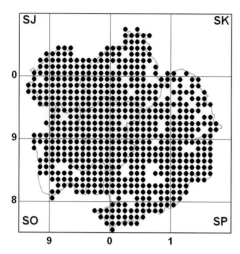

ground, developments and industry. It colonises industrial spoils and gravel of railways and driveways where its extensive rhizome can eventually stabilise the substrate. It is common on wasteland, roadsides, canal banks, parks, gardens and allotments, but also not uncommon in wet species-rich marsh and grassland. Tons of soil are moved around daily in B&BC and amongst it most certainly will be fragments of this species ready to colonise new sites. Found in damp to dry soils of moderate or high base and nutrient status, in the open or in partial shade. Ass: *Agrostis gigantea, Elytrigia repens, Ranunculus repens, Tussilago farfara.*

### *Equisetum sylvaticum* L.
### Wood Horsetail

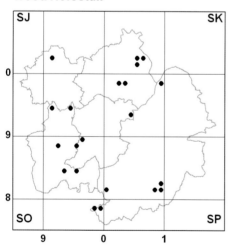

21. Native. Ax. A beautiful rhizomatous perennial, scarce in B&BC, where it grows in woodland, by streams and in marshy grasslands. Also on old but apparently post-industrial banks, at Darby's Hill quarry (SO969895) and Fens Pools (SO923887). It shows a NW distribution in the UK and B&BC sits at the edge of this main area. Its typical substrate is of intermediate fertility and base status, often flushed with base-rich ground water. Shade, shelter,

humidity and permanently damp ground are requirements. Records for Rakegate Wood (SJ9102) and for SO99 have not been verified. Ass: *Cirsium palustre, Corylus avellana, Dactylis glomerata, Dryopteris dilatata, Nardus stricta, Rumex sanguineus.*

### *Equisetum palustre* L.
### Marsh Horsetail

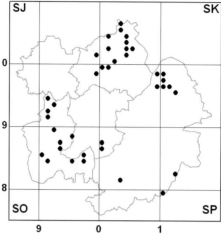

*39. Native. Ax. Perennial with an extensive rhizome system at some depth in the soil. Quite local in B&BC at pond and stream sides and in ditches, mainly in species-rich marsh and pasture vegetation, in infertile but fairly base-rich, moist to wet soils. The distribution in B&BC is mainly but not exclusively in the peripheral and countryside areas, although it is also a pernicious weed over a large area of Newhall Allotments, Sutton Coldfield, a stream valley site subject to flooding. Ass: *Equisetum fluviatile, Juncus acutiflorus, Juncus effusus, Juncus inflexus, Silene flos-cuculi.*

### *Equisetum telmateia* Ehrh.
### Great Horsetail

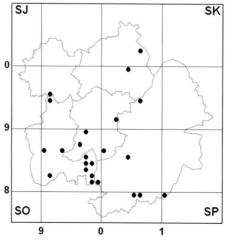

23. Native. Ax. A large perennial rhizomatous herb. Scarce in B&BC. Particularly associated with moist or

wet clay soils, nutrient-intermediate and base-rich, often base-flushed. Usually but not always in shade or semi-shade in woodland or woodland margins or hedgerows, not always obviously old sites, and occasionally in quarries and other secondary sites. Locally abundant in parts of Sandwell Valley particularly in Priory Woods and around the banks of Cascade Pool, also nearby on the M5 embankment at Junction 1. Ass: *Caltha palustris, Carex pendula, Epilobium hirsutum, Eupatorium cannabinum, Heracleum sphondylium, Urtica dioica.*

## LEPTOSPORANGIATE FERNS

### 6. OSMUNDACEAE

### *Osmunda regalis* L.
### Royal Fern
5. Native. A large fern found in a few mostly poolside locations in B&BC. Probably now always a relic of planting, although it was known, presumably as a native, in Sutton Park and reported by Bagnall as destroyed there in 1868. It is slow growing and very long-lived; huge plants can be over a century old. In the open or the semi-shade of woodland, on wet, usually peaty, moderately or very acid soil that may be infertile or moderately fertile. Twin ponds, Harborne (SP037854, F.C. & L.K. Whiston, 1987, seen again 2005); poolside, Southbourne Close (SP054826, MWP, ICT, L. Bastin & EMP, 2007); Edgbaston Pool (SP054841, R. Duff & C. Walker, 1997, seen again 2007, also recorded there in Cadbury *et al.* 1971); several, apparently planted, wet scrub E of Fens Pool (SO923889, ICT, MWP & A. Pritchard, 2008); persistent in the grounds of Merridale School, W'ton, from an original planting in 1983 (SO902981, CRP, 2000, still present 2010). A few old records may still be extant: at Merecroft Pool (SP043788) it was last recorded in 1994 and has been known there since at least 1975. At Moseley Bog (SP094821) it was last recorded in 1990, apparently a relic of cultivation, although it was frequently recorded on Moseley Common and bogs (SP0981 and SP0982) in the 19th century. Since the Victorians were notorious for digging up wild ferns it is possible that some of the planted plants were obtained locally.

### 8. MARSILEACEAE

### *Pilularia globulifera* L.
### Pillwort
0. Native. Extinct in B&BC. A small, scarce and declining grass-like fern that is easily overlooked, growing on infertile, non-calcareous mud in the drawdown zone at

the margins of ponds and lakes. Recorded in Sutton Park by Bagnall in 1875 and said in Cadbury *et al.* (1971) to be there until 1898.

## 9. SALVINIACEAE

### *Azolla filiculoides* Lam.
**Water Fern**

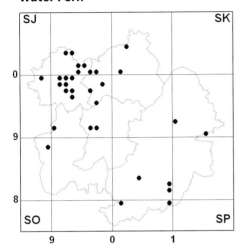

32. Neophyte. A small floating fern. In B&BC found in canals, lakes and pools. It seems to be frequently deliberately introduced. The distribution is scattered and sporadic, although in the survey period it was concentrated in canals in the NW. It can become dominant over considerable areas in suitable canals and pools but rarely seems to remain so for more than a few years. Grows in well-lit places or partial shade where the water is richly fertile and fairly base-rich. Ass: *Lemna minor, Lemna minuta, Riccia fluitans.*

## 11. DENNSTAEDTIACEAE

### *Pteridium aquilinum* (L.) Kuhn
**Bracken**

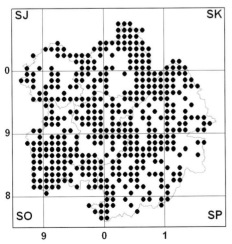

*442. Native. A large fern common throughout most of B&BC, particularly in some countryside areas, in open

spaces, woods, roadsides, hedgerows and gardens. It forms extensive colonies which exclude most other species, especially where woodland has been removed, or in heathland or acid grassland. Sometimes, however, dense stands can coexist with patches of *Hyacinthoides non-scripta* which flowers in the spring before *Pteridium* starts to grow. Although *Pteridium* can be an aggressive weed, it does not seem to be a regular early colonist of urban waste land, and may be largely dependent for its spread on accidental introductions of rhizome in soil or peat. It grows in open or semi-shaded situations on moist, usually deep, fairly acid and infertile soils. Ass: *Deschampsia flexuosa, Digitalis purpurea, Holcus mollis, Hyacinthoides non-scripta, Rubus fruticosus* agg.

We presume it is always the usual and widespread **subsp. *aquilinum***.

## 13. ASPLENIACEAE

### *Asplenium scolopendrium* L.
(*Phyllitis scolopendrium* (L.) Newman)
**Hart's-tongue**

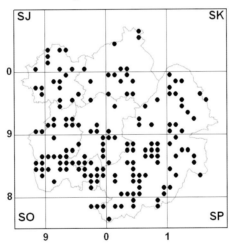

165. Native. An evergreen fern, frequent in B&BC, it was hardly recorded here in Cadbury *et al.* (1971), and was less common in the B&BC part of vc. 39 in Edees in 1972, suggesting that it has increased significantly in recent years. On shaded old industrial and residential walls, rail and canal bridges, especially those built with the Victorian type of engineering ('blue') bricks and lime mortar. On such walls plants tend to be small and numerous. Larger plants can be found growing on banks of streams and canals, and in woodland. A habitat it has found in our area is that under the roadside gutter grids, in the drains. Grows in sheltered positions on moist, at least modestly base-rich substrates of intermediate fertility. Ass: *Asplenium* spp., *Hedera helix, Mycelis muralis, Polypodium interjectum.*

▲ *Equisetum sylvaticum*

▲ *Equisetum telmataea* cones

▲ *Azolla filiculoides*

## *Asplenium adiantum-nigrum* L.
**Black Spleenwort**

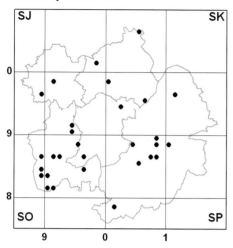

29. Native. Ax. All records are assumed to be the widespread **subsp. *adiantum-nigrum***. An evergreen fern, quite uncommon in B&C, but sometimes locally abundant, on old mortared (often 'blue'-brick) walls of railway viaducts, canal and railway bridges, gardens and churches. Also found on sandstone railway cuttings. It requires light, shelter, high humidity and a mild winter temperature. It grows on dry substrates of intermediate fertility and base status. Large colonies in the brickwork mortar on several of the Delph Locks in Brierley Hill. Ass: *Asplenium ceterach*, Asplenium *ruta-muraria*, Asplenium *scolopendrium*, Asplenium *trichomanes*.

## *Asplenium trichomanes* L.
**subsp. *quadrivalens*** D.E. Mey.
**Common Maidenhair Spleenwort**

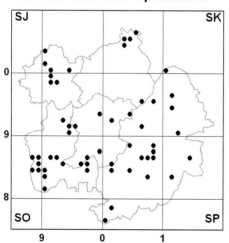

55. Native. A small evergreen fern. Uncommon in B&C, found on old mortared walls and bridges of railway and canal. Also walls of gardens and industrial buildings. Where these walls are sheltered and humid there can be a profusion of these spleenworts. A slightly more shade-loving spleenwort than *A. adiantum-nigrum*

or *A. ruta-muraria*, growing on dry, infertile, base-rich substrates. Ass: *Asplenium adiantum-nigrum, Asplenium ruta-muraria, Geranium robertianum*.

## *Asplenium ruta-muraria* L.
**Wall-rue**

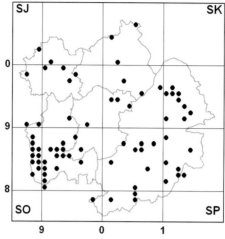

74. Native. The commonest small evergreen spleenwort in B&C on old mortared walls of railways, canals, churches and gardens. A profusion of robust plants can be found on some walls while on others, in drier exposed situations, plants are tiny and barely reach out from their mortared crack and can easily be overlooked. It is a short-lived fern that persists at its sites through continual re-establishment. It favours relatively well-lit, dry situations compared with sites favoured by *A. trichomanes*, on infertile, base-intermediate substrates. Ass: *Asplenium adiantum-nigrum, Asplenium scolopendrium, Asplenium trichomanes*, but often growing alone, or sometimes with *Cardamine hirsuta, Cymbalaria muralis, Sedum acre*.

## *Asplenium ceterach* L.
(*Ceterach officinarum* Willd.)
**Rustyback**

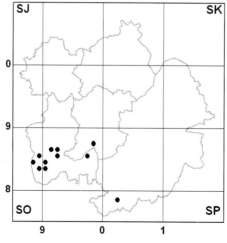

11. Native. Ax. Another small fern of old walls, rare in B&C, found mainly in

the Stourbridge area, matching its SW distribution in the British Isles as a whole. Large colonies in brickwork mortar of several of the Delph Locks, Brierley Hill. There are also records for both River Rea and rail bridges at Northfield (both SP0278, ARB, lost by 1996). It grows in well-lit, dry places on basic substrates that may be extremely infertile. It curls up to reduce water loss during times of drought. Ass: *Asplenium* spp.

## 14. THELYPTERIDACEAE

### *Thelypteris palustris* Schott
**Marsh Fern**
0. Native. Extinct in B&C. A Nationally Scarce plant of base-rich fens and fen woodlands. Recorded only from Sutton Park, last record in 1876 by Bagnall.

### *Oreopteris limbosperma* (All.) Holub
**Lemon-scented Fern**
2. Native. Ax. A medium-sized fern of streamsides and ditch banks on nutrient- and base-poor soils, nowadays largely confined to the uplands in England and Wales, on the verge of extinction in B&C. Long known in Sutton Park: Readett (1971) described it as rare on the railway bank in SP0998; it was still present, not far from the Roman Road, seen there by ARB within the modern survey period. A single plant was recently discovered with *Blechnum spicant* and *Athyrium filix-femina* in a deep ditch between pastures W of Brownhills Common (SK033064, ICT & SAHA, 2010). There are old records which may still be extant but were not refound in the survey: Edgbaston Pool (SP055842, D.A. Cadbury, 1935); Priory Woods, Sandwell Valley (SP027915, Sandwell Valley Naturalists Club, 1980, also seen there by ARB in the early 1990s); W bank of B'ham Level canal, Smethwick (SP017890, TCH & CRP, 1987, also seen there by ARB, and also possibly from S bank at SP013894, J. Wollner, 1986). Also recorded from Moseley Common (SP0981 and SP0982) in the 19th century.

## 15. WOODSIACEAE

### *Athyrium filix-femina* (L.) Roth
**Lady-fern**
*99. Native. Ax. Of medium to large size, it is locally frequent in B&C. Habitats include woodland, streamsides, canal sides, ditches and hedgerows, it appears to be much commoner in countryside than in urban habitats, but is not excluded from post-industrial sites, being present for example in Doulton's Clay Pit at Saltwells LNR (SO9387) and on damp, shady, furnace slag at Ladymoor Pool (SO9495). It grows in semi-

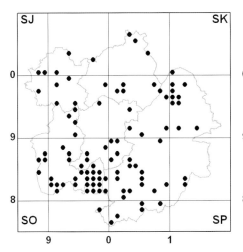

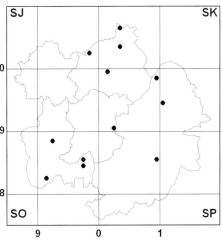

shade on soils that are constantly damp but with good drainage and therefore usually on sloping ground. Soil of intermediate fertility and base status. Ass: *Carex remota*, *Dryopteris filix-mas*, *Juncus effusus*.

### *Gymnocarpium dryopteris* (L.) Newman
### Oak Fern

0. Native. Probably extinct in B&BC and definitely so as a native, if it ever was. Once known from Darnell Hurst, Sutton Park (SP0997?, Bagnall, 1866), not seen since; and it was once recorded as introduced by a stream at Woodbrooke College, Selly Oak (SP036813, A.J.L. Fraser, 1975). In Britain it has a strong NW distribution not including our area. It is a fern of humid woodland and rocky places, in rather base- and nutrient-poor soils.

### *Gymnocarpium robertianum*
(Hoffm.) Newman
### Limestone Fern

0. Native. Extinct in B&BC. Recorded in Darnell Hurst in Sutton Park (SP0997?, Bagnall, 1866). Always amongst limestone rocks (rarely on walls) and therefore an odd record for Sutton Park, but supported by a herbarium specimen.

## 16. BLECHNACEAE

### *Blechnum spicant* (L.) Roth
### Hard-fern

12. Native. Ax. An evergreen fern, well-known to be a lime-hater, rare in B&BC as in other industrial areas possibly due to a sensitivity to air pollution, although there are records from near an old steelworks at Coombeswood (SO9785), on spoil at Fens Pools (SO9288) and an old record on wooded colliery excavations E of the claypit at Saltwells (SO937970) in the 1980s. It is abundant on a steep, wooded, acid bank in Ham Dingle, but is much more typically found as single plants, growing in semi-shade in woodlands in places with

an open field layer on moist, infertile, acid soils. In W Britain it is often frequent in heathland and moorland, but it is rarely in the open in our area; one example is on the banks of Longmoor Pool at Sutton Park (SP0985). Ass: *Deschampsia flexuosa*, *Dryopteris dilatata*.

## 17. ONOCLEACEAE

### *Onoclea sensibilis* L.
### Sensitive Fern

1. Neophyte. A medium-sized fern of creeping habit which can become naturalised on wet ground. One record only in B&BC, planted but spreading in a wooded area, 'Natureland', Lifford (SP059798, AEEP, 1995, not found 2007). Eastern N America and E Asia.

## 18. DRYOPTERIDACEAE

### *Polystichum setiferum* (Forssk.) T. Moore ex Woyn.
### Soft Shield-fern

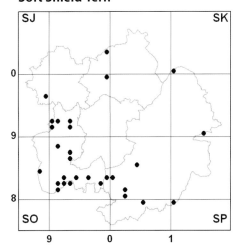

29. Native. Ax. A large, handsome fern. Scarce in B&BC on shady streambanks and in old woodland, apparently commonest in the Ash-Oak dingle woodlands of Dudley. It requires a humid sheltered position on permanently moist ground on slopes,

▲ *Asplenium ruta-muraria*

▲ *Asplenium ceterach*

▲ *Polystichum setiferum*

▲ Polystichum aculeatum

▲ Dryopteris affinis agg.

▲ Polypodium vulgare

typically on moderately base-rich, fertile clay soils. Ass: *Allium ursinum, Asplenium scolopendrium, Athyrium filix-femina, Carex pendula, Dryopteris dilatata, Dryopteris filix-mas*. The plant in dense carr woodland at Newtown Pool (SJ992038, ICT, 2008) is cultivar 'Divisilobum' with further divided pinnules, a popular and easily propagated garden plant which seems to be rarely encountered in the wild.

### *Polystichum aculeatum* (L.) Roth
### Hard Shield-fern

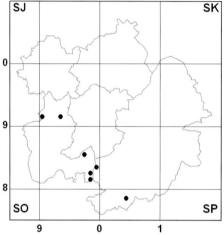

7. Native. Ax. Rarely recorded in B&BC, growing in similar habitats to *P. setiferum*, but usually associated with outcrops of basic rocks, and in our area it has also been found on walls of industrial buildings by canals, at several sites by the Dudley canal at Coombeswood (SO9785, JJD, 2000). Shade to half-shade on moist, fairly infertile, base-rich substrates. Only recently recorded at Wren's Nest (SO9391).

### *Dryopteris filix-mas* (L.) Schott
### Male-fern

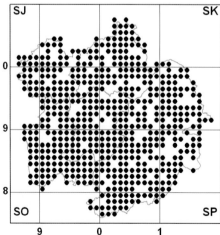

*571. Native. A long-lived fern, common throughout B&BC in old or recent woodland, where it can be abundant, but also on derelict land, in hedgerows,

roadsides, streamsides, churchyards, old gardens, canal and railway banks and colonising walls, including mortared walls, especially where supplied with moisture from leaking gutters. Found typically in semi-shade on moderately moist substrates of average base status and fertility but with a wide ecological amplitude, only really excluded from consistently wet sites. Ass: *Alliaria petiolata, Dryopteris dilatata, Epilobium montanum, Hedera helix, Mycelis muralis*.

### *Dryopteris* × *complexa* agg.
(*D. filix-mas* × *D. affinis* agg.)
### Hybrid Male-fern

1. Native. A very large and robust fern. Only a single plant is known from B&BC growing on a streamside in Coopers Coppice, Illey area (SO983821, RM & WAT, 2000, seen again, 2003). Although a hybrid it is true-breeding and has the potential to form a population if conditions are suitable. It grows on acidic soils.

### *Dryopteris affinis* agg.
### Scaly Male-fern

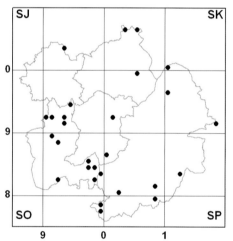

28. Native. Ax. Robust, long-lived ferns, uncommon in B&BC where they have a scattered distribution, being found rather more commonly in Dudley, usually singly or in small numbers. Usually in fairly well-lit, fairly dry or moist banks of woodland and scrub on rather nutrient-poor and base-poor soils, although there are also a few reliable records from old walls by canals. There are further records from the late 1980s and early 90s from Ham Dingle (SO9182), Wychbury Hill (SO9181) and Moseley Bog (SP0982). Many records have not been determined to what has now become species level, but **D. borreri** (Newman) Newman ex Oberh. & Tavel (**Borrer's Male-fern**) seems to be the common one, with a few plants keying out to **D. affinis** (Lowe) Fraser-Jenk. (**Golden-scaled Male-fern**). Ass (for *D. affinis*): *Anemone nemorosa*,

*Brachypodium sylvaticum, Deschampsia cespitosa, Hyacinthoides non-scripta.*

### *Dryopteris cristata* (L.) A. Gray
### Crested Buckler-fern

0. Native. A single unconfirmed record from Moseley Common (SP0982, M.A. Beilby, 1836), has been considered an error for more than a century (see discussion by Amphlett and Rea 1909).

### *Dryopteris carthusiana* (Vill.) H.P. Fuchs
### Narrow Buckler-fern

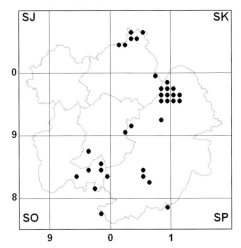

34. Native. Ax. Uncommon in B&BC, although frequent in Sutton Park, mostly in areas of seepage in old wet grassland and heath, also by pools and streams. Grows in the open or semi-shade on moist and wet, infertile, acid but base-flushed, usually peaty soils. Also tetrad SO98E. Ass: *Cirsium palustre, Dryopteris dilatata, Epilobium palustre, Juncus conglomeratus, Juncus effusus, Molinia caerulea.*

*Dryopteris × deweveri* (J.T. Jansen) Jansen & Wacht., the hybrid with *D. dilatata*, has not been recorded but is likely to be present where the two species occur together.

### *Dryopteris dilatata* (Hoffm.) A. Gray
### Broad Buckler-fern

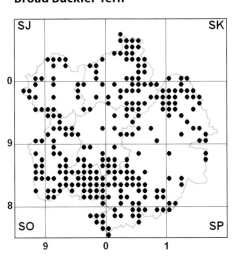

*267. Native. Common throughout B&BC in woodland, hedgerows and ditches, especially in countryside and outer suburban areas. It grows in shade or semi-shade, and can form large stands in suitable woodland, preferring poor drainage but not waterlogging and requiring a certain amount of shelter. Grows on base-poor soil of intermediate fertility. Ass: *Athyrium filix-femina, Dryopteris filix-mas, Hyacinthoides non-scripta, Pteridium aquilinum, Rubus fruticosus* agg.

## 19. POLYPODIACEAE

### *Polypodium vulgare* L.
### Polypody

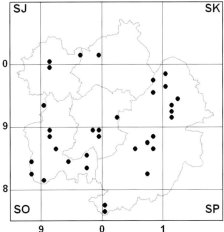

33. Native. Polypody ferns are recorded quite widely across B&BC, mostly in brickwork or stonework, especially by canals. Many are infertile or inaccessible for identification. **Polypodium vulgare** *sensu stricto* is a plant typically found in base-poor substrates, on rock outcrops, drystone walls and as an epiphyte. There were six positive attributions to this species within the survey period (mostly by JJD, JEH or ICT): a sandstone rock face on Worcester to Stourbridge railway (SO904819; JJD, 2003); Gospel End Road (SO909936, APD, 2004); planted in Rookery Park (SP112912, SB, 2003); Fens Pools (SO919880, JEH, 2004); Wyrley & Essington Canal (SJ994012, AB & S. Phipps, 2007); at two places in Moseley Bog as an epiphyte on large willows (one fallen and ±horizontal) (SP092820 & SP092821, F. Jarvis, conf. MWP & ICT, 2011). There are earlier records from Stourbridge Cemetery (SO886838, WAT, 1992); Sutton Park (Bagnall, 1897). Most Polypodys have been recorded as the aggregate, and all records are shown in the map.

### *Polypodium interjectum* Shivas
### Intermediate Polypody

8. Native. A slightly larger proportion of the aggregate records have been specifically

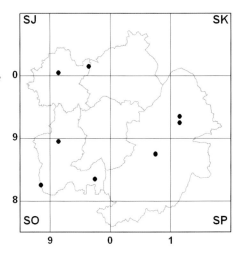

attributed to this species, which is characteristic of the mortar of old walls and base-rich rocks. Our records are from brick walls, a concrete slab in a canal bank, a wooded bank, and in a sandstone quarry Most of the aggregate records seem to be from similar habitats, especially on walls and bridges associated with canals, in dolerite quarries etc. suggesting that *P. interjectum* may be the commoner polypody in B&BC. Many plants inaccessible for definite identification are probably this species, for example plants on a column on platform two (SP069867, ICT, 2009) and on a wall by platform 12B (SP0686, ARB, 2007), both at New Street Station, B'ham.

## GYMNOSPERMS

### 20. PINACEAE

A number of species seem to exist in our area entirely as planted trees, and have occasionally been recorded. This includes: *Abies alba* Mill. (European Silver-fir); *Abies amabilis* Douglas ex Forbes (Red Fir); *Abies grandis* (Douglas ex D. Don) Lindl. (Giant Fir); *Abies nordmanniana* (Steven) Spach (Caucasian Fir); *Abies procera* Rehder (Noble Fir); *Calocedrus decurrens* (Torrey) Florin. (Incense Cedar); *Cedrus atlantica* (Endl.) Carrière (Atlas Cedar); *Cedrus atlantica* cultivar 'Glauca'; *Cedrus deodara* (Roxb. ex D. Don) G. Don (Deodar); *Cedrus libani* A. Rich. (Cedar-of-Lebanon); *Larix kaempferi* (Lamb.) Carrière (Japanese Larch); *Larix × marschlinsii* Coaz (L. decidua × L. kaempferi); *Picea breweriana* Watson (Brewer's Weeping Spruce); *Picea omorika* (Pancic) Purk. (Serbian Spruce); *Picea pungens* Engelm. (Colorado Spruce); *Picea sitchensis* (Bong.) Carrière (Sitka Spruce); *Pinus cembra* L. (Arolla Pine); *Pinus ponderosa* Douglas ex Lawson & C. Lawson (Western Yellow-pine); *Pinus strobus* L. (Weymouth Pine); *Pinus thunbergii* Parlatore. (Japanese Black Pine); *Pseudotsuga menziesii* (Mirb.) Franco (Douglas Fir); *Tsuga heterophylla* (Raf.) Sarg. (Western Hemlock-spruce).

## *Picea abies* (L.) H. Karst.
### Norway Spruce

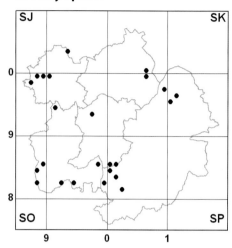

24. Neophyte. Quite widely but erratically recorded. Probably always planted, sometimes as a surviving cast-out Christmas tree. In Sutton Park, Readett (1971) recorded *P. abies* as planted in SP0997, SP1097 and SP1098, and *P. sitchensis* in SP1097.

## *Larix decidua* Mill.
### European Larch

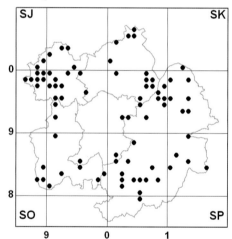

82. Neophyte. Widely planted in parks, gardens and plantations. Very few records of seedling regeneration (near Rowley Regis railways station, SO98 tetrad Y). Mapped records include many for *Larix* sp.; there are very few, and only planted, modern records for *Larix kaempferi*, or for *Larix × marschlinsii*.

## *Pinus sylvestris* L.
### Scots Pine

*198. Native in the Scottish Highlands and Nationally Scarce as a native, introduced in England. Mostly planted trees in parks, gardens and plantations, woodlands, but a scattering of records as self-set seedlings and trees in bare ground, grassy banks, sandstone railway cuttings and heathland, typically on base- and nutrient-poor soils.

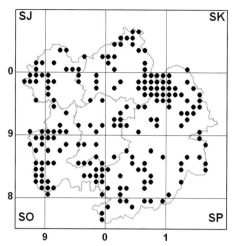

Ass: *Betula pendula, Betula pubescens, Quercus petraea, Quercus robur, Sorbus aucuparia.*

## *Pinus nigra* J.F. Arnold

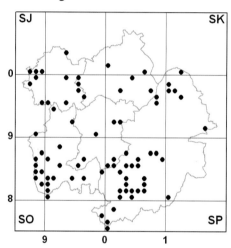

*80. Neophyte. Widely planted in parks, gardens, churchyards and woodland plantations. Few records have distinguished **subsp. nigra (Austrian Pine)** from **subsp. laricio** Maire (**Corsican Pine**), but both have been recorded.

## *Pinus contorta* Douglas ex Loudon
### Lodgepole Pine

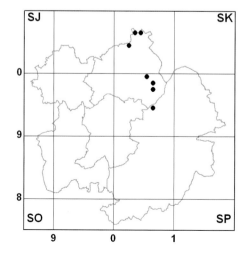

7. Neophyte. A few records as a planted tree and a few as a self-set seedling or sapling in heathland at Pelsall Common (SK0204), Brownhills Common (SK0306) and Barr Beacon (SP0697).

## *Pinus wallichiana* A.B. Jacks.
### Bhutan Pine

4. Neophyte. Occasionally planted in churchyards, parks, gardens and woodlands. All Saints church, West Bromwich (SP011921, MWP, 1996); several in woodland, Sandwell Valley (SP022922, MWP, 1998); planted by Stourbridge arm of the Dudley Canal (SO898848, APD, 1999); Greenfields Gardens (SO898840, APD, 1999). Three plants on a disused railway track were definitely self-sown from a planted park tree about 100m away. Specimens about 1.5m in height were growing along the old railway track bed. (SO997955, MWP, 2004).

## 21. ARAUCARIACEAE

### *Araucaria araucana* (Molina) K. Koch
### Monkey-puzzle

15. Neophyte. Seems to exist in our area entirely as a tree planted in parks and gardens, and has been recorded by some recorders. Chile & W Argentina.

## 22. TAXACEAE

### *Taxus baccata* L.
### Yew

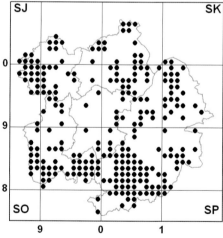

*260. Native, but widely planted and very widely disseminated in bird droppings. Most of our records are self-set seedlings, saplings and trees in shady places in gardens, parks, old woodlands and plantations, particularly but not exclusively on base-rich soils. The map suggests that it tends to be much less common in the old industrial heartlands and very frequent in the suburbs and some of the countryside areas, often in churchyards. Like many

evergreens it is sensitive to air pollution and has probably moved towards the centre of the conurbation since the Clean Air Acts of the 20th century. Ass: *Acer pseudoplatanus*, × *Cuprocyparis leylandii*, *Fraxinus excelsior*, *Quercus robur*.
The cultivars 'Fastigiata' and 'Fastigiata Aurea' are occasionally recorded from churchyards and gardens.

## 23. CUPRESSACEAE

A number of species seem to exist in our area entirely as planted trees, and have occasionally been recorded. This includes: *Chamaecyparis pisifera* (Siebold & Zucc.) Siebold & Zucc. (Sawara Cypress); *Cryptomeria japonica* (L. f.) D. Don (Japanese Red-cedar); *Cupressus goveniana* Gord. (Gowen Cypress); *Metasequoia glyptostroboides* Hu & W.C. Cheng (Dawn Redwood); *Sequoia sempervirens* (D. Don) Endl. (Coastal Redwood); *Sequoiadendron giganteum* (Lindl.) Buchholz (Wellingtonia); *Taxodium distichum* (L.) Rich. (Swamp Cypress); *Thuja plicata* Donn ex D. Don (Western Red-cedar); *Xanthocyparis nootkatensis* (D. Don) Farjon & D.K. Harder (Nootka Cypress).

### × *Cuprocyparis leylandii* (A.B. Jacks. & Dallim.) Farjon (× *Cupressocyparis leylandii* (A. B. Jack & Dallim.) Dallim.)
**Leyland Cypress**

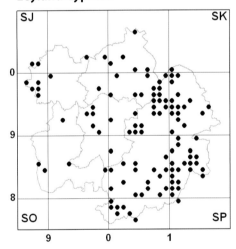

115. Neophyte. Widely planted in gardens, but most of the records refer to seedlings which clearly derive from planted trees, despite its reputation for sterility. Seedlings are found in existing and abandoned gardens, at the foot of walls outside gardens, in cracks in pavements, mainly in residential areas.

### *Chamaecyparis lawsoniana*
(A. Murray bis) Parl.
**Lawson's Cypress**
*154. Neophyte. Widely planted in parks, churchyards and woodland plantations but less common than × *Cuprocyparis leylandii* in private gardens and residential

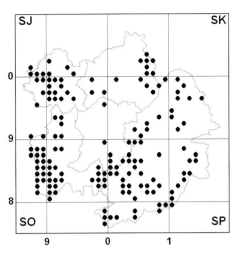

areas. Many of the records are for seedlings which may have been confused with those of × *Cuprocyparis leylandii*. The combined map below gives an impression of the high frequency of these species in B&BC, recorded from 237 monads collectively.

### × *Cuprocyparis leylandii* plus *Chamaecyparis lawsoniana*

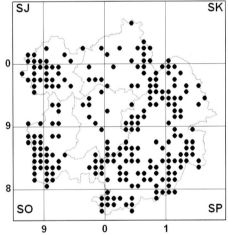

### *Juniperus communis* L.
**Common Juniper**
1. Native, but introduced in our area. Sect. 41. Common in gardens, but not normally recorded. There is a single recent record of seedlings in a roadside gutter and pavement (SO974944, MWP, ICT, JaH, SJC, EMP & A. Wood, 2007).

## ANGIOSPERMS

### PRE-DICOTS

### 25. NYMPHAEACEAE

#### *Nymphaea alba* L.
**White Water-lily**
*66. Native; probably mostly introduced, especially by anglers. An aquatic plant,

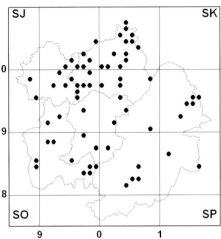

bottom rooted with floating leaves and flowers, growing in still or slow-moving water to about two metres deep. Prefers rather base-rich waters of average fertility, in a well-lit or partially shaded, sheltered situation. Found in canals, ponds and lakes but absent from areas of frequent navigation. There are a few records of **subsp. *alba*** and most of the records are probably referable to this. Ass: *Lemna minor*, *Lemna trisulca*, *Nuphar lutea*, *Potamogeton natans*.

Some of the plants are cultivars, sometimes with pink flowers, which are thought to be referable to *N. marliacea* Lat.-Marl. which covers various hybrids of *N. alba*.

#### *Nuphar lutea* (L.) Sm.
**Yellow Water-lily**

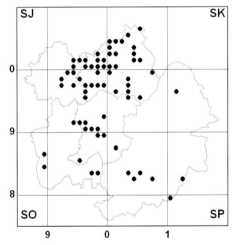

*68. Native, but also introduced, although generally disliked by anglers because of its far-spreading ability. An aquatic; bottom rooted with mature leaves both floating and submerged, growing in water up to 1.5 metres but often in much shallower water. Favoured by base-rich and quite nutrient-rich conditions, well-lit, but can stand a little shade. In B&BC found in canals, ponds and lakes where it can withstand more disturbance than *Nymphaea alba* by virtue of its submerged leaves which persist where floating leaves are lost or cannot develop, although still unlikely to thrive in fast-moving water or situations exposed to wind. It can completely dominate the beds of some of the less-used canals, such as parts of the Wyrley and Essington. Its apparent scarcity in the Dudley canals is intriguing. Ass: *Alisma plantago-aquatica, Alisma lanceolatum, Lemna minor, Lemna trisulca, Nymphaea alba, Potamogeton natans, Sparganium erectum.*

## 28. LAURACEAE

### *Laurus nobilis* L.
### Bay

2. Neophyte. A dioecious evergreen shrub or tree grown for the culinary use of its leaves and as a patio plant. Recorded from Red House Park (SP037945, M.G. Bloxham, 2002) and from a hedge in Daniels Lane (SP062999, JaH, 2007), both probably remants or discards from gardening. Mediterranean and Asia Minor.

## EU-DICOTS

## 29. CERATOPHYLLACEAE

### *Ceratophyllum demersum* L.
### Rigid Hornwort

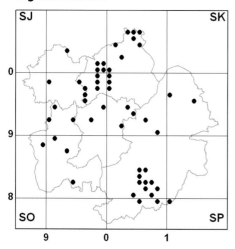

*53. Native. Submerged, rootless, perennial aquatic. Found in base-rich, nutrient-rich, still and very slow-flowing waters up to a depth of one metre. Found in canals, ponds and lakes but particularly characteristic of cut-off sections of canal, where, in fertile but unpolluted conditions, it can grow very rapidly and fill the water over appreciable distances, but usually only for a few years. Ass: *Elodea nuttallii, Lemna minor, Lemna trisulca, Myriophyllum spicatum, Potamogeton pectinatus.*

## 30. PAPAVERACEAE
## subfamily 1 – Papaveroideae

### *Papaver pseudoorientale* (Fedde) Medw.
### Oriental Poppy

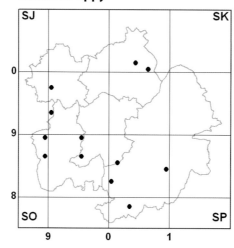

12. Neophyte. A large perennial herb, found infrequently, probably entirely as a garden discard or remnant, almost always in habitats adjacent to gardens. The map includes some plants described as *P. orientale* L. Also tetrad SO99X. SW Asia.

### *Papaver atlanticum* (Ball) Coss.
### Atlas Poppy

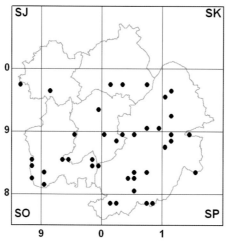

40. Neophyte. A perennial herb becoming quite frequent as an escape close to gardens, found as a pavement weed, on roadside verges, disturbed ground, post-housing sites, churchyards and once on a canal towpath. Often clearly regenerating from seed, and increasingly met with in the latter part of the recording period. Morocco. Ass: *Eschscholzia californica, Sisymbrium orientale.*

### *Papaver somniferum* L.
### Opium Poppy

*331. Archaeophyte. An annual weed of gardens, allotments, disturbed ground, streets, canals and parkland and still often

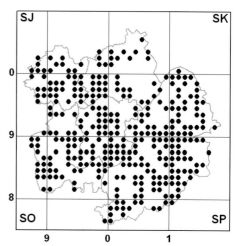

cultivated. It is a plant of well-lit places on dry to moist, richly fertile and moderately base-rich, well-drained, recently disturbed soils. The seed is very long-lived in soil, and the plant can be abundant on sites recently disturbed after many years (100+) of continual use, e.g. Devonshire Road School in Smethwick and parts of the old B'ham General Hospital B'ham in the 1990s. It has a long history of cultivation and escape that has hidden its native distribution which is probably in the E Mediterranean. Ass: *Chenopodium album, Lapsana communis, Papaver dubium, Papaver rhoeas, Sonchus oleraceus.*

We have no records of **subsp. setigerum** (DC.) Arcang. and assume all our records are **subsp. somniferum**, which has been specifically recorded occasionally.

### *Papaver rhoeas* L.
### Common Poppy

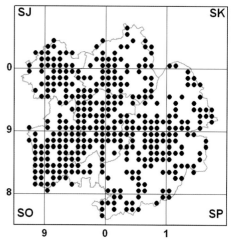

*384. Archaeophyte. An annual found on disturbed ground, demolition sites, canals, railways, streets, farmland, gardens, allotments and nature reserves. It grows in well-lit and well-drained situations on moist, quite base- and nutrient-rich, recently disturbed soils. The map suggests that it is a little scarcer in some of the countryside areas of B&BC and in some of the outer suburbs, but this is probably related mostly to the extent and frequency of disturbance. It is usually this species rather than *P. dubium* which suddenly becomes dominant in a failed agricultural crop, creating huge areas of red, as in SO8788 in 2011, where in some fields it was co-dominant with the white-flowered variant of *Rhaphanus raphanistrum*. S Europe. Ass: *Chenopodium album*, *Matricaria chamomilla*, *Senecio squalidus*, *Senecio vulgaris*, *Tripleurospermum inodorum*.

### *Papaver dubium* L.
### Long-headed Poppy

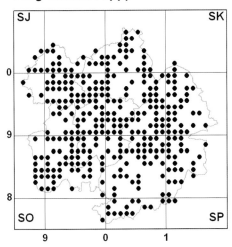

*340. Archaeophyte. An annual found on railways, canals, streets, wasteland, parkland, farmland, gardens, allotments and nature reserves. It grows in well-lit, well-drained places on moist, quite base-rich and nutrient-rich soils. It appears to be a little less common than *Papaver rhoeas*, although there are areas such as parts of Sutton where it seems to be commoner, and one frequently finds sites with just one of the two species. It has been suggested (Hill *et al.* 1999) that *P. rhoeas* is favoured by a slightly moister and more base- and nutrient-rich soil. There has long been experimental evidence that when sown together, the seedlings compete more strongly with others of their own species than they do between the species, suggesting some subtle differentiation in their use of the habitat. Europe. Ass: as *P. rhoeas*.

### *Papaver lecoqii* Lamotte
(*P. dubium* subsp. *lecoqii* (Lamotte) Syme)
### Yellow-juiced Poppy

1. Archaeophyte, casual in B&BC. Annual of cultivation and disturbance. Recorded in the pavement of West Park Avenue, Longbridge (SP012788, JJD, 2001).

### *Papaver hybridum* L.
### Rough Poppy

0. Archaeophyte. An annual of crops and disturbance. Probably at most a casual occurrence in B&BC: two 1980s unvalidated records from Brownhills (SK0306) and Valley Park (SJ9001).

### *Papaver argemone* L.
### Prickly Poppy

2. Archaeophyte. VU. An annual of arable crops and, rarely, waste land. In a pavement verge outside a petrol station on the A449 (SJ916037, ICT & EVJC, 2002); in an arable field with no crop present NE of Doe Bank Road, Barr Beacon (SP066967, ICT, MWP, PLR & JaH, 2006, seen again 2008). The latter record might be a remnant of an old arable weed flora. Also present were *Anchusa arvensis*, *Apera spica-venti*, *Avena fatua*, *Epilobium tetragonum*, *Sherardia arvensis*, *Spergula arvensis*, and *Veronica agrestis*. There are a very few earlier records, from Sutton Park (SP0997) in the 19th century, from Walsall (SK006000) and W'ton (SJ9001) in the 1980s and from N bank of reservoir at Hollymoor Hospital (SO998780, JJD, 1992).

### *Papaver nudicaule* L.
### Icelandic Poppy

1. Casual. A single record, from the golf course, Warley Park (SP010863, B. Westwood, 1996).

### *Meconopsis cambrica* (L.) Vig.
### Welsh Poppy

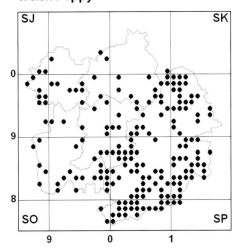

191. Native to Wales and Ireland, introduced in B&BC. Nationally Scarce as a native, where it grows in rocky woodlands and on cliff ledges, mostly in Wales. A long-lived perennial found in B&BC as a garden escape and an often tolerated weed in gardens, allotments, churchyards, pavements, roadside verges, on walls, in post-housing sites and on disturbed land. Particularly common in suburban residential areas and occasionally getting into suburban woodland dingles,

apparently much less common in the Black Country than in B'ham. Usually in cool, shady places on fairly fertile soils. First vc. 39 record was from Penn (SO8996, C.M. Hibbert, 1971); not recorded in Edees (1972) or Cadbury *et al.* (1971) and probably increasing in B&BC. Also tetrad SJ98E. Ass: *Cardamine flexuosa*, *Chelidonium majus*, *Epilobium montanum*, *Poa trivialis*, *Sonchus oleraceus*.

### *Glaucium corniculatum* (L.) Rudolph
### Red Horned-poppy

0. Casual. Annual, recorded in the California quarry in the Woodgate Valley (SP016831) in 1941 and 1945. S Europe.

### *Chelidonium majus* L.
### Greater Celandine

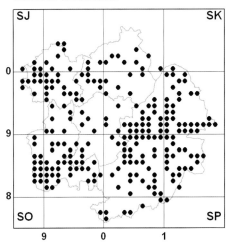

*242. Archaeophyte. A perennial herb and a cottage garden plant, once almost universally grown as a cure for warts. Now occasionally a garden weed but mainly escaped to sites recovering from disturbance: pavement cracks, the street, waste ground and allotments, churchyards, lanesides, canal banks and post-housing sites. Grows in the open, in shelter or in

▲ *Chelidonium majus*

slight shade on moist, base- and nutrient-rich soils. Double flowered forms are occasionally encountered. Distribution is concentrated in some of the older residential suburbs. Ass: *Alliaria petiolata*, *Epilobium ciliatum*, *Epilobium obscurum*, *Lamium album*, *Lapsana communis*, *Lolium perenne*, *Meconopsis cambrica*.

### *Eschscholzia californica* Cham.
### Californian Poppy

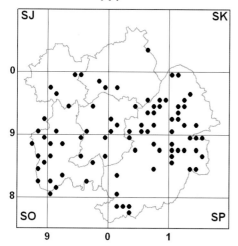

85. Neophyte. A perennial herb. In B&BC it is found as a weed of disturbed ground, edges of neglected gardens, pavements, allotments and post-housing sites. Western N America and Mexico.

### 30. PAPAVERACEAE
### subfamily 2 – Fumarioideae

### *Corydalis solida* (L.) Clairv.
### Bird-in-a-bush

0? Neophyte. A tuberous perennial herb. Between railway and Oldwinsford Church (SO909831, WAT, 1989). Two records for *Corydalis* sp. in the B'ham suburbs at SP0783 (1999) and SP0882 (2007) may have been this. Europe.

### *Corydalis cheilanthifolia* Hemsl.
### Fern-leaved Corydalis

1. Neophyte. Perennial. A single plant found growing in a pavement where it meets a garden fence in a track behind houses, Tettenhall Wood (SO878994, ICT & P. Millett, 2008). China.

### *Pseudofumaria lutea* (L.) Borkh.
### Yellow Corydalis

158. Neophyte. A perennial herb found growing from walls and pavement in the street and also in the brickwork of canals and railways. This is one of those 'weeds' that tends to be left alone by the gardener once it has arrived, thus travelling in the opposite direction to many of the plants we record, although like them it originated

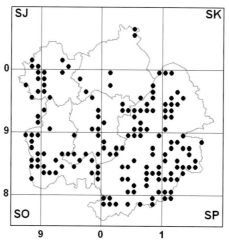

as a garden cultivated plant. It is a plant of well-lit and also shady places, rooting into damp, base-rich and infertile substrates. It may be increasing. Alps. Ass: *Asplenium ruta-muraria*, *Asplenium scolopendrium*, *Campanula trachelium*, *Cerastium fontanum*, *Cymbalaria muralis*, *Hedera helix*, *Poa annua*, *Senecio squalidus*, *Stachys sylvatica*.

### *Pseudofumaria alba* (Mill.) Lidén
### Pale Corydalis

0. Neophyte. Growing on walls in Hall Green (SP119815, CBW, 1994). Europe.

### *Ceratocapnos claviculata* (L.) Lidén
### Climbing Corydalis

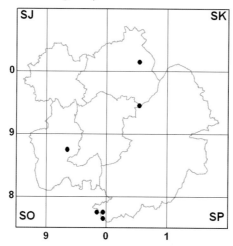

6. Native. Ax. A climbing annual found in the UK in deciduous and coniferous woodland and other shady places, on base-poor and nutrient-poor, often peaty soils. Not a strong competitor it benefits from a certain amount of disturbance. Rarely recorded in B&BC, its stronghold is on the edge of the Lickey Hills. Common on Rubery Hill (SO989777, JJD, 1990 & 2001) and in woodland on Rubery Hill (SO990778, JJD, 1992); also seen on a gorse bank, E of Cock Hill Lane (SO989778, MWP, 2007), in *Calluna vulgaris* – *Vaccinium myrtillus* community, Rednal Hill (SO996765, K.M.

Stephen, 1999). There are also other, scattered records from Saltwells Wood in Dudley (SO934870, APD, 1999); from Holly Wood in Perry Barr (SP053945, PWS & P. Meadows, 1997); from near Aldridge (SK0501, JEH, 2001) and an old record on an island of woodland on Dartmouth Golf Course, Sandwell Valley (SP0192, MWP, circa 1990). It was recorded from Sutton Park in 1873 and Gravelly Hill in 1817. Ass: *Digitalis purpurea*, *Holcus lanatus*, *Teucrium scorodonia*, *Ulex europaeus*.

### *Fumaria capreolata* L.
### White Ramping-fumitory

1. Native. A scrambling annual, recorded from an unshaded bank at Millgreen Farm near Aldridge (SK074015, JaH & SJC, 2006). There are two records from the 1830s, from SO9384 and SP18 tetrad I.

### *Fumaria muralis* Sond. ex W.D.J. Koch
### Common Ramping-fumitory

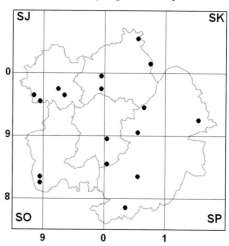

17. Native. Ax. An annual, found very occasionally, mostly on allotment sites, where it can be quite abundant on recently cultivated but currently neglected plots; also in gardens and pavement cracks, in moist, quite base- and nutrient-rich soil. Ass: *Anchusa arvensis*, *Fallopia convolvulus*, *Lapsana communis*, *Sonchus oleraceus*.

### *Fumaria officinalis* L.
### Common Fumitory

*203. Archaeophyte. An annual of cultivation and disturbed ground being found frequently in allotments, gardens, churchyards, waste ground, spoil heaps, railways, canals and a golf course. Grows in mainly open weed communities, usually well-lit, on moist to dry, but well-drained, fairly base- and nutrient-rich soils. Also tetrad SO99G. Ass: *Chenopodium album*, *Euphorbia helioscopia*, *Euphorbia peplus*, *Papaver rhoeas*, *Papaver somniferum*, *Poa annua*, *Senecio vulgaris*, *Sonchus oleraceus*, *Veronica persica*. Europe.

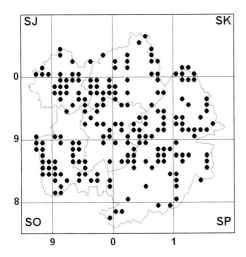

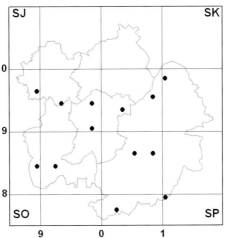

Lane Urban Park (SO976921, MWP, 1998) was the first vc. 39 record. China.

There are a few records specified as **subsp. officinalis**, thought to be the common subspecies, and a smaller number for **subsp. wirtgenii** (W.D.J. Koch) Arcang, the only records within the survey period for the latter are the steelworks site at Coombeswood (SO98S, WAT & CBW, 2000); and on the B'ham University campus close to the University station, growing with subsp. officinalis (SP0483, S.J. Whild, 2008), but there are older records from arable land at Park Limepits (SP0399, JPM, 1991); railway embankment at Wychall (SP037794, RM & JJD, 1991).

### Fumaria densiflora DC.
### Dense-flowered Fumitory
0. Archaeophyte. Nationally Scarce. An old record: in disturbed soil, Sandwell Park (SP0291, BRF, 1971).

## 31. BERBERIDACEAE

### Berberis vulgaris L.
### Barberry
2. Native or alien. A spiny deciduous shrub of hedgerows, in B&BC it has rare records from along railways and canals and in churchyards, mostly unconfirmed. Digbeth branch canal (SP080868, PWS & M. Kodaka, 2002); an undescribed site (SO896847, Wardell Armstrong surveyors, 2004). There are earlier records from St Mary's Church, Oldwinsford (SO907831, JJD, 1985); mixed scrub on the Worcester & B'ham canal (SP063863, F.C. Whiston, 1987): John the Baptist Church, Halesowen (SO966836, G. Peake, 1990).

### Berberis thunbergii DC.
### Thunberg's Barberry
13. Neophyte. A spiny deciduous shrub, a remnant of planting, garden throw-out, and bird-sown. Found growing from pavements, in hedgerows and churchyards, on railway and canal banks, in waste ground and in a car park. First

reported in vc. 39 in 1995 from near a canal bridge at Coseley (SO939949, PN). Japan.

### Berberis wilsoniae Hemsl.
### Mrs Wilson's Barberry
2. Neophyte. A spiny deciduous shrub. By the River Cole in Springfield (SP099819, WAT, 1999); edge of a disused railway, probably planted, Shepwell Green (SO97919881, JEH, 2007). China.

### Berberis gagnepainii C.K. Schneid.
### Gagnepain's Barberry
3. Neophyte. An evergreen shrub. Several self-sown plants found growing from a footpath at the base of a fence in Pedmore (SO900818, JJD, 2003); Oxbarn (SO8997, CBW, 2007); a bird-sown bush in Barnford Hill Park (SO996875, ICT, MWP, PLR & AWR, 2009). China.

### Berberis julianae C.K. Schneid.
### Chinese Barberry

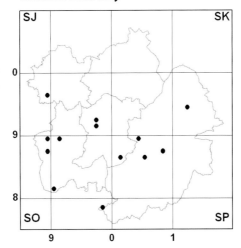

13. Neophyte. A large evergreen shrub, mostly found self-sown close to gardens along footpaths, on waste ground, a railway embankment and growing from the wall of B'ham Childrens Hospital. The record from SO9792, from Sheepwash

### Berberis darwinii Hook.
### Darwin's Barberry

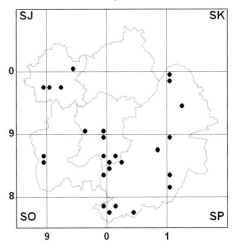

26. Neophyte. A spiny evergreen shrub. In B&BC it is found on railway embankments, in a derelict rail yard, but mostly close to gardens in pavements and hedges. Sometimes as a garden relic but often self-sown. S America.

### Berberis × stenophylla Lindl.
(*B. darwinii* × *B. empetrifolia* Lam.)
### Hedge Barberry

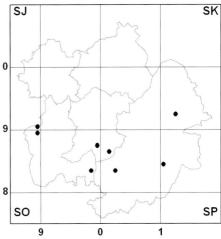

8. Neophyte. A large spiny evergreen shrub. Found as a relic of planting or sometimes bird-sown, in stream and canal corridors, in parks, on a conglomerate outcrop in Barnford Hill Park. A hybrid of garden origin.

### Berberis × frikartii C.K. Schneid. ex
H.J. van de Laar
(*B. candidula* (C. Schneider) C. Schneider × *B. verruculosa* Hemsl. et Wils.)
### Frikart's Barberry
1. Neophyte. Recorded at the E edge of a disused railway, S of road, Bentley (SO979988, JEH, 2007).

## *Mahonia aquifolium* (Pursh) Nutt.
**Oregon-grape**

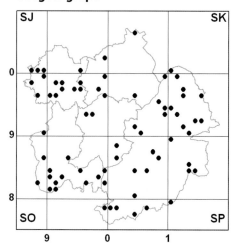

72. Neophyte. An evergreen shrub. Widely planted and bird-sown in B&BC, being found in hedgerows, woodland, rough ground, pavement cracks, walls, overgrown graveyards, disused railway lines and sewage works. Preferring semi-shade and dry to moist, fairly fertile soils, it naturalises well in hedgerows and woodlands despite often being planted in full sun. N America.

## *Mahonia japonica* (Thunb.) DC
1. Neophyte. Two plants recorded in 2003 from a footpath in Pedmore (SO908818, JJD, 2003). Probably native of Taiwan.

## 32. RANUNCULACEAE

### *Caltha palustris* L.
**Marsh-marigold**

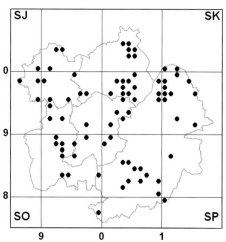

*79. Native. Ax. A perennial herb found especially in old, species-rich wet pastures and marshes, also in ditches, at water margins and in alder woodlands. It grows in muddy or peaty, fairly base-rich soils of intermediate fertility which are reliably damp to wet through the year. A long-lived plant, so despite a limited capacity for vegetative spread, it can form large stands by seeding

into areas where winter flooding prevents competition from tall herb dominants. It does not seem to appear spontaneously in new sites, but is frequently introduced around created ponds and seems to survive well. The distribution is focused on the countryside areas and many of the dingle woodland areas of B&BC, although it seems curiously uncommon around Illey. Also tetrads SJ90Q,V. Ass: *Cardamine amara, Cardamine pratensis, Chrysosplenium oppositifolium, Filipendula ulmaria, Juncus inflexus, Mentha aquatica, Silene flos-cuculi.*

## *Helleborus foetidus* L.
**Stinking Hellebore**

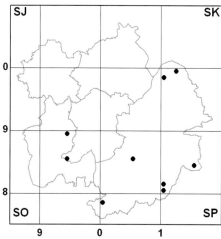

9. Native; usually introduced in B&BC. A garden reject or a seeding from a nearby garden. Nationally Scarce where a native, on shallow calcareous soils. Herbaceous perennial, in B&BC usually on base- and nutrient-rich, moist soils in sheltered positions. Records are mostly from residential areas in habitats marginal to private gardens and from churchyards. Also a persistent patch along old railway track bed, Blower's Green, Dudley.

## *Helleborus argutifolius* Viv.
**Corsican Hellebore**

4. Neophyte. Perennial. This species is not rhizomatous so is most likely to have self-sown from seed; very occasionally immature plants are found in paving and walls self-sown from nearby gardens but seldom reach maturity in these circumstances. Growing from the mortar of a brick wall, Warley (SP007854, CBW, 1997); Sandpits, B'ham (SP057874, MWP, 1999); Cole Valley Road (SP098805, MWP & ICT, 2007); verges and railings, Ham Lane, Kingswinford (SO831903, CBW, 2007). Corsica and Sardinia.

## *Helleborus viridis* L.
**Green Hellebore**

0. Perennial. Introduced with us although apparently native in woodlands on

calcareous soils in neighbouring counties. Long cultivation has obscured its native distribution in UK. Only an old record from Kings Heath Park pond (SP067816, JJB, 1990).

## *Helleborus orientalis* Lam.
**Lenten-rose**

2. Neophyte. A garden discard. Haden Hill Wood (SO962855, MWP & LG, 2005); Hill View, Oakham (SO954896, MWP, 2005). Turkey.

## *Nigella damascena* L.
**Love-in-a-mist**

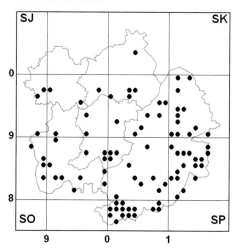

91. Neophyte. A garden annual that persists around gardens and allotments and escapes onto the street and into waste ground. It readily re-establishes itself from seed and will persist where the ground is regularly disturbed. Mediterranean.

## *Aconitum napellus* agg.
**Monk's-hood**

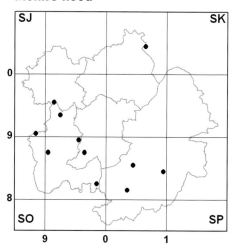

11. The aggregate mainly consists of *Aconitum napellus* L. (**Monk's-hood**), a native and Nationally Scarce species, plus *Aconitum × stoerkianum* Rchb. (*A. × cammarum* L., *A. napellus × A. variegatum*) (**Hybrid Monk's-hood**), a neophyte, a

sterile hybrid which can arise naturally in gardens but is more likely to have been purchased at a garden centre, although other hybrids and several subspp. of *A. napellus* may be involved. Most of our records are referred directly to *A.* × *stoerkianum*, the rest to *Aconitum napellus* agg. They are herbaceous perennial garden throw-outs which may become naturalised on suitable moist or damp soils in semi-shade, found on roadsides, pathsides and streamsides, often in rank vegetation.

### *Aconitum lycoctonum* L.
### Wolf's-bane
1. Neophyte. Herbaceous perennial, recorded in a garden, presumably a relic of past cultivation although not planted by the present owner (SO 975944, A. Wood, 2007).

### *Consolida ajacis* (L.) Schur
### Larkspur
3. Neophyte. An annual garden plant that was formerly a cornfield weed. Several plants on a disturbed footpath verge, Hasbury (SO950833, AWR, WAT & CBW, 2001); in a remnant of old garden (SP066908, MWP, 2005); on waste ground at Wordsley (SO8987, CBW, 2007). There is also an old record from ballast of an old railway line at Stechford Station (SP129875, CBW, 1989). Mediterranean and SW Asia.

### *Anemone nemorosa* L.
### Wood Anemone

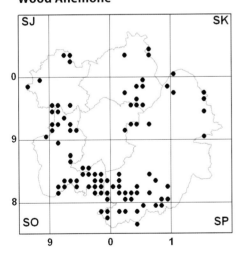

*93. Native. Ax. A rhizomatous perennial of old broad-leaved woods and hedgerows. Seed is rarely fertile so it spreads vegetatively, taking a hundred years to spread six feet (Mabey, 1997). This makes it an indicator of ancient woodland and the map gives a good impression of their distribution in B&BC. Found in semi-shade to shade, in moist, moderately fertile and not very base-poor soils. Ass: *Adoxa moschatellina*, *Carex sylvatica*, *Ficaria verna*, *Hyacinthoides non-scripta*, *Stellaria holostea*.

### *Anemone apennina* L.
### Blue Anemone
1. Neophyte. A rhizomatous perennial, probably entirely a relic of cultivation. Northycote Farm, by car park (SJ930031, PLR, 2008). From just before our survey period: grassy margin to moat (SP018776, JJD, 1994). Central S Europe.

### *Anemone blanda* Schott & Kotschy
### Balkan Anemone
3. Neophyte. A tuberous perennial, rarely persisting from cultivation. Spreading in a car park entrance, Sandwell Valley (SP029913, MWP, 1998); churchyard (SP097876, MWP, 1998); cemetery (SP059881, CRP & J. Rao, 2002). Balkans and SW Asia.

### *Anemone* × *hybrida* Paxton (*A. hupehensis* (Lemoine) Lemoine × *A. vitifolia* Buch.-Ham. ex DC)
### Japanese Anemone

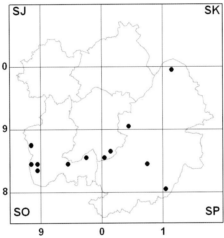

12. Neophyte. Tall perennial herb; a hybrid of garden origin. The few records are all of plants in pavement or tarmac cracks and the bases of walls near gardens. Europe.

### *Clematis vitalba* L.
### Traveller's-joy, Old-man's-beard

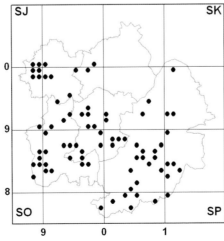

*78. Native; possibly sometimes introduced. Ax. A rampant climber, on the N edge of its

▲ *Caltha palustris*

▲ *Anemone nemorosa*

▲ *Anemone blanda*

native UK range in our area. It clothes large
areas of fence on industrial land and along
railways. The distribution in Sandwell and
B'ham may be following the rail network.
Also found in hedges, on waste land and
scrub on road banks and sometimes
allowed to persist in gardens. It grows in the
open and in partial shade on fairly or very
dry, base-rich or calcareous, moderately
nutrient-rich soils. Ass: *Artemisia vulgaris,
Buddleja davidii, Calystegia silvatica, Cytisus
scoparius, Reseda lutea.*

### Clematis tangutica (Maxim.) Korsh.
### Orange-peel Clematis
1. Neophyte. A deciduous climber. One
record, described as self-sown, from bare
waste ground in Norton (SO886825, WAT,
2001). China.

### Clematis montana Buch.-Ham. ex DC.
### Himalayan Clematis
5. Neophyte. A vigorous climber, usually
a relic of cultivation, reproduction from
seed being rare. Rarely recorded, growing
on fences and buildings: electricity sub-
station, W Smethwick (SP000894, CBW,
1997); works fence, Tat Bank (SO997891,
WAT, 2001); car park, Sutton Park (SP108971,
SPG, 1998); churchyard at Kingswinford
(SO895894, CBW, 2005); extensive patch
smothering hawthorn along the canal
towpath at Tettenhall Wood (SO885992,
MWP, 2005). The first vc. 39 record was two
plants from waste ground by Rolfe Street
Railway Station at Smethwick (SP022886, C.
Mansell & MWP, 1988). Asia.

### Ranunculus subgenus 1 –
### Ranunculus

### Ranunculus acris L.
### Meadow Buttercup

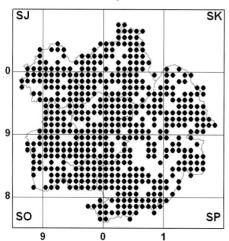

*538. Native. Perennial. Common
throughout B&BC in grassland, especially
permanent, overgrazed or mown farm
meadows and nature reserves, also by

ponds, pools and canals. In the open or
slight shade, on moist to rather damp, but
not totally waterlogged soils of average
fertility and base status. Ours is **subsp.
acris.** Ass: *Agrostis capillaris, Alopecurus
pratensis, Cerastium fontanum, Phleum
pratense, Rumex acetosa, Trifolium repens.*

### Ranunculus repens L.
### Creeping Buttercup
*689. Native. A creeping perennial,
common throughout B&BC from gardens,
roadside, woodland and arable land. An
invasive weed of cultivation which spreads
vegetatively by rooting at the nodes, also
prevalent in damp, disturbed, compacted
and over-fertile areas of pasture and lawn.
Grows in the open or semi-shade on
damp, often poorly drained soils that are
of average base status and usually richly
fertile. Ass: *Agrostis gigantea, Elytrigia
repens, Senecio jacobaea, Taraxacum* spp.,
*Urtica dioica.*

### Ranunculus bulbosus L.
### Bulbous Buttercup

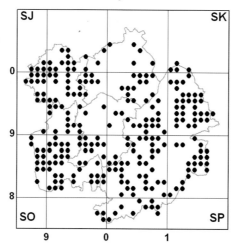

*266. Native. A grassland perennial with a
swollen stem-base. Particularly abundant
in dry, overgrazed, old pasture and dry
banks of fine open turf in parks and playing
fields. Somewhat less frequently recorded
in B&BC than *Ranunculus acris* or *R. repens*,
and possibly sometimes missed due to its
earlier growth and flowering period, with
dormancy often developing by July. Grows
in the open on dry to moist, well drained
and often drought liable, rather infertile
and base-rich soils. Ass: *Agrostis capillaris,
Bellis perennis, Festuca rubra, Luzula
campestris, Plantago lanceolata, Trifolium
pratense.*

### Ranunculus sardous Crantz
### Hairy Buttercup
0. Native or alien. An annual, lost from most
of its inland sites in UK by the 1930s. It was
recorded from Clayhanger (SK030046, A.

Sestakovs & S. Derry, 1987). This record has
not been confirmed, but this site was partly
ploughed at around this time and there are
other recent records from SJ90 in vc. 39.

### Ranunculus parviflorus L.
### Small-flowered Buttercup
3. Native. A small annual buttercup of dry,
disturbed habitats, of rare, and probably
essentially casual occurrence in B&BC.
Mown grass verge, alleyway off Chapel
Street, Stourbridge (SO901840, MES, 1996);
Clayhanger Village (SK047048, DH, 2004);
perhaps 30 plants in edge of mown grass
and gravel border behind conservatory,
West Park, W'ton (SO905993, ICT, 2008).
Ass (at West Park): *Catapodium rigidum,
Cerastium glomeratum, Poa annua.*

### Ranunculus arvensis L.
### Corn Buttercup
1. Archaeophyte. Sect. 41, BAP, CR. An
annual cornfield weed, rendered rare in
the UK by seed cleaning and herbicides.
Recently recorded from two places at the
edge of a cornfield in set-aside, Limepits
Farm (SP030996, M. Wilson, conf. MWP,
2006). Three plants were located elsewhere
in the same field on a follow-up visit (DH,
2007). This species has long-lived seed so
has the potential to reappear on cultivated
ground even in an urban setting. Bagnall
recorded it in Sutton Park (SP0997) in 1867
and 1876. There are also unconfirmed
records from Lindridge and Langley
Pools (SP154967) and Valley Park, W'ton
(SJ902014), both by J. Andrews in 1987
(Natural England files).

### Ranunculus auricomus L.
### Goldilocks Buttercup

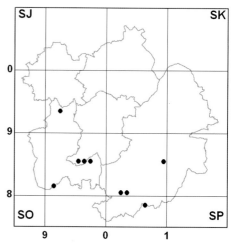

9. Native. Ax. A perennial, found very
infrequently in old broad-leaved
(particularly Ash-Oak) woodland and
hedgerows. Its strongholds seem to be
in Leasowes and Haden Hill Parks and
in some of the S B'ham dingle woods.

Grows in semi-shade on damp soils that are quite base-rich and of intermediate fertility. These plants are apomictics, producing seed without fertilisation and several hundred microspecies have been described from continental Europe. Ass: *Anemone nemorosa, Hyacinthoides non-scripta, Quercus robur*.

### *Ranunculus sceleratus* L.
### Celery-leaved Buttercup

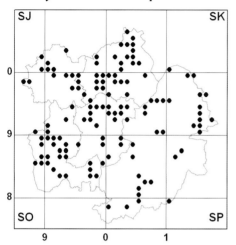

*129. Native. An annual found at streamsides, ponds, ditches and in marshy fields, usually as a colonist of bare, extremely fertile or even fertility-polluted, base-rich mud in the draw-down zone. Also tetrads SJ80Q, SO99D. Ass: *Apium nodiflorum, Lemna minor, Lemna minuta, Myosotis scorpioides, Persicaria amphibia*.

### *Ranunculus lingua* L.
### Greater Spearwort

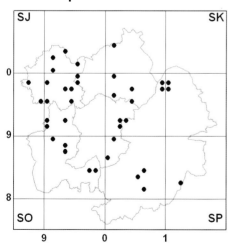

39. Native, but probably largely recently introduced in B&BC although our area is part of its presumed natural range and it has been known in Sutton Park since 1841. A stoloniferous perennial found at the edge of ponds and pools and also by a few canals and brooks. It seems to be more frequent in the Black Country than

in B'ham. A plant of well-lit places, rarely in partial shade, growing in shallow water or areas of seasonal inundation that are moderately base-rich and usually quite fertile, although it flourishes in some quite base- and nutrient-poor water at Sutton Park in Little Bracebridge Pool. Both Cadbury *et al.* (1971) and Edees (1972) accounted it rare, which it certainly is not now. It is a popular introduction in pond habitat creation and can spread rapidly once introduced. Ass: *Acorus calamus, Caltha palustris, Crassula helmsii, Epilobium hirsutum, Galium palustre, Glyceria maxima, Iris pseudacorus, Mentha aquatica, Menyanthes trifoliata, Schoenoplectus lacustris, Sparganium erectum, Typha angustifolia, Typha latifolia*.

### *Ranunculus flammula* L.
### Lesser Spearwort

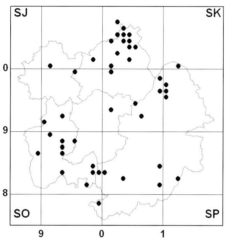

*45. Native. Ax. A perennial from ditches, flushes, marshes and marshy hollows in pasture, pond and river margins and places where ground is seasonally inundated. Grows best in short vegetation in well-lit places and is characteristic of old, relatively undisturbed, reliably wet, nutrient-poor and fairly base-poor situations. The distribution is centred in the countryside areas; it is very scarce in urbanised parts and confined to undamaged areas protected from water pollution. There may be some losses in S B'ham and Sutton Park since the 1980s. It is assumed all records are for **subsp. *flammula*.** Ass: *Carex panicea, Carex nigra, Galium palustre, Juncus acutiflorus, Juncus bulbosus, Myosotis laxa, Mentha arvensis*.

### *Ranunculus* subgenus 2 –
### *Batrachium* (DC) A. Gray

### *Ranunculus hederaceus* L.
### Ivy-leaved Crowfoot
9. Native. Ax. A procumbent annual or short-lived perennial found in bare mud

▲ *Ranunculus parviflorus*

▲ *Ranunculus sceleratus*

▲ *Ranunculus lingua*

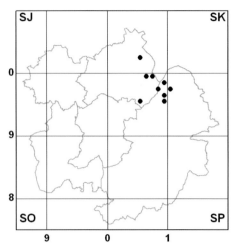

and peat or shallow water in the margins of ditches, pools, ponds, streams; also in a wooded area at Corporation Wood (SP0699). Grows in open situations or semi-shade on fairly base- and nutrient-poor soils and muds, particularly characteristic of the cattle-poached margins of water bodies. Considered indifferent to soil base or nutrient status, it is very much confined to base-poor and nutrient-poor areas in B&BC. They are all peaty sites. It was recorded in more squares at Sutton Park in the past, and also at two sites in marshy grassland at Warrens Hall Farm on the Rowley Hills (SO9588 and SO9689) in the 1980s. Ass: *Juncus bufonius*, *Juncus effusus*, *Juncus inflexus*, *Stellaria alsine*.

### *Ranunculus omiophyllus* Ten.
### Round-leaved Crowfoot

2. Native. Ax. A procumbent annual or short-lived perennial. Found on bare peat or mud in the edge of shallow water, on low fertility sites with low to medium base status. Its UK distribution is predominantly western and B&BC is on the eastern and lowland edge. Its habitat is similar to that of *Ranunculus hederaceus*, but in the UK generally it is much more confined to low-nutrient sites. In B&BC it has only ever been recorded from two areas. At Sutton Park, from five 1km squares by Readett (1971), and in the present survey it was only found in a ditch by the road, Longmoor Pool (SP092956, JWP & ICT, 2008) and in bare peat in a ditch by Little Bracebridge Pool (SP094983, JWP, 2008), but it is now spreading (with *R. hederaceus*) into shady, horse-poached bare areas close by the track (SP095983, ICT, J. Bailey, B. Opara, C. Tinstell, N. Crowley, D. Mattley, A. Freeman & C. Tregaskes, 2011). In 1871 it was last recorded by J. Matthews from The Birches, Hagley Brake (SO8981), which was probably just outside our boundary and Pedmore Common (SO8982, now largely within Stourbridge Golf Course, not seen there in recent surveys).

### *Ranunculus aquatilis* sensu lato
### Common Water-crowfoot

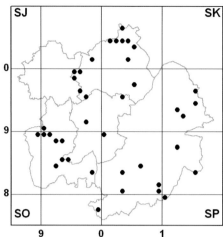

40. Native. Ax. The map includes all records for the aquatic Water-crowfoots *Ranunculus aquatilis* L. and *Ranunculus peltatus* Schrank, plus many which were not possible to distinguish as either, usually because of lack of flowers. They are rooted aquatic annuals or short-lived perennials with both submerged and floating leaves found in still or slow-flowing, shallow, clear water in ditches, pools, ponds, lakes, canals, rivers and at sewage works, growing in fairly nutrient-poor but base-rich water, and their presence suggests reasonable water quality. The two species are sometimes found together in the same pool. Records where it has been possible to distinguish between these species are given below.

### *Ranunculus aquatilis* L.
### Common Water-crowfoot

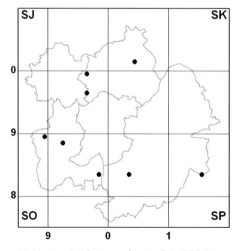

*8. Native. Ax. Scattered records in B&BC, in a variety of pools and small streams, probably less common than *Ranunculus peltatus*.

### *Ranunculus peltatus* Schrank
### Pond Water-crowfoot

*15. Native. Ax. Scattered records in B&BC, recorded entirely in ponds, apparently

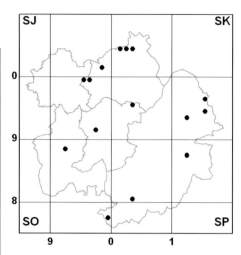

slightly commoner than *R. aquatilis*, sometimes in quite base-rich water associated with furnace spoil, but also in heathland. Old records in Sutton Park (SP0996, SP0997, SP1097, Readett, 1971).

### *Ranunculus penicillatus* (Dumort.) Bab.
### Stream Water-crowfoot

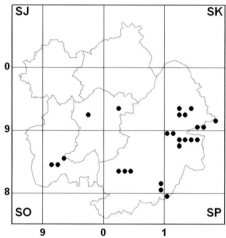

25. Native. The map combines almost all records of the submerged aquatic Water-crowfoots without floating leaves which are found in the less polluted, fairly clear, faster-flowing rivers and large streams of B&BC. Although some of these were recorded as *Ranunculus fluitans*, it is probable that all are *Ranunculus penicillatus*, a perennial of moderately rapidly flowing rivers, usually in nutrient-intermediate and base-rich clear waters. *R. penicillatus* has been reliably recorded (mainly by CBW) in the River Cole, the River Rea and the Bourn Brook, all in S B'ham. Most of our records have been attributed to **subsp. *pseudofluitans*** (Syme) S.D. Webster and in B&BC all probably belong to this subspecies.

Since neither *Ranunculus fluitans* and *Ranunculus penicillatus* will grow in rivers grossly polluted with nutrients or other contaminants, the map gives a useful impression of the state of our rivers (except the Stour, see under *R. fluitans*). It is interesting to note that these species were scarcely recorded in B&BC in the early 1970s by Eades (1972) and Cadbury *et al.* (1971) although there were many records, mostly for *R. penicillatus*, from the 19th and early in the 20th century. Ass: *Potamogeton pectinatus.*

### *Ranunculus fluitans* Lam.
### River Water-crowfoot

3. Native. It grows mainly in larger rivers in only moderately nutrient- and base-rich clear waters. WAT assigned the following intermediate-seeming plants in the River Stour to *R. fluitans* on grounds that N.T.H. Holmes determined colonies lower down the Stour in 1987 as this. Stambermill (SO911847 to SO916848, WAT, 2003); Lye (SO927849, WAT, 2003); Netherend (SO931852–934856, WAT, 2001).

### *Ranunculus circinatus* Sibth.
### Fan-leaved Water-crowfoot

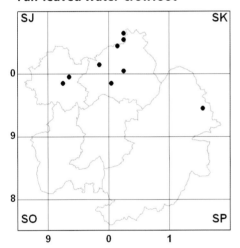

9. Native. Ax. Submerged aquatic perennial found typically in fairly deep, clear, moderately nutrient- and base-rich waters of ponds, but there are records from the Wyrley & Essington canal and it is also locally common in the muddy margins and in shallow water along an old railway track bed in the Mill Lane LNR, Walsall (SK0200). Ass: *Callitriche* spp.

### *Ficaria verna* Huds.
(*Ranunculus ficaria* L.)
### Lesser Celandine

*285. Native. Perennating by tubers. Found in woodland, hedges, stream banks, grassland including lawns, gardens and churchyards, it is typically one of the first, welcome flowers of spring but it can be a weed in (especially shady and damp) gardens. A plant of partial shade and damp soils that are moderately base-rich and fertile. The plant completely disappears by

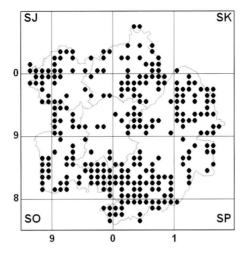

June so it may have been under-recorded, but the map does suggest that it is less common in the industrial heartlands. Many records are to species level only and this hides the distribution of our two native subspecies, **subsp. *verna*** and **subsp. *fertilis*** (Lawalrée ex Laegaard) Stace, (*Ranunculus ficaria* subsp. *ficaria*) both of which are thought to be present throughout our area. Subsp. *fertilis* is the commoner subspecies, which lacks tubers ('bulbils') in the leaf axils after flowering. Subsp. *fertilis* was specified on the recording sheet. Ass: *Anemone nemorosa, Bellis perennis, Cardamine flexuosa, Poa trivialis.*

### *Ficaria verna* Huds. **subsp. *verna***
(*Ranunculus ficaria* subsp. *bulbilifer* Lambinon)

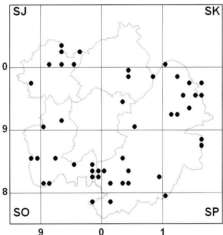

47. Native, but it is possible that these records include **subsp. *ficariiformis*** (F.W. Schultz) B. Walln., which is a similar garden escape. Subsp. *verna* is thought by Stace to be less tolerant of open conditions than subsp. *fertilis*, but it has also been suggested (Preston *et al.* 2002) that subsp. *verna* is more tolerant of disturbed situations. The map is unlikely to be a complete picture of the distribution of subsp. *verna*, but it does suggest that it is even more concentrated in the periphery

of the conurbation than the species as a whole. Also a record for tetrad SO99Z.

### *Myosurus minimus* L.
### Mousetail

0. Native or alien. An annual of seasonally flooded, disturbed land. Extinct in B&BC; there is a single record from Amphlett & Rea (1909) from the Harborne reservoir (SP0383, Garner, 1863).

### *Aquilegia vulgaris* L.
### Columbine

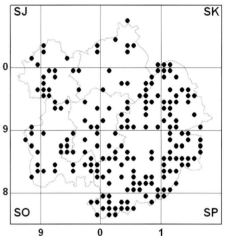

195. Native, but appearing to be entirely a garden escape in B&BC. A herbaceous perennial, found mainly in situations marginal to gardens: pavement cracks, road verges, allotments, churchyards, waste land, scrub, plantations and the occasional wall, mainly but not exclusively in residential areas. Grows in partial shade or in the open on moist to dry soils of intermediate base and nutrient status. Records may include some garden hybrids. Ass: *Anisantha sterilis, Epilobium montanum, Geranium robertianum, Hedera helix, Lamium album, Poa annua, Rubus fruticosus* agg.*, Senecio jacobaea, Veronica agrestis.*

▲ *Aquilegia vulgaris*

## *Thalictrum flavum* L.
### Common Meadow-rue

3. Native. Ax. A rhizomatous perennial, in the UK generally found as part of tall herb communities in old, wet, rather base-rich meadows and mires. Flood-plain meadow by the River Cole (SP154876, CRP, 2001) and at two places in the Sandwell Valley: scattered in the marsh at the RSPB Reserve (SP0392, MWP, 2003); in a ditch in the River Tame flood meadow (SP02719355, CRP, ICT, J. Miskin, M. Mansell, T. Hill, L. Copplestone & P. Shirley, 2011). There are further older records from the River Cole floodplain (SP136882 and SP155879, CW, 1990), also from Rotton Park reservoir (SP043867, Natural England files, 1986, seen again by CRP in 1990) and from Sheepwash Lane Urban Park (SO973921, P.L. Harris & JJB, 1987). Also another old record from Oxley sidings in W'ton (SJ905011, CW, PWS & JJB, 1989). Together these suggest a remnant of a natural presence in our area, plus some more casual occurrences. In 1972 Edees had a record for it from SP09G, which might be a Sandwell Valley record.

## *Thalictrum minus* L.
### Lesser Meadow-rue

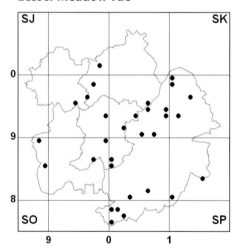

31. Native, but a garden relic or escape in B&BC. A perennial found on waste ground (post-housing), in pavement, canal towpaths, graveyards, allotments and in one instance the mortar on top of a wall. It can be very persistent, even in rough grassland. Grows in well-lit places on dry to moist soils that are base-rich and not very fertile.

## *Thalictrum speciosissimum* L.
### Dusky or Yellow Meadow-rue

1. Neophyte. A few plants recorded from a derelict site in Furlong Lane, Cradley (SO943847, MWP, 2003), seen again in 2004. No records in Clement &

Foster (1994) or Preston *et al.* (2002). SW Europe.

## 33. PLATANACEAE

### *Platanus* × *hispanica* Mill. ex Münchh.
(*P. occidentalis* L. × *P. orientalis* L.)
### London Plane

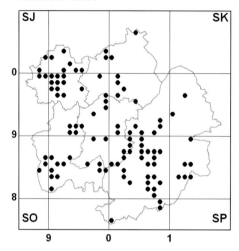

*103. All records appear to be of planted trees. There is no mention of seedlings, which one might expect from this fully fertile hybrid and which are reported elsewhere. Planted trees referred to as *Platanus orientalis* L. have been recorded by the then vc. 39 Recorder, BRF, from Regis School (SO874999, BRF, 1995) and in a garden by the Tettenhall Road (SO905987, BRF, 1990) and as planted in West Park (SO9099, B. Pugh, 1996).

## 34. BUXACEAE

### *Buxus sempervirens* L.
### Box

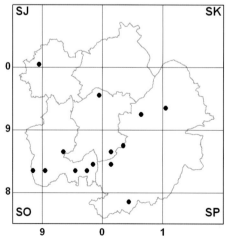

14. Introduced native. Evergreen shrub. The few records refer to planted specimens in parks and churchyards or garden plants persisting on post-housing sites where originally planted.

## 36. PAEONIACEAE

### *Paeonia officinalis* L.
### Garden Peony

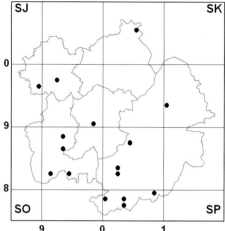

16. Neophyte. A perennial herb with a few B&BC records from waste land and old gardens, where if left undisturbed, it may persist for many years. S Europe.

## 37. GROSSULARIACEAE

### *Ribes rubrum* L.
### Red Currant

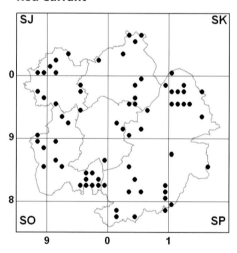

*72. Native or Alien. Widespread shrub, probably mostly a bird-sown introduction from cultivation. In river corridors, damp scrub and woodland but there are often extensive, low-growing patches in old, damp dingle woodland which appear to be part of the native flora. Europe.

### *Ribes spicatum* E. Robson
### Downy Currant

0. Native. Shrub. There are old records of this species from Alder Coppice (SO911948, by CRP & ST, 1986 and from the same place by J. Andrews, 1987, presumably an introduction) which have not been relocated.

## *Ribes nigrum* L.
## Black Currant

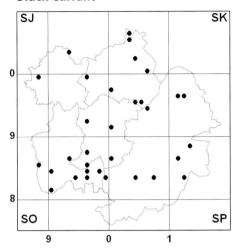

*32. Neophyte. Shrub. A widespread, bird-sown introduction in woodlands, sewage works, waste land, etc., and occasionally persisting from original plantings. Not really common, and less common than *R. rubrum*. Europe.

## *Ribes sanguineum* Pursh
## Flowering Currant

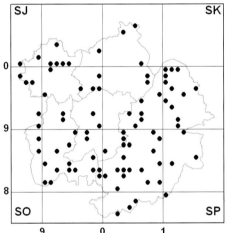

90. Neophyte. Shrub. Garden relic and throw-out, sometimes self-sown. Flowering in early spring. Road, canal and railway cuttings, hedgerows, edges of woodland, waste ground. Well-drained and moderately fertile soils. Also tetrad SO99A. W N America.

## *Ribes odoratum* H.L. Wendl.
## Buffalo Currant

2. Neophyte. Shrub. Current records from Lifford (SP058802, JWP, 1995) and Quinton (SO994853, WAT, 2001), the latter self-sown. There is also an old record: more or less naturalised in a hedge by a canal towpath, Wordsley (SO891863, BRF, 1987). C USA.

## *Ribes uva-crispa* L.
## Gooseberry, Goosegog

*91. Neophyte. Shrub. Widespread, mainly as

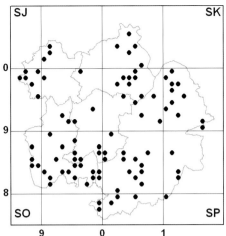

a result of bird sowings, mostly in hedges, scrub and woodlands but occasionally in post-industrial or post-residential waste ground and as a relic of cultivation around allotments and gardens. In moist or fairly dry, well-drained and moderately fertile soils. Europe.

## 38. SAXIFRAGACEAE

## *Bergenia crassifolia* (L.) Fritsch
## Elephant-ears

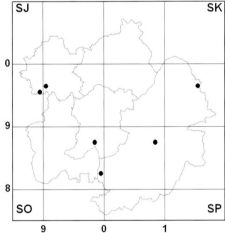

6. Neophyte. Rhizomatous perennial herb. A few records as a garden throw-out persisting on waste land. Siberia.

## *Bergenia cordifolia* (Haw.) Sternb.
## Heart-leaved Elephant-ears

1. Neophyte. Rhizomatous perennial herb. Grounds of Beacon View (SK063006, SMP, 2009). Old record, under trees by a canal towpath at Wordsley (SO8986, FGB, 1976). Garden escape. Siberia.

## *Bergenia × schmidtii* (Regel) Silva Tar.
(*Bergenia crassifolia × ciliata* (Haw.) Sternb.)
2. Neophyte. Recorded from wasteland along the A41, Sandwell Valley (SP021904, MWP, 1997), and in a grassy driveway behind houses, South Yardley (SP137857, MWP, ICT & PLR, 2006).

## *Darmera peltata* (Torrey ex Benth.) Voss ex Post & Kuntze
## Indian-rhubarb

1. Neophyte. Rhizomatous perennial herb. Margins of overgrown canal fragment, Great Bridge (SO977924, ICT, MWP, JaH & SJC, 2007). W USA.

## *Saxifraga × urbium* D.A. Webb
(*Saxifraga umbrosa* L. × *spathularis* Brot.)
## Londonpride

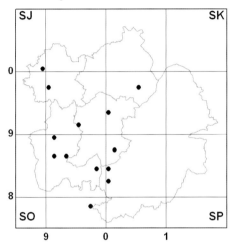

13. Neophyte. Stoloniferous perennial herb. A relic of cultivation in churchyards and cemeteries, sometimes escaping into hedgerows and (usually shady) waste land in the margins of gardens and occasionally naturalising in woodlands. Possibly declining: there were more records in the W in the 1980s and early 1990s. Garden origin.

## *Saxifraga granulata* L.
## Meadow Saxifrage

0. Native. Only old records: the most recent is: "Lineside, N Stourbridge Junction station" (SO909835, MES, 1988), refound in 1989 as on "ballast and thin soil at edge of track, sidings NE of Stourbridge Junction station" (SO909836, ST, 1989). Bagnall's record from Sutton Park in 1879 (SP098974) has also not been re-found.

## *Saxifraga hypnoides* L. hybrids
## Mossy Saxifrages

3. Native, but our records are of Garden Mossy Saxifrages (c.f. *Saxifraga × arendsii* hort., complex hybrids with *S. rosacea* Moench and other species) and are neophytes discarded from gardens or relics of planting. Pathside, along Orchard Close, Rowley Regis (SO965873, MWP & M. Goodby, 1998); neglected grave, Overend, Cradley (SO942842, WAT & CBW, 2001) bank of disused railway track, Netherton (SO951893, MWP & M. Goodby 2005). Garden origin.

## Saxifraga tridactylites L.
### Rue-leaved Saxifrage
2. Native. There is a diffuse population at Stourbridge Junction Railway Station: "large colony by railway track, N of Stourbridge Junction" (SO910836, MES, 1997) "frequent at southern end of Stourbridge Town platform" (SO909832, JJD, 2001). Recently it has appeared nearby on the kerb of a car park driveway, Heath Lane (SO904833, PLR, B. Westwood, 2009). It is a winter annual of drought-liable base-rich pockets of soil associated with calcareous rocks, sands and walls.

## Chrysosplenium oppositifolium L.
### Opposite-leaved Golden-saxifrage

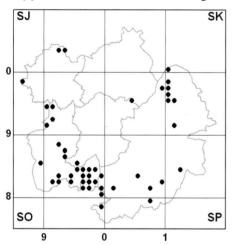

*47. Native. Ax. Perennial herb. In reliably moist (usually flushed) places in old woodlands, typically part of the field layer on moderately fertile and moderately base-poor to base-rich organic or siliceous soils in Alder woodlands. It can form extensive carpets in the spring but it may become hidden beneath taller forbs such as *Filipendula ulmaria*, *Epilobium hirsutum*, *Urtica dioica* and even *Impatiens glandulifera* later in the summer. Only really frequent in the Halesowen area, the map marks out the old dingle woodlands in the periphery of the conurbation. The relative absence from the dingle woods of Walsall is unexplained. Ass: *Alnus glutinosa*, *Caltha palustris*, *Cardamine amara*, *Cardamine flexuosa*, *Carex remota*, *Urtica dioica*.

## Chrysosplenium alternifolium L.
### Alternate-leaved Golden-saxifrage
1. Native. Perennial herb. This species seems to have very similar habitat requirements to *C. oppositifolium*, possibly preferring richer and less acid substrates. The two species often grow together, but *C. alternifolium* is generally scarcer. It is almost absent from the conurbation, occurring in the extreme S of the conurbation in oak-dominated woodland in the River Rea corridor

(Balaams Wood) (SO995784, P. Moore, 2001). In the past it has been recorded in Sutton Park SP0997, Bagnall, 1875), with an unvalidated record from Holly Wood, Queslett (SP0594, J. Little, 1988/9).

## Heuchera sanguinea Engelm.
### Coralbells

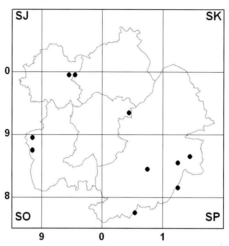

10. Neophyte. Several records as a garden escape, usually encroaching on to pavements, paths and waste ground. N America.

## Tellima grandiflora (Pursh) Douglas ex Lindl.
### Fringecups

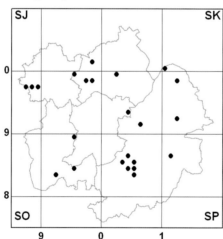

23. Neophyte. Perennial herb. An increasing and quite widespread garden escape, mostly found quite close to the garden origin in both shaded and open habitats but spreading (apparently by seed) from dumped material in several old woodlands including Marnell Drive (SO8997), Hill Hook (SK1000) and Rough Wood (SJ9801). Favoured by damp conditions, often close to streams. W N America.

## 39. CRASSULACEAE

### Crassula helmsii (Kirk) Cockayne
#### New Zealand Pigmyweed
28. Neophyte. Sch. 9 (invasive). Perennial

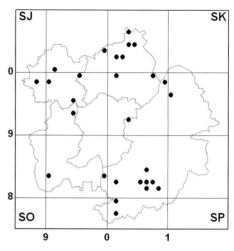

herb, quite widespread but apparently not common in large or small, still waterbodies, growing in draw-down zones and shallow water where it can become very abundant and often dominant. It is usually introduced with other aquatic plants in pond creation, or discarded into pools by aquarists, and it was still being sold in garden centres well into the present decade. No doubt also spread to new pools by birds and anglers (and possibly botanists). Recorded in lakes, ponds, ditches, wet hollows in fields, it is probably present in many small garden ponds not accessible to recorders. It seems to be favoured by clean, rather acid water but will grow in a wide range of substrates. Attempts at control, e.g. with herbicides, are usually not successful. First record in our area is by BRF in 1968 in his own garden in Tettenhall (SJ873002) but the next record was in 1988. Australia & New Zealand.

### Sempervivum tectorum L.
#### House-leek
0. Neophyte. Succulent evergreen perennial herb. Not encountered in the present survey, but Cadbury et al. (1971) suggest it might once have been recorded on walls and roofs in Sheldon (SP1584). C & S Europe.

### Sedum rosea (L.) Scop.
#### Roseroot
1. Native. Waste ground by hedge, residential area, presumed garden escape, Norton (SO885823, APD, 2003).

### Sedum praealtum A. DC.
#### Greater Mexican-stonecrop
1. Neophyte. Evergreen shrub, reported from a shaded footpath verge, Cot Lane Wordsley (SO884877, CBW, 2007). Mexico.

### Sedum spectabile Boreau
#### Butterfly Stonecrop
31. Neophyte. Perennial herb. A garden

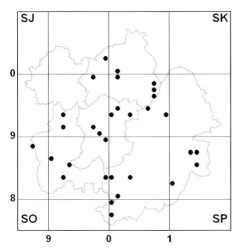

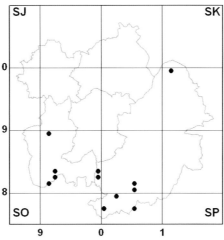

▲ *Chrysosplenium oppositifolium*

outcast in a wide range of habitats from post-industrial derelict land to woodland; most often observed in waste land at the 'rough grassland' stage of colonisation where it forms tight clumps within the sward. Many records are probably relics of cultivation in graveyards, gardens of demolished housing etc. Not usually in base- or nutrient-poor soils, although often in rubbly substrates or in cracks in concrete or pavements. Korea & Manchuria.

### *Sedum* 'Herbstfreude'
(*S. spectabile* × S. *telephium*)
**Autumn Stonecrop**

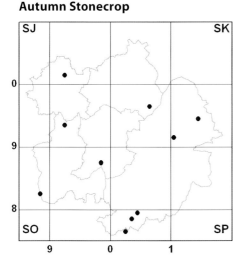

10. Plants referable to cultivar 'Herbstfreude' have not been consistently distinguished from *Sedum spectabile* but do occur in our area in a similar range of habitats e.g. in SJ1494, SP0276, SP0696, SP1091 and SP1494. Garden origin.

### *Sedum telephium* L.
**Orpine**

12. Native. Perennial herb. Only as a garden outcast in our area; usually small clumps in woodland, scrub or rough grassland and frequently recorded

as a casual. More commonly in the S in vc. 37.

### *Sedum kamtschaticum* Mast.
**Kamchatka Stonecrop**

1. Neophyte. Self-sown pavement weed, Yardley Wood (SP103805, CBW, 1998). E Asia.

### *Sedum spathulifolium* Hook.
**Colorado Stonecrop**

2. Neophyte. Naturalised all over a front garden in Sedgley (SO920935, MWP, 1997) and extending into pavement cracks from a garden border, New Oscott (SP098947, MWP, ICT & JaH, 2006). N America.

### *Sedum spurium* M. Bieb.
**Caucasian-stonecrop**

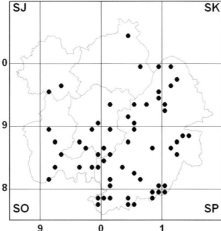

60. Neophyte. Perennial herb. Probably always a relic of or discard from garden cultivation, and not uncommon, although records are fewer in the N and W. Habitats include post-housing and post-industrial sites, abandoned quarries, heaps of rubble and soil, churchyards, urban concrete, but many records are just outside gardens. Mostly on dry, stony, base-rich and nutrient-poor substrates, often in some shade.

▲ *Tellima grandiflora*

▲ *Sedum spectabile*

## Sedum rupestre L.
## Reflexed Stonecrop

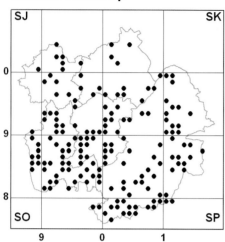

170. Neophyte. Perennial herb. Moderately common throughout as a garden escape, typically in residential areas in pavement cracks, at the foot of walls, in roof gutters (suggesting spread by seed?) and in graveyards but also in post-residential and post-industrial waste ground. Sometimes in quite shady garden hedgebanks but typically in very dry exposed situations. It is possible that we have been more willing to record it in marginal situations, but nevertheless it appears to have become much commoner in our area in the late 20th c.; Edees (1972) had only old records and Cadbury *et al.* (1971) none in the conurbation. Europe. Ass: *Aira caryophyllea, Aira praecox, Hedera helix, Hieracium* spp., *Hypochaeris radicata, Galium album, Sedum album, Taraxacum* spp., *Tragopogon pratensis, Urtica dioica.*

## Sedum forsterianum Sm.
## Rock Stonecrop

2. Native. Nationally Scarce perennial herb. Recorded on a wall in a residential area of Selly Oak (SP039823, WAT, 1998). Doubtless an escape from cultivation. A record from Pensnett High Street (SO912891, J. Whittock, 2007) has not been validated.

## Sedum acre L.
## Biting Stonecrop

*154. Native. Perennial herb. Often, but not always, an obvious escape from cultivation on gravestones, cracks in pavement and other habitats in garden margins in residential areas. Also in a variety of other drought-liable situations: old quarries, gravelly banks, building rubble, open grassland on blast-furnace spoil, blast-furnace clinker, usually on nutrient-poor and base-rich substrates and only producing large stands in relatively stable,

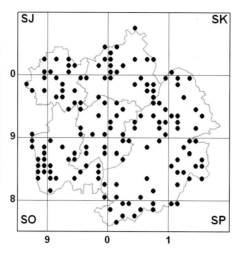

undisturbed sites. Seems to be more frequent, or at least more frequently recorded, than in either Edees (1972) or Cadbury *et al.* (1971). Ass: *Aira caryophyllea, Cymbalaria muralis, Erophila* sp., *Veronica arvensis.*

## Sedum sexangulare L.
## Tasteless Stonecrop

1. Neophyte. Unmetalled drive, Goldthorn Hill (SO916966, CBW, 2008). Also known from Lion Farm Estate, Oldbury, established on bare waste ground behind gardens (SO979885, WAT, 1992) but not found in 2001, feared lost.

## Sedum album L.
## White Stonecrop

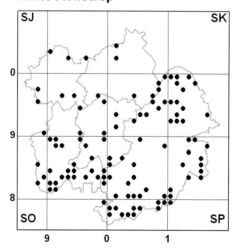

110. Neophyte. Perennial herb. Usually a clear escape from cultivation: small patches in cracks and edges of pavements, and other dry situations close to gardens, also in graveyards; occasionally more well established, e.g. on the Rowley Hills (SO9688). On nutrient-poor and base-medium to rich substrates. Europe. Ass: *Arabidopsis thaliana, Cardamine hirsuta, Epilobium obscurum, Festuca rubra, Veronica arvensis.*

## 40. HALORAGACEAE

## *Myriophyllum aquaticum* (Vell.) Verdc.
## Parrot's-feather

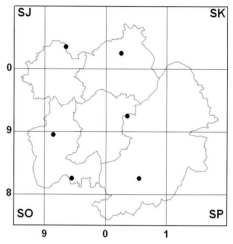

6. Neophyte. Sch. 9 (invasive). Emergent and submerged aquatic; once established, emergent masses can lead to total surface coverage within a very short space of time. First found in vc. 39 as three patches in the Daw End Branch canal, Aldridge (SK042060, JPM, 1990), also seen in the same canal at Clayhanger (SK045045, ICT, 1992, gone by 2008) and the Wyrley & Essington Canal at Rough Wood (SJ986005, ICT, 1992), but currently very few records, all for plants in small pools and almost certainly arising from deliberate introductions from garden ponds. S America.

## *Myriophyllum spicatum* L.
## Spiked Water-milfoil

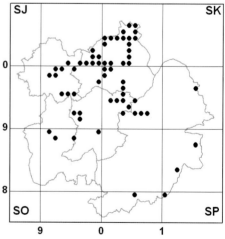

*62. Native. An aquatic perennial herb mainly confined to the Black Country canal network and a few base-rich ponds. Often the only submerged aquatic in canals subjected to periodic eutrophication, but clearly quite scarce in the more-navigated canals of B'ham & Dudley. Ass: *Ceratophyllum demersum, Elodea nuttallii, Potamogeton crispus, Potamogeton pectinatus.*

*Myriophyllum alterniflorum* DC.
**Alternate Water-milfoil**
1. Native. Recorded in the canal behind Walsall Art Gallery (SP0098, CBW, 2002). Also old records from Sutton Park (SP0997, Bagnall, 1876; SP0995 & 0998, Readett, 1971), last seen in Little Bracebridge Pool (SP0998) *circa* 1981.

## 41. VITACEAE

*Vitis vinifera* L.
**Grape-vine**

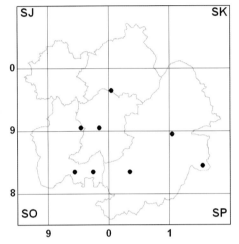

8. Neophyte. A vigorous scrambling, woody climber recorded from a few isolated places where it has become thoroughly naturalised, persisting as a relic of former cultivation or possibly growing from discarded pips. Ripe fruit are seldom if ever produced. Europe.

*Parthenocissus quinquefolia* (L.) Planch.
**Virginia-creeper**

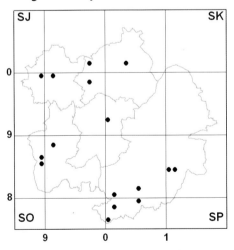

16. Neophyte. Sch. 9 (invasive). A far-reaching perennial climber often planted to screen out garden sheds and fencing and quickly outgrowing its intended purpose. Spreading vigorously from nearby gardens onto canal towpath vegetation, railway banks and rough ground where

it sometimes becomes naturalised. N America.

*Parthenocissus tricuspidata* (Siebold & Zucc.) Planch.
**Boston-ivy**
0. Neophyte. First record in vc. 39 was from a towpath at Wednesfield (SJ9400, FGB, 1975) and also recorded from Wordsley (SO8986, FGB, 1980), but no recent validated records. E Asia.

## 42. FABACEAE

*Robinia pseudoacacia* L.
**False-acacia**

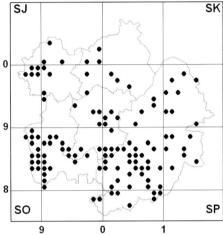

*121. Neophyte. A deciduous tree often planted in parks, estates and larger gardens and thriving in open, rather dryish soils that are not too fertile. Spreading by root-suckers and occasionally seeding into paving and waste ground. The form 'Frisia' has golden leaves remaining gold throughout the summer and many garden plantings are of this. N America.

*Phaseolus coccineus* L.
**Runner Bean**
1. Casual. An extensively grown, frost-sensitive, climbing perennial herb, seldom, if ever, surviving the British winter. One record only for a self-sown plant in abandoned allotment garden. Uplands, Handsworth (SP039909, MWP, 1998). Tropical America.

*Galega officinalis* L.
**Goat's-rue**
30. Neophyte. A perennial herb of irregular occurrence on recently created post-housing and industrial land, overgrown allotment plots, roadsides and railway banks. Sometimes persisting for a season or two when its showy, mauve to purple flowers create an eye-catching display. Competes poorly with more vigorous

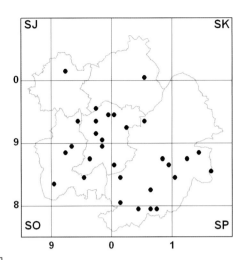

native perennials and populations soon dwindle. Europe.

*Colutea arborescens* L.
**Bladder-senna**
5. Neophyte. Deciduous garden shrub. One self-sown plant on waste ground, Bilston (SO9997, MWP & MHM, 1998); derelict nursery, Warley Park (SP011861, CBW, 1996); school grounds by Woodgate valley (SP013828, CBW, 2000); a few plants along Sneyd Brook, Pleck, Walsall, naturalised from original planting (SO967962, PN, 2001); pavement/fence by Music School, Lawnswood Road Wordsley (SO890870, CBW, 2008). S Europe.

*Onobrychis viciifolia* Scop.
**Sainfoin**

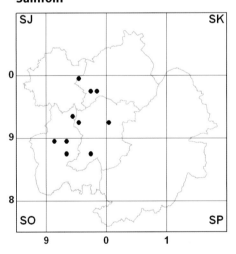

10. Native or alien. (alien with us). Perennial herb. Appearing, apparently only in the Black Country, infrequently on waste ground and at the side of tracks, where it may have been introduced as a grass-seed contaminant or constituent of a wild flower mix. Seldom persisting for more than a season or two.

*Anthyllis vulneraria* L.
**Kidney Vetch**
44. Native. Ax. A perennial herb of sharply

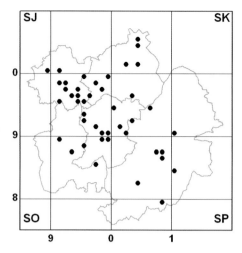

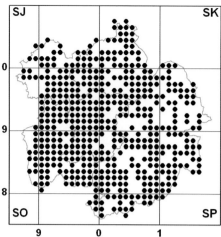

drained, open habitats in infertile soils such as those found on railway sidings and sunny banks and also appearing in waste and disturbed ground, sometimes deriving from grass-seed and wild flower mixes. Tends to be short-lived and erratic in its appearances but some colonies remain relatively stable. Ass: *Cytisus scoparius*, *Equisetum arvense*, *Medicago lupulina*, *Plantago lanceolata*, *Trifolium arvense*, *Trifolium dubium*.

Most records are for the agg. species and probably relate to the native **subsp. vulneraria**, but two introduced subspecies from Europe have been reliably recorded: **subsp. *carpatica*** (Pant.) Nyman **var. *pseudovulneraria*** (Sagorski) Cullen (SO995899 & SO994900, WAT, 2003) and **subsp. *polyphylla*** (DC.) Nyman (SO9298, 2007, SO9999, 2006 & SJ9100, 2004, SO98E, 2011, all JEH).

### *Dorycnium hirsutum* (L.) Ser.
### Hairy Canary Clover
1. Neophyte. A ground-covering sub-shrub with soft silver-grey foliage. One flowering specimen in pavement at base of outside garden wall, Jayshaw Avenue, Great Barr, B'ham (SP047938, MWP, 2005). Mediterranean region.

### *Lotus tenuis* Waldst. & Kit. ex Willd. (*L. glaber* Mill.)
### Narrow-leaved Bird's-foot-trefoil
2. Native. Sporadic occurrence. The only recent reliable records are from E of Colehall Lane (SP145879, CBW, 1997), and more recently frequent on a wasteland site by Moor Street Queensway, B'ham city centre (SP074869, MWP, 2011).

### *Lotus corniculatus* L.
### Common Bird's-foot-trefoil
*500. Native/alien. A generally well-distributed perennial herb of open, dryish places in soils that are more or less infertile and not too acidic. Frequent in roughish grassland, disturbed ground, old railway

track beds, canal towpaths and along road verges. Ass: *Agrostis capillaris*, *Festuca rubra*, *Hypochaeris radicata*, *Plantago lanceolata*.

### *Lotus corniculatus* var. *sativus* Hyl.

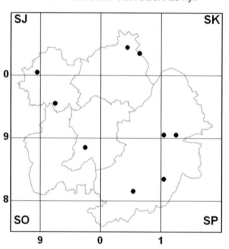

9. Neophyte. These alien genotypes introduced in seed mixtures have not been consistently separated from native populations in this survey, but 9 records are mapped. Europe?

### *Lotus pedunculatus* Cav.
### Greater Bird's-foot-trefoil

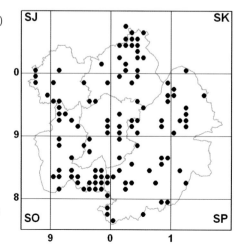

*116. Native. Ax. A perennial herb of open situations; typically in constantly moist grassy places and around the margins of lakes, ponds and ditches, on soils ranging from neutral to moderately acid. Mostly (although not exclusively) in old habitats. Ass: *Deschampsia cespitosa*, *Holcus lanatus*, *Juncus effusus*, *Juncus inflexus*, *Galium palustre*.

### *Ornithopus perpusillus* L.
### Bird's-foot

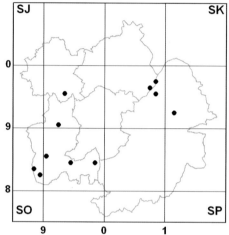

11. Native. Ax. A winter-germinating annual with a few widely scattered records in open, fairly bare grassland on freely draining, drought-liable slopes in heathland and acid grassland, also found in bare areas along the margins of amenity-sown lawns and paths in a few areas, where it is quick to colonise bare ground recently treated with glyphosate herbicide (e.g. at Homer Hill Recreation Gardens, Cradley, SO940849, MWP & ICT, 2008; Stourbridge Cemetery, SO886836, ICT & P. James, 2009), also rarely on blast furnace spoil. There are 1990 records (all by WAT, and probably still extant) for this species in SO8982 (Stourbridge Golf Course); SO8882 (Catholic Cemetery, Norton); SO8984 (Wollaston) and SO9081 (Pedmore). Ass: *Aira praecox*, *Anagallis arvensis*, *Aphanes arvensis*, *Erophila* sp., *Festuca ovina*, *Pilosella officinarum*, *Rumex acetosella*, *Trifolium dubium*, *Viola arvensis*.

### *Securigera varia* (L.) Lassen
### Crown Vetch
3. Neophyte. A deep rooted perennial herb of grassy waste places. Spreading patches in tall grassland between RSPB Centre and marsh, Sandwell Valley where it has persisted since its introduction in an acid-grassland mix in the 1980s (SP0392, MWP & MHM, 2001); locally abundant on bank and roadside within the grounds of Powertrain, Rednal, B'ham (SP009759, MWP, 2003); one plant in patch of rough

ground, The Flatts, Darlaston (SO985973, MWP, 2001). Europe.

### Scorpiurus muricatus L.
### Caterpillar-plant
0. Casual. Bird-seed-/wool-alien, appeared in a Smethwick garden (SP010885, C.F. Mansell, 1989).

### Vicia cracca L.
### Tufted Vetch

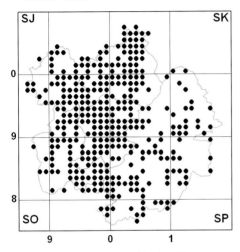

*348. Native. A perennial herb of frequent occurrence in scrubby grassland, moist meadows, old railway tracks, canal towpaths, hedgebanks, roadbanks and waste ground and showing a preference for open to partially shaded sites, in soils of intermediate fertility that remain moist for much of the year. Apparently considerably commoner in the Black Country than in B'ham. Ass: *Arrhenatherum elatius*, *Centaurea nigra*, *Lathyrus pratensis*, *Stellarea graminea*, *Stellaria holostea*.

### Vicia tenuifolia Roth
### Fine-leaved Vetch

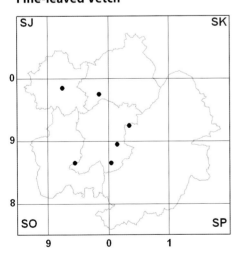

6. Neophyte. A scrambling, climbing, perennial herb similar in appearance to *Vicia cracca*. The few scattered records are for individual plants or small colonies growing

in scrubby grassland and banks in unmanaged sites, sometimes partially shaded. Europe. Ass: *Agrostis capillaris*, *Chamerion angustifolium*, *Galium aparine*, *Urtica dioica*.

### Vicia villosa Roth
### Fodder Vetch
2. Neophyte. A usually casual annual in B&BC; in rough grass, Broadwell Road, Oldbury (SO993897, WAT, 2003) and demolition area off Willenhall Road W'ton (SO939984, ICT & EVJC, 2004). There are scattered earlier records. Europe.

### Vicia hirsuta (L.) Gray
### Hairy Tare

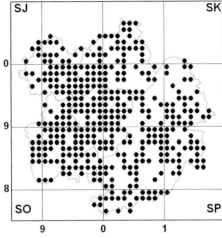

*396. Native. A common to locally abundant, scrambling annual of fairly fertile soils in occasionally disturbed, fairly open situations such as rough, unmanaged grassland, recently created post-industrial and housing land, banks of canals and railways. Also a weed of disturbed ground in allotments and gardens. Ass: *Arrhenatherum elatius*, *Dactylis glomerata*, *Equisetum arvense*, *Medicago lupulina*, *Vicia sativa* subsp. *segetalis*.

### Vicia tetrasperma (L.) Schreb.
### Smooth Tare

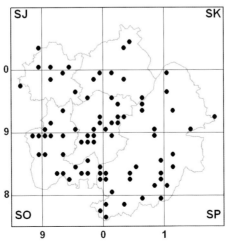

82. Native. Ax. Rough and disturbed ground in similar situations to *Vicia hirsuta* and occasionally growing mixed in with it but generally much scarcer and absent from many areas; possibly in relatively less disturbed and weedy situations. Not uncommon in uncultivated and overgrown allotment gardens. Ass: *Arrhenatherum elatius*, *Dactylis glomerata*, *Equisetum arvense*, *Festuca rubra*, *Medicago lupulina*, *Papaver rhoeas*, *Rumex acetosa*, *Urtica dioica*, *Veronica agrestis*, *Veronica hederifolia*, *Vicia hirsuta*.

*Vicia tetrasperma* (by Sue Nicholls)

### Vicia sepium L.
### Bush Vetch

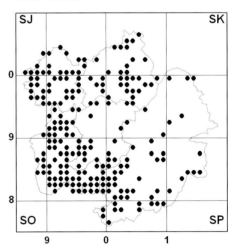

*219. Native. Scrambling perennial herb of rough, unmanaged, grassy places in open to lightly shaded sites and neutral or basic soils. Of common occurrence on hedge banks, woodland margins, in scrubby meadows, roadside, railway and canal banks. Generally well-distributed in suitable habitats throughout but clearly commonest in the Black Country and especially in the SW. Ass: *Alliaria petiolata*,

*Anthriscus sylvestris, Arrhenatherum elatius, Galium aparine, Veronica chamaedrys.*

### Vicia pannonica Crantz
### Hungarian Vetch

0. Casual. There are some old records for this species: waste ground, Bilston, four plants (SO945964, BRF, det. EJC, 1977); waste ground between Fens Pool and Simons Engineering (SO923889, ST, 1991).

### Vicia hybrida L.
### Hairy Yellow-vetch

0. Casual. Old record: four plants, Bilston (SO945964, BRF, det. G.A. Matthews, 1977).

### Vicia sativa L.
### Common Vetch

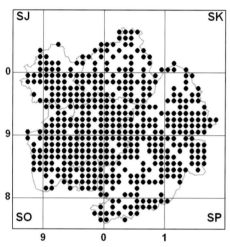

499. Plants of a wide range of fairly fertile soils in situations which are little cultivated, cut or grazed. The three subspecies have different habitats:

### Vicia sativa subsp. nigra (L.) Ehrh.

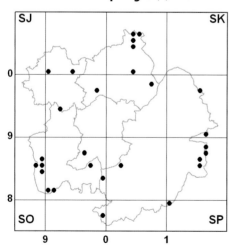

28. Native. A weakly climbing, scrambling or procumbent annual of natural and semi-natural open grassland on banks and slopes, in sunny, well-drained, fairly infertile soils. Not always recorded separately from subsp. *segetalis* but

generally considered rather infrequent due to the scarcity of suitable habitats in most of the built-up area and therefore found mainly in the periphery of B&BC. Also tetrad SO99A.

### Vicia sativa subsp. segetalis (Thuill.) Gaudin

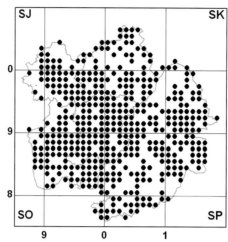

*459. Archaeophyte. A scrambling to weakly climbing annual of rough, grassy, open areas subjected to occasional disturbance, such as grass verges, roadside banks, field margins and woodland edges. Also regularly occurring on post-housing and industrial sites and margins of disturbance in allotment gardens. Tolerating a wide range of moisture and nutrient levels avoiding only the most acid soils. Ass: *Arrhenatherum elatius, Equisetum arvense, Galium aparine, Medicago lupulina, Vicia cracca, Vicia hirsuta.*

### Vicia sativa subsp. sativa

2. Archaeophyte. A robust annual formerly cultivated as a fodder crop and believed to be now almost absent from B&BC. One plant in waste ground, Cofton Park (SP002765, JJD, 1999); wildflower meadow, Woodgate Valley (SO994830, JJD, 2003). There are further records, which are probably mainly confusions with subsp. *segetalis*, and have not been accepted.

### Vicia bithynica (L.) L.
### Bithynian Vetch

1. Native. VU and a Nationally Scarce annual. A sizeable colony growing on a rubble strewn clay bank facing E into main quarry, Brick Kiln, Shelfield, Walsall (SK040024-5, L. Wilson & B. Hedley, 2004). Still there in 2007. Status uncertain but unlikely to be native in B&BC. Ass: *Helminthotheca echioides, Holcus lanatus, Tussilago farfara.*

### Vicia faba L.
### Broad Bean

4. Casual. Appearing rarely from cultivation as odd plants on spoil heaps,

waste ground and post-housing sites (SJ9004, SK1100, SP1082, SP1595). Origin uncertain.

### Lens culinaris Medik.
### Lentil

2. Casual. Two modern records. One plant on grassy verge, Clay Lane, Hall Green (SP130846, MWP & ICT, 2007); A few plants scattered over several metres in disturbed ground on the former site of Yardley Green Hospital, Yardley Green Road, Bordesley Green (SP115862, MWP, T. Oliver & L. Worledge, 2008). SW Asia.

### Lathyrus linifolius (Reichard) Bässler
### Bitter-vetch

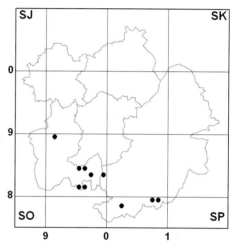

10. Native. Ax. An erect perennial herb of rather rare occurrence in a few undisturbed meadows, grassy banks and woodland margins in moist, infertile and moderately acidic soils mainly in the more rural and southern parts of the conurbation and largely absent from much of the urban area. Ass: *Achillea ptarmica, Agrimonia eupatoria, Carex flacca, Centaurea nigra, Festuca rubra, Filipendula ulmaria, Holcus mollis, Juncus inflexus, Potentilla erecta, Potentilla sterilis, Succisa pratensis.*

### Lathyrus pratensis L.
### Meadow Vetchling

*358. Native. A rhizomatous perennial herb more frequently encountered in unimproved and semi-improved grassland and grassy roadside, railway and canal banks and less commonly from disturbed ground in the more built-up areas. It spreads vigorously by rhizomes and considerable-sized populations occur in soils that are neutral and not excessively fertile (but not usually infertile) and moist but not very damp. Discouraged by heavy grazing or frequent mowing and more typical of undermanaged grassland being invaded

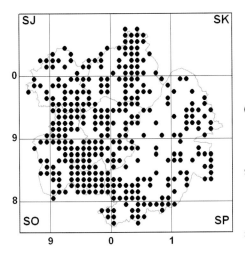

by scrub. Recorded from about half of the
1km squares in B&BC. Ass: *Arrhenatherum
elatius, Centaurea nigra, Cynosurus cristatus,
Dactylis glomerata, Ranunculus acris,
Ranunculus repens*.

### *Lathyrus grandiflorus* Sm.
### Two-flowered Everlasting-pea

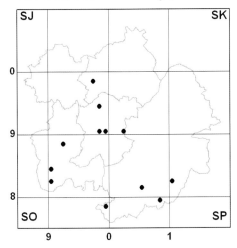

12. Neophyte. A climbing or scrambling
perennial herb well established as a relic
of cultivation and escaping into hedges
surrounding allotment gardens, roadside
banks and along a cemetery boundary
fence. Seldom reproducing from seed
but long-persisting and spreading
vigorously from a deep-rooted tuber. C
Mediterranean.

### *Lathyrus sylvestris* L.
### Narrow-leaved Everlasting-pea
4. Native, but with only a few, relatively
small and short-lived populations in B&BC.
Valley Park railway, W'ton (SJ896004,
R. Fussell & F. McCullagh, 1997); waste
ground, Newbridge (SJ897006, JVT, 2000);
Stourbridge Canal towpath (SO906864,
APD, 2002); Tansey Green claypit, Pensnett
(SO910896, AMG, 2003); Halesowen
Industrial Estate (SO971847, WAT & CBW,
2000).

### *Lathyrus latifolius* L.
### Broad-leaved Everlasting-pea

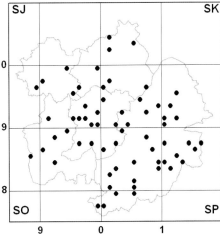

64. Neophyte. A well-naturalised,
scrambling, perennial herb of garden
origin, found in rough grassy places on
canal, railway and roadside banks,
derelict waste ground, margins of tracks
to the rear of houses and overgrown
allotment plots. Long-persisting once
established but generally not far from
habitation. Europe. Ass: *Agrostis
stolonifera, Anthriscus sylvestris, Crataegus
monogyna, Geranium robertianum,
Holcus lanatus, Melissa officinalis, Rubus
fruticosus* agg.

### *Lathyrus odoratus* L.
### Sweet Pea
3. Casual. Records are for odd plants
occurring in a soil heap (SO9887, WAT,
2001), by a canal (SP0397, TM, M. Kodaka,
2002) and in an allotment garden
among a potato crop (SP0193, MWP, 1998).
S Italy.

### *Lathyrus sativus* L.
### Indian Pea
2. Casual. One plant from spoil heap on
forecourt of abandoned petrol filling
station, Stratford Rd, Hall Green, B'ham
(SP103826, MWP, 2007) growing with
*Solanum tuberosum, Vicia faba*, and
*Solanum lycopersicum*. A record from
edge of footpath below dam of Frankley
Reservoir (approx SP002801, J. Clayfield,
2009) may just be in our area.

### *Lathyrus nissolia* L.
### Grass Vetchling
12. Native. Ax. A locally frequent but
easily overlooked annual of unmanaged,
open, grassy fields and tracksides in
moist, neutral soils. Extremely difficult
to detect when not in flower due to its
resemblance to the grasses with which
it grows and possibly under-recorded in
B&BC because of this. Ass: *Arrhenatherum*

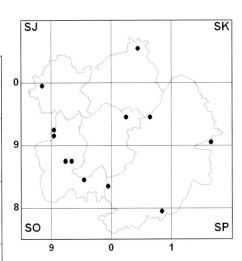

*elatius, Holcus lanatus, Ophrys apifera,
Vicia sativa*.

### *Lathyrus aphaca* L.
### Yellow Vetchling
1? Native or alien. VU and a Nationally
Scarce annual. At most a casual with us.
A patch (50 × 30m) was reported from
the top of a grassy bank in a waste area,
Hurst Lane, Dudley (SO930874, T. Benyon,
1994). A recent consultancy report gives
an unvalidated record: grassland by Asda
Superstore, Oldbury (SO988880, J. Glossop
& N. Betson, 2009).

### *Pisum sativum* L.
### Garden Pea
3. Casual. Isolated plants derived from
cultivation: disturbed soil on central
reservation of road (SO9590, MWP, 1997),
derelict waste ground (SP0886, MWP, 2004)
and abandoned allotment garden (SO9798,
MWP, SJC & JaH, 2003).
S Europe.

### *Cicer arietinum* L.
### Chick Pea
1. Casual. An annual, cultivated in some of
the allotment gardens in B'ham and Black
Country but seldom self-seeding. The
only record is for a few self-sown plants
in disturbed ground on the former site
of Yardley Green Hospital, Yardley Green
Road, Bordesley Green, where a few plants
were recorded growing with *Lens culinaris*.
(SP115862, MWP, T. Oliver & L. Worledge,
2008).

### *Ononis spinosa* L.
### Spiny Restharrow
2. Native, but probably only sporadic
introductions in B&BC. A small, but
well-established colony in clearings
among shrubs on the bank overlooking
a lake to the S of Queslett Road, Queslett
(SP06229434, JEH, 2005); unmown
parkland, Merridale (SO898982, JVT, 2005).

### *Ononis repens* L.
### Common Restharrow

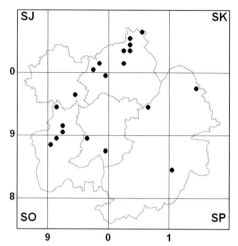

20. Native. Ax. In shortish, well-drained, nutrient-poor and base-rich, species-rich grassland, but also in the marginal grassland and track beds of railway walkways, canal towpaths and amenity sites. In some places it is likely to be a persistent introduction rather than a native plant, possibly being introduced in wildflower mixes as part of habitat-creation schemes or in hay fed to stock. Ass: *Agrimonia eupatoria, Euphrasia* sp., *Odontites vernus, Rubus fruticosus* agg., *Ulex europaeus*.

### *Melilotus altissimus* Thuill.
### Tall Melilot

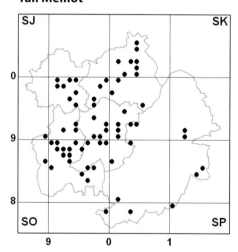

*67. Neophyte. A tall biennial herb forming patches on fairly moist, base-rich, waste ground and land recovering from disturbance where it is sometimes mixed in with populations of *M. officinalis* and *M. albus*. Displaying a higher salt-tolerance than *M. officinalis* and sometimes appearing along roadside verges and central reservations. The map suggests it is much commoner in the Black Country than in B'ham. Europe. Ass: *Artemisia absinthium, Chamerion angustifolium, Malva moschata, Melilotus officinalis, Reseda luteola*.

### *Melilotus albus* Medik.
### White Melilot

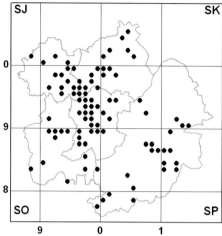

*91. Neophyte. A tall biennial herb of waste and disturbed places and railway sidings, sometimes found with the other tall, yellow-flowered Melilots, usually on well-drained, fairly base-rich and nutrient-poor, stony substrates, especially in the Black Country. Occasionally persisting to form colonies in cracks and crevices along central reservations of major roads where it is apparently moderately salt-tolerant. Europe. Ass: *Artemisia absinthium, Chamerion angustifolium, Epilobium ciliatum, Malva moschata, Medicago lupulina, Reseda luteola*.

### *Melilotus officinalis* (L.) Pall.
### Ribbed Melilot

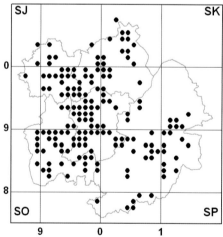

*168. Neophyte. The commoner of the two tall, yellow-flowering, biennial Melilots and often abundant on dry or fairly moist, fairly nutrient- and base-rich soil on waste ground recovering from recent disturbance, often forming a very tall, dense, continuous vegetation a few years after land is cleared. Sometimes growing alongside *M. altissimus*. Europe. Ass: *Artemisia absinthium, Chamerion angustifolium,*

*Malva moschata, Melilotus altissimus, Reseda luteola*.

### *Melilotus indicus* (L.) All.
### Small Melilot

2. Neophyte. Annual. Rarely recorded, as a casual, in situations suggesting introduction: Centre of the Earth garden centre (SP045881, G. Peake & AS, 1997); Three Crowns Special School grounds, Walsall (SP045979, AB, 2007). S Europe.

### *Trigonella foenum-graecum* L.
### Fenugreek

5. Casual. Annual. Self-sown plants in margins of allotment gardens near to original sowings at: Sandwell (SP031910, MWP, 1997); Holford Drive (SP072915, MWP, 2005); Uplands (SP0390, MWP, ICT, JaH, SJC & V. Lawrie, 2008); Woden Road, Wednesbury (SO9994, MWP, 2008); Kenrick Park Allotments (SP0190, MWP, 2008). E Mediterranean.

### *Medicago lupulina* L.
### Black Medick

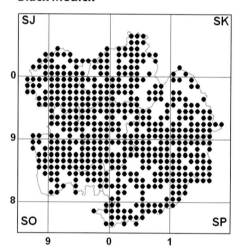

*532. Native. A very common to locally abundant annual or short-lived perennial herb of disturbed and waste ground, roadside verges, canal towpaths, disused railway tracks and garden borders and lawns in open, dryish, fairly infertile to moderately fertile, neutral or weakly basic soil. Slightly less common in the older suburbs. Ass: *Plantago lanceolata, Plantago major, Ranunculus repens, Trifolium pratense, Trifolium repens*.

### *Medicago sativa* L.
### subsp. *falcata* (L.) Arcang.
### Sickle Medick

0. Native. A Nationally Scarce perennial. Only old records, as a casual: one plant in rough ground on top of bank, Darby End, Dudley (SO956878, MWP & LG, conf. BRF, 1985); Great Bridge to West Bromwich railway (SO985925, JJB, A. Black & TCH, 1987).

### *Medicago sativa* L.
### **nothosubsp. *varia*** (Martyn) Arcang.
### **Sand Lucerne**

1. A hybrid between subsp. *falcata* and subsp. *sativa*, occurring spontaneously and also as an escape from cultivation. Recorded on waste ground at Monmore, W'ton (SO9397, PN, 1995).

### *Medicago sativa* L. **subsp. *sativa***
### **Lucerne**

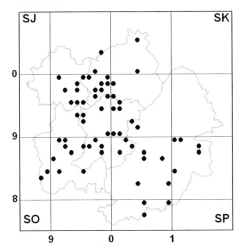

*64. Neophyte. A persistent colonist of grassy field margins, canal towpaths and recently created brownfield habitats, in open, well-drained sites that are not too fertile. Originally cultivated as a fodder crop and sometimes also included in grass-seed or wild flower mixes used in habitat creation schemes. Rather commoner in the Black Country than in B'ham. Mediterranean.

### *Medicago arabica* (L.) Huds.
### **Spotted Medick**

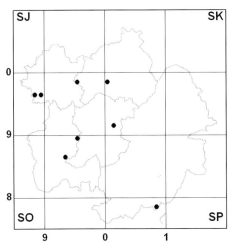

8. Introduced native. There are a few records for this procumbent to scrambling annual of colonies appearing in mown grassland along road verges and patches growing on rubble piles and house demolition sites in a few well-scattered locations. The BSBI Atlas (Preston *et al.* 2002) shows that this species is increasing in the Midlands, N of its main native range, possibly as a response to climate change. It is however not clear whether it usually exists here as a short-lived casual, although it has been present (and spreading) in its site in grass verges at SO893962 from first being noticed in 1999 to 2012. Ass: *Erodium cicutarium, Lolium perenne, Trifolium repens, Veronica chamaedrys.*

### *Trifolium repens* L.
### **White Clover**

*694. Native. The most commonly occurring clover in B&BC, recorded from all but the wettest and most acid or impoverished soils. It is tolerant of regular mowing and trampling and is one of the chief constituents of amenity grassland but is also common in pasture. Also found on disturbed and waste ground, in gardens, paths and paving but competing less well in taller grassland. Ass: *Achillea millefolium, Bellis perennis, Festuca rubra, Lolium perenne, Plantago lanceolata, Plantago major, Scorzoneroides autumnalis, Trifolium dubium, Trifolium pratense.*

### *Trifolium hybridum* L.
### **Alsike Clover**

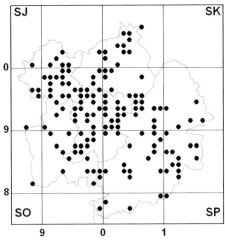

*150. Neophyte. An annual of frequent occurrence in grassy places along roadsides and on waste ground recovering from disturbance. Some of the records are for likely introductions in grass-seed mixes but although probably not persisting well in closed communities it appears to be quite well-established as a spontaneous colonist in rich or poor, dry or moist soils. Europe. Ass: *Agrostis stolonifera, Dactylis glomerata, Lolium perenne, Leucanthemum vulgare, Phleum pratense, Poa trivialis, Ranunculus repens, Sonchus asper.*

No attempt has been made to separate the cultivated neophyte subsp. *hybridum* from the native subsp. *elegans* (Savi) Asch. & Graebn.

### *Trifolium resupinatum* L.
### **Reversed Clover**

0. Neophyte. Old record of eight plants, edge of footpath, Park Lime Pits, Walsall (SP030999, JPM, 1991), with *Trifolium incarnatum*, probably from bird seed.

### *Trifolium campestre* Schreb.
### **Hop Trefoil**

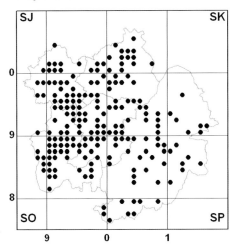

*199. Native. A winter-germinating annual of frequent occurrence in dry, sandy or stony, neutral and base-rich soils of intermediate fertility, such as those found on post-industrial land, furnace spoil, railway sidings, quarries and bare areas along canal towpaths, particularly in the Black Country. Considerably less common than *Trifolium dubium* but sometimes with it. Ass: *Centaurium erythraea, Erigeron acris, Hypericum perforatum, Medicago lupulina, Trifolium dubium, Trisetum flavescens.*

▲ *Trifolium campestre*

## Trifolium dubium Sibth.
### Lesser Trefoil

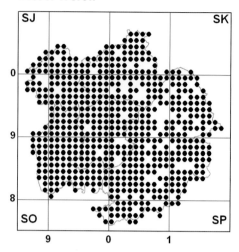

*608. Native. A very common winter-germinating annual found in a wide range of well-drained soil types and often abundant in lawns and amenity grassland kept short by mowing. Also a colonist of bare areas on post-housing and industrial land in open, sunny, moisture-retaining soils, but out-competed among taller vegetation. Ass: *Agrostis stolonifera, Bellis perennis, Festuca rubra, Geranium molle, Scorzoneroides autumnalis, Poa annua, Trifolium repens.*

## Trifolium micranthum Viv.
### Slender Trefoil

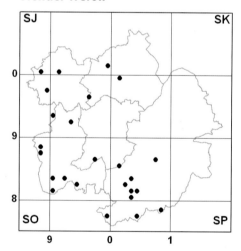

25. Native. Ax. Most records are for plants occurring in short, regularly maintained or trampled grassland on roadside verges and in amenity grassland where it often grows with *Trifolium dubium* and is easily overlooked. A more natural habitat is for plants occurring in short limestone grassland at the foot of the quarry at Wren's Nest NNR, Dudley, and it is almost always found in dry, fairly base-rich and nutrient-poor soils. Recorded from Sutton Park (SP1095) in Readett (1971). Ass: *Bellis perennis, Pilosella officinarum, Trifolium*

*campestre, Trifolium dubium, Trifolium repens.*

## Trifolium pratense L.
### Red Clover

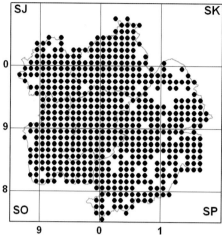

*603. Native. A perennial herb found in all but the most acidic or nutrient-poor soils but favoured by base- and nutrient-rich, moist, loamy soils and consistent management as meadow or pasture. Frequent in most non-acid grassland types and also a weed of waste and disturbed ground where it is often locally abundant. Selected variants are regularly included in grass mixes and some records might be for these; there is a single canal-side record for the agriculturally selected **var. sativum** Schreb. (SP054794, D. Broughton, 1997) but it is probably quite common. Ass: *Festuca rubra, Hypochaeris radicata, Lathyrus pratensis, Lolium perenne, Lotus corniculatus, Phleum pratense, Ranunculus acris, Trifolium repens.*

## Trifolium medium L.
### Zigzag Clover

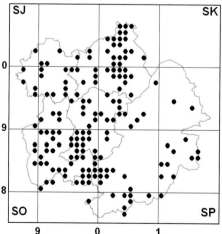

*165. Native. Ax. A rhizomatous perennial herb of medium to heavy, neutral to weakly basic, fairly dry soils. Of regular occurrence in roughish, unmanaged grassland on

railway and roadside banks, along canal towpaths and railway walkways and occasionally on more recently created post-housing and industrial sites in the Black Country, it is relatively uncommon in B'ham. It sometimes forms large patches, several metres across, and seems to be favoured in quite steeply sloping, fairly open but little-managed situations and disfavoured in tall, dense vegetation. Ass: *Centaurea nigra, Festuca rubra, Galium verum, Holcus lanatus, Potentilla reptans.*

## Trifolium incarnatum L.
### subsp. incarnatum
### Crimson Clover

1. Neophyte. Annual. Locally abundant in small area of grassland at the side of a path, the Cracker, N of Owen Street station, Tipton (SO953929, MWP, 1997, reappearing the following year but not seen since). Also old record from edge of footpath, Park Lime Pits, Walsall, probably from birdseed (SP030999, JPM, 1991). S Europe.

## Trifolium striatum L.
### Knotted Clover

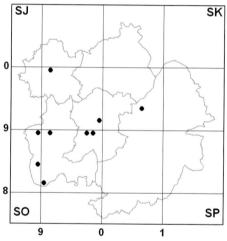

9. Native. Ax. Few records, from open vegetation on shallow, drought-liable, base-intermediate and often nutrient-poor soils. Well established in a small section of open, well-drained, sparsely vegetated, salt-splashed central reservation along Wolverhampton Road, Round's Green (SO980892, MWP & ICT, 2007); 30+ plants on traveller spoil, Wattle Street, Greets Green (SO991915, MWP, 2004). Other records are for a quarry, waste ground, playing fields and several road verges. Ass: *Geranium pusillum, Lolium perenne, Plantago lanceolata, Trifolium arvense, Trifolium repens.*

## Trifolium arvense L.
### Hare's-foot Clover

*132. Native. Ax. An annual pioneer species of open, sunny, well-drained situations in

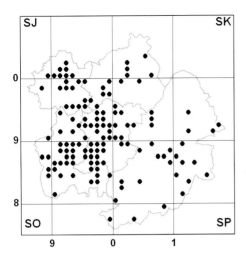

*Trifolium arvense* (by Sue Nicholls)

## Lupinus arboreus Sims
**Tree Lupin**

5. Neophyte. A distinctive, short-lived, semi-evergreen shrub recorded rarely (but sometimes in large populations) from post-housing land, post-industrial land and landfill sites in sunny, well-drained, low fertility conditions. Not likely to persist (frost-sensitive) but several populations have been quite long-lived and it could appear anywhere by virtue of its copiously produced long-lived seed. Bumble Hole (SO952882, R. Lester, 1995); two places S of Sandwell & Dudley station (SO992900, JJD, AWR, MWP & PLR, 2005); reclaimed land, West Bromwich (SP003927, MWP, 1997); post-housing site, Ley Hill Farm Road,

Frankley (SP0180, MWP, 2003); landfill site, Queslett (SP065943, SB, 2002). California.

## Lupinus × regalis Bergmans
(*L. arboreus* × *L. polyphyllus* Lindl.)
**Russell Lupin**

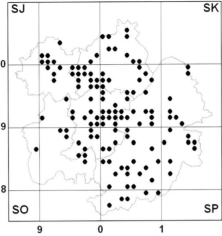

*130. Neophyte. A persistent escape that has become well-naturalised in many places. A coloniser of rough ground, railway sidings, roadside and canal banks, overgrown gardens and abandoned allotment plots in open, sunny sites. Flowering spikes are mainly blue in wild populations but pink, white and bi-coloured flowers are not uncommon. Records for *Lupinus polyphyllus* are all believed to refer to this. Garden origin. Ass: *Arrhenatherum elatius*, *Artemisia absinthium*, *Artemisia vulgaris*, *Calystegia sylvatica*, *Trifolium pratense*.

## Laburnum anagyroides Medik.
**Laburnum**

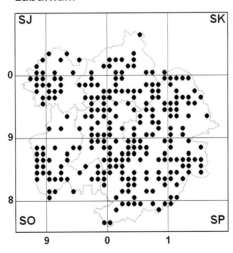

*261. Neophyte. Small tree, regularly grown in gardens and long persisting on post-housing sites when left undisturbed. In some years seeding is prolific and many seedlings appear in gardens, on waste and disturbed ground, in paving and paths. Many of the records are for

these and few survive to maturity. SC Europe.

## Laburnum × wateri (Wettst.) Dippel
(*L. anagyroides* × *L. alpinum*)
**Hybrid Laburnum**

1. Neophyte. Small tree. Planted in a car park, Hall Street, Willenhall (SO9698, BRF, 1995). Now the most commonly planted Laburnum, but apparently largely sterile. Wild European and garden origin.

## Laburnum alpinum (Mill.) J. Presl.
**Scottish Laburnum**

0. Neophyte. Tree, very similar to *L. anagyroides* and only rarely recorded but may be overlooked. One old record from waste land to the N of Stetchford Station (SP125875, CBW, conf. RM & WAT, 1989). SC Europe.

## Cytisus multiflorus (L'Her.) Sweet
**White Broom**

0. Neophyte. Shrub. Several recorded on waste ground, N side of railway, Stafford Road, W'ton (SJ912003, BRF, 1993), not seen within our recording period. Iberian Peninsula.

## Cytisus striatus (Hill) Rothm.
**Hairy-fruited Broom**

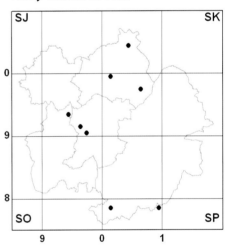

8. Neophyte. Shrub. A few records for possible self-sown plants from original plantings along roadside and canal banks, also in some quantity on Barr Beacon (SP0697).

## Cytisus scoparius (L.) Link
**Broom**

*438. Native. Shrub. Open aspects on heaths, banks of canals, roads and railway, waste ground and margins of woodland in stony and sandy, base-poor and nutrient-poor soils which are dry or fairly moist. It acts as a pioneer in the formation of scrub, especially after fire, but the individual bush tends to be short-lived and it is

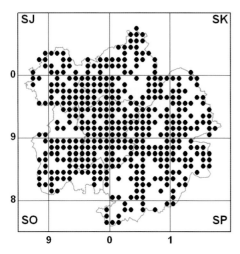

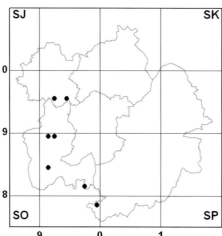

out-competed by other species as the scrub develops. Many plants in B&BC have red-tinged flowers suggesting origin as, or hybridisation with, garden cultivars. The Doomsday Book of 1086 refers to West Bromwich as "The little village on the heath of broom" which suggests it was very common at that time and has remained so to this day. Ass: *Betula pendula*, *Calluna vulgaris*, *Crataegus monogyna*, *Pinus sylvestris*, *Rubus fruticosus* agg., *Ulex europaeus*, *Ulex galli*.

### *Spartium junceum* L.
### Spanish Broom

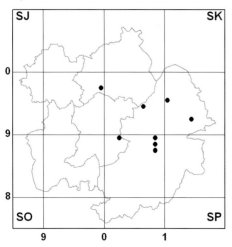

8. Neophyte. Long-flowering and occasionally self-sown on bits of waste land and roadside banks near to the original introductions. There is a fine stand in Birch scrub by the main railway line a mile E of B'ham New Street station (SP0887). Mediterranean.

### *Genista tinctoria* L.
### Dyer's Greenweed

7. Native. Ax. A small deciduous shrub absent from most of the conurbation but of rare occurrence in unimproved grassland in Lower Illey meadows and very few other outlying sites where its

native status is sometimes doubtful. Two populations at Springvale (SO9295) were definitely deliberate introductions but are well established since 1985, still present 2012. A large population on Barrow Hill, Pensnett (SO9189) was largely lost in housing and hospital developments in the 1990s. Ass: *Achillea millefolium*, *Centaurea nigra*, *Dactylis glomerata*, *Hypochaeris radicata*, *Lotus corniculatus*, *Plantago lanceolata*, *Senecio jacobaea*.

### *Genista anglica* L.
### Petty Whin

0. Native. Bagnall listed it for Sutton Park in 1877–8.

### *Genista hispanica* L.
### Spanish Gorse

1. Neophyte. Three small self-sown plants in roadside gutter on area of post-housing land recovering from recent disturbance. Western corner of Ley Hill Farm Road, Frankley (SP009801, MWP, 2003). SW Europe.

### *Ulex europaeus* L.
### Gorse

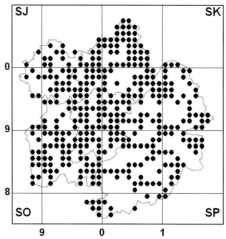

*371. Native. A shrub of infertile, mildly to moderately base-poor soils in open to partially shaded situations and much less

demanding in its soil requirements than *U. gallii*. Often acting as a first colonist in scrub formation in poorly managed grassland, coal spoil and spoil from open-cast coal mining, especially after fire, and regenerating well from seed after being burnt. Sometimes occurring in great abundance on canal, railway and roadside banks and also appearing in small colonies or in isolation on disturbed and waste ground and by roadsides. Ass: *Betula pendula*, *Calluna vulgaris*, *Cytisus scoparius*, *Pteridium aquilinum*, *Ulex gallii*.

### *Ulex gallii* Planch.
### Western Gorse

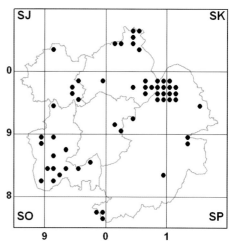

*57. Native. Ax. Most abundant on the very infertile, acidic, dry to moist soils of Sutton Park where it is common to locally dominant in sunny, open situations, often forming a well-marked community growing with *Calluna vulgaris*. There are further scattered records for plants in scrubby grassland in quarries (there has been a large population in the steep sides of Doulton's Clay Pit at Saltwells LNR – SO9387 – for many years) and on base-poor hillsides but it is generally quite an uncommon plant absent from most of the urban area. Also tetrad SO99A. Ass: *Betula pendula*, *Calluna vulgaris*, *Cytisus scoparius*, *Ulex europaeus*.

### *Arachis hypogaea* L.
### Ground-nut

2. Casual. Annual, rarely germinating from bird seed etc. Recorded twice by roads in Warley. Opposite Grove Road (SP009861, CBW, 1996); Abbey Crescent (SP006859, CBW, 1998). Brazil.

### 43. POLYGALACEAE

### *Polygala vulgaris* L.
### Common Milkwort

6. Native. Ax. A perennial herb of short, more or less infertile, old, base-rich to

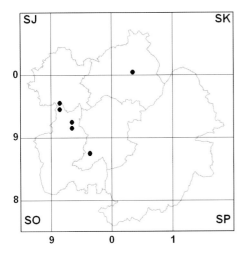

base-intermediate hillside grassland. Very occasionally in base-rich marshes. Recorded only rarely during the survey period. Locally frequent only perhaps on banks and slopes in Beacon Hill quarry (SO919949, E. McKay, 1998) and surrounding pastures (SO918957, ICT & C. Osborn, 2004). Also present at Wren's Nest (SO936920, ST, 1997, seen again 2007; SO935917–9, APD, 2004, seen again 2007); extensive along the plateau, Daw End railway cutting, Walsall (SK034002, DH, 2000); reported from quarried land E of Brickhouse Road, Rowley Regis (SO965875, MWP, LG, 1998) where the site has since scrubbed over and it has not been seen recently. There are one or two older records from more ruderal situations: a single plant from canal towpath, Bradley Arm Canal, Moorcroft Wood, Moxley (SO971950, DH, 1989) and also from the nearby (and now re-developed) Patent Shaft Steelworks site (SO975950, D. Vallance, TCH & A. Jervis, 1986). Readett (1971) reported it from Sutton Park as occasional from railway banks, and in grassland and marshes (SP0898, SP0998). Ass: *Brachypodium sylvaticum, Briza media, Bromopsis erecta, Leontodon hispidus, Linum catharticum*.

## Polygala serpyllifolia Hosé
### Heath Milkwort
1. Native. Recently found on a *Calluna*-vegetated coal spoil tip in fields W of Brownhills Common (SK032062, ICT & SAHA, 2010). This species, which grows in open situations in wet to dry acid grassland and heath, has been recorded in the past in Sutton Park (SP0991, Readett, 1971; SP0997, Bagnall, 1872) and may still be there. Some old records of *Polygala vulgaris* from Sutton Park could also be *P. serpyllifolia*. There is a further old record as locally common in damp grassland in the Woodgate Valley Country Park (SO998834, JJD, 1988) and another (A. Homer, 1987) from SO98 tetrad

A (possibly Wychbury Hill?). The reasons for the virtual absence of this species in our area are puzzling; it is present in all the surrounding counties and will grow on suitable secondary habitats e.g. heath on coal spoil mounds in Telford (vc. 40). Ass: *Agrostis capillaris, Calluna vulgaris, Festuca ovina*.

## 44. ROSACEAE

### Sorbaria sorbifolia (L.) A. Braun
### Sorbaria
1. Neophyte. Shrub. Several plants in mortar of old brick wall, Icknield Port Road (SP046871, MWP, 2006). N Asia.

### Sorbaria tomentosa (Lindl.) Rehder
### Himalayan Sorbaria
2. Neophyte. Shrub. Planted or introduced at two sites in Sheepwash Urban Park (SO976921, 1998; SO976919, 1998; both MWP). W Himalayas.

### Sorbaria kirilowii (Regel) Maxim.
### Chinese Sorbaria
1. Neophyte. Shrub. Several self-set plants, some quite large, from an original planting in a shrubbery to the rear of Hollyhurst Road, Bannersgate (SP088953, MWP, JMP, JaH, 2006). China.

### Spiraea sp.
### Brideworts

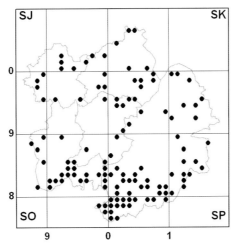

121. Neophytes. Common garden shrubs, widely and vigorously naturalising in waste ground, most likely entirely as garden remnants, throw-outs and by suckering from adjacent gardens. Found in waste ground, playing fields, churchyards and cemeteries, river flood plains, canal corridors, disused railway lines, etc. They are particularly common in hedges and can also form extensive thickets. The group is made up of several species and hybrids which can be difficult to distinguish, therefore maps for individual

segregates should be treated with some caution.

### Spiraea × rosalba Dippel
(*S. salicifolia* L. × *S. alba* Du Roi)
### Intermediate Bridewort
3. Neophyte. Waste land: large thicket near River Cole at Acocks Green (SP100837, CBW, 1996); huge stand off Hole Lane Northfield (SP034803, CBW, 1997); small bush N side of Addingsley Road, likely garden relic (SP034786, JJD, 2006). Garden origin.

### Spiraea × pseudosalicifolia Silverside
(*S. salicifolia* × *S. douglasii*)
### Confused Bridewort

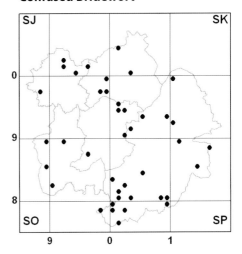

41. Neophyte. A high proportion of our *Spiraea* records are referred to this hybrid which seems to be widespread in our area . However it has been possible to refer some specimens only to "either × *pseudosalicifolia* or × *billardii*" and these have not been included in the map.

### Spiraea × billardii Herincq
(*S. alba* × *S. douglasii*)
### Billard's Bridewort
5. Neophyte. Very similar to *Spiraea × pseudosalicifolia* and possibly sometimes confused with it. However the following records are considered reliable: roadside, Grovelly Lane (SP013766, JJD, 1997); near River Cole, Springfield (SP099817, WAT, 1999); open space Woodgate – Kitwell (SO997820, JJD, 2003); derelict land off Bankfield Road (SO952959, MWP, 2004); large open area between housing and woodland, Streetly (SP079989, JEH, 2007). Also a slightly older record: near the River Rea at Moor Green (SP062824, CBW, 1993). Garden origin.

### Spiraea douglasii Hook.
### Steeple-bush
18. Neophyte. Widespread, but not as common as some of the hybrids. All

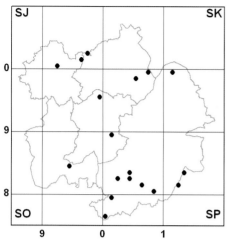

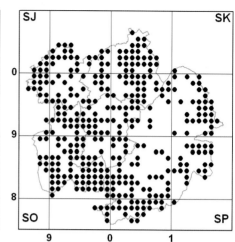

records characterised to subpecies are referred to **subsp. douglasii**. W N America.

### Spiraea japonica L.f.
### Japanese Spiraea

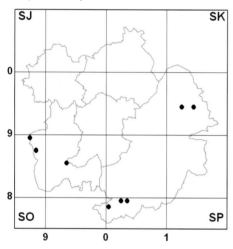

8. Neophyte. Widespread but not common. Some are large bushes but several records are for small plants in pavements and roadside gutters and appear to have seeded from neighbouring gardens. Japan.

### Spiraea × vanhouttei (Briot) Carriere
(*S. cantonensis* Lour. × *S. trilobata* L.)
### Van Houtte's Spiraea

1. Neophyte. Garden relic on post-housing land, Dovedale Road, Perry Common (SP091934, MWP, 2006). Garden origin.

### Aruncus dioicus (Walter) Fernald
### Buck's-beard

2. Neophyte. Perennial herb. Barrow Hill Dudley (SO915895, B. Marsh & N. Williams, 2003) and land at Queslett (SP065943, SB, 2002), also an older record from Beacon Hill, Sedgley (SO922946, P. Wilkinson, 1998). Europe.

### Kerria japonica (L.) DC.
### Kerria

26. Neophyte. A shrub; quite a widespread

garden relic or outcast in waste land, hedges, woodland margins. China & Japan.

### Prunus persica (L.) Batsch
### Peach

3. Neophyte. Cultivated tree recorded rarely as seedling from discarded stone: in River Rea corridor (SP082869, MWP, 2005); trading estate, Kingswinford (SO8989, CBW, 2005); bridleway by Goldthorn Avenue, W'ton (SO9096, CBW, 2006). Tibet and China.

### Prunus cerasifera Ehrh.
### Cherry Plum

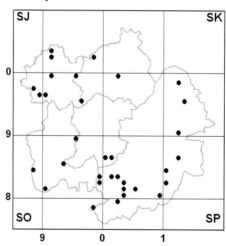

33. Neophyte. Shrub or small tree. Hedgerows, scrub and woodland margins, floodplains, parks, and other public open spaces. Often a relic of planting, currently it seems to be being planted more frequently in landscape schemes, and can spread by suckers and possibly by seeding. There are some records of quite large old shrubs by streams suggesting a preference for rich, moist soils. Because it flowers so early it may be under-recorded in some areas. SE Europe & SW Asia.

### Prunus spinosa L.
### Blackthorn

*369. Native. Strongly suckering shrub. Common except in some central parts of

B&BC, where, according to Edees (1972) and Cadbury *et al.* (1971), it always seems to have been scarcer. A plant of old hedges, woodland margins and forming impenetrable thickets on patches of waste ground if allowed. For this reason it was little used in 18th century enclosure hedges, but it has become a popular component in modern amenity plantings e.g. in 'species-rich hedges'. On moderately to very fertile, base-poor to base-rich, well-drained soils. Ass: *Acer campestre, Corylus avellana, Crataegus monogyna, Sambucus nigra*.

### Prunus × fruticans Weihe
(*P. spinosa* × *P. domestica*)

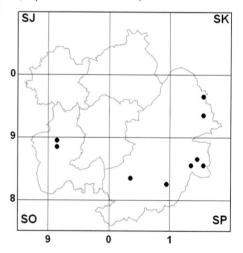

9. Native × alien. Occasionally recorded, sometimes with both parents but sometimes apparently as a relic of deliberate planting, in hedgerows and scrub. Probably quite common but forms an array of fertile intermediates between the parent species so may be recorded as either.

### Prunus domestica L.
### Wild Plum

*177. Archaeophyte. Shrub or small tree. Typically in old hedges and around allotments as a relic of small-scale

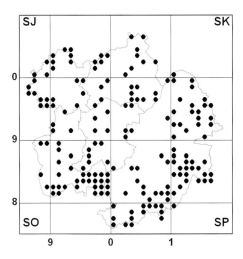

cultivation for the fruit. Appears to persist indefinitely, especially on rich, moist soil. Ass: *Corylus avellana*, *Crataegus monogyna*, *Ligustrum ovalifolium*, *Syringa vulgaris*.

Most records have not been allocated to subspecies and all subspecies records are included in the above map. We have very few records for **subsp. *domestica*** (**Plum**); we have only a single record for **subsp. × *italica*** (Borkh.) Gams ex Hegi (**Greengage**) (SP1492, SPG, 2000). There are 25 records for **subsp. *insititia*** (L.) Bonnier & Layens (**Bullace, Damson**) from across the range of the species, and many of our other records for *P. domestica* probably belong there.

### *Prunus avium* (L.) L.
### Wild Cherry

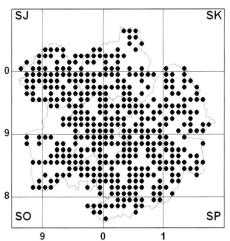

*429. Native. An almost ubiquitous tree in open woodland, scrub, hedgerows, by canals, railways, on amenity land, waste land and marginal habitats on base- and nutrient- medium to rich, fairly moist soils. It makes an excellent, fast-growing and attractively flowering amenity tree and is very widely planted. It seeds vigorously from such plantings. It is however also a component of semi-natural mixed-deciduous woodland and is probably present as such in some of our

old woodlands such as Ashen Coppice (SO9195), Ham Dingle (SO9182), Lutley Gutter (SO9483/4) and the Illey complex (SO9882). Ass: *Betula pendula*, *Fraxinus excelsior*, *Salix caprea*, but occurs with many deciduous trees and shrubs in plantings.

### *Prunus padus* L.
### Bird Cherry

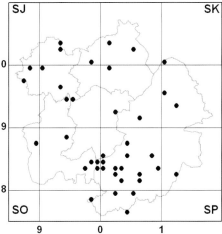

41. Native. Shrub or small tree. On the SE edge of its native range, but most records appear to be introductions. It is quite a common street tree, and many records are clearly seedlings or sucker growth from these in waste land, by railways and canals, or in amenity land. One population most likely to be native is in the old wet dingle woodland at Northycote Farm, W'ton (SJ9302-3) where there are several large thicket-like plants in the understorey under *Alnus glutinosa* and *Salix fragilis*. Even at that site there has been some tree planting in the past. There are also several in wet woodland on the edge of Powells Pool at Sutton Park (SP109954, MWP, ICT & JaH, 2005) and it was also recorded in the Park at SP098974 by Bagnall in 1891.

### *Prunus serotina* Ehrh.
### Rum Cherry

2. Neophyte. Recently discovered scattered across a furnace sand and slag spoil tip at Burnt Tree, Sandwell (SO95689138, 95729150 & 95819142, MWP & ICT, 2011); previously known from the grounds of Moxley Hospital (now Moorcroft Wood, Moxley) in the edge of woodland (SO970950, JPM, 1991), thought lost by 2009 but seen again on edge of the wood by the canal towpath (MWP, PWS & D. Hunt, 2011). E N America.

### *Prunus lusitanica* L.
### Portugese Laurel

15. Neophyte. Quite commonly planted, and many of our records are relics of planting in parks, churchyards, cemeteries,

▲ *Prunus domestica*

▲ *Prunus avium*

▲ *Prunus serotina*

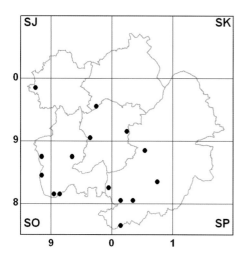

neglected shrubberies etc., but there are also records of seedlings.

## Prunus laurocerasus L.
### Cherry Laurel

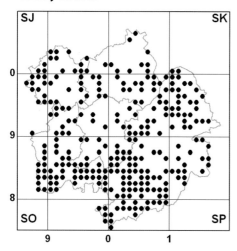

*282. Neophyte. Very widely planted in parks, cemeteries, churchyards, large public and private gardens and spreading from there both as discards and seedlings. Typically in waste and marginal habitats close to plantings, particularly by canals but also found in woodland plantations and in semi-natural woodlands, although rarely a serious threat in such situations. Disfavoured by nutrient- and base-poor soils, and preferring moist or damp conditions. The map suggests that it is particularly frequent in the more mature suburban residential areas. Surprisingly, the first record for vc. 39 was quite recent and just outside our area in 1991, and it was first recorded in vc. 38 in 1954, suggesting a rapid spread in recent years. SE Europe. Ass: *Acer pseudoplatanus*, *Corylus avellana*, *Ilex aquifolium*, *Sambucus nigra*.

There are also a few records of the following species, but probably always only as planted trees: *Prunus serratula* Lindl. (Japanese Cherry); *Prunus dulcis* (Mill.)

D.A. Webb (Almond); *Prunus pissardii* Carriere (Pissard's Plum).

## Chaenomeles speciosa (Sweet) Nakai
### Chinese Quince
5. Neophyte. A few records as a garden discard or possibly bird sown. Warley Woods, bird sown? (SP016858, CBW, 1998); (SP1691, SPG, 2000); Worcester & B'ham Canal (SP056800, PWS & D. Jones, 2002); Baptist Church, Lapal, relic of planting (SO988835, JJD, 2004); development land, Northfield (SP034787, JJD, 2006). China.

## Chaenomeles japonica (Thunb.) Spach
### Japanese Quince
2. Neophyte. Less frequently recorded than *C. speciosa*. Relic of cultivation in St John's churchyard, Wednesbury (SO987947, MWP, 1997); discard or bird sown, Balsall Heath (SP079849, CBW, 1999). Japan.

## Pyrus pyraster (L.) Burgsd.
### Wild Pear
4. Archaeophyte. Shrub or tree, with few records, mostly in old hedges but also in woodland. S side of disused railway bridge, Blakeley Green, Tettenhall (SJ898014, BRF, 1993); Church Walk, end of the churchyard of St. Michael's Church, Tettenhall (SJ891002, BRF, 1995 not found in 2008), Tettenhall College grounds (SO885995, PWS, 2000); Lickey Road, Longbridge (SP000765, JJD, 1999); West Heath recreation grounds (SP034784, JJD, 2006). The last record was identified as subsp. *achras* (Wallr.) Terpó. There are three further tetrad records from vc. 37: SP08K, SP08S & SP18P.

## Pyrus communis L.
### Pear

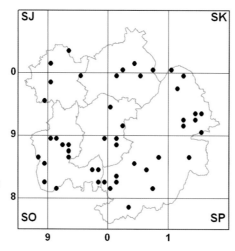

*47. Archaeophyte. Quite widely distributed as a relic of cultivation and possibly regenerating from discarded pips. Map includes plants recorded as *sensu lato* as well as *sensu stricto*.

## Malus sylvestris (L.) Mill.
### Crab Apple

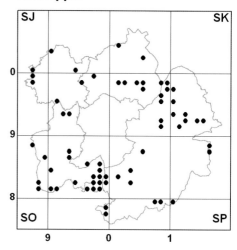

*65. Native. Ax. Mostly in old woodland and old hedgerows, and an indicator for such sites as is suggested by the map, but occasionally in churchyards, cemeteries etc, presumably as a relic of planting. On base- and nutrient-intermediate to rich, dry to damp soils. Also tetrads SJ90A,Q. Ass: *Acer campestre*, *Corylus avellana*, *Fraxinus excelsior*, *Prunus spinosa*, *Quercus robur*. There are also tetrad records for SP07E, J; SP08A, C, D, E, F, K, Q, R, V, W; SP18A, B, C, G, H, I, N.

## Malus pumila Mill. (*Malus domestica* Borkh.)
### Apple

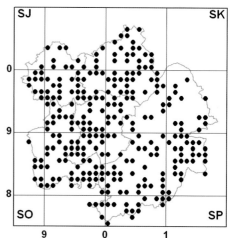

*286. Alien. Widespread as a relic of cultivation and from human-dispersed seeds in hedges, woodland, commons, public open spaces and in waste land especially by railways and canals and in river flood plains. On dry to damp soils with intermediate or high base and nutrient status. Intergrades with *Malus sylvestris*, probably largely as the result of hybridisation, and the map includes some intermediates and plants recorded as *M. sylvestris sensu lato*. Ass: *Acer pseudoplatanus*, *Crataegus monogyna*, *Sambucus nigra*, *Sorbus intermedia*.

***Malus floribunda*** Sieb. ex Van Houtte
**Japanese Crab**
1. Neophyte. Introduced into woodland, Sandwell valley (SP022922, MWP, 1998). Planting of ornamental crabs is common in the conurbation, but although there are many records of '*Malus* sp.', there are no others referred to specific cultivated species or cultivars.

***Sorbus aucuparia*** L.
**Rowan**

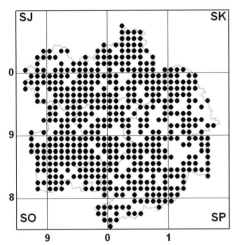

*525. Native. Almost ubiquitous tree; occasionally seeming to be part of the semi-natural woodland flora or as a solitary tree in heathland but usually a relic of planting, or developing from bird-sown seedlings in a wide range of open spaces, waste land and areas marginal to gardens. Found on a wide range of dry to moist, nutrient-poor and base-poor to base-rich soils. Ass: *Betula pendula*, *Crataegus monogyna*, *Ilex aquifolium*, *Ulex europaeus*.

***Sorbus intermedia*** agg.
**Swedish Whitebeam**

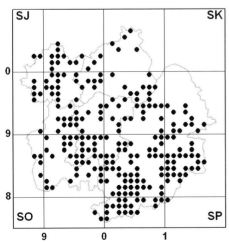

*242. Neophyte. Much planted as a street tree, but very widespread as a bird-sown seedling, sapling and mature tree on a wide variety of waste land, but particularly favouring quite open situations in quarries and other steep slopes on fairly base-rich soils and not often persisting in dense scrub or woodland. A proportion of these records have been specifically for **Sorbus intermedia** (Ehrh.) Pers. but all records are likely to be that microspecies. Baltic region.

***Sorbus aria*** agg.
**Common Whitebeam**

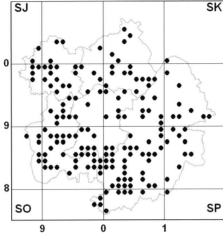

*171. Native. Much planted, and widespread as a bird-sown plant on habitats marginal to parks, cemeteries and gardens, on waste land by roads, canals and railways and in scrub and woodland especially on base-rich soil. Distribution similar to that of *Sorbus intermedia*, with some concentration in suburban areas. A few specimens included within this map, which shows all *Sorbus aria* agg. records, have been referred to **Sorbus aria** (L.) Crantz *sensu stricto* specifically, and almost all are likely to be that microspecies. Some sites have very old records for *Sorbus aria s.s.*, e.g. Sutton Park.

***Sorbus eminens*** E. Warb.
**Round-leaved Whitebeam**
1. Native; thought to be planted here. E.K. Horwood collected a *Sorbus* specimen from Bracebridge Pool, Sutton Park on 7 July 1954 which was noted as of interest by E.F. Warburg but he declined to name it (LTR). Further material was collected from the plantation woodland in June 2005 (SP100980) by JWP and was named as *S. eminens* and *S. aria* with possible hybrids by TCGR (NMW; Rich *et al.* 2010). This record of *S. eminens* is surprising because it is outside the expected range of a rare endemic, and presumably originated from a 'job lot' of nursery material from seed collected in SW England or Wales.

***Sorbus latifolia*** (Lam.) Pers.
**Broad-leaved Whitebeam**
2. Neophyte. Frequently planted, but rarely recorded as an escape. Northfield, possibly planted (SP0279, AEEP, 1999); Woodgate Valley, in grassland by school (SP012832, CBW, 1997). SW Europe.

***Sorbus croceocarpa*** P.D. Sell
**Orange Whitebeam**
1. Neophyte. Frequently planted street tree. Bird sown tree on waste ground, Hasbury (SO954829, AWR, WAT & CBW, 2001). Also reported from the bank of Long Meadow Pool, Moorcroft Wood, Moxley (SO970950, BRF, 1991).

***Sorbus torminalis*** (L.) Crantz
**Wild Service-tree**

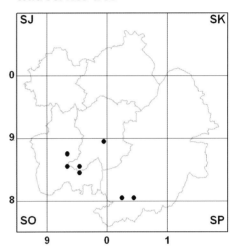

7. Native. Ax. Shrub or small tree of old woodland on base-rich, well-drained or moist, moderately nutrient-rich soils. Very uncommon in our area. Planted by the B'ham canal (SO999899, JJD, AWR & PLR, 2005), but there also appear to be two quite local clusters of records, both of which include possible relics of the natural distribution in ancient woodland and/or ancient hedges. In SO98 it has been known at Codsall Coppice (SO954857, CRP), a fragment of old woodland in Cradley Heath, since at least 1987 and was still present in 1998. It occurs nearby at Corngreaves Golf Course (SO956848, CRP, 1995) and at Mushroom Green (SO931872, J. Akers, 1999), both of which could be fragments of old woodland. Also an old record as a seedling in waste ground at Hawne Colliery workings (SO958848, WAT, 1991). The other cluster is in SP08, with 1996 and 1997 records from an old hedge in Manor Park Farm, Northfield (SP025806, B. Westwood, 1996), also at Rowheath Park, Bournville (SP042803, A. Sames, 2002) and older records: woodland at Sunderton Road (SP073801) in 1985 and 1987. There is also an old record for a third site – an old hedge in Bull's Lane, Over Green (SP151948), last seen in 1990. Ass: *Corylus avellana*, *Hyacinthoides non-scripta*, *Quercus robur*, *Sorbus aucuparia*.

***Sorbus thibetica*** (Cardot) Handel-Mazzetti
1. Alien. Woodgate Valley, by school
(SP012833, CBW, confirmed TCGR, 2000).

*Sorbus hupehensis* C.K. Schneid. (which is
possibly *Sorbus glabriuscula* McAllister) and
Sorbus 'Joseph Rock' have been recorded
as having been planted in West Park, W'ton
(SO9099, B. Pugh, 1996). There are records as
street trees for *Sorbus decipiens* (Bechst.) Irmisch
(SP0379), *Sorbus vilmorinii* Schneid. (SP0279)
and *Sorbus* 'Wilfred Fox' (SP0279), all AEEP
(1999), and *Sorbus* × *thuringiaca* (Ilse) Fritsch
(*S. aucuparia* × *S. aria*) (SP0084, SP0085 &
SP0787, all AS, 1999 & 2002). Himalayas.

***Amelanchier lamarckii*** F.G. Schroed.
**Juneberry**

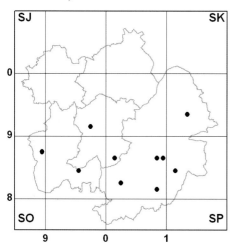

10. Neophyte. A few records from canal
banks, woodland, public open spaces, an
allotment; a relic of cultivation or self- or
bird-sown. N America.

***Cotoneaster* spp.**

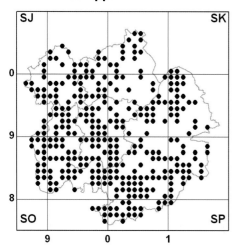

339. Neophytes. Records for 'Cotoneaster
sp.' have been combined with all named
*Cotoneaster* species records in the above
map which shows that this extremely
widely planted group of low shrubs is now
approaching ubiquitous spontaneous status

in B&BC. There were few records (and those
were all named as *Cotoneaster microphyllus*
Wall ex Lidl.) in Edees (1972) or Cadbury *et
al.* (1971) and no *Cotoneaster* records at
all from our area in the first BSBI Atlas
(Perring & Walters 1976). It must however be
acknowledged that modern recorders are
far more likely to record neophytes.

***Cotoneaster frigidus*** Wall. ex Lindl.
**Tree Cotoneaster**
2. Neophyte. A bird-sown juvenile by footpath,
Quarry Park Road, Pedmore (SO900818,
CBW, 2004); one mature tree, possibly
originally planted, Jubilee Mound, Sandwell
Valley (SP024923, MWP, 1998). Himalayas.

***Cotoneaster* × *watereri*** Exell
(*C. frigidus* × *C. salicifolius*)
**Waterer's Cotoneaster**

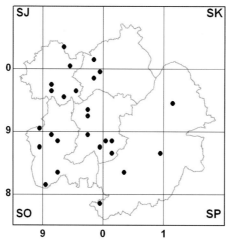

26. Neophyte. Erect, semi-evergreen
shrub or small tree surviving as a relic of
cultivation or bird-sown on waste ground,
along tracksides and fence margins.
Confused with *C. frigidus* but most (if not
all) of the tree cotoneaster records are
believed to be this. Garden origin.

***Cotoneaster salicifolius*** Franch.
**Willow-leaved Cotoneaster**

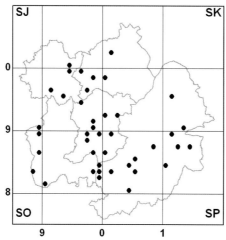

41. Neophyte. A large, arching, evergreen
shrub found on banks, roadsides, light
woodland, sites of dereliction and
occasionally as a relic of planting in shrub
beds. Almost certainly under-recorded in
our area due to immature plants providing
insufficient material for a positive
identication and possible confusion with
similar-looking Cotoneasters. Most
records are considered to be bird-sowings.
W China.

***Cotoneaster lacteus*** W.W. Sm.
**Late Cotoneaster**

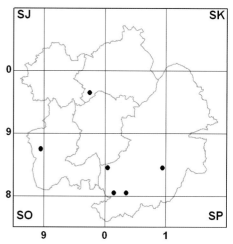

6. Neophyte. A popular late-flowering
garden shrub occurring rarely as bird-sown
individuals in a few scattered sites: back
alley, Ridgacre (SP004844, CBW, 1998); by
brook, Woodlands Park (SP038805, CBW,
1997); seedlings with planted parent, Greet
(SP099841, CBW, 1997); roadside verge
(SO9796, MWP & JaH, 2003); former housing
site (SP0180, MWP, 2003). SW China.

***Cotoneaster integrifolius*** (Roxb.) G. Klotz
**Entire-leaved Cotoneaster**

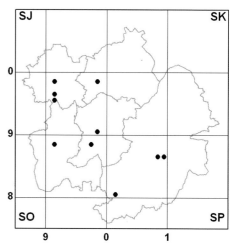

10. Neophyte. Sch. 9 (invasive). Isolated
records (which include four for *C.
microphyllus* agg.) of individuals or few
plants from quarry slope, canal towpath,

edge of factory, school grounds and self-sown from planters. Himalayas to W China.

### *Cotoneaster dammeri* C. Schneid.
### Bearberry Cotoneaster
4. Neophyte. Widely scattered records, established in a slag and ash heap, Vincent Drive (SP042833, MWP, 1997); in paving (SP126851, MWP, ICT & PLR, 2006); on a road verge (SP142918, MWP, JWP, conf. J. Fryer, 2007); and on an abandoned industrial site (SO982908, T. Oliver & MWP, 2009). This species is very similar to its frequently planted hybrid with *C. conspicuus*. Possibly some of these records could be *C. conspicuus* × *C. dammeri*. C China.

### *Cotoneaster* × *suecicus* Klotz
(?*C. conspicuus* × *C. dammeri*)
### Swedish Cotoneaster

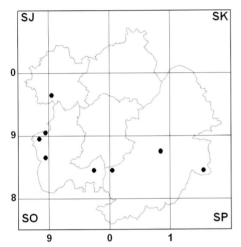

8. Neophyte. A low-growing shrub with long arching stems, often mass-planted on banks and in shrub beds (especially cultivars 'Skogholm' and 'Coral Beauty') as a ground-covering, weed-supressing, evergreen. Rarely surviving as a remnant of an original planting or throw-out in rough ground and on railway banks. Garden origin.

### *Cotoneaster conspicuus* C. Marquand
### Tibetan Cotoneaster
2. Neophyte. A stiffly erect evergreen shrub. Bare ground, Taylor Avenue, Bloxwich (SK009015, SMP & H. Simmons, 2005); self set in front garden outside derelict factories, Castle Vale (SP141917, MWP, JWP, conf. J. Fryer, 2007). Tibet.

### *Cotoneaster simonsii* Baker
### Himalayan Cotoneaster
109. Neophyte. Sch. 9 (invasive). The commonest of the erect, deciduous Cotoneasters, occurring individually or in small groups in scrubby fields, banks, quarries and on waste ground in open and partially shaded sites on soils of

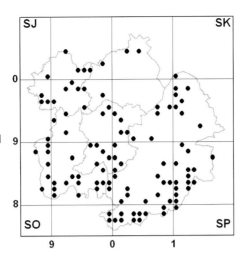

intermediate fertility. Mainly bird-sown. Himalayas.

### *Cotoneaster nanshan* M. Vilm. ex Mottet
### Dwarf Cotoneaster
4. Neophyte. A spreading, deciduous shrub rarely grown in gardens. Self-sown individuals in privet hedge (SP097797, JJD, 2000); in rough grassland (SP061812, JJD, 2001); at the base of wall (SP019781, JJD, 2001); large plant at wall base, Lapal (SO981833, JJD, 2003). W China.

### *Cotoneaster horizontalis* Decne.
### Wall Cotoneaster

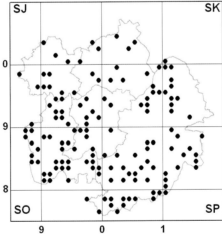

140. Neophyte. Sch. 9 (invasive). Horizontal or arching deciduous shrub well naturalised on sunny drought-liable banks, walls, quarry slopes, railway tracks and occasionally as a pavement weed in the urban area. By far the most frequent of the low-growing Cotoneasters in B&BC, although most of the records are quite recent: the first record for vc. 39 was in 1980 in our area (Wordsley, SO8986, FGB). W China.

### *Cotoneaster hjelmqvistii* Flinck & Hylmö
### Hjelmqvist's Cotoneaster
10. Neophyte. A deciduous, arching, low-

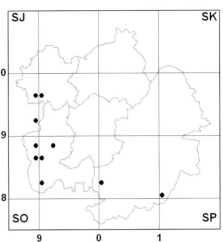

growing shrub. Similar to *C. horizontalis* and possibly overlooked. A record from a disused quarry near Fens Pools (SO923888, JEH, 2004) was the first record for vc. 39. Scattered records, self- or bird-sown under hedges and by paths in residential areas, in a churchyard, an old quarry, a railway track, a pavement crack. W China.

### *Cotoneaster divaricatus* Rehder & E.H. Wilson
### Spreading Cotoneaster

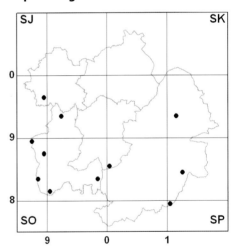

11. Neophyte. A wide-spreading, deciduous, arching shrub with a few confirmed records for individuals appearing on waste ground, a cemetery, a quarry, and hedgesides. All believed to be bird-sown. C China.

### *Cotoneaster bullatus* Bois
### Hollyberry Cotoneaster
19. Neophyte. Sch. 9 (invasive). A large deciduous shrub of uncommon occurrence. Records are mainly for one or few individuals on wooded roadside banks, in hedgerows and quarries, waste ground and secondary woodland. Most, if not all, spread by birds. First record for vc. 39 was from cracks in slabs of a disused railway station, Priestfield, Ettingshall (SO936969,

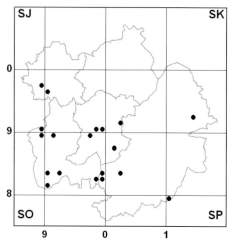

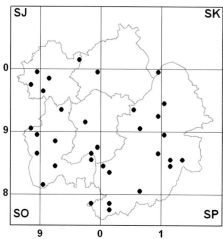

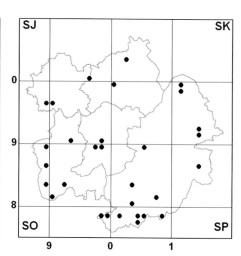

BRF, 1976, det. J.R. Palmer), still there in 1986. W China.

### *Cotoneaster rehderi* Pojark.
### Bullate Cotoneaster

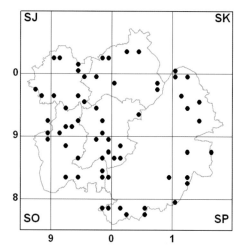

63. Neophyte. A medium to large, deciduous, arching shrub thoroughly naturalised on banks, hedgerows, waste ground and in secondary woodland where it is sometimes locally dominant from repeated bird-sowings. Much commoner than *C. bullatus*, the other medium to large, similar-looking *Cotoneaster* and much more frequent than records suggest due to non-fruiting material being overlooked. First record for vc. 39 was from the end of Wood Lane, Pelsall Common (SK015044, JPM, 1992). W China.

### *Cotoneaster franchetii* Bois
### Franchet's Cotoneaster

33. Neophyte. An arching evergreen shrub, extensively planted in shrubberies for its long-lasting, orange-red berries and evergreen foliage. Appearing spontaneously on walls, roadsides, waste ground and at the base of hedges often close to the original planting. Many immature non-flowering and non-fruiting

plants believed to be this are unrecorded because of possible confusion with *C. dielsianus* and *C. sternianus*. SW China.

### *Cotoneaster mairei* H. Lév.
### Maire's Cotoneaster

1. Neophyte. Erect evergreen shrub resembling *C. franchettii*. Between the rails, disused railway track, Bromley (SO903887, CBW, 2006). S China.

### *Cotoneaster sternianus* (Turrill) Boom
### Stern's Cotoneaster

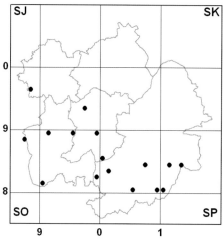

16. Neophyte. A medium-sized evergreen shrub occurring rarely on banks, along tracks and in roughish grassland presumably from bird-sowings. Very few confirmed records have been made as non-flowering material is often disregarded due to possible confusion with *C. franchetii*. SW China.

### *Cotoneaster dielsianus* E. Pritz. ex Diels
### Diels' Cotoneaster

30. Neophyte. An erect, arching, deciduous shrub sometimes persisting where originally planted. Bird-sown individuals are occasionally recorded from walls, pavement, waste ground and wooded banks. Some confusion may arise

with *C. franchetii* but the latter is evergreen. China.

### *Pyracantha* spp.
### Firethorns

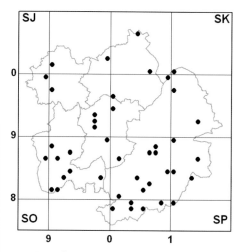

44. Neophytes. Shrubs, found occasionally as relics, discards or self-sown. Many of these records are refered to *P. coccinea* and *P. rogersiana*, which are mapped below.

### *Pyracantha coccinea* M. Roem.
### Firethorn

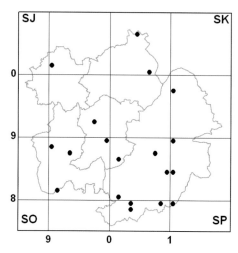

19. Neophyte. Shrub, occasional as a relic, a discard or self-sown, mainly in residential areas marginal to gardens or amenity plantings but also in graveyards, by canals, and on roadside waste land. Europe.

### *Pyracantha rogersiana* (A.B. Jacks.) Coltm.-Rog.
### Asian Firethorn

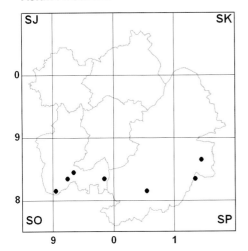

7. Neophyte. Fewer records than *P. coccinea* but there are a further fourteen records for *Pyracantha* sp. which may include this species. It grows in similar habitats and some records are convincingly bird- or self-sown. China.

### *Mespilus germanica* L.
### Medlar

2–3. Archaeophyte. Shrub or small tree, apparently relics of cultivation. Grassland on top of a bank by the M5, Sandwell Valley (SP020917, R. Croucher, 1998); woodland edge, Saltwells Nature Reserve, Dudley (SO931871, J. Akers, 1999). SE Europe.

Several plants in an old plantation, Streetly Road, Upper Whitton (SP097924, ICT & EVJC, 2006) might have been this or possibly a **× *Crataemespilus*** E.G. Camus (*Mespilus* × *Crataegus*) hybrid.

### *Crataegus crus-galli* L.
### Cockspurthorn

4. Neophyte. Relic of planting. Derelict shrubbery in Warley Park (SP010862, CBW, 1996); Warley Park Golf Course (SP011858, CRP, 2002); Friends' Meeting House, Selly Oak (SP040821, J. Osborne, 1998); E of main pool, Moorcroft Wood, Moxley (SO970952, ICT & MWP, 2011); also an old record from Edgbaston Pool (SP055842, D.A. Cadbury, 1935). E N America.

### *Crataegus persimilis* Sarg.
### Broad-leaved Cockspurthorn

4. Neophyte. Relic of planting. Woodland, the Dams, Norman Road, Smethwick (SP007867, MWP, 2001); road verge N side

of Birchfield Lane, Oldbury (SO984833, JJD, 2003); Moorcroft Wood (SO970952, MWP, 2008); Kitchen Lane open space (SJ964026, SAHA, 2010). Origin unknown.

### *Crataegus succulenta* Schrad.
### Round-fruited Cockspurthorn

1. Neophyte. Many seedlings around planted parent, Reddings Lane, Acocks Green (SP104834, CBW, 1996). E N America.

### *Crataegus monogyna* Jacq.
### Hawthorn

*690. Native. Although a wild shrub or tree, it is quintessentially an agricultural hedgerow plant, and it is still being planted in amenity hedges, often because its berries are an important winter food for many bird species. It probably owes its ubiquity to its pioneer strategy and the ease with which the seeds are bird-sown. It quickly appears and thrives in post-industrial land, abandoned fields, demolished houses, road verges, rail and canal banks, waste land and private and allotment gardens. It will successfully invade semi-natural grassland, heathland, woodland margins and clearings, particularly where there is environmental change, for example caused by undergrazing, excess soil fertility, lowering of the water table etc. Once established it will persist even in dense plantations, although it is not so common in old woodland and is not adapted to deep shade. It will grow on a wide range of soils except perhaps the most acid, the most nutrient-poor or the very wet. Ass: *Acer pseudoplatanus*, *Corylus avellana*, *Cotoneaster simonsii*, *Ilex aquifolium*, *Prunus domestica*, *Prunus spinosa*, *Sambucus nigra*.

We have not attempted to distinguish the native subsp. *nordica* Franco from the neophyte subsp. *azarella* (Griseb.) Franco, which is thought to have been widely planted in parks and gardens. The twice-flowering **Crataegus monogyna 'Biflora'** (**Glastonbury Thorn**) has been reported from Saltwells LNR in Dudley (SO953872, J. Akers, 1999).

### *Crataegus × media* Bechst.

(*C. × macrocarpa* Hegetschw., *C. monogyna* × *C. laevigata*)
17. Native. The two parent species are completely interfertile and intergrade, so that the hybrid is quite difficult to define and hence record. Nevertheless there are quite a few records in the S in both vc. 39 and vc. 37, many in old hedges associated with old grasslands or canals and a few in old dingle woodland. A few are sites where *C. laevigata* has been recorded in

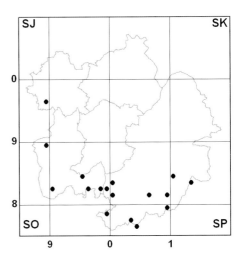

the past and might represent a change in assessment or a replacement of the species with the hybrid.

### *Crataegus laevigata* (Poir.) DC.
### Midland Hawthorn

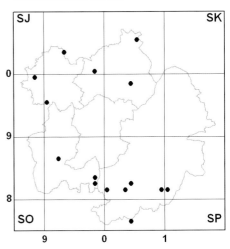

15. Native. A species of hedgerows and old woodland. It appears to be more shade-tolerant than *C. monogyna* and can be found in dense woodland. It seems to be on the NW margin of its natural distribution in our area, but it is still most often seen as a single tree in a hedge (usually but not always an old hedge). It is commoner in the SE of B&BC, although there seems to be quite a large number of old records in vc. 39 and vc. 38 which have not been refound in the modern survey. A few of the records in the NW are clearly introductions, such as the plants in a hedge at Northycote Farm, W'ton (SJ932033), known to have been planted in the 1980s. There seem to be no definite records of the pink-flowered *flore pleno* cultivars although they are not uncommon as street trees and in parks and gardens.

### *Crataegus orientalis* Pall. ex M. Bieb.
### Oriental Hawthorn

0. Neophyte. Recorded as planted in

Fowler's Park, W'ton (SJ919000, BRF, 1993). SE Europe & SW Asia.

### *Filipendula vulgaris* Moench
### Dropwort

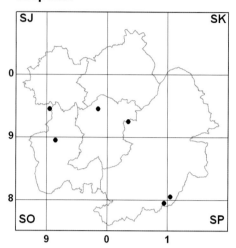

6. Native, but almost certainly always a garden escape in our area. Found in the edges of gardens, waste land by a freight terminal, in long-established debris by a track, foot of wall by a road. Old records from Hawthorn Wood, Park Lime Pits, Walsall (SK032001, P. Seccombe, 1984) and St Mark's churchyard, Pensnett (SO915894, G. Peake, 1991) have not been refound although it is now established in grassland in the quarry area on Barrow Hill near the latter (SO913897, ICT & B. Marsh, 2008).

### *Filipendula ulmaria* (L.) Maxim.
### Meadowsweet

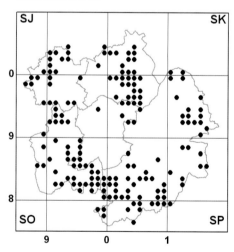

*169. Native. Ax. In B&BC it is found quite commonly in monads with semi-natural woodlands and grasslands but is almost absent from the more urban central areas. It is a plant of damp grasslands, woodland margins and road verges, ditches and canal and stream banks, where the ground water fluctuates and is not stagnant, and the soil is not nutrient-rich or base-poor. Ass: *Angelica sylvestris*, *Deschampsia cespitosa*,

*Epilobium hirsutum*, *Galium palustre*, *Juncus effusus*, *Juncus inflexus*, *Sanguisorba officinalis*, *Silene flos-cuculi*.

### *Rubus tricolor* Focke
### Chinese Bramble

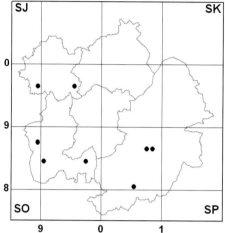

8. Neophyte. Occasionally becoming established in waste and marginal land from widespread plantings in car parks, amenity areas etc. China.

### *Rubus idaeus* L.
### Raspberry

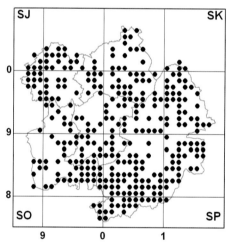

*325. Native. Common as an obvious throw-out or from colonising rhizomes, and possibly as a bird-sown seedling, from gardens and allotments. Also widespread in river, railway and canal corridors, in uncultivated grasslands and in woodland margins and clearings including in old woodland and in Sutton Park, although it is never possible to be sure it is not an escape. Apparently not so common in central urban areas nor in parts of Dudley. In a wide range of dry or damp soils except the most acid or nutrient-poor. Ass: *Arrhenatherum elatius*, *Chamerion angustifolium*, *Cytisus scoparius*, *Prunus spinosa*, *Rosa arvensis*, *Rubus fruticosus* agg.

### *Rubus spectabilis* Pursh
### Salmonberry

4. Neophyte. A few scattered records all suggesting garden discards. Moseley (SP0783, J. Rau, 2003); B'ham Botanical Gardens (SP049853, JWP, 2007); Stock's Wood (SP04528162, SAHA, 2007); Penn (SO9096, CBW, 2007). W N America.

### *Rubus cockburnianus* Hemsl.
### White-stemmed Bramble

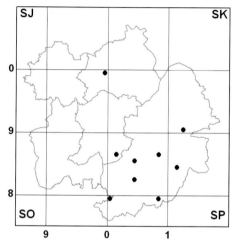

9. Neophyte. A few scattered records, never far from sites of cultivation in gardens, establishing into rough grassland or open scrub on banks and other waste uncultivated ground by suckering or as a garden discard. First recorded in our area in Warley Park (SP012861, CBW, 1996). China.

### *Rubus loganobaccus* L.H. Bailey
(*R. idaeus* × *R. vitifolius* Cham. & Schltdl.)
### Loganberry

2. Neophyte. A vigorous and recently much-cultivated plant, but rarely reported from the wild nationally and in B&BC. The earliest record in our area is from Stocks Wood, Bournville (SP045816, JJB, 1990); in our recording period are: High Heath Cottage, Sutton Coldfield (SP1497, SPG, 1998) and scrambling over dumped concrete, Selly Oak (SP042830, CBW, 2000). Garden origin.

### *Rubus* subgenus *Rubus*
### (*Rubus fruticosus* L. agg.)
### Brambles

*710. Ubiquitous in a wide range of uncultivated or little-cultivated habitats. The aggregate consists of 334 microspecies which were not distinguished in the present survey. An examination of the 10km square maps in Edees (1972) and Newton (1988) and Newton & Randall (2004) has suggested that the following microspecies are most likely to occur in our area, although no 10km square is entirely within the boundaries of B'ham and the Black Country and all records in Newton &

Randall, including pre-1988 records, have been used in making this assessment. Comments refer to recent records provided by vice-county Recorders, comments in brackets refer to records in Cadbury *et al.* (1971) and in Edees (1972).

Species marked with a double asterisk are considered by Newton & Randall (1988) to be of horticultural origin.

Subgenus *Rubus* Section RUBUS
*Rubus arrheniiformis* W.C.R. Watson
(old records from Sutton Park).
*Rubus bertramii* G. Braun
*Rubus nessensis* Hall
*Rubus plicatus* Weihe & Nees
(old records from Sutton Park).
*Rubus scissus* W.C.R. Watson
(old records from Sutton Park & vc. 39).

Subgenus *Rubus* Section GLANDULOSUS
Wimm. & Grab. (subsect. Hiemales E.H.L. Krause)
series SYLVATICI (P.J. Müll.) Focke
*Rubus albionis* W.C.R. Watson
(old records from Sutton Park).
*Rubus calvatus* Lees ex Bloxam
(old records from Sutton Park).
*Rubus gratus* Focke
(old records from Sutton Park).

** *Rubus laciniatus* Willd.

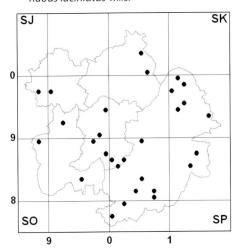

29. This highly distinctive cultivar is widely recorded in hedges, roadside verges, flowerbeds and pavements, often as a self-sown seedling (Edgbaston; Sutton Park; Small Heath).
*Rubus lindleianus* Lees
(old records from Minworth; Sutton Park & vc. 39).
*Rubus platyacanthus* P.J. Müll. & Lef.
*Rubus sciocharis* (Sudre) W.C.R. Watson
*Rubus varvicensis* Edees
(old records from vc. 39 part of Sutton Park).

series RHAMNIFOLII (Bab.) Focke
*Rubus amplificatus* Lees
*Rubus cardiophyllus* Lef. & P.J. Müll.

*Rubus nemoralis* P.J. Müll.
(old records from Sutton Park & vc. 39).
*Rubus polyanthemus* Lindeb.

series SPRENGELIANI Focke
*Rubus sprengelii* Weihe
(old records from Sutton Park & vc. 39).

series DISCOLORES (P.J. Müll) Focke
** *Rubus armeniacus* Focke.
'Himalayan Giant'
Widely recorded in vc. 37
*Rubus ulmifolius* Schott
Widely recorded or known from vc. 37 and 39. (old records from Sutton Park). Widespread, wholly sexual species.

series VESTITI (Focke) Focke
*Rubus criniger* (E.F. Linton) Rogers
(Old record from vc. 39)
*Rubus vestitus* Weihe
Recorded in vc. 37 (& old records from vc. 39

series MUCRONATAE (Focke) H.E. Weber
*Rubus egregious* Focke
(old records from vc. 39 part of Sutton Park are west of its accepted range and are now considered unlikely to be correct).

series RADULAE (Focke) Focke
*Rubus bloxamii* (Bab.) Lees
(old records from Sutton Park; vc. 39).
*Rubus echinatoides* (Rogers) Dallman
(old records from Sutton Park).
*Rubus echinatus* Lindl.
Recorded in vc. 37 and probably generally frequent.
*Rubus euryanthemus* W.C.R. Watson
(Sutton Park).
*Rubus flexuosus* P.J. Müll. & Lef.
*Rubus fuscus* Weihe
(old records from Sutton Park are now thought erroneous).
*Rubus insectifolius* Lef. & P.J. Müll.
(old records from Sutton Park).
*Rubus longithyrsiger* Lees ex Focke
Recorded in vc. 39 in vicinity of Sutton Park.
*Rubus pallidus* Weihe
(old records from Sutton Park not mapped by Newton & Randall 2004).
*Rubus rufescens* Lef. & P.J. Müll.

series MICANTES Sudre ex Bouvet
*Rubus leightonii* Lees ex Leighton
(old records from Sutton Park; Minworth; also vc. 39).
*Rubus trichodes* W.C.R. Watson
(old records from Sutton Park are not now considered to be correct).

series ANISACANTHI H.E. Weber
*Rubus anglofuscus* Edees
*Rubus infestus* Weihe ex Boenn.
*Rubus pascuorum* W.C.R. Watson

series HYSTRICES Focke
*Rubus dasyphyllus* (W.M. Rogers) E.S. Marshall
(old records from vc. 39).
*Rubus murrayi* Sudre
(old records from Sutton Park).

series GLANDULOSAE (Wimm. & Grab.) Focke
*Rubus hylonomus* Lef. & P.J. Müll.

Subgenus *Rubus* Section CORYLIFOLII Lindl.
*Rubus conjungens* (Bab.) Rogers
(old records from Sutton Park).
*Rubus pruinosus* Arrh.
(old records from Sutton Park & vc. 39).
*Rubus tuberculatus* Bab.
Widely recorded in vc. 37 and 39

Subgenus *Rubus* Section CAESII Lej. & Courtois
*Rubus caesius* L.
Dewberry
Recorded in vc. 37, and by our recorders in SP0178, SP0792, SP1491 and SP1595; this species is however often confused with members of sect. Corylifolii.

### *Potentilla fruticosa* L.
### Shrubby Cinquefoil
1. NT Native, but ours is a garden cultivar. Outside Majestic Wine, Tettenhall (SO891999, CBW, 2005). Old record as a relic of cultivation: St John the Baptist's, Halesowen (SO966836, G. Peake, 1991).

### *Potentilla anserina* L.
### Silverweed

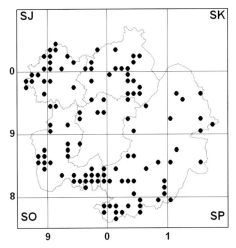

*117. Native. Stoloniferous perennial herb. Widespread but rather unevenly distributed, being less common in Sandwell and central B'ham. A colonist of periodically disturbed or lightly trampled, usually damp situations, particularly where they are subjected to winter-flooding or have impeded drainage. Pool margins, canal towpaths, road verges with impeded drainage, damp edges of cultivation. Soils are usually base-intermediate and fairly nutrient-rich. It may have some salt tolerance but is not part of the road margin community. Ass: *Agrostis stolonifera, Holcus lanatus, Persicaria maculosa, Ranunculus repens.*

### *Potentilla indica* (Jacks.) Wolf
(*Duchesnea indica* (Jacks.) Focke)
**Yellow-flowered Strawberry**
2. Neophyte. Stoloniferous perennial herb. Saltwells LNR, Dudley (SO937871, APD & J. Akers, 1999); a mat of it on waste land, Chapel Street, Wall Heath (SO878897, CBW, 2007). S & E Asia.

### *Potentilla argentea* L.
**Hoary Cinquefoil**
1. Native; probably casual in B&BC. NT. Perennial herb. Disturbed ground 5m inside entrance to Streetley cemetery (SP066988, JEH, 2007).

### *Potentilla recta* L.
**Sulphur Cinquefoil**

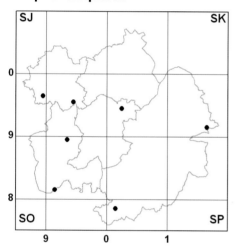

7. Neophyte. Perennial herb. Garden discard or from seed, usually close to gardens, on pavements, by paths or on walls, but in the recent past has been quite well established in post-industrial land on dry banks. There are also old records from the 1980s and 1990s from the Sandwell Valley complex (SP0292, SP0191, SP0392); blast furnace spoil banks (Ladymoor Road, Bilston, SO9495) and limestone at Sedgley Beacon (SO9190, *circa* 1970). Europe.

### *Potentilla intermedia* L.
**Russian Cinquefoil**
1. Neophyte. Biennial or perennial herb. Several plants in canal towpath, Rounds Green (SO983897, ST, 1998, still there 2005). Russia.

### *Potentilla erecta* (L.) Raeusch.
**Tormentil**
*87. Native. Ax. Perennial herb. Fairly local in B&BC, typically on base-poor and fairly nutrient-poor, slightly moist soils, and almost always in undisturbed and

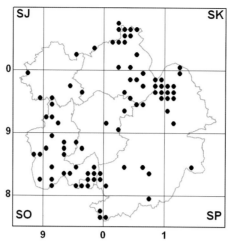

agriculturally unimproved semi-natural habitats such as heaths, old grassland and drier parts of mires, including sometimes places where these occur in very small fragments. It will persist both into the margins of scrub and under heavy grazing, and some of the occurrences especially in the southern fringes of the conurbation are in slightly more base-rich grassland, but almost always more or less unimproved and with nutrient-poor soils. There are no records of the upland subsp. *strictissima* (Zimmeter) A.J. Richards and all our material is thought to be **subsp. erecta.** Ass: *Calluna vulgaris, Deschampsia flexuosa, Festuca ovina, Galium saxatile, Luzula campestris.*

### *Potentilla* × *suberecta* Zimmeter
(*P. anglica* × *P. erecta*)
0. Native. Old record from rough grassland on the E side of the River Cole at Springfield (SP099827, JJD, 1993).

### *Potentilla anglica* Laichard
**Trailing Tormentil**
5. Native. Ax. Perennial herb. There are a number of old records, mostly from farm grassland, but very few records from our period, from rough grassland or grassy banks. NW Bloxwich (SJ98160318, JEH, 2004); grassy area in a churchyard, Amblecote (SO8985, APD, 2008); Doulton's Clay Pit, Saltwells (SO935870, APD & J. Akers, 1999); amenity grassland, Beeston Close, Aston (SP085896, D. Wall, 2008); Chester Road, B'ham (SP1293, SPG, 1998). There are also several tetrad records: SO88X, SO88Z, SO89U, SO98E, SO99A, SP09S, and SP09X, suggesting that this species has probably been under-recorded. Possibly some of our records for *Potentilla* × *mixta* (see below) are *P. anglica.*

### *Potentilla* × *mixta* Nolte ex Rchb.
(*P. anglica* × *P. reptans* plus
*P. erecta* × *P. reptans*)
**Hybrid Cinquefoil**
24. Native. Ax. It seems to be impossible to

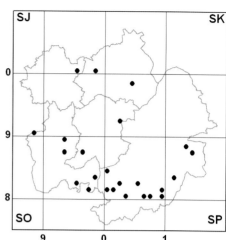

separate these two hybrids, and they are also often confused with *Potentilla anglica*, with which they seem to form a hybridising complex. We have more records for *P.* × *mixta* than for *P. anglica*, some from old grassland but also from much more secondary habitats such as lawns, concrete hard standing, churchyards and cemeteries, low walls and waste ground. The uneven distribution suggests that this complex may be under-recorded. There are further tetrad records from SO88Z and SO98E and JWP recorded it in Sutton Park in SP1197 in 1990.

### *Potentilla reptans* L.
**Creeping Cinquefoil**

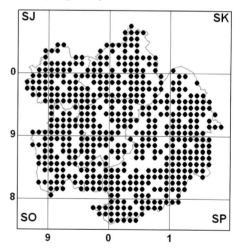

*529. Native. Perennial herb with runners rooting at the nodes. Almost ubiquitous in grassy situations. Old grasslands, secondary grasslands, road, canal and railway banks, river corridors and also as a colonist in bare ground and persisting in rough uncultivated grassland, hedgerows and open scrub and woodland margins. Discouraged by close and frequent mowing and mostly only in the trampled and/or weed-killed margins of lawns and grass verges. Found on most dry to damp soils except where very base- and nutrient-poor. Ass: *Alopecurus pratensis, Arrhenatherum elatius, Centaurea nigra, Cirsium arvense, Dactylis glomerata, Festuca rubra, Holcus lanatus, Prunella vulgaris, Ranunculus acris, Ranunculus repens.*

### *Potentilla sterilis* (L.) Garcke
### Barren Strawberry

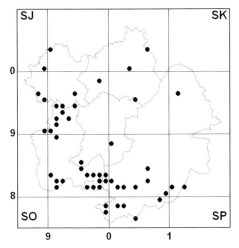

*51. Native. Ax. Commoner in the S and W of the conurbation, it is perhaps most at home in humid, sheltered, semi-shaded situations such as open scrub or grassy banks in old dingles. Also in similar sheltered situations in moist but relatively open grassland, typically on steep banks, often with bare patches and rock outcrops. Soils are usually moist and intermediate in base and nutrient status. Only occasionally seen in more secondary habitats such as tumbledown walls, lawns, old railway banks, shady canal cuttings, quarries. Ass: *Agrostis capillaris, Prunella vulgaris, Veronica chamaedrys, Viola riviniana.*

### *Comarum palustre* L.
(*Potentilla palustris* (L.) Scop.)
### Marsh Cinquefoil

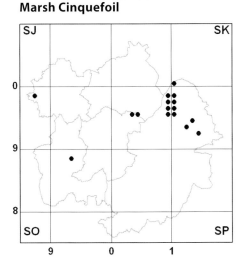

16. Native. Ax. Still quite common in Sutton Park, but presumed lost from some of its sites (e.g. Jockey Fields, Walsall,

SK038025; Moseley Bog, SP094821; Greet Mill Meadows on the River Cole SP099824; Fox Hollies SP128824, all last recorded in the early 1990s) although it never appears to have been very frequent in our area. The site in W'ton (SO8798), a small pond in relict pasture, Smestow Valley LNR, has also recently lost this species. Found in wetlands, typically long-established ones, particularly pond margins and wet hollows in fields, under nutrient-poor and fairly base-poor conditions and is therefore an indicator of good quality water and wetlands little affected by fertiliser runoff. Probably threatened by nutrient enrichment of water, drainage and the scrubbing-over of undergrazed wetland sites. Rarely in shade. Sometimes planted in pond creation schemes but seldom survives for long. Ass: *Galium palustre, Juncus conglomeratus, Menyanthes trifoliata, Molinia caerulea.*

### *Fragaria vesca* L.
### Wild Strawberry

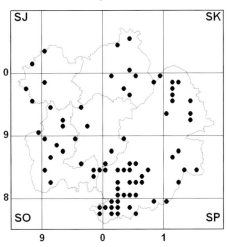

*78. Native. Ax. Not uncommon. Typically in open vegetation on shallow, droughty soils. At a wide range of light situations from moderate shade in open woodland, woodland margins and hedgerows, to full exposure in quarries and on other rock outcrops and stabilised rubble such as old railway ballast but usually in places with some shelter and protection from disturbance. Although the map suggests that it is less common in the central urban areas, it is occasionally found there in gardens in residential areas, where it is presumably in deliberate cultivation, from which it can escape into marginal habitats such as paths and hedgebanks by means of its far-reaching stolons or as a discard. Soils are typically nutrient-poor and base-medium to -rich. Ass: *Agrostis capillaris, Festuca rubra, Geranium robertianum, Prunella vulgaris, Sagina apetala sensu lato.*

▲ *Potentilla sterilis*

▲ *Comarum palustre*

▲ *Fragaria vesca*

## *Fragaria ananassa* (Duchesne) Duchesne
**Garden Strawberry**

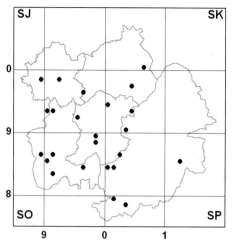

24. Neophyte. Garden and allotment relic and discard in waste land and edge habitats, sometimes appearing to colonise via its extensive stolons and very occasionally forming larger, more persistent patches on disused railway sidings and by canal towpaths. Usually in rich, garden or allotment soil in sheltered and not frequently disturbed situations. Garden origin. Ass: *Calystegia sylvatica, Elytrigia repens, Geranium endressii, Lamium album, Rubus fruticosus* agg.

## *Geum rivale* L.
**Water Avens**

4. Native. Ax. Perennial herb. A plant of base-enriched flushes, especially in woodland by streams but also in old species-rich grassland, it is undergoing a marked decline in lowland Britain which seems to be reflected in B&BC. It has been recorded in a few, scattered, typical habitats, fairly recently in Park Coppice, W'ton (SO910957, 1987), Cuckoo's Nook and the Dingle, Walsall (SP054987, SP052991, 1990), Balaam's Wood, B'ham (SO996784, 1990) and in several woods and pastures in the Illey complex, Dudley (SO9681, SO9781, 1990), but none of these have been confirmed within our time period. The few extant records could all easily represent introductions from garden cultivation: Tansey Green Claypit, Dudley (SO911895, ST, 1997, seen again 2008), Fens Pool, Dudley (SO918887, ICT & EVJC, 2007), pool in B'ham Botanical Gardens (SP047853, JWP, MWP & EVJC, 2007); (SP1292, SPG, 1996).

## *Geum × intermedium* Ehrh.
(*Geum rivale* × *G. urbanum*)
**Hybrid Avens**

1. Native. Ax. A common and fertile hybrid where the two parent species grow together or have grown together previously, it has been recorded in the past

in Park Coppice, W'ton (SO910957, L Park & ICT, 1989) and recently in Dudley by Illey Brook (SO975811, RM, 2003) and in Lower Illey Dingle (SO975812, RM, 2003).

## *Geum urbanum* L.
**Wood Avens**

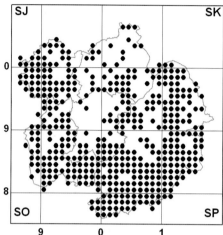

*458. Native. Perennial herb. A ubiquitous species in most parts of our area, occurring in fertile, fairly moist, base-intermediate soils in woodlands (although often not in old woodlands) and to an increasing extent as a weed of cultivation even without much shade in gardens and allotments and in other intermittently disturbed habitats in residential areas. Its apparent scarcity in much of Walsall and in the central urban areas is only partly explained by the idea (Gilbert, 1989) that it is a member of relatively advanced successional communities which rarely have time to develop in central urban areas. It is frequently quite an aggressive weed in allotments and gardens. Ass: *Galium aparine, Geranium robertianum, Lapsana communis, Poa trivialis, Ranunculus repens, Urtica dioica.*

## *Agrimonia eupatoria* L.
**Agrimony**

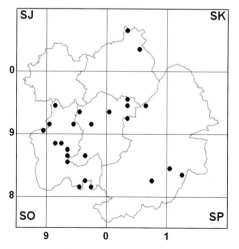

24. Native. Ax. Perennial herb, in old grassland, but probably favoured by under-management and often concentrated in field margins, rough grassland, grassland/woodland interfaces, hedgebanks, etc., especially on banks and on well-drained, fairly nutrient-poor and moderately or very base-rich soils. Sometimes found in similar soils in more secondary situations such as old quarries. Ass: *Achillea ptarmica, Carex flacca, Centaurea nigra, Filipendula ulmaria, Juncus inflexus, Lathyrus linifolius, Ononis repens, Ophioglossum vulgatum, Potentilla erecta, Succisa pratensis.*

## *Sanguisorba officinalis* L.
**Great Burnet**

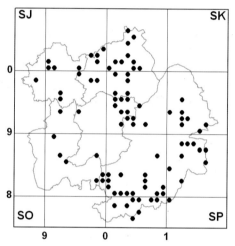

*91. Native. Ax. Perennial herb. Old, unimproved, usually damp or even wet grassland; not uncommon and quite widespread in B&BC although apparently less common in Sandwell and Dudley. A few of its sites are old species-rich meadows, but most are quite species-poor and managed for amenity or little-managed. In some cases it may be persisting in semi-improved species-rich grassland or colonising from remnants or even from hay fed to stock. As such it is present in a wide range of river corridor flood plain grasslands, in grazing land by canals, and in Black Country post-industrial horse pastures which may have a remnant or seed bank from old grassland. It was also once included in agricultural seed mixtures and is now included in amenity seed mixes and in hay strewn in habitat creation, but these are probably only minor components of its present distribution. Soils intermediate in base and nutrient status, often silty or peaty. Ass: *Alopecurus pratensis, Conopodium majus, Dactylorhiza praetermissa, Filipendula ulmaria, Juncus effusus, Juncus inflexus, Ranunculus acris, Rumex acetosa.*

## Poterium sanguisorba L.
(*Sanguisorba minor* Scop.)
**Salad Burnet**

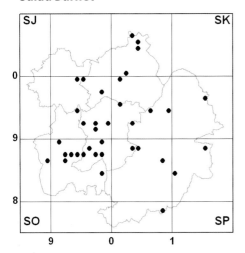

36. Native and Neophyte. Subsp. *sanguisorba* is Ax. Perennial herbs. Most (22) of these records are for **subsp. balearicum** (Bourg. ex Nyman) Stace (subsp. *muricata* (Gremli) Briq.) (**Fodder Burnet**) which is mapped below.

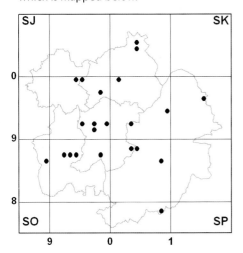

This is a neophyte from S Europe, a remnant of old agricultural seed mixtures and also often inappropriately included in modern habitat creation seed mixtures. In B&BC it seems to operate mainly as an introduction in landscaping schemes and occasionally as a casual in dry, base-rich soils and spoils.

A few records (5) are for **subsp. sanguisorba** (*Sanguisorba minor* subsp. *minor*), the true native Salad Burnet (Ax). This is a plant of limestone rock ledges and limestone grassland and other very base-rich substrates. It is known currently from a small number of sites which are most likely also introductions: rough grassland, Mill Lane nature reserve, Walsall (SK0200, MWP & JaH, 2001) and also nearby in short grassland near path (SP0199, MWP & JaH, 2001); path adjacent to meadow, Saltwells LNR Dudley (SO935871, J. Akers,

1999); in gully in quarry grassland, Barrow Hill (SO913897, ICT & B. Marsh, 2008); the Cracker, Tipton (a site of spread limestone) (SO954928, MWP, 1997). There are also a number of old records of this species which have not been re-found, which were mostly attributed to subsp. *sanguisorba* and may represent remnants of native populations, particularly at Beacon Hill, Sedgley (SO922946, PW, 1987), Park Lime Pits, Walsall (SK032001, SK030004, both JJB, 1989), Cooper's Bank, Barrow Hill, Dudley (SO918903, J. Andrews & ICT, 1987) and Rowley Hills (SO975890, TCH, A. Black & A. Brown, 1987; SO977894, W.G. Teagle, 1975).

## Acaena anserinifolia (J.R. & G. Forst.) Druce
**Bronze Pirri-pirri-bur**
1. Neophyte. Perennial, woody at the base. Growing out of a garden into tarmac drive edges, Coventry Road, B'ham (SP156837, MWP, JWP, ICT & L. Bastin, 2007). New Zealand.

## Acaena ovalifolia Ruiz & Pav.
**Two-spined Acaena**
1. Neophyte. Perennial, woody at the base. Appears to be spreading locally from one site of cultivation: lawned area at side of buildings, in mown grass around drain cover, Winterbourne Gardens (SP052838, JWP & MWP, 2007); single plant in woodland W of Edgbaston Pool (SP053839, ICT, M. Kingsbury & T. Holland, 2009); several plants at the back of a tee near a small pool at Edgbaston Golf Course (SP056839, JWP & MWP, 2007). S America.

## Alchemilla alpina L.
**Alpine Lady's-mantle**
2. Native; casual with us. Perennial herb. Pavement weed, Aversley Road (SP040779, JJD, 2000); cemetery, Handsworth (SP029906, ICT & B. Bridges, 2002).

## Alchemilla conjuncta Bab.
**Silver Lady's-mantle**
4. Neophyte. Perennial herb. Brickwork at the entrance to the Coseley Canal tunnel, where it forms a large patch on the N-facing wall (SO941939/40, BRF, 1987; still present 1998). Other sites are more casual: seedlings by road verge, Warley (SP006860, CBW, 1996); self-sown from garden in pavement (SP104833, CBW, 1996); in paving, Sara Close (SP109993, MWP, JWP & PLR, 2006). Alps.

## Alchemilla filicaulis Buser
**subsp. vestita** (Buser) M.E. Bradshaw
**Hairy Lady's-mantle**
29. Native. Ax. Perennial herb of old, species-rich grassland on soils of intermediate base status, fairly low in

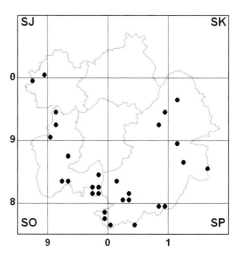

nutrients, usually in damp (often flushed) patches in the meadow. Present in grazed and hay swards, but discouraged by under-management or applications of artificial fertilisers. Almost all of our records are in the periphery of the conurbation, although there are older records from similar but more central sites which have not been re-found in the present survey: Wren's Nest Dudley (SO937920, 1985), Coopers Bank, Dudley (SO918803, 1987), Sutton Park (SP098974, 1867; SP1097, 1971), Rectory Park, Sutton Coldfield (SP129962, 1981). It is still quite frequent in the Illey area. Ass: *Agrostis capillaris*, *Cardamine pratensis*, *Filipendula ulmaria*, *Ranunculus acris*, *Rhinanthus minor*.

## Alchemilla mollis (Buser) Rothm.
**Soft Lady's-mantle**

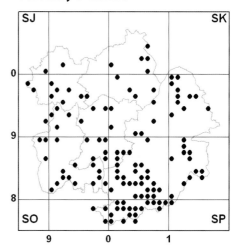

129. Neophyte. A vigorous garden perennial herb, readily escaping locally, mainly by seed, and widely found in garden peripheries in paths, pavements in waste areas and on walls, as a relic of cultivation in abandoned gardens and allotments and in graveyards, sometimes persisting in rough grassland, very occasionally in more species-rich grassland and by ponds and streams. Carpathians. Ass: *Alliaria petiolata*,

*Chamerion angustifolium, Geranium robertianum, Geum urbanum, Holcus mollis, Hyacinthoides × massartiana.*

### *Aphanes arvensis* agg.
### Parsley-pierts

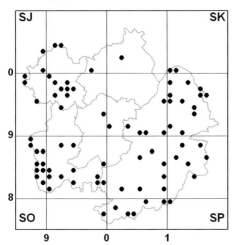

81. Native. Winter- or spring-germinating annuals of bare ground or open vegetation developing in situations liable to summer drought, on a wide range of light, sandy soils. Heaths, golf courses, dry grassy banks in parks, drought-liable areas of road verges and path sides, especially where there is trampling or intermittent weed-killing, crop margins in allotments and agricultural fields. Some fruiting specimens have been attributed to the two species in the aggregate and these records are mapped below. Also tetrad SO99Z. Ass: *Aira praecox, Catapodium rigidum, Erophila* sp., *Rumex acetosella, Veronica arvensis, Vulpia bromoides.*

### *Aphanes arvensis* L.
### Parsley-piert

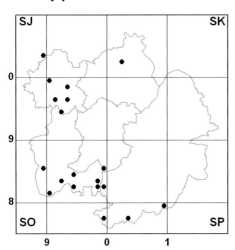

19. Native. Mostly described from road verges and lawns. Also tetrad SO99Z.

### *Aphanes australis* Rydb.
### Slender Parsley-piert
5. Native. Fewer plants conform to this

description than to that of *Aphanes arvensis*. They are mostly from less urban, acid grasslands, but also found by roadsides and in residential areas: bare ground, car park, W'ton town centre (SO913984, ICT, 1999); verge of B4187 near Trehearns (SO907810, JJD, 2003); steep bank in *Festuca rubra* grassland, Fens Pools (SO921887, ICT & EVJC, 2007); gravel bank by Bannersgate car park, Sutton Park (SP0995, MWP, ICT & JWP, 2008); Stourbridge Golf Course, edges of bunkers and raised greens (SO8982, WAT, 1992, seen again at SO896827, 2010). Also older records from Stourbridge cemetery (SO885838, 1990; SO887837, 1992, both WAT); dry bank in pasture, Wollaston (SO887858, WAT, 1990).

### *Rosa multiflora* Thunb.
### Many-flowered Rose

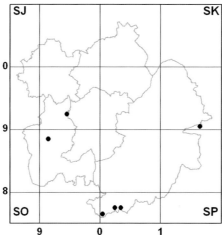

6. Neophyte. A scrambling shrub, sometimes huge. A few scattered records probably always as a remnant of cultivation, garden reject or deliberate introduction. Found scrambling over hedges or scrub or in rough grassland. Also older record by an old church hall, Weoley Castle (SP023827, CBW, 1989). E Asia.

### *Rosa luciae* Franch. & Rochebr. ex Crép.
### Memorial Rose
1. Neophyte. Recorded in a hedge (SO899920, APD & CBW, 2007); plant now lost.

### *Rosa arvensis* Huds.
### Field-rose or Field Rose
*201. Native. Patches in open scrub, also in woodland and along hedges on a wide range of fairly dry, not very acid or impoverished soils. Common in Dudley and Walsall, its scarcity in W'ton, Sandwell and central B'ham is difficult to explain, especially since it is sometimes used in landscaping schemes. Ass: *Crataegus*

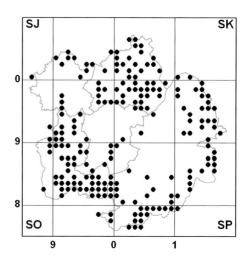

*monogyna, Prunus spinosa, Rubus fruticosus* agg.

### *Rosa × irregularis* Déségl. & Guillon
(*R. × verticillacantha* Mérat; *R. arvensis × R. canina* and *R. canina × R. arvensis*)
5. Native. Hedgerows and scrub. Remarkably few records for these hybrids between two common rose species; not recorded in our part of vc. 39 despite being not uncommon in the non-B&BC parts. Certainly under-recorded. In our area most records are with *R. arvensis* as the female parent which is more easily recognised. Wylde Green Road (SP130953, M.J. Hill, P.J. Copson, B. Rowe, A.L. Primavesi & PC, 1997); hedgerow SW of Lower Illey, with *canina* the female parent (SO978811, RM, 1997); Mill Lane, Northfield, with *canina* the female parent (SP022787, RM, 1999); field hedge, Illey (SO984819, RM & WAT, 2000); large patch in scrub W of Lutley Lane (SO941823, RM & WAT, 2000); and earlier records from the Leasowes (SO976838, WAT, 1993 ); River Rea (SP062833, RM, 1993); Yardley Cemetery (SP127843, P.G. Garner, 1993).

### *Rosa spinosissima* L.
(*Rosa pimpinellifolia* L.)
### Burnet Rose

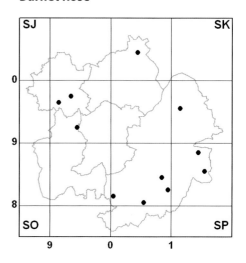

11. Native. Probably entirely escapes from cultivation in our area – discards or vigorous suckerings from plantings on amenity sites, often forming quite large patches, but sometimes clearly a bird-sown seedling. Found in scrub developing on neglected amenity land, waste land, hedgerows, quarries, canal towpaths. There are records from old semi-natural woodland sites: Moseley Bog (SP091820); Balaam's Wood (SO995784).

### *Rosa rugosa* Thunb.
### Japanese Rose

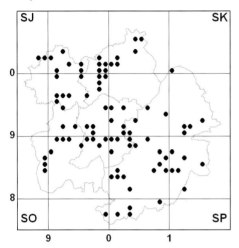

91. Neophyte. Schedule 9 (invasive). Usually clearly a relic of planting or a throw-out, often forming large stands in neglected public open spaces and in hedges and demolished housing. Cadbury *et al.* (1971) record only a single record in our part of vc. 38 and Edees (1972) has no records anywhere in vc. 39, but it now seems particularly common by canals, also by ponds and in river, railway and motorway corridors. Occasionally in more semi-natural habits, e.g. Beacon Hill, Sedgley (SO9294), Hill Hook, B'ham (SK1000), Sandwell Valley (SP0492), but generally there it is the result of misguided amenity planting. The map suggests that it is quite scarce away from the urban centres. The national distribution confirms its concentration in the centres of population, where it is both planted and spreading in the urban environment. Ass: *Acer campestre, Cornus sanguinea, Crataegus monogyna, Viburnum opulus.*

### *Rosa* 'Hollandica'
### Dutch Rose

11. Neophyte. A plant of hybrid origin, one parent being *Rosa rugosa*, the other obscure. Widely used as a rootstock in horticulture and found as a garden relic, discard, and spreading out of gardens and from amenity planting by suckers. Recorded quite frequently in vc. 37 in a

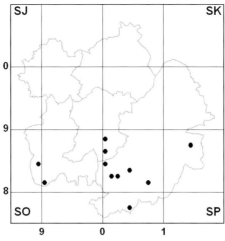

wide range of marginal situations such as periphery of recreation grounds; naturalised in parks, including Woodgate Valley and on a factory waste site. Doubtless occurs elsewhere in B&BC and may be being confused with *Rosa rugosa*.

### *Rosa virginiana* Mill.(non Herrm.)
### Virginian Rose

2. Neophyte. Two well-established bushes on an old pig farm, Yardley Wood (SP102793, CBW, det. RM, 1996); single plant in margins of Dunstall Park racecourse, W'ton (SJ903010, ICT & EVJC, det. RM, 2007). E N America.

### *Rosa gallica* L.
### Red Rose of Lancaster

0. Neophyte. An old record as a garden escape from the top of a disused brick quarry behind a house, Latham's Bridge, Walsall Wood (SK043026, BRF, 1991).

### *Rosa ferruginea* Vill.
(*Rosa glauca* Pourret non Vill. ex Loisel.)
### Red-leaved Rose

9. Neophyte. As a relic of planting, as a garden discard, and also as a bird-sown seedling, around gardens and allotments, on a road central reservation, and in scrub developing on waste land.

### *Rosa canina* L.
### Dog-rose

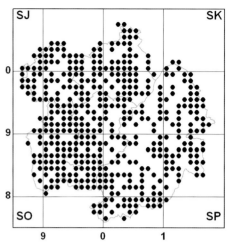

*456. Native. Almost ubiquitous, although the spontaneous distribution has been much confused in recent years by widespread planting in landscaping schemes. Common in hedgerows, spontaneous and planted scrub, in plantations and older woodlands, especially in the margins. It is frequently spread by birds and found in road, rail and river corridors and many types of infrequently disturbed waste land. It occurs as a seedling almost anywhere, although it is rarely found in the most nutrient- and base-poor soils and requires dry or only moderately damp soil conditions. Some, e.g. Graham & Primavesi (1993), recognise the groups Dumales, Lutetianae, Pubescentes and Transitoriae within *Rosa canina* based mainly on differences in indumentum, and all of these groups have been recorded in our part of vc. 37. Ass: *Crataegus monogyna, Prunus spinosa, Sambucus nigra, Rubus fruticosus* agg.

### *Rosa* × *dumalis* Bechst.
(*R. canina* × *R. caesia* or *R. caesia* × *R. canina*; both subsp. of *R. caesia*)

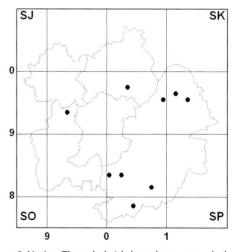

9. Native. These hybrids have been recorded reliably throughout our area, mostly in

waste land. Many free-standing bushes were recorded in Sutton Park in the Longmoor enclosure (SP095959, M.J. Hill, P.J. Copson, B. Rowe, A.L. Primavesi & PC, 1997). In some cases the hybrid is specified as being with *R. caesia* subsp. *vosagiaca* as the female parent.

### *Rosa* × *dumetorum* Thuill.
(*R. canina* × *R. obtusifolia* and *R. obtusifolia* × *R. canina*)
3. Native. Recorded from Sutton Park (SP114963, HHF, ALP, 1996); E of Hodge Hill (SO933832, T.D. Knight, RM & J.W. Meiklejohn, 2001); Peddimore Lane (SP153933, JWP, MWP, ICR & JaH, 2006). In the first two cases *Rosa canina* is given as the female parent. The first record in vc. 39 was from W'ton (SO99, Bagnall, 1896, det. ALP from BIRA specimen).

### *Rosa* × *scabriuscula* Sm.
(*R. canina* × *R. tomentosa*)
0. Native. First record for vc. 39 was from W'ton (SO99, J. Fraser, 1876, det. ALP from BIRA herbarium specimen). Not recorded in our area more recently.

### *Rosa* × *nitidula* Besser
(*R. canina* × *R. rubiginosa* and *R. rubiginosa* × *R. canina*)

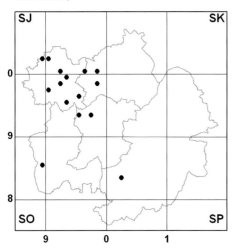

15. Native. First record for vc. 39 was from Tettenhall (SO89, J. Fraser, 1878, det. ALP from British Museum herbarium specimen). Not uncommonly recorded, particularly in the Black Country, by footpaths, in hedges by amenity grassland, by roadsides, on reclaimed ground and by a towpath. Records mainly by JEH, who considers that it is always planted by local authorities in our area. Difficult to separate from planted forms of *R. rubiginosa*.

### *Rosa caesia* Sm. **subsp. *vosagiaca***
(N.H.F. Desp.) D.H. Kent (subsp. *glauca* (Nyman) G.G. Graham & Primavesi nom. inval.)
**Glaucous Dog-rose**
1. Native. 10+ bushes almost certainly

planted, in scrub by the Bourne Brook at Lodge Hill, Woodgate Valley (SP025831, RM, 2002).

### *Rosa obtusifolia* Desv.
**Round-leaved Dog-rose**
2. Native. Recorded twice in scrub in the Illey area. Adjacent to Breach Dingle (SO960812, RM, 2004) and SW of Lower Illey (SO977811, RM, 1997).

### *Rosa sherardii* Davies
**Sherard's Downy-rose**
1. Native. Few bushes in a field hedge, meadow near Lower Illey (SO978810, RM, 2003).

### *Rosa rubiginosa* L.
**Sweet-briar**

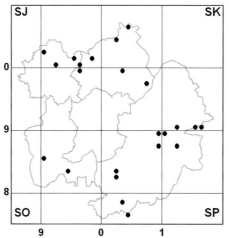

23. Native. Quite commonly recorded in hedgerows, waste land, patches of scrub in pasture, river corridors, abandoned railway tracks, although not all records have been verified by either RM or JEH. Apart from an old record from Sutton Park (SP098974, Bagnall, det. rev. ALP, 1871) *R. rubiginosa* is probably best seen as a modern introduction in local authority planting schemes, although at least some of the records are in distinctly non-amenity, waste land situations suggesting spread by birds.

### *Rosa micrantha* Borrer ex Sm.
**Small-flowered Sweet-briar**
1. Native. A single record: scrub, W of California, near Woodgate Valley (SP013827, RM, 2002). Status uncertain.

### *Rosa agrestis* Savi
**Small-leaved Sweet-briar**
1. Native. NT. One bush reported in scrub by Bourn Brook at Lodge Hill (SP025831, RM, 1998). Almost certainly introduced with other *Rosa* species.

## 45. ELAEAGNACEAE

### *Hippophae rhamnoides* L.
**Sea-buckthorn**

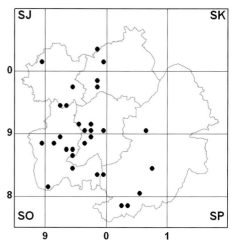

30. Introduced native. A salt-tolerant, thorny, deciduous shrub used in planting schemes along roadsides, on banks and around buildings and occasionally spreading from established plantings or from bird-sowings onto banks and waste ground. Rarely achieving maturity in these situations. Also tetrad SO90A.

### *Elaeagnus pungens* Thunb.
**Spiny Oleaster**
1 Neophyte. A large spiny bush, apparently self sown in an old hedge, path off Meadowsweet Avenue, Hawkesley (SP049778, JJD, 2000). Japan.

## 46. RHAMNACEAE

### *Rhamnus cathartica* L.
**Buckthorn**
5. Native. Ax. Spiny shrub, rarely found, usually in hedgerows, sometimes planted. Blackroot Pool car park, Sutton Park (SP108971, SPG, 1999); Plants Brook Valley (SP1492, L. Holmes, 1998); Tenacre Fields, Parkes Hall Pool (SO930928, A. Glaisher, 2003); hedge border, disused railway, Tipton Green/Bloomfield (SO953927, JEH, 2007); hedge bordering disused railway, Tibbington (SO95379303, JEH, 2007).

### *Frangula alnus* Mill.
**Alder Buckthorn**
34. Native. Ax. Shrub. Typically found in semi-shaded situations in broad-leaved, semi-natural woodland sites of some antiquity, in moist or damp, but not continuously waterlogged, usually peaty soils that are neutral to moderately acid. Seldom in any quantity and more often occurring as a very few isolated individuals. Recorded in 10 squares in Sutton Park in 1971. Also now deliberately planted in

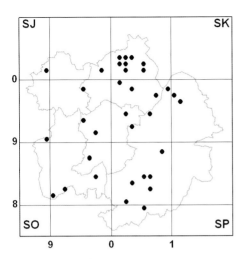

habitat creation schemes, confusing its true native range. Also recorded from tetrad SO98E. Ass: *Betula pubescens, Molinia caerulea, Quercus petraea, Quercus robur, Salix cinerea.*

## 47. ULMACEAE

### *Ulmus glabra* Huds.
### Wych Elm

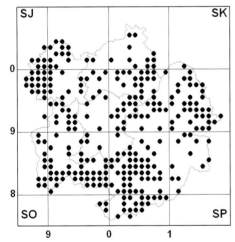

*289. Native. Severely hit by Dutch Elm disease and now survives mainly as seedlings and saplings and possibly regrowth in scrub and old woodland and in hedgerows, frequently succumbing to fresh attacks. The concentration of the records in the peripheral and countryside areas of B&BC reflects the distribution of old woodlands and hedges. It prefers moist, fairly fertile and base-rich soils. Ass: *Fraxinus excelsior, Ilex aquifolium, Quercus robur, Ulmus procera.*

### *Ulmus glabra* × *U. procera*
1. Native? Recorded in Furnace Coppice Halesowen (SO965845, JJD, 2003).

### *Ulmus glabra* × *U. minor*
3. Native. Said by Stace to be a common hybrid, a cluster of records in the Lapal

area of Halesowen have been identified as *U. glabra* × *U. minor sensu* Stace: hedgebank, Lapal Lane South (SO986829, JJD, 2003); footpath to Lye Close (SO984827, JJD, 2003); Lapal Pool (SO981835, JJD, 2003); Lye Close Brook Dingle (SO984824, JJD, 2003). Another elm, identified as *U.* × *vegeta* (Loudon) Ley (**Huntingdon Elm**), also *U. glabra* × *U. minor*, was recorded as planted in St Paul's Churchyard, Blackheath (SO977862, WAT, 2001) and also, earlier, by a canal (SP064795, WAT, 1993).

### *Ulmus* × *hollandica* Mill.
(? *U. glabra* × *U. minor*, or *U. glabra* × *U. minor* × *U. plotii*)
### Dutch Elm

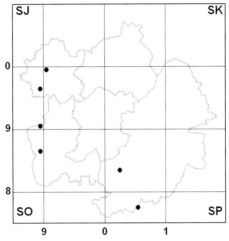

6. Native. A natural hybrid which is also planted, e.g. in West Park W'ton (SO9099), also recorded from hedgerows and churchyards.

### *Ulmus procera* Salisb.
### English Elm

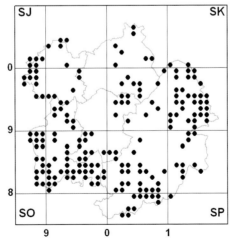

*196. Native or alien. Common and sometimes abundant in old hedgerows where it is quite frequently the only species; now often seen as sucker regrowth after Dutch Elm disease. Much less recorded in the heavily urbanised

areas and seems less common generally than *Ulmus glabra*, although the new growth after attacks is sometimes difficult to ascribe definitely to either species (*U. glabra* is said not to sucker). Grows in moist, fertile soils. Ass: *Fraxinus excelsior, Ilex aquifolium, Quercus robur.*

### *Ulmus minor* Mill.
### Small-leaved Elm
0. Native. Old record from Monyhull, on wooded bank above canal (SP071793, JJD, 1993), also some unverified records from the 1980s from Park Limepits (SP0399), the Wren's Nest (SO9392) and Northycote Farm (SJ9303). Also mapped in SP19C and SP19E in 1971 (Cadbury *et al.*), but presumably from outside Sutton Park since not recorded there by Readett (1971).

### *Ulmus plotii* Druce
### Plot's Elm
0. Native. Cadbury *et al.* gave Four Oaks (SP1199) as a site for this Nationally Scarce species in 1971.

## 48. CANNABACEAE

### *Cannabis sativa* L.
### Hemp

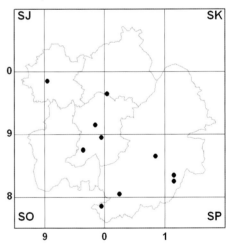

10. Casual. An annual arising from birdseed or from bait used by anglers which sporadically appears along disturbed roadside verges, on post-housing sites, etc. It is also cultivated illegally both on waste land and in houses and factories. Bagnall recorded it from the railway embankment in Sutton Park (SP1097) in 1877. Asia.

### *Humulus lupulus* L.
### Hop
*61. Native and also a frequent escape from cultivation. A perennial climber quite frequently found along railways, canals and in woodland and farmland, almost always scrambling through hedges or fences. Grows in the open or in partial shade in

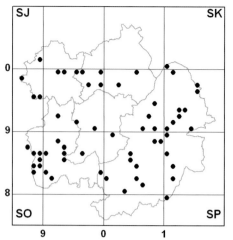

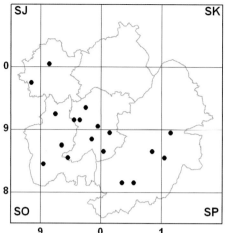

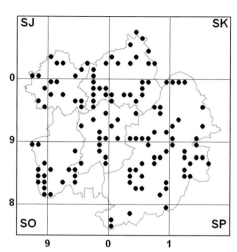

moist, richly fertile soil. Also tetrad SO98E. Ass: *Calystegia sepium*, *Calystegia sylvatica*, *Lonicera* spp., *Urtica dioica*.

### *Humulus lupulus* L.
### 'Op

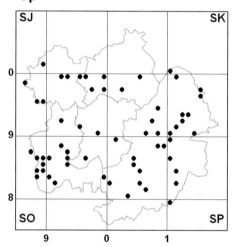

*61. Nairtive. Fun all around eya, Dudley, Tipp'n, Crairdley, Umpshear, Darlo, Wassul, Carma, Wolvo, an' Odebry, Smerik an' Brumajum. It ochis itsen ova railway bonks, is fun up the cut, an' grows ova 'edgis on the fodes an' lezzers. An' op 'n a catch alung th'oss rowd. We evun sid paiylins bostid unda its waiyte. Many an ode mon 'as 'ops ut wum weya it teks its ook ova the paiylins. It dus awraiyt on wairta an' 'oss muk. Cor grow itsen on sond bin as 'ow it's tew dry. As bin fun wi goosegogs, oppuls an' 'tween tairtus ut th'olltmunts weya blokes dow arf tek th'ommbridge wi it. Ass: *Calystegia sepium*, *Calystegia sylvatica*, *Lonicera* spp., *Urtica dioica*.

### 49. MORACEAE

### *Ficus carica* L.
### Fig

18. Neophyte. A deciduous shrub or sometimes quite a substantial tree, with records from canals, railways, riverbanks

and in paving. Sometimes a relic of planting or an escape from a nearby garden, but a number of trees appear to be spontaneously established. Two impressive examples cover the bank of the derelict railway where it crosses Sedgley Road East in Tipton. E Mediterranean and SW Asia.

*Morus nigra* L. (**Black Mulberry**) is rarely recorded, and only as a planted tree, in parks and old gardens, etc.

### 50. URTICACEAE

### *Urtica dioica* L.
### Common Nettle

*711. Native. A rhizomatous and/or stoloniferous perennial herb common on richly fertile, moist or winter-wet soils characterised by high phosphate and a history of disturbance, although it will persist long after disturbance has ceased and it is a natural constituent of the field layer in many types of Alder wood. Relatively indifferent to soil base status and thriving in full sun or moderately deep shade in a wide range of habitats: woods, scrub, hedgerows, allotments, gardens, stream and river margins and rubbish dumps of all kinds. Ass: *Anthriscus sylvestris*, *Arctium minus*, *Calystegia* spp., *Cirsium arvense*, *Galium aparine*, *Lapsana communis*, *Rumex obtusifolius*, *Symphytum* × *uplandicum*.

The non-stinging subsp. *galeopsifolia* (Wierzb. ex Opiz) Chrtek from damp and non-weedy sites has so far (rather understandably) not been recorded in B&BC.

### *Urtica urens* L.
### Small Nettle

131. Archaeophyte. An annual herb, found quite frequently on disturbed and cultivated ground. Like *Urtica dioica* it is a fertility indicator, but more confined to well-lit and frequently disturbed situations,

and is not usually found in base-poor soils. A weed of arable, but often well-established in allotments, rose beds, shrubberies, probably originally imported in farmyard manure. Also around rabbit warrens in fields and with an uncommon and limited casual occurrence in disturbed situations by roads etc. Ass: *Chenopodium album*, *Euphorbia helioscopia*, *Fallopia convolvulus*, *Gnaphalium uliginosum*, *Lamium amplexicaule*, *Lamium purpureum*, *Senecio vulgaris*, *Sonchus oleraceus*, *Veronica persica*.

### *Parietaria judaica* L.
### Pellitory-of-the-wall

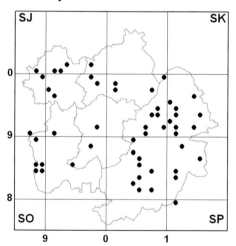

53. Native. Typically found at the base of walls and in paving, also on the walls themselves, usually in shady, sheltered positions in dry to moist, base-rich mortar or soil of intermediate fertility. Not at all uncommon in many residential areas in habitats marginal to gardens, and often seems to spread sporadically over several hectares where it occurs. Also occasionally found in city centre areas, as in Wheeler's Fold, W'ton (SO915987, ICT, 2008) and on the walls of canal locks. Little recorded in B&BC by Edees (1972) or Cadbury *et al.* (1971), it may be increasing. Ass:

*Asplenium ruta-muraria, Cymbalaria muralis, Meconopsis cambrica, Stellaria media, Soleirolia soleirolii.*

### *Soleirolia soleirolii* (Req.) Dandy
**Mind-your-own-business**

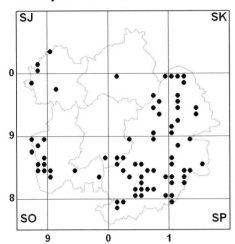

75. Neophyte. An evergreen, carpet-forming, perennial herb found occasionally in rather sheltered shady situations on garden steps, the base of walls, in paving, and adjacent to long-term dripping gutters and drains. It has also been found on the side of a ditch and a stream bank, a habitat it may come to exploit more. Grows in shade or semi-shade, on wet or damp soils of intermediate fertility and base status. Ass: *Hedera helix, Rubus fruticosus* agg., bryophytes. W Mediterranean islands.

### 51. NOTHOFAGACEAE

### *Nothofagus obliqua* (Mirb.) Blume
**Roble**
5. Neophyte. A few scattered records of this large deciduous tree, almost all recent plantings, but there are records for possibly self-set plants from Valley Parkway, Northfield (SP029801, CBW, 1997) and Lodge Hill (SP029829, CBW, 1997). S America.

There are other, unconfirmed records of plantings of at least two other Southern Beeches: *Nothofagus antarctica* (Forster f.) Oersted, (Antarctic Beech) and *Nothofagus alpina* (Philippi) Dmitri & Milano (Rauli) e.g. at West Park, W'ton (SO9099).

### 52. FAGACEAE

### *Fagus sylvatica* L.
**Beech**
*330. Native. A large deciduous timber tree; probably entirely planted or naturalised from cultivation in B&BC and more characteristic of residential than industrial areas. Apparently somewhat commoner

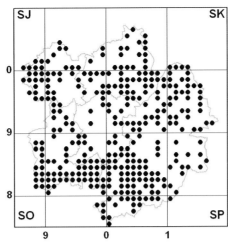

in the S of the area. Common as clipped garden hedging and as mature trees and saplings in hedgerows, woodland, plantations, nature reserves and street plantings but not associated with old woodlands and preferring well-drained soils. Quite readily developing from seed where trees have been planted in woodland. Ass: *Acer pseudoplatanus, Fraxinus excelsior, Quercus robur, Pinus sylvestris.*

Four cultivars have been recorded from our area, all probably entirely plantings: *F. sylvatica* forma *purpurea* (Aiton.) C.K. Schneid (**Copper or Purple Beech**) is quite widespread. Other cultivars have been only rarely recorded: cultivar 'Dawyck' (West Park, SO9099), 'Aspleniifolia' (**Fern-leaved Beech**) in Sandwell Valley (SP0291), Plantsbrook (SP1392) and Highbury Park (SP0682), and 'pendula' (**Weeping Beech**) at Edgbaston (SP0485).

### *Castanea sativa* Mill.
**Sweet Chestnut**

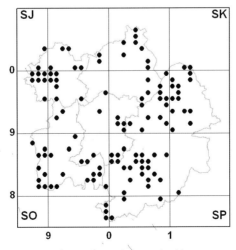

*123. Archaeophyte. A large deciduous tree recorded from woodland, farmland, nature reserves, parks and as a roadside tree on a wide range of soils. Widely planted in the past as a timber tree, and in mixed deciduous woodland generally,

including some considerable-sized trees. No definite records of regeneration from seed. Planted trees irregularly recorded. S Europe, N Africa and Asia Minor. Ass: *Acer pseudoplatanus, Fagus sylvatica, Pinus sylvestris, Quercus robur, Tilia × europaea.*

### *Quercus cerris* L.
**Turkey Oak**

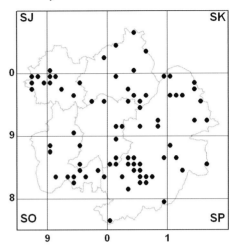

*79. Neophyte. A deciduous tree, not common but found in a wide range of habitats: mixed deciduous woodland, hedgerows, by canals and railway lines, sewage works, cemeteries, golf courses, university grounds, but especially in parkland. Largely planted, but it certainly has the potential to spread by seed, especially on sandier soils, and it is probable that the records on post-industrial sites include some self-generated from seed. Turkey Oak has an ecological impact, it is host for the Knopper Gall wasp (*Andricus quercuscalicis*) which affects acorns of nearby English Oaks. Grows on average to dry soils that are intermediate in base status and fairly fertile. Europe and Asia.

### *Quercus cerris* L. × *Q. robur* L.
1. Mill Lane nature reserve, Walsall (SP017999, M.G. Bloxham & N. Curnow, 2008), but Stace (2010) considers intermediate plants to be one or other parent with unusual leaf-shapes.

### *Quercus × crenata* Lam.
(*Q. cerris × Q. suber*)
**Lucombe Oak**
3. Neophyte. A large semi-evergreen tree. Park Farm Wood, Sandwell Valley (SP020913, M.G. Bloxham, 2001); old plantation woodland at Saltwells LNR (SO931873, J. Akers, 1998); The Leasowes Park (SO980841, H. Edwards, 2006). Old record: Europa Copse, Sandwell Valley (SP018912, TCH, 1988). All B&BC records are probably planted and are likely to originate from the hybrid which arose in

W. Lucombe's nursery in Exeter in 1762, however in Europe this hybrid can occur naturally wherever the parent species grow together; it is fertile and can be self-sown. Backcrosses do occur.

### *Quercus ilex* L.
### Evergreen Oak; Holme Oak

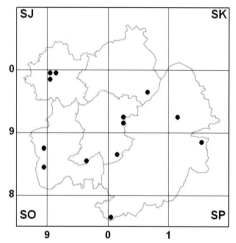

13. Neophyte. An evergreen tree found planted in woodland and parkland; there are two lovely specimens either side of the main road by the Molineux football stadium in W'ton (SO912992, ICT, 2006). The first records for vc. 39 were from near Holy Well, Sandwell Park (SP025913, BRF) & in the Nature Trail Guide for Haden Hill (SO9585, Anon.) both 1975. None of these records seem to be spontaneous, although several bushes in the woodland understorey at Doe Bank Wood (SP066962, MWP, ICT, PLR & JAH, 2006) may be regeneration rather than plantings. Mediterranean.

### *Quercus petraea* (Matt.) Liebl.
### Sessile Oak, Durmast Oak

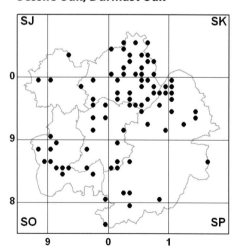

*84. Native. Ax. A deciduous tree, recorded from woodland, nature reserves, farmland, golf courses, railway and canal banks. It is rarely as common as *Q. robur*, and often occurs as isolated individuals, suggesting

planting. Nevertheless it is quite frequent in some areas, and across Sutton Park and in some smaller old woodlands (often now surrounded by housing) in the Sutton area and E Walsall it can be abundant. Like *Q. robur* it does not require rich soil, and it is probably favoured over *Q. robur* in more acid, damper soils. Ass: *Betula pendula*, *Ilex aquifolium*, *Quercus × rosacea*, *Quercus robur*, *Sorbus aucuparia*.

### *Quercus × rosacea* Bechst.
(*Q. petraea* × *Q. robur*)
Sometimes called **Hybrid Oak**

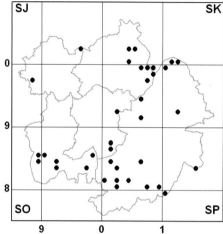

37. Native. A large deciduous tree, fertile and interfertile with both parents and showing a varying range of combination of, and intermediates between, the characters of the parent species. This together with the variability of the parents may have led to under-recording. Recorded from woodland, parkland, river and streamsides, scrub and street verges, often but not always with one or both of the parents.

### *Quercus robur* L.
### Pendunculate Oak, English Oak

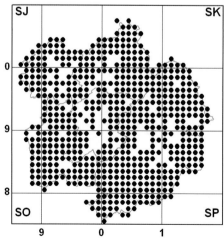

*615. Native. A long-lived deciduous tree and a dominant canopy tree in many of our old woods. In B&BC it is much

commoner than *Q. petraea* and found just about everywhere, either spontaneously or as a planted tree. Roadside, woodland, scrub, nature reserves, railways, canals, tips, farmland, parkland, church grounds, hedgerows, golf courses, quarries, hospital grounds, sewage works, allotments, common land, colonising the remains of Walsall power station, a rock escarpment in Sedgley, a racecourse and a BMX track. The map suggests that it may be slightly discouraged in some of the inner urban areas. Grows in damp to dry soils with a wide range of, but essentially intermediate, fertility and base status. Ass: *Acer pseudoplatanus*, *Betula pendula*, *Fagus sylvatica*, *Fraxinus excelsior*, *Ilex aquifolium*, *Quercus × rosacea*, *Quercus petraea*, *Sorbus aucuparia*.

### *Quercus rubra* L.
### Red Oak

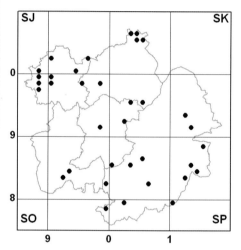

34. Neophyte. A large deciduous tree recorded from parkland, woodland, farmland, common land and as a roadside tree. Mostly planted trees, rarely appearing self-set. N America.

Other records of planted Oak species from within our period include: *Quercus castaneifolia* C.A. Mey. (Chestnut-leaved Oak) and *Quercus garryana* Douglas ex Hook. (Garry Oak or Oregon White Oak), both from West Park W'ton (SO9099); *Quercus coccinea* Münchh. (Scarlet Oak) recorded in Sutton Park (SP1195, SP1196) and from the Northfield area, SP0279; *Quercus pubescens* Willd. (Downy Oak) in High Street, Tettenhall (SJ885000); *Quercus × turneri* Willd. (*Q. ilex* × *Q. robur*) (Turner's Oak) recorded from a car park at the Eye Hospital, Chapel Ash, W'ton (SO903986, BRF, 1996).

### 53. MYRICACEAE
*Myrica gale* L. (Bog-myrtle) was planted in a bog garden at Merridale School, W'ton in 1984, and was still there in 2008 (SO9087, ICT, 2008).

## 54. JUGLANDACEAE

### *Juglans regia* L.
### Walnut

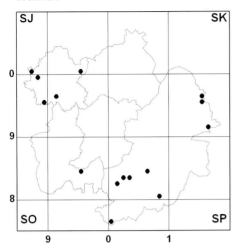

15. Neophyte, although it has probably been grown in gardens since Roman times. A large deciduous tree, the few records are mostly planted in hedgerows, woodland, the grounds of large houses (now often parks) and on golf courses. There are doubtless more in parks and gardens which have not been recorded. Rarely, the record suggests self-setting: e.g. a seedling in Phoenix Street, Brierley Hill (SO918689, CBW, 2006). Walnut has an ecological impact: chemicals in the rooting area of up to 12–18m inhibit the growth of some plants. Asia.

*Pterocarya fraxinifolia* (Poir.) Spach (Caucasian Wingnut) is a rarely planted tree: West Park (SO9099, B. Pugh, 1996), a grove in Cofton Park (SP003763, ICT, MWP, EMP & R. Seadon, 2007) and Highbury Park (SP067825, EMP, 2007).

## 55. BETULACEAE

### *Betula pendula* Roth
### Silver Birch

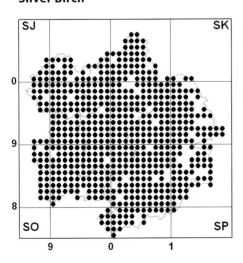

*614. Native. A deciduous pioneer tree, common throughout, colonising open areas in woodland, heathland, and under-managed grassland, also house clearance sites, waste land, railway and canal banks, quarries, post-industrial sites, sometimes high on the walls of derelict buildings and occasionally surprisingly large specimens. Also abundantly planted in parks, as a street tree and in amenity woodland plantings. Relatively short-lived especially in deep shade. Not always easy to distinguish from *Betula pubescens* or the hybrid between the two, but it seems to be favoured by drier, lighter nutrient-poor soils, from base-poor to base-rich. One cultivar has been recorded from our area, **B. pendula cultivar 'Laciniata' (Swedish Birch or Cut-leaved Birch)** (SK0402, JEH, 2001). Ass: *Betula pubescens, Crataegus monogyna, Cytisus scoparius, Pteridium aquilinum, Quercus robur, Salix caprea, Ulex europaeus.*

### *Betula* × *aurata* Borkh.
(*B. pendula* × *B. pubescens*)
5. Native. Rarely recorded; possibly some records of *Betula pubescens* are this. Usually with one or both parents. There are five recent records from B&BC, from Walsall Wood (SK045032, JEH, 2001); Brownhills (SK047069, JEH, 2001); Lane Avenue Allotments (SO995989, ICT & JaH, 2008); Rotton Park Reservoir (SP043867, P. Orwin, 2002); *Betula pubescens* woodland, Sutton Park (SP097984, ICT, MWP & JWP, 2008). Older records from Pelsall Common (SK0104).

### *Betula pubescens* Ehrh.
### Downy Birch

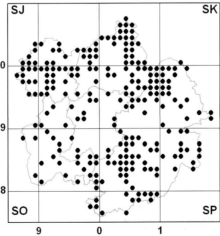

*239. Native. A deciduous, pioneer tree, somewhat less common than *B. pendula*, but probably under-recorded. In a similar wide range of habitats but with a tendency towards damper situations and much less frequently planted. Ass: *Betula pendula, Pteridium aquilinum, Quercus petraea,*

*Quercus robur, Salix cinerea, Ulex gallii, Ulex europaeus.*

There is an old record for **subsp. tortuosa** (Ledeb.) Nyman, Sutton Park (SP0998, E. F. Warburg, 1971?). This subsp. is associated with upland areas of N Britain, where it replaces the lowland **subsp. pubescens**, to which otherwise all B&BC material is likely to belong.

*Betula papyrifera* Marshall (Paper-bark Birch) is known from two plantations, in Haden Hill Park (SO958852, CRP, 2002) and, less recently, dominant in Merry Hill woodland (SO886974, PWS & D. Morse, 1988).

A few other *Betula* spp. have been recorded as planted: *Betula utilis* D. Don (*B. jaquemontii* Spach) (Himalayan Birch) in West Park, W'ton (SO9099), and in Woodland Walk, Penn (SO8996, BRF, 1993); *Betula maximowicziana* Regel (Monarch Birch): two on the edge of the railway, by waste pasture, Deepfields, Coseley (SO941947, BRF, 1991); *Betula nigra* L. (River Birch): The Cedars, Compton (SO887987, BRF, 1992).

### *Alnus glutinosa* (L.) Gaertn.
### Alder

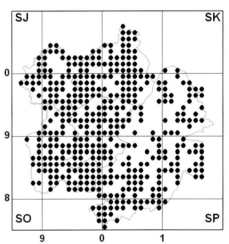

*433. Native. A deciduous tree associated with water margins. Via a micro-organism it can extract and use nitrogen from the air. Common almost throughout and recorded by rivers, streams, brooks, canals, lakes, pools, reservoirs, and from woodland, farmland, meadows, nature reserves, parkland and in amenity tree plantings especially on post-industrial sites. Favoured by wet to damp soils, often poorly drained with a fluctuating water table, usually of intermediate base and nutrient status. Three kinds of Alder woodland are recognised in the National Vegetation Classification and at least two are found in B&BC. The *Alnus glutinosa – Carex paniculata* woodland is found in Sutton Park (and possibly elsewhere: there is a last remnant at Edgbaston Pool). The more widespread type is the *Alnus glutinosa – Urtica dioica* woodland. Alder is also present in some kinds of damp Oak woodland, and it has been planted in almost every recent tree plantation on wet and post-industrial sites. A stand on the summit of a coal spoil heap at Peascroft Wood, Bilston was planted there *circa* 1900. Ass: *Salix cinerea, Salix fragilis, Salix viminalis*.

The cultivar 'Laciniata' was planted by the stream bank, Wightwick Manor (SO8698, BRF, 1991).

### *Alnus* × *hybrida* A. Braun ex Rchb.
(*A. glutinosa* × *A. incana*)

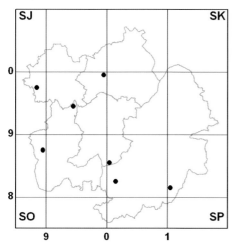

7. Native × Neophyte. Occasionally recorded, usually in plantings of either or both parents. It is rarely clear whether these are spontaneous hybrids or were planted with the parents.

### *Alnus incana* (L.) Moench
**Grey Alder**

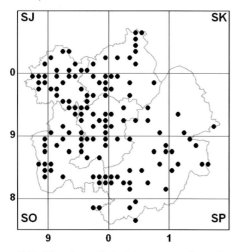

*134. Neophyte. A deciduous tree planted in woodland, parkland, farmland, nature reserves, rivers, streams, brooks and canals. Spreading by suckers and occasionally by seed. Grows best on damp, but not waterlogged, soils of intermediate base status and quite low fertility. W Europe.

### *Alnus cordata* (Loisel.) Duby
**Italian Alder**

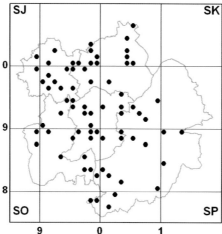

74. Neophyte. A deciduous tree, widely recorded in amenity plantings in parks and on waste land, on canal towpaths, stream and pool banks, railway and motorway embankments and on commons. Usually they are young planted trees, but quite often these are recorded with seedlings or self-sown young trees and the plant is currently increasing in frequency. Thrives on drier, poorer soils than other Alders. Italy and Albania.

### *Carpinus betulus* L.
**Hornbeam**

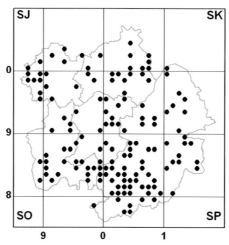

145. Native, but almost always appears to be introduced in B&BC. A long-lived deciduous tree recorded from woodland (including old woodland), parkland, common land, playing fields, hedgerows and churchyards. Thrives in moist soils of intermediate fertility and base status. Self-set trees or seedlings are recorded, and when an old Hornbeam plantation in Windmill Hill Wood, W'ton (SO872982) was thinned in the 1980s, quite a dense understorey of seedlings appeared briefly. Also tetrad SO98E.

### *Corylus avellana* L.
**Hazel**

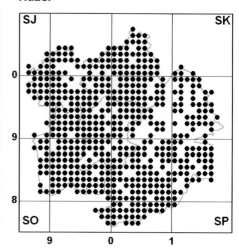

*560. Native. A deciduous multi-stemmed shrub or small tree. It is common throughout B&BC as an understorey in old Oak and Oak-Ash woodland, especially where there is a coppicing history and it is also abundant in old hedges. It is also enthusiastically planted in amenity planting schemes in parks, public open spaces, waste land and reclamation sites. It is usually stripped of its fruit by Grey Squirrels, but (possibly as a result) seedlings can be frequent. Grows well in open to medium-shaded situations on most soils which are not waterlogged or seriously impoverished. Ass: *Acer campestre, Crataegus monogyna, Fraxinus excelsior, Prunus spinosa, Quercus robur*.

### *Corylus maxima* Mill.
**Filbert**
0. Neophyte. Recorded on waste ground at Ettingshall (SO9396, PN, 1994) as the cultivar 'Purpurea'.

### *Corylus colurna* L.
**Turkish Hazel**
1. Neophyte. Land off Teddesley Street, Walsall (SP015990, N. Sibbett, 2008). Quite commonly planted as a street tree, e.g. in B'ham city centre.

## 56. CUCURBITACEAE

### *Bryonia dioica* Jacq.
**White Bryony**
*214. Native. A dioecious, scrambling, tuberous, perennial herb, found predominantly in hedges, also in scrub, woodland and on fences and not confined to old or mature habitats. Found throughout B&BC but apparently much commoner in the NE and the SW fringe. It was the first plant to reappear after a hedgerow in Tipton was pulled out and replaced with a metal fence. Grows in

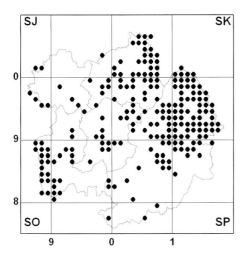

well-lit or shaded, sheltered places on moist, fairly base- and nutrient-rich soils. Its distribution pattern in B&BC is unusual; in Britain as a whole it seems to disappear at quite moderate altitudes, but this cannot be the factor operating here. Ass: *Alliaria petiolata, Galium aparine, Lamium album, Rubus fruticosus* agg.

### *Cucumis sativus* L.
### Cucumber
1. Casual. One well grown plant on disturbed ground edge of tarmac path, Hawkesley (SP041786, JJD, 2001).

## 57. CELASTRACEAE

### *Euonymus europaeus* L.
### Spindle

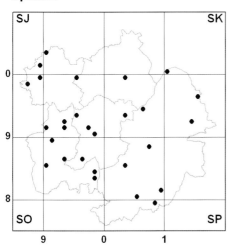

28. Native introduction? A deciduous shrub or small tree of semi-shaded, base-rich soils of intermediate fertility, particularly overlying limestone. In B&BC most often a persistent introduction in planting schemes. Possibly native on Wren's Nest (SO9392, SO9492).

### *Euonymus japonicus* Thunb.
### Evergreen Spindle
2. Neophyte. Garden outcast. By the River

Cole at Stechford (SP131881, CBW, 1997); Sutton Park (SP101979, SPG, 1998). First record for vc. 39: footpath, by the fence of an old cottage, Mushroom Green, Dudley (SO93648656, BRF, 1992). Japan.

## 58. PARNASSIACEAE

### *Parnassia palustris* L.
### Grass-of-Parnassus
2. Native. Ax. Perennial herb. Scattered in an extensive base-enriched flush on the western margin of the stream feeding Longmoor Pool, Sutton Park. The flush, which extends into two 1km squares (SP0995, SP0996), is the only site for the species in the vice-county. Also recorded from SP0997 in 1841 and in SP0998 by Cadbury *et al.* (1971). Ass: *Galium uliginosum, Valeriana dioica.*

## 59. OXALIDACEAE

### *Oxalis corniculata* L.
### Procumbent Yellow-sorrel

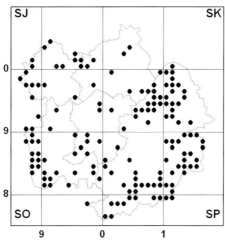

151. Neophyte. This procumbent, short-lived perennial herb usually enters gardens and allotment sites as a weed in pot plants from garden centres. Its ripe seeds are ejected explosively from the capsules into nearby paths, borders, pavement cracks and disturbed ground where it rapidly becomes established. **Var. *atropurpurea*** Planch. is more strictly correct for most of our purple-leaved plants. Seldom far from habitation, distribution distinctly suburban. Native range unknown. Ass: *Arabidopsis thaliana, Cardamine hirsuta, Epilobium montanum, Lamium amplexicaule, Plantago major, Poa annua, Polygonum aviculare, Sagina apetala sensu lato, Sagina procumbens, Senecio vulgaris, Trifolium dubium, Viola × wittrockiana.*

### *Oxalis exilis* A. Cunn.
### Least Yellow-sorrel
77. Neophyte. A prostrate annual or short-

▲ *Bryonia dioica*

▲ *Parnassia palustris*

▲ *Oxalis corniculata*

▲ *Oxalis articulata*

▲ *Oxalis acetosella*

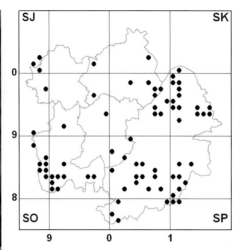

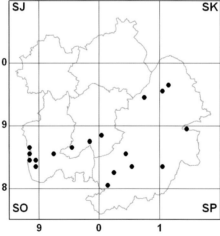

lived perennial herb seemingly restricted to garden lawns, paving and paths and along the base of walls and crevices in paved areas in sunny, well-drained sites in B&BC. Most plants are likely to have arrived as pot plant weeds from garden centres and become established in much the same way as *O. corniculata*. New Zealand and Tasmania. First vc. 39 record: 50 plants between paving slabs at Highfield School, W'ton (SO880963, CBW & BRF, 1983). Ass: *Bellis perennis, Elytrigia repens, Oxalis corniculata, Prunella vulgaris, Taraxacum* spp., *Poa annua*.

### *Oxalis stricta* L.
### Upright Yellow-sorrel

18. Casual. Similar to *O. corniculata* but always erect with slightly larger leaves and flowers. Occasionally becoming established in overgrown gardens, paths and cultivated land, seldom if ever far from habitation and almost certainly introduced into gardens with pot plants. More tolerant of shaded or semi-shaded situations than either *O. corniculata* or *O. exilis*. N America.

### *Oxalis articulata* Savigny
### Pink-sorrel

15. Neophyte. The few records for this perennial herb are for isolated individuals

or small groups in disturbed areas and on waste ground near to habitation. The first convincing record outside cultivation in vc. 39 was a small patch on the side of a footpath over the canal at Coseley (SO941943, WAT, 1987). E S America.

### *Oxalis acetosella* L.
### Wood-sorrel

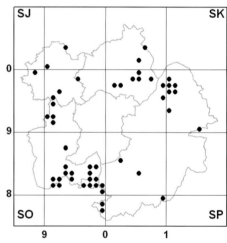

*51. Native. Ax. A creeping, patch-forming, perennial herb of moisture-retentive moderately acid, more or less infertile soils in deciduous woodland, dingles, coppices and shady hedgerow banks. Predominately associated with old woodlands. Declining in B&BC in recent years due largely to habitat loss, it is less common than many of its woodland associates in otherwise suitable habitats which are subject to disturbance or competition from faster-growing species. Ass: *Anemone nemorosa, Hyacinthoides non-scripta, Stellaria holostea, Viola riviniana*.

### *Oxalis debilis* Kunth.
### Large-flowered Pink-sorrel

7. Neophyte. Perennial herb. Modern records are all apparently garden rejects or relics of cultivation and all are unconfirmed field identifications: in pavement at the

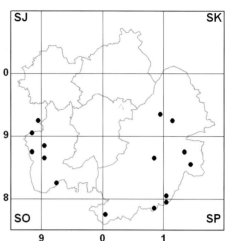

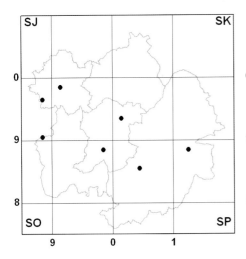

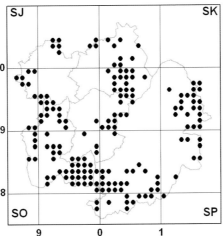

foot of a garden wall, Alum Rock Road (SP121881, MWP & ICT, 2006); B'ham Botanical Gardens (SP049853, JWP, 2007); Strathfield Walk, W'ton (SO880966, ICT, 2007); waste land by ring road, W'ton (SO917980, ICT & JaH, 2007); Newton Street Allotments (SP014931, MWP, 2008). S America.

### Oxalis latifolia Kunth
### Garden Pink-sorrel
2. Neophyte. Records both from roadside verges, both unconfirmed field identifications: Longdale Road (SP052777, ICT, MWP & JaH, 2007) and Fox Hollies Road (SP144942, ICT, MWP & EVJC, 2007). C & S America.

### Oxalis tetraphylla Cav.
### Four-leaved Pink-sorrel
1. Neophyte. Cultivated plot, Quinton Nurseries Allotment (SO995845, MWP, 2008). Mexico.

### Oxalis incarnata L.
### Pale Pink-sorrel
2. Neophyte. Well established beneath window and spreading along path near warm air outlet, Alcester Road South, Kings Heath (SP0781, MWP, 2000); small patch established at foot of tower-block wall, Severn Road, Cradley (SO939842, WAT, 2001). S Africa.

## 60. EUPHORBIACEAE

### Mercurialis perennis L.
### Dog's Mercury
*173. Native. Ax. Rhizomatous perennial herb. Frequent to locally common in many of the older deciduous woodlands and hedge bases in shaded and semi-shaded situations in intermediate to moderately fertile soils. Absent from many parts of the built-up area except where tiny fragments of hedges and woodland have survived as in parks and large gardens but the distribution clearly has a strong rural bias.

Its frequency in E Sutton and E B'ham is not strongly paralleled in other old woodland species. Ass: *Anemone nemorosa, Carex sylvatica, Circaea lutetiana, Ficaria verna, Stellaria holostea.*

### Mercurialis annua L.
### Annual Mercury

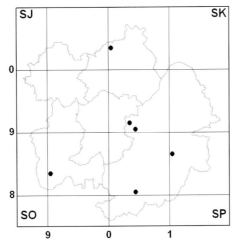

6. Archaeophyte. An annual of rare occurrence with only a scattering of records for individuals or small populations appearing as a weed of cultivation in gardens, allotments and in paving. Probably essentially casual in our area; at least one population (SP1086) is thought to have arrived in an allotment "in a packet of vegetable seeds".

### Euphorbia dulcis L.
### Sweet Spurge
1. Neophyte. Perennial herb, in plots and waste areas and under hedges, Jeffcock allotments, W'ton (SO900973, CBW, 2008).

### Euphorbia oblongata Griseb.
### Balkan Spurge
5. Neophyte. Perennial herb. Small patch in grass behind houses, off Manor Way, Lapal (SO976832, WAT, 2001); compacted, open area on a plot of post-industrial land, New Bond Street, Bordesley, 20+ plants growing

with several other garden derivatives (SP084862, MWP, conf. EJC, 2004); disturbed ground (SP043878, MWP, 2006); disturbed ground by Walsall Road (B4151) (SP106989, MWP, 2007); allotment gardens, Sutton Road, Walsall, a few plants seeded into paving (SP032979, MWP, ICT, JaH, SC & J.M. Hughes, 2008). Balkans and Aegean.

### Euphorbia platyphyllos L.
### Broad-leaved Spurge
0. Casual. Annual. Old record: Seven plants amongst the rubble of demolished houses, Terrace Street, Blackheath (SO968864, LG, 1987).

### Euphorbia helioscopia L.
### Sun Spurge

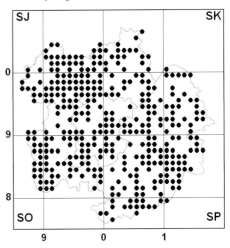

*361. Archaeophyte. An annual of sunny, well-drained, fertile sites and particularly common in the well-cultivated soil typically found in allotment gardens. Also a common weed of spoil heaps and post-housing sites subjected to recent disturbance. Ass: *Arabidopsis thaliana, Capsella bursa-pastoris, Euphorbia peplus, Fumaria officinalis, Papaver somniferum.*

### Euphorbia lathyris L.
### Caper Spurge

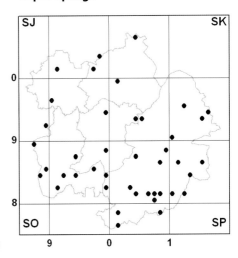

42. Introduced native. A glabrous biennial of infrequent and rather erratic occurrence, appearing in neglected and abandoned gardens and allotments, on traveller spoil, post-housing and industrial land recovering from recent disturbance. Sometimes a weed of gardens but invariably weeded-out before reaching maturity.

### *Euphorbia exigua* L.
**Dwarf Spurge**

2. Archaeophyte. NT. The sole known extant spontaneous site for this nationally declining annual is a small, persistent colony, growing in the Scree Garden in Winterbourne Botanical Gardens, Edgbaston, where it co-exists among alpines and is thought to have been introduced into the bed at some time with one of the plantings. Plants appear annually despite being "periodically weeded-out" (SP052838, MWP & JWP, 2007). This population has been deliberately and successfully introduced into the garden of one of the authors (SO959894, MWP, 2008) as a conservation measure and appears annually in sink gardens and in paving cracks.

### *Euphorbia peplus* L.
**Petty Spurge**

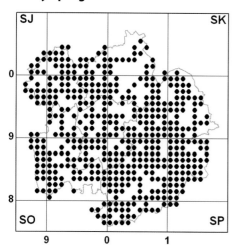

*487. Archaeophyte. A very common annual of nutrient-rich, sunny sites in gardens, allotments and spoil heaps and by far the most frequently occurring spurge to appear in paving and paths. Ass: *Arabidopsis thaliana, Capsella bursa-pastoris, Euphorbia helioscopia, Fumaria officinalis, Papaver somniferum, Poa annua.*

### *Euphorbia esula* agg.

A very difficult group; the next six taxa from the aggregate have been reported from our area.

### *Euphorbia waldsteinii* (Soják) Czerep.
**Waldstein's Spurge**

1. Neophyte. Reported by a roadside hedge, Penn, W'ton (SO8894, CBW, 2003). Europe & Asia.

### *Euphorbia × pseudovirgata* (Schur) Soó
(*E. waldsteinii* (Soják) Czerep. × *E. esula*)
**Twiggy Spurge**

1. Neophyte. There are a number of old records for this taxon: railway station, Smethwick (SK0288, WHH, 1952); a small patch on waste ground near the railway, Wallbrook (SO947931, WAT, det. E.R. Smith 1987); occasional on rough pasture and a spoil bank at Deepfields, (SO942947, BRF, det. A.R. Smith, 1991); a few by the towpath at Dudley Port, (SO971916, BRF, det. A.R. Smith, 1991); N side of Northfield Road, by railway, Netherton (SO948878, ST, 1991); quarry, Pouk Hill (SO9999, JPM, 1991); (SP0987, JWP, A. Radcliffe-Smith, 1989). The only record from the current recording period is a few plants on a grassy bank against fence, B'ham Canal towpath (SO947935, APD, 2004).

### *Euphorbia esula* L.
**Leafy Spurge**

1. Neophyte. Perennial herb. Small colony on derelict railway track bed, Blowers Green, Dudley (SO944897, MWP, 2003). Several more plants 300 yards away in 2004. Europe. A specimen was shown to EJC who thought it could be *E. × gayeri* Boros & Soó (*E. waldsteinii* (Soják) Czerep. × *E. cyparissias*) but it was not confirmed.

### *Euphorbia cyparissias* L.
**Cypress Spurge**

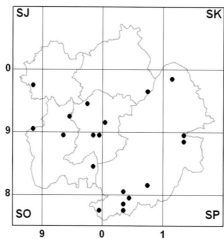

19. Neophyte. A rhizomatous, patch-forming perennial herb found in a number of widely scattered sites. Most of the records are for patches spreading into nearby paving from gardens in residential

areas, but a few represent much larger, more significant populations, for example the one well-naturalised on the bank and along the disused railway track bed, Blowers Green, Dudley (SO937892, MWP, 2006).

### *Euphorbia boissieriana* (Woronow) Prokh.
**× *E. esula* L.**

0. Neophyte. Reported from railway sidings at Small Heath, B'ham, where it covered 2–3 square metres and was there for at least 3 years (SP095872, JWP, det. A.R. Radcliffe-Smith, 1989). The site is now believed to be built over.

### *Euphorbia × pseudolucida* Waldst.
(possibly *E. lucida* Waldst. × *E. waldsteinii*)

0. Neophyte. Another member of the *E. esula* group, reported as a single plant in a strip of rough grazing between the Stour Valley and Lye Industrial Estate (SO928849, WAT, det. A.R. Radcliffe-Smith, 1988). First UK record.

### *Euphorbia amygdaloides* L.
**subsp. *amygdaloides***
**Wood Spurge**

1. Native. Tufted perennial. In B&BC probably at the N edge of its range in UK. There is only one definite record, from a glade in woodland associated with the colleges E of Griffin's Hill, Selly Oak (SP038815, CBW, 1997). It is not completely impossible that some records ascribed to subsp. *robbiae* may actually be this.

### *Euphorbia amygdaloides* L.
**subsp. *robbiae* (Turrill) Stace**

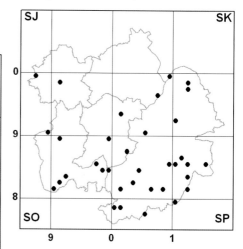

35. Neophyte. A frequently cultivated, ground-covering, rhizomatous perennial herb spreading from gardens or persisting as a garden throw-out in a few places, usually in shady road verges rich in leaf mould in residential areas. Its scarcity in W'ton and the Black Country is difficult to explain. NW Turkey.

### *Euphorbia characias* L.
### Mediterranean Spurge

3. Neophyte. Perennial herb; all records are thought to be subsp. *venata* (Willd.) Litard. (subsp. *wulfenii* (Hoppe ex Koch) Radcl.-Sm.), a popular garden plant. A persistent patch on rough grassy mound, Haden Hill Park, Halesowen (SO957853, MWP, 2005); derelict site, Holford Way, Witton (SP079914, MWP, 2005); former Bean Road foundry site, Tipton (SO945927, MWP & T. Oliver, 2009).

### *Euphorbia griffithii* Hook f.
### Griffith's Spurge

1. One record for this popular garden plant. Persistent garden throw-out of cultivar 'Dixter' in waste ground / scrub, Belle Vale, Halesowen (SO955845, WAT, 2001). Bhutan & Tibet.

### *Euphorbia myrsinites* L.
### Broad-leaved Glaucous-spurge

1. Neophyte. Three or four sprawling plants in an otherwise abandoned grassy garden, Russell's Hall (SO927903, CBW, 2006). SE Europe & Asia Minor.

## 62. SALICACEAE

### *Populus alba* L.
### White Poplar

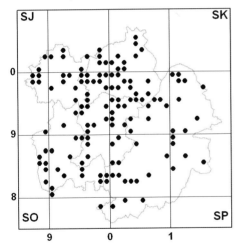

*134. Neophyte. A freely suckering tree, commonly planted and spreading vigorously especially when felled. Particularly common as part of multi-species urban planting schemes on motorway embankments, playing fields, parks, golf courses, public open spaces, amenity plantings. Mature trees not common. Central & SE Europe.

### *Populus* × *canescens* (Aiton) Smith
(*P. alba* × *P. tremula*)
### Grey Poplar

*80. Neophyte. A planted tree, found occasionally in parks, churchyards,

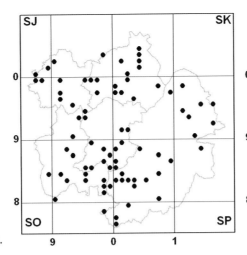

golf courses, gardens and in old mixed deciduous plantations and also in recent amenity plantings. Also tetrad SO98E. Europe.

### *Populus tremula* L.
### Aspen

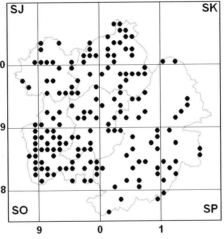

*168. Native. A tree, often forming thickets by suckering, often planted in mixed deciduous woodlands, parks, golf courses, amenity plantings, etc. Also with an apparently spontaneous distribution in old dingle woodlands and in hedges on base-intermediate and often nutrient-poor moist or damp soils. Also in quarries and post-industrial sites, not necessarily damp, sometimes deliberately planted but also sometimes acting as a colonising species in relatively bare areas with poorly developed soils. Ass: *Betula pendula*, *Betula pubescens*, *Alnus glutinosa*, *Salix caprea*, *Salix cinerea*.

### *Populus nigra* L. subsp. *betulifolia*
(Pursh) Dippel.
### Black-poplar

26. Native, but possibly largely planted in B&BC. Ax. This is the distinctive broadly spreading tree typically found by water courses which has been largely replaced by

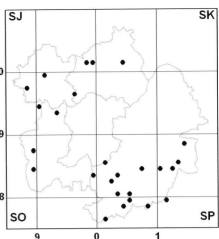

hybrids with *P. deltoides*. Recorded, typically as isolated trees, from brook sides, flood plains, remnant old hedges, sometimes apparently as boundary markers; but also sometimes clearly planted in parks, cemeteries, golf courses, etc. Typically on moist to damp, nutrient- and base-rich soils. Ass: *Alnus glutinosa*, *Fraxinus excelsior*, *Quercus robur*, *Salix fragilis*.

### *Populus nigra* L. – Fastigiate cultivars
### Lombardy Poplars

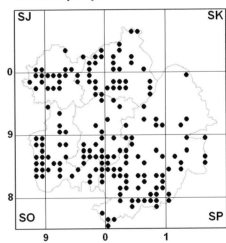

*175. Neophytes. Several fastigiate poplars have been widely planted in B&BC, mostly in residential areas in garden boundaries, hedges, parks, cemeteries, golf courses, by canals, often in rows. They include the narrowly fastigiate male true Lombardy Poplar, 'Italica', which is most commonly recorded, the more broadly fastigiated male 'Planteriensis', which is a hybrid between 'Italica' and subsp. *betulifolia*, which has been recorded by Rowley Regis railway station (SO979865, JJD, 2005) and by Sarehole Mill (SP098818, JWP, 1995) and the much broader female 'Gigantea' which has not so far been distinguished in B&BC. These plants do not spread by seed but may sucker. Garden origins.

### *Populus × canadensis* Moench
(*P. nigra × P. deltoides* Marshall)
**Hybrid Black-poplar**

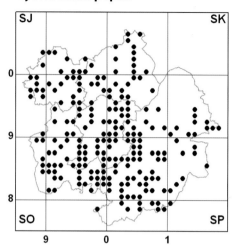

*223. Neophyte. Widely planted in mixed deciduous plantations, amenity plantings, parks, golf courses, cemeteries etc. and rapidly becoming massive trees, which often lean alarmingly and are as a result preferentially felled. Still however widely recorded. Garden origin.

It exists in numerous cultivars, which have sometimes been recorded. Cultivar 'Serotina' (*P. nigra* subsp. *nigra × P. deltoides*) (Black-Italian Poplar) may be the commonest, but the only records are old: Scott's Green, Dudley (SO932892, BRF, 1987) and by Bourne Brook, Harborne (SP0381, BRF, 1987). Cultivar 'Gelrica' has been recorded twice: Bournville (SP048804, EMP & A. Millward, 2004); Cocks Moors Woods golf course (SP0780, A. Millward & EMP, 2006). Cultivar 'Eugenei' (*P.* 'Regenerata' × *P. nigra* 'Italica') (Carolina Poplar) was recorded in SK0401, SK0402 & SK0404 by JEH in 2001.

### *Populus × jackii* Sarg.
(*P. deltoides × P. balsamifera*)
**Balm-of-Gilead**

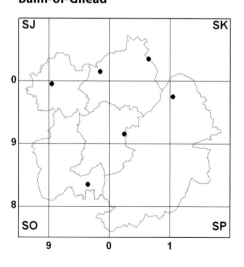

6. Neophyte. Probably always planted in B&BC. West Park W'ton (SO9099, B. Pugh, 1996), Rough Wood (SJ985012, PN, 2007); Castlebank Plantation (SK061034, ICT, 2008); Sutton Park (SP1097, SB, 1997); off Dog Kennel Lane (SO968832, ST, 1998). A tree in the bank of Ice House lake in the Sandwell Valley (SP021914, MWP, 1999) is probably also this. N America & garden origin.

### *Populus trichocarpa* Torr. & A. Gray ex Hook.
**Western Balsam-poplar**

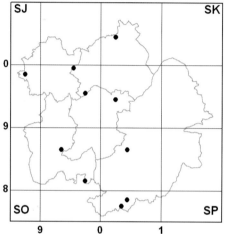

10. Neophyte. Commonly planted for rapid production of timber, it is recorded from public open spaces, golf courses, etc. W N America.

### *Populus* 'Balsam Spire'
(*P. trichocarpa × P. balsamifera*)
**Hybrid Balsam-poplar**
1. Neophyte. Now commonly planted in UK as a windbreak and for timber, in B&BC it is reported from Lark Rise Fields area (SK123001, SAHA & PWS, 2004). N America.

### *Populus balsamifera* L.
**Eastern Balsam-poplar**
4. Neophyte. Planted for ornament and for timber. A group of six near an industrial estate, Mill Race Lane, Amblecote (SO902847, APD, 1998); B'ham city centre E (SP077876, AS, 2002); Stechford (SP120862, ICT, DJA, DH, C. Gleeson & C. Wilmer, 2004); former Bean Road Foundry (SO945927, MWP & T. Oliver, 2009). E N America.

### *Salix pentandra* L.
**Bay Willow**
14. Native, but probably always planted in B&BC. A large shrub or small tree with a few records from recent amenity plantations on commons, in parks, on waste land, by canals. Grows on damp or

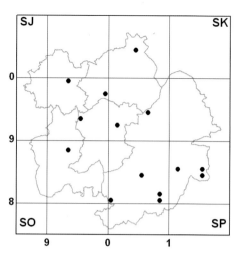

wet, base and nutrient-poor to -medium soils.

### *Salix × meyeriana* Rostk. ex Willd.
(*S. pentandra × S. fragilis*)
**Shiny-leaved Willow**
1. Hybrid between native × alien species. A large shrub or small tree. Hay Barn recreation grounds (SP113854, ICT, MWP, PLR & A. Rostański, 2006). There is also a pre-survey record from bank of River Rea (SP028789, JJD, 1994). The records for *S. pentandra* might include more *S. × meyeriana*. Spontaneous hybrid.

### *Salix × ehrhartiana* Sm.
(*S. pentandra × S. alba*)
**Ehrhart's Willow**
1. Neophyte. Recent tree plantation at Moseley Bog (SP092821, ICT, MWP, JWP & PLR, 2007). Garden origin.

### *Salix fragilis* L.
**Crack-willow**

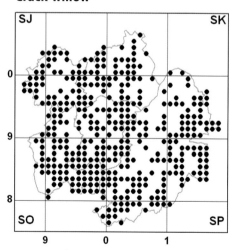

*399. Archaeophyte. A large tree or pollard, commonly planted throughout B&BC, but regenerating spontaneously from shed twigs under wet conditions. Prefers damp or wet, base- and nutrient-medium to rich soils. Found beside rivers, streams and ditches, in hedges, and sometimes in extensive stands in wet woodland, often with other *Salix* spp., suggesting the remains of old osier beds. Ass: *Alnus glutinosa, Fraxinus excelsior, Salix cinerea, Salix viminalis.*

There are a few records for the male **var. furcata** Ser. ex Gaudin: wet woodland at Northycote Farm (SJ935030 & SJ934029, ICT & C. Waterson, 2005); woodland plantation, Greadier St (SJ975005, ICT, 1999); Buckpool area (SO895869, ICT, 2008). There are only old records for the female **var. russelliana** (Sm.) W.D.J. Koch (**Bedford Willow**): Sutton Park (SP0483, Cadbury *et al.*, 1971); five by the canal at Compton (SO883989, BRF, det. RDM, 1986); site of an old garden, roadside, Pearson Street, W'ton (SO915976, BRF, det. RDM, 1986) but this is almost certainly the predominant variety. The male var. *decipiens* (Hoffm.) W.D.J. Koch and the female var. *fragilis* have not been recorded in our area but may well be present.

### *Salix* × *rubens* Schrank
(*S. alba* × *S. fragilis*)
**Hybrid Crack-willow**

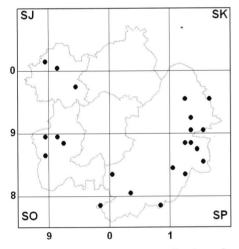

22. Archaeophyte. A large, usually planted, tree or pollard; some material planted in recent years by local authorities as '*Salix alba*' seems to be this hybrid. There are a few records from parkland, an industrial estate, canals, rivers, streams and brooks, including a plant from the Woodgate Valley perceived as a "young spontaneous sapling" (SP000834, CBW, 1996).

### *Salix* × *pendulina* Wender.
(*S. fragilis* × *S. babylonica* L.)
**Weeping Crack-willow**

2. Neophyte. A planted 'weeping willow', less common than *S.* × *sepulcralis* but probably under-recorded in B&BC. Perry Park Tree Nursery and BMX Track (SP069926, SAHA & M.J. Latham, 2008); a few trees planted on the Bourn Brook at Selly Oak (SP037832, CBW, 1997). Possibly

sometimes recorded as *S. babylonica* (see under *Salix* × *sepulcralis*).

### *Salix alba* L.
**White Willow**

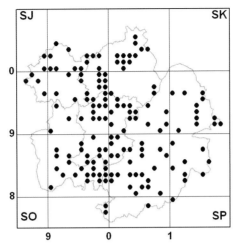

*154. Archaeophyte. A widely planted tree established typically in damp, fertile, base-rich soils across B&BC at the sides of canals, rivers, lakes, ponds and sewage works and also on waste land, industrial land, woodland and railway land. Also tetrad SO98E. Ass: *Alnus glutinosa, Fraxinus excelsior, Salix fragilis, Salix viminalis.*

There are two recent records of **var. vitellina** (L.) Stokes (the often planted **Golden Willow**): land at Delph Road (SO914862, J.G. Kelcey, 1997); Swan Pool and the Swag (SK040020, CRP, 1997). There is a single old record of **var. caerulea** (Sm.) Dumort. (**Cricket-bat Willow**) from by the River Rea (SP022788, AEEP & A. Reeves, 1988).

### *Salix* × *sepulcralis* Simonk.
(*S. alba* × *S. babylonica*)
**Weeping Willow**

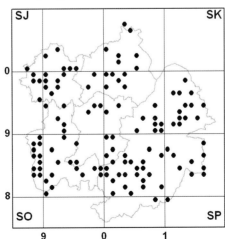

126. Neophyte. A tree planted throughout B&BC, although apparently less common in parts of Sandwell. It is frequently found in parks and public areas at the side of

rivers, pools and ponds. Also found in churchyards, by canals and on railway land. The first record for vc. 39 was from a canal towpath in Wednesfield (SJ9400, FGB, 1975). A large number of records made for *S. babylonica* L. have been added to the map, since the latter species is not hardy in the Midlands and almost all are likely to be this hybrid. It is possible that this means that some specimens of *S.* × *pendulina* have been included in the map for *S.* × *sepulcralis*. **Nothovar. Chrysocoma** (Dode) Meikle has occasionally been recorded. Garden origin.

### *Salix triandra* L.
**Almond Willow**

2. Archaeophyte. A streamside shrub or small tree only very occasionally recorded: Boots Land, Wightwick Wedge, probably planted (SO881985, SRP, M. Bryant, B. Hickey & P. Hodgson, 1995); small tree by stream, Cheviot Way, Lutley (SO948829, AWR, WAT & CBW, 2001). There are also some tetrad records from 1989–1994: SP08B, SP08F, SP08G, SP08L and SP18N (all CBW).

### *Salix* × *mollissima* Hoffm. ex Elwert
(*S. triandra* × *S. viminalis*)
**Sharp-stipuled Willow**

2. Archaeophyte. A shrub, often found in old osier beds. By the River Cole at Kitts Green (SP154876, CBW, 1997); by Merritts Brook, Manor Farm Park (SP023803, CBW, 1997); an earlier record is by the Bourn Brook, Selly Oak (SP035832, CBW, 1989).

### *Salix purpurea* L.
**Purple Willow**

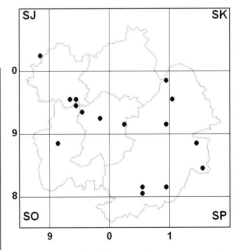

16. Native. A shrub or small tree, recorded from beside streams and rivers, at pool margins and in wet hollows on damp to winter-wet, base- and nutrient-medium to rich soils. Some records by the Rivers Rea and Cole are considered introductions, and in the UK it has been much planted as an osier in the past. At at least one site it

appears to have been brought in recently with canal dredgings, but there are others such as Fens Pools (SO9188) where it forms extensive and widespread stands. Ass: *Alnus glutinosa, Salix cinerea, Salix fragilis, Salix viminalis.*

### *Salix × rubra* Huds.
(*S. purpurea × S. viminalis*)
**Green-leaved Willow**
0. Native. Old record: several at the base of a railway bank, Wallbrook, Coseley (SO947925, BRF, 1988).

### *Salix × forbyana* Sm.
(*S. purpurea × S. viminalis × S. cinerea*)
**Fine Osier**
1. Native × native × alien. Another plant with a history as an osier crop plant. A single bush recorded from the River Rea (SP057799, JJD, 2001).

### *Salix daphnoides* Vill.
**European Violet-willow**

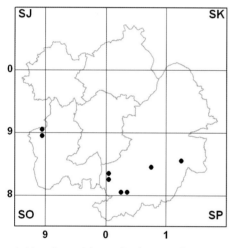

8. Neophyte. A large shrub or small tree, mostly planted as an amenity tree in our area, mostly on river banks and by pools but also in disused allotments and other drier open spaces. Europe.

### *Salix acutifolia* Willd.
**Siberian Violet-willow**
4. Neophyte. A large shrub or small tree, occasionally recorded from amenity plantings. Stechford Bridge (SP128878, CBW, 1997); Balsall Heath (SP083845, CBW, 1998); near Pensnett Church (SO916894, CBW, 2007) and on an industrial estate, W'ton (SO912972, CBW, 2007). E Europe.

### *Salix viminalis* L.
**Osier**
*182. Archaeophyte. Shrub or small tree, spreading readily from twigs and by seed. Found along rivers, streams, brooks, rarely by canals, in remnant osier beds, in hedgerows, on waste land, in scrub and

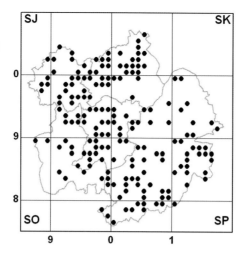

included in amenity planting mixtures. Grows best on damp or wet soil of intermediate base status and fertility. Ass: *Alnus glutinosa, Fraxinus excelsior, Phalaris arundinacea, Salix cinerea, Salix fragilis.*

### *Salix elaeagnos* Scop.
**Olive Willow**

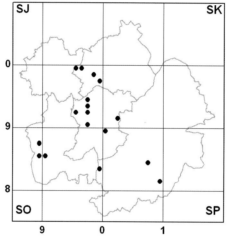

17. Neophyte. A shrub or small tree, used in amenity plantings, often as a screen by canals or lakes, but also in waste ground and in street beds, where seedlings have been reported. Also tetrad SO98J. S Europe.

### *Salix × smithiana* Willd.
(*S. × sericans* Tausch ex A. Kern., *S. viminalis × S. caprea*)
**Broad-leaved Osier**
42. Native × Alien. A shrub or small tree, possibly unevenly recorded, spread fairly thinly across our area and recorded from rivers, brooks and pools, scrub, waste ground, spoil, recreation grounds and hedgerows, typically singly, sometimes, but not always, in drier situations than *S. viminalis*. Some records are recent amenity plantings, other are growing with other willows in remnant osier beds

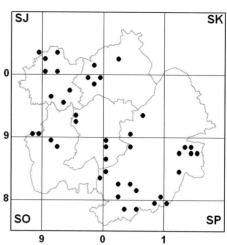

and some may have arisen as spontaneous hybrids.

### *Salix × calodendron* Wimm.
(*S. viminalis × S. caprea × S. cinerea*)
**Holme Willow**
3. Neophyte. A shrub or small tree, rare in B&BC where it is recorded by a ditch, Victoria Common, Northfield (SP029801, CBW, 1997); as part of an amenity planting in Balsall Heath (SP079849, CBW, 1999); two, presumed to be planted, by a pond, Kingswinford (SO892895, CBW, 2005). There is also an interesting older record from waste ground at Oldbury Sports Centre, where a single plant was growing with much *S. caprea*. The recorder noted "this plant is not the distinct clone *S. calodendron*, but a different hybrid with the same parentage" (SO979891, WAT, conf. RDM, 1990).

### *Salix × holosericea* Willd.
(*S. smithiana* auct. Non Willd., *S. viminalis × S. cinerea*)
**Silky-leaved Osier**

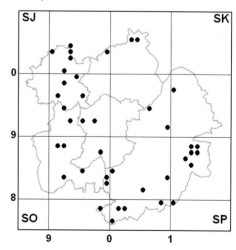

41. Native × Alien. A shrub or small tree, not common in B&BC and possibly unevenly recorded. It is recorded mainly from river and stream corridors, but also from

hedgerows, shrubberies, rough grassland, recreation ground and in a willow copse on farmland. As with *S.* × *smithiana*, some records are in mixtures with other willows in recent amenity plantings and in much older remnant osier beds and some may have arisen as spontaneous hybrids.

### *Salix caprea* L.
### Goat Willow

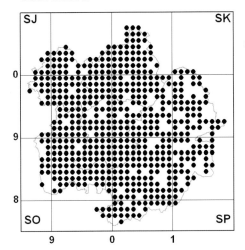

*565. Native. A shrub or small tree, although occasionally very large old trees are encountered in woodland. Common throughout, because wind-borne seed makes it possible for it to colonise bare places in a wide range of habitats, especially after disturbance: industrial spoil, abandoned railway ballast and sidings, canal and railway embankments, housing clearance areas and other waste land, hedges, scrub and clearings in woodland. It grows preferentially in damp soils, though usually not waterlogged, but it can colonise drier places than other willows. It is usually associated with quite base-rich and nutrient-rich soils but it can establish itself on rubbly, skeletal post-industrial substrates which may be quite nutrient-poor. Ass: *Betula pendula, Betula pubescens, Crataegus monogyna, Salix* × *reichardtii, Salix cinerea.*

All our plants are likely to be **subsp. *caprea*** for which there are some specific records.

### *Salix* × *reichardtii* A. Kern.
(*S. caprea* × *S. cinerea*)
30. Native. A fertile spontaneous hybrid occurring with the parents, with populations potentially showing a complete gradation between the two species. There are however relatively few records from B&BC, often in fairly damp places, in Sutton Park, along river valleys, by canals, and also in damp, clayey areas of disturbed post-industrial ground, in other

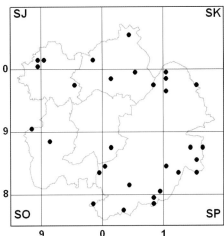

words in situations intermediate between those favoured by the parent species. Possibly under-recorded.

### *Salix* × *capreola* Jos. Kern. ex Andersson
(*S. caprea* × *S. aurita*)
1. Native. Ax. A single unconfirmed record from Longmoor Valley, Sutton Park (SP0996, SPG, 1999).

### *Salix cinerea* L.
### Grey Willow

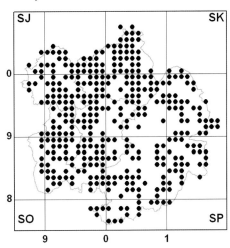

*378. Native. A shrub or small tree, common throughout from a range of wet or damp natural habitats, particularly pond, lake and river margins, mires, wet heathland, damp woodland and from damp areas of waste ground, quarry bottoms etc. Grows on fairly base-poor to base-rich soils of intermediate or quite low fertility, but the range may be extended into drier habitats probably by hybridisation with *S. caprea*. The map suggests that it is partly excluded from some of the inner city areas. Ass: *Alnus glutinosa, Betula pubescens, Salix caprea, Salix viminalis.*

**Subsp. *oleifolia*** Macreight has been specifically recorded across the range and is likely to account for all species records.

### *Salix* × *multinervis* Döll
(*S. cinerea* × *S. aurita*)

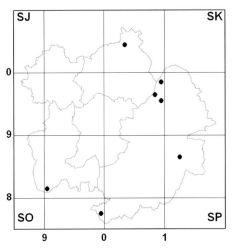

7. Native. Ax. A shrub or small tree, typically found in damp acid places where the parents come together, and this accounts for its distribution in wet ground and heathland in Sutton Park. There are however also a few reliable records from scattered sites, some of which are not notably base- and nutrient-poor: the River Cole, a recreation ground and from a construction site.

### *Salix aurita* L.
### Eared Willow

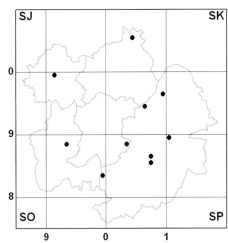

10. Native. Ax. A shrub, normally found in damp or wet sites in base- and nutrient-poor, peaty soils in heathland and moorland. In B&BC it occurs rarely, and recently almost entirely in secondary habitats. In Readett (1971) it was listed as well distributed in typical habitats in Sutton Park (SP0997, SP0998, SP1096, SP1097, SP1098) but the current survey mainly revealed *S.* × *multinervis* there, with only two records of *S. aurita* in SP0996 NW of Longmoor Pool, both sides of the stream. Some of the other modern records are fairly clearly planted (SO9388; SP0785; and SP0982, E of Moseley Bog, "a good many"). The rest are mostly in marginal habitats

▲ *Salix aurata*

▲ *Viola riviniana*

▲ *Viola reichenbachiana*

close to canals possibly representing some pattern of dispersal or on quarry sites where there is a slight possibility they are a relic of heathland habitats. It was also recorded in the 19th century from Northfield (SP07J) presumably from Victoria Common. Ass: *Betula pubescens*, *Salix cinerea*.

### *Salix eriocephala* Michx.
### Heart-leaved Willow
1. Neophyte. A shrub, naturalised at the N end of Longmoor Pool in Sutton Park. First noted by HHF in SP0996 in 1976, it was recorded there by BRF in 1979 and was determined by RDM. It was still present in 2012, forming an extensive stand in shallow water (from SP094960 to SP093961, JWP MWP & ICT, 2008). NW N America.

### *Salix myrsinifolia* Salisb.
### Dark-leaved Willow
0. Native. A shrub or small tree of river banks and lake shores almost entirely in Scotland and Ireland, it would be an introduction in B&BC. There are no current survey records but it was seen earlier in a hedge at the Hayes (SO934841, DH, 1986) and in scrub by the River Tame at Minworth Sewage Works (SP169916, R. Normand, J. Turner & N.R. Hewitt, 1987), although neither of these records were refereed.

### *Salix repens* L.
### Creeping Willow
0. Native. A low shrub, typically found at its UK inland sites in peaty mires on nutrient-poor and base-poor or base-rich peats. The prostrate **var. *repens*** was long known in Sutton Park and was recorded (as rare in marshes) in SP0895 and SP0998 by Readett in 1971 but was not located there in the present survey.

### 63. VIOLACEAE

### *Viola odorata* L.
### Sweet Violet

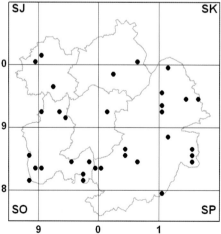

33. Native. There are a few records from old woodland (e.g. Ham Dingle, SO9182) but it appears largely introduced in B&BC. A perennial herb recorded from woodland, hedgerows, parkland, nature reserves, churchyards, canals and disturbed ground and also from roadside verges and pavements. Grows mostly in semi-shade on moist, fertile, base-rich soils. Ass: *Alliaria petiolata*, *Arum maculatum*, *Galium aparine*, *Geum urbanum*, *Hyacinthoides* × *massartiana*.

### *Viola hirta* L.
### Hairy Violet
1. Native. A woodland margin plant, usually on calcareous soils. There are two old records for this species from Wren's Nest (SO937920, J. Box, 1986) and (SO936915, ST, 1989) and this population has been recently refound on the steep SW slope behind the Seven Sisters security fence in the edge of hawthorn scrub, within two metres of our only site for *Gentianella amarella* and growing with *Brachypodium sylvaticum*, *Carex flacca*, *Carex sylvatica*, *Centaurea nigra*, *Cotoneaster horizontalis*, *Cotoneaster simonsii*, *Fragaria vesca*, *Galium album*, *Hedera helix*, *Leontodon hispidus*, *Leucanthemum vulgare*, *Viola riviniana*, *Crataegus monogyna* seedings and *Prunus spinosa* suckers (SO935915–936916, MWP, ICT, PLR & A. Coward, 2010).

*Viola hirta* (by Teresa Bailey)

### *Viola riviniana* Rchb.
### Common Dog-violet
*292. Native. A perennial herb found both in old woodlands and as a tolerated garden weed throughout our area, although the map suggests that it is scarcer in the inner urban areas and commonest in some of the older suburbs. Also found in the open or in semi-shade in many lightly managed areas of parks, cemeteries, canal and railway corridors and sometimes in grassland or as a pavement weed. On most damp to dry soils except the most nutrient-rich. Ass: *Fragaria vesca*, *Galium aparine*, *Geranium robertianum*, *Hyacinthoides non-scripta*.

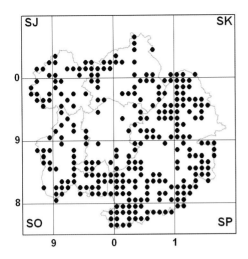

There is additionally a pre-survey record of **subsp. minor** (Murb. ex Greg.) Valentine from marshes and bogs, Sutton Park (SP0998, Readett, 1951, still present in 1991). Also the purple-leaved horticultural cultivar *Viola riviniana* 'Purpurea Group' has been recorded as a garden escape self-sown in tarmac at Fox Hollies (SP121827, CBW, 1998) and in pavement at Lutley (SO944823, AWR, WAT & CBW, 2001).

### Viola × bavarica Schrank
(*V. riviniana × V. reichenbachiana*)
2. Native. A hybrid which may occur where the parent species overlap. In our area it has been recorded as a single plant in the valley bottom of the Dingle, near Hayhead (SP046983, ICT, 2006) where it was growing with a predominance of *V. reichenbachiana* and in a roadside ditch in old woodland, in the grounds of Northfield Manor House (SP028810, ICT, MWP, JWP, AWR, JaH & L. Bastin, 2008), growing with *V. riviniana*. Another plant recorded in Hardwick Wood, Walsall (SP081991, JaH & SJC, 2007) as *V. reichenbachiana* may also have been this hybrid.

### Viola reichenbachiana Jord. ex Boreau
**Early Dog-violet**

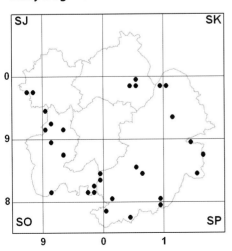

30. Native. Ax. A perennial herb, recorded mainly from old woodlands and hedgerows, where it typically occurs in shadier and damper situations than *V. riviniana*, and in more consistently nutrient-poor and base-rich soils. Also occasionally in disturbed urban habitats such as pavement cracks in residential areas. Probably under-recorded in all its habitats due to its early flowering. Ass: *Alliaria petiolata*, *Allium ursinum*, *Arum maculatum*, *Brachypodium sylvaticum*, *Crataegus monogyna*, *Ficaria verna*, *Fraxinus excelsior*, *Hedera helix*, *Mercurialis perennis*.

### Viola canina L.
**Heath Dog-violet**
0. Native. NT. A perennial herb of heathland, on moist, nutrient- and base-poor, usually peaty soils, declining severely in the UK. It was not recorded during the survey, however there is a reliable 1992 record from Stourbridge Golf Course: 10–12 plants on edge of bunker near 8th Green (SO899822, WAT, not refound in 2010). There are also earlier records from Rubery Hill (SO9977, W.H. Hardaker, circa 1939) and from Sutton Park in the 1870s (SP0997, Bagnall, 1875), where the records were for **subsp. canina**, as are probably all our records.

### Viola palustris L.
**Marsh Violet**
4. Native. Ax. A perennial herb of nutrient- and base-poor mires, probably declining in B&BC and only recorded recently from four squares in Sutton Park: muddy margins of stream, Longmoor Valley (SP090966, MWP, ICT & PLR, 2006); boggy ground (SP0998, SB, 1997); stream from Boldmere to Wyndley (SP1095, SB, 2002); valley mire (SP102977, MWP, ICT, PLR, DJA & J. Antrobus, 2007). Readett (1971) also recorded it in three more Sutton Park squares, SP0897, SP1997 & SP1096. J.P. Martin recorded it from Rough Wood (SJ9800) in 1991 and from Clayhanger Village (SK045052) in 1990. The latter site must be the mire by the canal at the swingbridge (recently rebuilt), which is still extant and has other acid mire records, but it has not been seen there on more recent visits. There are 19th century and early 20th century records from the Moseley Heath bogs (SP0982), Birches Hagley Brake (SO8981), Rednal Hill (SO9976), Bog Meadow Coppice (SP015834) and Moseley Wake Common (SP08W). W. Withering recorded it from B'ham Heath (SP08) in 1787. Ass: *Carex echinata*, *Carex panicea*, *Menyanthes trifoliata*, *Succisa pratensis*.

### Viola cornuta L.
**Horned Pansy**
0. Neophyte. An annual or short-lived perennial. Once recorded from Moseley Parish (SP0783, W.B. Grove, 1883).

### Viola tricolor L.
**Wild Pansy**

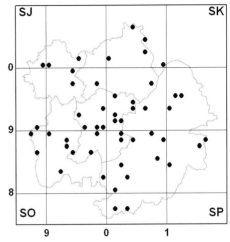

52. Native. NT. An annual or perennial herb, found mostly in disturbed situations in field margins, allotments, waste land, road verges, churchyards, parkland, canal and rail corridors and only occasionally in rather more semi-natural situations in country parks etc. Some populations appear to grade into *Viola × wittrockiana*. Usually in light, well-drained, rather impoverished but moderately base-rich soils. Ass: *Papaver* spp., *Polygonum aviculare*, *Urtica dioica*.

### Viola × wittrockiana Gams ex Kappert
(cultivars probably derived from *V. tricolor × V. arvensis*)
**Garden Pansy**

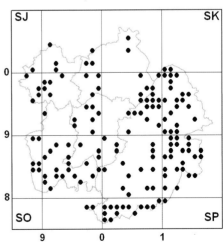

152. Neophyte or casual of garden origin. Annual or perennial herbs, recorded from lawns, paving, grass verges, post-housing sites and other waste land, allotments, churchyards and even road gutters,

usually but not always close to gardens in residential areas. Ass: *Agrostis capillaris, Bromus hordeaceus, Epilobium montanum, Fumaria officinalis, Hypochaeris radicata, Poa annua, Polygonum aviculare, Senecio vulgaris, Trifolium dubium.*

### *Viola arvensis* Murray
### **Field Pansy**

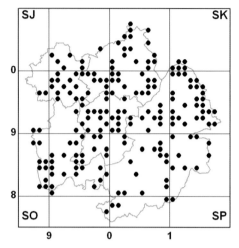

*195. Archaeophyte. An annual weed of bare, disturbed places in cultivated and waste ground, recorded from field margins, allotments, gardens, around buildings and building sites and on road margins and the central reservations. A light-loving plant of moist to dry, averagely fertile and base-rich soils. Also tetrad SO99A. Ass: *Capsella bursa-pastoris, Cardamine hirsuta, Euphorbia peplus, Matricaria chamomilla, Myosotis arvensis, Papaver rhoeas.*

### *Viola labradorica* Schrank.
### **Labrador Violet**

1. Neophyte. A garden perennial resembling *V. riviniana.* Reported from Wordsley: a dozen or so under Sycamore (SO 886872, CBW, 2007).

### 64. LINACEAE

### *Linum bienne* Mill.
### **Pale Flax**

2. Native; introduced in our area. Biennial or perennial. Small isolated colonies on raised banks and along path margins at Mill Lane Nature Reserve, Ryecroft, Walsall and alongside the path on the rough grassy banks on land between Mill Lane and the railway to the rear of Ashfield Close (SP015998, MWP, 2001). It is believed to have been introduced with ballast or similar at a time when the whole area was railway sidings, turntable and locomotive shed; Fibbersley (SO957996, DH & S.J. Lawley, 1999). There ais also an older record from the Cracker (SO953928, CRP & ST, 1985).

### *Linum usitatissimum* L.
### **Flax**

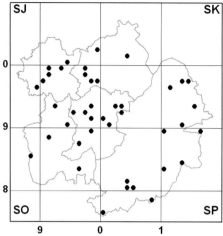

42. Neophyte, essentially casual with us. Annual. Records for gardens, roadsides verges, spoil heaps and post-housing sites usually from bird seed and often with other species from the same source. Origin in cultivation. Ass: *Helianthus annuus, Phalaris canariensis, Triticum aestivum.*

### *Linum perenne* L.
### subsp. *anglicum* (Mill.) Ockendon
### **Perennial Flax**

0. Native in E England. Nationally Scarce. Bagnall reported it from Aldridge (SK00) in 1901.

### *Linum catharticum* L.
### **Fairy Flax**

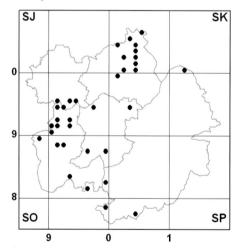

*35. Native. Ax. An annual or biennial herb typically found in calcareous and base-rich, infertile sites in open situations such as quarries, railway sidings, furnace spoil and other anthropogenically created substrates. Widely distributed at least in the Black Country, with good local populations but generally scarce. Ass: *Briza media, Carex flacca, Centaurium erythraea, Euphrasia* spp., *Festuca rubra, Lotus corniculatus.*

### *Linum flavum* agg. (cf *L. flavum* L.)
### **Yellow Flax**

1. Neophyte. A well-established, spreading patch, growing among *Hypericum perforatum* at the edge of the old railway track walkway to the rear of Asda Supermarket in Tipton, was confirmed, at the time, as a first record out of a garden for this plant in Britain. Its pale-yellow, five-petalled flowers appear continuously from June to September and merge in well with similar coloured flowers growing in the same vicinity (SO965940, MWP, conf. EJC, 2001, still present but reduced 2011). S, C & E Europe.

### *Linum grandiflorum* Desf.
### **Crimson Flax**

1. Casual. Annual. A number of plants self-sown from the previous year's planting in the flower-bed along the central reservation in front of the old B'ham Childrens Hospital, Ladywood Middleway, B'ham (SP054862, MWP, 1997). N Africa.

### 65. HYPERICACEAE

### *Hypericum olympicum* L.
### **Mount Olympus St John's-wort**

2. Neophyte. A solitary plant rooted in pavement, Streetly (SP073975, MWP, ICT & PLR, 2006); Money Hill Road (SP126946, MWP & ICT, 2007). Balkans.

### *Hypericum calycinum* L.
### **Rose-of-Sharon**

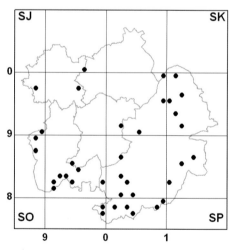

38. Neophyte. A rhizomatous shrub found on waste ground, roadsides, in pavements, parks, churchyards, old gardens and by canals, being favoured by moist soils and semi-shade. Chiefly a throw-out or persisting from old plantings. Viable seed is said to be rare, so garden escapes are patches of vegetative growth, which can be fairly extensive, near to or continuous with the garden of origin. It is not immediately clear why it has been so rarely recorded in the Black Country. Bulgaria and Turkey.

### *Hypericum pseudohenryi* N. Robson
**Irish Tutsan**

1. Neophyte. A semi-evergreen shrub, recorded in a shrub belt by a service road by the A491, where it is likely to be a survival from a planting (SO911819, JJD, 2003). China.

### *Hypericum* 'Hidcote'

3. Neophyte. A deciduous shrub; a garden throw-out or relic of a planting. A sterile cultivar and probable hybrid. Abandoned allotments at Vincent Drive (SP041834, N.M. Wyatt, 2000); Selly Oak Park (SP0582, E. Powell & A. Millward, 2003); grounds of Beacon View (SK063006, SMP, 2010).

### *Hypericum androsaemum* L.
**Tutsan**

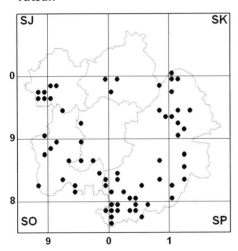

66. Native, but possibly entirely introduced in B&BC. A shrub found by pools, streams, canals, on post-housing sites, recreation grounds, churchyards, allotments, in lanes and in pavement cracks all of which suggests bird-sowings and garden discards and relics. It grows in semi-shade on moist to damp soils intermediate in base and fertility status. Its absence from our old woodlands is noticeable, although it can be found in some fragments of semi-natural stream valley. Ass: *Betula pendula*, *Hedera helix*, *Hyacinthoides non-scripta*, *Rubus fruticosus* agg., *Symphoricarpos albus*, *Urtica dioica*.

### *Hypericum* × *inodorum* Mill.
(*H. androsaemum* × *H. hircinum*)
**Tall Tutsan**

4. Neophyte. A shrub with a few records from secondary sites: garage entry, Lutley Grove Woodgate (SO998820, JJD, 2003); development site, West Heath, Northfield (SP034786, JJD, 2006); waste ground, edge of cemetery, Cinder Hill (SO925944, JEH, 2007); edge of pavement and factory compound, Ocker Hill (SO974933, JEH, 2007). Also two earlier records in scrub near Manor Farm Park (SP024804, CBW, 1989) and a thicket of it by the River Rea, Moor Green (SP062824, CBW, 1993). SW Europe.

### *Hypericum hircinum* L.
**Stinking Tutsan**

3. Neophyte. A shrub, with three pavement sites in the Woodgate area, all probable bird sowings (SO994821, SO996821 & SO994821, all JJD, 2003); towpath, Worcs & B'ham canal (SP054803, MWP, 2007); garden paving and brickwork, Moseley (SP080836, ICT & MWP, 2007). Mediterranean. The UK plant is **subsp. majus** (Aiton) N. Robson.

### *Hypericum perforatum* L.
**Perforate St John's-wort**

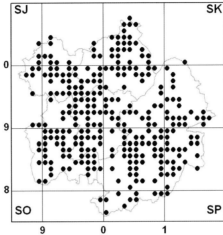

*299. Native. A rhizomatous perennial herb, found throughout in a wide range of habitats but usually in full daylight or slight shade in unmanaged but fairly open vegetation, often recovering from disturbance. It grows in dry, fairly base-rich and fairly nutrient-poor, often thin or skeletal soils, such as on furnace spoil, consolidated rubble, in quarries and by railways and canals. Also tetrad SJ90Q. Ass: *Centaurium erythraea*, *Festuca rubra*, *Linaria vulgaris*, *Pilosella officinarum*, *Silene vulgaris*.

### *Hypericum* × *desetangsii* Lamotte
(*H. perforatum* × *H. maculatum*)
**Des Etangs' St John's-wort**

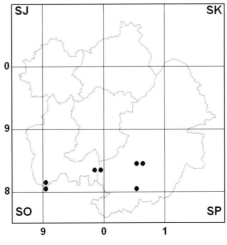

### *Hypericum maculatum* Crantz
**Imperforate St John's-wort**

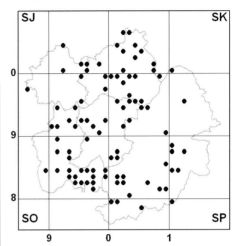

7. Native. Few records for this hybrid perennial, which is probably under-recorded, mostly from rough grassland from the Woodgate Valley and from railway sites. The first vc. 39 record was from Hay Head, Walsall (SP0499, DH, conf. N.K.B. Robson, 1993).

*93. Native. A rhizomatous perennial herb of hedgebanks, rough grasslands and post-industrial habitats: street, railway and canal sides, wasteland, a refuse tip, gasworks, an old power station; occasionally in old grassland. Often in unmanaged sites recovering from disturbance similar to those with *H. perforatum*, but less common and typically on moister or even damp or clayey, slightly more fertile soils. Also tetrad SJ90A. Ass: *Arrhenatherum elatius*, *Carex hirta*, *Centaurea nigra*, *Lathyrus pratensis*, *Vicia cracca*.

All our material referred to subspecies appears to be **subsp. obtusiusculum** (Tourlet) Hayek, which was recorded throughout the range in B&BC.

### *Hypericum tetrapterum* Fr.
**Square-stalked St John's-wort**

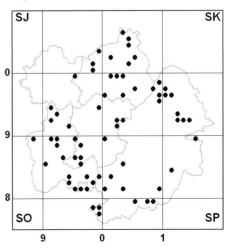

*68. Native. Ax. A rhizomatous perennial herb, found in a variety of soggy places. The majority of records are from undergrazed or ungrazed, relatively long-undisturbed wet grasslands and marshes with records from pools, ponds, canalsides, river corridors, reservoirs and damp roadsides. Grows in open situations or partial shade, on damp or wet soils of intermediate fertility and intermediate base status. Much scarcer in the urban and residential centres, despite the fact that it regenerates from seed abundantly, even in dry soils, when cultivated. Ass: *Epilobium hirsutum, Epilobium palustre, Filipendula ulmaria, Galium palustre, Mentha aquatica, Juncus inflexus, Silene flos-cuculi.*

### *Hypericum humifusum* L.
### Trailing St John's-wort

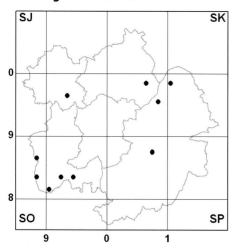

10. Native. A short-lived perennial herb, colonising open, often compacted situations on banks, tracksides and in lawns on light, sandy, fairly base- and nutrient-poor soils. Also with a few casual-seeming records on tarmac paths and garden walls in residential areas. Ass: *Achillea millefolium, Lotus corniculatus, Prunella vulgaris, Trifolium dubium.*

### *Hypericum pulchrum* L.
### Slender St John's-wort

4. Native. Ax. A perennial herb not uncommon in the UK in open woodlands on unimproved heathy soils but is almost absent from B&BC. There are a very few recent records in the S periphery of the conurbation: Woodgate Valley (SO999835, JJD, 2003 and SP08B, RM, 1998); dry grassy S-facing slopes of the stream with *Rumex acetosella* at Uffmoor (SO956824, ST, 1998); in scrub in the Stour corridor with *Calluna vulgaris* at Stambermill (SO910845, ST, 1997). Also an older record in the Illey area: a single plant in a bare place in a meadow W of the M5 (SO987822, WAT, 1992). There is also an isolated

record on the bank of the Walsall canal (SO994975, MWP, 2001). It seems to have last been seen in Sutton Park by Bagnall in 1867 and there is an even older record from Edgbaston Park (SP08, Miss Withering, 1796). Ass: *Calluna vulgaris, Deschampsia flexuosa, Rumex acetosella, Scorzoneroides autumnalis, Teucrium scorodonia.*

### *Hypericum hirsutum* L.
### Hairy St John's-wort

2. Native. This perennial herb of base-rich grassland and woodland habitats appears to be only a rare adventive in B&BC. It was only found twice during the survey period, a single plant on a rough grassy bank in Coombeswood (SO973851, WAT, 2000); and a path-side bank in the neighbouring square at Halesowen Industrial Park (SO972847, WAT, 2001). The only other record is an unconfirmed one from Doulton's Clay Pit at Saltwells Nature Reserve in 1974 (SO9387, M. Joachim).

### *Hypericum elodes* L.
### Marsh St John's-wort

0. Native. Extinct in B&BC. This plant of base- and nutrient-poor pools and mires has been largely annihilated from the English midlands. It was known from B'ham Heath (SP08) in the 18th century (W. Withering, 1787) and from both 1km squares of Moseley Common (SP0981 & SP0982) in the 19th century and was last recorded there in 1836.

### 66. GERANIACEAE

### *Geranium endressii* J. Gay
### French Crane's-bill

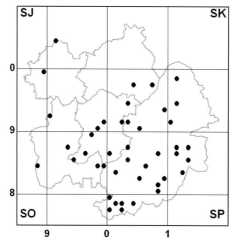

43. Neophyte. A vigorous, patch-forming, rhizomatous, perennial herb. Often out-growing its former location in gardens and thrown out or planted in rough grassland, waste ground, banks and

tracks, where it frequently becomes established. Its similarity to *G. × oxonianum* may have led to some confusion. Extensively naturalised to the rear of houses, St Brade's Close, Rowley Regis. S Europe, W Asia. Ass: *Anthriscus sylvestris, Plantago lanceolata, Potentilla reptans, Rubus fruticosus* agg., *Urtica dioica.*

### *Geranium × oxonianum* Yeo
(*G. endressii × G. versicolor*)
### Druce's Crane's-bill

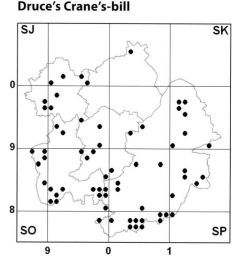

66. Neophyte. A free-flowering hybrid perennial herb, persisting where planted or discarded from gardens, on banks, verges and rough grassland near to habitation. A very variable hybrid and there are some records as "*G. endressii* or *G. × oxonianum*" which are not mapped. Ass: *Anthriscus sylvestris, Crocosmia × crocosmiiflora, Plantago lanceolata, Potentilla reptans, Rubus fruticosus* agg., *Saponaria officinalis, Urtica dioica.*

### *Geranium versicolor* L.
### Pencilled Crane's-bill

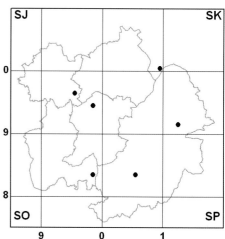

6. Neophyte. Very few records for this rhizomatous perennial herb. Persisting as a garden throw-out or possibly

spontaneous introduction in hedgebases and overgrown gardens. C Mediterranean.

## Geranium rotundifolium L.
### Round-leaved Crane's-bill

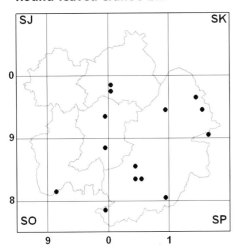

14. Native. A persistent annual, typically found in grassy verges, rough banks and neglected bits of stony ground in dry, sunny places. A generally scarce species throughout the conurbation but small densely populated colonies are sometimes encountered. Ass: *Oenothera glazioviana*, *Rumex obtusifolius*.

## Geranium sylvaticum L.
### Wood Crane's-bill

2. Introduced native, almost certainly always a garden discard in B&BC. Stow Heath lane open space (SO942979, ICT & EVJC, 2007); Jeffcock Road Allotments (SO900973, ICT & EVJC, 2007).

## Geranium pratense L.
### Meadow Crane's-bill

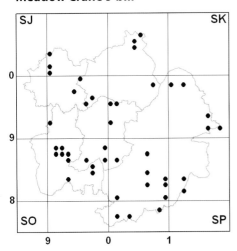

45. Native. A showy perennial herb, naturalised on roadside banks and in other unmanaged grassy places in open and marginally shaded situations, on moist, neutral soils of intermediate fertility. Occasionally found in semi-

natural sites, e.g. floodplain meadow, by River Tame (SP182918, ICT, JJB & SAHA, 2006), but never in great quantity and its habitats and infrequency across the conurbation suggests it is almost entirely an introduction in B&BC. Ass: *Alopecurus pratensis*, *Arrhenatherum elatius*, *Centaurea nigra*, *Galium aparine*, *Heracleum sphondylium*, *Urtica dioica*.

## Geranium himalayense Klotzsch
### Himalayan Crane's-bill

1. Neophyte. Rhizomatous perennial. A garden throw-out with a single unconfirmed modern record from a passageway near lock-up garages between Toll House Rd and Bristol Rd South, Rednal (SP004774, MWP, 2005).

## Geranium sanguineum L.
### Bloody Crane's-bill

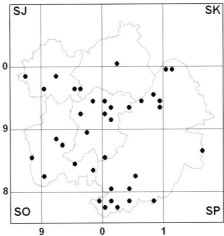

37. Introduced native. An attractive perennial herb, frequently grown in gardens and occasionally persisting on post-housing sites or as a throw-out in rough grassland, waste ground and on spoil heaps. Never occurring in any sites where it could be considered native. Ass: *Agrostis* spp., *Arrhenatherum elatius*, *Lysimachia nummularia*.

## Geranium columbinum L.
### Long-stalked Crane's-bill

2. Native. Annual. This plant of calcareous grassland has been reported from the old town gasworks, Dudley (SO901849, AMG, 2000) and a cricket field, Tettenhall (SJ885003, JVT, 2000).

## Geranium dissectum L.
### Cut-leaved Crane's-bill

*381. Archaeophyte. A generally common, erect annual of hedge banks, roadside verges, unmanaged grassy places, land recovering from recent disturbance and arable field margins in open, moist, fertile soils. Ass: *Chenopodium*

▲ *Hypericum pulchrum*

▲ *Geranium rotundifolium*

▲ *Geranium dissectum*

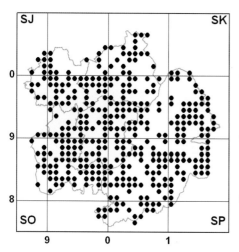

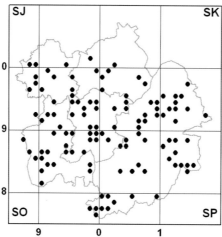

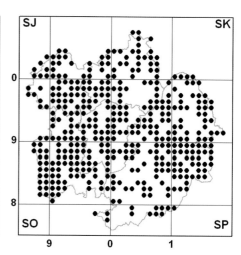

album, Elytrigia repens, Plantago major, Sisymbrium officinale, Tripleurospermum inodorum.

### Geranium × magnificum N. Hyl.
(*G. ibericum* Cav. × *G. platypetalum* Fisch. & C.A. Mey.)
**Purple Crane's-bill**

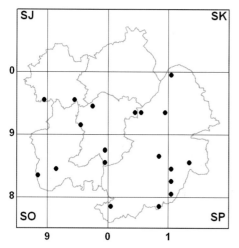

Festuca rubra, Galium aparine, Geranium molle, Geranium lucidum, Lolium perenne, Taraxacum spp., Urtica dioica.

### Geranium pusillum L.
**Small-flowered Crane's-bill**

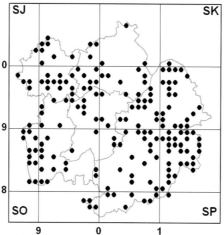

Trifolium dubium, Trifolium repens, Veronica chamaedrys.

White flowered populations sometimes occur (*G. molle* var. *album* Picard?).

### Geranium macrorrhizum L.
**Rock Crane's-bill**

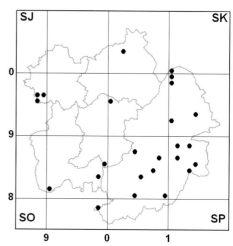

19. Neophyte. An abundantly flowering, sterile, clump-forming, perennial herb, sometimes persisting where discarded from gardens along tracks to the rear of houses, around groups of lock-up garages, on canal towpaths, on waste ground and post-housing land. Apparently less frequent in these situations in B&BC than *G. pratense*.

### Geranium pyrenaicum Burm. f.
**Hedgerow Crane's-bill**
115. Neophyte. A perennial herb of frequent occurrence on railway and canal banks, along road verges, on waste ground and field margins in open, unshaded situations. More showy plants with white flowers sometimes occur and might be of garden origin. It was rarely recorded here by Edees (1972) or Cadbury *et al.* (1971). S Europe & SW Asia. Ass: *Agrostis stolonifera, Anisantha sterilis, Anthriscus sylvestris, Arrhenatherum elatius, Crepis vesicaria,*

183. Native. An annual of open, well-drained, fertile soils, readily colonising regularly mown grassy places along roadside banks, verges and lawns and also a weed of fairly bare places on waste ground and cultivated land. Ass: *Cerastium glomeratum, Epilobium ciliatum, Erodium cicutarium, Euphorbia helioscopia, Fallopia convolvulus, Geranium molle, Lolium perenne, Poa annua, Trifolium dubium, Trifolium repens, Veronica arvensis.*

### Geranium molle L.
**Dove's-foot Crane's-bill**
*416. Native. A very common, patch-forming annual of open habitats, typically found in regularly maintained grassland such as roadside verges, lawns and sports fields. Also a weed of waste ground, cultivated land and fairly bare places alongside paths. Ass: *Cerastium fontanum, Crepis capillaris, Scorzoneroides autumnalis, Lolium perenne, Poa annua,*

25. Neophyte. A patch forming garden perennial, persisting where thrown-out or planted, in rough, grassy verges and tracks usually not far from habitation, sometimes in shade. Several named cultivars are grown but no distinction has been made for plants recorded out of gardens. Mountains of S Europe. Ass: *Alliaria petiolata, Urtica dioica.*

### Geranium dalmaticum (G. Beck) Rech. f.
**Dalmatian Crane's-bill**
2. Neophyte. A cushion forming, glossy-leaved perennial herb. Spreading onto tarmac path from a garden, Robin Hood Crescent, Yardley Wood (SP103808, CBW, 1998); in a wall, Surrey Drive, Wordsley (SO895875, CBW, 2007). SE Europe.

### Geranium lucidum L.
**Shining Crane's-bill**
167. Native. An annual of roadside verges, paving, tracks between houses, waste and

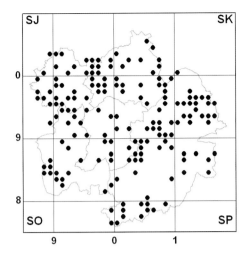

derelict land in open and partially shaded situations. Fairly common in urban areas and occasionally cultivated or tolerated in gardens where its attractive shiny, green foliage is utilised as a rather short-lived ground-cover in dry, shady spots. Also tetrad SO88Z. Ass: *Capsella bursa-pastoris, Carex hirta, Conyza floribunda, Epilobium montanum, Galium aparine, Lobularia maritima, Poa annua, Sagina procumbens, Senecio squalidus, Sonchus oleraceus, Taraxacum* spp.*, Urtica dioica, Viola tricolor.*

### Geranium robertianum L.
### Herb-Robert

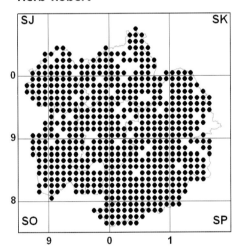

*620. Native. A very common annual or biennial found in a wide range of soil types avoiding only the most acidic and least fertile. Shade-tolerant and appearing in woodland, shady hedgerows, developing scrub and young tree plantations, roadside verges, waste ground, and a prolific coloniser in cultivated land and gardens and bare shady places generally. A less invasive white-flowered form is occasionally found. Ass: *Epilobium montanum, Galium aparine, Geum urbanum, Lapsana communis, Poa trivialis, Viola riviniana.*

### Geranium phaeum L.
### Dusky Crane's-bill

4. Neophyte. This shade-tolerant perennial herb, which was often planted in churchyards due to its rather sombre colouring, naturalises in shady hedgebanks and roadsides and areas around gardens but appears to be very scarce in our area. There are only four modern records: Highbury Park Allotments (SP079824, A. Millward & EMP, 2006); occasional, naturalised, woodland edge, Saltwells LNR (SO931871, J. Akers, 1999); lots, edge of garage/commercial premises, N of Brownhills, probably not planted (SK055060, JEH, 2001); (SP118952, MWP, 2005). C Europe.

### Geranium thunbergerii Siebold ex Lindl. & Paxton
### Thunberg's Geranium

1. Neophyte. A perennial garden cranesbill, reported from the middle of a grassy back alley, Hall Green (SP108819, CBW, det. P.F. Yeo, 1998). Temperate Asia.

### Erodium moschatum (L.) L'Hér.
### Musk Stork's-bill

2. Archaeophyte. This mainly coastal species was found in short grass near a lamp post, Near Mason Hall, University of B'ham Grounds (SP051846, D. Wrench, 2002). It occurred in some quantity along the fenceline and near the discus/hammer net in Alexander Stadium, Perry Barr (SP066926, JEH, 2005). Seed probably came with imported sand used in the stadium.

### Erodium cicutarium (L.) L'Hér.
### Common Stork's-bill

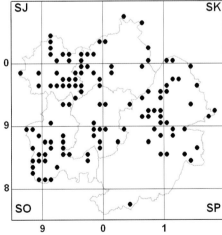

118. Native. An annual of open, well-drained, fairly bare places along the margins of roadside verges, rough and waste places and along old railway tracks and sidings usually in fairly skeletal soils and sometimes in cracks between paving stones. Rarely really common in our area but smallish

populations occasionally take advantage of bare ground previously treated with glyphosate, and sometimes roadside populations extend over hundreds of metres. Ass: *Arabidopsis thaliana, Geranium pusillum, Trifolium dubium, Trifolium repens.*

### Erodium manescavii Coss.
### Garden Stork's-bill

1. Neophyte. Perennial. Self-sown into paving from original planting nearby, in the alpine yard, B'ham Botanical Gardens (SP048854, MWP & JWP, 2007). Pyrenees.

### 67. LYTHRACEAE

### Lythrum salicaria L.
### Purple-loosetrife

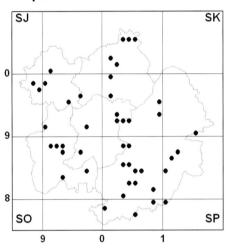

46. Introduced native? A tall perennial herb naturally occurring in water-saturated and periodically inundated neutral to weakly acid soils in open, well-lit situations. Records are mainly from

▲ *Lythrum salicaria*

marginal vegetation of small pools and ditches where small to moderately sized populations are present. Almost certainly native in our area in the past, these populations would have been gradually lost to urban spread and most of the modern records suggest introduction in habitat creation schemes. It also appears rarely in drier soils on post-housing sites where it survives as a relic of herbaceous border or garden pond plantings. There were few records from our parts of vc. 39 and vc. 37 in the 1970s Floras.

### Lythrum portula (L.) D.A. Webb
### Water-purslane

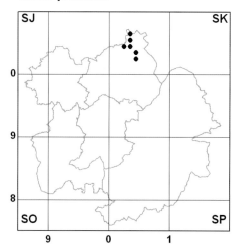

6. Native. Ax. A light-loving annual of constantly moist, moderately acid, infertile soils and shallow standing water. Quite frequent in seasonally inundated pasture and margins of a few shallow pools at three sites in Walsall: Clayhanger (SK033046 & SK035046, ICT & EVJC, 2006); Jockey Fields (SK0402 & SK0403, C. Walker, C. Daguet, S. Wilson & H. Griffiths, 2002); and Friar Pool, Pelsall Common (SK021045, ICT, 2008); quite frequent in wet pastures W of Brownhills Common (SK032061, SK034059 & SK033061, ICT & SAHA, 2010). Ass: *Agrostis stolonifera, Crassula helmsii, Gnaphalium uliginosum, Hydrocotyle vulgaris, Mentha aquatica, Myosotis laxa, Ranunculus peltatus, Stellaria alsine, Veronica scutellata.*

### 68. ONAGRACEAE

### Epilobium hirsutum L.
### Great Willowherb

*657. Native. A tall, rhizomatous perennial herb of pond and canal margins, streamsides, wet grassland and waste ground, in open, neutral to base-rich, very fertile soils. Forming pure stands in ditches, choked up ponds and sites of impeded drainage where it is often an indicator of eutrophication, but also found in drier

disturbed situations where it is far less dominant. Increase is from both seed and by spreading rhizomes. Very common. Ass: *Glyceria maxima, Solanum dulcamara, Sparganium erectum, Typha latifolia, Urtica dioica.*

### Epilobium × novae-civitatis Smejkal
(*E. hirsutum × E. ciliatum*)

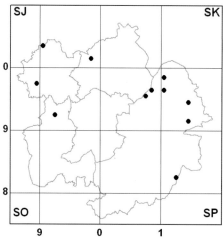

11. Neophyte × native. A few records for isolated plants or small groups in paving, rough grassland and stream bank with, or in the absence of, one or both parents.

### Epilobium parviflorum Schreb.
### Hoary Willowherb

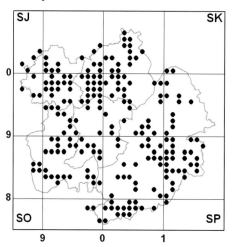

*218. Native. A frequently encountered perennial herb perennating by leafy stolons and readily spreading from seed along pond margins, in flushes, canal towpaths, areas of impeded drainage and also in drier and somewhat disturbed marginal habitats in allotments, gardens and on waste ground. Also tetrad SO99A. Ass: *Apium nodiflorum, Carex otrubae, Epilobium hirsutum, Senecio aquaticus*, but perhaps more commonly in drier habitats with other *Epilobium* spp., *Atriplex patula, Chenopodium album, Senecio squalidus.*

### Epilobium × floridulum Smejkal
(*E. parviflorum × E. ciliatum*)
5. Native × neophyte. Single or small groups of plants in a quarry (SK041025, ICT, MWP & AB, 2007), but mostly in pavement cracks: (SP021914, MWP, 1998); (SP052812, ICT, MWP, L. Bastin, EMP, 2007); (SP099996, MWP & ICT 2006); (SP096954, MWP & ICT, 2006).

### Epilobium montanum L.
### Broad-leaved Willowherb

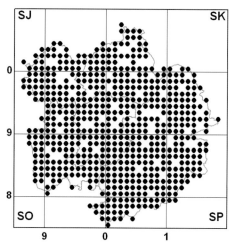

*601. Native. The most shade-tolerant of the willowherbs and found in a wide range of habitats and soil types throughout B&BC. Frequently occurring in paving, allotments, garden borders, all sorts of disturbed and typically shady waste ground and in more natural situations in woodland margins and clearings. Ass: *Alliaria petiolata, Cardamine hirsuta, Cardamine flexuosa, Epilobium ciliatum, Epilobium obscurum, Geum urbanum.*

### Epilobium × interjectum Smejkal
(*E. montanum × E. ciliatum*)
3. Native. Recent records from Bourn Brook (SP025831, RM, 1998); one plant along paving at the edge of a shrub bed (SP055858, ICT, MWP & JWP, 2007); Kinfare Rise (SO921919, APD, 2007). First found in vc. 39 on a roadside bank, a churchyard and three waste places in Sedgley (SO931937, SO915949, SO916936, SO918935 & SO927943, WAT, 1986). Probably commoner and under-recorded.

### Epilobium tetragonum L.
### Square-stalked Willowherb
86. Native. A perennial herb of waste ground, roadsides and gardens in well-lit or slightly shady, dry to moist soils of moderate fertility. Mostly occurring in small localised colonies or as isolated, individual plants mixed in with other *Epilobium* species. Possibly under-recorded and confused with *E. obscurum*, and

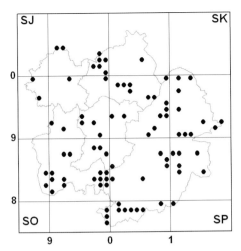

scarcely recorded for vc. 39 and vc. 38 in the 1970s Floras. Also tetrad SO99A. The subsp. have not been distinguished. Ass: *Capsella bursa-pastoris, Epilobium ciliatum, E. montanum, E. obscurum, Hordeum murinum, Poa annua, Polygonum aviculare.*

## *Epilobium obscurum* Schreb.
## Short-fruited Willowherb

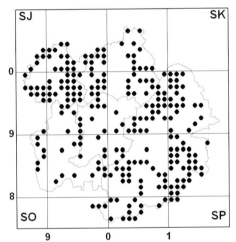

248. Native. Increasingly encountered perennial weed of paving, gardens, allotments and waste ground in well-lit, fairly moist soils of average pH and fertility. Recorded from virtually all of the allotment sites visited during the survey and probably under-recorded in many areas due to confusion with similar willowherbs. Also seems to be the predominant willowherb in old graveyards especially where maintained with glyphosate. Cadbury *et al.* (1971) and Edees (1972) considered it a plant predominantly of watersides and marshes. Ass: *Agrostis stolonifera, Anisantha sterilis, Arabidopsis thaliana, Capsella bursa-pastoris, Cardamine hirsuta, Catapodium rigidum, Conyza canadensis, Epilobium ciliatum, Epilobium montanum, Equisetum arvense, Hedera helix, Holcus lanatus, Hordeum murinum, Juncus effusus, Lactuca serriola, Poa annua, Poa*

*trivialis, Senecio vulgaris, Trifolium dubium, Tussilago farfara, Vulpia myuros.*

## *Epilobium* × *vicinum* Smejkal
(*E. obscurum* × *E. ciliatum*)
1. Described by Stace as one of the commonest hybrids in Britain, possibly overlooked. The only recent record: flowering in pavement, Pinfold Street, B'ham city centre (SP069867, ICT, 2007).

## *Epilobium roseum* Schreb.
## Pale Willowherb

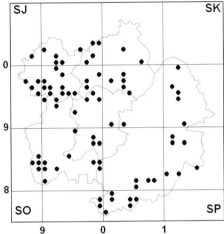

82. Native. A perennial herb of roadsides, paving and marginally disturbed, often slightly shady habitats on the edges of allotments and gardens, in open, moisture-retaining, moderately fertile to richly fertile soils. Appearing later in the year than other Willowherbs and often a casualty of weedkilling before reaching maturity in paving and paths. Undoubtedly under-recorded in the urban area. Ass: *Cardamine hirsuta, Epilobium ciliatum, Epilobium montanum, Euphorbia peplus, Holcus lanatus, Poa annua, Polygonum aviculare, Senecio jacobaea.*

## *Epilobium ciliatum* Raf.
## American Willowherb

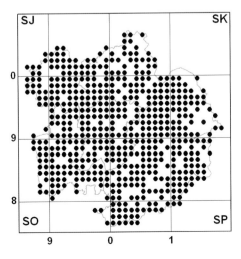

▲ *Lythrum portula*

▲ *Epilobium hirsutum*

▲ *Epilobium roseum*

*547. Neophyte. A very common perennial herb of open, fertile, moist soils, and readily seeding into paving, paths, bases of walls, waste and cultivated ground. Also a weed of disturbance on post-housing and industrial land throughout the conurbation. Its spread across B&BC is fairly recent but it was already quite common in the 1970s Floras. N America. Ass: *Arabidopsis thaliana, Capsella bursa-pastoris, Persicaria maculosa, Poa trivialis, Senecio vulgaris, Sisymbrium officinale.*

### *Epilobium palustre* L.
### Marsh Willowherb

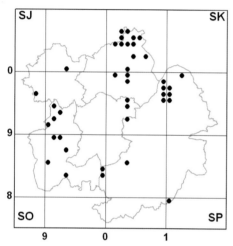

*41. Native. Ax. Locally frequent in open, moderately acid, infertile, constantly moist to wet soils in some of the flushed and marshy sites in undeveloped parts of B&BC such as at Sutton Park and Clayhanger. Does not appear as a weed in the urban area. Ass: *Cardamine pratensis, Juncus acutiflorus, Juncus conglomeratus, Juncus effusus, Mentha aquatica, Myosotis laxa, Silene flos-cuculi.*

### *Epilobium brunnescens* (Cockayne) P.H. Raven & Engelhorn
### New Zealand Willowherb
0. Neophyte. An old record from Illey Brook (SO98Q, R. Cooper, 1982). New Zealand.

### *Chamerion angustifolium* (L.) Holub
### Rosebay Willowherb
*683. Native. Ubiquitous and frequent in B&BC, colonising by means of its wind-borne seeds and often becoming dominant in a wide range of open situations on damp to dry soils over a wide range of base and nutrient status: clearings and burnt areas in woodlands and heaths, especially around the margins, coal and furnace spoil (especially burnt spoil), intermittently managed waste land, abandoned allotments and gardens, housing and factory clearance areas, and as individual plants in almost any

open vegetation. Intolerant of continual disturbance and trampling, heavy shade and consistent waterlogging and favoured by any act which leaves bare ground undisturbed and without a vigorous seedbank. Ass: *Arrhenatherum elatius, Artemisia vulgaris, Epilobium hirsutum, Rubus idaeus, Tussilago farfara, Urtica dioica.*

### *Oenothera glazioviana* P. Micheli
### Large-flowered Evening-primrose

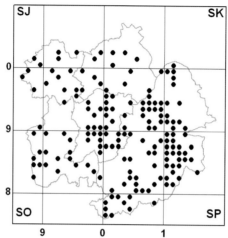

167. Neophyte. A tall biennial found on waste land, neglected gardens, railway and canal banks, overgrown allotments and post-industrial and housing sites in well-drained, sunny situations, particularly on lighter soils. Quickly colonises newly created habitats and sometimes forms large colonies (especially in allotments, where it is sometimes tolerated in unused areas) but decreasing as sites mature. The commonest evening-primrose by far in the urban area. N America. Also tetrad SO99A. Ass: *Anisantha sterilis, Aquilegia vulgaris, Arrhenatherum elatius, Artemisia vulgaris, Conyza canadensis, Conyza sumatrensis, Dactylis glomerata, Hypericum perforatum, Lamium album, Rubus fruticosus* agg., *Rumex obtusifolius, Senecio jacobaea, Urtica dioica, Veronica agrestis, Viola × wittrockiana, Vulpia myuros.*

### *Oenothera × fallax* Renner
(*O. glazioviana × O. biennis*)
### Intermediate Evening-primrose
3. Neophyte. Neglected garden, Court Farm Rd (SP10059272, MWP & JWP, 2006); track near railway, Ackers Adventure Park (SP102847, MWP & JWP, 2006); Waste ground, W'ton (SO926988, JEH, 2006).

### *Oenothera × britannica* Rostański
(*O. cambrica × O. glazioviana*)
0. Neophyte. Two plants found in disused railway sidings at Bushbury, W'ton, growing with both *O. glazioviana* and *O. cambrica*, may have been this (SJ917021, BRF, 1992).

### *Oenothera biennis* L.
### Common Evening-primrose

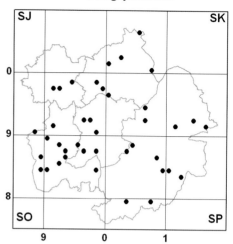

40. Neophyte. Small colonies or individuals occasionally appear on post-housing and other similar recently disturbed sites and in marginal vegetation along streams, canal banks and railway embankments in sunny, well-drained more or less infertile sites. N America or Europe.

### *Oenothera biennis* L. × *O. cambrica* Rostański
3. Neophyte. Railway waste ground, Bournville (SP051805, JWP, det. J.C. Bowra, 1995); cemetery, Smethwick (SP015873, WAT, det. J.C. Bowra, 1996); a small population on grassy slopes on western platform of Gravelly Hill station (SP100907, ICT, MWP, JWP, JaH & SJC, 2007).

### *Oenothera cambrica* Rostański
### Small-flowered Evening-primrose
Stace (2010) has included this species as a segregate within *Oenothera biennis*.

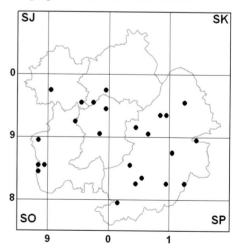

24. Neophyte. A medium to tall biennial occasionally appearing as individuals or in small groups on recently created post-housing sites, in neglected bits of roadside vegetation and unmanaged overgrown gardens. First record for vc. 39: canal

towpath, Compton, W'ton (SO8898, BRF, 1969). N America or Europe.

## Oenothera stricta Ledeb. ex Link
### Fragrant Evening-primrose

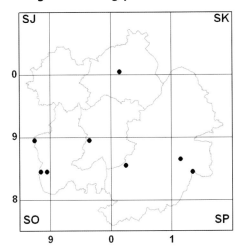

8. Neophyte. Very few widely scattered records for individual or small groups of plants in paving by gardens and roadside verges in sunny situations. Chile.

## Clarkia unguiculata Lindl.
### Clarkia
1. Neophyte. Hardy annual frequently sown in gardens. Pavement weed, Willow Road, Balsall Heath (SP072842, CBW, 1997). California.

## Clarkia amoena (Lehm.) A. Nelson & J.F. Macbr.
### Godetia
1. Neophyte. Hardy annual frequently sown in gardens. A few plants on a small area of post-housing land, Pleck, Walsall (SO996973, MWP, 2001). W N America.

## Fuchsia magellanica Lam.
### Fuchsia

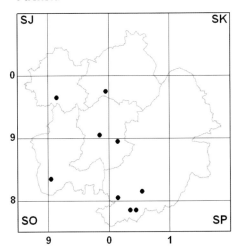

9. Neophyte. Relic of cultivation, typically in post-housing land, or rarely a seedling. Records include Fuchsia 'Riccartonii', which is a hardy, sterile, cultivar frequently grown

in gardens and occasionally surviving on post-housing sites. Chile & Argentina.

## Fuchsia 'Corallina'
(possibly F. splendens Zucc. × F. globosa Benth.)
### Large-flowered Fuchsia
1. Neophyte. Hardy deciduous shrub. A relic of cultivation. One mature shrub on large area of post-housing council estate, Northfield, B'ham (SP0180, MWP, 2003). Garden origin.

## Circaea lutetiana L.
### Enchanter's-nightshade

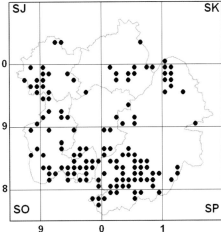

*136. Native. A perennial herb found in the shadiest areas of deciduous semi-natural woodland, on wooded stream banks and occasionally (fairly frequently further N in Staffordshire) as a weed of cultivation in gardens and allotments. It spreads rapidly by its hooked fruits and its long, brittle rhizomes and is at an advantage in disturbed habitats where shade reduces the vigour of other plants. Preferring moist, but not wet, soils of intermediate fertility and base status; unlike most woodland species its main period of growth is in summer. Ass: *Chrysosplenium oppositifolium, Ficaria verna, Geum urbanum, Glechoma hederacea, Silene dioica, Mercurialis perennis, Veronica montana.*

## 69. MYRTACEAE
There are records only for planted specimens of *Eucalyptus gunnii* Hook f., the Cider Gum, a moderately hardy deciduous tree from S Australia and Tasmania, in B&BC.

## 71. ANACARDIACEAE

## Rhus typhina L.
### Stag's-horn Sumach
52. Neophyte. A frequently grown deciduous shrub or small tree sometimes persisting for a short time on post-

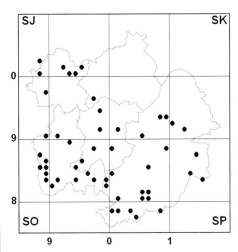

housing sites where it was originally planted. Suckering vigorously from garden specimens and forming small localised patches up to some distance away on roadside and railway banks and neglected bits of land. No records of self-seeding have been reported. Also tetrad SK00R. Eastern N America.

## Cotinus coggygria Scop.
### Smoke-tree
1. Neophyte. Shrub. Disused railway, The Cracker, Princes End (SO958938, PWS, 1998). S Europe.

## 72. SAPINDACEAE

## Aesculus hippocastanum L.
### Horse-chestnut

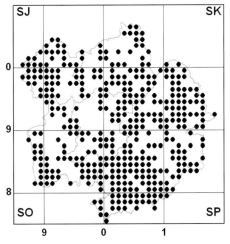

*403. Neophyte. A widely planted tree in the urban landscape, along roads, in parkland and churchyards, and also frequently planted and regenerating in deciduous woodland. Often self-sown in hedgerows, gardens and on waste land but rarely attaining maturity in these situations. The foliage of most trees in B&BC has in recent years been ravaged by Horse Chestnut Leaf Miner (*Cameraria ohridella*) and there has been significant dieback on some trees due to Bleeding Canker of Horse Chestnut (*Phytophthora*) which could result in many of our trees being lost over the coming years. Balkan Peninsula.

### *Aesculus carnea* J. Zeyh.
**Red Horse-chestnut**

1. Neophyte. Occasionally planted in parks and estates and as a street tree, eight records as such. Four small plants on a roadside verge seeded below specimen tree, Croftdown Road, Harborne (SP0285, MWP, 2004). Garden origin.

### *Acer platanoides* L.
**Norway Maple**

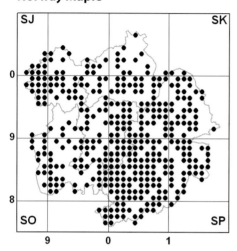

*399. Neophyte. A widely planted deciduous tree along roads, in parks, and other amenity areas. Frequently self-sown on waste land, in plantations and secondary woodland where it is often naturalised. A common roadside weed from nearby plantings but seldom attaining maturity in this situation, nevertheless greatly increasing in the urban area. Europe.

### *Acer cappadocicum* Gled.
**Cappadocian Maple**

1. Neophyte. Infrequently planted deciduous tree. The few records for this are mostly for planted specimens, but seedlings and saplings reported in pavement and gardens near a planted tree in Hazelbank (SP041785, JJD, 2001) and another seedling at Grassmoor Road (SP041787, JJD, 2001). SW and C Asia.

### *Acer campestre* L.
**Field Maple**

*457. Native. A tree or shrub of lightly shaded to semi-shaded habitats in neutral to weakly acid soils of average fertility. Widely planted in hedgerows and extensively used in habitat creation schemes, often seeding but also often difficult to determine if planted or naturally occurring. Rarely found

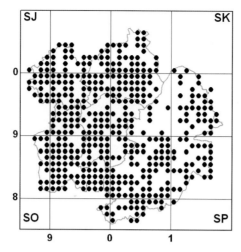

in old woodland but quite frequent in old, species-rich hedgerows. Ass: *Corylus avellana, Cornus sanguinea, Crataegus monogyna, Quercus robur, Ulmus* spp.

### *Acer pseudoplatanus* L.
**Sycamore**

*682. Neophyte. The most frequently recorded tree in B&BC. Commonly planted, and in some years prolifically seeding in woods, gardens, on waste ground, roadside verges and into paving. Well-naturalised in semi-natural and secondary deciduous woodland throughout the conurbation where it often dominates the understorey to the detriment of native trees and shrubs. Tolerant of all soil types avoiding only waterlogged soils and the most acidic. Occasionally completely absent from old, semi-natural woods e.g. Park Coppice, W'ton (SO9195). *A. pseudoplatanus* cultivars 'Brilliantissimus' and 'Purpureum' have also been occasionally recorded. Europe. Ass: *Acer platanoides, Crataegus monogyna, Fraxinus excelsior, Sambucus nigra*.

### *Acer saccharinum* L.
**Silver Maple**

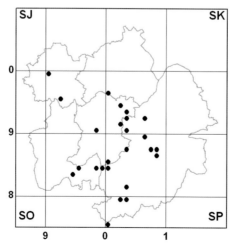

25. Neophyte. A medium-sized deciduous tree frequently planted in parks,

school grounds and used in landscape creation schemes. Records are mainly for established plantings, but note the following records: many seedlings in a shrubbery, near Walsall Football Ground (SP0096, MWP, JaH & SJC, 2001); several small self-seeded plants below mature tree at entrance to Uplands Allotment Gardens, Handsworth (SP0390, ICT, MWP, JaH, SJC & V. Lawrie, 2008). 'Laciniate group' also recorded. Eastern N America.

### *Acer palmatum* 'Atropurpureum'
**Japanese Maple**

1. Neophyte. One small plant seeded into paving from planted specimen in nearby garden, Sutton Coldfield (SP116953, MWP, L. Bastin, JaH & S. Carvalho, 2005). *Acer palmatum* was also recorded as a street tree, planted by the Worcester Road (B4187) at intervals across the monad (SO9081, JJD, 2003).

There are also records of planted specimens of the following neophytes: *Acer davidii* Franch. (Snakebark); *Acer griseum* (Franch.) Pax (Paperbark Maple); *Acer heldreichii* Boiss. & Hedr. (Heldreich's Maple); *Acer negundo* L. (Ashleaf Maple); *Acer pennsylvanicum* L. (Striped Maple); *Acer rubrum* L. (Red Maple); *Acer rufinerve* Siebold & Zucc. (Grey-budded Maple); *Acer saccharum* Marshall (Sugar Maple).

### 73. RUTACEAE

### *Skimmia japonica* Thunb.
**Skimmia**

3. Neophyte. An evergreen shrub, occasionally found as a relic of cultivation. Well-rooted garden discard on footpath behind houses, near Weoley Castle (SP022825, CBW, 1995); Hole Lane, Northfield (SP032799, AEEP, 1999); edge of woodland, S of High Haden Road, Haden Cross (SO962855, MWP & LG, 2005). Japan.

### *Ruta graveolens* L.
**Rue**

3. Casual. A mature plant on waste ground, possibly thrown-out from a nearby garden, Balsall Heath (SP079849, CBW, 1999); established by path, Woodlands Walk, Penn (SO895961, CBW, 2007); one plant, almost certainly originally planted, in St Mary's churchyard, Handsworth (SP055903, MWP, 2008). E Mediterranean.

### 74. SIMAROUBACEAE

### *Ailanthus altissima* (Mill.) Swingle
**Tree-of-Heaven**

13. Neophyte. A fast-growing tree occasionally grown in gardens but more

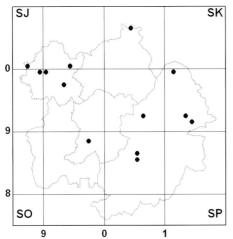

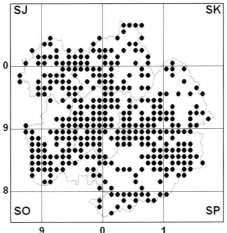

often in mixed tree and shrub plantings by roadsides and on central reservations. The few records are for planted trees or rarely for suckering plants very close to original plantings. China.

## 75. MALVACEAE

### *Malva moschata* L.
### Musk-mallow

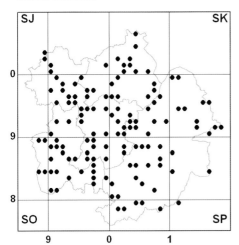

*132. Native. A perennial herb found mainly on intermittently mown road verges and canal and railway banks in warm, sunny situations on fairly dry, moderately base-rich and not over-fertile soils. Also recorded from post-industrial sites and waste land associated with playing fields, allotments etc. and occasionally as a street weed. It is an easily grown and an attractive plant and is much sown by wild flower lovers and included in a variety of 'wildflower' seed mixtures. Ass: *Arrhenatherum elatius*, *Centaurea nigra*, *Lathyrus pratensis*, *Malva sylvestris*, *Silene latifolia*, *Vicia cracca*.

### *Malva alcea* L.
### Greater Musk-mallow

7. Neophyte. A perennial herb, found rarely as a garden escape or throw-out, in vacant, uncultivated land on post-housing sites,

in allotments, in abandoned flower beds, by the Metro tram line and as seedlings in pavement. Europe. Ass: *Lepidium didymum*, *Euphorbia peplus*, *Urtica dioica*, *Viola arvensis*.

### *Malva sylvestris* L.
### Common Mallow

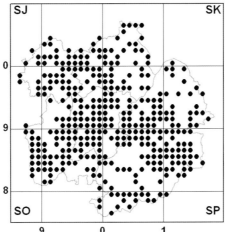

*369. Archaeophyte. A widespread perennial herb, commonest in some of the inner urban areas, found particularly on disturbed roadside hedgebanks and little-cut road verges, also on railway and canal banks, and waste or rough ground recovering from disturbance generally. A light-loving plant of average to dry, fairly base- and nutrient-rich soils. Ass: *Artemisia vulgaris*, *Arrhenatherum elatius*, *Rubus fruticosus* agg., *Silene latifolia*, *Sisymbrium officinale*, *Vicia sativa*.

### *Malva parviflora* L.
### Least Mallow

3. Neophyte, essentially casual. An annual herb, usually introduced with wool shoddy, bird seed, etc., but probably arriving in B&BC in manure delivered to allotments. A large stand on a manure heap, Woden Road South Allotments, Sandwell (SO991945, MWP, 2008); Wheelers Lane Allotments, Kings Heath (SP082814, MWP,

▲ *Acer platanoides*

▲ *Acer campestre*

▲ *Malva parviflora*

*Malva parviflora* (by Anne Bebbington)

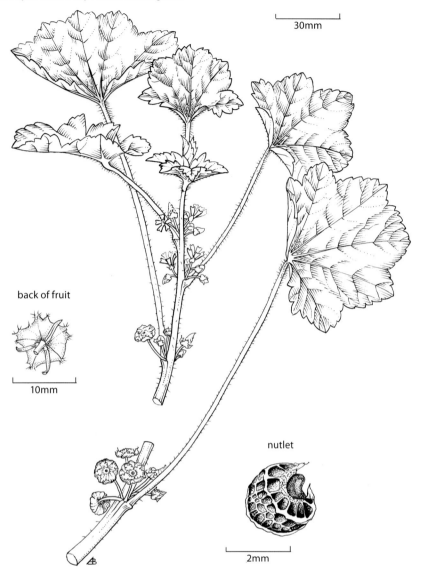

30mm

back of fruit

10mm

nutlet

2mm

ICT & EMP, 2008); among potato plants, Jeffcock Road Allotments, W'ton (SO9097, CBW, 2010). Recorded prior to the survey in 1992 as a single large plant in an arable field, Pedmore (SO906815, B. Westwood). Mediterranean and Central Asia.

### *Malva pusilla* Sm.
### Small Mallow
0. Casual. Found on a compost heap at Highfields School, Penn (SO880963, CBW, 1991). Europe.

### *Malva neglecta* Wallr.
### Dwarf Mallow
23. Archaeophyte. Annual (sometimes overwintering) which grows in bare patches on shallow, drought-liable base-rich and nutrient-intermediate soils. Intolerant of competition with vigorous species, its records from B&BC include some from pavement cracks, tarmac drives, spoil mounds, an old steelworks

site, a road island and as an allotment and lawn-edge weed. Also records from a neglected garden border, parkland, lane banks and a cemetery. Also tetrad SJ90A. Ass: *Euphorbia peplus*, *Taraxacum* sp., *Trifolium dubium*.

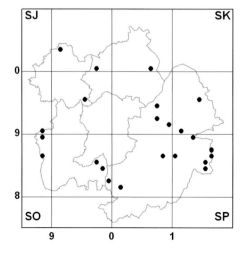

### *Malva verticillata* L.
### Chinese Mallow
1. Neophyte. Recorded from Wheelers Lane Allotments, Kings Heath (SP082814, MWP, ICT & EMP, 2008), where it had probably been originally introduced deliberately as an exotic salad or medicinal plant, but it had since spread to unused parts of several plots, apparently by seed. E Asia.

### *Malva setigera* Schimp. & Spenn.
(*Althaea hirsuta* L.)
### Rough Mallow
0. Casual. An annual, according to Cadbury *et al.* (1971) recorded once only in a waste place, Edgbaston (SP0584, C.M. Goodman, 1957). Europe.

### *Malva arborea* (L.) Webb & Berthel.
(*Lavatera arborea* L. )
### Tree-mallow

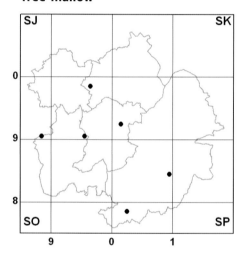

6. Native (by the sea). A large monocarpic herb which is accounted not frost-hardy inland. Nevertheless there are a few verified records from waste and marginal habitats usually close to gardens in B&BC.

### *Malva* × *clementii* (Cheek) Stace
(*Lavatera* × *clementii* Cheek, *Lavatera thuringiaca* L.; *M. olbia* (L.) Alef. × *M. thuringiaca* (L.) Vis.)
### Garden Tree-mallow
84. Neophyte. A shrub recorded quite frequently as a garden escape, discard and relic, sometimes as apparently self-sown seedlings (it is considered by some to be fertile, by others to be largely sterile), found mostly in waste land in residential areas, in post-housing sites, along canals, in rough grassland, in moist, base- and nutrient-intermediate, loamy soils. Recorded mostly as **L. thuringiaca** L., it appears that most or all records are ***Malva* × clementii**, although few plants have so far been positively identified as *L.* × *clementii*: near the River Cole (SP099817, CBW, 1999); Woodgate Valley Country Park

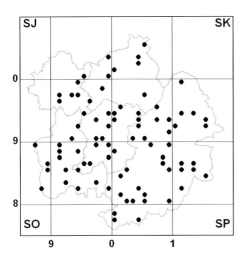

(SP009836, CBW, 2004); scrubby grassland, Fens Pools (SO915887, CBW, 2006); SO99R; SJ90V. SE Europe.

### Malva trimestris (L.) Salisb.
### (Lavatera trimestris L.)
### Royal Mallow
0. Casual. A rare garden escape or from bird seed. First reported in vc. 39 from a nature trail along the disused railway at Brownhills Common (SK0306, JPM, 1991). Mediterranean.

### Alcea rosea L.
### Hollyhock

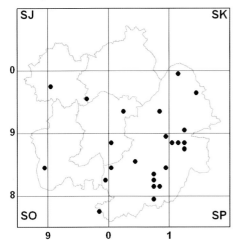

24. Neophyte. A biennial or perennial herb occurring as a self-sown garden escape or discard, mostly in pavements or along paths close to gardens or allotments, but also a few canal towpath and railway bank records and one from amenity grassland. Garden origin.

### Sidalcea malviflora (DC.) A. Gray ex Benth.
### Greek Mallow
3. Neophyte. A perennial escaping or being discarded from gardens. Roadside, Gorsey Mead Grove, Frankley (SP0078, MWP, 2003); neglected rough grassland, Hawkesley (SP051776, JJD, 2000). UK plants of Greek

Mallow are hybrids of unknown origin and *S. malviflora* (from N America) may or may not be in the parentage.

From the same botanical complex, BRF recorded six plants of **Sidalcea campestris** Greene from a sunny bank at Saltwells Nature Centre (SO931872, 1995).

### Tilia platyphyllos Scop.
### Large-leaved Lime

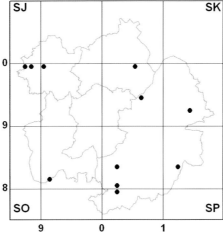

11. Native. Nationally Scarce; only a few planted trees have been recorded in B&BC, found as mature specimens in parks, and in similar amenity plantings in residential areas, although at least one plant at Manor Park Farm (SP029809, B. Westwood, 1996) was thought to be a self-sown from a nearby mature tree.

### Tilia × europaea L.
### (T. platyphyllos × T. cordata)
### Lime

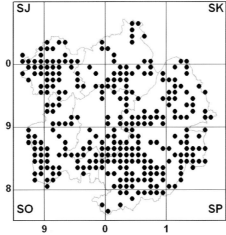

*308. A native hybrid, but thought to be almost entirely planted in B&BC, although it is easily propagated from suckers. It is partially fertile yet we have only two records of saplings, from Wordsley (SO883869, CBW, 2007) and Penn Fields (SO896968, CBW, 2007). Mature trees line many streets and it can also be

found in parks, churches, parkland and other old amenity plantings. The map suggests a concentration in the older suburbs and a scarcity in the industrial areas and more recently developed residential areas.

### Tilia cordata Mill.
### Small-leaved Lime

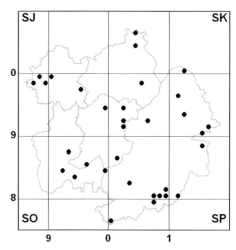

33. Native. Ax. A tree or coppice stool. Many of the records are for trees planted in amenity woodlands in parks, churchyards, playing fields, golf courses etc. The modern landscape architect specifies it rather than *T. × europaea*. There are however quite a few records suggesting an ancient presence in B&BC both in scattered old hedges, and in old woodland such as Park Hall Wood (SP1590 & SP1691) and Saltwells Wood (SO9387 and an old record for SO9388). It is favoured by moist, base-rich soils of intermediate fertility. Ass: *Acer campestre, Fraxinus excelsior, Quercus robur, Ulmus glabra*.

In addition to the above, there are a few records for (mostly recent) plantings of the following two neophyte limes: **Tilia 'Petiolaris'** (**Pendant Silver-lime**) was reported in the 1980s and early 1990s from Tettenhall College Woods (SO8899), Merridale Cemetery (SO9097) and Fowler's playing fields (SJ9200), all in W'ton and more recently at Highbury Park (SP0682, EMP, 2008) in B'ham. **Tilia × euchlora** K. Koch (**Caucasian Lime**) is now being planted as a street tree and was first recorded in vc. 39 in Yew Tree Lane in Tettenhall (SO8799) in 1992.

## 78. TROPAEOLACEAE

### Tropaeolum majus L.
### Nasturtium
30. Casual. A frost-sensitive annual including many cultivars. Plants recorded in habitats marginal to gardens, on

▲ Tropaeolum majus

▲ Reseda alba

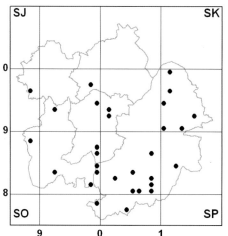

recently cleared post-housing land and on spoil heaps to the rear of houses. Peru.

## 79. LIMNANTHACEAE

### *Limnanthes douglasii* R. Br.
### Meadow-foam

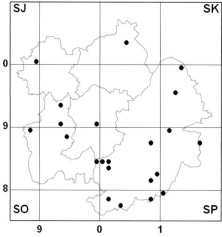

22. Casual. A showy, hardy annual, frequently grown in sunny spots in gardens and allotments and occasionally self-seeding into nearby paving and verges and persisting in neglected, grassy verges to the rear of houses. Plants also appear sporadically in cultivated ground where they have been grown previously, and, from time to time, on post-housing sites or spoil mounds. California.

## 80. RESEDACEAE

### *Reseda luteola* L.
### Weld

*357. Archaeophyte. A biennial herb. Found throughout our area though more concentrated in the Black Country and along the main transport corridors in B'ham. Typically on waste land, recently disturbed or recovering from disturbance, and commoner in industrial and inner urban areas than in residential areas. Many

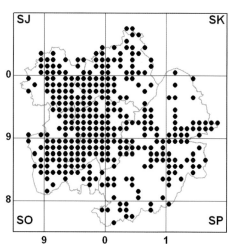

records are associated with canal land, also disused railways, brickworks, sewage works, landfill sites, country parks, playing fields etc., on moist or dry, well-drained, base-rich and fertile, often rubbly soils. Ass: *Artemisia vulgaris*, *Epilobium ciliatum*, *Linaria vulgaris*, *Senecio squalidus*, *Silene alba*, *Vicia sativa* subsp. *segetalis*.

### *Reseda alba* L.
### White Mignonette

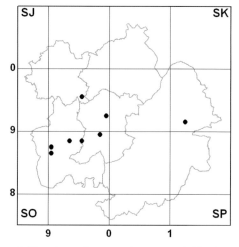

8. Neophyte. An annual or perennial herb with a few records from disturbed ground and ground recovering from disturbance on post-industrial waste land, roadsides, a car park, ruins of a bridge. On dry to moist, base- and nutrient-intermediate, often stony soils. Mediterranean.

### *Reseda lutea* L.
### Wild Mignonette

*110. Native or alien. Ax. A biennial or perennial herb, mainly found in the Black Country although it extends across B'ham associated with transport corridors. Recorded from waste land, disturbed ground, housing demolition sites, canal towpaths and road verges and especially close by railways. Its strong affinity with railways accounts for the linear patterns on the map. Grows in

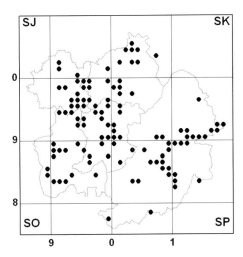

reasonably well-lit places, on dry to moist, base-rich (often calcareous) and fairly nutrient-poor to intermediate soils. Ass: *Epilobium ciliatum, Linaria vulgaris, Senecio viscosus, Verbascum thapsus, Vulpia myuros*.

## 81. BRASSICACEAE

### *Erysimum cheiranthoides* L.
### Treacle-mustard

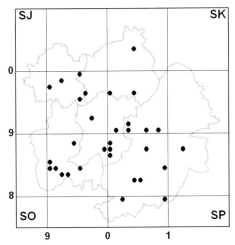

32. Archaeophyte. An uncommon annual colonist or weed of waste, disturbed or cultivated ground, including flowerbeds, allotments, roadsides, dumped soil, a car park and as a pavement weed. There is also a record from grassland over colliery spoil at the former Hawne Colliery and it has been found on industrial spoil in other areas. It is found in well-lit situations on moist to fairly dry, base- and nutrient-intermediate to rich soils. Ass: *Lepidium didymum, Lapsana communis, Papaver* sp., *Raphanus raphanistrum, Senecio vulgaris, Sonchus oleraceus*.

### *Erysimum × marshallii* (Henfr.) Bois
(*E. decumbens* (Schleich. ex Willd.) Dennst. × *E. perofskianum* Fisch. & C.A. Mey.)
### Siberian Wallflower
2. Neophyte, essentially casual with us,

escaping from garden cultivation. A dozen or so as pavement weeds, Balsall Heath (SP069845, CBW, 1997); a disturbed path edge, Saltwells LNR (SO932875, J. Akers, 1998 and again in 1999). Probably of garden origin.

### *Erysimum cheiri* (L.) Crantz
### Wallflower

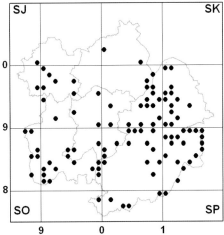

103. Archaeophyte. A perennial herb with fairly frequent scattered records which show an eastern bias. A light-loving plant of sunny but sheltered situations on dry, base-rich and moderately fertile or fairly infertile soils or crumbling mortar. It is found predominantly on pavements and other places peripheral to gardens, largely as a self-seeder from cultivation, but it also occurs on walls, rubble piles, waste ground, by railways and canals. Ass: *Centranthus ruber, Lobularia maritima, Senecio jacobaea, Senecio squalidus*.

### *Arabidopsis thaliana* (L.) Heynh.
### Thale Cress

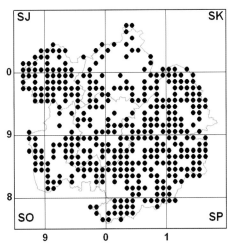

*409. Native. A widespread pioneer species on bare ground, on road verges, especially where regularly treated with herbicides (such as around street signs), railway land, canal towpaths, churchyards, recreation grounds, car parks, allotments, gardens.

It is typically an early-flowering winter-annual and may have been missed in areas visited late in the year. Favoured by dry, stony, base- intermediate and fairly nutrient-poor soils, but can operate as a weed of cultivation on quite fertile light soils. Appears to be much more commonly recorded than by Edees (1972) or Cadbury *et al.* (1971) in the mid-20th century. Ass: *Capsella bursa-pastoris, Cardamine hirsuta, Cerastium glomeratum, Erophila* sp., *Poa annua, Sagina apetala sensu lato*

### *Camelina sativa* (L.) Crantz
### Gold-of-pleasure
1. Archaeophyte, casual in B&BC. Annual, once a bad weed of flax. Recorded from Allsops Hill Quarry Complex (SO968878, ST, 1998). Older records: near the Visitor's Centre of the RSPB reserve, Sandwell Valley (SP0392, MWP, 1990) probably from bird-seed, not seen since; Tansey Green Claypit at Pensnett (SO910895, ST, 1986). It was also one of the many casuals recorded on the railway line at Sutton Park in the 1870s (SP1097, Bagnall, 1877).

### *Camelina alyssum* (Mill.) Thell.
0. Casual. One old record only, California Quarry, Woodgate Valley (SP0183, WHH, 1941).

### *Neslia paniculata* (L.) Desv.
### Ball Mustard
0. Casual. An annual, usually a birdseed alien or a seed contaminant, recorded only once, from before the survey period, at Balls Hill Branch Canal embankment (SO989906, JJB & P.L. Harris, 1987).

### *Capsella bursa-pastoris* (L.) Medik.
### Shepherd's-purse
*656. Archaeophyte. An annual, common everywhere where dry to damp, fertile soil is disturbed except in shade or on very base-poor soil, producing several generations per year and flowering throughout much of the year. Well-adapted to conditions of frequent disturbance, especially cultivation, and resistant to trampling and mowing. Ass: *Euphorbia peplus, Matricaria discoidea, Poa annua, Polygonum aviculare*.

### *Turritis glabra* L.
(*Arabis glabra* (L.) Bernh.)
### Tower Mustard
0. Native. Sect. 41, BAP, Nationally Scarce, EN. A biennial, not recorded during the present survey but with a history in our area, at least recently essentially as a casual. It was last seen on a track by the railway at Bushbury (SP0291, BRF, 1993); 20–30 plants on waste ground off Market Street, Stourbridge (SO900843, H.E.E. Babb, conf.

WAT, 1989); Coseley (SO938945, N.R. & G.C. Hewitt, 1988). There are also eight old records from between 1805 and 1939 from the Stourbridge area (SO9084 & SO9182), from hedgebanks etc. which might include native occurrences.

### Barbarea vulgaris W.T. Aiton
### Winter-cress

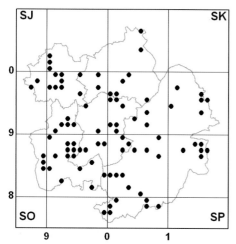

*90. Native. Biennial or perennial, quite widespread and locally frequent in some areas. Records include banks of the Rivers Stour and Rea, brooks including Bourne Brook in Woodgate Valley Park and canals, also ditches, but also recorded from farmland, waste ground, road verges, churchyards and sewage works. Usually found on somewhat disturbed, moist to damp (but not waterlogged), base- and nutrient-rich soils in full daylight. Also tetrad SK00A. Ass: *Euphorbia helioscopia*, *Holcus lanatus*, *Poa trivialis*, *Ranunculus repens*, *Rumex obtusifolius*.

### Barbarea stricta Andrz.
### Small-flowered Winter-cress

0. Neophyte; a rare casual in our area and not recorded in the present survey. A biennial or perennial herb, recorded as a casual on the canal towpath, Broad Street to Railway Drive, W'ton (SO918988, BRF, 1988). There is another pre-survey record from the River Cole, Bordesley Green (Anon., SP122868, 1992). Nationally this species has an interesting distribution concentrated in a zone from the mouth of the Severn to that of the Humber and passing through B&BC, so there could well be more of it in our area. Europe.

### Barbarea intermedia Boreau
### Medium-flowered Winter-cress

4. Neophyte, essentially a rare casual in B&BC. Usually a biennial herb. Several, roadside and garden, Selcombe Way, Hawkesley (SP049773, JJD, 2000); one plant in mown verge, Boleyn Road, Frankley (SO984786, JJD, 2001); one

plant on disturbed ground, B4187, Worcester Lane (SO905819, JJD, 2003); Barnford Farm Allotments (SO995875, ICT, MWP, PLR & AWR, 2008). NW Africa and W Europe.

### Barbarea verna (Mill.) Asch.
### American Winter-cress

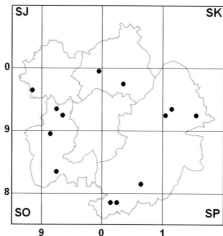

13. Neophyte. A biennial or annual, widely cultivated as a watercress substitute, it can form a persistent seedbank in allotments and six of the recent records are as a garden or allotment weed. Other records appear to be casual occurrences from disturbed situations, mostly on fairly moist, fertile soil in a river corridor, post-industrial land, and by a path in open scrub on Mons Hill.

### Rorippa palustris (L.) Besser
### Marsh Yellow-cress

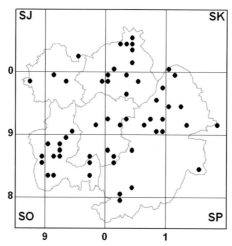

*56. Native. A spring-germinating annual, recorded from the margins of rivers, canals, a reservoir, pools, also in damp ground, waste ground and playing fields. It seems to be rarer in the SE. It grows in full daylight on fairly fertile and base-rich areas of wet mud, either at the edge of receding water bodies or around areas of disturbance and impeded drainage. Also tetrads SJ90Q,V. Ass: *Agrostis stolonifera*, *Alopecurus geniculatus*, *Ranunculus sceleratus*.

### Rorippa sylvestris (L.) Besser
### Creeping Yellow-cress

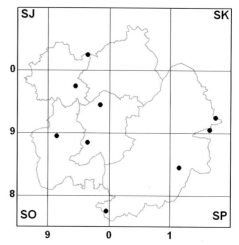

9. Native. A rather uncommon perennial of damp, bare and disturbed ground, found in similar habitats to *Rorippa palustris* but often in less reliably wet situations, so that it is found near the top of the draw-down zone around ponds, pools and canals and occasionally in muddy roadside gutters and pavements, puddly waste land, sewage works and even cultivated soil as a weed in flower beds. Soils are damp or winter-wet, base-rich and fertile. So far there are no reports here of European polyploidy races which are extremely aggressive weeds of cultivation and waste ground. Ass: *Agrostis stolonifera*, *Alopecurus geniculatus*, *Plantago major*, *Potentilla anserina*, *Sagina procumbens*.

### Rorippa amphibia (L.) Besser
### Great Yellow-cress

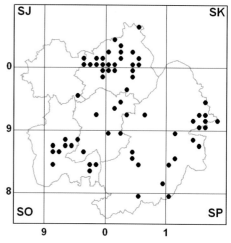

*65. Native. A perennial associated with standing water margins, and very abundant in the shallow water of canal margins in some areas of B&BC, but not in others, also in the edges of some of the main rivers and streams. A light-loving plant of sites which have fluctuating water levels, but are reliably wet throughout the year, on fairly base-

and nutrient-rich substrates. Ass: *Apium nodiflorum, Epilobium hirsutum, Glyceria maxima, Myosotis scorpioides, Nasturtium officinale* agg., *Solanum dulcamara*.

## Nasturtium officinale agg.
(*Rorippa nasturtium-aquaticum* agg.)
### Water-cress

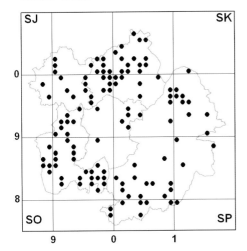

*123. Native. Perennial herbs associated with water. Recorded from streams, brooks, canals, pools and ponds, wet woodland and willow carr, growing in well-lit places and also partial shade, mostly in clear, shallow running water of intermediate base and nutrient status over sandy or gravelly substrates. At least a quarter of the records are from canals, another quarter from ponds and pools, the rest nearly all from running water. The aggregate is apparently less common in the W'ton/Sandwell/B'ham corridor. Ass: *Apium nodiflorum, Callitriche* spp., *Myosotis scorpioides, Veronica beccabunga*.

The aggregate consists of two species and their hybrid, which can only be satisfactorily distinguished in fruit:

## Nasturtium officinale W.T. Aiton
(*Rorippa nasturtium-aquaticum* (L.) Hayek)
### Water-cress, Green Water-cress

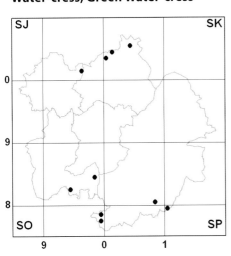

10. Native. Perennial recorded in Walsall, W'ton, Dudley and S B'ham in ponds, streams and canals.

## Nasturtium × sterile (Airy Shaw) Oefelein
(*Rorippa × sterilis* Airy Shaw; *N. officinale* × *N. microphylla*)
### Hybrid, Brown or Winter Water-cress

4. Native. This is the most commonly cultivated watercress. It has been recorded only rarely: small flush at foot of bank, Shelah Road, Hawne (SO965845, WAT, 1995); large patch in stream along ditch, Sandwell Valley (SP019921, MWP, 2005); by base-poor stream, Sutton Park (SP101977, MWP, ICT, PLR, DJA & J. Antrobus, 2007); in quarry, Brick Kiln SLINC (SK038023, ICT & A. Blackshaw, 2007). This hybrid is probably under-recorded where it has not been possible to decide whether immature fruits are definitively sterile. Also a record for tetrad SJ90Q.

## Nasturtium microphyllum (Boenn.) Rchb.
(*Rorippa microphylla* (Boenn.) Hyl. ex Á. & D. Löve)
### Narrow-fruited or One-rowed Water-cress

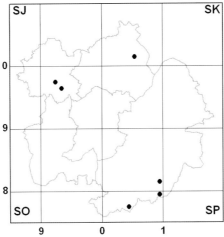

6. Native. Perennial, with records from ponds, canals and a ditch. A small pond, Swanshurst Park (SP094816, JWP, 1995); ditch S of Scribers Lane (SP099797, JJD, 2000); canal, W'ton (SO928971 and SO931967, ICT & EVJC, 2001); Shannon Road, Hawkesley, small area of flushed grassland along roadside (SP044775, MWP, 2007); in canal at Stubbers Green, Walsall (SK050010, ICT, 2008).

## Armoracia rusticana P. Gaertn., B. Mey. & Scherb.
### Horse-radish

*383. Archaeophyte. A perennial, sterile in the UK, but a fairly common relic of cultivation in allotments and gardens, almost impossible to eradicate and spreading readily from root cuttings. It is also found on a wide range of waste ground as a garden discard or in dumped

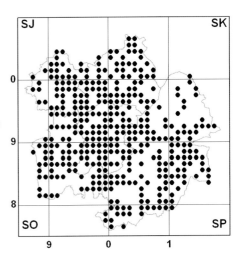

soil, and it seems to be particularly common in the caps of old landfill sites. It persists well in many types of rough, uncultivated, undergrazed and little-trampled grassland and open scrub on fairly deep, moist, base-intermediate and nutrient-rich soils. Ass: *Alopecurus pratensis, Cirsium arvense, Dactylis glomerata, Equisetum arvense, Rumex obtusifolius*.

## Cardamine amara L.
### Large Bitter-cress

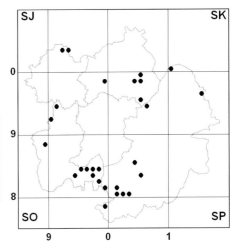

28. Native. Ax. A perennial associated with permanently wet, organic or silty substrates of intermediate base and nutrient status. Very occasionally seen in open situations in wet grassland, it is almost always found in moderate shade in old Alder woodland along streams and rivers or by substantial pools, and seems to be particularly abundant where water is flushing out of the banks throughout the year. Ass: *Angelica sylvestris, Caltha palustris, Chrysosplenium oppositifolium, Epilobium hirsutum, Ficaria verna, Filipendula ulmaria*.

## Cardamine pratensis L.
### Cuckooflower

*256. Native. A perennial, found throughout on damp grasslands including

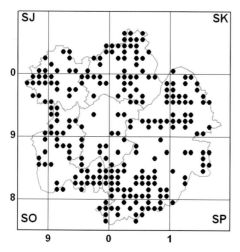

lawns, churchyards and amenity grasslands but commonest in old, species-rich stands of vegetation, also in marshes, streamsides and even open woodland, but not persisting well in tall, dense vegetation or deep shade. The map suggests that it is scarcer in many of the inner, heavily urbanised areas. Grows best in not very fertile soils of intermediate base status. This species has many variants, often with distinct chromosome numbers, that as far as we are aware have not been distinguished in B&BC or indeed hardly in the UK as a whole. Possibly B&BC would be a fertile area in which to study this differentiation in view of the extreme range of conditions found in a small area. Ass: *Galium palustre, Juncus effusus, Ranunculus acris, Ranunculus flammula, Rumex acetosa.*

▲ *Cardamine pratensis*

### *Cardamine impatiens* L.
### Narrow-leaved Bitter-cress

2. Native. NT & Nationally Scarce. A biennial, typically found in bare places in woodland and usually on stabilised screes, especially on limestone. Edees (1972) noted that it had been known in the dolerite quarries of Barrow Hill and at Sedgley (presumably on Sedgley Beacon) since at least 1801, and it is still present on Barrow Hill, along the shady ride from Pensnett Church, most recently in 2007 (SO915895, ICT & MWP). It was also recorded along the line of a filled-in canal known as Castle Walkway, Selly Oak (SP031829, CRP, 2002). There is also an old, unconfirmed record from woodland in the grounds of Woodbrooke, Bournville (SP036814, T. Thompson, 1985).

### *Cardamine flexuosa* With.
### Wavy Bitter-cress

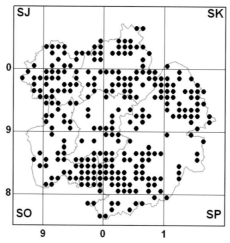

*289. Native. A winter- or summer-annual most commonly encountered as a colonist of bare, damp or wet places such as ditches in woodland, especially but not always old woodland, and it can also sometimes be found as a garden weed. Usually, but not always, in moist, shady situations and generally on base- and nutrient-intermediate, damp soils. The map shows a relative scarcity in the central areas and some clustering of the distribution around the countryside areas. Ass: (in woodlands) *Caltha palustris, Chrysosplenium oppositifolium, Epilobium montanum, Solanum dulcamara.*

### *Cardamine hirsuta* L.
### Hairy Bitter-cress

*480. Native. A winter annual found throughout in many habitats but particularly on cultivated ground and as a garden weed, tending to colonise bare areas on shallow soils such as driveways, paths, rockeries, roofs and wall tops. A light-loving plant growing on soils of

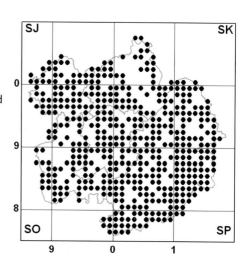

average fertility and base status which tend to dry out in summer. Many fewer records from B&BC in the 1970s vc. 39 and vc. 38 Floras. Ass: *Arabidopsis thaliana, Cerastium glomeratum, Erophila* sp., *Sagina apetala sensu lato, Stellaria media.*

### *Cardamine corymbosa* Hook. f.
### New Zealand Bitter-cress

2. Neophyte. An annual spread by horticulture, found as three or four plants as a weed in a Bournville garden centre in Stockswood Road (SP046816) in 1995 by JWP. Still present, as a single plant, in 2003 (WAT). Further plants were noted in pots supplied by Hill Cottage Alpines in the B'ham Botanical Gardens shop (SP0485, JWP, 2007). It may be overlooked for *C. hirsuta* elsewhere. New Zealand.

### *Lepidium sativum* L.
### Garden Cress

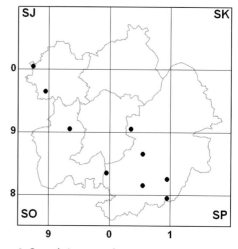

9. Casual. An annual, occasionally recorded as a relic of allotment cultivation but there are older records from Park Lime Pits and Tansey Green claypits. Egypt and SW Asia.

### *Lepidium campestre* (L.) W.T. Aiton
### Field Pepperwort

6. Archaeophyte. Annual to biennial. A

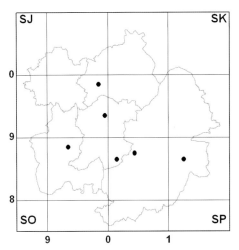

few records from disturbed, dry, soil of intermediate nutrient and base status, mostly as a street weed or on post-industrial sites. Also tetrad SJ90V.

### Lepidium heterophyllum Benth.
### Smith's Pepperwort
1. Native. Perennial. Usually from droughty bare patches in acid grassland, it was found on waste land near houses, Ridgeacre (SP012844, CBW, 1997). Two slightly older records: waste land, Enville Street (SO896854, R.E. Smith, 1989, now lost); sandy, bare hedgebank, Burys Hill (SO898816, WAT, 1991).

### Lepidium ruderale L.
### Narrow-leaved Pepperwort

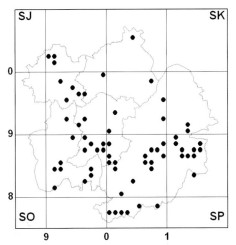

65. Archaeophyte. An annual, recorded occasionally from dry waste ground and disturbed places, mostly from post-industrial sites such as quarries and an old brickyard, but since the mid-1990s (and initially in the S) found in the margins and central reservations of busy roads (especially in the cracks between kerbstones) apparently as a roadside halophyte. It is now frequently abundant and spreading for some distance in roadside habitats, which now account

for most of its distribution in B&BC and it continues (2012) to become more abundant there. Ass: *Cochlearia danica*, *Matricaria discoidea*, *Plantago coronopus*, *Polygonum aviculare*, *Puccinellia distans*, *Sagina apetala sensu lato*, *Spergularia marina*.

### Lepidium latifolium L.
### Dittander

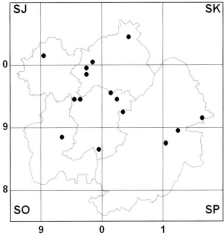

15. Native in some coastal areas and Nationally Scarce there. Inland, an escape from cultivation as a culinary herb, becoming replaced in that role in the 17th century by Horseradish (Pearman in Preston *et al.* 2002). A rhizomatous perennial herb found in moist to damp, fertile, soil recovering from disturbance on roadsides, railway sidings, river corridors, waste land. In some quantity infesting a riverside horse-grazed pasture subjected to periodical flooding between Sandy Lane and the River Tame near Junction 8 of the M6 (SP0195). Ass: *Anthriscus sylvestris*, *Cirsium arvense*, *Hordeum murinum*, *Persicaria amphibia*, *Rumex obtusifolius*, *Tripleurospermum inodorum*, *Urtica dioica*.

### Lepidium graminifolium L.
### Tall Pepperwort
0. Neophyte. Few, mainly old, records in UK, with one very old record from California Quarry, Woodgate Valley (SP0183, WHH, 1952). S Europe.

### Lepidium draba L.
### Hoary Cress
51. Neophyte. A rhizomatous perennial herb, found mainly in the Black Country, unlike the other members of the genus which are more widely spread. In rough grassland and waste ground, particularly on canal banks and towpaths and by roads, where it can occupy large areas of grassed verges, also on miscellaneous waste and post-industrial sites. A light-loving plant of dry to moist, base-rich soils of intermediate fertility, it can withstand a certain amount

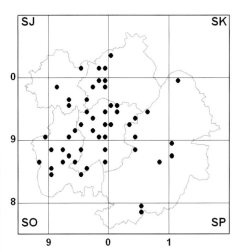

of mowing, trampling and disturbance and has become well-established on some sites although it does not seem to be spreading to new sites very quickly. S Europe and SW Asia. Ass: *Anisantha sterilis*, *Anthriscus sylvestris*, *Artemisia vulgaris*, *Cirsium arvense*, *Fallopia japonica*, *Geranium pyrenaicum*, *Poa trivialis*, *Rubus fruticosus* agg., *Rumex obtusifolius*, *Silene latifolia*, *Urtica dioica*.

**Subsp. *draba*** is specified by most recorders and all records are thought to be this although subsp. *chalapense* (L.) Thell. (Green Pepperwort) was once naturalised not far from B&BC at Burton-on-Trent in Staffordshire.

### Lepidium coronopus (L.) Al-Shehbaz
(*Coronopus squamatus* (Forssk.) Asch.)
### Swine-cress

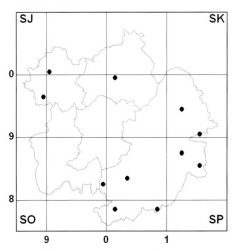

11. Archaeophyte. An annual with a few records mainly from the E of the area, mainly as a pavement weed but also in bare places in amenity grassland and grass verges and in areas of disturbed or trampled ground and very rarely seen in the inner urban areas.

### Lepidium didymum L.
(*Coronopus didymus* (L.) Sm.)
### Lesser Swine-cress
206. Neophyte. An annual or biennial, it

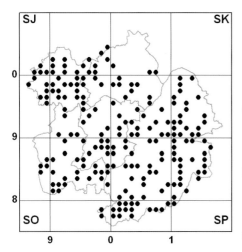

can be an abundant weed of cultivation, particularly in allotments but also in gardens and arable fields, but it is also quite frequent as an opportunist coloniser of a wide variety of disturbed or trampled bare areas. It is quite a frequent pavement and tarmac weed and occurs in the herbicided margins of mown-grass road verges. It thrives in moist, but well-drained, base- and nutrient-rich allotment soils but also in pavement cracks, between paver bricks, on trampled paths, a bonfire site, once in shade. It was much less common in 1971 according to both Edees (1972) and Cadbury *et al.* (1971) and is probably still increasing. Europe and N & S America. Ass: *Capsella bursa-pastoris, Cirsium arvense, Gnaphalium uliginosum, Poa annua, Polygonum aviculare, Trifolium repens, Veronica arvensis, Viola arvensis.*

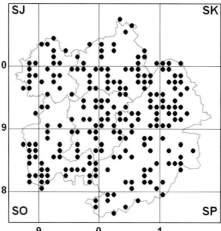

### *Lunaria annua* L.
### Honesty

*226. Neophyte. A biennial garden plant which has become widely naturalised along lanes, footpaths, canal hedgerows, woodland margins, in abandoned gardens, churchyards etc. and spreading into waste ground and plantations. It can be quite abundant and persistent, preferring moist, rich soil in semi-shade which is occasionally disturbed. Ass: *Epilobium montanum, Geum urbanum, Hyacinthoides × massartiana.*

Our British plant is **subsp. *annua***, a cultivated plant of unknown origin.

### *Lunaria rediviva* L.
### Perennial Honesty

1. Neophyte. Naturalised from cultivation, broad-leaved woodland, the Duckery, Great Barr Park (SP051959, PWS & P. Meadows, 1997). Europe.

### *Aurinia saxatilis* (L.) Desv.
### (*Alyssum saxatile* L.)
### Golden Alison

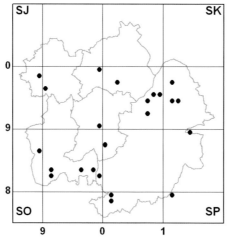

23. Neophyte. A garden perennial, occasionally self-seeding on walls and in pavements in residential areas but apparently always a casual. Europe and SW Asia.

### *Berteroa incana* (L.) DC.
### Hoary Alison

0. A rare casual in UK, with one old record from Boldmere, near Sutton (Bagnall, 1874).

### *Lobularia maritima* (L.) Desv.
### Sweet Alison

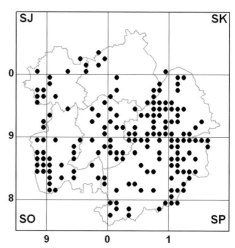

174. Neophyte, probably essentially casual in B&BC. An annual to perennial garden escape with a sporadic distribution in B&BC. Typically found on pavements, or at the foot of walls, in close proximity to gardens. Unlike some other garden escapes, it is still widely cultivated. There are a few records from waste ground, along paths, on canal towpaths, through rough grass, in a sports ground, on a disused railway, and persisting on sites of demolished housing. It grows in full sun on dry, rather nutrient-poor but base-rich soils. Coasts of SW Europe and the Mediterranean. Ass: *Arabidopsis thaliana, Centranthus ruber, Eschscholtzia californica, Euphorbia peplus, Geranium lucidum, Lamium amplexicaule, Lamium purpureum, Linaria purpurea, Poa annua, Sagina procumbens, Stellaria media, Senecio squalidus, Veronica agrestis.*

### *Descurainia sophia* (L.) Webb ex Prantl
### Flixweed

2. Archaeophyte. Annual or biennial. On a tip/bank/waste ground at Hay Mills (SP116847, WAT, 1998); locally common along a footpath in an arable field and extending into the hedgebank, field margin and farmyard at Langley Hall (SP150956–151956, ICT, MWP & JWP, 2006). Also an earlier record of a single plant on urban waste ground at Oldbury (SO997887, JJD, 1987).

### *Arabis caucasica* Willd. ex Schltdl.
### Garden Arabis

4. Neophyte. A perennial garden plant, which can naturalise on walls and rock outcrops but appears only to occur as

▲ *Lepidium didymum*

a roadside casual in B&BC. It has been recorded as a self-set pavement weed from Warley (SP006854, CBW, 1997); by the verge of Kent Road, Lapal (SO985844, CBW, 2000); by the Ashted Circus (SP0887, MWP, 2004); Wall Heath (SO883896, CBW, 2005). S Europe, N Africa and *SW* Asia.

### *Arabis hirsuta* (L.) Scop.
### Hairy Rock-cress

1. Native. A plant normally found in crevices in limestone and other calcareous rocks; here it was recorded from uncultivated farmland (SJ882018, JVT, 2000), not from a typical habitat and is likely to be a casual introduction at most.

### *Aubrieta deltoidea* (L.) DC.
### Aubretia

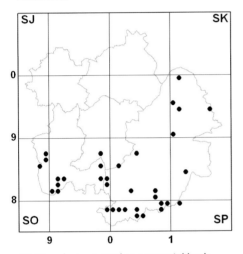

35. Neophyte. A garden perennial herb, widely naturalised in England, especially in the SW. Most of our records are essentially as casual pavement weed seedlings but there are a few more permanent escapes onto walls and embankments. Apparently escaping more commonly in the S. Sicily, Balkans and SW Asia.

### *Erophila* DC.
### Whitlowgrasses

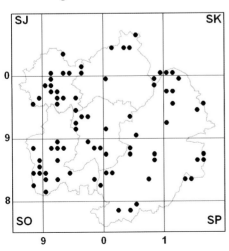

79. Native. Ax. *Erophila* spp. are key components of the ephemeral winter-annual community found on open ground on shallow soils, typically S-facing, which warm up very early in spring but are liable to dry out completely in summer. Typically the soil is skeletal, fairly base-rich and quite nutrient-poor. Classical examples are on rock exposures in the hills, and we have some examples in B&BC, e.g. in the Rowley Hills and also in a few places on blast furnace spoil. However *Erophila* spp. may also be found on driveways, pavement edges and bare areas of grass verges damaged by car parking or enthusiastic herbicide application, also in churchyards, on stone canal embankments, gravelled amenity areas, crumbling pavements etc. They are certainly under-recorded, due to the early-flowering time and small size, but our recorders consider that they are becoming commoner in some of these secondary urban sites. Ass: *Arenaria serpyllifolia sensu lato, Cerastium glomeratum, Cerastium semidecandrum, Festuca ovina, Festuca rubra, Poa annua, Taraxacum sect. Erythrosperma, Veronica arvensis.*

Stace recognises three species in this aggregate, two of which have been recorded in B&BC, although the majority have been recorded as the aggregate.

### *Erophila verna* (L.) DC.
### Common Whitlowgrass

14. Native. Ax. This segregate is probably the commonest, but has been distinguished by only a few recorders, in all parts of B&BC.

### *Erophila glabrescens* Jord.
### Glabrous Whitlowgrass

2. Native. Ax. Streetly, both found at the junction between pavements and lawns (SP081988 & SP080990, both JEH, 2008).

### *Conringia orientalis* (L.) Dumort
### Hare's-ear Mustard

0. Casual. An annual of arable and waste places, in the UK it was originally a contaminant of imported crop seed and later became a rare bird seed alien. Not seen in the present survey but recorded twice by BRF: Oak Street, W'ton (SO902982, 1972); W'ton Street, Bilston (SO943963, 1983). C & S Europe, the Mediterranean region and W Asia.

### *Diplotaxis tenuifolia* (L.) DC.
### Perennial Wall-rocket

26. Archaeophyte. A perennial herb, found in the UK mainly in urban areas and particularly ports. Strongly urban-centred in B&BC, it grows mainly in open situations

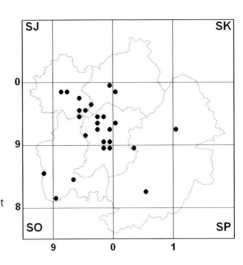

or sparse grassland in post-industrial areas, on waste ground, as a pavement weed, by canals and roadsides, usually in dry, skeletal soils or well-drained slopes, occasionally on rubble and walls on base-rich soils of variable fertility. It seems to be particularly frequent in the Oldbury area. There are a few records from scrub and allotments on richer soils and seed is being sold and grown for salading as 'wild rocket'. Ass: *Capsella bursa-pastoris, Conyza* spp., *Epilobium ciliatum, Hordeum murinum, Poa annua, Senecio squalidus, Sisymbrium officinale, Vulpia myuros.*

### *Diplotaxis muralis* (L.) DC.
### Annual Wall-rocket

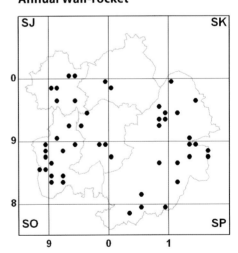

48. Neophyte. An annual or short-lived perennial, in similar habitats to *D. tenuifolia* but distributed more in the periphery of B&BC, often in residential areas, increasing. It grows in open situations, particularly as a street weed in pavements and at the foot of walls but is also associated with old railways and other post-industrial sites, only rarely on canal sites or as a garden or allotment weed although it too has been sold as 'wild rocket' or as a green manure. Also recorded on the limestone at Wren's Nest NNR. Well-lit situations on

sharply drained, base-rich and nutrient-intermediate soils. C & S Europe and N Africa. Ass: *Capsella bursa-pastoris, Chenopodium album, Epilobium ciliatum, Epilobium montanum, Festuca rubra, Geranium robertianum, Hordeum murinum, Lamium album, Senecio squalidus*.

### *Brassica oleracea* L.
### Cabbage

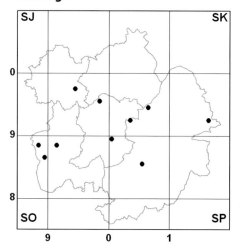

10. Native or alien. Nationally Scarce as a native on sea cliffs. A perennial herb, rarely recorded and usually essentially a casual in B&BC, although occasionally it persists for some years. Apparently always an escape from cultivation. Found in waste land, often by canals, also in rough grass at Burbury Brickworks (SP099836) and high on retaining wall at S end of Fiveways railway station, within ornamental brick arch feature, rooted in mortar (SP059858, lost by 2012).

**Var. capitata** L. (**Cabbage**) and **var. botrytis** L. (**Cauliflower, Broccoli**) have been recorded.

### *Brassica napus* L.

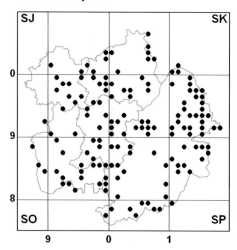

*146. Neophyte, probably essentially a casual in B&BC, but widespread. An annual or biennial, found as a crop relic on farms which spreads into bare places along roadsides, canals and railways. Frequent also on demolition land and other waste places and has been recorded from churchyards and playing fields. Soils dry to moist, intermediate or high in base and nutrient status. Cultivated origin. Ass: *Anisantha sterilis, Artemisia vulgaris, Elytrigia repens, Epilobium ciliatum, Senecio jacobaea, Senecio squalidus*.

There are few records specifically for **subsp. oleifera** (DC.) Metzg. (**Oil-seed Rape**), but practically all our records for *B. napus* are thought to be for this subspecies. **Subsp. rapifera** Metzg. (**Swede**) was recorded on the fringes of Queen's Lea Allotments (SJ9700, ICT, 2006).

### *Brassica rapa* L.
### Turnip

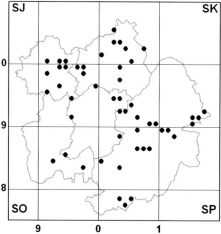

51. Archaeophyte. Annual or biennial, recorded from disturbed ground, waste ground, parkland, canal, disused railway and from farmland where it is a relic of cultivation. Grows in reasonably well-lit places on moist, fairly fertile and base-rich soils. **Subsp. rapa** (**Turnip**) is probably the subspecies to which most of our records should be referred, although there are no specific records for it. **Subsp. oleifera** (DC.) Metzg. (**Turnip-rape**) has been recorded only once in an RSPB Field, Sandwell Valley Complex. Almost certainly a bird-seed casual. **Subsp. campestris** (L.) A.R. Clapham (**Wild Turnip**) is recorded occasionally from riversides and canals and has been seen on a nature reserve and a golf course. Ass. for subsp. *campestris*: *Anthriscus sylvestris, Alliaria petiolata, Urtica dioica*.

### *Brassica tournfortii* Gouan
### Pale Cabbage
1. Casual, rare in UK. Roadside bank, Amberway, Halesowen (SO9685, CBW, 2005).

### *Brassica juncea* (L.) Czern.
### Chinese Mustard
11. Casual. An annual, recorded from

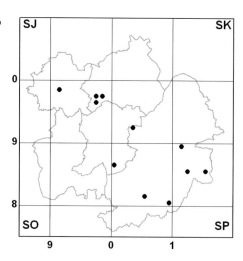

disturbed waste ground including that of demolished houses, derelict land, a path side, allotments and as a flower-bed weed. From bird-seed, and possibly increasing due to cultivation by ethnic groups and gourmets. Usually on moist, fairly fertile soil. S & E Asia.

### *Brassica nigra* (L.) W.D.J. Koch
### Black Mustard

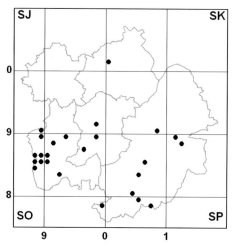

25. Native or alien. An annual, found occasionally on waste and disturbed ground, by roadsides and canals, and in allotments. Apart from a few records in the edges of canals, it does not seem to occur in its typical habitat in river margins in B&BC and is probably largely an escape from cultivation. The cluster of roadside records in the Stourbridge area may derive from River Severn-side occurences a few km beyond B&BC in vc. 39. A light-loving plant found on moist, fertile and fairly base-rich soils. Ass: *Brassica napus, Papaver rhoeas, Rhaphanus raphanistrum, Sisymbrium orientale, Urtica dioica*.

### *Sinapis arvensis* L.
### Charlock
*164. Archaeophyte. An annual found in disturbed ground, originally a weed

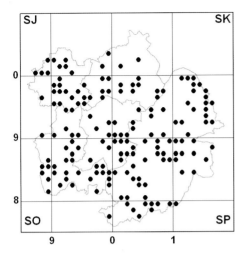

of arable, it is still found in arable field margins and on spare ground in allotments. However it is now, thanks to its control by selective herbicides, far more an opportunist coloniser of bare soil along lanes, roadsides and central reservations, recent plantations and miscellaneous habitats by canals, in churchyards, parks, rubbish dumps, nature reserves etc, possibly often generated from a long-lived soil seed bank after disturbance. It prefers reasonably moist, fertile and base-rich soil although it can sometimes flower in a dwarfed condition on poorer soil. It is not resistant to trampling or mowing. Also tetrad SO98E. Ass: *Avena fatua*, *Fallopia convolvulus*, *Papaver rhoeas*, *Raphanus raphanistrum*, *Sonchus oleraceus*, *Tripleurospermum inodorum*.

### *Sinapis alba* L.
### White Mustard
5. Archaeophyte. An annual, widespread in UK as an arable and opportunist weed and now grown in the fields for pheasants, but rarely recorded in B&BC. May Lane Allotments, Kings Heath (SP078802, WAT, 1999); near car park, Saltwells LNR (SO934869, APD, 1999); Amblecote (SO896847, Wardell Armstrong consultants, 2004); cornfield margins, Limepits Farm (SP031998, MWP, 2006).

**Subsp.** *alba* was specifically recorded at a road junction at Greets Green (SO985917, MWP, 1997).

### *Eruca vesicaria* (L.) Cav.
### Garden Rocket
3. Casual. An annual, long cultivated as a medicinal plant and currently with some popularity as a garden and allotment salad plant, but as yet rarely observed growing spontaneously. Tansey Green brickworks (SO905895, AMG, 2002); Smithy Lane (SO911901, AMG, 2002). Mediterranean and SW Asia.

**Subsp.** *sativa* (Mill.) Thell. was recorded on waste ground, New Bond Street (SP085863, MWP & JWP, 2004).

### *Erucastrum gallicum* (Willd.) O.E. Schulz
### Hairy Rocket
1. Neophyte. An annual, widespread on the chalk of Salisbury Plain as a result of army activity. Only casual records in B&BC; one recent: Lodge Hill Cemetery (SP025824, K. Barnett, AWR & CBW, 1998); older records (1950–1992), probably from bird seed, from West Bromwich, W'ton and Dudley. A plant recorded as *Erucastrum* sp. at the former Hawne Colliery site in Dudley (SO956846, ST, 1997) may also have been this. Pyrenees & C Europe.

### *Erucastrum nasturtiifolium* (Poir.) O.E. Schulz
### Watercress-leaved Rocket
0. Casual. Once recorded from Sutton Park (SP0997, Bagnall, 1877).

### *Hirschfeldia incana* (L.) Lagr.-Foss.
### Hoary Mustard

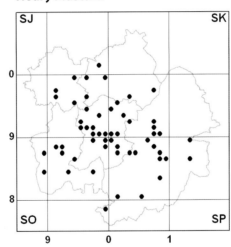

56. Neophyte. Annual or short-lived perennial, not mentioned in Cadbury *et al.* (1971) or Edees (1972) and with few records in our parts of vc. 39 and vc. 37 before 1990, it has become much more frequent in the Black Country, especially in the Tipton to Oldbury area, and to some extent in central parts of B'ham, during the survey period. Records are mostly from waste ground on post-industrial sites, associated with railways and along canals but also occasionally on former housing sites, in residential areas and as a pavement and trackside weed. Well-lit, disturbed situations on dry to moist, base-rich and nutrient-medium, usually but not always skeletal soils. SW Europe, the Mediterranean and SW Asia. Ass: *Agrostis capillaris*, *Cirsium arvense*, *Erigeron acris*, *Potentilla reptans*, *Sedum spurium*, *Urtica dioica*.

### *Coincya monensis* (L.) Greuter & Burdet
### subsp. *cheiranthos* (Vill.) Aedo, Leadlay & Muñoz Garm.
### Wallflower Cabbage
5. Neophyte. An annual or biennial, mostly recorded as a casual in the Black Country, but it seems to be increasing and there are some quite large populations which seem to be established more permanently. There are records from four areas within our survey period: established in quantity, roadside bank, verges & waste ground, Amber Way and footpath towards canal, Halesowen Industrial Park (SO970846, WAT, 1992 and still established there in 2000); a large colony associated with a disused railway, Wednesbury (SO9894, MWP, 2001); Coseley (SO946978, PN, 2001); several records over two monads in the Round Oak area, Dudley: on the towpath of the Stourbridge Canal (SO926880–SO925879, APD & ICT, 2002) and along the Pedmore Road (SO929885–SO927879, APD & ICT, 2002). There are older records: it was first recorded in vc. 39 on a canal towpath at Millfields (SO938963, BRF, 1980); later in a car park, Broad Street Bilston (SO946964, BRF 1983); in Pensnett churchyard (SO915893, BRF, 1987); Worcester Lane, Pedmore (SO906816, WAT, 1991); some 30 plants on dumped soil at old Hawne Colliery site (SO958847, WAT, 1991); disused railway sidings, Springvale (SO938953, BRF, 1993). It grows in bare areas or on rough grass banks in dry, skeletal, fairly nutrient-poor and fairly base-rich soil, often based on furnace spoil. W Europe. Ass: *Agrostis capillaris*, *Deschampsia flexuosa*, *Hieracium* spp., *Inula conyza*, *Pteridium aquilinum*, *Rubus fruticosus* agg., *Urtica dioica*.

### *Rapistrum rugosum* (L.) Bergeret
### Bastard Cabbage

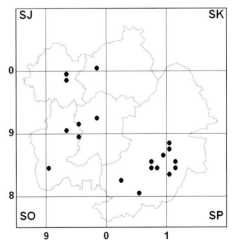

19. Neophyte. Annual or short-lived perennial. A scattering of mostly essentially casual records, although sometimes forming quite large persistent populations

as on roadside banks at Brickfield Road, Hay Mills (seen in 1998 independently by CBW & MWP at SP115847 and SP116848, and still present in 2007). Recorded from bare or grassy situations recovering from disturbance on waste land both in industrial and residential areas, in well-lit places, on dry to moist, usually moderately base- and nutrient-rich soils. Mediterranean and SW Asia. Ass: *Anisantha sterilis, Crepis capillaris, Equisetum arvense, Hordeum murinum, Melilotus officinalis.*

### Crambe cordifolia Steven
**Greater Sea-kale**
0. Neophyte. A single plant, a presumed garden discard, established on canal towpath, Horseley Fields, W'ton (SO9298, FGB, 1975, persisted at least into the 1980s).

### Raphanus raphanistrum L. subsp. raphanistrum
**Wild Radish**

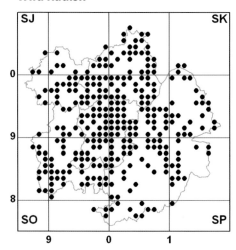

*307. Archaeophyte. An annual, fairly common on recently disturbed or cultivated ground in post-industrial and countryside areas, less so in the major country parks and in some residential areas although sometimes present in allotments where it may coexist with *Raphanus sativus*. It was once a serious weed of arable, but has been largely defeated by selective herbicides, and now its distribution in B&BC is clearly urban-centred, although the white-flowered variant was co-dominant with *Papaver rhoeas* in a series of bean fields S of Wall Heath (SO876889) in 2011. Recorded from arable fields, waste land, scrub, parks, churchyards, lanes and verges, canal towpaths, quarries. Grows mainly in well-lit places on moist to dry, well-drained, quite fertile and base-medium soils. Ass: *Anisantha sterilis, Geranium dissectum, Matricaria chamomilla, Papaver rhoeas, Sinapis arvensis.*

### Raphanus sativus L.
**Garden Radish**

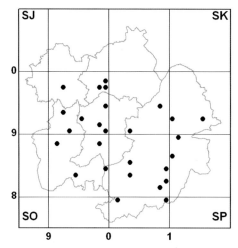

27. Casual. An annual herb; an escape from cultivation mainly in unused allotment land although occasionally a street weed. Found in recently disturbed, moist, fertile, base-intermediate soil. The hybrid with the Wild Radish (*R.* × *micranthus*) has not been recorded but could occur in allotments where both parent species often occur together.

### Sisymbrium altissimum L.
**Tall Rocket**

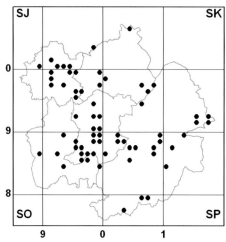

*67. Neophyte. Annual found growing on disturbed and waste ground, dumped soil, scrub, railway sidings and canal towpaths in well-lit sites usually in pockets of fairly moist, fairly base-rich and moderately fertile soil, very largely urban-centric and in industrial areas. According to the New BSBI Atlas (Preston *et al.* 2002) it was a contaminant of grass-seed and bird-seed but became much more common when introduced from the First World War battlefields by returning troops. Although still widespread in B&BC it does not seem to be spreading like *S. orientale* and it might even have become scarcer since the 1980s. E Europe and W Asia. Ass: *Aethusa*

*cynapium, Anisantha sterilis, Artemisia vulgaris, Epilobium ciliatum, Sisymbrium officinale, Sisymbrium orientale.*

### Sisymbrium orientale L.
**Eastern Rocket**

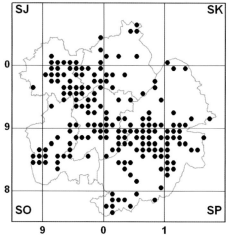

*190. Neophyte. Annual of disturbed ground, recorded from pavements and roadsides, fragments of waste land, canal towpaths and railway land, mainly in the industrial areas but also occasionally in the busier residential areas, in well-lit places on dry to moist, fairly base-rich and nutrient-intermediate, sometimes rather stony soils. Distinctly commoner than *S. altissimum*, and probably increasing in frequency, and unlike many similar plants equally common in B'ham as in the Black Country. The fruiting plant consists largely of an inflorescence spreading widely in three dimensions which can become uprooted and trundle around the streets in the wind as an urban 'tumbleweed'. S Europe, the Mediterranean and W Asia. Ass: *Aethusa cynapium, Anisantha sterilis, Artemisia vulgaris, Epilobium ciliatum, Sisymbrium officinale.*

### Sisymbrium officinale (L.) Scop.
**Hedge Mustard**

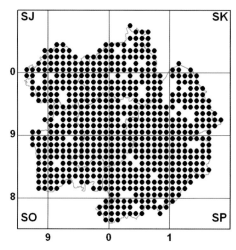

*635. Archaeophyte. Annual or biennial, common throughout in many disturbed and cultivated situations whether urban or rural (except in Sutton Park), in fairly open situations, on dry to moist, fairly base-rich and fertile soils. Path, track and roadsides, canal towpaths, allotments, arable land, industrial and residential waste land. Ass: *Anisantha sterilis, Artemisia vulgaris, Epilobium ciliatum, Hordeum murinum.*

A plant with glabrous fruits, **var. leiocarpum** DC., was reported by F.M. Day, Penn, SO8995, in 1941 and has been recorded much more recently on a development site on the Oddingley Road at West Heath, Northfield (SP034786, JJD, 2006).

### *Sisymbrium austriacum* Jacq.
**Austrian Rocket**
0. Casual. Once recorded by WHH from California Quarry, Woodgate Valley (SP0183, 1952). S Europe.

### *Sisymbrium polyceratium* L.
**Many-podded Hedge Mustard**
3. Casual, rare in UK. Annual, recorded twice in Walsall as single plants: outside an electricity station, Bentley Lane (SO995993, ICT, det. TGCR, 2000); Navigation Street (SP00986, CBW, conf. TGCR, 2002) and in B'ham in some quantity where the pavement meets the front wall of terraced housing in Carlisle Road, Lozells (SP065895, MWP, det. EJC, 2005), where it persisted for at least two years. S Europe.

### *Isatis tinctoria* L.
**Woad**
2. Archaeophyte. Grown as a dye-plant in ancient times but now a scarce casual in UK and probably always a deliberate introduction in 'wildflower seed' in B&BC. A biennial or perennial herb, recorded twice at Saltwells LNR on spoil by Hurst Lane (SO9387, T. Beynon, 1996) and by a path on disturbed ground (SO932875, J. Akers, 1999). Also on waste ground by a canal, Walsall (SP0097, JaH, 1999).

### *Alliaria petiolata* (M. Bieb.) Cavara & Grande
**Garlic Mustard**
*565. Native. Biennial (or monocarpic), common throughout in a wide range of partially shaded habitats particularly woodland margins or clearings, hedgerows, stream and river margins, canal towpaths, wooded gardens and sometimes as a street weed or on waste land. Typically forming dense colonies on moist, nutrient-rich and fairly base-rich soil (usually also rich in well-decayed leaf litter); favoured by occasional disturbance and more associated with plantations than with

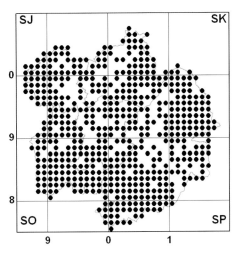

old woodland. Ass: *Anthriscus sylvestris, Calystegia sepium, Calystegia sylvatica, Galium aparine, Lamium purpureum, Urtica dioica.*

### *Teesdalia nudicaulis* (L.) W.T. Aiton
**Shepherd's Cress**
0. Native. NT. There is a report of this winter annual species from an industrial waste tip near Middle Pool at Fens Pool, Dudley (SO917886, W. Prestwood & R. Dibble, 1977). Natural England files suggest that it was recorded there again by an un-named Wildlife Trust recorder in 1984. It was not found at this site (which also boasts *Cerastium arvense*) in the present survey.

### *Thlaspi arvense* L.
**Field Penny-cress**

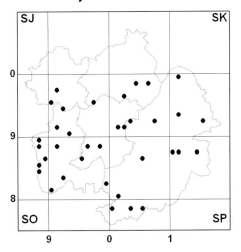

36. Archaeophyte. Ax. An annual weed of cultivated and disturbed ground recorded rather infrequently from allotments and arable fields, with a few records also from construction sites, post-housing sites, railways, canals, by the A456, churchyards and as a street weed. Grows in well-lit places on light, dry to moist, moderately fertile and base-rich soils. Ass: *Aethusa cynapium, Anagallis arvensis, Arabidopsis thaliana, Capsella bursa-pastoris, Lepidium

*didymum, Fallopia convolvulus, Lamium hybridum, Lobularia maritima, Papaver rhoeas, Sonchus oleraceus, Veronica agrestis, Viola arvensis.*

### *Hesperis matronalis* L.
**Dame's-violet**

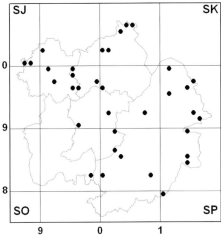

35. Neophyte. An uncommon perennial or biennial garden escape, as a street weed, on road verges (especially in shallow ditches), on waste ground, in spare land on allotments, from railway and canal land, and pre-survey from the banks of the River Rea. Grows usually in slight shade, on moist to damp, quite base- and nutrient-rich soils. S Europe and W Asia. Ass: *Alliaria petiolata, Anisantha sterilis, Holcus lanatus, Taraxacum* spp., *Urtica dioica.*

### *Matthiola incana* (L.) W.T. Aiton
**Hoary Stock**
0. Neophyte. Annual or perennial, woody below, quite well naturalised in coastal areas of UK, but with just one old record in B&BC as a garden escape with double, pink flowers: roadside, Bloxwich (SJ982020, BRF, 1976). Mediterranean.

### *Malcolmia maritima* (L.) W.T. Aiton
**Virginia Stock**
2. Neophyte. In B&BC a rare casual annual escaping from gardens, recorded from a street junction in B'ham (SP072873, MWP, 1997) and from waste ground at Tividale (SO9690, MWP & MHM, 2001). Italy and the Balkans.

### *Cochlearia danica* L.
**Danish Scurvygrass**
220. Native. A winter annual, native to maritime coastal habitats, it has spread inland along salt-treated roads since the early 1980s. In vc. 39 its first appearance on a roadside was on the central reservation of the A449, Lloyd Hill, W'ton (SO884949, CBW & BRF, 1983). After only a few years, major routes sported an almost unbroken

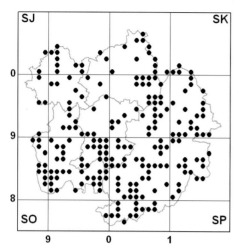

line of pale pink (turning white) flowers along the salt-washed kerb in (February–) March–May. It is noticeable that on some of the motorway central reservations, where there was only a barren concrete strip and a barrier, there is now a flora of *Cochlearia danica* with a sprinkling of *Conyza* species and the saltmarsh grass *Puccinellia distans*. The central reservations of many major dual carriageways in B&BC now often resemble maritime swards, with *Cochlearia danica*, and *Plantago coronopus* dominant, and with *Lepidium ruderale*, *Spergularia marina* and *Puccinellia distans* often present. In recent years the lesser through-roads have also started showing healthy populations, and *Cochlearia danica* has spread so rapidly through our area during the survey period that it is effectively under-recorded. It grows in full sun on typically moist soils contaminated with salt, and is rarely found away from the immediate edge of roads, usually replacing amenity grass or bare mud but capable of growing on some gravelly or crumbling tarmac substrates and occasionally appearing on nearby wall tops directly affected by road spray and around the bases of lampposts and signposts.

▲ *Cochlearia danica*

## *Iberis sempervirens* L.
**Perennial Candytuft**

3. Neophyte. A sprawling perennial garden shrub. Several plants on a wooded bank, Brook Holloway, Wollescote (SO927836, JJD & G.H. Green, 2001); St Michael's churchyard, Boldmere (SP109939, SPG, 1998); Jeffcock Road, W'ton (SO902974, CBW, 2008). There are also two records from the 1980s in SP09, both probably garden relics. Mountains of S Europe, N Africa and SW Asia.

## *Iberis umbellata* L.
**Garden Candytuft**

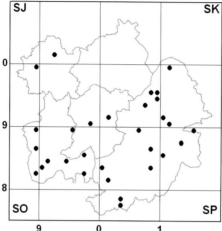

30. Casual. An annual which seems to need to be continuously replenished from garden cultivation and is almost always close to its garden source, at the foot of walls, in pavements, on grass verges, etc., although it can be found further afield when fly-tipped onto waste ground and in one case it was recorded from a golf course. Mediterranean.

## 82. SANTALACEAE

## *Viscum album* L.
**Mistletoe**

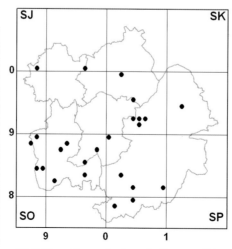

25. Native. Atmospheric pollution possibly contributes towards the scarcity of this

species in B&BC with records for isolated individuals found in scattered locations on a number of different host species. Small localised populations occur on street and park trees in Hampstead (SP0492), which are believed to have arisen from seed deposited by birds from plants parasitising a planted apple tree in a nearby garden. Other sites include a few individuals on street trees in High Park Avenue (SO8884) and neighbouring roads in Wollaston, Stourbridge, and two well-established colonies comprising around fifteen plants on two Lime trees just inside the main entrance to Haden Hill Park, Halesowen (SO9685). The remainder are from widely scattered individual plants mainly found high up on street trees. Host species include *Malus* spp., *Tilia* × *europaea*, *Populus* × *italica*, *Sorbus aucuparia* and *Robinia pseudoacacia*.

## 84. TAMARICACEAE

## *Tamarix gallica* L.
**Tamarisk**

2. Neophyte. A suckering shrub, usually a relic of planting. Recorded twice in adjacent squares on post-industrial sites in Tipton: Princes End disused railway (SO958938, PWS, 1998); (SO953929, PN, 2007). SW Europe.

## 85. PLUMBAGINACEAE

## *Armeria maritima* (Mill.) Willd.
**Thrift**

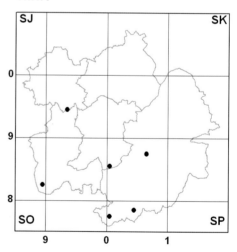

6. Native in maritime habitats. A perennial herb and a garden escape in B&BC. Rough grassland, Longbridge (SP002775, JJD, 1999); central B'ham (SP069872, N. Walker, 1999); a small plant in a gutter, Mullion Croft, West Heath (SP041781, JJD, 2001); also three records immediately by major roads, quite possibly growing as a roadside halophyte: A451 near Norton

Covert (SO890824, B Westwood, 1998); two clumps in the central reservation, A4123, Warley (SP006857, CBW, 2000); W verge of the A4123, Coseley (SO938941, MWP, 2008).

## 86. POLYGONACEAE

### *Persicaria alpina* (All.) H. Gross
### Alpine Knotweed
1. Neophyte. A rhizomatous perennial, a mountain plant from S, C & E Europe, rarely grown in gardens in the UK. A patch persisted for 15 years near the junction of Cyprus Street and Broadwell Road, Oldbury, near the park against the railings in a small, triangular-shaped fenced-off area enclosing a brick-built gas installation. It grew with Pyracantha, Sycamore saplings and Rosebay (SO993895, MWP & LG, first recorded there in 1983, last seen in 1998). It is known to have established itself on river shingle and elsewhere at a few sites in Scotland, but this may have been the only site in England.

### *Persicaria campanulata* (Hook. f.) Ronse Decr.
### Lesser Knotweed
5. Neophyte. A stoloniferous perennial herb. There is an extensive population in marshy ground above Blackroot Pool, Sutton Park (now dense scrub) where it has persisted since being first recorded (SP108974, R.C.L. Burges, 1933, still there 2005); spreading into wet woodland from an original introduction, Winterbourne Gardens (SP0583, MWP & JWP, 2007); a naturalised colony in wet woodland where the Chad Brook meets the railway embankment, on the site of the old TV gardens, now a wild area, in the grounds of B'ham Botanical Gardens (SP050849, MWP, JWP & EVJC, 2007); Hill Hook, from a wet woodland clearing (SK106002, MWP, ICT & AB, 2007); damp, shady pathside, Woodlands Walk, Penn (SO895962, CBW, 2006, probably now destroyed). Himalayas.

### *Persicaria bistorta* (L.) Samp.
### Common Bistort
*56. Native. Ax. A patch-forming perennial herb, found in damp to wet grassland on somewhat fertile and base-rich soils in fairly sheltered, open or slightly shaded places. Many of the records are in semi-improved grassland in river and stream corridors, and many of these could possibly be native occurrences, but others in churchyards, parkland, hedgerows, by canals and railways are more clearly introductions from cultivation. Ass: *Alopecurus pratensis*, *Cirsium palustre*, *Juncus effusus*, *Lotus*

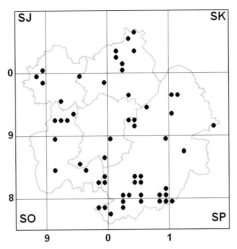

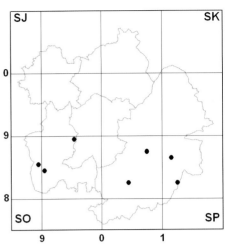

*pedunculatus*, *Mentha aquatica*, *Rumex acetosa*, *Silene flos-cuculi*.

### *Persicaria amplexicaulis* (D. Don) Ronse Decr.
### Red Bistort
3. Neophyte. A tufted perennial herb, a garden escape, probably always via rhizomes. Shaded verge opposite houses, Old Swinford (SO902826, WAT, 2003); Small stand in rough grassland, Woodgate Valley (SO996828, JJD, 2003); in paving, close to specimen in garden (SP056857, MWP, JWP & ICT, 2007). Asia.

### *Persicaria affinis* (D. Don) Ronse Decr.
### Himalayan Bistort, Fleece Flower
1. Neophyte. A casual or persistent garden escape, in pavement, against a fence, Pear Tree Drive, Pedmore (SO902826, MWP & APD, 2003). Himalayas.

### *Persicaria capitata* (Buch.-Ham. ex D. Don) H. Gross
### Pink-headed Knotweed
7. Neophyte, probably only casual. There

*Persicaria capitata* (by Anne Bebbington)

are few records of this small perennial from B&BC however expect to see more of it in the future. Where it is used in hanging baskets, the following year plants will be found in paving cracks beneath. In subsequent years it may spread quite well both vegetatively and by seed. It may or may not be frost-hardy. First recorded in B&BC in Worcester Street, Stourbridge (SO900840, CBW, 1995). Himalayas.

### *Persicaria wallichii* Greuter & Burdet
(*Polygonum polystachum* Wall ex Meissner)
### Himalayan Knotweed
1. Neophyte. A tall rhizomatous perennial, semi-naturalised in some quantity in the margin of Brookvale Park boating lake, presumably from an original planting (SP094911, ICT, JaH & EVJC, 2006). Himalayas.

### *Persicaria amphibia* (L.) Delarbre
### Amphibious Bistort
*217. Native. Occurs both as a floating

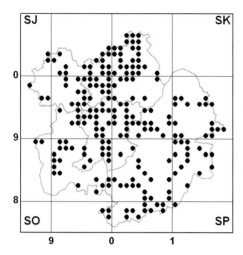

aquatic perennial herb and also as
a terrestrial plant. The same plant
can develop into either according
to conditions, but it tends to flower
much more freely in open water.
Characteristically in draw-down zones of
ponds, lakes, rivers and brooks, growing
out across the open water, also in ditches
and in unmanaged, usually damp grassland
in the open and in semi-shade. Can persist
in quite dry situations where dredged out
of ponds and dumped. Soils are usually
quite base- and nutrient-rich but it is
tolerant of poorer soils also. Ass: Aquatic:
*Myriophyllum spicatum, Nuphar lutea,
Potamogeton natans;* Terrestrial: *Eleocharis
palustris, Glyceria maxima, Holcus lanatus,
Lycopus europaeus.*

### *Persicaria maculosa* Gray
**Redshank**

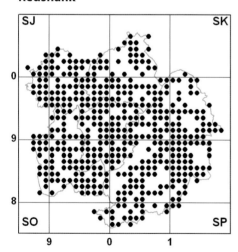

*471. Native. An annual herb, common
on waste, cultivated and other areas of
bare ground, growing on fertile or very
fertile, moist, damp, or winter-wet, base-
intermediate soils. Seeds germinate mainly
in early spring. Ass: *Anagallis arvensis,
Euphorbia peplus, Papaver dubium, Papaver
rhoeas, Matricaria chamomilla, Spergularia
arvensis, Tripleurospermum inodorum.*

### *Persicaria lapathifolia* (L.) Delarbre
**Pale Persicaria**

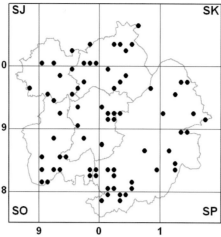

74. Native. An annual herb of cultivated
and otherwise disturbed ground, recorded
from allotments, farmland, lane and
canal sides, derelict land and sewage
works. Grows in very similar places to *P.
maculosa*, and often with it, but much less
frequently. It is typically a larger plant and
may need more time between episodes of
disturbance to set seed successfully. Ass:
*Capsella bursa-pastoris, Fallopia convolvulus,
Fumaria officinalis, Hordeum murinum,
Lobelia erinus, Persicaria maculosa,
Ranunculus repens, Reseda luteola, Senecio
vulgaris, Urtica dioica.*

### *Persicaria hydropiper* (L.) Delarbre
**Water-pepper**

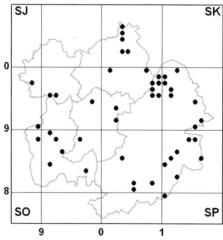

*47. Native. Ax. An annual herb found
colonising open vegetation or bare soil
and persisting in disturbed pasture in
damp, often winter-wet, fertile or fairly
fertile soils of intermediate or quite low
base status, in full light and in shade.
Recorded from damp woodland and farm
pastures, reservoir, pond, stream, canal and
track margins and ruts, ditches and an osier
bed. Almost absent from post-industrial
and built-up areas, it is only common in

Sutton Park, other large open spaces and
peripheral areas, usually where there is
stock trampling. Also tetrad SO99A. Ass:
*Alopecurus geniculatus, Agrostis stolonifera,
Cirsium palustre, Epilobium hirsutum, Juncus
articulatus, Juncus bufonius, Juncus effusus,
Myosoton aquaticum.*

### *Persicaria minor* (Huds.) Opiz
**Small Water-pepper**
1. Native. VU. A small, nationally scarce
annual of wet, often trampled situations,
in B&BC it has only ever been recorded in
Sutton Park. Bagnall had it from the top
end of Bracebridge Pool (probably SP0998)
in 1880, and Readett (1971) from a marsh
near Little Bracebridge Pool (SP0998),
probably Bagnall's original station. Up to
1995 it used to be quite common in the
ditch running alongside the road from the
Banners Gate entrance to Longmoor Pool
(*circa* SP093956, HHF, PC & MWP, 1995)
but this site has become overgrown. Also
recorded from SP0995 by SB in 1997.

### *Fagopyrum esculentum* Moench
**Buckwheat**

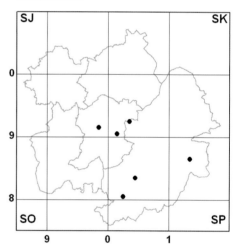

6. Neophyte, essentially a casual in B&BC.
An annual, often grown as a green manure,
self-seeding from cultivation in cultivated
or disturbed soil. Rarely persists. Asia.

### *Polygonum aviculare* agg.
**Knotgrasses**
*643 Native and archaeophytes. Prostrate
annuals which are vigorous colonists
of bare and trodden ground, on a wide
variety of dry to damp soils whether
base- or nutrient-poor or rich. Recorded
particularly in the street, in pavement
cracks, bare patches in the grass verges,
gateways, the edge of paths, and similar
situations. Also found on waste ground,
rubbish dumps, on brick and concrete
rubble, manure heaps and arable fields and
there are records from churchyards and
quarries. The majority of the records

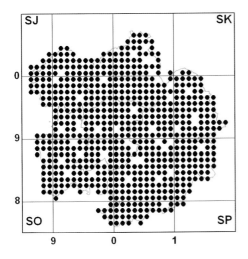

▲ *Persicaria amphibia*

were made for the aggregate, which is made up of four species, of which only two, **P. arenastrum** Boreau (**Equal-leaved Knotgrass**) (83 monads) which is an archaeophyte, and **P. aviculare** L. (**Knotgrass**) (108 monads) which is a native species, have been widely recorded in B&BC. Where records have been made systematically (mainly in B&BC areas in vc. 39 and vc. 38 ), both these species have been recorded in the same range of habitats ascribed to the aggregate, and at similar frequencies.

### *Polygonum patulum* M. Bieb.
### Red-knotgrass

0. Casual. Much confused with *Polygonum arenarium* Waldst. & Kit., an erect or decumbent annual, recorded prior to the survey as locally abundant in a marl pit/brickyard (SP0987, D.A. Cadbury, 1964). Habitat since destroyed.

### *Fallopia japonica* (Houtt.) Ronse Decr.
### Japanese Knotweed

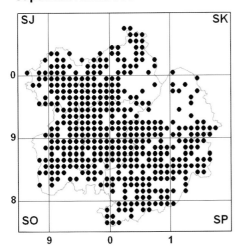

*442. Neophyte. Sch. 9 (invasive). A large rhizomatous, thicket-forming perennial herb, common throughout B&BC where it is an aggressive invader of waste places, unused gardens, neglected public open

spaces, railway land and the banks of water courses. The thickets shade out the existing vegetation and it is therefore of conservation concern. Strenuous efforts are currently being made (2011) to control this species using herbicides. The plant is successful in open and semi-shade, favoured by shelter and deep, moist to damp, fertile soil. Still appears to be fairly uncommon in the countryside areas of Walsall and Sutton, and in the more semi-natural peripheral areas generally, but otherwise it appears to be ubiquitous. This seems to have been largely the case by 1971 in Cadbury *et al.* and in Edees (1972). Japan.

### *Fallopia* × *bohemica* (Chrtek & Chrtková) J.P. Bailey (*F. japonica* × *F. sachalinensis*)
### Conolly's Knotweed

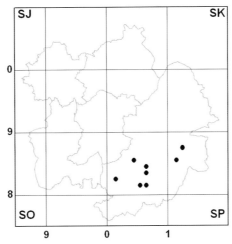

8. Neophyte. Sch. 9 (invasive). A large rhizomatous perennial herb, mostly forming large colonies in S B'ham river corridors, also in B'ham Botanical Gardens and Cannon Hill Park. It is not clear whether these are spontaneous hybrids or became naturalised from cultivation, but the distribution does not mirror that of *F. sachalinensis*. Europe.

### *Fallopia sachalinensis* (F. Schmidt) Ronse Decr.
### Giant Knotweed

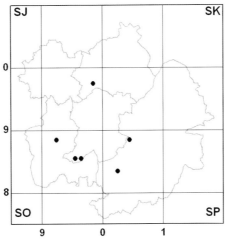

▲ *Persicaria maculosa*

▲ *Fallopia japonica*

6. Neophyte. Sch. 9 (invasive). An even larger rhizomatous, thicket-forming perennial herb than *Fallopia japonica*, with a few sites in B&BC including a canal, railway land and Haden Hill Park. Some sites may have been lost due to control measures having been taken, and it is possible that some of those may have been *Fallopia × bohemica*. E Asia.

### *Fallopia baldschuanica* (Regel) Holub
**Russian-vine**

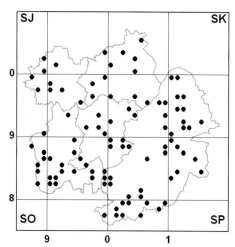

98. Neophyte. A rampant climbing perennial. A frequent garden relic, throw-out or escape in B&BC found sprawling over derelict industrial sites, waste land, railway embankments, unused allotments and various wire fences, hedges and walls. Sometimes planted to cover garden structures such as sheds and detached garages, and then proceeds to take over large areas of unused garden so that it is often difficult to decide whether a plant is spontaneous in origin. Favoured by deep, moist, fertile soil. C Asia.

### *Fallopia convolvulus* (L.) Á. Löve
**Black-bindweed**

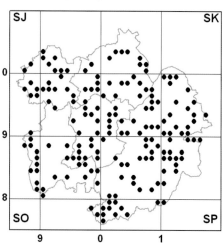

177. Archaeophyte An annual herb, found in cultivation and other disturbed places:

arable field edges, as a weed of gardens and allotments, rubbish tips and as a street weed. Grows in fairly base- and nutrient-rich, moist soil. Ass: *Euphorbia peplus, Chenopodium album, Lamium purpureum, Persicaria maculosa, Senecio vulgaris.*

### *Rheum × rhabarbarum* L.
(*Rheum × hybridum* Murray)
**Rhubarb**

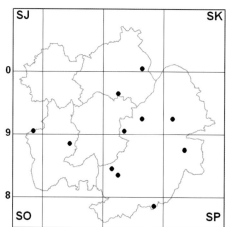

11. Neophyte. A rhizomatous perennial herb. A garden relic or throw-out on waste land where there were formerly houses and gardens. Few records. Garden origin from N Chinese or E Siberian parents.

### *Rumex acetosella* L.
**Sheep's Sorrel**

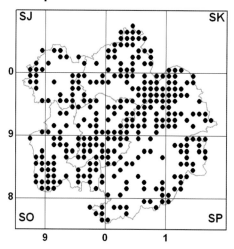

*321. Native. A rhizomatous perennial herb. Common throughout B&BC in short, heathy grassland and on dry grassy banks, verges and lawns and as a colonist of bare patches on fairly or very nutrient-poor and base-poor, usually sandy or stony and shallow, dry to moist soils. A regular component of old, dry, heathy grassland but also common in secondary situations. Ass: *Aira praecox, Agrostis*

*capillaris, Festuca ovina, Galium saxatile, Pilosella officinarum.*

There are a few records assigned specifically to **subsp. acetosella**, which is the common subspecies, and only one for **subsp. acetosella var. tenuifolius** Wallr., from Sutton Park (SP0997, Bagnall, 1873). There is a single record for **subsp. pyrenaicus** (Pourr.) Akeroyd, from dry, acid heath at Swanshurst Park (SP094814, JWP, conf. RM, 1995).

### *Rumex scutatus* L.
**French Sorrel**
3. Neophyte. Colonising paths and waste ground by seeding from cultivation, allotments at Newhall (SP1295, ICT & MWP, 2008); Richmond Park (SO883898, ICT & MWP, 2008); Wheelers Lane (SP082814, MWP, ICT & EMP, 2008).

### *Rumex acetosa* L.
**Common Sorrel**

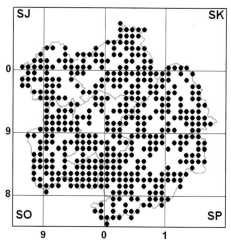

*462. Native. A tufted perennial herb, common throughout B&BC in a wide range of old and more recent grasslands, lawns and grassy woodland rides whether species-rich or quite species-poor, in full daylight or slight shade on moist soils of intermediate fertility and base status but over quite a wide range and perhaps most typically mildly acid. Ass: *Agrostis capillaris, Centaurea nigra, Cerastium fontanum, Festuca rubra, Holcus lanatus, Ranunculus acris.*

Many records are for **subsp. acetosa** and it is assumed that almost all our records are for this subspecies. There are however six records for **subsp. ambiguus** (Gren.) Á. Löve, which are given below.

### *Rumex acetosa* subsp. *ambiguus*
(Gren.) Á. Löve
6. Neophyte originating in cultivation where selection has produced larger leaves than wild form. Occurs as an outcast from

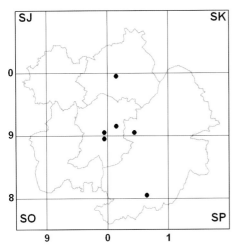

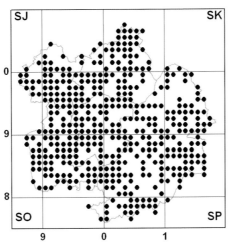

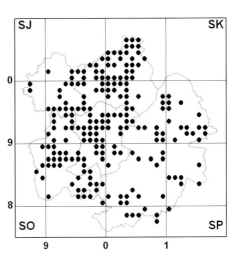

allotments and cottage gardens, also on waste ground, usually, but not always, near allotments.

### Rumex hydrolapathum Huds.
### Water Dock

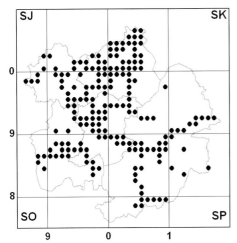

*189. Native. A large tufted perennial herb, found along brooks and rivers and by pools but predominantly in the margins of canals. The map gives a good impression of the distribution of the canals of B&BC and it seems to be able to survive even in some of the heavily managed and utilised canals of B'ham. Grows in well-lit places and also partial shade, in shallow water, on fairly base- and nutrient-rich substrates. Ass: *Alisma lanceolatum, Alisma plantago-aquatica, Glyceria maxima, Sparganium erectum, Typha latifolia.*

### Rumex crispus L.
### Curled Dock

*441. Native. 'Injurious weed'. An annual to short-lived perennial herb, common in a wide range of cultivated land, disturbed situations and rough grasslands. A light-loving plant found on moist to damp, base- and nutrient-medium to -rich soils. Often grows with *Rumex obtusifolius*, but not so

frequent and more confined to recently disturbed situations. Ass: *Artemisia vulgaris, Cirsium arvense, Rumex obtusifolius, Senecio jacobaea.*

Some records are referred specifically to **subsp. crispus** and all records are assumed to be for that subspecies.

### Rumex × pratensis Mert. & W.D.J. Koch
(*R. crispus* × *R. obtusifolius*)

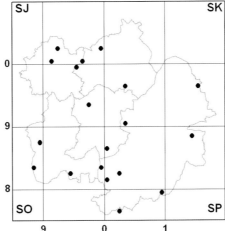

19. Native. This hybrid has been occasionally recorded, from abandoned and cultivated fields, allotments and pavement edges, canal and pool margins, usually with both parents. Probably under-recorded.

### Rumex conglomeratus Murray
### Clustered Dock

*213. Native. A perennial herb, common in damp places and at water margins. Found by canals (particularly in the brickwork of the canal column), by brooks, pools, farm ponds and in winter-wet or flushed areas in pastures and woodland margins, usually on quite base- and nutrient-rich soils in well-lit situations. Apparently commoner in the Black Country than in B'ham, possibly due to its high frequency by Black Country canals.

Ass: *Agrostis stolonifera, Carex hirta, Carex otrobae, Holcus lanatus, Juncus effusus, Lycopus europaeus, Rumex hydrolapathum, Scutellaria galericulata.*

### Rumex × abortivus Ruhmer
(*R. conglomeratus* × *R. obtusifolius*)
2. Native. Perry Park (SP0692, G. Kitchener, 2005); Sedgley (SO9293, CBW, 2008).

### Rumex sanguineus L.
### Wood Dock

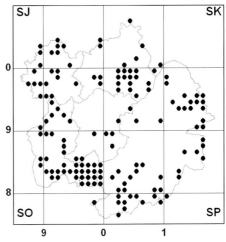

*147. Native. A perennial herb, found in woodland, which is often but not exclusively old, in lane hedges, parkland and churchyards. Grows in semi-shade on damp to moist, base- and nutrient-medium to rich soils. Scarce in central urban areas and also some rural ones, probably due to lack of suitable woodland habitats. Ass: *Brachypodium sylvaticum, Carex remota, Circaea lutetiana, Geum urbanum, Poa trivialis, Rubus fruticosus* agg.

**Var. viridis** Sibth. is also recorded, from Sutton Park. Almost all records are probably this variety, although **var. sanguineus**, a rare garden escape, has been recorded in paving, gravel beds and bare ground at Harborne Lane Allotments (SP041829, MWP, 2004).

### *Rumex × dufftii* Hausskn.

(*R. sanguineus* × *R. obtusifolius*)
2. Native. Below the dam at Bartley reservoir, with both parents (SP008815, CBW, conf. J.R. Akeroyd, 1998); waste ground, near Walsall Art Gallery (SP010986, CBW, 2002). Also earlier records from Sedgley (SO917937, CBW, 1987) and waste land W of Moseley Bog (SP092821, CBW, 1989).

### *Rumex obtusifolius* L.
### Broad-leaved Dock

*705. Native. 'Injurious weed'. A ubiquitous perennial herb, common throughout in disturbed, cultivated and waste land and grassland. It colonises similar sites to *R. crispus*, but persists better after recovery from disturbance and is therefore present in a wide range of scrub, woodland margins, weedy pasture, rough grassland and road verges as well as in a wide range of disturbed situations. Grows in well-lit places and slight shade, on moist to winter-damp, fertile or extremely fertile soils of intermediate or high base status. Ass: *Artemisia vulgaris, Dactylis glomerata, Elytrigia repens, Heracleum sphondylium, Ranunculus repens, Urtica dioica*.

### *Rumex palustris* Sm.
### Marsh Dock

0. An uncommon native annual to short-lived perennial of wetlands, it is only a casual in B&BC. A few on a demolition site, Regent Street, Old Hill (SO954866, B. Westwood, conf. J.R. Akeroyd, 1989).

### *Rumex maritimus* L.
### Golden Dock

2. Native. An annual to short-lived perennial herb, normally found in pool, lake and stream margins, it is rarely recorded in B&BC. Streamside in Sutton Park (SP094982, MWP & ICT, 2005); Bagnall recorded it there (SP0997) in 1880; in imported soil filling a hole left by a removed street tree, B'ham (SP058857, ICT, MWP & JWP, 2007).

### *Oxyria digyna* (L.) Hill
### Mountain Sorrel

1. Native. From mountain areas in UK, a single plant appeared in the car park of the Conservative Club, Oak Street, Kingswinford (SO885884, CBW, 2005).

## 87. DROSERACEAE

### *Drosera rotundifolia* L.
### Round-leaved Sundew

2. Native. Ax. An insectivorous, rosette-forming perennial herb, growing among *Sphagnum* mosses or on extremely nutrient-poor and base-poor damp or

wet peat. Recorded, only recently in Sutton Park: in the mire in Longmoor valley (SP092963, MWP, ICT & PLR, 2006); at Pool Hollies, in a tiny mire where it is almost extinct (most recently SP102977, PLR, MWP, ICT & PC, 2009). In the same square it has been recorded recently in wet birch woodland near Blackroot Pool car park (SP108971, SPG, 1998) and in 1977 at Blackroot Pool (SP107972, WarNaCT & Warks BRC). It was described as locally abundant at Sutton in the same two squares in Readett (1971) but it is now extremely local and diminishing. It was last seen at Stubber's Green SSSI in 1990 (SK046016, CW). It grew there in a *Sphagnum* lawn which has developed in a pool margin over a considerable depth of *Typha latifolia* peat. The site is now scrubbed over and partially drained. It was last seen on Moseley Common (SP0982) *circa* 1860, on Pedmoor Common near Stourbridge (SO8982) in 1835, and on B'ham Heath (SP08, W. Withering and probably SP0488) in 1787. Ass: *Carex echinata, Polytrichum commune, Sphagnum* spp., *Triglochin palustris*.

### *Drosera intermedia* Hayne
### Oblong-leaved Sundew

0. Native, once deliberately introduced in B&BC. In the early 1990s *Drosera intermedia* was introduced into the mire at Pool Hollies (SP101977, MWP), along with *Sarracenia* sp., but neither survived for long.

## 88. CARYOPHYLLACEAE

### *Arenaria serpyllifolia* sensu lato
### Thyme-leaved Sandwort

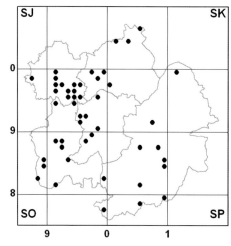

48. Native. Ax. Winter annuals recorded from railway sidings, quarries, limestone and other droughty grassland, also from blast furnace spoil and other derelict land, churchyards, canalsides (including a canal wall), as a street weed and in one instance as a border and lawn weed. They grow in drought-liable shallow, often

stony, nutrient-poor to medium, fairly base-poor to base-rich soils. Ass: *Cerastium semidecandrum, Daucus carota, Erodium cicutarium, Erophila* sp., *Sagina apetala sensu lato, Taraxacum* section Erythrosperma, *Trifolium arvense, Vulpia bromoides*.

Most recorders did not distinguish the two species *Arenaria serpyllifolia* L. (**Thyme-leaved Sandwort**) and *Arenaria leptoclados* (Rchb.) Guss. (**Slender Sandwort**). Most which were so distinguished were recorded as *A. serpyllifolia sensu stricto*. Only one recent record was for *A. leptoclados*, from a canal towpath between Spring Vale and Lanesfield (SO937954, JEH, 2007), although in the past it has been reliably recorded on Pelsall North Common (SK0104, JPM, 1991). Readett (1971) recorded both species from Sutton Park, *A. leptoclados* from the railway track (SP0898, SP0998, 1971), *A. serpyllifolia* from rough grassland and railway banks.

### *Arenaria balearica* L.
### Mossy Sandwort

0. Neophyte. Reported in Edees (1972) as established in turf in Handsworth cemetery (SP0590, WHH, 1958). W Mediterranean islands.

### *Moehringia trinervia* (L.) Clairv.
### Three-nerved Sandwort

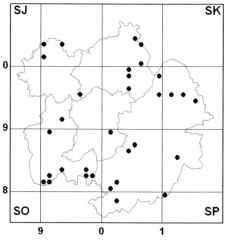

*32. Native. Ax. An uncommon annual, largely confined to peripheral areas of the conurbation, recorded mainly from bare and slightly disturbed areas in (usually old) deciduous woodland, hedgerows and scrub, golf courses, farmland. Grows in shade or semi-shade on dry to moist soils of average base and nutrient status. Ass: *Digitalis purpurea, Ficaria verna, Galium aparine, Poa trivialis*.

### *Stellaria nemorum* L.
### Wood Stitchwort

0. Native. Only a 19th century record from Hob Lane, Yardley (SP1185, M.A. Beilby,

1836), and that was not widely accepted at the time, but it sits nicely between its main distribution in N England and its populations in Wales.

### *Stellaria media* (L.) Vill.
### Common Chickweed

*662. Native. An annual or short-lived perennial herb, common throughout, from a wide range of habitats on cultivated, disturbed and trampled ground in richly fertile, base medium to rich, moist soils, in the open or in slight shade. Particularly characteristic around the bases and among the surface roots of mature street trees. Ass: *Capsella bursa-pastoris*, *Lamium purpureum*, *Lolium perenne*, *Poa annua*, *Poa trivialis*.

### *Stellaria pallida* (Dumort.) Crép.
### Lesser Chickweed

5. Native. Ax. An annual which flowers very early in dry, sandy sites and rarely persists beyond the spring, it has been very rarely recorded in B&BC but may not always have been distinguished from *S. media*, which it closely resembles, or it may have been missed in surveys later in the season. Two plants in the sandy, windblown entrance to a disused shop/factory on the E side of Bell Place, W'ton (SO909980, CBW, 2002) and two records from the Stourbridge area; junction of Greenfield Avenue with Bath Road (SO899841, B. Westwood & PLR, 2009); grass verge, corner of Kempton Way (SO891833, B. Westwood & PLR, conf. ICT, 2009); Stourbridge Golf Course, Pedmore Common (SO896827, ICT, PLR & JH, 2010); many plants on a steep grass verge, SE side of Granville Street, central B'ham (SP062863, ICT, 2011). Also an old sighting from a bare place on steep slope, Warrens Hall Farm, Sandwell (SO957888, ICT, 1990).

### *Stellaria neglecta* Weihe
### Greater Chickweed

0. Native. An annual or short-lived perennial herb, usually found in hedgebanks and associated ditches and in woodland margins, but remarkably absent from B&BC. A few old records, mostly in the periphery: Sheldon Country Park (SP163855, CRP, ST & TCH, 1985); Tansley Hill, Warrens Hall (SO957891, CRP, 1986); Radley's Walk (SP164858, CRP, ST & TCH, 1985); Rough Wood Wedge (SJ986006, CW, P.L. Harris, 1988); (SP08W, JJD, 1993).

### *Stellaria holostea* L.
### Greater Stitchwort

*140. Native. Ax. An evergreen perennial herb characteristic of fairly open old deciduous woodlands, woodland margins and old hedgebanks, it grows in semi-

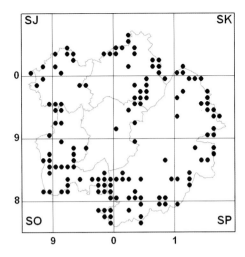

shade on moist soils with intermediate base and nutrient status. It is found in these habitats in B&BC, but is quite strongly confined to peripheral and countryside areas. It is very rarely found in secondary habitats although it survives quite well when introduced in woodland habitat creation schemes. Ass: *Ficaria verna*, *Glechoma hederacea*, *Holcus mollis*, *Hyacinthoides non-scripta*, *Pteridium aquilinum*.

### *Stellaria graminea* L.
### Lesser Stitchwort

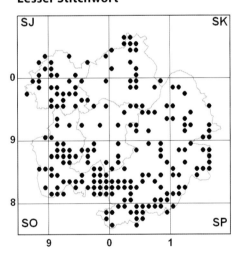

*212. Native. A perennial herb which seems to be adapted to scrambling up amongst tall grasses in under-managed, but moderately species-rich permanent grassland. In B&BC it is recorded from woodland margins, hedgebanks and road, railway and canal banks, on dry or moist, moderately base- and nutrient-rich soils. It is also found in rough grassland in waste areas, quarries, churchyards, golf courses, playing fields etc., and sometimes persists as a lawn weed originally introduced with the turf. Ass: *Arrenatherum elatius*, *Centaurea nigra*, *Dactylis glomerata*, *Holcus lanatus*, *Lathyrus pratensis*, *Rumex acetosa*.

▲ *Moerhingia trinervia*

▲ *Stellaria holostea*

## Stellaria alsine Grimm
(*S. uliginosa* Murray)
### Bog Stitchwort

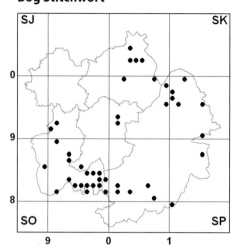

*44. Native. Ax. A mat-forming, perennial herb associated with disturbed situations in old, moderately nutrient-rich and base-poor to medium mires in the open or in light shade. It colonises bare areas and clambers up rushes and other tall species as the vegetation closes. It is recorded from clearings and margins of woodland (including pinewood), scrub, old wet grassland, wet hollows in drier grassland, by ponds, pools, brooks, streams, canals, marshes and osier beds. Largely found in the countryside areas, rare or absent in the industrial and residential areas in B&BC. Ass: *Carex leporina*, *Juncus articulatus*, *Juncus bufonius*, *Juncus effusus*, *Myosotis laxa*, *Phalaris arundinacea*.

## Cerastium arvense L.
### Field Mouse-ear
1. Native. Long known from Fens Pools (SO916887–SO918887, MHM, 1987, still there 2007), where it grows quite extensively on S-facing slopes of coal spoil NE of Middle Pool with *Festuca rubra*, *Lotus corniculatus*, *Pilosella officinarum*,

▲ *Cerastium arvense*

*Ranunculus bulbosus*, *Rumex acetosella*, *Trifolium dubium*, *Vulpia bromoides*. Two strong colonies were recorded on/by the 16th fairway at Stourbridge Golf Course in 1992 (SO903825, WAT, not seen 2010). It was also recorded at Hawthorn Wood, Park Lime Pits in 1984 (SK032001, P. Seccombe).

## Cerastium arvense × Cerastium tomentosum
3. Native × alien. This hybrid is said by Stace to occur with both parents, but in B&BC it has been recorded in the absence of *C. arvense* on and near an old tomb in SE corner of Holy Trinity churchyard, Wordsley (SO893878 & SO892879, MES, det. A.C. Leslie, 2001, still there in 2007); amongst rubble, Fighting Cocks, Goldthorn Hill, W'ton (SO915966, CBW, 2008); on Portway Hill, Rowley Regis (SO971885, R. Branscombe, 1997).

## Cerastium tomentosum L.
### Snow-in-summer

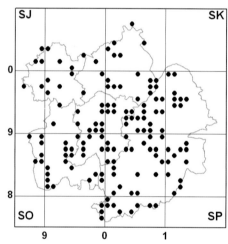

*148. Neophyte. A mat-forming perennial herb. A garden throw-out or relic, recorded from grassland, wasteland, post-housing sites, as a street weed, on disused railway lines and railway embankments, in churchyards and farmland. It prefers well-lit, well drained sites on dry soils or furnace spoils but is a good competitor even in dense, tall grassland. There is no evidence of generation from seed. Italy.

## Cerastium fontanum Baumg.
### Common Mouse-ear
*648. Native. A practically ubiquitous tufted or mat-forming, genetically variable perennial herb, spreading rapidly by seed and found in a wide variety of grassy places and in soils from base-intermediate to -rich, nutrient-poor to -rich, dry to damp, usually well-lit and in open vegetation, but also in slight shade. Recorded from permanent pasture, sown and mown grassland, as a street weed, from parkland,

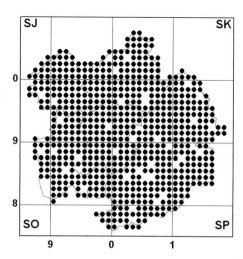

farmland, wasteland, meadows, common land, by canals and railways. Ass: *Agrostis capillaris*, *Festuca rubra*, *Lolium perenne*, *Poa trivialis*, *Trifolium repens*.

Where a subspecies has been recorded, it is almost always **subsp. *vulgare*** (Hartm.) Greuter & Burdet. There are also three old records for **subsp. *holosteoides*** (Fr.) Salman, Ommering & de Voogd: two on the Mousesweet Brook at Saltwells LNR (SO936858 & SO937861, CRP & E. McKay, 1994); hedgerow at Quinton Expressway (SO993839, AS & J. Price, 1994). This almost glabrous plant from wet places may be commoner than the records suggest and not recorded.

## Cerastium glomeratum Thuill.
### Sticky Mouse-ear

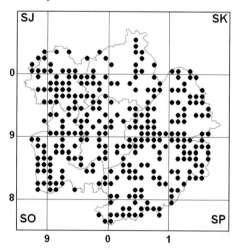

312. Native. An annual herb found throughout, colonising a wide variety of open habitats, on base-intermediate and nutrient-poor to -rich, dry to damp soils and sometimes prominent as a winter annual on sites which dry out in summer, fruiting and disappearing early in the season. Recorded from wasteland, streets, canals, railway, churchyards, parkland, common land, grassland, farmland and nature reserves. The map suggests that it

may be less common in the countryside areas. Ass: *Aira praecox, Arabidopsis thaliana, Capsella bursa-pastoris, Cerastium fontanum, Cerastium semidecandrum, Epilobium ciliatum, Filago minima, Poa annua, Stellaria media, Trifolium dubium.*

### *Cerastium diffusum* Pers.
### Sea Mouse-ear

3. Native. An early-flowering, winter-annual herb with a natural distribution around the coasts of the UK. Scarce inland, where it has been associated with railways, but the BSBI Atlas (Preston *et al.* 2002) reports that it is now being recorded by salt-treated roadsides. In B&BC there are both types of record: several colonies over kerb top, edge of B4187 Worcester Lane (SO905819, JJD, 2003); Northfield Railway station (SP024789, JWP, MWP, ICT, JJD, JaH & PLR, 2008); bare gravelly patch by A449, Penn with *Matricaria discoidea, Plantago coronopus, Plantago lanceolata, Poa annua,* and *Trifolium dubium* (SO896958, ICT, 2007 & 2008). Also Readett (1971) reported it from by the railway in Sutton Park. It should be looked for in suitable habitats flowering in March and April.

### *Cerastium semidecandrum* L.
### Little Mouse-ear

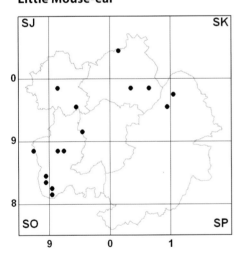

15. Native. Ax. A winter annual, usually flowering in early spring and disappearing by May, growing in bare places on dry, shallow, usually base-intermediate and nutrient-poor to intermediate soil which dries out in summer. In B&BC it is not confined to S-facing rock outcrops and droughty sand patches in semi-natural habitats, although it is perhaps commonest in these situations, in Sutton Park, on Barr Beacon and assorted golf courses. It is however also found on spoil tips (especially blast furnace spoil) and even in more disturbed habitats such as road verges. Ass: *Arenaria serpyllifolia sensu lato, Aira praecox, Cerastium glomeratum, Erophila* sp., *Filago minima.*

### *Myosoton aquaticum* (L.) Moench
### Water Chickweed

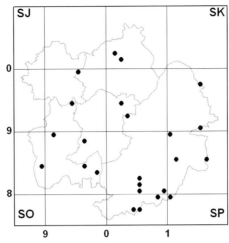

24. Native. A spreading perennial of pool and canal banks and occasionally flooded areas of stream and river banks on moderately base- and nutrient-rich, damp to wet, often heavy soils. The very patchy distribution may reflect the fact that its riverside and streamside habitats are often extremely fertile in the urban area and readily becomes dominated by taller, ranker vegetation.

### *Moenchia erecta* (L.) P. Gaertn., B. Mey. & Scherb.
### Upright Chickweed

0. Native. A winter annual of shallow soils and open situations, typically on S-facing rock outcrops and drought-liable sand patches. It is almost extinct in the Midlands away from the counties bordering Wales. Bagnall recorded it in Sutton Park in 1876, but it has not been seen there since. In 1992 it was recorded at Stourbridge Golf Course, in quantity by a bunker by the 9th green (SO897826, WAT & MES; not found there in 2010).

### *Sagina nodosa* (L.) Fenzl
### Knotted Pearlwort

3. Native. Ax. A perennial herb of old, base-rich, nutrient-poor mires and flushes, tolerant of trampling and grazing but not of competition. Known from Sutton Park since 1787, recorded there by Readett (1971) from SP0995, SP0996 and SP0998, it is still recorded from the banks of Longmoor Pool (SP092964, MWP, ICT & PLR, 2006, also SP0995, JWP, 2006), also further E (SP1095, SB, 1998). An old record from Water Orton Sidings (SP172914, HHF, 1973) is probably just outside our boundary.

### *Sagina procumbens* L.
### Procumbent Pearlwort

*543. Native. A small, mat-forming perennial herb, a common plant colonising bare places in paving cracks, cracks in

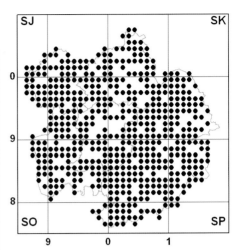

concrete, mortar near the base of old walls, flower beds with impoverished soils, crevices in piles of brick rubble, cinders and blast furnace spoil. Also recorded from wasteland, canal and railway banks, quarries, churchyards, sewage works, parkland, farmland and nature reserves, where it can grow in short, open, waterside or water-flushed semi-natural grassland. Typically it grows in base- and nutrient-intermediate, often winter-wet soils and not usually in particularly dry situations. It resists trampling but is easily overtopped and outcompeted. Ass: small mosses, *Epilobium ciliatum, Poa annua,* small seedlings of other colonising species.

### *Sagina apetala* sensu lato
### Annual Pearlwort

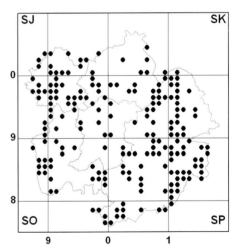

192. Native. Small annual herbs colonising similar places to *Sagina procumbens*, but generally on sites which are less sheltered and more likely to dry out completely in summer, and usually on substrates which are somewhat less base- and nutrient-rich. Recorded as a weed of streets, paths, car parks and churchyards, also canalside and railway habitats, wasteland, and farmland. Early in the season probably

sometimes mistaken for *S. procumbens* and hence under-recorded. Ass: Small mosses and *Anchusa arvensis*, *Aphanes arvensis*, *Lepidium didymum*, *Erodium cicutarium*, *Matricaria chamomilla*, *Oxalis corniculata*, *Poa annua*, *Poa compressa*, *Plantago lanceolata*, *Tripleurospermum inodorum*, *Veronica arvensis*.

Many recorders have not distinguished the two species **S. apetala** Ard. (**Annual Pearlwort**) and **S. filicaulis** Jord. (**Slender Pearlwort**) now recognised by Stace (2010) and the map shows the aggregate. Nevertheless both species have been widely recorded in B&BC. Occasionally they have been recorded together.

### *Sagina apetala* Ard.
### Annual Pearlwort

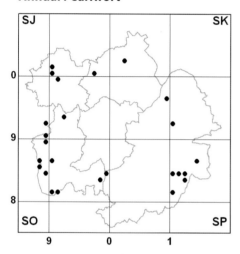

25. Native. Recorded less frequently than *Sagina filicaulis*, in the range of habitats of the aggregate.

### *Sagina filicaulis* Jord.
(*S. apetala* subsp. *erecta* F. Herm.)
### Slender Pearlwort

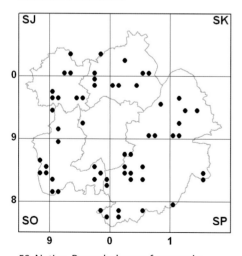

59. Native. Recorded more frequently than *S. apetala*, in the range of habitats of the species but perhaps more usually in farmland.

### *Scleranthus annuus* L.
### Annual Knawel

0. Native. An annual or biennial herb found in the UK in drought-liable sandy situations, including both heaths and cultivated land. There are old records in Readett (1971) from rough grassland in Sutton Park (SP0997, SP1196) but it has not been found in the current survey. There are also two more recent records from newly turned soil near Wychall reservoir (SP038794, AEEP, 1987), and from a bank above the playing fields at High Park School, Wollaston (SO882843, WAT, 1990). Both these records were ascribed to the commoner **subsp. *annuus***.

### *Spergula arvensis* L.
### Corn Spurrey

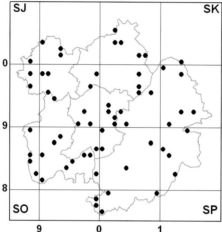

63. Archaeophyte. VU. An annual weed of cultivation and disturbed situations, it seems to be fairly uncommon in B&BC, especially in B'ham. It is recorded from arable and other types of farmland, municipal flower beds, allotments, cemeteries, streets, canalsides, golf courses, a cricket ground and a racecourse. It is often in only moderately fertile soils and sometimes in quite damp (or even winter-wet) situations. Ass: *Chenopodium album*, *Chenopodium polyspermum*, *Matricaria chamomilla*, *Persicaria maculosa*, *Tripleurospermum inodorum*.

### *Spergularia marina* (L.) Besser
### Lesser Sea-spurrey

21. Native in coastal habitats, it has colonised inland roadsides since the late 1970s. An annual herb, it is has started to appear in B&BC fairly recently. It seems to have been first noticed by CBW in 1998 by the A4123 (SP007856) and by the A456 (SP016854), both in Warley and by Robin Hood Lane in Yardley Wood (SP104807). The relative lack of records from the W may be because much of Dudley and W'ton was recorded in the early years of the survey.

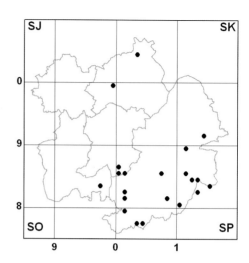

Ass: *Cochlearia danica*, *Plantago coronopus*, *Puccinellia distans*.

### *Spergularia rubra* (L.) J.& C. Presl
### Sand Spurrey

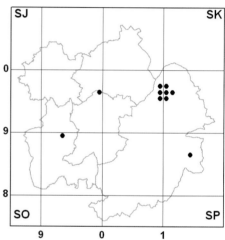

10. Native. Ax. An annual or biennial herb, typically found in the UK in sparse or trampled vegetation on base- and nutrient-poor stony or sandy substrates in heaths and moorland, but also with a distribution in more artificial habitats such as railway land and waste ground. In B&BC it has been recorded from eleven squares in Sutton Park in the past and is still quite frequent there in heathland and acid grassland. It was also found at Sheldon Heath (SP144864, MWP & ICT, 2007). It was at Stourbridge Golf Course in 1992 (SO899822, WAT) and is probably still there. Other records are very scarce within our time period, one from the banks of the River Tame (SO994969, MWP & JaH, 2003), also by the Dudley Canal (SO932891, PN & JVT, 2004), although there are five more from the 1980s from widely scattered post-industrial and waste land sites suggesting a very limited and casual distribution in secondary sites in B&BC. Ass: *Aira praecox*, *Cerastium glomeratum*, *Cerastium semidecandrum*, *Filago minima*, *Rumex acetosella*.

## *Agrostemma githago* L.
## Corncockle

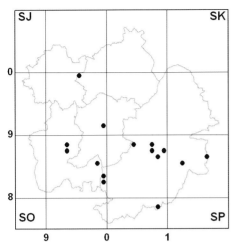

15. Archaeophyte. An annual herb, now considered extinct in UK as an arable weed, it had already disappeared locally by the time of the Edees (1972) and Cadbury *et al.* (1971) Floras. Now found occasionally as a casual, escaping from cultivation or sown deliberately in habitat creation seed mixes where it may persist for a few years if disturbance allows seed to germinate. Recorded from fairly fertile soils in waste land, railways, canals, as a street weed, in public open spaces, on a cleared factory site, and from a grave in Quinton Cemetery.

## *Silene vulgaris* (Moench) Garcke
## Bladder Campion

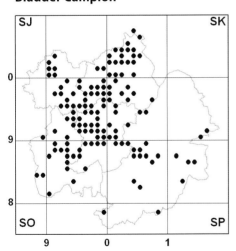

*136. Native. Ax. A perennial herb from open vegetation on dry, rather impoverished or skeletal, base-rich or base-contaminated soils, closely associated with post-industrial areas in B&BC. Common in the Black Country, much less common in B'ham and in countryside and residential areas generally. Habitats include railway ballast, canal, road and railway corridors, spoil and refuse tips, quarries, rock outcrops and parched grassland on shallow soil. Ass: *Artemisia absinthium*,

*Festuca rubra, Hieracium* spp., *Hypericum perforatum, Leucanthemum vulgare, Reseda lutea, Trifolium dubium, Trisetum flavescens.* Our plant is **subsp. vulgaris**.

## *Silene uniflora* Roth
## Sea Campion

2. Native on coastal cliffs, casual in B&BC. A perennial herb cultivated in garden rockeries and escaping rarely as seedlings: paving and edge of garden path, Edgbaston (SP044846, MWP, 2006); track to lock-up garages, Sheldon (SP152839, MWP & ICT, 2007).

## *Silene armeria* L.
## Sweet-William Catchfly

4. Neophyte. Annual rarely escaping from cultivation. Scattered in a garden/orchard, Northfield, not planted (SP019789, AEEP & A. Reeves, 1995); one plant on a post-housing site, S of Oddingley Road, Northfield (SP034786, MWP & ICT, 2006); six plants on a post-housing site on the W side of Lichfield Road, A5127, Four Oaks (SP113992, MWP, JWP & PLR, 2006); track entering Bowman's Harbour landfill site, W'ton (SO940990, P. Millett & ICT, 2008). Also two older records: on reclaimed ground, bank top, S of the River Tame, Wood Green (SO997964, BRF & JPM, 1991); industrial estate, The Leys, Brierley Hill (SO905875, ST, 1991).

## *Silene latifolia* Poir.
## White Campion

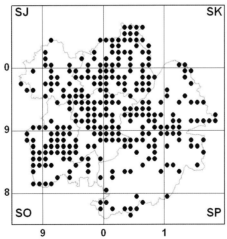

*298. Archaeophyte. An annual, biennial or short-lived perennial, common in colonising vegetation on well-lit ground recovering from disturbance, or in sites kept open by drought. Typically on light, dry but fairly fertile and base-rich soil. The map suggests that it is scarcer in predominantly residential areas and prefers industry and the countryside. Recorded as a street weed, from lane-side hedges, waste land, churchyards, nature

▲ *Agrostemma githago*

▲ *Silene vulgaris*

▲ *Silene armeria*

▲ *Silene coronaria*

▲ *Silene flos-cuculi*

▲ *Saponaria officinalis*

reserves, parkland, common land, rail and canal. Particularly likes road, rail and canal embankments. Our plants are **subsp. *alba*** (Mill.) Greuter & Burdet. Ass: *Arrhenatherum elatius, Artemisia vulgaris, Crepis capillaris, Festuca rubra, Leucanthemum vulgare, Sonchus arvensis, Trisetum flavescens.*

### *Silene × hampeana* Meusel & K. Werner
(*S. latifolia × S. dioica*)

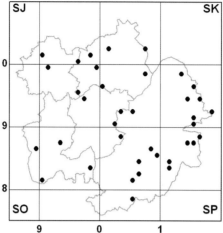

37. Archaeophyte × native. A fertile spontaneous hybrid found commonly where the parent species come into contact; back-crossing may form hybrid swarms. Usually with one or both parents, but particularly in the well-lit, disturbed or droughty habitats on road, rail and canal embankments favoured by *S. latifolia*. Also recorded from waste and derelict land, canal towpaths, river corridors and, rarely, from woodland.

### *Silene dioica* (L.) Clairv.
### Red Campion

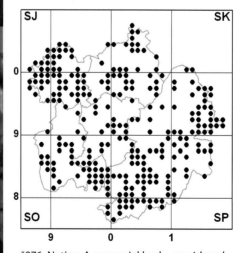

*276. Native. A perennial herb, considered to be short-lived, common in a range of shady places, especially open woods, woodland margins, scrub, hedgerows, shady gardens and allotments, and not confined to old habitats. It is often sown

in gardens and habitat creation schemes and can persist under suitable conditions. It often extends into fairly unshaded habitats especially when they are slightly disturbed, and it is excluded by deep shade. It seems to operate at least in part as a colonist of open, slightly disturbed but sheltered and lightly shaded situations on most moist or damp soils except the most nutrient-rich or base-poor. The distribution in B&BC appears to be concentrated in the older suburbs and the more wooded countryside areas and is to some extent a negative reflection of the distribution of *Silene latifolia*. Ass: *Alliaria petiolata, Circaea lutetiana, Ficaria verna, Hyacinthoides non-scripta, Mercurialis perennis, Scrophularia nodosa, Stellaria holostea.*

### *Silene gallica* L.
### Small-flowered Catchfly

0. Archaeophyte. Sect. 41, BAP, EN, Nationally Scarce. An overwintering annual mainly from poor, droughty arable land it is now largely confined to coastal sites in the UK. Recorded in Sutton Park by Bagnall in 1877.

### *Silene conica* L.
### Sand Catchfly

0. Native. VU, Nationally Scarce. An annual herb of open sandy places, it was recorded in 1832 from 'Iverley Common' (SO8882), which was probably on our border.

### *Silene cretica* L.
### Cretan Catchfly

0. A rare casual, it was recorded by Bagnall in 1877, on a railway bank in Sutton Park.

### *Silene coronaria* (L.) Clairv.
(*Lychnis coronaria* (L.) Murray)
### Rose Campion

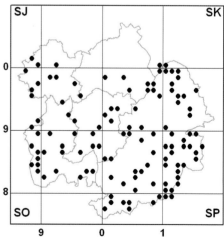

116. Neophyte. A garden escape, found quite commonly in pockets of soil in pavement cracks, also in allotments, waste ground, dumped garden waste, an old car park, and other habitats marginal to

gardens. Often generating from seed. Naturalised across a large area of sandy industrial spoil E of the A4123 at Burnt Tree (SO957914). S & SE Europe and SW Asia. Ass: *Arrhenatherum elatius, Iberis umbellata, Rubus fruticosus* agg., *Rumex obtusifolius, Fraxinus excelsior* seedlings.

### *Silene flos-cuculi* (L.) Clairv.
(*Lychnis flos-cuculi* L.)
**Ragged-Robin**

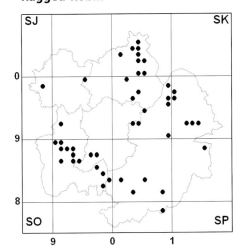

*48. Native. Ax. A perennial herb found in fairly lush vegetation in marshes, wet meadows, rush pastures and flushes in permanently wet to damp, fairly base-rich and not too fertile soils and peats. Most of the records are in countryside areas and it seems to be particularly common in the nature reserves and countryside of Dudley but it is also, rarely, found in canal margins and sewage works. Also in grassland generated from habitat creation seed mixes or hay strewing but rarely persists in them. Ass: *Achillea ptarmica, Carex panicea, Eleocharis palustris, Galium palustre, Juncus articulatus, Juncus effusus, Mentha aquatica, Triglochin palustris*.

### *Saponaria officinalis* L.
**Soapwort**

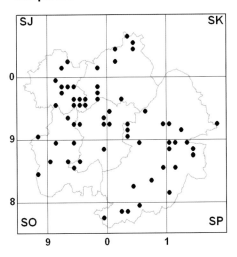

64. Archaeophyte. A rhizomatous perennial garden escape or throw-out in B&BC found mostly in post-industrial habitats, on waste land, roadsides, railway and canalside habitats, allotments, churchyards, recreation grounds, probably usually regenerating vegetatively and showing no signs of invading semi-natural streamside and damp woodland habitats as in SW England and N Wales. The flowers are often double. Found in well-lit situations on a wide range of moist, less impoverished, reasonably base-rich soils. Ass: *Arrhenatherum elatius, Artemisia vulgaris, Cirsium arvense, Centaurea nigra, Crocosmia × crocosmiiflora, Eupatorium cannabinum, Geranium × oxonianum, Ranunculus repens*.

### *Vaccaria hispanica* (Mill.) Rauschert
**Cowherb**
0. Neophyte. An annual with two old casual records: as a bird-seed alien in a garden in Sedgley (SO9294, A.M. Price, 1967); from the railway bank in Sutton Park (Bagnall, 1877). S & C Europe.

### *Gypsophila paniculata* L.
**Baby's-breath**
1. Neophyte. A perennial herb, recorded once, in disturbed land, Water Lane Middleway/Coventry Road traffic island (SP085861, MWP, 1997). C and E Europe and W and C Asia.

### *Dianthus caryophyllus* L.
**Clove Pink**
0. Neophyte. A tufted perennial herb, once recorded in California Quarry (SP016831, W.H. Hardaker, 1953).

### *Dianthus plumarius* L.
**Pink**
2. Neophyte. The familiar garden pink. Waste ground/playing field near Ruiton (SO919918, BH, 2001); a clump in a pavement in Lapal (SO989836, JJD, 2003). E and C Europe.

### *Dianthus deltoides* L.
**Maiden Pink**
4. Native; probably always introduced in B&BC. NT and Nationally Scarce as a native. A perennial herb, occurring as a spontaneously-sown garden escape or throw-out. It grows in well-lit situations in poor, dry, fairly base-rich soils, usually in rough or cultivated grassland, often close to quarries or old sites of quarrying. Mushroom Green (SO9386, T. Beynon, 1996, seen 1999); Saltwells LNR (SO938872, A. Harris, 1998); grassy bank, roadside edge, Shire Ridge (SK056035, SJC, 2006); self set in edge of lawn, Stirchley (SP050814, MWP, ICT, EMP & L. Bastin, 2007). There are quite

a few older records: waste ground, Rowley Regis (SO968878, MWP, 1988); patch in rough grass/scrub Homer Hill, Cradley (SO937848, WAT, 1992, lost by 1994). Also recorded from California Quarry (SP016831) and Manor Pit, Halesowen (SO9783) by WHH *circa* 1952.

### *Dianthus barbatus* L.
**Sweet-William**
4. Neophyte. The familiar garden biennial or short-lived perennial herb, very occasionally flowering as a casual from seed in dumped garden waste etc. (SO961967, PN, 1998); St Michael's Church, Boldmere (SP109939, SPG, 1998); (SO906943, BH, 1999); by pond (SP048772, JJD, 2000). S Europe.

### *Dianthus armeria* L.
**Deptford Pink**
0. Native; a rare casual in B&BC. Sch. 8, Sect. 41, BAP, EN and Nationally Scarce as a native. An annual or short-lived perennial herb, only recorded prior to the survey, from Water Orton Sidings (SP166913, CRP, P.R. Shirley & HHF, 1992) and on an embankment of the Tame Valley Canal (SP029947, JJB, 1987).

## 89. AMARANTHACEAE
(Including CHENOPODIACEAE)

### *Chenopodium bonus-henricus* L.
**Good-King-Henry**
4. Archaeophyte. VU. A patch-forming perennial once much escaping from cultivation into waste land and found in base- and nutrient-rich, moist soil, but with few modern records: Percy Sturmer School (SP075850, G.C. Slawson, 1998); Brandwood End Cemetery (SP071798, B. Bridges, 2002); landfill at Queslett (SP065943, SB, 2002); rank grassland, Bury Hill Park, Rowley Hills (SO970889, MWP, ICT, JaH, EMP & EVJC, 2007, still there in 2011). There were a dozen records, from all parts, in the 1980s. Mountains of central and S Europe.

### *Chenopodium glaucum* L.
**Oak-leaved Goosefoot**
1. Archaeophyte, with a huge geographical range in the temperate zone. VU. An annual of disturbed ground with two close recent casual records: a front garden in Vicarage Street, Langley (SO999881, MWP, 2003) and from the rear garden at the same address. These appeared spontaneously several years after a deliberate introduction.

### *Chenopodium rubrum* L.
**Red Goosefoot**
39. Native. An annual of base-rich and extremely nutrient-rich muds by water

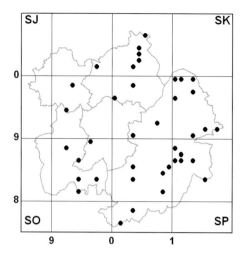

margins (e.g. around sewage works) and constantly moist or damp, nutrient-polluted disturbed land such as allotment manure heaps, dumped soil and suitable places on farmland, also occasionally a street weed. Prefers sheltered but sunny situations. Ass: *Atriplex prostrata, Chenopodium polyspermum, Stellaria media, Urtica dioica, Urtica urens.*

### *Chenopodium polyspermum* L.
### Many-seeded Goosefoot

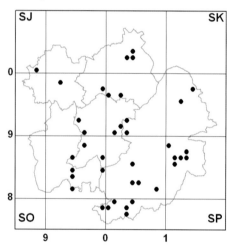

39. Archaeophyte. Ax. A spreading annual of recently disturbed, base-rich, fertile or very fertile, moist to damp but well-drained soil. Recorded from arable fields, gardens, allotments, path sides, street margins, recreation grounds, waste ground and dumped soil. The distribution may suggest some clustering of sites and some association with canal and stream corridors. Ass: *Chenopodium album, Euphorbia peplus, Persicaria maculosa, Senecio vulgaris, Stellaria media, Urtica urens.*

### *Chenopodium vulvaria* L.
### Stinking Goosefoot

0. Archaeophyte. Sch. 8, Sect. 41, BAP, EN. A prostrate annual of disturbed ground. In 1971 Cadbury *et al.* recorded it from

an old tip near Sutton Coldfield (SP1495) and there were several records from the Cradley area (SO9484) at the end of the 19th century.

### *Chenopodium hybridum* L.
### Maple-leaved Goosefoot

0. Archaeophyte. Erect annual. Only old records. Beechwood Hotel (SP061840, R.A. Jones & J. Turner, 1987); Sewage works wetland, Lindridge and Langley Pools (SP155967, D. Morse & T. Morris, 1988).

### *Chenopodium ficifolium* Sm.
### Fig-leaved Goosefoot

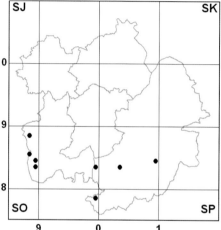

8. Archaeophyte. An annual of disturbed and particularly fertile and base-rich cultivated ground. Recorded from waste ground, a pony field, by roads and a footpath, on dumped soil, a manure heap and as a flowerbed weed. There do not appear to be any old records in B&BC, the oldest is from 1992 and its expansion from the Fens and the London area seems to be generally very recent.

### *Chenopodium opulifolium* Schrad.
### ex W.D.J. Koch & Ziz
### Grey Goosefoot

0. Neophyte. An annual of waste ground and in the past a seed impurity. Recorded by Bagnall by roads in Sutton Park (SP0997, 1891) and in West Bromwich in 1948 (SO99, V. Jacobs, det. J.M.P. Brennan). Europe.

### *Chenopodium album* L.
### Fat-hen

*465. Native. An annual of recently disturbed ground, recorded from arable land, allotments, waste ground, as a street weed, from playing fields, by canals, railways, in churchyards and sewage works. Grows, often in quantity, in moist, fertile, base-rich, recently disturbed soils in well-lit situations. Ass: *Atriplex patula, Capsella bursa-pastoris, Fallopia convolvulus,*

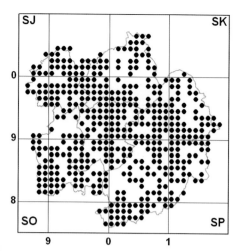

*Persicaria maculosa, Senecio vulgaris, Sonchus oleraceus.*

### *Chenopodium giganteum* D. Don
### Tree Spinach

1. Casual. Large annual, Originally grown from seed at Wheeler's Lane, Moseley allotments and now part of the weed flora on several plots (SP081814, EMP, 2011). India.

### *Bassia scoparia* (L.) Voss
### Summer-cypress

2. Neophyte. An annual herb, a garden escape or possibly from bird seed. Recorded in a double hedge in the RSPB reserve in the Sandwell Valley (SP035927, MWP, 1996); waste land, Warren Road, Washwood Heath (SP101889, MWP, 1997). Temperate Asia.

### *Spinacia oleracea* L.
### Spinach

1. Casual. Cultivated annual. Only one record, from bare ground adjacent to gardens, Evesham Crescent, Bloxwich (SJ986032, MWP, ICT, JaH & SJC, 2007). Asia.

### *Atriplex hortensis* L.
### Garden Orache

3. Neophyte. An annual herb, occurring as a garden escape. Tip, scrub on edge of playing field, Stechford (SP138876, CBW, 1997); Uplands Allotments (SP038910, ICT, MWP, JaH, SJC & V. Lawrie, 2008); Lower Tinker's Farm Allotments (SP017798, MWP & ICT, 2008). Central Asia.

### *Atriplex prostrata* Boucher ex DC.
### Spear-leaved Orache

*177. Native. An annual herb of slightly damp, disturbed, base-rich and fairly to very fertile, recently disturbed soils, intolerant of grazing or trampling. Recorded particularly in the extreme margins of roads, demonstrating its known salt tolerance, but also by pools, reservoirs, rivers, brooks, canals and sewage works

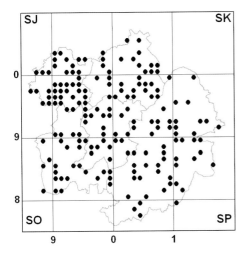

and in farmland, waste places, railway land and churchyards. It may also be more tolerant of mineral-rich but nitrogen-poor spoily substrates than *Atriplex patula*. Ass: *Artemisia vulgaris, Atriplex patula, Chenopodium album, Cirsium arvense, Persicaria maculosa, Plantago major, Polygonum aviculare, Senecio squalidus*.

### *Atriplex littoralis* L.
### Grass-leaved Orache

1. Native of saltmarshes. Found between paving cracks by the A47 Heartland Parkway (SP104894, JWP, MWP, ICT & PLR, 2006), growing with *Puccinellia distans* in a concrete desert.

### *Atriplex patula* L.
### Common Orache

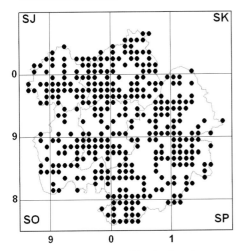

*364. Native. An annual herb of moist to damp, fairly base-rich, fertile, recently disturbed soils, intolerant of grazing or trampling. Recorded from cultivated land, waste land, manure heaps, as a street weed, from quarries, a disused railway line, parkland, common land, nature reserves, canals and river banks and like *Atriplex prostrata*, with which it often grows, it shows salt tolerance and may be found in the edges of roads. Ass: *Atriplex prostrata,*

*Chenopodium album, Persicaria maculosa, Polygonum aviculare, Senecio vulgaris, Stellaria media*.

### *Beta vulgaris* L.
### Beet

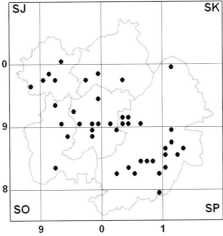

41. Native biennials but almost entirely escapes from cultivation in B&BC. The map shows all records. The native **subsp. maritima** (L.) Arcang. **(Sea Beet)** was recorded from under a hide, lake margin, Forge Mill RSPB reserve, Sandwell Valley (SP0392, J. Forty, 1992). There are a few scattered records for **subsp. vulgaris** (**Root Beet** – Sugar Beet, Beetroot, etc.). **Subsp. cicla** (L.) Arcang. **(Foliage Beet** – Spinach Beet, Swiss Chard, etc.) is quite commonly recorded, usually as a temporary relic of cultivation or as self-set seedlings in uncultivated parts of allotments, but also occasionally from waste land, including an old factory site.

### *Amaranthus* spp.

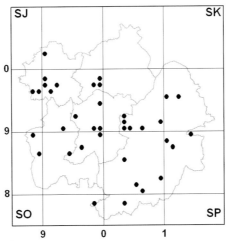

37. Neophytes. Frost-tender annual herbs extensively grown in allotments, especially associated with Caribbean cooking when the resultant mixture of closely related species is called 'Callaloo' and recommended strongly as a green leaf vegetable. Callaloo appears largely to consist of *A. retroflexus*

and *A. hybridus*. Once introduced they seed readily and appear to become part of the seed bank, appearing spontaneously across plots and in marginal situations. The map includes non-flowering plants not immediately referable to particular species which have been observed in allotments in most areas of B&BC. Temperate and tropical America. The exotic seeds collection programme at Ryton Gardens in Coventry has collected seed from B'ham allotments and referred them (S. Cunningham 2010) to *A. caudatus* L. (Love-lies-bleeding), *A. cruentus* L. (Purple Amaranth) and strains from India referred to *A. gangeticus* L. (Elephant-head Amaranth). These are however probably plants directly in cultivation

### *Amaranthus retroflexus* L.
### Common Amaranth, Callaloo

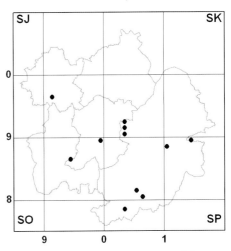

11. Neophyte. Annual herb. Most of the records are from allotments, usually with *A. hybridus*, but there are also records from waste land and as a casual in a gutter and on the RSPB reserve at Sandwell Valley, where it might have arrived in bird seed. N America.

### *Amaranthus hybridus* L.
### Green Amaranth, Callaloo

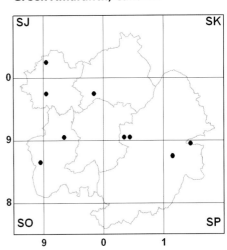

9. Neophyte. An annual herb extensively grown on allotments with *Amaranthus retroflexus* as 'Callaloo' and becoming semi-naturalised on such sites. There are also a few records from roadside gardens, from a canal bank, and by the River Cole. In allotments, plants intermediate between the two species occur and may be the hybrid *A. × ozanonii* (Thell.) C. Schust. & M. Goldshm. (*A. retroflexus × A. hybridus*), e.g. at Pereira Road Allotments (SP033853, ICT, 2008). Tropical and subtropical America.

### Amaranthus caudatus L.
### Love-lies-bleeding

4. Casual. A garden annual, recorded as spontaneous seedlings from a few B'ham allotments (SP0391, SP0390, SP0991, SP0581). This species originated in cultivation.

### Amaranthus albus L.
### White Pigweed

2. Neophyte. An annual herb recorded around a paved landing stage at Powell's Pool, Sutton Park (SP104955, ICT, MWP & JaH, 2005); in the market area, W'ton (SO901982, CBW, 2005). N America.

## 93. MONTIACEAE

### Claytonia perfoliata Donn ex Willd.
### Springbeauty

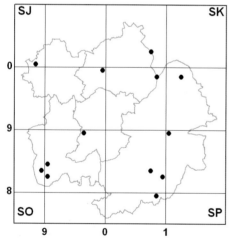

13. Neophyte. An annual herb escaping from gardens and becoming quite well established in woodland, brooks, churchyards, golf courses, hedgerows and as a street weed. In partial shade to full light, preferring light but moist soils of intermediate fertility and base status. Western N America.

### Claytonia sibirica L.
### Pink Purslane

10. Neophyte. An annual herb occasionally becoming well-naturalised and even abundant in damp woodland, for example

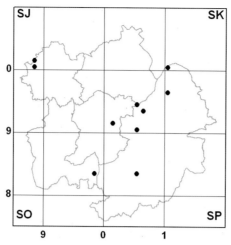

in Holly Wood W of the M6 (SP0594). Also recorded from hedgerows, field, nature reserves, churchyards, waste land and stream sides. Grows in semi-shade on damp, often heavy soils of intermediate base and nutrient status. E Asia and western N America.

### Montia fontana L.
### Blinks

4. Native. Ax. An annual or perennial, in damp to wet, nutrient-poor and slightly base-enriched situations such as bryophyte-rich flushes. Currently only from Sutton Park: wet area, Longmoor Pool (SP093958, MWP & ICT, 2005); above Longmoor Pool (SP0996, SB, 1997); Little Bracebridge Pool, streamside area (SP094982, MWP & ICT, 2005). It was recorded by Readett (1971) in SP0995, SP0996, SP0998, SP1095, SP1096, SP1097 and SP1195 in 1971, so there may have been losses. There is also an old record for Edgbaston Pool (SP055842, D.A. Cadbury, 1935) and an unconfirmed record from Park Coppice (SO900957, L. Parkes, 1989).

Three of the four subspecies known in Britain have been described in Sutton Park: **Subsp. amporitana** Sennen, an aquatic in permanently wet places, is in Bagnall's herbarium, dated 1868, from SP0997. It was refound in 1986 (SP091966, J.C. Bowra) and a more recent record (SP0996, SB, 1997) was ascribed to this subspecies. Readett (1971) ascribed specimens from SP0998 and SP1096 to **subsp. variabilis** Walters, which is also a plant of permanently wet places.

**Subsp. chondrosperma** (Fenzl) Walters, which is a winter annual characteristic of sites which dry out in summer is also in Bagnall's herbarium from Sutton Park (SP0997) dated 1874 and was acknowledged as still present in SP0998 in Readett (1971). It has recently been recorded as frequent towards the mown corner of a grass field in Sutton Park

(SP113966, BL, conf. J. Poland & M. Rand, 2011).

## 95. CORNACEAE

### Cornus sanguinea L.
### Dogwood

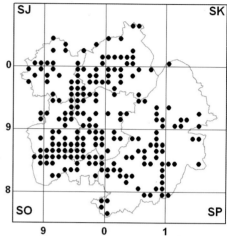

*214. A native, deciduous shrub of woodland and (especially old) hedgerows in partially shaded to open situations on neutral to base-rich soils of intermediate fertility. Also very occasionally as a small tree. Confusion arises as to its true native status in B&BC due to introductions in landscaping and habitat-creation schemes. Many of those may be the introduced subsp. *australis* (C.A. Mey) Jáv. rather than the native subsp. *sanguinea* although no specific records exist. There may have also been confusion with *C. sericea* and *C. alba* in the urban area. Ass (in old hedgerows): *Acer campestre, Corylus avellana, Crataegus monogyna, Prunus spinosa*.

### Cornus sericea L.
### Red-osier Dogwood

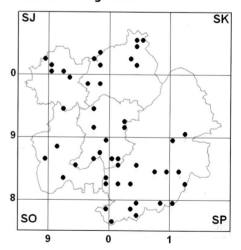

48. Neophyte. An introduced deciduous shrub frequently utilised in planting schemes for its decorative red-stemmed winter shoots. Extensively planted in shrub

beds along roadsides and canal towpaths, around car parks, industrial estates and in country parks. When left, it suckers extensively, and often forms persistent thickets away from the original plantings. N America.

### *Cornus alba* L.
### White Dogwood

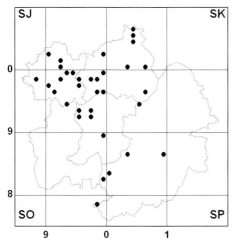

35. Neophyte. A deciduous, suckering shrub, highly esteemed for its brightly coloured winter shoots and widely planted in shrubberies in much the same way as *C. sericea*. Suckering extensively from original plantings but rarely, if ever self-seeding. Differences from *C. sericea* are not always apparent. Also tetrad SP09S. E Asia.

### 96. HYDRANGEACEAE

### *Philadelphus* spp.
### Mock-orange

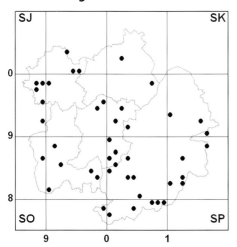

45. Neophytes. Shrubs; often, but not always, relics of cultivation in abandoned gardens and old churchyards, but also occasional seedlings. Typically in hedgerows and scrub in canal and river corridors on rich, moist soil but also on railway embankments and post-industrial waste land and even in old woodland.

Many have been determined to species or hybrids and these are dealt with below.

### *Philadelphus coronarius* L.
### Mock-orange

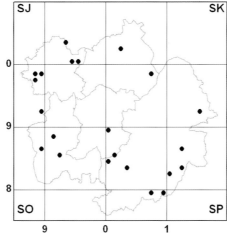

22. Neophyte. The most commonly recorded Mock-orange in the conurbation. All records of seedlings identified to species are attributed to this species. Europe.

### *Philadelphus* 'Lemoinei group'
(incl. *P. coronarius* × *P. microphyllus* A. Gray = *P. lemoinei* Lemoine)
### Hairy Mock-orange

1. Neophyte. Long-established in St. John's churchyard, Wednesbury (SO987947, MWP, 1997). Garden origin.

### *Philadelphus* 'Virginalis group'
(incl. *P.* × *virginalis* Rehder (*P. coronarius* × *P. microphyllus* A. Gray × *P. pubescens* Loisel.))
### Double Mock-orange

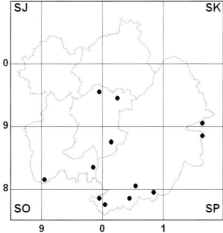

12. Neophyte. Similar habitats to *Philadelphus coronarius*. It is possible that some records of *Philadelphus coronarius* are actually this hybrid. Garden origin.

### *Deutzia scabra* Thunb.
### Deutzia

1. Neophyte. Shrub; a relic of cultivation,

long-established in St John's churchyard, Wednesbury (SO987947, MWP, 1997). China & Japan.

### *Hydrangea macrophylla* (Thunb.) Ser.
### Hydrangea

1. Neophyte. Shrub; a rare relic of cultivation, or garden throw-out in woodland. St Mary's, Kingswinford (SO894893, MWP, 1997). Japan.

### *Hydrangea petiolaris* Siebold & Zucc.
### Climbing Hydrangea

2. Neophyte. Woody climber. By path in a dry part of a wet woodland, Hill Hook (SK106001, MWP, ICT & AB, 2007); grounds of Beacon View (SK063006, SMP, 2009). Japan.

### 97. BALSAMINACEAE

### *Impatiens capensis* Meerb.
### Orange Balsam

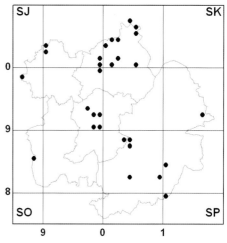

29. Neophyte. An annual of open, water-saturated soils along the margins of canals, pools and ditches generally occurring in small, localised colonies among other pool or canalside emergents. Generally quite scarce throughout B&BC, but now

▲ *Impatiens capensis*

in most of our canals. It was not recorded in our area in either Cadbury *et al.* (1971) or in Edees (1972) and our first records are in the 1980s. N America. Also tetrad SP09R. Ass: *Berula erecta, Glyceria maxima, Iris pseudacorus, Rumex hydrolapathum, Sparganium erectum, Typha latifolia.*

### *Impatiens parviflora* DC.
### Small Balsam

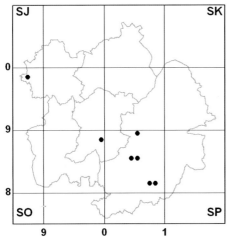

7. Neophyte. Woodland clearings, neglected fragments of ground near habitation and cultivated land; in small localised populations, usually on nutrient-rich soil or rubbish in shady, sheltered situations. A scattering of records for this annual but nowhere really well established, despite being apparently widely recorded in our part of vc. 38 in Cadbury *et al.* 1971 (but not our part of vc. 39 in Edees 1972). C Asia.

### *Impatiens glandulifera* Royle
### Indian Balsam, Himalayan Balsam

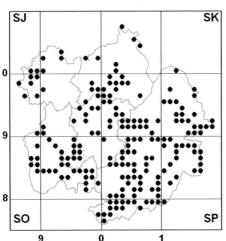

*198. Neophyte. Sch. 9 (invasive). A tall annual, forming continuous stands along streams and river banks in damp woodland and also in more open situations on base- and nutrient-rich soils and muds, frequently invading and often dominating old Alder and Willow carr

woodlands. Also, less vigorously, on waste ground and gardens in drier soils. These latter habitats seem to be invaded more vigorously in wet seasons, and can act as 'staging posts' for the colonisation of new damp woodland areas, although it mainly travels down river and canal corridors. Viewed with mixed feelings in B&BC. Its gaudy, large pink to purple, sickly-sweet smelling flowers are a cheery sight along the banks of urban water courses in the late summer. 'Balsam Bashing' by Natural History Societies and local groups is a regular task for those who regard Indian Balsam as an aggressive, rampant species shading out more choice native plants. Still spreading, however its apparent scarcity in parts of the Black Country was also visible in Edees (1972). Himalayas. Ass: *Caltha palustris, Chrysosplenium oppositifolium, Circaea lutetiana, Eupatorium cannabinum, Geranium pratense, Phalaris arundinacea, Solanum dulcamara, Urtica dioica.*

### *Impatiens walleriana* Hook. f.
### Busy Lizzie
1. Casual. Escaped from gardens on to walls and pavements, Broad Street, Kingswinford (SO886884, CBW, 2005).

### 98. POLEMONIACEAE

### *Polemonium caeruleum* L.
### Jacob's-ladder

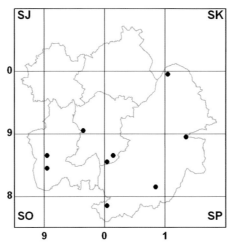

9. Considered native in the Peak District and further N, but no more than a garden escape in B&BC. Frequently cultivated perennial herb, sometimes quick to self-sow in garden borders and flower-growing allotment plots and very occasionally appearing briefly on post-housing land recovering from recent disturbance.

### *Polemonium pauciflorum* S. Watson
### Yellow Jacob's-ladder, Few-flowered Jacob's-ladder
1. Neophyte. Six plants on post-housing

site, junction of Newtown Lane & Foxoak Street, Cradley Heath (SO946862, JEH & MWP, 2005). Arizona & N Mexico.

### *Phlox paniculata* L.
### Phlox
1. Neophyte. Several patches in rough area to rear of gardens, Great Barr, Sandwell Valley (SP0492, MWP, 1999). N America.

### 99. PRIMULACEAE

### *Primula vulgaris* Huds.
### Primrose

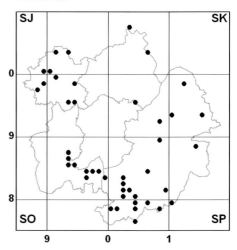

44. Native. An evergreen perennial herb which is found in a variety of half-shaded situations, usually in moist to damp soils of intermediate fertility and base status. There is a scattering of records particularly from churchyards and from hedgerows and waste ground and other habitats marginal to gardens in residential areas. Most records are obviously or probably from original introductions or are garden escapes. A few are long-established from deliberate introductions in habitat creation. Occasionally plants have pink rather than yellow flowers. Also tetrad SO99A. Ass: *Fragaria vesca, Narcissus* spp., *Symphytum × uplandicum, Viola odorata.*

### *Primula × polyantha* Mill.
(*P. vulgaris × P. veris*)
3. Native, but also the basis of the garden *Polyanthus* group. All records probably of horticultural origin rather than spontaneous hybrids: River Rea corridor (SP017783, MWP, ICT, JWP, JJD, AWR & JaH, 2008); St. Peter's, Homer Hill (SO942851, MWP & ICT, 2008); Quinton cemetery (SO9885, CBW, 2000). There is also a scattering of ten records for *Primula* spp., which probably include further records of the *Polyanthus* group and possibly *P. × pruhonicensis.*

### Primula elatior (L.) Hill
### Oxlip
1. Native; introduced in B&BC. NT and Nationally Scarce in its native range in East Anglia. Seedlings from garden planting, in a woodland margin, Moor Hall Drive (SP125982, MWP, ICT, JWP & JaH, 2006).

### Primula veris L.
### Cowslip

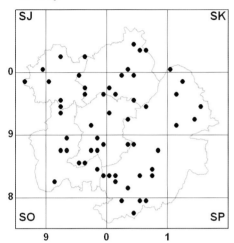

*57. Native. A perennial herb. A few records in semi-natural grassland may be native, others by canal towpaths, in parks and other public open spaces are doubtfully so, and many in churchyards, road verges, islands and central reservations and in habitat creation schemes are clearly introductions. In the Lower Illey meadows (SO9781) there only appear to be records up to 1986. In usually short, open, fairly species-rich grassland on moist, typically base-rich or calcareous, fairly infertile to moderately fertile soils. Also tetrad SO99A. Ass: *Cynosurus cristatus, Festuca rubra, Lotus corniculatus, Ranunculus acris, Ranunculus bulbosus, Trifolium pratense.*

### P. × pruhonicensis Zemann ex Bermans
(*P. vulgaris* × *P. juliae* Kusn.)
### Hybrid Primrose
1. Neophyte. This relic and throwout from gardens is represented by a single record for the cultivar 'Wanda', found on waste ground by Winson Green Road (SP044877, MWP, 1998), but it could be elsewhere, unrecorded except as '*Primula* sp.' . Garden origin.

### Hottonia palustris L.
### Water-violet
0. Native. Unconfirmed 18th century record from the B'ham Heath (probably SP0487).

### Lysimachia nemorum L.
### Yellow Pimpernel
*23. Native. Ax. A procumbent, evergreen, perennial herb of woodlands and other

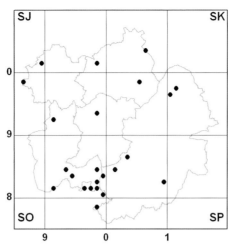

shady places, recorded occasionally, usually on steep slopes in old dingle woodland, but there are one or two records from churchyards and post-industrial land. Grows in semi-shade in relatively bare patches of damp, rather base- and nutrient-poor soils. Ass: *Epilobium montanum, Lamiastrum galeobdolon, Milium effusum, Poa nemoralis, Viola riviniana.*

### Lysimachia nummularia L.
### Creeping-Jenny

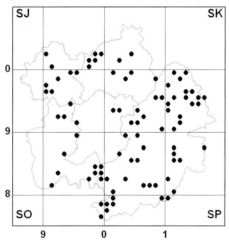

86. Native; probably largely introduced in B&BC. A procumbent, evergreen, perennial herb found in damp to wet soil of intermediate base and intermediate to fairly high nutrient status, usually as an understorey in tall herb vegetation or in scrub or woodland margins. It is found in a wide range of mostly secondary communities which have developed on waste ground, road verges, pavement, railway land, canal banks, hedge banks and churchyards, often by water, and also in the margins of gardens and allotments. It gives every appearance of being a garden escape even when it is present in old grassland or woodland; possibly native e.g. in wet woodland near Wyndley Pool in Sutton Park. Also recorded in tetrad SO98E. Ass:

▲ *Impatiens glandulifera*

▲ *Primula vulgaris*

▲ *Lysimachia nummularia*

▲ *Anagallis tenella*

▲ *Anagallis arvensis* subsp. *arvensis*

▲ *Anagallis arvensis* subsp. *foemina*

*Agrostis stolonifera, Epilobium hirsutum, Geum urbanum, Myosotis scorpioides.*

### *Lysimachia vulgaris* L.
### Yellow Loosestrife

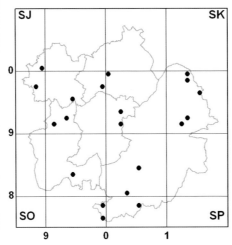

20. Native. Ax. A semi-evergreen perennial herb characteristic of water margins and wet woodlands. In B&BC there is a scattering of records, mostly in lake and pond margins, often in public or private parks, nature areas or quarries and sometimes clearly introduced. Grows in the open or in shade, on wet soils, intermediate or fairly rich in bases and nutrients. Ass: *Carex acutiformis, Carex rostrata, Epilobium hirsutum, Equisetum fluviatile, Galium palustre, Scutellaria galericulata, Sparganium erectum.*

### *Lysimachia ciliata* L.
### Fringed Loosestrife

2. Neophyte. Two records, both from shady spare ground in allotments, either persisting from cultivation or garden discards. Kent Road Allotments (SO981847, ICT & L. Worledge, 2008); Pereira Road Allotments (SP032853, ICT, 2008). N America.

### *Lysimachia punctata* L.
### Dotted Loosestrife

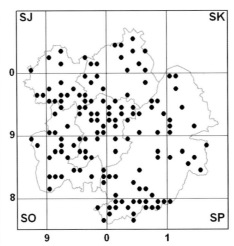

\*142. Neophyte. An evergreen perennial herb; a garden throw-out frequently naturalised in rough grassland, by canals, in a variety of waste ground, along roadsides, along a disused railway etc. and also appearing by pools and occasionally surviving in disturbed areas in old wet woodland. In well-lit or slightly shaded situations in damp to moist, fairly base- and nutrient-rich soils. Europe and Asia. Ass: *Arrhenatherum elatius, Chamerion angustifolium, Epilobium hirsutum, Pentaglottis sempervirens.*

### *Anagallis tenella* (L.) L.
### Bog Pimpernel

3. Native. Ax. A prostrate, evergreen perennial herb which grows in short, open vegetation in nutrient-poor, slightly base-flushed mires. It is a poor competitor with taller vegetation. It is recorded from two areas in Sutton Park: near Little Bracebridge Pool (SP094983, MWP & ICT, 2005, seen again 2009) and in the Longmoor Valley (SP093962, MWP, ICT & PLR, 2006). Readett (1971) described it as locally frequent and recorded it from two more squares, SP0995 and SP1096. It is also present in the mire by the canal on Clayhanger Common (SK045053, DH, 2003) where turf stripping (as a conservation measure) seems to have regenerated a large population over several square metres when last seen in 2010. There is an old record from a swamp in Holly Wood (SP053945, J. Little, 1981, seen again in 1983). Ass: *Carex hostiana, Carex panicea, Cirsium dissectum, Dactylorhiza fuchsii, Pedicularis palustris, Pinguicula vulgaris, Triglochin palustris.*

### *Anagallis arvensis* L.
### Scarlet Pimpernel

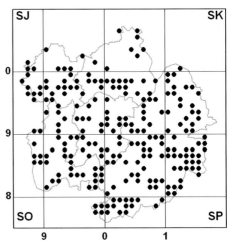

\*237. Native. A prostrate winter-annual, sometimes perennating. From recently disturbed or cultivated ground in gardens, allotments, arable land and development sites, growing in well-lit places or a little shade on moist to dry soils, intermediate in base and nutrient status. In some allotments it is extremely abundant, in others very scarce or absent. It seems to prefer sandy, sharply drained sites. Also tetrad SO98E. Ass: *Arabidopsis thaliana, Cardamine hirsuta, Myosotis arvensis, Stellaria media, Veronica persica.*

Some records are for **subsp. *arvensis*** and practically all our records are likely to be of this subspecies, although Cadbury *et al.* (1971) have a record for the Nationally Scarce **subsp. *foemina*** (Mill.) Schinz & Thell. (subsp. *caerulea* Hartman) (**Blue Pimpernel**) from a roadside in SP08I, and blue-flowered plants have been noted in Uplands Allotments (SP0390 or SP0391, MWP & A.J. Purcell, 2010).

### *Cyclamen hederifolium* Aiton
**Sowbread**

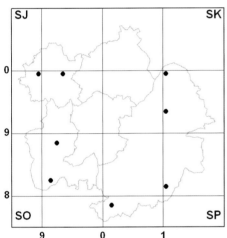

8. Neophyte. A perennial herb and a rare garden escape or relic of planting in grassed road verges, hedgerows, churchyards etc.; sometimes well-naturalised and spreading quite widely at suitable sites e.g. in Holy Trinity churchyard, Heath Town (SO931998, MWP & ICT, 2011). Europe and Turkey.

### 101. SARRACENIACEAE

### *Sarracenia purpurea* L.
**Pitcherplant**

0. Neophyte. Introduced by unknown persons into the Pool Hollies mire in Sutton Park in the 1980s (SP101977, MWP) where it survived for at least one winter. Photographs dated 1986 suggest that the plant might actually have been *Sarracenia alata* (Wood) Wood (Pale Pitcherplant).

### 102. ERICACEAE

### *Empetrum nigrum* L. **subsp. *nigrum***
**Crowberry**

2. Native. Ax. An evergreen shrub, on the

extreme SE edge of its distribution in the UK in B&BC. Recorded by Readett (1971) from five Sutton Park squares (SP0898, SP0996, SP0997, SP0998 and SP1097) but only found in SP1097 in the present survey, by SB in 1997 and in 2007 in a single mire site (SP103975, MWP, ICT, PLR, DJA & J. Antrobus). More recently it has also been found close to the railway line in an area of tree regeneration of birch, willow and pine (SP089984, BL, 2009). There are older records from two locations on Brownhills Common (SK042063, JPM, 1990), and it was mentioned as a colonist of open-cast and bell pit workings near Brownhills by Rees & Skelding (1950), but has not been seen there since 1993. It is still present near Brownhills on Chasewater (SK0407) not far outside our boundary. It is a plant of damp and dry extremely base-poor and nutrient-poor peat, in shade or full sun. Ass: *Calluna vulgaris, Deschampsia flexuosa, Vaccinium myrtillus, Vaccinium oxycoccus, Vaccinium vitis-idaea.*

### *Rhododendron ponticum* L.
**Rhododendron**

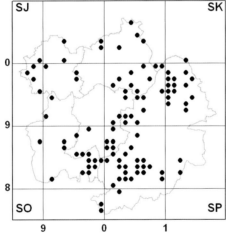

*103. Neophyte. Sch. 9 (invasive). An evergreen shrub, notorious in UK as a potentially invasive plant forming dense, impenetrable understories in old woodland on base-poor soils, especially where they are moist and nutrient- poor. In B&BC it is common as a garden plant and is planted or naturalised by seeding in woodlands quite widely. It is recorded from riversides and brooksides, nature reserves, parkland, woodland, scrub and churchyards but rarely seems to be a serious problem. At many sites it is removed in management, and it is probably excluded from much of the Black Country by the lack of sufficiently acid soils. In Sutton Park, where acid, peaty soil might be expected to encourage *R. ponticum*, it is present but the native *Ilex aquifolium* is the dominant (and invasive) undershrub,

so possibly it outcompetes *R. ponticum*. SE Europe and the Iberian peninsula.

### *Rhododendron luteum* Sweet
**Yellow Azalea**

0. Neophyte. Sch. 9 (invasive). A deciduous shrub. Two pre-survey records: by a pond off Hampshire Drive (SP043856, S. Derry & S. Ginley, 1988); Manor Farm Park (SP028808, JJB, 1990). These were probably relics of planting. Europe.

### *Calluna vulgaris* (L.) Hull
**Heather**

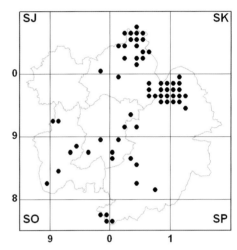

*64. Native. Ax. A low shrub found on moist to damp, very base- and nutrient-poor, often peaty soils and the characteristic dominant species of heathland. The major concentrations of *Calluna* in B&BC in the areas of Brownhills Common, Barr Beacon, Sutton Park and Rednal show the major remnants of heathland in the conurbation and possibly suggest where these might be extended by management. At many existing sites appropriate management by local authorities has reinvigorated the heather cover in recent years. Many of the isolated records for *Calluna* represent railway embankments or exposures of base-poor rock; there seems to have been very little significant development of *Calluna* on coal spoil (some small stands W of Brownhills Common in SK0406), but of course there are remarkably few sizeable remnants of coal spoil in B&BC. Ass: *Deschampsia flexuosa, Festuca filiformis, Festuca ovina, Nardus stricta, Pteridium aquilinum, Ulex gallii.*

### *Erica tetralix* L.
**Cross-leaved Heath**

*13. Native. Ax. A low shrub, the characteristic species of wet heaths, found on wet to damp soils, usually waterlogged at least in winter, usually peaty, very base- and nutrient-poor, or on pure peats. Only known from the core heathland

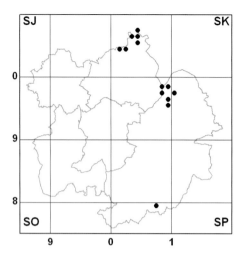

areas of B&BC: Sutton Park, Brownhills Common, and Pelsall Common. Rarely at all frequent at any of these sites. Also a few plants at the canal-side mire on Clayhanger Common at SK045053. Readett (1971) recorded it from twelve monads at Sutton Park; it may be diminishing at that site, possibly due to scrubbing over of heathland, or it may have been under-recorded in the present survey. The record for Brandwood Cemetery (SP0779, B. Bridges, 2002) is considered an introduction, essentially in cultivation. It was also recorded on Moseley Common (SP0982) and in the Stourbridge area (SO98) in the 19th century. Ass: *Anagallis tenella, Calluna vulgaris, Drosera rotundifolia, Eriophorum angustifolium, Sphagnum* spp., *Vaccinium oxycoccos*.

### *Erica cinerea* L.
### Bell Heather

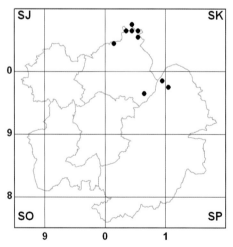

9. Native. Ax. A low shrub of dry heathland or well-drained patches in wet heathland, on very base- and nutrient-poor, shallow or sharply drained peaty or siliceous soils. Still quite abundant on Brownhills Common, and present at several points along the nearby portion of the Wyrley & Essington Canal by Chasewater, but increasingly rare

elsewhere. It was last seen at its old sites at Pelsall Common (SK014045) in 2009. Similarly at Sutton Park, where Readett (1971) recorded it from six squares: SP0896, SP0995, SP0996, SP0997, SP0998 & SP1097, and described it as "occasional in bog and heath", it appears now to be very scarce. PC recorded it from SP1097 in 1999 and last remembers seeing it in the Park in SP0998 in 2002. The record from SP0696 is from Barr Beacon, where it appears to have been introduced in heather brash strewn on the site from Brownhills Common in the 1990s. There are also old records from the Rough Wood wedge (SJ986015 & SJ988010, M.E. Evans, 1980), the latter site in grassland at the rear of the Frank F. Harrison Comprehensive School; neither plant was refound. It was also recorded on Moseley Common (SP0982) and in the Stourbridge area (SO8982, probably Pedmore Common) in the 19th century. Ass: *Calluna vulgaris, Carex pilulifera, Molinia caerulea, Rumex acetosella, Ulex gallii.*

### *Vaccinium oxycoccos* L.
### Cranberry

3. Native. Ax. A trailing shrub, growing, usually amongst *Sphagnum*, on wet, extremely base- and nutrient-poor peat in well-lit or slightly shaded places. Only from Sutton Park where it was recorded in three squares: the mires above Longmoor Pool (SP093957, MWP & ICT, 2005); (SP092964, MWP, ICT & PLR, 2006) and in quantity in a mire between Bracebridge and Blackroot Pools (SP103975, MWP & ICT, 2005, seen again in 2009). In 1971 Readett (1971) recorded it as locally abundant in bog and marsh at Sutton Park in seven squares: SP0898, SP0995, SP0996, SP0997, SP0998, SP1096 and SP1097. It also occurs just over the border of Walsall at Chasewater. There are also 19th century records from Pedmore Common (SO8982), the Stourbridge district (SO98) and Moseley Common (SP0982). Ass: *Erica tetralix, Eriophorum angustifolium, Eriophorum vaginatum, Hydrocotyle vulgaris, Sphagnum* spp.

### *Vaccinium vitis-idaea* L.
### Cowberry

8. Native. Ax. A low shrub found in heathland, growing in moist, extremely base- and nutrient-poor peaty substrates in full daylight or part shade. It is at its UK SE limits in B&BC. Brownhills Common: (SK035064 & SK038063, DH, 1998 and at SK042063, JPM, 1990, but not found in the latter square in the present survey). Sutton Park: small patch S of Gun Targets (SP088966, Warwickshire Butterfly Conservation, 2009); Streetley Clumps (SP089984, BL, 2009); damp heathland

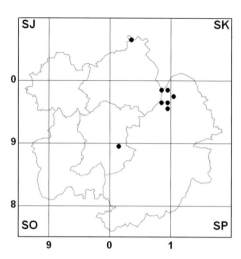

above Longmoor Pool (SP092956, MWP & ICT, 2005); (SP0996, SPG, 1999); Streetley Wood area (SP090984, MWP & ICT, 2005); between Bracebridge and Blackroot Pools (SP103975, MWP, ICT, PLR, DJA & J Antrobus, 2007); Readett (1971) listed it for only four squares in the Park. It is also present on the high embankments of the B'ham Canal complex in the Galton Valley (SP017890, TCH & CRP, 1987, still there in 1998), where it grows with other heathland species. Ass: *Calluna vulgaris, Deschampsia flexuosa, Hypochaeris radicata, Nardus stricta, Ulex europaeus, Vaccinium myrtillus, Vaccinium oxycoccos.*

### *Vaccinium × intermedium* Ruthe
(*V. vitis-idaea × V. myrtillus*)

0. Native. Recorded from Sutton Park in 1889 by Bagnall (SP0997).

### *Vaccinium myrtillus* L.
### Bilberry

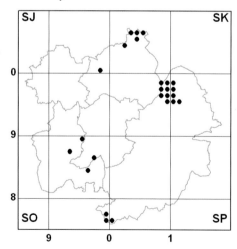

*25. Native. Ax. A low shrub of heathland and heathy woodland, growing in full daylight to half shade, in moist to damp, fairly well-drained, peaty or stony, extremely base- and nutrient-poor soils. Recorded from the main heathland areas of Pelsall Common, Brownhills Common,

Sutton Park and Rednal. Readett (1971) recorded it at three more squares than in the present survey in Sutton Park (SP0895, SP1196 and SP1197) but it seems to have held its own better there than have many other members of Ericaceae. There are also other scattered records from woodlands on acid soils and from steep river and railway embankments. It was last recorded at Pedmore Common near Stourbridge (SO8982) in 1986; it had been known there since 1832. Ass: *Calluna vulgaris, Deschampsia flexuosa, Galium saxatile, Potentilla erecta*.

## *Hypopitys monotropa* Crantz
(*Monotropa hypopitys* L.)
### Yellow Bird's-nest
2. Native. Sect. 41, BAP, EN. A saprophytic perennial herb. It appeared on a dump of contaminated limestone rubble at the Bilston gasworks site, SW of Dudley Priestfield railway: a thousand or more plants over 5 × 10 m (SO937966, EVJC, P. Millett, B. Tokarska-Guzik & A. Rostański, 1999). It grew under *Salix/Betula* scrub which had developed around bare areas. Unfortunately the site was lost to development in 2002. At that time it was discovered that there were several large colonies across the scrub-dominated part of the site. There is however a newly discovered site, on a canal bank in Selly Oak, in *Hedera* 'Hibernica' in a woodland plantation on a bank of the Worcester & B'ham canal S (and a little N) of the Bristol Road railway bridge (SP043827, O. Pescott, 2008). This is thought to be **subsp. hypophegea** (Wallr.) Tzevelev.

## 103. GARRYACEAE

### *Aucuba japonica* Thunb.
### Spotted-laurel

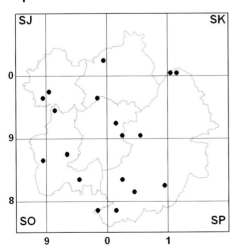

18. Neophyte. There are few records for this frequently planted, shade tolerant, evergreen shrub, but it is sometimes

present in old woodland. Persistent relics of planting, or possibly self-set individuals, in woodland at Hill Hook, Sandwell Valley, Harborne Hall, Moseley Bog, Alder Coppice, also canal embankment Selly Oak and a few records from roadsides and churchyards in residential areas. Japan.

## 104. RUBIACEAE

### *Sherardia arvensis* L.
### Field Madder

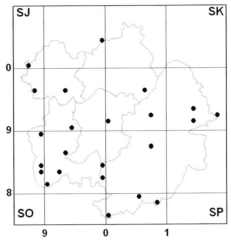

23. Native. Ax. Annual in grassland on dry, sunny and well-drained, base- and nutrient-intermediate soils: managed verges, banks, close-mown lawns. Only rarely as a weed of arable land: growing with *Papaver argemone* in arable fields to the N of Doe Bank Lane, Pheasey (SP066967, MWP, ICT, JaH & PLR, 2006). Ass: *Agrostis capillaris, Bellis perennis, Cerastium fontanum, Festuca rubra, Hypochaeris radicata, Lolium perenne, Plantago lanceolata, Trifolium dubium, Trifolium repens, Veronica arvensis*.

### *Phuopsis stylosa* (Trin.) Benth. & Hook. f. ex B.D. Jacks
### Caucasian Crosswort
1. Neophyte. A mat-forming perennial occasionally grown in gardens. A small patch seeded on to the top of a garden wall, Weeford Road, Sutton Coldfield (SP135996, MWP, ICT & PLR, 2007). Caucasus and Iran.

### *Galium odoratum* (L.) Scop.
### Woodruff
34. Native. Ax. Perennial herb from shaded, damp deciduous Ash/Oak and Alder woodland in neutral and often base-rich soils. An ancient woodland indicator plant and native populations still occur in B&BC. However it also occurs as a persistent garden throw-out, occasionally forming extensive patches from its creeping rhizomes. Approximately 60%

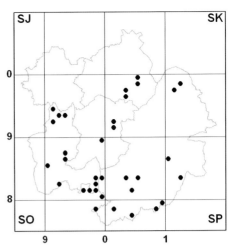

of the mapped records come from old woodlands. Tetrad records for SO89X & Y, SO99D. Ass (in woodlands): *Anemone nemorosa, Cardamine amara, Hyacinthoides non-scripta, Lamiastrum galeobdolon, Oxalis acetosella, Sanicula europaea, Veronica montana*.

### *Galium uliginosum* L.
### Fen Bedstraw
2. Native. Ax. Scrambling perennial, only confirmed from two sites in Sutton Park where small colonies occur in base-enriched flushes in Longmoor Valley (SP093962, MWP & ICT, 2006) and near Little Bracebridge Pool (SP094982, MWP & ICT, 2005). In 1971, Readett (1971) recorded it in SP0995 and SP1096, and Bagnall in 1873 in SP0997. Ass: *Dactylorhiza praetermissa, Hydrocotyle vulgaris, Isolepis setacea, Menyanthes trifoliata, Nymphoides peltata*.

### *Galium palustre* L.
### Common Marsh-bedstraw

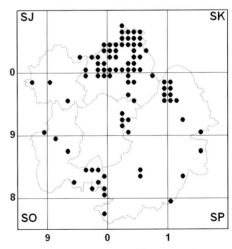

*88. Native. Ax. Perennial from margins of ponds, ditches and wet meadows and rush-pastures in unshaded situations on a wide range of soil types. Also in the mortar of permanently moist brickwork along canal edges. Typically it scrambles up amongst the rushes in the reedswamp and marsh communities. Its distribution suggests that it is only a common feature of canal margins in the waters derived more directly from Chasewater in the Walsall area. Ass: *Berula erecta, Juncus acutiflorus, Juncus effusus, Juncus inflexus, Mentha aquatica, Myosotis scorpioides, Silene flos-cuculi.*

Most of our modern records do not indicate the subspecies, but there are records for **subsp. palustre** throughout the range and most are likely to be this. There is one modern record for **subsp. elongatum** (C.Presl) Arcang. from Edgbaston Pool (SP0583, JWP & MWP, 2007) and an old record from Merecroft Pool & Meadowland (SP043787, B'ham Natural History Society, 1974; T.J. Pickvance & AEEP, 1975) .

### Galium verum L.
### Lady's Bedstraw

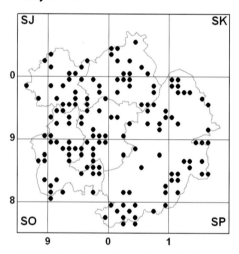

*149. Native. Perennial herb, relatively common in lawns, grassy verges and roadside banks on dry, moderately acid to quite base-rich, infertile soils in open and sunny situations. Tolerant of regular mowing and often prevented from flowering in such situations. Its presence in garden lawns is very patchy and it may sometimes be an introduction in turf from old meadows. Also tetrad SK00A. Ass: *Agrostis capillaris, Betonica officinalis, Festuca ovina, Festuca rubra, Pilosella officinarum, Rumex acetosella.*

### Galium × pomeranicum Retz.
(*G. verum × G album*)
2. Native. Of rare occurrence where *G. verum* and *G. album* grow within close proximity. Recorded from Mill Lane Nature Reserve, Coal Pool, Walsall, with parents on a grassy bank where two railway lines diverge (SP017998, MWP, 2001) and a little way N of this where more plants occur on grassy banks and paths (SK0200, JaH & MWP, 2001).

### Galium album Mill.
(*Galium mollugo* L.)
### Hedge Bedstraw

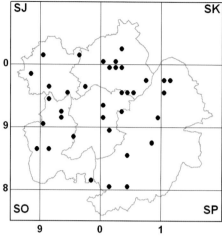

36. Native/Introduced native. Ax. Perennial herb from open to slightly shaded well-drained situations on base-rich or calcareous soils. Widespread but generally uncommon in hedge margins, railway and canal embankments, limestone quarries and other unmanaged grassy areas. Often included in wildflower seed mixes and some plants are almost certainly from deliberate introductions, e.g. at Phoenix Park, W'ton (SO918967) and field by Blue House Farm, Barr Beacon (SP070972). Ass: *Brachypodium sylvaticum, Bromopsis erecta, Epilobium parviflorum, Heracleum sphondylium, Holcus lanatus, Lolium perenne, Plantago lanceolata, Polygala vulgaris, Plantago media.*

### Galium saxatile L.
### Heath Bedstraw

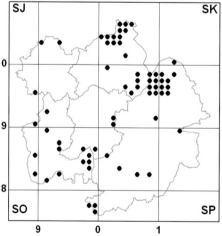

*65. Native. Ax. A frequent to very common perennial of dry (but not droughty) heathland in infertile, acidic soils in open, sunny situations. Scarce elsewhere; occasionally seen in short-mown lawns on sandy banks. Ass: *Calluna vulgaris, Deschampsia flexuosa, Erica tetralix, Festuca filiformis, Festuca ovina, Potentilla erecta.*

### Galium aparine L.
### Cleavers, Goosegrass
*694. Native. Ubiquitous autumn-germinating annual of shady and open situations. Waste ground, hedges, cultivated and disturbed ground, gardens, typically scrambling through and over tall weeds, bushes and young trees. Favoured by rich, fertile soils and by periods without cultivation, so tends to be commonest in woodland margins, hedges and young tree plantations treated intermittently with herbicides, etc. Ass: *Anthriscus sylvestris, Rumex obtusifolius, Sambucus nigra, Symphytum × uplandicum, Urtica dioica, Veronica hederifolia.*

### Cruciata laevipes Opiz
(*Galium cruciata* (L.) Scop.)
### Crosswort

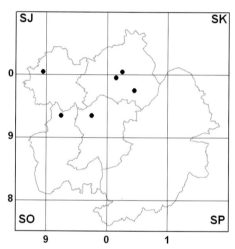

6. Native. This perennial herb of hedgerows and woodland margins in fairly nutrient- and often very base-rich, moist soils is quite common in the countryside further W, but is rare in B&BC. It occurs mainly on the limestone and along abandoned railway lines: Hurst Hill Wood (SO928937, E. McKay, 1998); wooded abandoned railway sidings, Smestow LNR (SJ897006, PWS & CRP, 2000); rough calcareous grassland on a disused railway line, Mill Lane nature reserve, Ryecroft (SP0200, MWP, 2001; SP019999, PWS, TM, M. Kodaka & S. Woods, 2002); hedgerow, Skip Lane, Walsall (SP043975, JaH & SJC, 2007); Ocker Hill, Tipton (SO9793, JEH, 2007). It is possibly declining: it was more widespread on Hurst Hill in the 1980s and nearby in the Gorge, Sedgley (SO928942), also on the Wren's Nest (SO937920) and Fens Pools (SO917886). The only records from the B'ham side of the conurbation are very old and from Sutton Park (SP0997, Bagnall, 1876). Ass: *Anthriscus sylvestris, Arrhenatherum elatius, Urtica dioica.*

## 105. GENTIANACEAE

### *Centaurium erythraea* Rafn
### Common Centaury

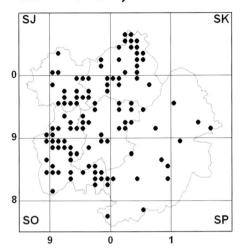

*113. Native. Ax. Open vegetation on well-drained, mildly acidic to base-rich soils in a wide range of habitats which include shortish grassland, railway tracks, canal towpaths, areas recovering from recent disturbance and spoil including coal spoil. Much commoner in the Black Country than in B'ham and apparently commoner now than in Edees (1972). A population of white-flowered plants grow on the banks of Forge Mill Lake, Sandwell Valley. Ass: *Carex flacca*, *Erigeron acris*, *Linum catharticum*, *Hypericum perforatum*, *Lotus corniculatus*, *Poa compressa*.

### *Blackstonia perfoliata* (L.) Huds.
### Yellow-wort

4. Native. Ax. Possibly native in open, well-drained, calcareous grassland, Hill Farm Bridge Fields, Great Barr (SP032949–SP033951, MWP, 1998), where it seems to have been known since at least 1986; in a tiny area of unimproved grassland between Fort Parkway and M6 motorway, Nechells (SP116894, MWP, 2006); a few plants on clayey waste ground off Cole Hall Lane, Colehall (SP148877, CBW, 1997). There are older records from Ryecroft cutting near Park Lime Pits in Walsall (SP019998, R. Normand, 1988), from a scrubby bank in pasture, Frankley (SO999783, JJD, 1992) and from industrial spoil by the railway, Wood Green, Wednesbury (SO995965, J. Andrews, 1988), from where it was reported by several people in 1987–9, and was lost in the construction of the Junction 9 trading estate. Some was translocated locally to an area between the motorway slip road embankment, the railway and the River Tame at SO997964. Edees (1972) quotes *Blackstonia* as being 'in great abundance upon the lime hills near Dudley Castle' in

1801. Ass: *Carex flacca*, *Centaurea erythraea*, *Linum catharticum*, *Ophrys apifera*.

### *Gentianella amarella* (L.) Börner
### Autumn Gentian

1. Native. A few plants in open grassland on Silurian Limestone on the steep W-facing slope of the Wren's Nest NNR, behind the safety fence (SO936916, A. Coward & ICT, 2008), where it has been known since at least 1983 (SO937920, A. Whitbread) and appears to be increasing (16 plants in 2010). Ass: *Briza media*, *Ctenidium molluscum*, *Leontodon hispidus*, *Linum catharticum*, *Lotus corniculatus*, *Pilosella officinarum*.

## 106. APOCYNACEAE

### *Vinca minor* L.
### Lesser Periwinkle

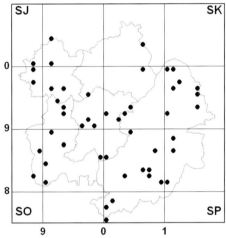

49. Archaeophyte. Prostrate, perennial sub-shrub naturalised and sometimes forming extensive patches in light woodland, shady roadside banks and along tracks and drives near to habitation. More shade-tolerant than *V. major*. A variegated cultivar ('Argenteo-variegata'), with leaves variegated cream and yellow has been reported. SW & C Europe. Ass: *Alliaria petiolata*, *Epilobium montanum*, *Galium aparine*, *Glechoma hederacea*, *Tellima grandiflora*, *Viola riviniana*.

### *Vinca major* L.
### Greater Periwinkle

73. Neophyte. A widely cultivated, vigorously spreading, evergreen sub-shrub used as ground cover and self-rooting from gardens into drives and tracks to the rear of houses. Also persisting where discarded on waste ground, spoil heaps, banks and hedgerows in open and slightly shaded situations. Variegated forms are frequently grown and sometimes spread from gardens. Mediterranean. Ass: *Chamerion angustifolium*, *Epilobium*

▲ *Centaurium erythraea*

▲ *Gentianella amarella*

▲ *Vinca major*

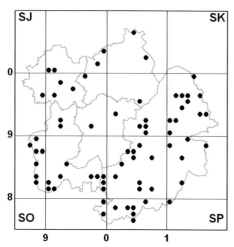

montanum, Galium aparine, Glechoma hederacea, Poa trivialis.

## 107. BORAGINACEAE

### Lithospermum officinale L.
### Common Gromwell

2. Native. First recorded at the Wren's Nest NNR (SO9391) in 1864; rediscovered there in limestone grassland in 1990 (SO936915, N. Williams); still present there but now inaccessible behind the Seven Sisters security fence, and seen there in the edge of scrub and along a track and also at SO935917 in 2010. It is however also present and accessible in the Wren's Nest quarry area (SO937920, ST & N. Williams, 1989); (SO936920, ST, 1997) and seen there again in 2007. Also recorded from a small fragment of limestone grassland on the neighbouring Mons Hill (SO936924, ICT, EVJC, JaH, SJC & PLR, 2007). Similar limestone habitats occur nearby but there have been no further records. Ass: Brachypodium sylvaticum, Briza media, Carex flacca, Carex sylvatica, Centaurea nigra, Hedera helix, Linum catharticum, Plantago media, Trifolium repens.

### Echium vulgare L.
### Viper's-bugloss

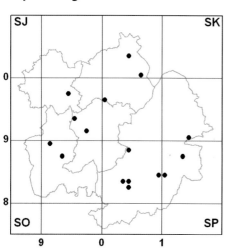

16. Native. An occasional introduction or adventive on dry, sunny sites, on banks, disturbed road verges, railway land, canal towpaths and land recovering from recent disturbance. Sometimes a relic of cultivation in gardens and allotments or possibly a relic of habitat creation, but also has a long history in vc. 39 and vc. 38 as a weed of sandy fallow fields. Rarely persists for more than a few years. Ass: Leucanthemum vulgare, Matricaria chamomilla, Polygonum aviculare, Reseda luteola.

### Pulmonaria officinalis L.
### Lungwort

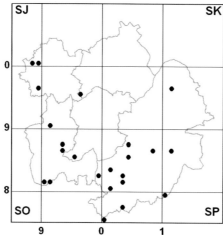

23. Neophyte. An early-flowering perennial herb, persisting in old gardens, churchyards, on rough grassy banks, waste places and woodland, usually as a garden outcast and often in the shade and on base- and nutrient-rich loamy soil. About 15 species of Pulmonaria are known and many cultivars are grown. Some records could be for these. Seldom far from habitation. Europe. Ass: Symphytum × uplandicum.

### Symphytum officinale L.
### Common Comfrey

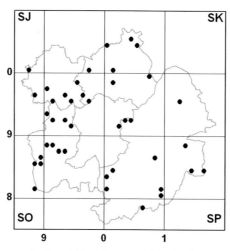

42. Native. A hispid perennial herb of banks of rivers and streams and also, but

less often, in rough, unmanaged places among tall herbs and grasses, in moist, fertile soils. Non-flowering plants of S. × uplandicum, which is much the commoner plant in the urban area are possibly sometimes erroneously recorded for this. Ass: Eupatorium cannabinum, Epilobium hirsutum, Rumex obtusifolius, Urtica dioica.

### Symphytum × uplandicum Nyman
(S. officinale × S. asperum Lepeche)
### Russian Comfrey

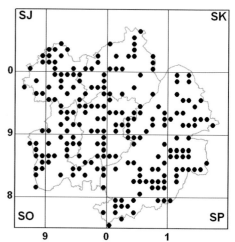

*221. Neophyte. In rather drier situations than S. officinale and far more frequently encountered. Roadsides, railway and canal banks, rough ground, neglected bits of land to the rear of gardens and around buildings and allotments, in open to lightly shaded places in moderately to very fertile, fairly base-rich, moist loamy soils. Caucasas. Ass: Anthriscus sylvestris, Geum urbanum, Heracleum sphondylium, Rumex obtusifolius, Urtica dioica.

### Symphytum tuberosum L.
### Tuberous Comfrey

3. Native; introduced in B&BC. A well established colony in bare, well-consolidated soil on bank near pool and a further colony between shrubs and roadside fence in the same area, Haden Hill Park (SO958851, also (probably nearby) in SO9685, CRP, 1995 & 2002); steep bank of abandoned railway line S of A4101 (SO9089, B. Marsh, 2008).

### Symphytum × hidcotense P.D. Sell
(S. grandiflorum × ?S × uplandicum)
### Hidcote Comfrey

2. Neophyte. First record in vc. 39 was eight plants from the N shaded side of a path at Wrekin Lane, Tettenhall (SJ869001, BRF, 1983). A hybrid consisting of two cultivars 'Hidcote Blue' and 'Hidcote Pink', our records are for 'Hidcote Blue'. A small patch on top of wooded bank, Elizabeth Grove, Oakham, Dudley (SO956893, MWP,

2006); large patch in overgrown shrubbery, Brades Road, Oldbury (SO9889, MWP, 2000).

### Symphytum grandiflorum DC.
### Creeping Comfrey

5. Neophyte. A creeping, rooting plant often grown in gardens as ground cover. The recent records are for plants that have spread from an original planting or as persistent garden throw-outs. Friends Meeting House, Selly Oak, not deliberately introduced (SP0482, AEEP, 1997); spreading in rough grass, Northfield (SP023797, AEEP, 1997); by garages, Rood End (SP004886, CBW, 1997); County Lane, Iverley (SO888815, JJD, 2002); B'ham Botanical Gardens (SP049850, MWP, 2008). NE Turkey, Georgia.

### Symphytum orientale L.
### White Comfrey

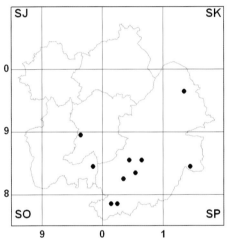

10. Neophyte. Garden outcast or possibly originally deliberately planted. Isolated plants or small patches in rough herbage and neglected fragments of ground near buildings, sometimes in quite sandy, dryish soils. Also tetrad SP09H. S Russia, Caucasus, NW Turkey. Ass: *Anthriscus sylvestris*, *Arrhenatherum elatius*, *Urtica dioica*.

### Brunnera macrophylla (Adams) I.M. Johnst.
### Great Forget-me-not

1. Neophyte. Perennial herb. Single large clump in rough grassland, N side of Bourne Brook, Woodgate Valley Country Park (SO996835, JJD, 2003). It was also recorded in 1991 as a casual in waste ground, rear access road to Combermere Arms, Chapel Ash, W'ton (SP905987, BRF). Caucasus, Georgia, NE Turkey.

### Anchusa officinalis L.
### Alkanet

3. Neophyte. Perennial herb. Sporadic garden escape. By the River Tame (SP157911, CW, 1996); edge of stream bank, between Fox Hill & Bristol Road (SP034815, AS, 1997);

Harborne Railway (SP0386, AS, 2000). Also three 1987 records from SO968864, SP061854 and SP079918. Europe.

### Anchusa azurea Mill.
### Garden Anchusa

1. Neophyte. Two patches among tall herbage on a post-housing site, Willenhall (SO955982, ICT, 2008). S Europe.

### Anchusa arvensis (L.) M. Bieb.
### (Lycopsis arvensis L.)
### Bugloss

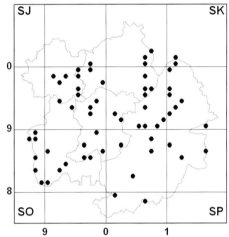

62. Archaeophyte. An annual weed of arable field margins, allotments and recently disturbed ground and occasionally on post-industrial sites. In sunny, well-drained soils of average to moderate fertility. Ass: *Arabidopsis thaliana*, *Capsella bursa-pastoris*, *Galium aparine*, *Raphanus raphanistrum*, *Reseda luteola*, *Urtica dioica*, *Viola arvensis*.

### Pentaglottis sempervirens (L.) Tausch ex L.H. Bailey
### Green Alkanet

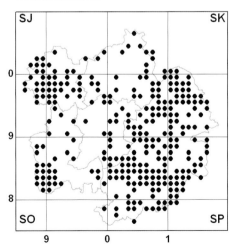

*294. Neophyte. An invasive, deep-rooted garden perennial, extremely difficult to eradicate once firmly established. Well-naturalised in rough ground, bits of waste ground to the rear of houses, path, track

▲ *Echium vulgare*

▲ *Pentaglottis sempervirens*

and road verges especially where they are backed by walls, fences or hedges, railway and canal banks and neglected, overgrown gardens, often in light shade. Usually close to habitation, preferring the moist, nutrient- and base-rich soils of residential areas and apparently less common in both the industrial areas of the Black Country and the countryside areas. SW Europe. Also tetrad SJ90V. Ass: *Arrhenatherum elatius, Artemisia vulgaris, Campanula trachelium, Geranium endressii, Rumex obtusifolius.*

### *Borago officinalis* L.
### Borage

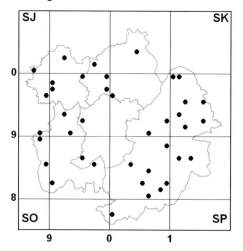

39. Neophyte. A frequently grown and occasionally self-seeding annual herb of allotment sites and gardens, in rich, fertile soil. Rarely persists for long in any one place but often has a semi-permanent scattered spontaneous population in allotment gardens. Grown for its young leaves and flowers which are used in salads and garnishes and possibly tolerated when self-sown. C & S Europe.

### *Amsinckia micrantha* Suksd.
### Common Fiddleneck
1. Neophyte. Annual of arable and light ground. Three plants on old steelworks site, Coombeswood (SO972851, JJD, 2000). W N America.

### *Myosotis scorpioides* L.
### Water Forget-me-not
*87. Native. A coloniser of shallow margins of pools, ditches and streams in fairly nutrient-and base-rich muds in open situations. Often among canal emergent vegetation growing through patches of *Typha latifolia, Sparganium erectum* and other emergent marginal vegetation, although clearly not a plant of densely urban areas. Ass: *Alisma lanceolatum, Berula erecta, Rorippa amphibia, Solanum*

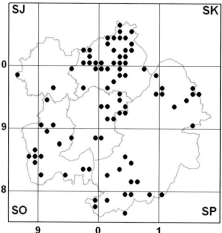

*dulcamara, Sparganium erectum, Veronica beccabunga.*

### *Myosotis secunda* Al. Murray
### Creeping Forget-me-not
1. Native. This erect to ascending annual or perennial is only known from small areas of poached, boggy ground and margins of acid, peaty streams draining into Little Bracebridge Pool, Sutton Park, where it is locally frequent (SP094982, MWP & ICT, 2005). Bagnall also recorded it in SP0997 and Cadbury *et al.* (1971) recorded it in SP1096.

### *Myosotis laxa* Lehm.
### subsp. *caespitosa* (Schultz) Hyl. ex Nordh.
### Tufted Forget-me-not

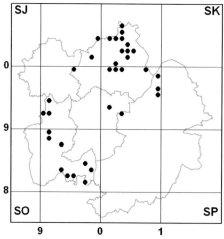

*35. Native. This annual or biennial is a plant of marshy pastures and margins of pools and ditches in similar habitats to *M. scorpioides* with which it is sometimes found, but it is not so tolerant of tall vegetation, or deep water or nutrient-rich substrates and is apparently rare in canals and from all B'ham sites except in Sutton Park. There is an old 1991 record from SP0379 (JJD) and a modern tetrad record for SO99A. Ass: *Agrostis stolonifera, Alopecurus geniculatus, Galium palustre, Ranunculus flammula.*

### *Myosotis sylvatica* Ehrh. ex Hoffm.
### Wood Forget-me-not

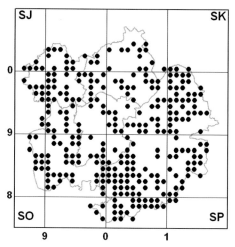

*312. Native, but usually or entirely introduced in B&BC. Spring-flowering biennial or short-lived perennial commonly grown in gardens and prolifically seeding into paths, paving, roadside banks, waste ground and woodland in open and shaded situations. Sometimes present in older bits of woodland but much commoner in secondary woodland and disturbed places generally. Ass: *Geranium robertianum, Geranium endressii, Geum urbanum, Poa trivialis.*

### *Myosotis arvensis* (L.) Hill
### Field Forget-me-not

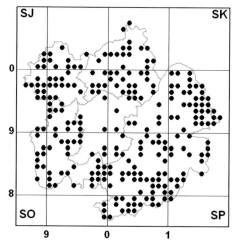

*253. Native. Field margins, cultivated and waste ground, gardens, paving and neglected patches of ground near to habitation in open, dry, usually only moderately nutrient- and base-rich soils. The marked scarcity in Sandwell and NE B'ham is difficult to explain. Ass: *Anagallis arvensis, Arabidopsis thaliana, Papaver rhoeas, Veronica persica, Viola arvensis.*

### *Myosotis ramosissima* Rochel
### Early Forget-me-not
6. Native. Winter annual, elsewhere

typically found in summer-droughted shallow soils associated with S-facing rock outcrops, but with a very small and probably essentially casual urban distribution in B&BC. Roadside bank, Sandwell Valley (SP045932, MWP, 1997); (SP1092, N. Walker, 1998); Saltwells (SO931871, J. Akers, 1999); pavement crack, Wordsley (SO892873, APD, 2002); Bushbury (SJ929032, JEH, 2004). Ass: *Cerastium glomeratum*, *Valerianella locusta*.

### *Myosotis discolor* Pers.
### Changing Forget-me-not
3. Native. A winter annual, but also found in disturbed ground, in sandy arable fields and even in slightly damp, but always open grassland sites. In B&BC apparently of only very infrequent casual occurrence. One plant in meadow to rear of Gospel End Sewage Works (SO902943, BH, 1999); plants in gravel triangle in private road, Sutton Coldfield (SP127982, MWP, ICT, JWP & JaH, 2006); single plant (**subsp. *dubia*** (Arrond.) Blaise) in long grass, off St Paul's Drive, Blackheath (SO978863, WAT, 2001).

### *Cynoglossum officinale* L.
### Hound's-tongue
1. Native. NT. This plant of dry stony or sandy places is known only from bare areas in the quarries at Barrow Hill (SO914896, P. Hancox & B. Jones, 1998, seen again up to 2010). In 2005 the Barrow Hill population was described as "about eighty plants on the S- and E-facing slopes of an old spoil-heap, W of the junction of tracks" (SO915895, MES & A.M. Pettigrew). In 2010 the population was much smaller. Its late appearance at this well-known site suggests a recent introduction.

### *Phacelia tanacetifolia* Benth.
### Phacelia
4. Neophyte. A constituent of bee and butterfly seed mixes and also sold as a green manure for allotments. Rarely appearing as a casual on spoil heaps and disturbed ground or persisting for a year or two after cultivation in allotments. Edgehill Road (SP100998, MWP, JWP & ICT, 2006); Sheepwash Urban Park (SO976920, MWP, ICT, JaH & SJC, 2007); Pereira Road Allotments (SP033853, ICT, 2008); Court Lane Allotments (SP105928, ICT, 2008). California.

### *Nonea lutea* (Desr.) DC.
### Yellow Nonea, Yellow Monkswort
1. Casual. An ultra-hardy, early spring-flowering annual, native to Russia where it overwinters beneath the snow and begins flowering as its covering recedes. A garden introduction by one of the authors and

self-seeding into crazy-paving to the rear of gardens a few metres away, Langley (SO999881, MWP, 2001, seen again 2002, 2003). Not seen since.

### *Cerinthe major* L.
### subsp. *purpurascens* (Boiss.) Selvi & Cecchi
### Greater Honeywort
1. Neophyte. Cultivated annual; in paving at edge of garden, Westwood Road (SP088954, MWP, JWP & JaH, 2006). Mediterranean.

## 108. CONVOLVULACEAE

### *Convolvulus arvensis* L.
### Field Bindweed

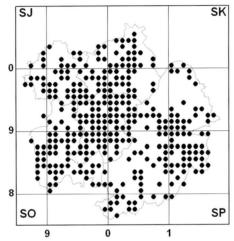

*344. Native. A common to locally abundant twining or climbing perennial herb of dryish, open situations in moderately fertile soils on banks, walls and rough ground. Particularly common along railway tracks and canal towpaths and a vigorous weed of cultivated ground on allotment sites and margins of arable land. Scarcer in much of suburban B'ham. Ass: *Anagallis arvensis*, *Lapsana communis*, *Persicaria maculosa*, *Viola arvensis*.

### *Calystegia sepium* (L.) R. Br.
### Hedge Bindweed

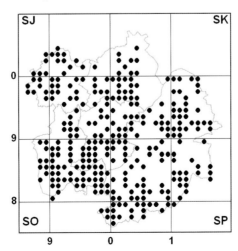

*296. Native. Twining through tall, herbaceous vegetation and shrubs, on banks, through hedges and up fences in open situations on moist, fertile soils. Especially abundant on overgrown abandoned cultivation sites but also a weed of cultivation. Similar habitats to *C. silvatica* but less frequent in the urban area. All records refer to **subsp. *sepium***. Ass: *Artemisia vulgaris*, *Calystegia silvatica*, *Rumex crispus*, *Rumex obtusifolius*, *Urtica dioica* and see list for *C. silvatica*.

**Forma *schizoflora*** (Druce) Stace has been recorded: one plant in roadside hedge near the railway bridge, the Crescent, Willenhall (SO975983, MWP, JaH & SJC, 2003).

### *Calystegia* × *lucana* (Ten.) G. Don
(*Calystegia sepium* × *C. silvatica*)

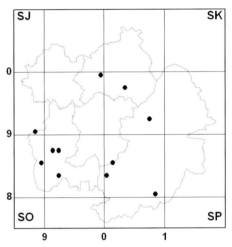

11. Native × neophyte. Occurs occasionally where *C. sepium* and *C. silvatica* grow together.

### *Calystegia pulchra* Brummitt & Heywood
### Hairy Bindweed

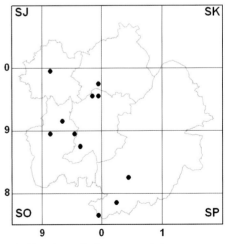

11. Neophyte. A vigorous, twining, herbaceous perennial occasionally forming dense patches in hedges, over fences and on banks in dryish, fertile soils. Of infrequent occurrence and generally not

far from habitation. Origin unknown. Ass: *Cornus* sp., *Hedera helix*, *Rubus fruticosus* agg., *Urtica dioica*.

### *Calystegia* × *howittiorum* Brummitt
(*C. pulchra* × *C. silvatica*)
2. Neophyte × neophyte. Two records from 2002. A well established colony twining through trees in the grounds of New Bradley Hall, Barnett Lane, Kingswinford (SO885883, APD, 2002); Wren's Nest Nature Reserve (SO9391, R. Labrenz, conf. R.K. Brummitt, 2002).

### *Calystegia silvatica* (Kit.) Griseb.
### Large Bindweed

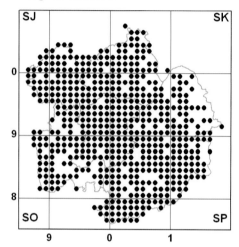

*561. Neophyte. A vigorous twining climber, rapidly dominating shrubberies, hedges, fences, railway, river and canal banks and waste ground in both open and semi-shaded situations on moderate to richly fertile soils. Much more aggressive and competitive than *C. sepium* and quick to colonise newly created habitats in the urban area. Also a pernicious weed in almost all cultivated allotment plots and in gardens. S Europe. Ass: *Elytrigia repens*, *Euphorbia peplus*, *Lapsana communis*, *Taraxacum* spp., *Veronica persica*, see also list for *Calystegia sepium*.

**Var. *quinquepartita*** N. Terracc. has been recorded: a single specimen growing with the regular flowered form (SP067895, MWP, 2005).

### *Cuscuta campestris* Yunck.
0. Neophyte. A rootless complete parasite. Only one old record as a casual with us: on *Pelargonium* and other species in the garden of Highfields School, W'ton (SO880963, CBW, det. J. M. Mullin, 1988).

## 109. SOLANACEAE

### *Lycium barbarum* L.
### Duke of Argyll's Teaplant
39. Neophyte. A suckering, deciduous, berry-producing, spiny shrub found

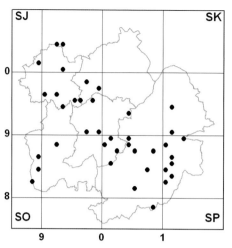

sporadically on banks, waste ground and in hedges, particularly in river and canal corridors. Some plants growing along fencelines may be planted but the possibility of spread through bird-defecation of seeds cannot be ruled out, despite production of the sweet-tasting fruit (believed by some authorities to be poisonous and by others to be the elixir of life) often being very low. China. Ass: *Corylus avellana*, *Crataegus monogyna*, *Fallopia japonica*, *Pteridium aquilinum*.

### *Lycium chinense* Mill.
### Chinese Teaplant
1. Neophyte. Neglected edge of factory yard, Tibbington (SO951936, JEH, 2007). China.

### *Atropa belladonna* L.
### Deadly Nightshade

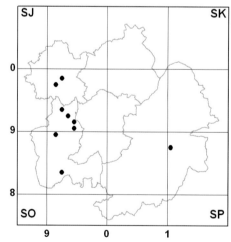

9. Native. Introduced in B&BC? Early records for this deadly poisonous plant are mainly from the Silurian limestone of Dudley Castle Hill and in broad-leaved woodland nearby. In the past occurring quite frequently and sometimes in quantity on the castle ruins but less so in recent years. Also long known in the nearby Wren's Nest National Nature Reserve where it has been seen recently along a shady woodland

path on Mons Hill (SO936925, ICT, EVJC, SJC, JaH & PLR, 2007). In the 1990s there were several plants on the spoily banks of a disused railway track at Horseley Fields, W'ton (SO9298) and on the quarry spoil of Barrow Hill, Pensnett (SO9189) although neither of these have been seen since 2000. Other sightings are in urban streets: a few plants growing through shrubs in the grounds of council buildings in Ednam Road, Dudley, a large plant at the side of the path near a railway footbridge, Ludlow Road, Washwood Heath, and in Marston Road, W'ton; also in an allotment in Wollescote, Dudley. Cadbury *et al.* (1971) remark that it was recorded by Ray from Sutton Coldfield in 1724 and they map it as frequent to abundant in SP08I (Smethwick).

### *Hyoscyamus niger* L.
### Henbane
0. Introduced native. VU. A few old records only. A few seen on towpaths near Wednesfield (SJ9501, FGB, 1975). A solitary plant on a post-housing site at the junction of Park Road and Berry Street Winson Green (SP0489, S. Hadley & A.D. Skelding, 1980), was discovered by a child who picked a flower to show her teacher at the school nearby. Attempts to germinate seed collected from the plant were unsuccessful. Waste ground, Regent Street, Old Hill, Rowley Regis (SO954866, BRF, 1989).

### *Nicandra physalodes* (L.) Gaertn
### Apple-of-Peru

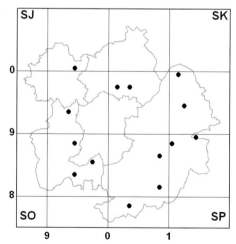

14. Casual. Often called 'Shoo-fly plant' by gardeners: reputed to repel flies. Frost-sensitive perennial occasionally grown and also spontaneous from bird-seed. The few recent records are from post-housing land and from allotment gardens where it may sometimes be seeding spontaneously. Peru. Ass: *Chenopodium album*, *Euphorbia peplus*, *Lamium purpureum*, *Persicaria maculosa*, *Poa annua*.

## *Datura stramonium* L.
## Thorn-apple

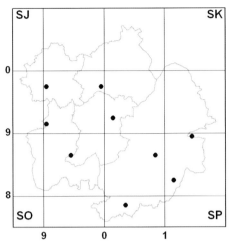

9. Neophyte. There are recent records from post-housing sites, allotments and spoil heaps. In the 1980s it occurred in great abundance for several hundred metres along the grass verges of the A4123 in Oldbury when road-widening was taking place. America. Ass: *Ambrosia artemisiifolia*, *Chenopodium polyspermum*.

## *Datura ferox* L.
## Longspine Thorn-apple

1. Neophyte. One confirmed record from a spoil heap on housing development land, Heathland Avenue, Buckland End (SP128943, JWP & MWP, 2007). E Asia.

## *Salpichroa origanifolia* (Lam.) Thell.
## Cock's-eggs

1. Neophyte. A few immature plants seeded into the paving below a nearby planted specimen, in terrace bed near Winterbourne House, Winterbourne Botanical Gardens, Edgbaston (SP0583, JWP & MWP, 2007). S America.

## *Physalis alkekengi* L.
## Japanese-lantern

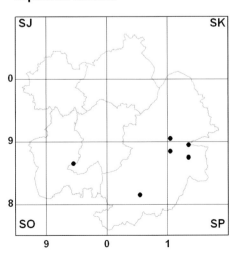

6. Neophyte. A few records for solitary individuals or small colonies of plants in rough, grassy fragments of waste ground left following housing demolition, or self-sown in overgrown and neglected garden borders and paving near to original plantings. Europe.

## *Physalis peruviana* L.
## Cape-gooseberry

1. Neophyte. Minworth Sewage Works. Frequent large flowering plants scattered over steep slopes of rubbly material tipped over the sewage beds (SP173917, ICT, JJB & SAHA, 2006). America.

## *Solanum nigrum* L.
## Black Nightshade

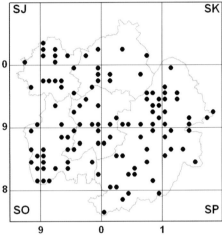

113. Native or alien. An annual of cultivated and recently disturbed soil in gardens, allotments and margins of arable land, waste ground, spoil heaps, land recovering from recent disturbance in open situations and fertile soils. Particularly frequent in allotments. Also tetrad SJ90V. Ass: *Aethusa cynapium*, *Chenopodium album*, *Lepidium didymum*, *Fallopia convolvulus*, *Poa annua*, *Polygonum aviculare*, *Trifolium dubium*, *Trifolium repens*, *Urtica dioica*, *Veronica arvensis*, *Viola arvensis*.

Some were recorded as, and probably all are, **subsp. *nigrum***, although there is a record of the neophyte **subsp. *schultesii*** (Opiz) Wessely as a casual, a single plant growing as a weed in a flower pot in a garden centre in Erdington (SP107920, JWP & MWP, 2006).

## *Solanum physalifolium* Rusby
## Green Nightshade

3. Neophyte. An annual of cultivated land, now increasing rapidly in UK. In southern periphery of B&BC, mainly in arable land. Abundant at one end of a beet field, Stourbridge (SO898815, APD, 2003); car park and surrounds, B'ham Great Park, Rubery (SO998779, JJD, 2005);

▲ *Lycium barbatum*

▲ *Atropa belladonna*

▲ *Nicandra physalodes*

field S of Quarry Park Road, Pedmore, in cereal stubble (SO9081, JJD, 2003); arable headland, Pedmore parish (SO902811, JJD, 2003). S America.

### Solanum dulcamara L.
### Bittersweet

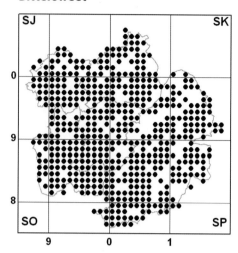

*533. Native. Typically in partially shaded situations on moist to wet, nutrient-rich and base-medium to -rich soils. Among the tall, unmanaged vegetation at the edge of pools, canals and river banks, in the scrub covering overgrown ponds and in Alder carr woodlands, but also on waste and disturbed ground in more open and much drier situations. Ass: they range from *Alnus glutinosa*, *Lycopus europaeus*, *Myosotis scorpioides*, *Phalaris arundinacea*, *Typha latifolia* to *Arrhenatherum elatius*, *Epilobium ciliatum*, *Rumex obtusifolius*, *Trifolium repens*, *Urtica dioica*.

### Solanum tuberosum L.
### Potato

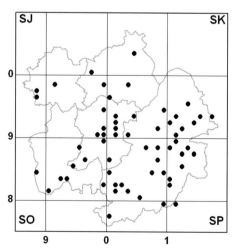

60. Neophyte. A frost-tender cultivated plant often occurring on spoil heaps, post-housing sites, gardens and allotments from discarded tubers or peelings; like Tomato, seems to be commoner in the E. S America. Ass: *Fumaria officinalis*,

*Raphanus raphanistrum*, *Tripleurospermum inodorum*.

### Solanum lycopersicum L.
(*Lycopersicon esculentum* Mill.)
### Tomato

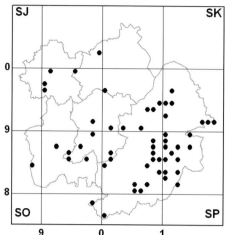

56. Neophyte. Disturbed land, spoil heaps, sewage works, paving and anywhere fruit has been discarded, apparently more commonly in the E. Young plants are frequent but few reach maturity. One enormous plant with abundant ripe fruit on heap of dumped soil on a post-industrial site near the centre of B'ham (SP080879, MWP, October 2003). C & S America. Ass: *Atriplex patula*, *Chenopodium album*, *Persicaria maculosa*, *Urtica urens*.

### Solanum rostratum Dunal
### Buffalo-bur
1. A casual from bird-seed. Post-housing site, Oddingley Road, West Heath (SP034786, JJD, 2006). Older records: building site, Ridgeacre Road Quinton (SP010847, LG, det. MWP, conf. A. Grenfell, 1989); disturbed ground, by the A4123, Rowley Regis (SO972900, MWP & LG, conf. S. Knapp, 1994). America.

### Solanum chacoense Bitter
### Chaco Potato, known locally as 'Jack Hawkes' Potato'
1. Neophyte. An invasive pest in the regularly cultivated herbaceous borders and at the base of hedges at B'ham University Botanic Garden, Winterbourne. A further small colony of seven plants beyond the perimeter fence in the playing fields of King Edward VI School for Girls, Edgbaston (SP052838, JWP & MWP, conf. S. Knapp, 2007 & 2008). The recorders considered that the colony had arisen by rhizomatous growth. It was growing with *Urtica dioica* and *Fallopia japonica*, partly shaded by an ornamental *Prunus* sp. It is a widespread and aggressive weed in S America, and was probably originally

cultivated in the Botanic Garden by Prof. J.G. Hawkes. Garden staff consider it ineradicable and had been aware of it as a weed for at least 10 years.

### Nicotiana sylvestris Speg. & Comes
### Argentine Tobacco
1. Casual. A colony of 20+ self-sown plants in a disused glasshouse border, B'ham University Botanical Gardens, Winterbourne, Edgbaston (SP0583, MWP & JWP, 2007). Argentina.

### Nicotiana × sanderae W. Watson
(*N. alata* Link & Otto × *N. forgetiana* Hemsl.)
### Flowering Tobacco

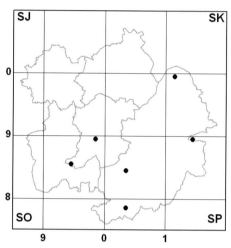

6. Neophyte. A frost-sensitive garden annual, very rarely self-seeding on dumped soil, post-housing land and waste ground but not persisting. S America.

### Petunia × hybrida P.L. Vilm.
(*P. axillaris* (Lam.) Britton, Stearns & Poggenb. × *P. integrifolia* (Hook.) Schinz & Thell.)
### Petunia

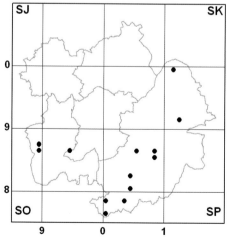

13. Casual. A frost-sensitive garden annual occasionally appearing as isolated plants on post-housing sites, waste ground and in garden borders, occurring in many different shades and colour forms

including bi-colours, often clearly self-set from seed. Garden origin. The trailing form grown in hanging baskets: cultivar 'Surfina', has also been recorded, presumed via vegetative propagation.

## 110. OLEACEAE

### Forsythia Vahl.
### Forsythias

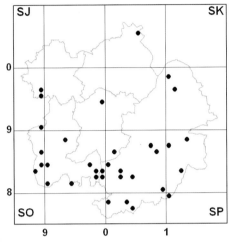

34. Neophytes. Deciduous, suckering shrubs, persisting where originally planted in overgrown shrubberies and post-housing sites. Many garden cultivars are grown and some records might be for *Forsythia suspensa* (Thunb.) Vahl., but almost all have been recorded as *Forsythia × intermedia* Zabel (*F. suspensa × F. viridissima* Lindl.). Despite the lack of recent records in the N, the first records for vc. 39 were on the canal opposite to towpath at W'ton, SO9399 and Wednesfield, SJ9400 (both FGB, 1975). Garden origin.

### Jasminum officinale L.
### Summer Jasmine
2. Neophyte. Scrambling shrub. Land off Broad Lane (SP068794, SAHA, 2005); probably bird-sown, bridleway, Penn (SO906965, CBW, 2007). Caucasus to China.

### Jasminum beesianum Forest & Diels
### Red Jasmine
1. Neophyte. Spreading patch from original planting on post-housing site, Dovedale Road, Perry Common (SP092933, MWP, 2006). China.

### Jasminum nudiflorum Lindl.
### Winter Jasmine
3. Neophyte. Persisting where planted B'ham and Fazeley Canal (SP153924, PS & M. Kodaka, 2003); Rectory Park (SP1296, SPG, 1998); two patches under *Ulmus × hollandica*, by road, Wordsley (SO899868, CBW, 2010). China.

### Fraxinus excelsior L.
### Ash
*668. Native. A timber tree, almost ubiquitous in woodland and hedgerows and often planted. In some years producing copious amounts of winged seed that readily germinate in paving cracks, unmanaged gardens, areas of waste ground, around neglected buildings and in woodlands. Favoured by moist, at least moderately fertile soils and one of the characteristic tree species of old woodland on base-rich soils. It is also the characteristic tree species in woodland on dry, impoverished limestone soils. A fast growing pioneer, quickly colonising to create pockets of urban woodland where waste ground is left undisturbed. 'Pendula' (Forma *pendula* (Ainton) Schelle, Weeping Ash) is occasionally planted as a specimen tree in parks and churchyards. Ass: *Acer pseudoplatanus, Buddleja davidii, Corylus avellana, Cotoneaster* spp., *Quercus robur, Salix caprea, Sambucus nigra,*.

### Fraxinus ornus L.
### Manna Ash
4. Neophyte. Deciduous tree. 4 recent records, all almost certainly persisting from original plantings: SJ9300; SO9099; SP0085; SP0682. S Europe and Asia Minor.

### Syringa vulgaris L.
### Lilac

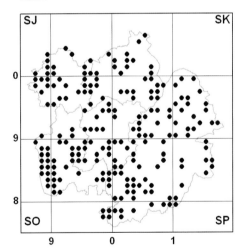

*211. Neophyte. A strongly suckering, deciduous shrub often persisting in old hedgerows and on post-housing and industrial sites from original plantings. Some small plants on waste ground are possibly self-sown. SE Europe.

### Ligustrum vulgare L.
### Wild Privet
*96. Native evergreen shrub, probably entirely introduced in B&BC. Most of the records are for persistent plantings in old neglected hedges and shrubberies where

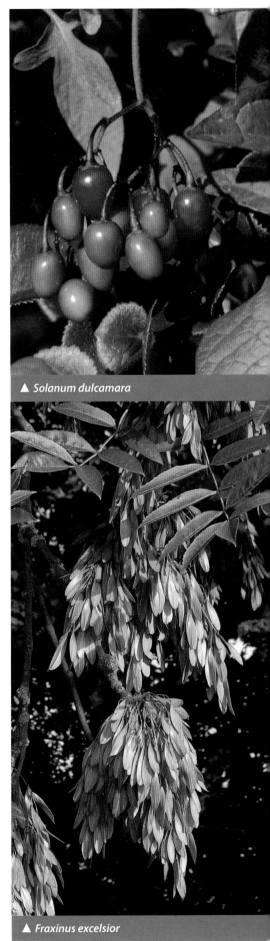

▲ Solanum dulcamara

▲ Fraxinus excelsior

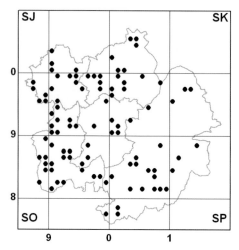

it is sometimes mixed in with, or used as an alternative to *L. ovalifolium*. Bird-sown plants may occur.

### *Ligustrum ovalifolium* Hassk.
**Garden Privet**

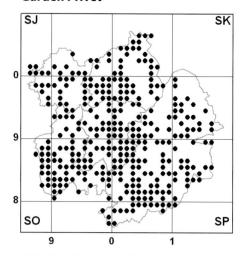

*333. Neophyte. A traditionally planted, semi-evergreen, hedging shrub, typically once bordering most urban gardens, but in recent years, much less often planted and regularly ripped-out to create car-parking space or replaced by quick-growing conifers or fencing panels. An occasional introduction in woodland or persistent remnant of an old garden boundary where, if left undisturbed, it forms dense thickets. Doubtfully spontaneous. Japan.

### 113. VERONICACEAE

### *Digitalis purpurea* L.
**Foxglove**

*495. Native, and also a garden escape. A biennial or short-lived rosette-forming perennial, found with other tall herbs and ferns in partially shaded or open situations on at least moderately acid soils of intermediate to low fertility. It requires patches of bare soil for successful establishment from its tiny seed but it is associated particularly

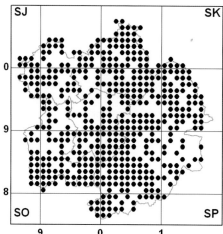

with disturbed rather than necessarily bare habitats. Typically it grows on steep banks where soil slip or periodic flooding create the required bare patches. Frequent to locally abundant on canal and railway, stream and river banks, rough grassland, spoil tips, woodland margins and clearings (where it can be abundant after tree felling), disturbed areas of heathland. Less frequent in neglected gardens and similar areas recovering from disturbance. The map may reflect some lack of base-poor situations in some of the areas where it is relatively infrequent. White-flowered plants often occur. Ass: *Chamerion angustifolium, Dryopteris dilatata, Holcus lanatus, Holcus mollis, Hyacinthoides non-scripta, Pteridium aquilinum, Teucrium scorodonia.*

### *Erinus alpinus* L.
**Fairy Foxglove**

1. Neophyte. Patches of this short-lived perennial are firmly established in brickwork mortar of the reception building at the entrance to B'ham University Botanical Gardens, Winterbourne, Edgbaston (SP0583, JWP & MWP, 2007). SW Europe.

### *Veronica officinalis* L.
**Heath Speedwell**

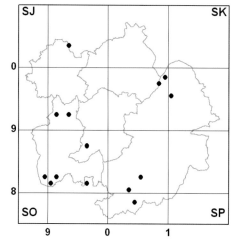

14. Native. Ax. A perennial, uncommon on well-drained, unimproved grassy banks and managed grassland in churchyards and roadside verges in open habitats on sandy and heathy soils. Very rarely recorded as a garden lawn weed and then likely to have been introduced with the turf. Also tetrads SO98E, SP09J. Ass: *Agrostis capillaris, Deschampsia flexuosa, Festuca ovina, Galium saxatile, Potentilla erecta, Potentilla sterilis, Rumex acetosella.*

### *Veronica montana* L.
**Wood Speedwell**

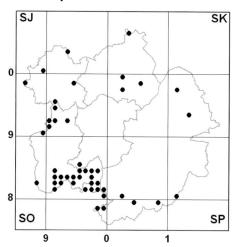

*47. Native. Ax. A plant of long-established, mixed deciduous woodland and shady, wooded stream banks on damp, mildly acid soils. Its low scrambling stems root readily to produce extensive clonal patches and stem fragments can be carried along streams, but seed production is only very modest and dispersal is poor, so it does not otherwise colonise new habitats readily. Frequent in dingles and other remnants of old woodland in rural parts of the conurbation, especially in the S & W, absent from much of the built-up areas where suitable locations are also largely absent. Confined to unimproved habitats and seldom, if ever, occurring as a weed unlike many speedwells. The record from SO9498 is a deliberate introduction in a habitat creation scheme. Ass: *Chrysosplenium oppositifolium, Circaea lutetiana, Mercurialis perennis, Oxalis acetosella, Viola reichenbachiana.*

### *Veronica scutellata* L.
**Marsh Speedwell**

5. Native. Ax. Perennial herb, very uncommon in B&BC and still being lost. In good quantity by a field pond in unimproved marshy pasture, Lower Illey Meadows (SO977811, WAT, 1988) and was still there in 1997; the record of a few plants in a marsh, Woodgate Valley, last recorded in 1994 (SO998834, RM) may still hold good;

it is still just present at Turner's Pool, W'ton (SO877982, SRP, 1995, last seen 2011). It has been recorded in three squares in Sutton Park in the past (SP0997; SP0998; SP1096, Readett, 1971) but was not seen there in the present survey. There are however three extant records in Walsall: on the edge of a lake, and in ditches and bare patches in pasture, Clayhanger (SK035046, ICT & EVJC, 2006); Friar Pool, Pelsall Common (SK021045, ICT & N. Musgrove, 2008) and it has also appeared in the edge of a new lake on Blackcock Farm (SK042034, ICT & AB, 2006). Ass: *Juncus articulatus, Lythrum portula, Myosotis laxa, Ranunculus flammula*.

### *Veronica beccabunga* L.
### Brooklime

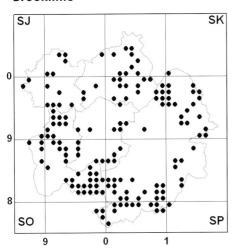

*158. Native. Ax. A quite frequently occurring perennial herb, found in margins and shallows of ditches, pools, streams and marshy hollows in meadows, in all but the most infertile soils, typically in open situations but tolerant of light to moderate shade. The map suggests that it is largely confined to the countryside areas of B&BC and most of the records are from old sites. Ass: *Agrostis stolonifera, Apium nodiflorum, Glyceria fluitans, Ranunculus flammula, Nasturtium officinale*.

### *Veronica anagallis-aquatica* L.
### Blue Water-speedwell

2. Native. Rarely recorded in B&BC, and possibly confused with *V. catenata* or *V. anagallis-aquatica* × *V. catenata*. Brick Kiln, Clayhanger (SK042037, L. Wilson, 2004); Clayhanger SSSI (SK035045, ICT, 2008); There is an old record for Sutton Park (SP0997, S. Freeman, 1841).

### *Veronica catenata* Pennell
### Pink Water-speedwell

7. Native. Ax. A generally scarce but locally frequent short-lived perennial. Long-established at some sites but an early colonist at others. Well established in

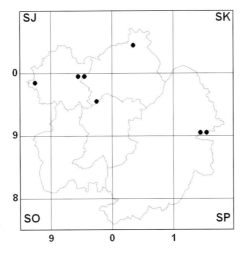

the margins and spreading into deeper, clear water, in Moxley Pool, Darlaston; locally common to abundant in the shallows of recently created pools and ditches, Bowmans Harbour, but now lost from Turner's Pool, W'ton (SO877982, SRP, 1995); occasional in bed of dried up pool, Clayhanger; large patches around pool margins in Park Hall Nature Reserve, Castle Bromwich. Ass: *Agrostis stolonifera, Eleocharis palustris, Juncus articulatus, Lycopus europaeus, Myosotis laxa*.

### *Veronica serpyllifolia* L.
### Thyme-leaved Speedwell

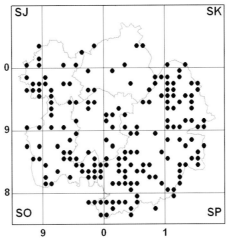

183. Native. A creeping, low-growing perennial herb, frequent in paths, roadside grass verges, waste ground and also a weed in lawns and borders in fairly dry to moist sunny and slightly shaded situations in soils of intermediate fertility and base status. Our plant is **subsp. serpyllifolia**. Ass: *Bellis perennis, Cerastium fontanum, Crepis capillaris, Poa annua, Ranunculus bulbosus, Ranunculus repens, Taraxacum* spp., *Trifolium dubium*.

### *Veronica longifolia* L.
### Garden Speedwell

7. Neophyte. Persisting from original

▲ *Digitalis purpurea*

▲ *Veronica montana*

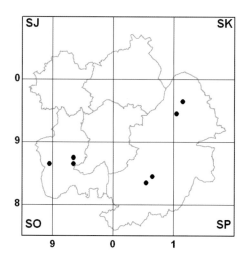

planting on post-housing land or as a pavement weed or garden discard in a few places. First record for vc. 39 was on a canal bank at New Cross (SO935997, BRF, 1974). N & C Europe.

### *V. longifolia* × *V. spicata*

1. Neophyte × native. This hybrid was recorded from Bromwich Wood (SO998811, J. Parsons, L. Hamill & S. Needle, 2007).

### Veronica spicata L.
### Spiked Speedwell

1. Native; introduced in B&BC. Sch. 8, Nationally Scarce. One spreading patch persisting from original planting in rough grassland on post-housing site, Dovedale Road, Perry Common (SP099934, MWP & JWP, 2006).

### Veronica hederifolia L.
### Ivy-leaved Speedwell

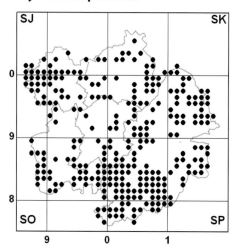

*294. Archaeophyte. A rapidly maturing, spring- and early summer-flowering annual of bare and disturbed ground, gardens, paving, hedge borders, spoil heaps and arable land in nutrient-rich soils in sun and partial shade. Undoubtedly under-recorded in the present survey due to its earliness in maturing and

virtual disappearance from early summer onwards. Ass: *Arabidopsis thaliana*, *Geranium robertianum*, *Lamium purpureum*, *Poa annua*, *Senecio vulgaris*, *Stellaria media*.

The two subspecies have not been consistently distinguished but both **subsp. hederifolia** and **subsp. lucorum** (Klett & Richt.) Hartl have been recorded throughout. Subsp. *lucorum*, which apparently tolerates shade better, was recorded twice as often as subsp. *hederifolia*.

### Veronica crista-galli Steven
### Crested Field-speedwell

2 Neophyte, casual in B&BC. Recorded from an extensive re-seeded landfill site at Queslett (SP065943, SB, 2002); weed in an undug plot, Jeffcock Road Allotments, Bradmore (SO99D, CBW, 1999). Also an early record in the grass of an abandoned school garden, Highfields School, W'ton (SO880963, CBW & S. O'Donnell, 1992). Caucasus.

### Veronica filiformis Sm.
### Slender Speedwell

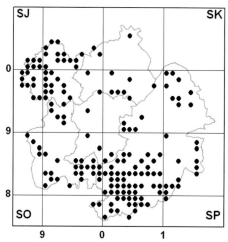

*172. Neophyte. A low-growing perennial herb increasing in grassy banks and verges, garden lawns and amenity grassland in sunny, moisture-retaining soils. Readily colonising areas of managed grassland in which it spreads by fragmentation of the vegetative shoots transferred on the blades of mowing machines. Often creating a blue haze throughout the sward in early summer between grass cuts. Its high frequency in W'ton and S B'ham is difficult to explain. Also recorded from tetrad SO98E. Turkey and Caucasus. Ass: *Achillea millefolium*, *Agrostis capillaris*, *Bellis perennis*, *Lolium perenne*, *Ranunculus repens*.

### Veronica agrestis L.
### Green Field-speedwell

176. Archaeophyte. Along with *V. persica* this rapidly maturing annual was recorded from almost every one of the allotment

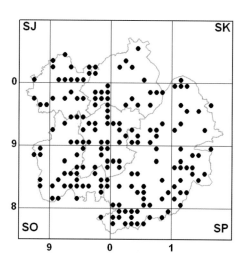

gardens surveyed during 2008 and in many it was recorded as being common to locally abundant. It also occurs in other areas of disturbance such as garden borders and soil heaps and less so as an opportunist annual in road verges and pavement cracks. Prefers rich, fertile soil. Also tetrads SK00A, SO98E. Ass: *Chenopodium album*, *Lamium amplexicaule*, *Lamium purpureum*, *Solanum nigrum*, *Veronica persica*.

### Veronica polita Fr.
### Grey Field-speedwell

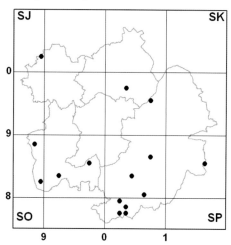

15. Native. Ax. This annual was recorded only very infrequently in the survey and seems to be very scarce in B&BC compared with *V. agrestis*. Isolated records from disturbed or cultivated ground: paths, gardens, allotments, around buildings etc. in open, sunny, well-drained fertile soils.

### Veronica persica Poir.
### Common Field-speedwell

*373. Neophyte. A very common, rapidly maturing weed of disturbance, in open, dry to moist, fertile soils in gardens, allotments, roadsides, field margins and paving. SW Asia. Ass: *Chenopodium album*, *Euphorbia helioscopia*, *Euphorbia peplus*, *Lamium*

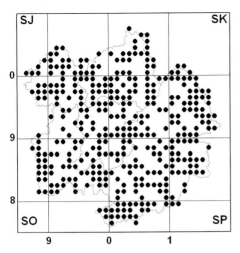

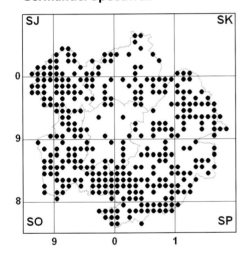

amplexicaule, *Lamium purpureum, Solanum nigrum, Veronica agrestis, Polygonum aviculare.*

### *Veronica chamaedrys* L.
### Germander Speedwell

*354. Native. A common perennial herb of hedgebanks, roadside verges, waste ground and woodland margins and also a frequent weed in managed grassland and garden lawns on dry to slightly moist, moderately fertile soils. There is some sign of it being less common in the central areas of Sandwell, and also in the more base-poor soils of N Walsall. Ass: *Agrostis capillaris, Bellis perennis, Festuca rubra, Lotus corniculatus, Prunella vulgaris, Trifolium repens.*

### *Veronica arvensis* L.
### Wall Speedwell

*371. Native. Sunny, open, well-drained, often drought-liable situations in moderately base-poor to base-rich, rather infertile soils in bare areas on road verges, banks, gardens and waste ground. A common pavement weed. Apparently scarcer in Walsall. More commonly recorded than in the 1970s Floras. Ass: *Aphanes arvensis, Arabidopsis thaliana,*

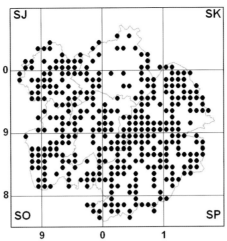

*Erophila* sp., *Sagina apetala, Trifolium dubium.*

### *Veronica salicifolia* G. Forst.
(*Hebe salicifolia* (G. Forst.) Pennell)
### Koromico
2. Neophyte. Shrub. Garden relic or discard. Ridgacre, by a brook (SP006844, CBW, 1997); recreation grounds, Shenley Fields (SP016805, CBW, 1997). New Zealand and Chile.

### *Veronica × franciscana* Eastw.
(*Hebe × franciscana* (Eastw.) Souster, *V. elliptica* G. Forst. × *V. speciosa* R. Cunn. ex A. Cunn.)
### Hedge Veronica
5. Neophyte. Shrub. Mostly small self-sown plants on and at the base of walls from nearby garden plantings, and usually with a N exposure. There are records from SO9883, SP0084, SP0086, SP0681 and SP0895. Cultivar 'Blue Gem' (Kingstanding Road, SP080953, MWP, JWP & JaH, 2006) is used for hedging usually in maritime situations. Wind and salt tolerant. Hardy to -10 Celsius. Garden origin.

### *Veronica brachysiphon* (Summerh.) Bean.
(*Hebe brachysiphon* Summerh.)
### Hooker's Hebe
1. Neophyte. Shrub. One mature plant on quarry slope, Rowley Hills 1999, still there 2011 (SO9789, MWP, LG). New Zealand.

### *Veronica dieffenbachii* Benth.
(*Hebe dieffenbachii* (Benth.) Cockayne & Allan)
### Dieffenbach's Hebe
3. Neophyte. Relic of cultivation. Derelict shrubbery, Warley Park (SP010862, CBW, 1996); hedge, by canal near Dunstall Park (SJ908007, JEH, 2004); Four Oaks Road, Sutton Coldfield (SP112989, MWP & ICT, conf. EJC, 2006). Chatham Island.

### *Antirrhinum majus* L.
### Snapdragon
144. Neophyte. A short-lived perennial

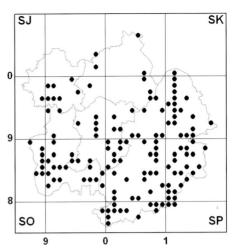

herb regularly cultivated in gardens and discarded after flowering. Readily seeding onto and along the base of garden walls, onto paths and in paving cracks. Sporadically appearing on post-housing sites and land recovering from recent disturbance but seldom found too far from habitation. A wide range of colour forms are known. Ass: *Campanula persicifolia, Cerastium tomentosum, Epilobium montanum, Hordeum murinum, Sedum rupestre, Taraxacum* spp., *Trifolium repens.*

### *Chaenorhinum minus* (L.) Lange
### Small Toadflax

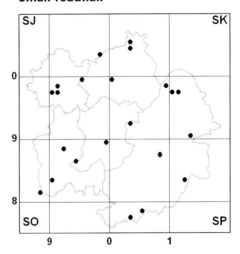

22. Archaeophyte. Ax. This annual is an infrequent coloniser of open, dry, water-stressed places on base- and nutrient-rich substrates, showing a distinct preference for anthropogenically created substrates such as compacted clinker and ash and often occurring in temporary car parks, derelict railway sidings and ground near electricity sub-stations, where it is probably encouraged by intermittent treatment of stone mulches with herbicides. Ass: *Agrostis stolonifera, Atriplex patula, Sisymbrium officinale, Sonchus oleraceus.*

▲ *Misopates orontium*

▲ *Linaria vulgaris*

*Misopates orontium* (by Anne Bebbington)

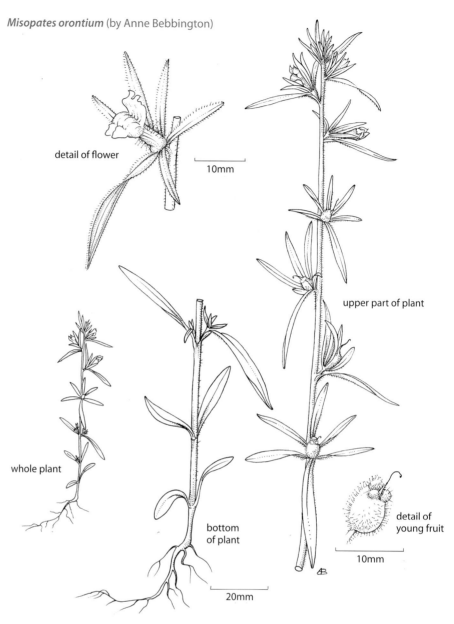

detail of flower

10mm

upper part of plant

whole plant

bottom of plant

detail of young fruit

10mm

20mm

### *Misopates orontium* (L.) Raf.
### Weasel's-snout

4. Archaeophyte. VU. At least 50 plants distributed in three allotment garden plots, Spring Meadow, Old Hill (SO957861, MWP, 2008); a single plant which appeared on banks of Moorcroft Pool after extreme draw-down in 2011 (SO9795, MWP). Also a persistent weed of cultivation after being originally deliberately introduced at two sites: a garden at Langley, Oldbury (SO999881, MWP, 1998 & 2003) and an allotment at Windsor Rd, Penn (SO892967, ICT, 1999 & 2011).

### *Cymbalaria muralis* P. Gaertn., B. Mey. & Scherb.
### Ivy-leaved Toadflax

*102. Neophyte. A trailing, herbaceous perennial, well-established in cracks of old walls and in the brickwork of canal, road and railway bridges and also on blast furnace slag in open to partially shaded situations.

More rarely, it becomes established in mortar joints along the edge of canal towpaths. Becoming rare outside the urban area and usually found not too far from habitation. Also tetrad SO88Z. C S Europe.

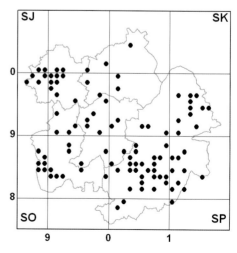

Ass: *Asplenium ruta-muraria, Centranthus ruber, Sedum acre, Senecio jacobaea.*

All are thought to be **subsp. *muralis***. A white-flowered form occurs.

## *Cymbalaria pallida* (Ten.) Wettst.
### Italian Toadflax

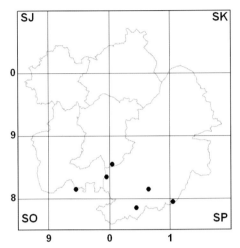

6. Neophyte. This trailing herbaceous perennial, larger in all parts than *C. muralis*, is only rarely encountered. The few records we have are for well-established and spreading patches on the pavement side of garden walls and are likely to have spread from cultivation nearby. Italy.

## *Linaria vulgaris* Mill.
### Common Toadflax

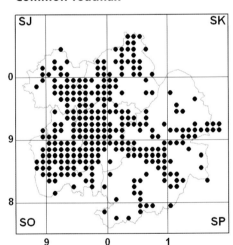

*304. Native. Perennial herb of rough grassy places, post-industrial land, walls, quarries, spoil heaps, canal banks, railways tracks, in sunny, open, well-drained aspects. Our records suggest this species favours the artificially created sites and soils typically associated with the Black Country and is generally regarded as a good 'Black Country Plant'. Although often recorded in B'ham squares it is much scarcer and tends to be transient or restricted to railway corridors. Ass: *Artemisia absinthium, Artemisia vulgaris, Festuca rubra, Hypericum*

*perforatum, Leucanthemum vulgare, Senecio squalidus, Silene vulgaris.*

## *Linaria × sepium* G.J. Allman
(*L. vulgaris × L. repens*)

4. Native × alien. Hybrid swarms occur predominately along railway tracks, both derelict and live, where *L. repens* and *L. vulgaris* occur together. Large colonies recorded from Langley Loop, Oldbury (SO994888, BRF & MWP, 1988, seen again 1998 and 2004); derelict railway trackbed, Cinder Bank, Dudley (SO941894, MWP, 2003); grassy slope, Turner's Hill (SO963881, ST, 1998); A47 Heartland Parkway (SP109896, MWP, ICT, JWP & PLR, 2006).

## *Linaria purpurea* (L.) Mill.
### Purple Toadflax

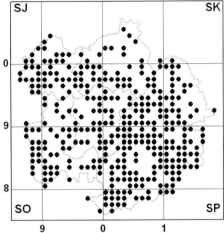

*355. Neophyte. A perennial herb of garden origin that has become thoroughly naturalised in residential areas, and to a degree in industrial areas, in open, dry situations on waste ground, roadsides, gardens, railway and canal banks, walls and paving. Pink-flowered plants sometimes occur (cultivar 'Cannon').

## *Linaria × dominii* Druce
(*L. purpurea × L. repens*)

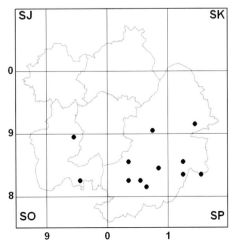

12. Alien × native. A few records of this variable hybrid occur in railway ballast where *Linaria purpurea* and *L. repens* grow together, but there are also records from around gardens and allotments in residential areas, where it sometimes appears to be tolerated and treated as a garden plant.

## *Linaria repens* (L.) Mill.
### Pale Toadflax

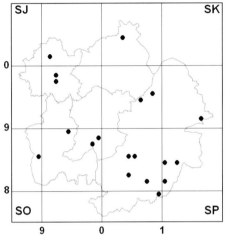

19. Archaeophyte. Found in a range of sharply drained, artificially created substrates including brick mortar, ballast, cinder and industrial spoil on walls and waste ground in sunny, open situations. Particularly associated with railway corridors and often forming colonies in disused railway-track beds and sidings. Ass: *Epilobium ciliatum, Linaria vulgaris, Sagina apetala sensu lato, Senecio viscosus, Vulpia myuros.*

## *Linaria maroccana* Hook. f.
### Annual Toadflax

1. Casual. One record from a disused railway track, Pelsall (SK025033, MWP, JaH & SJC, 2004). Morocco.

### 114. PLANTAGINACEAE

## *Plantago coronopus* L.
### Buck's-horn Plantain

97. Native; largely naturalised in B&BC. A colonist of dry, open, well-trodden salt-rich situations. Very common to abundant in the salt-splash zone of many of the major roads throughout the conurbation, where it colonises the short, regularly mown strip along central reservations and bare, compacted soil along the road-edges and can become abundant or even dominant. It is now commoner than is suggested by the map in the Black Country, which was mostly surveyed in the early years of the project. There are also a few records (e.g. in Sutton Park, where it was first recorded in 1859 on gravel paths) representing an

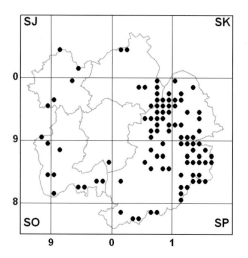

earlier heathland presence not connected with road salting. Ass: *Agrostis stolonifera, Atriplex patula, Cochlearia danica, Geranium pusillum, Lolium perenne, Plantago major, Poa annua, Polygonum aviculare, Scorzoneroides autumnalis, Trifolium dubium.*

## *Plantago major* L.
### Greater Plantain
*703. Native. Perennial. Compacted and heavily trampled soils along paths, on grass verges and lawns. Very common in nutrient-rich, improved grassland and on land recovering from recent disturbance. Avoiding only the most acid of soils. Ass: *Agrostis stolonifera, Bellis perennis, Poa annua, Polygonum aviculare.*

Generally the subspecies have not been distinguished, and most records are thought to be of **subsp. major**, although the smaller **subsp. intermedia** (Gilib) Lange., associated with damper situations, has been recorded from Burbury Brickworks (SP099836, JJD, 2004) and from Oddingley Road, West Heath (SP034786, JJD, 2006).

## *Plantago media* L.
### Hoary Plantain

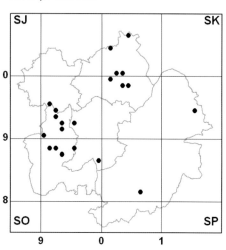

21. Native. Ax. In a few places in moderately short, well-drained limestone grassland in sunny, open aspects where it sometimes forms substantial colonies. Also, rarely, as a weed in managed lawns where it is likely to have been introduced with the original turf, its prostrate rosette of leaves avoiding the mower blades, although seldom flowering in such situations. Ass: *Briza media, Carex flacca, Cynosurus cristatus, Festuca ovina, Leontodon hispidus, Linum catharticum, Trifolium pratense, Trifolium repens.*

## *Plantago lanceolata* L.
### Ribwort Pantain
*705. Native. Widespread and extremely common perennial in all types of managed grassland where it is tolerant of mowing and trampling. Also found on banks, waste ground, paving and many other situations, avoiding only dense shade, permanently waterlogged soils and the most acid soils. Ass: *Agrostis capillaris, Centaurea nigra, Festuca rubra, Hypochaeris radicata, Scorzoneroides autumnalis, Poa trivialis, Taraxacum* spp., *Trifolium repens.*

## *Littorella uniflora* (L.) Asch.
### Shoreweed
0. Native. This perennial herb of the margins of nutrient- and base-poor lakes is rare and probably retreating in the lowland Midlands and was not encountered in the survey. There are old Sutton Park records for Bracebridge Pool (SP0998) seen as recently as 1934 (Cadbury *et al.*, 1971) and SP0997 (Bagnall, 1889).

## 115. HIPPURIDACEAE

## *Hippuris vulgaris* L.
### Mare's-tail

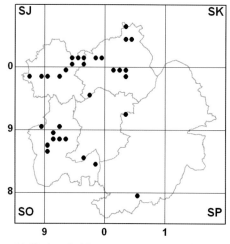

32. Native. A rhizomatous perennnial aquatic herb of local occurrence in the Black Country (rare in B'ham) submerged

in shallow to relatively deep water of pools and canals in nutrient-rich, open or partially shaded situations. Much more rigid, erect shoots emerge from the surface in early summer, sometimes forming substantial colonies. The distribution could represent a number of distinct populations. It often appears to be associated with coarse fishing. Ass: *Elodea nuttallii, Nuphar lutea, Persicaria amphibia, Potamogeton pectinatus, Ranunculus aquatilis, Zannichellia palustris.*

## 116. CALLITRICHACEAE

## *Callitriche* spp.

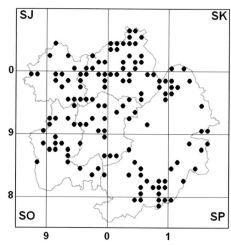

138. Native. These plants of still or slowly moving water, most also having terrestrial forms on mud, have been widely recorded in the conurbation but often cannot be identified to species in the absence of fruits.

## *Callitriche hermaphroditica* L.
### Autumnal Water-starwort
1. Native. The only record for this submerged aquatic plant of clear but base-rich and fairly nutrient-rich waters is from SW corner of Longmoor Pool, Sutton Park (SP0995, JWP, J.C. Bowra & P.J. Copson, 1990). It was seen there again in the same pool in 2006 by JWP.

## *Callitriche stagnalis* Scop.
### Common Water-starwort
*84. Native. By far the commonest species, usually recorded in very shallow base- and nutrient-rich water around the edges of lakes, ponds, canals and slow reaches of streams and rivers, on mud by water and in relatively ephemeral puddles and wheel-ruts in woodland and other shaded places. Much less common in deeper water, and some of our records from deeper water are probably non-flowering plants of other species. Also tetrad SO99A. Ass: *Agrostis stolonifera,*

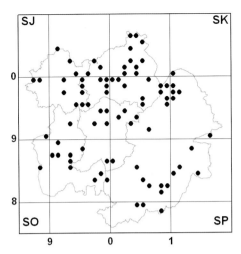

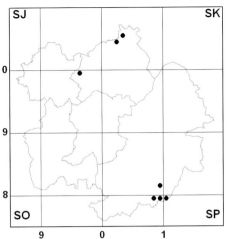

*Alopecurus geniculatus, Apium nodiflorum, Eleocharis palustris, Juncus effusus, Lemna minor.*

### *Callitriche platycarpa* Kütz.
### Various-leaved Water-starwort
3. Native. Reliably recorded from deep water in subsidence pools on blast furnace slag at Moxley Hospital (SO971952, MWP, 2001), from Fens canal feeder pools by Round Oak steelworks (SO913883, JEH, 2004) and from the Wyrley and Essington canal at Wednesfield (SJ944002, JEH, 2004). Said by Lansdown (2008) to be a plant of base-rich waters. Probably under-recorded. Bagnall, also Readett (1971), recorded it from several squares in Sutton Park and there are 1970s records from Merecroft Pool (SP0478) and Rough Wood (SJ9800). Also a modern tetrad record from SK00A.

### *Callitriche obtusangula* Le Gall
### Blunt-fruited Water-Starwort
2. Native. A species characteristic of base-rich waters. Plentiful in Billesley Common brook (SP085805, JWP & J.C. Bowra, 1995); ponds in stream descending into the Dingle, Cotwall End (SO915923, ICT & AMG, 2000). Readett (1971) and Bagnall in the 19th century both recorded it in Sutton Park.

### *Callitriche brutia* Petagna
### subsp. *brutia*
### Pedunculate Water-starwort
0. Native. Only one old record: from Sutton Park (SP0998, Cadbury *et al.* 1971).

### *Callitriche brutia* Petagna
### subsp. *hamulata* (Kütz. ex W.D.J. Koch)
### 0. Bolòs & Vigo
### Intermediate Water-starwort
7. Native. According to Lansdown (2008), this is a plant found in a wide range of water bodies, but especially in permanent, more oligotrophic or acid water. A few

scattered records in small ponds, pools and ditches, some associated with coal spoil, and with old records in Sutton Park.

## 117. SCROPHULARIACEAE

### *Verbascum blattaria* L.
### Moth Mullein
4. Neophyte. Casual. Annual to biennial. Eight plants on waste ground, by the canal, Hay Mills industrial area (SP105846, CBW, 1998); one plant near Boldmere entrance to Sutton Park (SP105956, MWP, 1997); introduced with garden compost at Jeffcock Road Allotments, W'ton (SO900973, CBW, 2008); bank by car park, Servosteel, Dudley (SO921891, BL, 2011). Europe.

### *Verbascum virgatum* Stokes
### Twiggy Mullein
3. Native; introduced in B&BC? Nationally Scarce. Tall biennial herb. A small colony of no more than a dozen plants growing with *Verbascum thapsus* in the sparsely vegetated, W-facing bank of the artificially created North Island in Forge Mill Lake, Sandwell Valley (SP031928, MWP, 2004). In 1990 a solitary plant was recorded from the pathside vegetation near the R Tame to the SE of this site (J. Little, det. V. Johnstone) and the more recently discovered colony could have resulted from its copious long-lived seed. There are also unconfirmed reports from pathsides, after resurfacing, in Walsall woods at the Dingle (SP047982, DH, 1998) and Hay Head (SP044990, DH, 1998); the plants did not reappear. Also an old record from the grounds of Woodbrooke (SP036814, T. Thompson, 1985).

### *Verbascum bombyciferum* Boiss.
### Broussa Mullein
1. Casual. One plant on a small patch of rough ground, Castle Vale (SP149914, JWP & MWP, 2007). Turkey.

### *Verbascum phlomoides* L.
### Orange Mullein
0. Casual. One old record: waste ground, West Bromwich (SP009913, BRF & MWP, 1991). Europe.

### *Verbascum densiflorum* Bertol.
### Dense-flowered Mullein
4. Casual. Beside approach road, RSPB Sandwell Valley (SP035927, MWP, 1996 & 2002, also SP036928, 1997); Canal bank, Tipton Road, Dudley Port (SO969910, MWP, 1997); a weed in an ornamental flower tub, W'ton Railway Station (SO919989, CBW, 2001); near road, base of reclaimed quarry mound, Darby Hill (SO969895, JEH, 2007).

### *Verbascum thapsus* L.
### Great Mullein

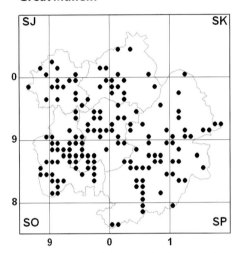

*154. Native. A tall biennial herb of rough grassy places, waste ground, spoil heaps, railway sidings and disused tracks, quarries, canal and railway banks, overgrown gardens and ground recovering from recent disturbance. Prefers open, dry, well-drained situations on soils of intermediate fertility, avoiding only the most acid. Often grown or tolerated in gardens and producing copious, very small, long-lived seed. SW Europe. Ass: *Chamerion angustifolium, Daucus carota, Hypericum perforatum, Reseda luteola, Sagina apetala sensu lato, Silene vulgaris*.

### *Verbascum nigrum* L.
### Dark Mullein
3. Introduced native. Speedwell Road, Hay Mills (SP114848, CBW, 1998); Sandwell Valley (SP0192, MWP, 2001); the Ackers, Small Heath, B'ham (SP104846, SAHA, 2005). It also appeared in a clearing in Upper Nuthurst, Sutton Park (SP1097, C. Podmore, det. HHF, 1993).

### *Verbascum speciosum* Schrad.
### Hungarian Mullein
2. Neophyte. Known for some years from

a mixed shrub/perennial bed near the road island at the junction of Watery Lane Middleway/Coventry Road Island (SP085861, MWP, 1997), where it was undoubtedly originally introduced but has gone on to produce new plants; also a small colony on overgrown bank on an area of post-industrial land off Bankfield Road, Bradley (SO952959, MWP, det. V. Johnstone, 2004). SE Europe.

### Verbascum pulverulentum Vill.
### Hoary Mullein
0. Native or alien. Nationally Scarce as a native. Only known as growing from a wild flower seed mix at Saltwells LNR, Dudley (SO931871, BRF, 1994).

### Verbascum lychnitis L.
### White Mullein
4. Native/Introduced native. Nationally Scarce as a native. Reported from waste land in W'ton in 1981 (SO9198, P. Hodgson) but all recent records are confined to an area around Barrow Hill, Fens Pools and Buckpool Nature Reserve, Dudley. One plant in railway bridge brickwork and another nearby in ballast at the junction of Stourbridge Canal and the old freight line (SO908877, M. Richardson, 1995, seen again 2010); S-facing slope of spoil heap, Barrow Hill (SO915895, B. Marsh & N. Williams, 2003, also seen in 2005 and at SO914896 by CBW in 2006); by disused railway near Fens Pool (SO918885, SO922888 & SO922886, JEH, 2004, seen again 2010); in a grassy clearing on the edge of secondary woodland NE of Fens Pool (SO923887, MWP, ICT & A. Armstrong, 2008).

### Scrophularia nodosa L.
### Common Figwort

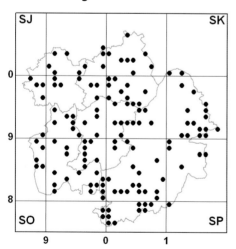

*141. Native. A perennial herb of damp woodland rides and clearings, stream banks, canal road and railway embankments often among tall vegetation in both open and shaded habitats and

showing a preference for moist, fertile soils. Appearing more rarely in drier situations on neglected waste sites and land recovering from disturbance in urban areas. Also tetrad SO99A. Ass: *Alliaria petiolata, Arrhenatherum elatius, Geum urbanum, Heracleum sphondylium, Silene dioica*.

### Scrophularia auriculata L.
### Water Figwort

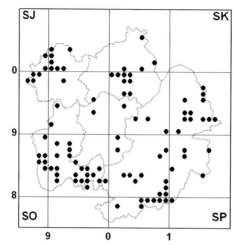

*99. Native. This perennial herb is rather less common than *S. nodosa* and more choosy in its habitat requirements. Confined to constantly moist, open to slightly shaded situations on the edges of streams, rivers, ditches, ponds, canals and wet woodland in quite base- and nutrient-rich soils. Its apparent scarcity in the N Walsall canals is interesting; perhaps the waters are too base- and nutrient-poor. There are one or two reliable records from waste land. Ass: *Filipendula ulmaria, Myosotis scorpioides, Oenanthe crocata, Phalaris arundinacea, Senecio aquaticus*.

### Scrophularia vernalis L.
### Yellow Figwort
0. Neophyte, casual with us. Once recorded in the overgrown rubble of demolished houses, Terrace Street, Blackheath (SO968864, LG, 1987).

### Phygelius capensis E. May. Ex Benth
### Cape Figwort
1. Neophyte. Shrub. One well-established plant growing among Honeysuckle near garden boundary fence N of Kenniford Close. Blue Rock Quarry, Rowley Regis (SO9788, MWP, 2010). S Africa.

### Sutera cordata (Thunb.) Kuntze
### Bacopa
1. Casual. Tender perennial. Often grown in hanging baskets and occasionally found (probably as seedlings) in pavement cracks etc. beneath, but not persisting and rarely recorded. Cultivar 'Snowflake' self-set

in hospital car park from previous year's plantings, Fiveways, B'ham (SP054862, MWP, 1997). S Africa.

### Limosella aquatica L.
### Mudwort
1. Native. Nationally Scarce. Annual. Hundreds of plants appeared in drying out mud in a horse field, Walsall, 2010. *Agrostis stolonifera, Juncus bufonius, Ranunculus sceleratus, Rorippa palustris*.

### Buddleja alternifolia Maxim.
### Alternate-leaved Butterfly-bush
3. Neophyte. Records all thought to be from original plantings. Darby End disused railway (SO961863, PS, 1998); well established on banks along old railway walkway, The Flatts, Darlaston (SO982971, MWP & MHM, 2001); Wednesfield (SJ943002, PN, 2002). SE Gansu, China.

### Buddleja davidii Franch.
### Butterfly-bush

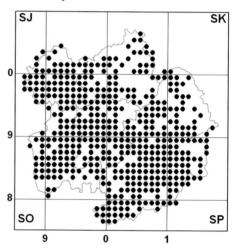

*475. Neophyte. Shrub. An increasing feature of the urban area, on walls, buildings and in paving cracks. Also very common along railway corridors throughout the region in both brickwork and on trackside ballast. A rapid coloniser after disturbance on recently demolished industrial and post-housing sites, seeding profusely, and where left undisturbed, forming dense thickets and rapidly creating 'urban woodland' along with *Salix caprea, Betula pendula* and *Fraxinus excelsior*. Thickets can develop in 2–3 years, suppressing much diversity in the early successional annual plant communities. Cadbury *et al.* (1971) had six records in vc. 38, and described it from "bombed sites in B'ham" (Burges & Andrews, 1947). In 1972 it was not mentioned by Edees (1972), and it was first recorded in vc. 39 in 1977 in waste ground, Mill Street, Wordsley (SO894866, WAT). Our records suggest a major expansion started in B&BC in the mid-1980s, and that it is now uncommon only in the countryside areas. White-flowered plants are not uncommon. China. Ass: *Betula pendula*, *Cotoneaster* spp., *Crataegus monogyna*, *Dryopteris filix-mas*, *Pseudofumaria lutea*, *Salix caprea*, *Senecio squalidus*.

### Buddleja × weyeriana Weyer
(*B. davidii* × *B. globosa*)
**Weyer's Butterfly-bush**
5. Neophyte. Shrub. Isolated records on banks and waste ground near to habitation. Warley Park, derelict shrubbery, "probably spontaneous" (SP010862, CBW, 1996); two plants with parents, University of B'ham grounds (SP0483, MWP, 2000); towpath, Leybrook Allotments (SP000778, MWP, 2005); Sheldon Country Park (SP152845, MWP, ICT, JWP & L. Bastin, 2007); waste ground by River Rea culvert, Digbeth (SP082868, MWP & ICT, 2007). Garden origin.

### Buddleja globosa Hope
**Orange-ball-tree**

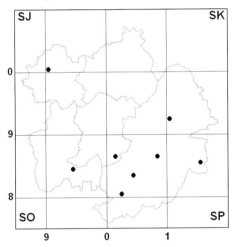

8. Neophyte. A large deciduous shrub persisting where thrown out or deliberately planted but doubtfully arising spontaneously. Chile and Peru.

### Nemesia strumosa Benth.
**Cape Jewels**
1. Casual. Garden annual. Disturbed land on post-housing site, Ley Hill Farm Road, Frankley (SP0180, MWP, 2003). S Africa.

### Diascia barberae Hook. f.
**Twinspur**
1. Casual. Tender perennial garden plant, pavement weed, Cot Lane, Wordsley (SO886876, CBW, 2007). S Africa.

## 118. LAMIACEAE

### Stachys byzantina K. Koch
(*S. lanata* Jacq. Non Crantz)
**Lamb's-ear**
26. Neophyte. Occasionally seeding into paving cracks and paths from garden

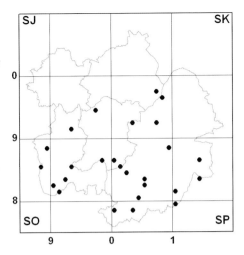

plants but seldom attaining maturity. Well established patches in rough grassland near the site of the old RSPB Centre, Sandwell Valley (SP035928, MWP, 2006). N Turkey, S Caucasus, N Iran.

### Stachys sylvatica L.
**Hedge Woundwort**

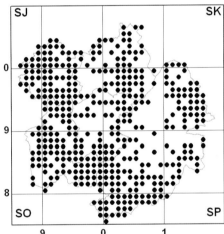

*431. Native. A common perennial herb of hedgebanks, woodland margins, rough and unmanaged grassy areas, gardens and land recovering from disturbance in open to moderately shaded places in moist, moderately fertile soils. Will sometimes survive the development of quite dense shade in, for example, Hawthorn scrub. Appears to be scarcer in some of the more intensely industrial or highly populated areas and also in parts of Sutton Park. Ass: *Galium aparine*, *Geranium sanguineum*, *Geum urbanum*, *Poa trivialis*, *Urtica dioica*.

### Stachys × ambigua Sm.
(*S. sylvatica* × *S. palustris*)
**Hybrid Woundwort**
1. The only modern records are from Park Hall Nature Reserve (SP162910, SAHA, 2006), plus a Walsall tetrad record from SP09E.

▲ *Limosella aquatica*

▲ *Buddleja davidii*

▲ *Stachys sylvatica*

### *Stachys palustris* L.
### Marsh Woundwort

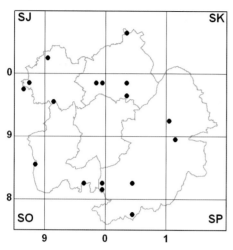

17. Native. Ax. An uncommon herbaceous perennial growing among other tall herbs in moist waterside meadows and canal-side vegetation. Rarely in drier uncharacteristic places on derelict land in moderately fertile neutral soils; sometimes a relic of wetlands in these situations. Also tetrad SP09E in Walsall. Ass: *Carex otrubae, Glyceria maxima, Iris pseudacorus, Juncus effusus, Persicaria lapathifolia.*

### *Stachys annua* (L.) L.
### Annual Yellow-woundwort

0. Casual. Recorded by Bagnall, above Blackroot Pool, Sutton Park (SP19, Bagnall, 1891).

### *Stachys arvensis* (L.) L.
### Field Woundwort

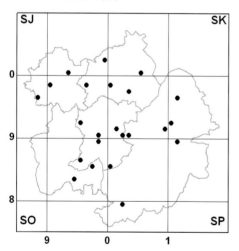

23. Archaeophyte. NT. Ax. Annual. Recorded widely across the conurbation but almost exclusively confined to allotment gardens, where it occurs as a weed of cultivation, particularly in potato plots. Populations vary from a few isolated plants to large local populations and are generally confined to one or two plots per site. The few non-allotment records are

*Stachys arvensis* (by Anne Bebbington)

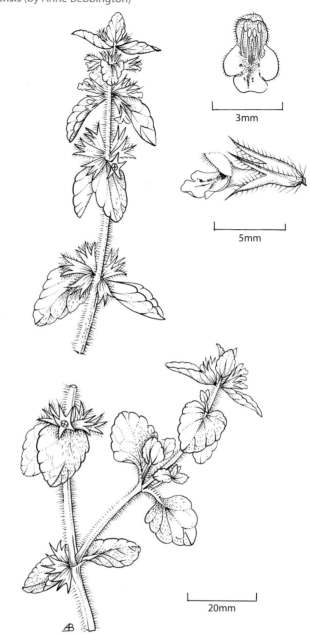

from garden paths and paving and ground recovering from disturbance in well-lit, open vegetation on soils of intermediate fertility and base-status. Ass: *Lamium amplexicaule, Lamium hybridum, Lamium purpureum, Poa annua, Polygonum convolvulus, Stellaria media, Trifolium dubium.*

### *Betonica officinalis* L.
(*Stachys officinalis* (L.) Trevis.)
### Betony

*53. Native. Ax. Unimproved meadows and grassy hillsides on mildly acidic, infertile, well-drained sites with sunny open aspects. Some native populations still occur but records are often for isolated plants. Ass: *Holcus lanatus, Knautia arvensis, Lotus corniculatus, Rumex*

acetosa, Sanguisorba officinalis, Succisa pratensis.

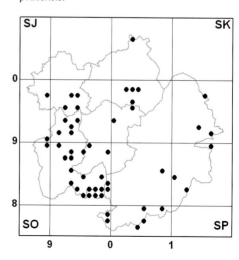

### *Ballota nigra* L.
### Black Horehound

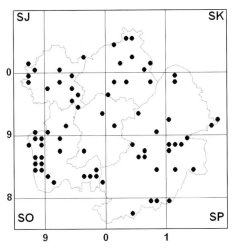

72. Archaeophyte. Among tall herbs and grasses on unmanaged banks and road verges and in neglected bits of wasteland near buildings in moist, fertile soils. Often in isolation or a few individuals. There are further tetrad records in vc. 37, also SO98E. Ass: *Anisantha sterilis, Elytrigia repens, Hordeum murinum, Lamium album, Lapsana communis, Sisymbrium officinale.*

### *Leonurus cardiaca* L.
### Motherwort

2. Neophyte. A small colony has persisted for at least 29 years at the base of shrubs along the canal towpath at Titford Lakes, Oldbury (SO988878, MWP, most recently 2012). In most years towpath strimming reduces plants to a few inches from the ground but when seed production has been successful new plants appear the following year. The best recorded year was 1989 when approximately 60 flowering spikes were counted. Two other casual records: one plant in vegetable patch, Beeches Road, West Bromwich (SP010910, J. Little, 1997) and an old record of one plant on waste ground, Terrace Street, Blackheath (SO968864, MWP & LG, 1987). Europe.

### *Lamiastrum galeobdolon* (L.) Ehrend. & Polatschek
### subsp. *montanum* (Pers.) Ehrend. & Polatschek
### Yellow Archangel

*91. Native. Ax. Quite strongly associated with woodlands of some antiquity. Still frequent in dingles and remnants of old woodland in shade, on moist or damp, base-intermediate to base-rich soils of intermediate fertility chiefly in the fringes of the urban area. The map includes some records without the subspecies being identified (to do this was possible on the recording sheet). Ass: *Anemone nemorosa,*

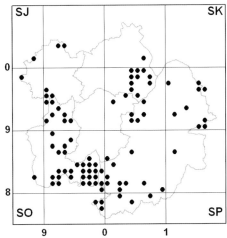

*Arum maculatum, Carex sylvatica, Hyacinthoides non-scripta, Mercurialis perennis.*

### *Lamiastrum galeobdolon*
### subsp. *argentatum* (Smejkal) Stace
### Yellow Archangel

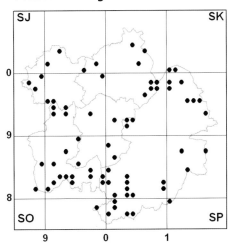

74. Neophyte. Sch. 9 (invasive). A persistent escape and garden throw-out which has become thoroughly naturalised, frequently forming extensive spreading patches. It can usually be easily distinguished from subsp. *montanum* by its conspicuous whitish leaf-blotch throughout the year and its larger flowers. It is sometimes found in old deciduous woodland (e.g. in Rough Wood, SJ9801; Sutton Park, SP0897 & SP1097; Alder Coppice, SO9194 and Ham Dingle, SO9182) and therefore must be accounted as a potentially invasive alien species. It is most commonly found on shady banks, tracksides and shrubberies and in deciduous woodland plantations. E Europe. Ass: see subsp. *montanum*, also *Anisantha sterilis, Anthriscus sylvestris, Artemisia vulgaris, Fallopia japonica, Geranium pyrenaicum, Poa trivialis, Rubus fruticosus* agg., *Rumex obtusifolius, Silene latifolia, Urtica dioica.*

▲ *Stachys arvensis*

▲ *Leonurus cardiaca*

▲ *Lamiastrum galeobdolon* subsp. *montanum*

**Lamium album** L.
**White Dead-nettle**

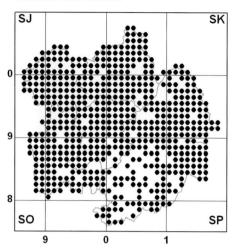

*593. Archaeophyte. Almost ubiquitous on canal and railway banks, hedgerow banks, spoil heaps, waste ground, neglected bits of land between buildings and on land recovering from recent disturbance. Frequently growing with *Urtica dioica*, usually in fairly moist, fertile soil. The scarcity of records in the S Birmingham suburbs is partly due to tetrad recording in vc. 37 but to some extent extends into two vice-counties. Ass: *Anthriscus sylvestris*, *Arrhenatherum elatius*, *Elytrigia repens*, *Galium aparine*, *Ranunculus repens*, *Rumex obtusifolius*, *Urtica dioica*.

**Lamium maculatum** (L.) L.
**Spotted Dead-nettle**

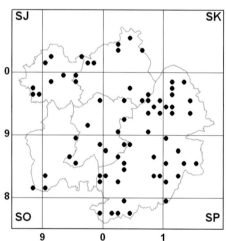

72. Neophyte. Garden throw-out or escape in grassy places on waste land and neglected areas between buildings and occasionally in paving. Persistent and patch-forming when left undisturbed in open and semi-shaded situations on fairly fertile soils. Europe. Ass: *Acer campestre*, *Alliaria petiolata*, *Anthriscus sylvestris*, *Holcus lanatus*, *Persicaria maculosa*, *Rubus idaeus*, *Urtica dioica*.

**Lamium purpureum** L.
**Red Dead-nettle**

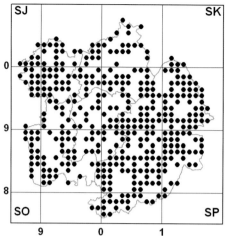

*401. Archaeophyte. Hedge banks, gardens, waste areas, cultivated land and sites recovering from recent disturbance in rich, fertile soils. A colonist of disturbed ground in allotment gardens in association with other rapid-maturing annuals. Ass: *Chenopodium album*, *Euphorbia peplus*, *Polygonum aviculare*, *Stellaria media*, *Veronica agrestis*, *Veronica persica*.

**Lamium hybridum** Vill.
**Cut-leaved Dead-nettle**

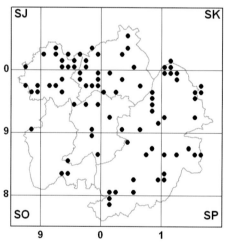

87. Archaeophyte. Arable land, field borders, allotment gardens. Generally uncommon but locally frequent particularly along margins of arable fields. Often with *L. purpureum* but in some allotments more frequent. Apparently scarcer in the S. Ass: *Capsella bursa-pastoris*, *Fallopia convolvulus*, *Fumaria officinalis*, *Lamium amplexicaule*, *Lamium purpureum*, *Matricaria chamomilla*, *Poa annua*, *Polygonum aviculare*, *Senecio vulgaris*, *Veronica agrestis*.

**Lamium amplexicaule** L.
**Henbit Dead-nettle**

139. Archaeophyte. A weed of disturbance

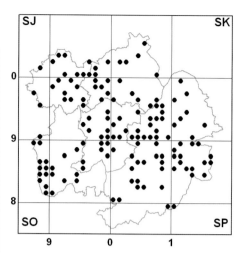

in field borders, gardens and allotment plots in open, sunny places on light but fertile soils. Ass: *Arabidopsis thaliana*, *Capsella bursa-pastoris*, *Epilobium ciliatum*, *Fallopia convolvulus*, *Galinsoga parviflora*, *Galinsoga quadriradiata*, *Lamium hybridum*, *Poa annua*, *Stellaria media*, *Urtica urens*, *Veronica agrestis*, *Veronica hederifolia*, *Veronica persica*.

**Galeopsis angustifolia** Ehrh. ex Hoffm.
**Red Hemp-nettle**
0. Archaeophyte. BAP, CR, Nationally Scarce. Old record from a lime quarry at Sedgley Beacon (SO9194, M.H. Bigwood, 1952). The site of the species was destroyed when a new reservoir was created there in 1970, although much of the quarry is still present.

**Galeopsis speciosa** Mill.
**Large-flowered Hemp-nettle**
2. Archaeophyte, probably no more than a casual in B&BC. VU. Golf course, W'ton (SJ884009, JVT, 2000); several plants in arable field subjected to recent disturbance, Sandwell Valley (SP018921, MWP, 2005). There are also older records from a road verge at Lutley Gutter (SO9483, F. Fincher, 1963), Ham Dingle (SO915827, D. Oakley, 1973) and Wyndley Wood (SP110953, J. Maiden, R. Jones & J. Turner, 1987).

**Galeopsis tetrahit** agg.
**Common Hemp-nettle**
*178. Native. Annuals. Most of our records are for the aggregate, relatively few for either **G. tetrahit** L. *sensu stricto* or for **G. bifida** Boenn., so all records are mapped together. Arable land, field margins, light woodland, hedgerows and allotment gardens in open and moderately shaded places in a wide range of soils including some quite damp pond-side and streamside habitats. Ass: *Alliaria petiolata*,

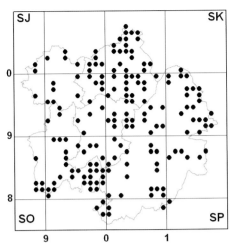

Digitalis purpurea, Galium aparine, Lapsana communis.

### Galeopsis bifida Boenn.
### Bifid Hemp-nettle

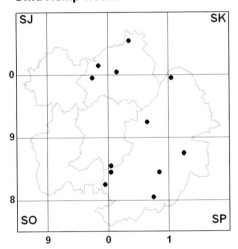

12. Native. Annual of field margins, arable land, disturbed ground in similar situations to *G. tetrahit* with which it sometimes grows. Some records for the aggregate will be for this as the two are indistinguishable when not in flower. Also tetrad SP09P.

### Phlomis fruticosa L.
### Jerusalem Sage
1. Neophyte. Evergreen shrub. One plant, either self-set or adventitious, Hullbrook Road, Billesley (SP092805, CBW, 1999). Mediterranean.

### Melittis melissophyllum L.
### Bastard Balm
0. Native. Perennial herb. Historical record, described as a garden escape, Sycamore Wood, land S of Hardwick Wood (SP080990, DH, 1986).

### Scutellaria galericulata L.
### Skullcap
*157. Native. A colonist of the permanently saturated brickwork mortar just above

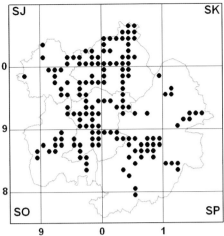

the water-line along all but the most used canals throughout the conurbation. Also in the marginal vegetation of pools and ditches on moderately fertile soils in well-lit, open situations. Ass: *Carex otrubae, Bidens frondosa, Oenanthe crocata, Rumex conglomeratus, Rumex hydrolapathum.*

### Scutellaria minor Huds.
### Lesser Scullcap
1. Native. Ax. This plant of nutrient- and base-poor peaty mires is now largely confined to Wales and the Welsh borders in midland Britain. It is sometimes confused with pink-flowered forms of *Scutellaria galericulata*, and that may account for some of the seven historical records in B&BC, e.g. from Merecroft Pool in Walsall. However it has been more plausibly recorded at Stubbers Green in Walsall (SK044020, H.G. Owens, 1972) and in the mire by the canal at the swingbridge (recently rebuilt) near Clayhanger Village (SK045052, JPM, 1990, also seen by ICT and last seen 1992). Both sites are greatly changed and *Scutellaria minor* can no longer be found there, although the latter site still has *Anagallis tenella* and *Carex echinata*. However *S. minor* still exists in Sutton Park: Readett (1971) recorded it in SP0996 & SP0998 and although it was not found in the present survey a small population was recently recorded in a small open grazed piece of the heath that is beginning to get scrubbed over near the railway line (SP091983, BL, 2009). The species was also recorded in similar vegetation on Penn Common, just outside our borders in vc. 39 (SO8994, BRF, 1990) and taken together these records suggest that, as with other species associated with similar mires, *S. minor* once had a more extensive distribution in lowland Britain.

### Teucrium scorodonia L.
### Wood Sage
*64. Native. Ax. Hedgebanks, scrubby

▲ *Lamium amplexicaule*

▲ *Galeopsis speciosa*

▲ *Scutellaria galericulata*

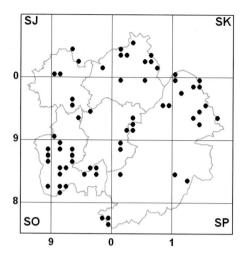

grassland and wood margins in open and semi-shaded places on moderately acid, nutrient-deficient soils. Seems to be almost entirely confined to the countryside areas of B&BC. Ass: *Deschampsia flexuosa, Digitalis purpurea, Galium saxatile, Rumex acetosella.*

### *Teucrium chamaedrys* L.
### Wall Germander
0. Neophyte. An old BRF record: on a hedgebank, Wrekin Lane, Tettenhall (SJ871001, 1989) may just be in our area. Europe.

### *Ajuga reptans* L.
### Bugle

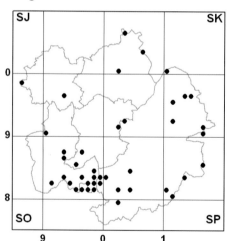

*42. Native. Ax. A herbaceous perennial found in damp grassland and shady situations, in dingles, woodland rides, streamsides and other moist, cool, shady places, usually on quite base-rich but only moderately nutrient-rich, often clay soils. Its low creeping habit enables it to form large clonal patches, though it does not compete well with taller vegetation. Only really frequent in the Illey/Woodgate Valley area and becoming quite scarce in the built-up areas. Plants with dark purple shining leaves (cultivar 'Atropurpurea'),

are occasionally found spreading into paving cracks and overgrown borders from original garden plantings. Also tetrad SO98E. Ass: (in woodlands) *Cardamine flexuosa, Carex remota, Carex sylvatica, Ficaria verna, Poa trivialis, Schedonorus giganteus.*

### *Nepeta cataria* L.
### Cat-mint
1. Archaeophyte. VU. Seen by BRF, by the canal, near Broad Street, W'ton, SO918988, in 1988; probably still in the same place in 1999 (towpath, SO917989, ICT, 1999). Also appeared for a few years in *Chrysanthemum* pots at Highfields School, W'ton (SO8896, CBW, *circa* 1990) and once known from the ruins of Dudley Castle (Withering 1796).

### *Nepeta* × *faassenii* Bergmans ex Stearn
(*N. racemosa* Lam. × *N. nepetella* L.)
### Garden Cat-mint
5. Neophyte. A sprawling, aromatic, semi-evergreen herb often grown in gardens. Self-set in edge of shrubbery, Warley Park (SP012861, CBW, 1996); waste ground between road and railway, Warren Road (SP101889, MWP, 1997); unused pasture by Park Hall reserve (SP162908, MWP, ICT & JWP, 2006); pavement cracks, Harrisons Road (SP044846, MWP, 2006); pavement crack, Darnick Road (SP097949, MWP, ICT & JaH, 2006). Garden origin.

### *Glechoma hederacea* L.
### Ground-ivy

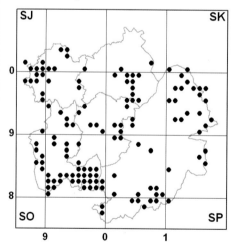

*135. Native. A low, stoloniferous perennial, forming large patches along woodland margins, hedgerows and wooded stream and river banks in lightly to moderately shaded, slightly disturbed situations on soils of average or quite high fertility and base status. Typically the site is cool and damp, with poorly drained, often winter-wet, clay soil. Largely confined to the margins of (or close to) semi-natural

vegetation in our area and rare or absent elsewhere. Native plants and bronze-leaved cultivars are grown in gardens and can persist in lawns. Ass: *Cardamine flexuosa, Ficaria verna, Geum urbanum, Poa trivialis, Schedonorus giganteus, Urtica dioica.*

### *Prunella vulgaris* L.
### Selfheal

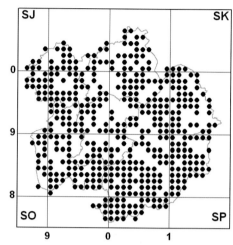

*469. Native. A very common, patch-forming perennial of open situations or very short turf. Moist lawns and grassy roadside verges, damp to dry meadows and relatively open woodland margins in soils of average fertility and intermediate base status. Some lawns are almost exclusively this. Ass: *Bellis perennis, Lotus corniculatus, Plantago lanceolata, Trifolium dubium, Trifolium repens.*

### *Melissa officinalis* L.
### Balm

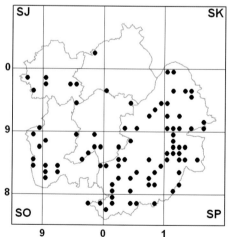

89. Neophyte. A perennial herb grown in gardens for its aromatic, lemon-scented leaves and frequently seeding into paving, roadside verges, garden paths and neglected bits of waste land. Generally not too far from habitation, but probably becoming commoner in B&BC: very few records either in Cadbury *et al.* (1971) or

in Edees (1972). S Europe. Ass: *Agrostis stolonifera, Alliaria petiolata, Lathyrus latifolius, Senecio squalidus, Urtica dioica*.

### *Clinopodium ascendens* (Jord.) Samp.
**Common Calamint**
1. Native; casual in B&BC. A perennial of dry hedgebanks and rock exposures on base-rich soils, with a recent record from a grassy drive to garages, New Street, Wordsley (SO890869, CBW, 2008).

### *Clinopodium vulgare* L.
**Wild Basil**
3. Native. A rhizomatous perennial herb of verges and hedgebanks on limestone soils. The only site where it appears to be native in B&BC is the Wren's Nest, Dudley, on dry limestone grassland banks (SO936917, ST, 1997) and with older records at SO937920 (A. Whitbread, 1983, seen again 1985). It was also introduced on to Bushbury Hill road verge in strewn hay (SJ925021, ICT) in 1987, and persisted there until at least 2007. It has also been seen in secondary grassland over coal spoil at Stow Lawn, Bilston (SO940978, ICT & EVJC, 2007), where it also appears to be an introduction although there are no records to support this.

### *Clinopodium acinos* (L.) Kuntze
(*Acinos arvensis* (Lam.) Dandy)
**Basil Thyme**
0. Native. Sect. 41, BAP, VU. Only old records for this annual of base-rich soils: Beacon Hill, Sedgley (SO922946, PW, 1987); Sutton Park (SP0997, Bagnall, 1868).

### *Hyssopus officinalis* L.
**Hyssop**
1. Casual? A single flowering shrub on waste land N of Moor Street Queensway and W of Priory Queensway in central B'ham (SP074870, ICT & D. Harrison, 2011). S Europe.

### *Origanum vulgare* L.
**Wild Marjoram**

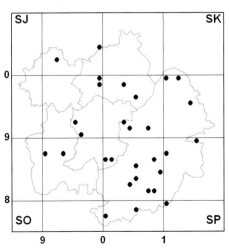

30. Native; probably always introduced in B&BC. The records are for isolated plants on dry, grassy banks and rough ground, and as a pavement weed, seeding from nearby gardens. Occasionally spreading onto paths or self-seeded from original plantings in allotment gardens. Ass: *Linaria vulgaris, Tanacetum vulgare, Vicia hirsuta*.

### *Thymus vulgaris* L.
**Garden Thyme**
1. Neophyte. Evergreen shrub. B'ham Canal, Telford Way to Brasshouse Lane (SP017891, TM, 2003), presumed garden escape.

### *Thymus polytrichus* A. Kern. ex Borbás
**subsp.** *britannicus* (Ronniger) Kerguélen
(*T. drucei* Ronniger)
**Wild Thyme**
3. Native; always introduced in B&BC? Dwarf shrub. Only isolated plants in open, bare ground: Coney Green (SO908840, APD, 1998); B'ham & Fazeley Canal (SP071877, TM, 2002); patch on bank of derelict railway track, Blower's Green (SO941893, MWP, 2004).

### *Thymus × citriodorus* Pers.
(*T. vulgaris × T. pulegioides* L.)
**Lemon Thyme**
1. Neophyte. Recorded as a pavement crack casual, the Brambles, Pedmore (SO918833, WAT, 2003). Garden origin.

### *Lycopus europaeus* L.
**Gypsywort**

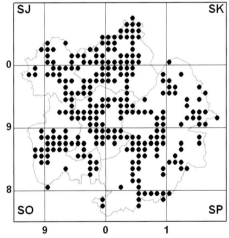

*271. Native. Perennial. Open or shaded situations in shallow, standing-water around pools and ditches, and present almost everywhere in the tall herb and reedswamp community along the canal network. In moderately base-rich, fertile substrates. Fairly shade tolerant and often in Alder and Willow carr. Ass: *Berula erecta, Carex otrubae, Glyceria maxima, Scutellaria galericulata, Solanum dulcamara*.

### *Mentha arvensis* L.
**Corn Mint**

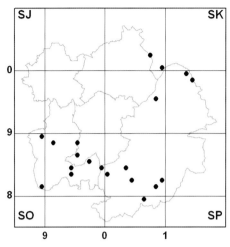

*20. Native. Ax. A rhizomatous perennial found infrequently in marshy pastures, mires and edges of ponds, pools and reservoirs, in sun or partial shade, typically where there is a fluctuating water table, but otherwise in habitats similar to those of *M. aquatica* and sometimes with it. No records from its arable fields habitat. Ass: *Agrostis stolonifera, Dryopteris dilatata, Filipendula ulmaria, Galium palustre, Juncus effusus, Myosotis laxa, Urtica dioica*.

### *Mentha × verticillata* L.
(*M. arvensis × M. aquatica*)
**Whorled Mint**
4. Native. Marsh, Oval Pool, Warrens Hall (SO955885, ST, 1997); edge of lake, West Smethwick Park (SP004888, CBW, 1997); Stratford Canal (SP084796, JJD, 2000); Senneleys Park (SP011818, CBW, 1996). Also from SO99C and SO89X (BH, 1999). These sites do not have records for *M. arvensis*.

### *Mentha × smithiana* R.A. Graham
(*M. arvensis × M. aquatica × M. spicata*)
**Tall Mint**
1. Neophyte. A garden throw-out first recorded in vc. 39 from waste ground, Roebuck Lane, Smethwick (SP0189, MWP, 1989). There is a more recent record from Uplands Allotments, Perry Barr (SP0391, ICT, MWP, JaH, SJC & V. Lawrie, 2008). ?garden origin.

### *Mentha aquatica* L.
**Water Mint**
*161. Native. A rhizomatous perennial of open or semi-shaded sites in permanently wet situations where it often grows partially submerged. Margins of pools, ditches, streams, rivers and canals and in wet woodland on a wide range of soil types. Ass: *Deschampsia cespitosa, Filipendula ulmaria, Holcus lanatus, Juncus*

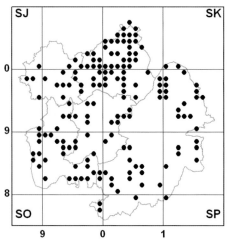

*effusus, Juncus inflexus, Lycopus europaeus, Myosotis scorpioides, Silene flos-cuculi.*

### *Mentha* × *piperita* L.
(*M. aquatica* × *M. spicata*)
**Peppermint**
2. Native × Archaeophyte. Poolside marsh, the Dingle, Leasowes Park (SO983842, WAT, 1989 & RM, 2004); River Cole (SP102795, CBW, 1996); also old record from Wood Farm (SJ984017, CRP & JJB, 1989). **Var. *citrata*** (Ehrh.) Briq. (**Eau de Cologne Mint**) was recorded in a track verge by Midland Road, Four Oaks (SP113970, ICT, EVJC & S.M. Phipps, 2005), and probably occurs as an escape elsewhere.

### *Mentha spicata* L.
**Spear Mint**

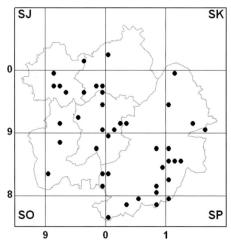

42. Archaeophyte. A relic of cultivation and established garden outcast in rough and neglected grassy places and unmanaged gardens where it frequently forms large patches from its creeping rhizome. Probably our commonest naturalised garden mint. Ass: *Artemisia absinthium, Juncus inflexus.*

### *Mentha* × *villosonervata* Opiz
(*M. spicata* × *M. longifolia* (L.) Huds.)
**Sharp-toothed Mint**
2. Neophyte. Village Road, Four Oaks

(SP115992, MWP, JWP & PLR, 2006); near Longmoor Pool, Sutton Park (SP098960, B. Rowe, det. EJC, 1995). ?garden origin.

### *Mentha* × *villosa* Huds.
(*M. spicata* × *M. suaveolens*)
**Apple-mint**

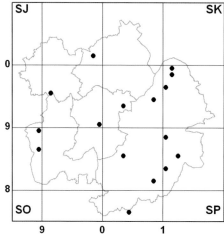

16. Neophyte. A garden escape, mostly in waste land but also in Rough Wood (SJ9801) and by the River Tame (SP0393). Some records have been referred to **var. villosa** and others to **var. alopecuroides** (Hull) Briq. ?Garden origin.

### *Mentha* × *rotundifolia* (L.) Huds.
(*M. longifolia* × *M. suaveolens*)
**False Apple-mint**
1. Neophyte. West Hill College (SP035824, DJA, 2003). Europe.

### *Mentha suaveolens* Ehrh.
(*M. rotundifolia* auct. Non (L.) Huds.)
**Round-leaved Mint**
1. Native; garden outcast in our area. A single unconfirmed record: Hobmoor playing fields (SP125855, A. Gleeson, 2004).

### *Mentha pulegium* L.
**Pennyroyal**
2. Native. Sch. 8, BAP, EN, nationally rare. Modern records are casual garden escapes or persisting from cultivation. Brewery Fields Allotments, Dudley (SO953902, R. Billingsley, 2000); by the canal at Freezeland, Bilston (SO937963, PN, 2006). Recorded at the side of a pool at Erdington (SP19) in 1787 by W. Withering, according to Cadbury *et al.* (1971).

### *Mentha requienii* Benth.
**Corsican Mint**
1. Neophyte. Flower bed and paving, Golden Hop Terrace, B'ham University Botanical Gardens, Winterbourne (SP0583, MPW & JWP, 2007). Corsica and Sardinia.

### *Lavandula angustifolia* Mill.
**Garden Lavender**

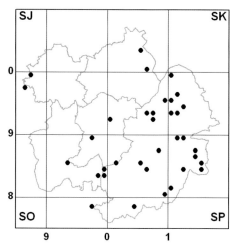

35. Neophyte. Evergreen shrub. Small plants are often found along roadside margins and paving seeded from mature plants in nearby gardens. Few survive to maturity. These plants were all recorded as *Lavandula* × *intermedia* Loisel. (*L. angustifolia* Mill. × *L. latifolia* Medik.) but this is now considered to be sterile. W Mediterranean.

### *Rosmarinus officinalis* L.
**Rosemary**

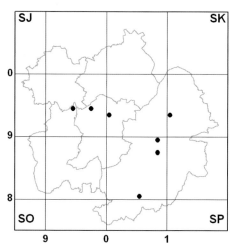

7. Neophyte. Evergreen shrub. Garden discards and self-sets, isolated plants in residential areas, a woodland plantation, canalsides, a churchyard. Mediterranean.

### *Salvia pratensis* L.
**Meadow Clary**
1. Native or alien. Sch. 8, NT. Near Greenleighs (SO9195, BH, 2000), habitat not specified. A very old record from Rubery (SO9977): "leaves of a sage there, 1908, Amphlett" (Amphlett & Rea, 1909)

### *Salvia verbenaca* L.
**Wild Clary**
4. Native; presumed introduced in B&BC.

Large patch in canal bank vegetation, Tame Valley Canal, Hamstead (SP042934, MWP, 1997); a few, edge of fire breaks, Saltwells Nature Reserve (SO935879 & SO938881, J. Akers, 1998, seen by APD, 1999); four large plants, in gravelly, weedy patch between track and fishing lake, W of Bloxwich (SJ984020, JEH, 2004); several flowering plants and hundreds of seedlings appeared on an area of waste land by Moor Street Queensway in central B'ham (SP074870, D. Harrison, conf. MWP, 2011).

### Salvia verticillata L.
### Whorled Clary
0. Neophyte. Persisting for a while as eight patches on a strip of rough grass by the railway, Wallbrook (SO947930, WAT, 1987). S Europe.

### Salvia splendens Ker Gawl.
### Scarlet Sage
1. Casual. Frost-sensitive perennial grown as a summer bedding plant and usually discarded after flowering. One plant in pavement crack at the base of a garden wall, New Mills, Walsall (SP002968, MWP & JaH, 2003). Brazil.

### Physostegia virginiana (L.) Benth.
### Obedient Plant
1. Neophyte. Waste land between road and railway, Warren Road, Washwood Heath B'ham (SP101889, MWP, 1999). US.

### Agastache foeniculum (Pursh) Kuntze
### Anise Hyssop
1. Casual. Perennial herb. Garden escape. Self-seeded at base of old stable wall, Wightwick Manor, W'ton (SO8698, CBW, 2000). N America.

## 119. PHRYMACEAE

### Mimulus moschatus Douglas ex Lindl.
### Musk
0. Neophyte. Recorded in paved area at rear of Wightwick Manor (SO8698, M.E. Harthill 1985 & JPM, 1990, probably still present). Western N America.

### Mimulus guttatus DC.
### Monkeyflower
16. Neophyte. Constantly wet, badly aerated, nutrient- and base-intermediate substrates in open to slightly shaded situations, sometimes forming large colonies along the margins of pools and ditches. Frequent along the ditch between the car park and Longmoor Pool, Sutton Park, and also extensively around the

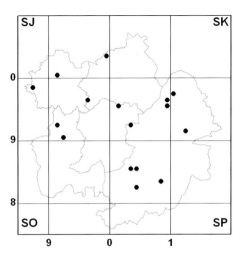

margins of that pool (SP0995). Western N America.

## 121. OROBANCHACEAE

### Melampyrum pratense L.
### Common Cow-wheat
1. Native. Ax. Heathland and dry birch and oak woodland in shady, nutrient- and base-poor soils. Declining; perhaps now only in heathland on Rednal Hill (SO996766, R.A. Jones & R. M. Busbridge, 1987, still there in 2005, SAHA). Formerly listed in Readett (1971) in Sutton Park (SP0897, SP0898, SP0997, SP1097 & SP1098), but not re-found in the recent survey although thought to be still present (PC, pers. comm.). There are further old records for Bromwich Woods (SO998811, Natural England, 1981); woodland at Illey (SO984821, Natural England, 1981); woods at Edgbaston (SP08, W. Withering, 1796). Ours is **subsp. pratense**.

### Euphrasia officinalis sensu lato
### Eyebrights

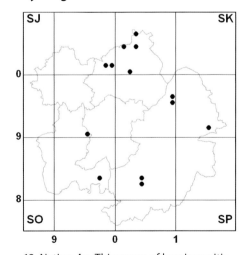

13. Native. Ax. This group of hemiparasitic annual microspecies, mainly found in old grassland, are scarce in B&BC. The most recent sightings are: Rough Wood Wedge

and Wyrley & Essington canal, Bloxwich, in poorly drained pasture (SJ9801, 2007 & SJ9901, 2007); Pelsall Common, in both heathy grassland and grassland on furnace spoil (SK0104, 2008); Daw End Fields, Walsall, base-rich pasture (SK0200, 2001 & SK0300, 1989); Clayhanger SSSI, wet pastures (SK0304, 2006); Brownhills Common, damp, heathy pastures (SK0306, 2010); The Leasowes, Halesowen, base-rich pasture (SO9783, 1998); Hilltop, Langley Reservoir, B'ham, grassland (SP0086, 1991); Canal towpath, Selly Oak, and widespread on the disturbed grassland and open vegetation of a development site by the canal (SP0482, 2008 & SP0483, 1997, still abundant, 2010); Brookvale Park, Gravelly Hill, B'ham, mesotrophic grassland (SP0990, 1987); Sutton Park, heathy pasture (SP0997, 1866; SP0995, SP0996, SP0998, all 1971; still present in the Park at Longmoor, recorded as *E. nemorosa*, (SP0995/SP0996, HHF, 1995); By dismantled railway, Dudley (SO9590, AMG & CRP, 2001); Railway triangle (SP1591, CW, 1996).

The few identifications to microspecies have all been to **Euphrasia nemorosa** (Pers.) Wallr. (**Common Eyebright**). There were some short-term introductions in W'ton (mostly in SJ9202 and SJ9303) in the 1990s and 2000s using hay from Stiperstones in Shropshire.

### Odontites vernus (Bellardi) Dumort.
### Red Bartsia

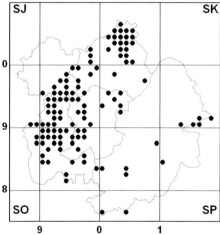

*117. Native. Ax. A moderately common, hemiparasitic annual herb, typically found on moist, open and often trampled pastures, grassy tracks, banks, canal towpaths and waste places in moderately nutrient-poor but fairly base-rich soils, often with a poor structure and impeded drainage due to trampling. Widespread in the unintensively managed, 'tumbledown' horse pastures which have long been a feature of the Black Country landscape and are also particularly common in the

▲ *Odontites vernus*

▲ *Parentucellia viscosa*

▲ *Rhinanthus minor*

Walsall countryside. These are often made by enclosing small areas of waste land and industrial spoil or are sometimes unfenced and grazed by tethered ponies. So ubiquitous is this species where horses are grazed that it is possibly spread in hay, although it flowers a little late to contribute much seed to hay. Ass: *Agrostis capillaris, Agrostis stolonifera, Centaurea nigra, Centaurium erythraea, Cynosurus cristatus, Festuca rubra, Plantago lanceolata, Ranunculus acris, Trifolium repens*.

Subsp. *serotinus* (Syme) Corb. appears to occur throughout the range in B&BC, also white-flowered plants.

### *Parentucellia viscosa* (L.) Caruel
### Yellow Bartsia

2. Native. Probably our only extant site for this hemiparasitic annual is a large population in a 50 × 25 metre patch within poorly drained, Soft-rush-dominated pasture on land between the M6 motorway and Walsall Canal S of the A4124 and W of Bloxwich (also known as Wood Farm). First reported in 1991 (SJ985015, DH) and still present and abundant in 2007. A single plant appeared in soil imported for landscaping a golf range at Queslett (SP061939, ICT & EVJC, 2002). There is an old record for about 17 plants on the E bank of a canalised part of the River Tame, Sheepwash Lane, Sandwell (SO977922, TCH & ICT, 1987, the first record for vc. 39). Ass: *Agrostis stolonifera, Alopecurus geniculatus, Juncus articulatus, Juncus effusus, Lotus pedunculatus, Ranunculus acris, Senecio aquaticus*.

### *Rhinanthus minor* L.
### Yellow-rattle

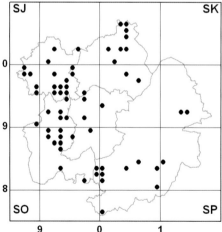

*62. Native. Ax. Unimproved dry (occasionally damp) pasture, shortish or fairly open patches of grassland and also abandoned railway sidings and other post-industrial sites in moderately acid to basic soils of intermediate or low fertility. Favoured by hay meadow management

and disfavoured by heavy grazing. Commoner in some of the industrial parts of the Black Country as well as in the countryside areas; the natural distribution of this species in our area is somewhat confused by some of the records deriving from wild flower mixes and hay strewing. Introductions definitely account for the records in SJ9202, SO8798, SO8898, SO8995, SO8996, SO9295, SO9396 and SP0684. Ass: *Anthoxanthum odoratum, Centaurea nigra, Cynosurus cristatus, Hypochaeris radicata, Lotus corniculatus, Ranunculus bulbosus, Trifolium pratense*.

### *Pedicularis palustris* L.
### Marsh Lousewort

2. Native. Ax. Hemiparasitic, annual to short-lived perennial herb, restricted to small colonies growing in nutrient-poor mires with base-enriched but acid flushes near Little Bracebridge Pool (most recently SP094983, MWP & ICT, 2005, seen again 2011) and in similar vegetation in Longmoor Valley, Sutton Park (most recently SP093961, MWP, ICT & PLR, 2006). Readett (1971) recorded it also in SP0995 and SP1097, and Bagnall recorded it in 0997 in 1867. There are very few other sites for this species in the lowland Midlands and it is the only site in vc. 38. Ass: *Anagallis tenella, Carex hostiana, Carex panicea, Cirsium dissectum, Dactylorhiza fuchsii, Pedicularis sylvatica, Pinguicula vulgaris, Triglochin palustris*.

### *Pedicularis sylvatica* L.
### Lousewort

3. Native. Ax. A perennial hemiparasitic herb in small quantities in damp to wet, infertile, acid heathland in three places in Sutton Park: near Little Bracebridge Pool (SP0998, SB, 1997) and N of Longmoor Pool (SP0996, SB, 1997; SP093958, MWP & ICT, 2005). Readett (1971) also recorded it from SP1096 and SP1097 and Bagnall from SP0997 in 1874. It is also recorded on Brownhills Common, growing in the fringe of a pool with *Erica tetralix* and *Sphagum* spp. (SK035064, DH, 2002). There are also old records from the mire by the canal at Clayhanger (SK045052, J. Andrews, 1987, seen again by JPM, 1990, not seen there by ICT in 2008 or 2010) and from marshy grassland, Illey (last seen SO977811, A. Fraser, 1976). It occurs in drier and more base-poor sites than *P. palustris* and is much commoner than that species in the surrounding rural counties. Ass: *Carex panicea, Dactylorhiza fuchsii, Nardus stricta, Potentilla erecta*.

### *Lathraea squamaria* L.
### Toothwort

6. Native. Ax. A perennial root-parasite found on woodland banks, especially

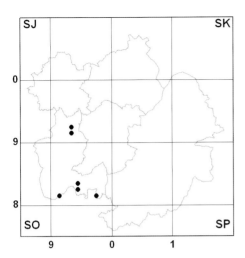

above streams, on moisture retaining, moderately fertile and base-rich soils where it usually grows on the roots of Hazel. In spring 2009, well over a thousand flower spikes were visible at the base of Hawthorn, Sycamore and Hazel, on wooded banks near Seven Sisters Caves and on the steep-sided wooded bank overlooking the quarry at Wren's Nest NNR (SO9391). Also reported growing around the base of a Cotoneaster in nearby Mons Hill College campus and on Sycamore and Hawthorn elsewhere. Other recent records are from from Illey, Lutley Gutter, and Wychbury Hill. Ass: *Acer pseudoplatanus*, *Corylus avellana*, *Crataegus monogyna*, *Ulmus glabra*.

### *Orobanche minor* Sm.
### Common Broomrape
5. Native. Ax. Almost all the few modern records for this annual root parasite are for plants growing in canal towpath or embankment vegetation. One population, on *Trifolium repens* and *Trifolium pratense* in compacted vegetation by the Tame Valley Canal, Great Barr has been known there since 1987 (SP029947, JJB; most recent record SP026948, MWP, 1998). In some seasons none are found but plants may often be cut down before reaching maturity in towpath management. Elsewhere: towpath, Wyrley & Essington canal, Heath Town (SO930992, P. Millett, 2000); post-industrial land 50 metres from the B'ham canal, W'ton Science Park (SJ915003, ICT & P. Millett, 2007; this was probably the same population seen by BRF in 1993 and 1997 on railway waste at N side of bridge, Stafford Road, Bushbury); one plant in a recently planted shrub bed, Castle Bromwich (SP140909, MWP, ICT & JaH, 2006) was probably introduced there with the shrubs. Shortly before the publication of this Flora a significant colony was discovered on the footprint of

the former Cradley High School in Homer Hill Park, Cradley. Hundreds of flowering spikes appeared among extensive patches of *Trifolium repens* which dominated the site. Spikes were also noted in clumps of *Medicago lupulina* and further plants were found among *Vicia hirsuta* although the latter was not confirmed as the host plant. There are older (1987) canalside records from SO951882, SO956924, SO953923, SO966918, SO970914, SO978929 and SO980907.

## 122. LENTIBULARIACEAE

### *Pinguicula vulgaris* L.
### Common Butterwort
2. Native. Ax. Known for many years (since 1852, C.R. Jordan, SP0997) from two mires in Sutton Park, where small populations grow in open, sunny aspects on permanently wet, infertile soils in strongly base-enriched areas of acid flushes. Locations are near Little Bracebridge Pool (most recent SP0998, AB, 2007, seen again 2011) and to the N of Longmoor Pool (most recent SP0996, MWP, ICT & PLR, 2006, seen again 2011). Readett (1971) also recorded it in SP0995. Ass: *Anagallis tenella*, *Carex hostiana*, *Carex panicea*, *Cirsium dissectum*, *Dactylorhiza fuchsii*, *Pedicularis palustris*, *Triglochin palustris*.

### *Utricularia* L.
### Bladderworts
3. Native. Free-floating insectivorous perennials, present in Sutton Park. A population was recorded in peaty water among *Menyanthes* on the W side of Blackroot Pool (SP1097, R.C. Palmer, 1997). An extensive colony was discovered in similar situations along the shady margins of Bracebridge Pool (SP098979, MWP, ICT, JaH & EVJC, det. rev. JJD, 2005). Since then follow up visits to locate flowering material have been unsuccessful, hampering a conclusive identification, although the leaf-segments of material from Bracebridge Pool have bristle-bearing teeth and the bladders have hairs characteristic of **Utricularia vulgaris** L. or **Utricularia australis** R. Br. as opposed to *U. minor*. The plant has now been observed in the fringes of the reedswamp all around Bracebridge Pool, and more recently it has also been observed in the reedswamp around Little Bracebridge Pool (SP095982, MWP, 2009).

### *Utricularia minor* L.
### Lesser Bladderwort
0. Native. One historical record for Sutton Park (SP0998, Bagnall, 1875). This may be the plant described in the previous entry.

▲ *Pedicularis sylvatica*

▲ *Orobanche minor*

▲ *Utricularia* sp. at Sutton Park

## 123. ACANTHACEAE

### *Acanthus spinosus* L.
### Spiny Bear's-Breeches
1. Neophyte. A robust perennial herb persisting where originally planted, in tall, coarse, infrequently cut herbage along a canal towpath, Smethwick (SP024889, MWP, 2004, and known at that site for 15 years). C Mediterranean.

## 123A BIGNONIACEAE
*Catalpa bignonioides* Walter (Indian Bean Tree) is grown in parks and gardens and has been occasionally recorded as a planted tree. There are mature trees on Aston University campus (SP0787), 1, Gorway Gardens Walsall (SP0297), West Park W'ton (SO9099), E end of New Hampton Road E, W'ton (SO9199) and doubtless elsewhere. SE USA.

## 124. VERBENACEAE

### *Verbena officinalis* L.
### Vervain
3. Archaeophyte. Rarely recorded. Solitary plant on derelict land, Bordesley, B'ham (SP0886, MWP, 2003); shrub holding area, B'ham Botanical Gardens (SP048852, MWP, JWP & EVJC, 2007); path, B'ham University Botanical Gardens, Winterbourne (SP0583, MWP, JWP, 2007).

### *Verbena bonariensis* L.
### Argentinian Vervain

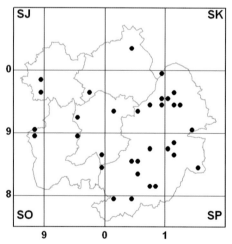

33. Neophyte. This tall herbaceous garden perennial was not considered to be hardy in Britain until quite recently but warmer summers and milder winters have seen a marked increase in its popularity and many plants now survive from one year to the next. Towards the end of the recording project seedlings and immature plants have increasingly appeared in paving cracks, gutters, garden paths, around the base of street

trees and in allotment plots and paths. S America.

## 125. AQUIFOLIACEAE

### *Ilex aquifolium* L.
### Holly

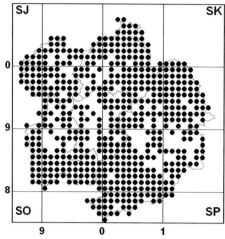

*564. Native. An evergreen shrub or small tree especially common in old hedgerows and in deciduous woodlands in fairly base-poor soils of average fertility where it is often the dominant understorey shrub. Forming pure Holly woodland or a dense understorey on dryish, acid soils in many parts of Sutton Park. Also widely planted and naturalised in more recent hedgerows, shrubberies and gardens, into which it spreads spontaneously in bird droppings. Appears to be slightly scarcer in the central urban areas. Ass: *Hedera helix, Lonicera periclymenum, Quercus robur.*

### *Ilex × altaclerensis* (Loudon) Dallim.
(*I. aquifolium × I. perado* Alton)
### Highclere Holly

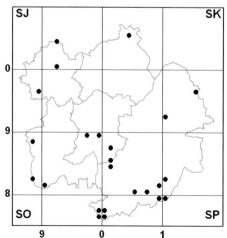

24. Neophyte. A large evergreen shrub or small tree persisting in woodland, parks and estates as a relic of cultivation or rarely possibly self-sown (e.g. seedlings

and saplings on waste ground, Lifford SP051802, CBW, 1998). Garden origin.

## 126. CAMPANULACEAE

### *Campanula patula* L.
### Spreading Bellflower
2. Native. Sect. 41, BAP, Nationally Scarce, EN. A biennial, in B&BC confined to dry, well-drained, open, sandstone faces and grass margins above and at the base of the steep-sided railway cutting of the Worcester to B'ham railway line to the W of the B4187 near Hagley (SO904814, ST & CRP, 1993, seen in 1999 & 2003). In some years populations have been known to exceed 1000 individuals (JJD, 2003). There is also an unverified record for Pedmore Lane, opposite houses (SO9182, Worcestershire Wildlife Trust, 2001).

### *Campanula persicifolia* L.
### Peach-leaved Bellflower

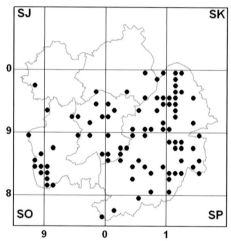

91. Neophyte. A showy, short-lived perennial, often appearing on post-housing and industrial sites recovering from recent disturbance. Also regularly appearing in neglected garden borders and paths and in paving along the base of garden walls. The frequency of this species tends to fluctuate from year to year but the patchiness of the distribution of this and several other garden Campanulas is not fully explained. White-flowered plants are quite common. Europe. Ass: *Antirrhinum majus, Arrhenatherum elatius, Cirsium vulgare, Meconopsis cambrica, Rubus fruticosus* agg., *Sedum rupestre, Tragopogon pratensis, Urtica dioica.*

### *Campanula medium* L.
### Canterbury-bells
3. Neophyte. A showy, garden biennial appearing very rarely on waste land and post-housing sites where it might be self-sown. Three post-1994 records: housing demolition site (SP009892, MWP, 1997); edge of car park (SO903844, APD, 1998);

Thimble Mill Road (SP087893, TM, PWS & M. Kodaka, 2002). Italy & SE France.

### Campanula glomerata L.
### Clustered Bellflower

1. Native; probably a garden escape in B&BC. Established colony, trackside off Redditch Road (SP039778, JJD, 1999).

### Campanula portenschlagiana Schult.
### Adria Bellflower

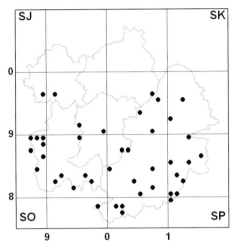

43. Neophyte. The less frequently recorded of the two low-growing, trailing *Campanula* colonists in the urban area. Well established patches are often met with, following lines of brickwork mortar and cloaking front garden walls of many of the Victorian and Edwardian terrace type houses, which characterise many parts of B'ham. Often becoming firmly established in paving and paths where the showy long-lasting flowers ensure plants are left undisturbed when occasional tidying up is carried out. Seldom far away from gardens. Croatia. Ass: *Centranthus ruber, Pseudofumaria lutea*.

### Campanula poscharskyana Degen
### Trailing Bellflower

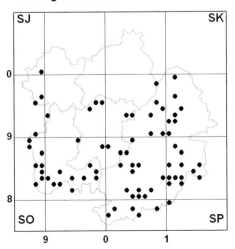

76. Neophyte. This low-growing, trailing perennial is firmly established and

colonises many garden walls and paving cracks in the urban area, particularly in the small front gardens of many of the Victorian and Edwardian terraces. Once established it rapidly colonises adjoining garden walls, where, because of its attractive, long-flowering, blue-grey, star-shaped flowers, it is often spared when weeding is carried out. More frequently escaping from habitation than *C. portenschlagiana* and recorded from both railway and canal bridge brickwork mortar. Serbia. Ass: *Centranthus ruber, Clematis vitalba, Geranium lucidum, Pseudofumaria lutea, Ranunculus repens, Urtica dioica*.

### Campanula latifolia L.
### Giant Bellflower

0. Native. Recorded in the grounds of Park House, Sutton Park (SP1196, HHF, 1988, seen again 1990 by JMP). Presumed an introduction. Not seen in present survey.

### Campanula trachelium L.
### Nettle-leaved Bellflower

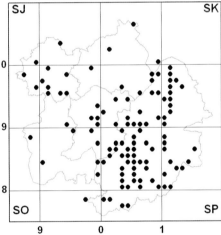

108. Native, doubtfully so in B&BC, and rarely seen in the old woodlands which are its natural habitat especially further south in UK. A plant of dry to moist, calcareous or base-rich soils, seeding prolifically into an array of habitats such as gardens, paving cracks, canal, railway and roadside hedgebanks and margins of shrub and tree plantations in semi-shaded situations. In B&BC it most frequently appears in small, rather neglected, terrace gardens in densely urbanised parts of B'ham, Sandwell and W'ton. Also rarely introduced in woodland habitat creation schemes. More noticeable white-flowered forms often occur. Ass: *Anthriscus sylvestris, Alchemilla mollis, Arrhenatherum elatius, Geranium lucidum, Geranium robertianum, Geum urbanum, Hedera helix, Mercurialis perennis, Pseudofumaria lutea, Rubus fruticosus* agg., *Urtica dioica*.

▲ *Campanula poscharskyana*

▲ *Campanula trachelium* 'Alba'

▲ *Pratia pedunculata*

▲ *Menyanthes trifoliata*

▲ *Nymphoides peltata*

### *Campanula rapunculoides* L.
### Creeping Bellflower

2. Neophyte. Rhizomatous perennial herb. An uncommon garden escape. Dry grassland, near a hedge at Bantock Park, Penn (SO896977, CBW, 2006); W of Brockmoor (SO9087, B. Jones, 1999).

### *Campanula rotundifolia* L.
### Harebell

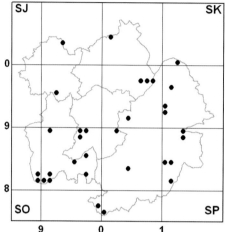

*32. Native. Ax. A widely distributed, but rapidly declining plant of old sites with open aspects and dry, infertile, and (usually) base-poor soils. Sometimes on sandstone rock faces and on scarp slopes. Old sites have often not been refound, and even when still present, it is often in much reduced numbers and a cause for concern. It has however reappeared in pasture at Northycote Farm Country Park, W'ton since grazing was reinstated (SJ933032, I. Nichols, 2007). Ass: *Agrostis capillaris*, *Galium verum*, *Pilosella officinarum*, *Rumex acetosella*, *Teucrium scorodonia*, *Ulex europaeus*, *Ulex gallii*.

### *Wahlenbergia hederacea* (L.) Rchb.
### Ivy-leaved Bellflower

0. Native. Extinct in B&BC. Sutton Park (SP0997, A.W. Wills, 1891).

### *Jasione montana* L.
### Sheep's-bit

0. Native. Extinct in B&BC. This plant of dry, sunny rock outcrops and similar stony sites is declining sharply in the English Midlands and SE. There is an old record from Sutton Park (SP0997, Bagnall, 1867) and a more doubtful one from Clayhanger, but the only definite native site in B&BC was from a tiny fragment of acidic grassland off Bustleholme Lane, Stone Cross, West Bromwich (SP015945, CW, 1993) where a population of around 100 plants was destroyed for housing in 1993. Translocation of plants and seed to similar sites nearby was unsuccessful.

### *Lobelia erinus* L.
### Garden Lobelia

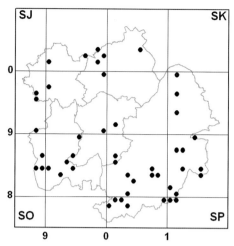

48. Neophyte. A frost-sensitive, garden perennial, grown as a summer bedding plant and generally discarded after flowering. Occasionally (and more often in recent years), plants appear in garden paths, paving cracks and on post-housing and recently disturbed ground. Trailing varieties have been recorded as self-sown below window boxes and baskets. First recorded in vc. 39 from waste ground at Sandwell Park (SP0291, BRF, 1971). S Africa.

### *Pratia pedunculata* (R. Br.) Benth.
### Blue Star-creeper, Matted Pratia

3. Neophyte. A creeping, normally dioecious, mat-forming perennial. Spreading throughout a neglected rockery, Redmoor Gardens, Penn (SO902961, CBW, 2006); plentiful in a close-cut lawn, Wordsley (SO881872, CBW, 2007); spreading through part of a regularly mown front lawn in Darbys Hill Road, Rowley Regis (SO964895, MWP, 2009), house owner recalls it being there for over 20 years. Australia and Tasmania.

### 127. MENYANTHACEAE

### *Menyanthes trifoliata* L.
### Bogbean

13. Native. Ax. Forming extensive patches along the margins and in the shallow water around Little Bracebridge Pool, Sutton Park in permanently wet, nutrient-poor and base-poor peaty soils in open and slightly shaded situations and in other similar places around the Park. It was known there to Bagnall in the 19th century. It also occurs in a wider range of ponds and pools, in other areas of B&BC, often in much more nutrient- and base-rich conditions. Some may well be deliberate introductions although often the populations are large, vigorous and well-established and may sometimes represent

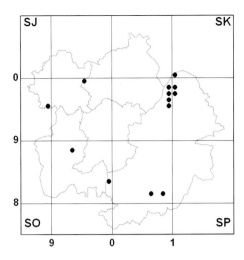

survival subsequent to some nutrient-enrichment. Ass: *Acorus calamus, Carex rostrata, Comarum palustre, Nymphoides peltata, Ranunculus lingua.*

### *Nymphoides peltata* Kuntze
**Fringed Water-lily**

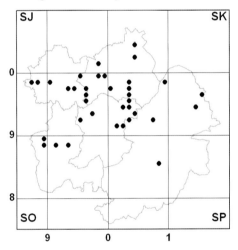

36. Introduced native. Nationally Scarce as a native in the Fens and the Thames Valley. An aquatic, rhizomatous perennial, its distribution in B&BC is believed to be chiefly from deliberate or accidental introductions of discards from garden ponds or possibly on the feet of water fowl. It has become firmly established in pools and some of the quieter sections of canals mainly in the N of our area, and where left unrestricted, often forms extensive patches across the water surface. It had no or very few records in our area in the 1970s. Ass: *Ceratophyllum demersum, Galium uliginosum, Hydrocotyle vulgaris, Lemna minor, Menyanthes trifoliata, Nuphar lutea, Persicaria amphibia, Potamogeton pectinatus.*

### 128. ASTERACEAE

### *Echinops exaltatus* Schrad.
**Globe-thistle**
1. Neophyte. Well established garden

escape growing among tall perennials on the top of a railway bank in Coalpool Lane, Walsall (SP0199, MWP & ICT, 2001). E & SE Europe.

### *Echinops bannaticus* Rochel ex Schrad.
**Blue Globe-thistle**
5. Neophyte. Biennial to perennial herb, first reported in vc. 39 from a canal towpath at Wordsley (SO8986, FGB, 1980). Recent records: Dads Lane, Ten Acres recreation ground (SP060818, JWP, 1995); waste ground, Hill Top (SP001869, B. Westwood, 1996); Small Heath, derelict ground near church (SP097846, CBW, 1997); derelict allotment, Yardley (SP125855, CBW, 1997); abandoned garden, Pheasey playing fields (SP066963, MWP, ICT, PLR & JaH, 2006). SE Europe.

### *Carlina vulgaris* L.
**Carline Thistle**
2. Native. Ax. A monocarpic perennial or biennial of skeletal soils and screes on limestone and other basic rocks. At two B&BC sites: Sedgley Beacon, in lightly grassed slopes in the limestone quarry (SO919949, BH, 1999, still present 2011), also recorded there at SO922946 in the 1980s. In the 1980s it was also abundant on rubble slopes in the dolerite quarries on Barrow Hill, where it has been long known and has been recorded at several locations (SO914896, SO915895, SO916896) but is now becoming scarce due to scrubbing over. (SO914896, CBW, 2006) seems to be the most recent record there.

### *Arctium lappa* L.
**Greater Burdock**

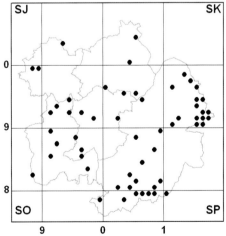

57. Archaeophyte. Biennial to perennial herb. Rough ground, canal, river and railway banks, sewage works where small localised colonies occur growing with tall perennials of disturbed places. Open situations in fairly nutrient and base-rich soils. Commoner in parts of the E than

in the W, and may sometimes have been over-recorded for large varieties of *A. minus*. Ass: *Arrhenatherum elatius, Artemisia vulgaris, Cirsium arvense, Rumex obtusifolius.*

### *Arctium minus* sensu lato
**Lesser Burdock**

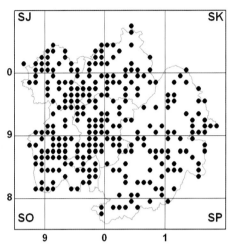

*285. Native. Biennial or monocarpic perennial of roadside, railway and canal banks, rough and waste ground in open and shady places in all but the most acid, but usually nutrient-rich, soils, particularly frequent along shady path margins. Ass: *Alliaria petiolata, Arrhenatherum elatius, Artemisia vulgaris, Cirsium arvense, Geum urbanum, Rumex obtusifolius.*

Three taxa have been recognised but have not been consistently separated in the survey. Two make up ***Arctium minus*** (Hill) Bernh. Of these **subsp. *minus*** seems to be the commonest, being described throughout the range. **Subsp. *pubens*** (Bab.) P. Fourn. has two records: Stockland Green (SP0791, MWP, 2005) and rough, grassy area of a public open space, Titford/Whiteheath (SO983883, WAT, conf. RM, 1992). A third taxon constitutes ***Arctium nemorosum*** Lej. (**Wood Burdock**) which is found particularly in open woods and other shady places. This has two old records in vc. 37 (SO98W and SO98Y, both by JJD in the 1980s), one recent tetrad record (SO88Z, CBW, 2005) and our records for *Arctium minus sensu lato* may well include further records.

### *Carduus crispus* L.
(*C. acanthoides* auct. Non L.)
**Welted Thistle**
24. Native. Tall biennial of river, canal and railway banks, field borders, riverside meadows, amongst tall, coarse vegetation on fertile soils. Widely distributed but relatively uncommon and often occurring as isolated individuals or in small groups. Many of the records seem to be associated with the River Tame corridor and there

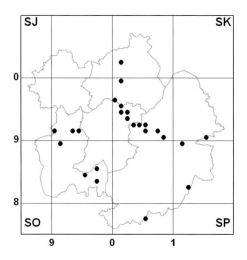

are also populations on the limestone areas associated with the Wren's Nest and Park Lime Pits. There are also old records from Sutton Park. Ass: *Anthriscus sylvestris*, *Artemisia vulgaris*, *Arrhenatherum elatius*, *Brassica napus*, *Cirsium* spp., *Petasites hybridus*.

## *Carduus nutans* L.
## Musk Thistle

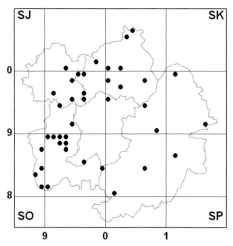

*40. Native. Biennial to perennial. Widely distributed but generally scarce and often not long persisting. In a wide range of open situations from cultivation to grassland in well drained calcareous and base-rich, fairly nutrient-rich substrates. Recorded from roadside, canal and railway banks and individually or in small groups on post-housing and industrial sites. Ass: *Agrostis stolonifera*, *Artemisia absinthium*, *Cirsium vulgare*, *Crepis vesicaria*, *Linaria vulgaris*.

## *Cirsium eriophorum* (L.) Scop.
## Woolly Thistle

0. Native. This biennial of lime-rich soils may have a rare casual occurrence in B&BC. A few old reports and none from our limestone areas: single plant, edge of field/pathside, Woodgate Valley Country

Park (SO995830, WAT, 1992); grounds of Woodbrooke (SP036814, T. Thompson, 1985); Radleys Walk and adjacent land (SP160858, J. Turner & J. Maiden, 1987); Home Wood (SP133954, JPM & A. Sestakovs, 1987).

## *Cirsium vulgare* (Savi) Ten.
## Spear Thistle

*668. Native. 'Injurious weed'. Very common biennial on roadside verges, waste ground, in grassland, neglected gardens and lawns. In similar situations to, and often with, *Cirsium arvense* but never as invasive. Ass: *Arrhenatherum elatius*, *Artemisia vulgaris*, *Cirsium arvense*, *Elytrigia repens*, *Rumex obtusifolius*.

## *Cirsium dissectum* (L.) Hill
## Meadow Thistle

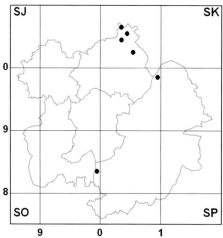

6. Native. Ax. Perennial herb. Nutrient-poor and acid but base-enriched marshy fields and flushes in waterlogged soil in sheltered, sunny, open situations. Very local. Long-known from Sutton Park but seems much declined since Readett's Flora of Sutton Park (1971) which recorded it in SP0995, SP0996 and SP1096 and earlier (Bagnall, 1876) in SP0997; recently only found in mires near Little Bracebridge Pool (SP0998, MWP & ICT, 2005). A second surviving cluster of sites is in Walsall, where it persists in some quantity in wet grazing land E of the main subsidence pool on Clayhanger SSSI (last seen SK0360444–6, ICT & EVJC, 2006) although it seems to have been more widespread and abundant in the 1980s before the site was partly ploughed. Individual small patches or individual plants occur on Clayhanger Common (last seen SK045052, ICT, 2008); in Castlehill fields (last seen at SK053026, ICT, 2008) and in an old pasture near Brownhills Common (SK033064, ICT & SAHA, 2010). Also recorded from wet meadow in Woodgate Valley (S0998834, ICT, 1998, seen again 2006). Records for Lark Rise

fields (SK124000, J. Turner, 1987) and Holly Wood (SP053945, DH & P. Allenby, 1984) have not been refound. Ass: *Achillea ptarmica*, *Anagallis tenella*, *Carex hostiana*, *Carex panicea*, *Centaurea nigra*, *Dactylorhiza fuchsii*, *Odontites vernus*, *Pedicularis palustris*, *Pinguicula vulgaris*, *Ranunculus acris*, *Senecio aquaticus*, *Succisa pratensis*, *Triglochin palustris*.

## *Cirsium × forsteri* (Sm.) Loudon
(*C. dissectum* × *C. palustre*)
0. Native. In the herbarium of R.C.L. Burges collected in 1937 from a moist pasture above Little Bracebridge Pool at Sutton Park (?SP0997) according to Readett (1971).

## *Cirsium palustre* (L.) Scop.
## Marsh Thistle

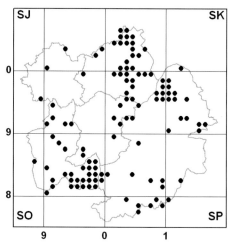

*112. Native. Ax. Biennial. Locally common in marshy fields, riverside and poolside meadows, edges and clearings in wet woodlands in full light to slight shade in poorly drained, moist to wet, moderately acid, infertile soils. In B&BC it mainly occurs in the countryside areas and in remnants of unimproved land. Ass: *Agrostis canina*, *Deschampsia cespitosa*, *Dryopteris carthusiana*, *Holcus lanatus*, *Juncus effusus*, *Juncus inflexus*, *Mentha aquatica*, *Molinia caerulea*, *Senecio aquaticus*, *Succisa pratensis*.

## *Cirsium arvense* (L.) Scop.
## Creeping Thistle

*703. Native. 'Injurious weed'. Rough and waste ground, field borders, cultivated land, neglected gardens, overgrazed pasture, habitat creation schemes etc. Very common in a wide range of situations and soil types, avoiding only the most acidic. Particularly abundant on fertile ground where large stands form from creeping lateral rhizomes if its presence is ignored. Ass: *Arrhenatherum elatius*, *Artemisia vulgaris*, *Cirsium vulgare*, *Elytrigia repens*, *Lolium perenne*, *Rumex obtusifolius*, *Trifolium repens*.

The white-flowered form has been recorded in SO9897 and doubtless occurs elsewhere.

## *Onopordum acanthium* L.
## Cotton Thistle

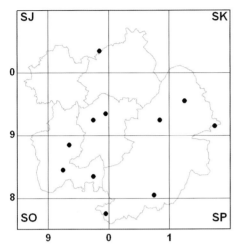

11. Archaeophyte. Tall biennial of roadside banks, rough ground and spoil heaps. Often observed as a first year rosette and not surviving to flower the second year. Occasionally creating a spectacular show with its flowering spikes attaining well over two metres in height. Best considered as a casual garden escape. Europe.

## *Serratula tinctoria* L.
## Saw-wort

1. Native. Perennial of old species-rich grassland, only recorded in our area as one small patch in damp, modestly species-rich grassland adjacent to E side of M5 in the Pinewood area of the Woodgate Valley (SO989821, CRP, 1997, seen again 2003 & 2009). Ass: *Anthoxanthum odoratum*, *Betonica officinalis*, *Centaurea nigra*, *Poa humilis*, *Sanguisorba officinalis*, *Succisa pratensis*.

## *Centaurea scabiosa* L.
## Greater Knapweed

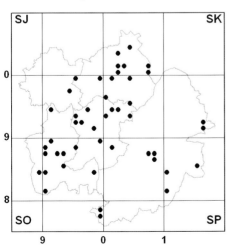

*47. Native. Ax. Perennial herb. Railway, canal and roadside banks and limestone and dolerite quarries in warm, sunny, open situations on well-drained calcareous to slightly acidic, infertile, usually stony or gravelly soils and spoils. Often deliberately introduced and persisting in 'wild flower mixes' along canal towpaths and walkways with other showy plants such as *Centaurea cyanus*, *Glebionis segetum*, *Knautia arvensis*, *Malva moschata*, etc. Otherwise ass: *Agrimonia eupatoria*, *Briza media*, *Bromopsis erecta*, *Chamerion angustifolium*, *Knautia arvensis*, *Leontodon hispidus*, *Leucanthemum vulgare*, *Linaria vulgaris*, *Linum catharticum*, *Picris hieracioides*, *Senecio erucifolius*.

## *Centaurea montana* L.
## Perennial Cornflower

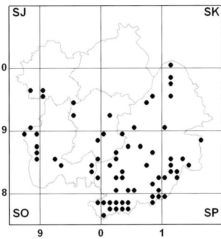

69. Neophyte. An erect rhizomatous perennial herb often discarded from gardens and persisting on roadside banks, recently cleared post-housing sites, banks of traveller spoil and sometimes spreading from gardens into nearby paving cracks, apparently especially in the S and W. Mountains of C & S Europe.

## *Centaurea cyanus* L.
## Cornflower

19. Archaeophyte. Sect. 41, BAP, Nationally Scarce. This beautiful weed of arable field crops, especially cereals, was defeated by seed cleaning and selective herbicides and had very few records in our area in Edees (1972) and Cadbury *et al.* (1971). It is now commonly included in 'wild flower mixes' and deliberately sown along canal towpaths, school wildflower gardens and suchlike where new plants appear for a year or two. Rarely, casuals appear on post-housing sites and in paving cracks, self-sown from nearby garden plantings. Seed is however thought to remain viable in soil for many years and there is one

▲ *Carduus nutans*

▲ *Cirsium dissectum*

▲ *Cirsium palustre*

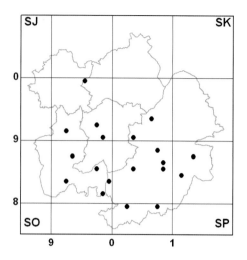

modern record from a recently ploughed and reseeded ley, Illey Lane (SO983817, ST, 1997), well away from the urban area. Ass: *Glebionis segetum, Agrostemma githago, Leucanthemum vulgare*

### Centaurea × gerstlaueri Erdner
### Hybrid Knapweed

0. Native. This plant was recorded by G.C. Druce in Tipton (SO99) in 1923 and in rough grassland by a canal in Edgbaston (SP0685, D.A. Cadbury, 1935–51, seen again 1971). It is considered to derive from crosses between *C. debeauxii* Gren. & Godr. And *C. nigra* or between their hybrid and the formerly naturalised *C. jacea* L., or from plants introduced with *C. jacea*.

### Centaurea nigra L.
### Common Knapweed

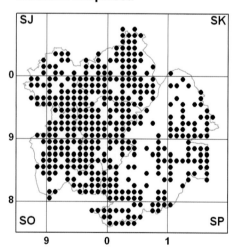

*425. Native. A perennial herb of canal, railway and roadside banks and areas of waste ground and often abundant in impoverished rough grassland, it is also a characteristic ('constant') species of our typical lowland, species-rich haymeadow and pasture, mesotrophic ('neutral') grassland type. Occurs on sunny to partially shaded sites on a wide range of soil types avoiding only the most acid, the

permanently waterlogged, the very dry and the most nutrient-rich. Surprisingly local in parts of B'ham. Ass: *Agrostis capillaris, Arrhenatherum elatius, Dactylis glomerata, Festuca rubra, Lathyrus pratensis, Lotus corniculatus, Plantago lanceolata, Ranunculus acris, Ranunculus bulbosus, Trifolium pratense, Trifolium repens.*

Many segregates have been described within this species and have not been distinguished in our survey. Plants in which the outer flowers are much longer than the inner (as in *C. scabiosa*) are rare in our area and are usually associated with introductions, e.g. at Kitchen Lane, W'ton (SJ964026).

### Centaurea debeauxii Gren. & Godr.
### (C. nemoralis Jord.)
### Chalk Knapweed

0. Native. This possibly much overlooked species of light, often calcareous soils, which is either very similar to, or alternatively not distinct from, *C. nigra*, was once recorded in Beaconhill Quarry, Sedgley (SO9194, BRF, 1974).

### Carthamus tinctorius L.
### Safflower

1. Casual. From a post-housing site in Greets Green, West Bromwich (SO985917, MWP, 1997). The source was apparently parrot food. Also an old record from dumped soil, roadside bank, Ryecroft (SP016998, JPM, 1990). SW Asia.

### Cichorium intybus L.
### Chicory

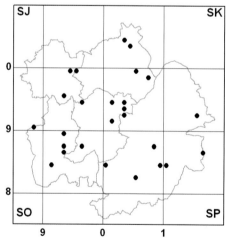

26. Archaeophyte. An uncommon perennial herb found occasionally in rough grassland and roadside banks and verges and generally considered as naturalised from original introductions. Long-persisting in rough grassland at the RSPB Reserve in Sandwell Valley (SP035927) since its introduction in an 'acid grassland' seed mix in the 1980s.

### Lapsana communis L.
### Nipplewort

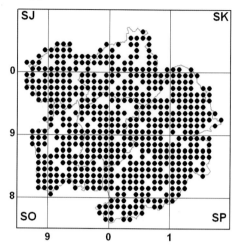

*585. Native. Annual of open and shaded situations in hedge banks, wood margins, field borders, roadsides, waste ground and a weed of cultivation in allotments etc. Found in all but the most acidic and impoverished of soils. Often forming sizeable colonies where left undisturbed. Ass: *Alliaria petiolata, Epilobium montanum, Geranium robertianum, Geum urbanum, Urtica dioica.*

### Hypochaeris radicata L.
### Cat's-ear

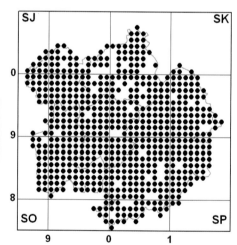

*635. Native. A very common perennial herb of grassy banks, roadside verges, waste ground and other neglected but not frequently disturbed areas in sunny well drained situations in base-poor to base-rich, fairly nutrient-poor soils. Also a common weed of amenity grassland and well-manicured lawns where it tolerates regular mowing although seldom allowed to flower in such situations. Also a regular constituent of unimproved grasslands. Ass: *Agrostis capillaris, Bellis perennis, Festuca rubra, Lolium perenne, Plantago lanceolata, Trifolium repens.*

### *Hypochaeris glabra* L.
### Smooth Cat's-ear

1. Native. Perennial. One robust plant appeared on ground laid to plastic mesh with sandy, possibly imported, soil, W of main entrance, Russell's Hall Hospital Dudley (SO920894, MES, 2012). Ass: *Anagallis arvensis, Conyza canadensis, Conyza sumatrensis, Trifolium arvense* and other spp. typical of sandy waste ground.

### *Scorzoneroides autumnalis* (L.) Moench
(*Leontodon autumnalis* L.)
### Autumn Hawkbit

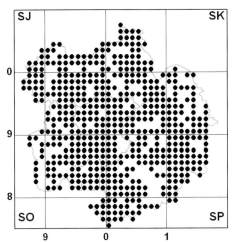

*542. Native. A small perennial of roadside verges, amenity grassland, lawns, paving, waste ground and other grassy areas. One of the commonest yellow-flowering Composites and often forms a cheerful sight along grassy central reservations and roadside verges where abundant flowering can continue well into the autumn when the cutting regime tapers off. Also a frequent weed of poorly drained, compacted lawns and amenity grassland and a constituent of damper species-rich grasslands. In all soil types, avoiding only the most acid, and made up of a large number of ecological types. Ass: *Agrostis capillaris, Cerastium fontanum, Hypochaeris radicata, Taraxacum* spp., *Trifolium repens*.

### *Leontodon hispidus* L.
### Rough Hawkbit

*65. Native. Ax. A widespread but infrequent perennial herb of dry, well-drained, nutrient-poor, base-rich and calcareous soils and a constituent of old, species-rich grassland. Typically found on rough grassy banks and in open grassland and only seldom occurring as a 'weed' in the managed grassland areas associated with the built-up areas where it is generally scarce and restricted to tiny pockets of suitable vegetation. From the map such sites are clearly much commoner in the

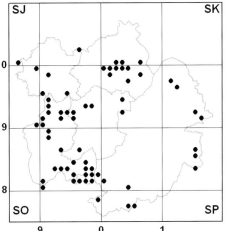

Black Country than in B'ham, both in countryside and industrial areas. Ass: *Carex flacca, Cynosurus cristatus, Daucus carota, Festuca rubra, Linum catharticum, Lotus corniculatus, Rhinanthus minor, Trifolium dubium*.

### *Leontodon saxatilis* Lam.
(*L. taraxacoides* (Vill.) Mérat)
### Lesser Hawkbit

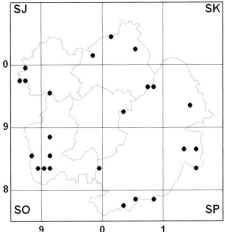

*24. Native. In fairly dry pastures and quarries and in urban areas on well-drained grassy banks, roadside verges and lawns on usually base-intermediate (but occasionally quite base-poor), fairly nutrient-poor soils in open, sunny situations. In suitable habitats large colonies may occur and populations along well-drained roadside verges and central-reservation grassland seem unaffected by regular mowing. Very rarely as a weed in garden beds and paving. Ass: *Agrostis capillaris, Bellis perennis, Cynosurus cristatus, Festuca rubra, Hypochaeris radicata, Polygonum aviculare, Sagina procumbens, Scorzoneroides autumnalis*.

### *Picris hieracioides* L.
### Hawkweed Oxtongue

12. Native. Ax. Quarries, canal banks,

▲ *Centaurea nigra*

▲ *Cichorium intybus*

▲ *Leontodon hispidus*

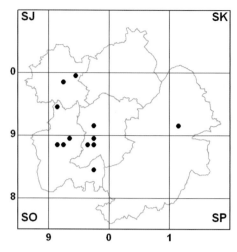

maculosa, *Phleum pratense, Ranunculus repens, Rubus fruticosus* agg. *Senecio jacobaea, Sisymbrium orientale, Sonchus oleraceus.*

### *Tragopogon pratensis* L.
### Goat's-beard

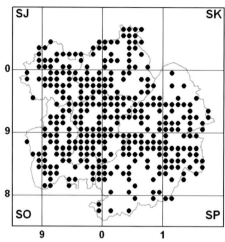

\*354. Native and Alien. A common annual or biennial appearing in a wide range of unmanaged habitats such as canal, railway and roadside banks, rough grassy places, neglected and disturbed ground, roadside verges and overgrown gardens in industrial and residential areas and less commonly in countryside areas although it will sometimes survive well in dry pasture and meadows. Typically in sunny, exposed sites on nutrient- and base-medium to -rich soils and often growing amongst tall grasses and herbs. Ass: *Arrhenatherum elatius, Artemisia vulgaris, Dactylis glomerata, Holcus lanatus, Linaria vulgaris.*

Segregation of the three subspecies has often not been attempted by our surveyors but most records so identified refer to the native **subsp. minor** (Mill.) Wahlenb. A few are for the neophyte **subsp. pratensis**: Saltwells LNR disused car park and roadside verge (SO932875, J. Akers, 1998); Amblecote (SO895858, APD, 2008); by cycle path in long grass, Stirchley (SP057814, D. Broughton, 1997) and a slightly earlier record from a grassland mound at Bartley Green (SP007825, CBW, 1994). Europe.

### *Tragopogon porrifolius* L.
### Salsify

9. Neophyte; casual in B&BC. A biennial, rarely escaping from cultivation as self-sown individuals in neglected allotment gardens and even less commonly on to waste land, pavements and grassy verges. Very similar to *Tragopogon pratensis* so could possibly go

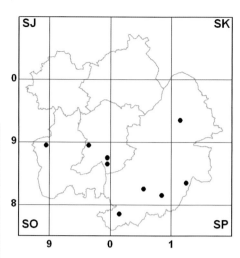

unnoticed in the absence of flowers. Mediterranean

### *Sonchus arvensis* L.
### Perennial Sowthistle

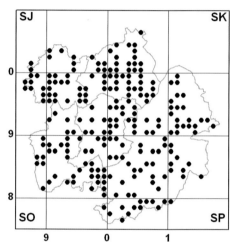

\*227. Native. A summer-flowering perennial herb of frequent occurrence, found in open situations along roadside verges (typically the very edge), on waste ground, arable field borders, canal and railway banks and neglected gardens. Showing a preference for nutrient-enriched soil. Ass: *Arrhenatherum elatius, Cirsium arvense, Elytrigia repens, Lactuca serriola, Rumex obtusifolius, Senecio jacobaea.*

### *Sonchus oleraceus* L.
### Smooth Sowthistle

\***657**. Native. A very common annual or overwintering weed in the urban area and found in all sorts of disturbed ground, allotments, gardens, paving, roadside verges, field borders and also in the more rural areas as a weed of arable field margins. Typically in sites with sunny, open aspects and tolerant of a wide range of soil types avoiding only the most acidic. Frequently growing with or near *Sonchus asper*. Ass: *Chenopodium album, Cirsium vulgare, Polygonum aviculare,*

roadside verges, derelict railway tracks in drought-liable, nutrient-poor, base-rich soils in open, sunny situations. Infrequent in the urban area but where it does appear, becoming locally common and more persistent than *Helminthotheca echioides*. Large colonies seem to be increasing along the derelict railway track at Blowers Green, Dudley and on the nearby roadside verges along the A461 Dudley Southern By-pass. Alien and native subsp. have not been distinguished. Ass: *Centaurea scabiosa, Leontodon hispidus, Linaria vulgaris, Senecio erucifolius, Trifolium arvense.*

### *Helminthotheca echioides* (L.) Holub
(*Picris echioides* L.)
### Bristly Oxtongue

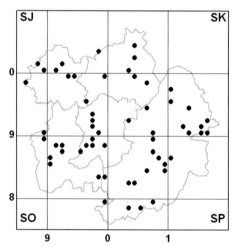

58. Archaeophyte. An annual or biennial of infrequent but widespread occurrence and generally associated with waste and disturbed bare ground and roughish, unmanaged banks in open, sunny situations. Populations tend to be transient and very small or restricted to the odd individual. This is possibly a species which spreads on the tyres of construction vehicles. Ass: *Cirsium arvense, Dactylis glomerata, Persicaria*

*Rumex obtusifolius, Senecio vulgaris, Sonchus asper.*

### *Sonchus asper* (L.) Hill
### Prickly Sowthistle

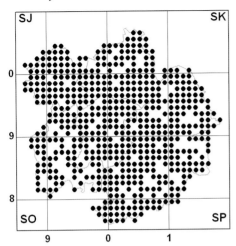

*577. Native. Annual of disturbed and waste ground, gardens, paving, roadside verges, field borders, etc. on dry to damp well-drained soil. Much the same habitat requirements and associated species as *Sonchus oleraceus* but perhaps slightly less common.

**Subsp. *glaucescens*** (Jord.) Ball is a biennial variant which has been recorded three times in SP08 and SO98 and is probably more widespread.

### *Lactuca serriola* L.
### Prickly Lettuce

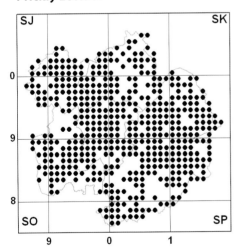

*500. Archaeophyte. An increasingly common, overwintering or spring-germinating annual of roadsides, railway and canal banks, disturbed waste ground, neglected gardens, paving and bare areas around shrub borders, especially those which have been irregularly treated with glyphosate herbicide. Usually on nutrient-rich and base-rich soils. Ass: *Artemisia vulgaris, Campanula trachelium, Epilobium ciliatum, Senecio jacobaea, Sonchus arvensis, Urtica dioica.*

Two forms have been recognised, **forma *integrifolia*** (Gray) S.D. Prince & R.N. Carter, with stem-leaves undivided and **forma *serriola*** with stem-leaves deeply pinnately lobed. The former is by far the more frequent of the two but mixed populations are found. Generally they have not been distinguished in this survey.

### *Lactuca sativa* L.
### Garden Lettuce
2. Casual. In a pavement crack (SO9292, MWP & APD, 2004) and an allotment (SP0982, ICT, 2008). Origin in cultivation.

### *Lactuca virosa* L.
### Great Lettuce

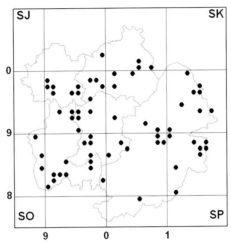

67. Native. Evidence suggests that this tall annual or biennial herb has increased during the survey period. The first reliable record for vc. 39 was in 1990, from a building plot, Regis Road, Tettenhall (SJ882009, BRF). Plants are typically found in rough, coarsely vegetated grassy field borders, among unmanaged canal towpath vegetation and less often on land recovering from recent disturbance such as recently abandoned allotments where records are generally for individual plants. Small to medium sized colonies discovered on other sites appear to be more permanent, and where these have been checked in subsequent years populations appear to be increasing annually. Ass: *Arrhenatherum elatius, Digitalis purpurea, Urtica dioica.*

### *Cicerbita macrophylla* (Willd.) Wallr.
### Common Blue-sowthistle
5. Neophyte. All records close to gardens: overgrown allotments, Lifford (SP064803, JWP, 1995); garden, Pedmore (SO916824, JWP & CRP, 1999); large patch behind houses, Lodge Hill (SP029832, CBW, 1997); two patches by a stream, Dogkennel Lane, Halesowen (SO968830, WAT, 2001); a small persistent colony established on a roadside

verge at the junction of Grove Lane, Ox Leys Road, Sutton Coldfield (SP166950, MWP, ICT, JaH & JWP, 2006). Also old record from Sutton Park (SP1197).

### *Mycelis muralis* (L.) Dumort.
### Wall Lettuce

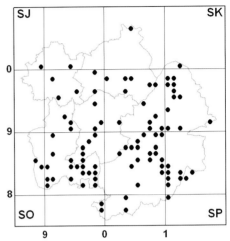

94. Native. A widely distributed but rather uncommon perennial herb of dry, well drained, moderately acid to calcareous soils in shady situations and typically found growing from cracks on garden walls and on shady hedge banks and woodland margins. Usually colonies are relatively small or restricted to a very few individuals. Ass: *Alliaria petiolata, Cymbalaria muralis, Epilobium montanum, Geranium robertianum.*

### *Taraxacum* spp.
### Dandelions
*706. Ubiquitous species of pastures, meadows, lawns, roadside verges, gardens, disturbed ground in open, sunny aspects but also tolerant of some shade. Colonists of lawns and amenity grassland subject to regular mowing.

The genus has not been systematically studied in B&BC. The following account is based entirely on data kindly provided from the National *Taraxacum* Database, which holds all UK validated records for BSBI. This was significantly supplemented for B&BC by a series of field visits in the vc. 37 part of B&BC led by A.W. Reid and J.J. Day in March–May 2008. The B&BC list focuses on records from the period 1995 to 2010, although earlier records are mentioned. The treatment of the genus follows that of Dudman & Richards (1997) as slightly modified in Sell & Murrell (2006). Records are from vc. 37 except where indicated.

### Section 1. Erythosperma (H. Lindb.) Dahlst.
Small to medium-sized perennial herbs found in dry places in rocky and sandy

ground and in short grassland, usually on S-facing, unshaded slopes in shallow soil. Candidate axiophytes.

Plants of this character occur on blast furnace spoil at Fens Pools (SO9288) and on Pelsall Common (SK01046), but records have not been validated.

**Taraxacum lacistophyllum** (Dahlst.) Raunk.
Thin grassland on conglomerate mound, Barnford Hill Park, SO9987.

**Taraxacum brachyglossum** (Dahlst.) Raunk.
1950 record from Sutton Park, vc. 38 (SP0895).

### Section 4. Spectabilia (Dahlst.) Dahlst.
Small to medium-sized perennial herbs from damp, usually acid places. Mostly montane or submontane, although one species (*T. faeroense*) is Britain's most widespread dandelion. Candidate axiophytes.

**Taraxacum faeroense** (Dahlst.) Dahlst.
Unimproved mesotrophic grassland, SO9982. Records from 1950s from S B'ham (SP08) and Sutton Park, vc. 38 (SP0998, SP1096, SP1097, SP1098).

### Section 6. Naevosa M.P. Christ.
Small to robust perennial herbs with leaves heavily spotted with large dark spots, and generally with a northern and western distribution in the UK. Candidate axiophytes.

**Taraxacum euryphyllum** (Dahlst.) Hjelt
Pasture, Lower Illey, SO9881.

### Section 7. Celtica A.J. Richards
Medium-sized perennial herbs. Species of old hedgerows, woodland margins and riversides. Candidate axiophytes.

**Taraxacum gelertii** Raunk.
Illey pasture (SO9881); Damp wooded roadside bank, Manor Farm Park, Northfield (SP0281).

**Taraxacum bracteatum** Dahlst.
Clent Breccia outcrop, hill slope, trackside and grassland (some unimproved). SO9788, SO9982, SP0178, SP0180, SP0278, SP0280. Old record from 1950s from a B'ham street, vc. 38 (SP0786).

**Taraxacum subbracteatum** A.J. Richards
In grass by River Rea, SP0177; disturbed trackside, River Rea corridor, SP0178; scrubby bank, Fox Hollies Park, SP1282.

**Taraxacum duplidentifrons** Dahlst.
Two 1952 records from Sutton Park, vc. 38, both from SP1096.

**Taraxacum celticum** A.J. Richards
Unimproved hill grassland, SO9181; garden, Selly Oak SP0482.

**Taraxacum hesperium** C.C. Haw.
Allotments verge, Oldbury, SO9987.

**Taraxacum excellens** Dahlst.
Nettles under Oak by path, SO9583.

**Taraxacum nordstedtii** Dahlst.
Unimproved grassland, Lyeclose Farm W of M5, SO9882; roadside grass verge, Hawkesley, SP0477; 1878 record, Sutton Coldfield, vc. 38, SP19. Also a 1951 record: locally abundant in mire, Sutton Park, vc. 38, SP0998.

**Taraxacum unguilobum** Dahlst.
Croftdown Road, Harborne, vc. 39, SP0184. Also a 1951 record from Sutton Park, vc. 38, SP0998.

### Section 8. Hamata H. Øllg.
Mostly medium-sized perennial herbs. Ecology predominantly 'weedy'.

**Taraxacum hamatum** Raunk.
Both wasteland and unimproved grassland sites, SO9788, SO9881, SO9882, SP0078, SP0178, SP0280. Also a 1878 record from Sutton Coldfield, vc. 38, SP19.

**Taraxacum subhamatum** M.P. Christ.
Longbridge, SP0076.

**Taraxacum hamiferum** Dahlst.
Base of conglomerate mound, SO9987; road verge, SP1080; base of roadside tree, SP1283.

**Taraxacum quadrans** H. Øllg.
Fox Hollies Park Round Pool – scrubby bank, SP1282.

**Taraxacum pseudohamatum** Dahlst.
Grassland in road and track verges, in allotments, by streams, a wooded bank. SO9783, SO9788, SO9978, SO9986, SP0076, SP0078, SP0178, SP0181, SP0278, SP0281, SP0477, SP0482.

**Taraxacum prionum** Hagend., Soest & Zevenb.
Manor Farm Park near Merritts Brook – damp grassland, SP0280.

**Taraxacum boekmanii** Borgv.
Gardens, road verges, waste ground, in mostly recent but some old grassland. SO9788, SO9789, SO9881, SO9978, SO9986, SP0083, SP0177, SP0178, SP0181, SP0477, SP0478, SP1080.

**Taraxacum atactum** Sahlin & Soest
Roadside marl bank, SP0078; grass by river,

SP0178; damp wooded roadside bank, SP0281.

**Taraxacum hamatiforme** Dahlst.
Allotments, road verges, a hedgebank, grassland by stream; all secondary sites. SO9783, SO9978, SO9986, SO9987, SP0178, SP0181, SP0980, SP1081.

### Section 9. Ruderalia Kirschner, H. Øllg. & Štìpánek
Usually robust perennial herbs. Very common plants of grassland, waste places, paths, roadsides and walls. By far the largest section, with many introduced species.

**Taraxacum pannucium** Dahlst.
Cofton Park, road edge, SP0076.

**Taraxacum alatum** H. Lindb.
By road edge, SP0078, grass verge, SP0477. Also a 1954 record, from vc. 38 (SP0484).

**Taraxacum insigne** Ekman ex M.P. Christ. & Wiinst.
Edge of industrial units, Hawkesley, SP0477; 1986 record: wood clearing, Tettenhall, vc. 39, SO8899.

**Taraxacum laticordatum** Markl.
Laneside, Lappal, SO9783; road verge, SP1080.

**Taraxacum lepidum** M.P. Christ.
Scarp grassland, Wychbury Hill, SO9181.

**Taraxacum croceiflorum** Dahlst.
Grass by Mill Race bridge, SP1081, rough grass, SP0177.

**Taraxacum lacerifolium** G.E. Haglund
Grassland, Bury Hill, SO9789.

**Taraxacum stenacrum** Dahlst.
Allotment, Oldbury, SO9987.

**Taraxacum cherwellense** A.J. Richards
(*T. stenoglossum* Dahlst. Non Brenner)
Grassland, Bury Hill, SO9788. A 1986 record: mortared wall crevice, vc. 39, SO8899.

**Taraxacum undulatiflorum** M.P. Christ.
Grassland on road verges, base of street tree, by a stream, on a golf course, on a quarry slope, SO9788, SO9789, SO9986, SO9986, SP0177, SP0178, SP0477, SP0478, SP0478.

**Taraxacum piceatum** Dahlst.
Bury Hill grassland, SO9788; A441 central reservation, SP0377.

**Taraxacum tumentilobum** Markl. ex Puol.
Woodgate Valley Country Park, SP0083.

**Taraxacum ancistrolobum** Dahlst.
Pasture, Illey, SO9881.

**Taraxacum sellandii** Dahlst.
Grassy banks by roads, by a river, in a car park, in a park, on a golf course, SP0177, SP0178, SP0278, SP0477, SP0478, SP0981.

**Taraxacum angustisquameum** Dahlst. ex H. Lindb.
Pavement edge, SP0981.

**Taraxacum adiantifrons** Ekman ex Dahlst.
Grassy edge of scrub, SP0477.

**Taraxacum retroflexum** H. Lindb.
Foyle Road, Hawkesley – disturbed ground, SP0478.

**Taraxacum aequilobum** Dahlst.
Grassy road verges, an allotment, SO9986, SO9987, SP0178, SP0181, SP0477, SP0478. A 1974 record from B'ham, vc. 38 (SP0485).

**Taraxacum latissimum** Palmgr.
Cofton Park, SP0076.

**Taraxacum exacutum** Markl.
Road edge, SP0981. 1986 record from Tettenhall, vc. 39 (SJ8800).

**Taraxacum leptodon** Markl.
Grassy road verge, Frankley, SO9978.

**Taraxacum rhamphodes** G.E. Haglund
Roadside marl bank, Frankley, SP0078.

**Taraxacum cordatum** Palmgr.
Grassland, SO9789; road verge, SP0278; garden lawn, SP0477.

**Taraxacum sagittipotens** Dahlst. & R. Ohlsen ex G.E. Haglund
Old Hawne Colliery, SO9584.

**Taraxacum ekmanii** Dahlst.
Old wood bank, SP0477.

**Taraxacum oblongatum** Dahlst.
Damp wooded roadside bank, Manor Park Farm, SP0281.

**Taraxacum cophocentrum** Dahlst.
Scrubby grassland, Bury Hill, SO9788.

**Taraxacum pachymerum** G.E. Haglund
Shenley Fields Allotments, SP0181; grass bank, Yardley Wood, SP1080.

**Taraxacum dilatatum** H. Lindb.
By mill race, SP0177; road verge, SP0178; trackside SP0278.

**Taraxacum polyodon** Dahlst.
Wall base by A4123, SO9986; Shenley Road

Allotments, SP0181; edge of industrial units, also in mown grass, SP0477.

**Taraxacum xanthostigma** H. Lindb.
Grassland, Bury Hill, SO9788.

**Taraxacum 'anceps'** H. Øllg. ined.
Grass verge, SP0478.

**Taraxacum fasciatum** Dahlst.
Old Hawne colliery, SO9584.

### *Crepis paludosa* (L.) Moench
**Marsh Hawk's-beard**
0. Extinct in B&BC? Native. Recorded by Bagnall in Sutton Park (SP0997, 1866).

### *Crepis biennis* L.
**Rough Hawk's-beard**
5. Native; probably entirely introduced in B&BC. Biennial. Well-established in a hay meadow created at Kitchen Lane, W'ton by strewing hay from Eades Meadow in Worcestershire in 1994 (SJ964026, CRP, 2000, still there in 2009). In the late 2000s it appeared on another created meadow in Wolverhampton at Bushbury Hill (SJ926023, ICT & P. Millett, 2010), presumably transferred either by botanists' feet or with grass-cutting equipment. There are a few other unconfirmed records: Quinton Meadows (SO993835, C. Wishart, 2007) and monad records without habitat details from SP007844 (AS, 1999) and (SP1592, SPG, 2000). It was also recorded twice at Hill Hook (SK106004) in the 1980s.

### *Crepis capillaris* (L.) Wallr.
**Smooth Hawk's-beard**

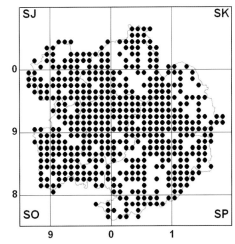

*526. Native. A very common annual or biennial species, found in fairly open vegetation on roadside verges, and colonising waste and disturbed land. Tolerant of mowing or trampling so commonly occurring in lawns and amenity grassland in open, sunny situations in a wide range of soil types avoiding only

the most acid or wet. Plants can vary greatly in height and vigour depending on the habitat circumstances. Ass: *Agrostis capillaris, Cerastium fontanum, Lolium perenne, Plantago lanceolata, Plantago major, Poa annua, Trifolium dubium, Trifolium repens*.

**Var. glandulosa** Druce was recorded in a woodland strip by the railway, Havacre Lane/Darkhouse Lane, Coseley (SO941947, E. Lomas & H. Bowler, 2004).

### *Crepis vesicaria* L.
**Beaked Hawk's-beard**

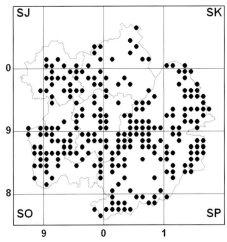

*251. Neophyte. An early summer-flowering biennial of sunny, warm, open situations in well-drained, fairly nutrient-poor but base-rich soils on roadsides, railways, derelict and waste ground, shrub borders and neglected gardens. Often locally abundant and forming large colonies on railway ballast and post-industrial sites particularly on skeletal, unbalanced or polluted soils. Rapidly maturing during the spring months and quickly disappearing after flowering suggesting that its true distribution may not be fully recognised. All records in vc. 39 were considered uncertain by Edees (1972) and there were few records in our part of vc. 38 in Cadbury *et al.* (1971). It appears to be spreading N and W in the UK. Our plant is **subsp. taraxacifolia** (Thuill.) Thell. ex Schinz & R. Keller. Ass: *Arrhenatherum elatius, Festuca rubra, Silene vulgaris, Trifolium arvense, Trifolium dubium*. Europe.

### *Crepis setosa* Haller f.
**Bristly Hawk's-beard**
1. Casual. Single plant on disturbed verge, A484, Mucklow Hill (SO975842, JJD, 2000). Also old records: two plants on waste ground, and eight, 100 metres or so away on the site of demolished houses, Old Hill, Blackheath (SO953865 & SO955866, LG, 1991). Three specimens on a disused railway, Roebuck Lane, Smethwick (SP017895, MWP, 1991). S Europe.

## *Pilosella officinarum* F.W. Schultz & Sch. Bip.
## Mouse-ear-hawkweed

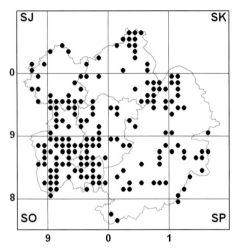

*185. Native. Roadside, railway and canal banks, short grassland, waste ground, roadside verges and lawns, quarries, furnace spoil and other man-created substrates. A stoloniferous, perennial herb of base-rich to base-poor, nutrient-poor, often skeletal soils, often locally dominant on dry moisture-stressed S-facing banks and in lawns. Present throughout B&BC but curiously concentrated in Dudley and the Sutton/Walsall borderlands, both areas with much high land which lack geological drift material. Also tetrad SJ90V. Ass: *Aira praecox*, *Hieracium* spp., *Hypochaeris radicata*, *Pilosella praealta*, *Sedum rupestre*.

Seven subspecies are described in Sell and Murrell (2006) and three have been recorded on the old quarry workings on the Rowley Hills (SO9789, WAT, 2001): **subsp. *euronota*** (Nägeli & Peter) P.D. Sell & C. West; **subsp. *officinarum***, and **subsp. *tricholepia*** (Nägeli & Peter) P.D. Sell & C. West.

## *Pilosella flagellaris* (Willd.)P.D. Sell & C. West
## subsp. *flagellaris*
## Spreading Mouse-ear-hawkweed

2. Neophyte. Well naturalised in grassland and alongside the path in Saltwells Nature Reserve. First observed on top of a clay bank (SO935869, APD, conf. J. Bevan, 1993). In subsequent years it was observed spreading in grassland along the edges of the path by the pool. By 1998 it was abundant there and well naturalised, and seen also at SO935870 and near the main Saltwells car park (SO934869, APD, 1999). It is a garden escape, introduced and naturalised on grassy roadsides and railway banks. This plant should not be confused with the endemic subspecies *bicapitata* P.D. Sell & C. West which is only known from three localities in Shetland. C & E Europe.

## *Pilosella praealta* (Vill. ex Gochnat) F. W. Schultz & Sch. Bip.
## Tall Mouse-ear-hawkweed

2. Neophyte. Recently discovered growing abundantly on a steep-sided, S-facing, moisture-stressed slope on an old quarry site on land S of Bury Hill Park in the Rowley Hills (SO976889, ICT, MWP, EVJC, JaH & EMP, det. WAT, 2007). Two further colonies are established in the grassland lower down the hillside towards Wolverhampton Road (SO979891, MWP, 2012). Another small colony has appeared at Fens Pools in Dudley growing in furnace spoil on a steep, S-facing, moisture-stressed slope (SO917885, MWP, ICT & APD, 2007). Plants grow mixed in with *Pilosella officinarum* and other similar composites. Absence of stolons suggest our plant is **subsp. *praealta***. Europe.

## *Pilosella aurantiaca* (L.) F.W. Schultz & Sch. Bip.
## Fox-and-cubs

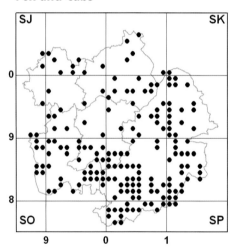

184. Neophyte. A stoloniferous or rhizomatous perennial herb, often persisting and spreading where planted or discarded from gardens and possibly also spreading by seed. Typically found in lawns and short grassland, on waste ground and roadside banks, on dry soils. Often carpeting frequently managed, well-drained lawns where its presence becomes apparent when flowering is able to take place between cuts. In some graveyards it becomes the predominant species over large areas.

Most recorders have not attempted to separate the two subspecies in the present survey; **subsp. *aurantiaca*** does appear to be (rarely) present, but **subsp. *carpathicola*** (Nägeli & Peter) Soják with above-ground stolons seems to be predominantly recorded throughout. N & C Europe. Ass: *Achillea millefolium*, *Agrostis capillaris*, *Cerastium fontanum*,

*Festuca rubra*, *Plantago lanceolata*, *Trisetum flavescens*.

## Genus *Hieracium* spp.
## Hawkweeds

A large group, consisting almost entirely of apomictic microspecies – Sell & Murrell (2006), whose classification is followed here, describe 412 species. The microspecies offer serious problems of identification, and with few exceptions require expert determination of specimens, which facility has not been available for this survey. For these reasons only the two sections which probably account for almost all the records in this lowland area have been mapped. We have nevertheless been fortunate in that much material for vc. 37 has been authoritatively named at the species level and that this information has been kindly made available to us. We have restricted our account to modern records.

## *Hieracium* spp.
## Hawkweeds

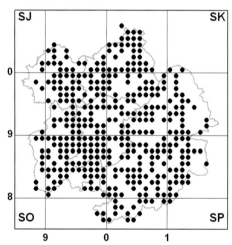

*389. Native and introduced. Perennial herbs with a marked preference for lighter soils and well-drained situations, found characteristically on rock outcrops, quarries, spoil heaps, waste ground of derelict industrial sites, dry roadsides, canal, road and railway cuttings, walls and bridges, clearly very widely distributed in B&BC. Divided into 17 sections, but practically all B&BC material belongs to two sections, Sabauda and Vulgata.

**Section 1. Sabauda** (Fr.) Arv.-Touv.
156. Almost all plants in B&BC with stem-leaves normally more than 15, and no leaf rosette at flowering, belong to this section. They are widespread in lowland Britain, found in open woodlands, on road, railway and canal banks, rock outcrops, and walls and in waste land.

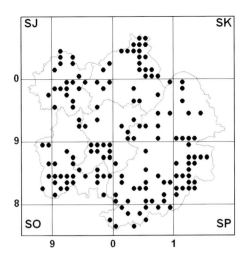

Widely distributed in B&BC and the commonest section recorded specifically.

### Hieracium vagum Jord.
**Glabrous-headed Hawkweed**
Native. A common plant, usually in small numbers in rough grass by railways, canals, rivers, in quarries and colliery waste and once in cracks in pavement. Essentially a species of man-made habitats in vc. 37 and probably throughout, with a handful of records from woodland and heathland. Plentiful at Langley Reservoir, on rough acid grassland banks, with *H. sabaudum, H. salticola* & *H. umbellatum* (SP000869, WAT, 2006).

### Hieracium salticola (Sudre) P.D. Sell & C. West
**Bluish-leaved Hawkweed**
This rather characteristic species is widely described in the literature as being particularly found "in the B'ham area". It has been recorded abundantly in the vc. 37 part of B&BC, mostly in urban areas, on grassy slopes, canal banks, colliery and quarry waste, along roadsides, in gardens and on wall tops, and there are records (many unvalidated) from every 10km square in B&BC. Mainly found in man-made habitats in our area, but showing signs of spreading into more 'natural' habitats. Frequent, railway bank, Spring Road Station, growing with *H. sabaudum* forma *bladonii* (SP111829, WAT, 2006).

### Hieracium prominentidens P.D. Sell
**Large-toothed Hawkweed**
Native. A segregate from *H. salticola*, described from Surrey, Middlesex and Montgomeryshire, which is now known to be more widely distributed. There are three records (all WAT) in B&BC, from SO9584 (2004), SO9383 (2006) and SP1283 (2006), on old colliery workings and a canal bank.

### Hieracium sabaudum L.
**Autumn Hawkweed**
Native. Recorded quite frequently in the

vc. 37 part of B&BC, mostly as **forma sabaudum**, but also occasionally as **forma bladonii** (Pugsley) P.D. Sell. Sometimes with *H. vagum* or *H. salticola*, but primarily a rural species of lanesides and open woodlands in vc. 37 and less often found on post-industrial sites. Very locally frequent, old spoil-heaps, Oldnall Colliery, with *H. eboracense, H. salticola* and *H. vagum* (SO933839, also SO937838, WAT, 2004).

### Section 2. Hieracioides Dumort.
**Hieracium umbellatum L.**
**Umbellate Hawkweed**
Native. Very scarce in B&BC. The only authoritatively named recent material (of **subsp. umbellatum var. umbellatum**) is from Langley Reservoir, scattered on rough acid grassland banks with *H. sabaudum, H. salticola* and *H. vagum* (SP001869, WAT, 1996 & 2006).

### Section 4. Tridentata (Fr.) Arv.-Touv.
**Hieracium eboracense Pugsley**
**Northern Hawkweed**
Native. A quarry (SO9789), a sandstone outcrop (SO9977) and a factory yard (SO9283). Old quarry spoil banks, Bury Hill, Rowley Hills, growing with *H. salticola* and *H. vagum* (SO977890, WAT, 2005).

### Section 16. Vulgata (Griseb.) Willk. & Lange

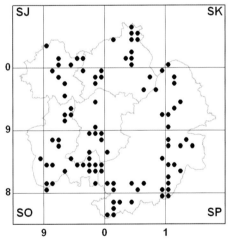

97. Plants with few to numerous, usually enlarged basal leaves and two to eight stem-leaves. They have been recorded throughout B&BC, and the range of habitats is much the same as for Sect. Sabauda and for the genus *Hieracium* as a whole. Currently no records from central B'ham.

### Hieracium vulgatum Fr.
**Common Hawkweed**
Native; probably introduced in lowlands. Recorded occasionally throughout B&BC. In old pasture, rough grassland, lanesides, hedgebanks, canal and railway banks, walls and railway bridges, all in our part of

vc. 37 referable to forma *vulgatum*. Strong colony with *H. argillaceum*, dry bank below the canal, close to the Leasowes Park (SO973836, WAT, 2006).

### Hieracium asperatum Jord. ex Boreau
**Rough Hawkweed**
Possibly introduced. This is one of four taxa with maroon-marbled leaves and two to five stem-leaves which were formerly known collectively as *Hieracium maculatum* auct.; none now have this name. A close-grouped colony of 50+ plants on edge of clearing in secondary Birch woodland, Woodgate Valley (WAT, conf. D.J. McCosh, 2006).

### Hieracium daedalolepidoides (Zahn) Roffey
**Petite-leaved Hawkweed**
Native. Two recent records from SO8882 and SO9383 in sandy grassland and colliery spoil. On spoil heaps of the former Oldnall Colliery workings (SO937838, WAT, det. D. J. McCosh, 2004).

### Hieracium anglorum (Ley) Pugsley
**Anglian Hawkweed**
Native; probably introduced in B&BC. So far only recorded in vc. 37 and showing a preference for sandy soils. Recorded from SO9081, SO9383, SO9485, SO9783, SO9786, and SP0176 (and elsewhere before 1995) on colliery spoil, sandy acid banks, often in railway cuttings. Rowley Regis Railway Station (SO979865, WAT, 2006).

### Hieracium acuminatum agg.
This group of microspecies is widely recorded across B&BC from rough grass, colliery spoil, canal and railway banks, waste ground, usually in small numbers. There is one confirmed record for **Hieracium acuminatum** Jord. (**Tall Hawkweed**): a single plant in light shade under trees on edge of Cofton Park (SP006765, WAT, conf. D.J. McCosh, 2004). **Hieracium consociatum** Jord. ex Boreau (**Sociable Hawkweed**) has been quite frequently recorded throughout our part of vc. 37. Occasional in major colony of *H. acuminatum* agg. on spoil-banks of old quarry, Bury Hill, Rowley Hills (SO977890, WAT, 2006). **Hieracium argillaceum** Jord. (**Southern Hawkweed**) has also been frequently recorded throughout our part of vc. 37: very locally frequent with *H. consociatum* and *H. anglorum*, dry grassy slope, Cradley Church (SO942852, WAT, 2004).

### Section 17. Hieracium
Plants with strongly maroon-spotted and marbled leaves without, or with only one stem-leaf are not uncommonly grown in gardens. They seed freely and are occasionally found self-sown near habitation.

They belong to this section and are currently assigned to **Hieracium scotostictum** Hyl. (**Dappled Hawkweed**) although there may be more than one taxon involved. Reported in pavers from Wordsley, SO8987 and pavement weeds recorded as *H. maculatum* in SP1197 and SP0494 may well belong here but have not been verified.

### Filago vulgaris Lam.
### Common Cudweed

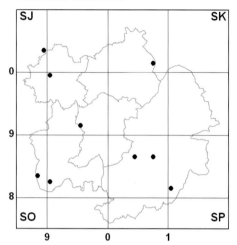

9. Native. NT. Ax. An annual of open, well drained, skeletal, acid soil with very few recent records. It seems to have almost a casual status in B&BC, appearing briefly in paving or at the edge of paths. Very rarely are there larger populations which might be more stable: a colony of 100+ plants colonising an area of compressed cinder in the disused car park of the abandoned Moor Green football ground (SP104813, MWP, ICT, JWP & EMP, 2007); a number of colonies several metres across scattered across a huge furnace sand and slag spoil tip at Burnt Tree, Sandwell (SO957913, MWP & ICT, 2011). There is also a recent record of a sizeable colony from derelict land by Moor Street Queensway in central B'ham (SP074869, MWP, 2011). In the early 1980s there was a large population (growing with *Filago minima*) on abandoned railway sidings in W'ton (SO916993) (now part of a builders' yard). Ass: *Achillea millefolium*, *Festuca rubra*, *Trifolium arvense*, *Trifolium repens*, *Urtica urens*.

### Filago minima (Sm.) Pers.
### Small Cudweed

3. Native. Ax. This annual is currently known from two sites at Sutton Park: dry heathy, sparsely vegetated, compacted soil along the margins of a path (SP104978, ICT & MWP, 2005, seen again by BL in 2010). BL also has a 2010 record from Sutton Park from SP102960. It might be native in Sutton Park, growing with *Aira praecox*, *Cerastium semidecandrum*, *Festuca filiformis*, *Veronica*

*arvensis*, although it is surprising that it had not previously been recorded there. There is however an 1896 Bagnall record for *Filago vulgaris* from SP0997. *Filago minima* is also nearby Sutton Park in Vesey Close, Sutton (SP107989, MWP, ICT & JWP, 2007). This, and two 1980s records in W'ton from railway sidings and by the Bentley canal suggest it might have a rare casual distribution in B&BC like *F. vulgaris*.

### Anaphalis margaritacea (L.) Benth.
### Pearly Everlasting

1. Neophyte. Annual garden escape. One small clump in a development site N of Oddingley Road, West Heath, Northfield (SP034786, JJD, 2006). N America.

### Gnaphalium uliginosum L.
### Marsh Cudweed

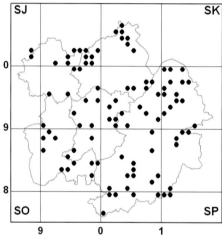

97. Native. This annual is frequently encountered in ground subject to impeded drainage such as well-trodden field entrances, seasonally wet muddy pool margins, in wheel ruts or around puddles on earth tracks. It can also occur as a weed of cultivation in garden paths, borders and allotment gardens showing a preference for soils that are damp and intermediate in base and nutrient status. By far the most common cudweed in the urban environment. Ass: *Cerastium glomeratum*, *Juncus bufonius*, *Plantago major*, *Poa annua*, *Polygonum aviculare*.

### Gnaphalium luteoalbum L.
### Jersey Cudweed

3. Native or alien, probably just an adventive in B&BC. Sch. 8. Until recently it was thought only to grow in the Channel Islands, having apparently become extinct in the Brecklands. It now appears to have developed a scattered occurrence as a casual in England and Scotland. In 2003 a colony of 200 + plants was discovered in compacted, sparsely vegetated, drought-liable, acid soil alongside a path running

through Homer Hill Park in Cradley (SO940849, MWP, conf. F. Rose, 2003). Associates were *Capsella bursa-pastoris*, *Erophila* sp., *Lamium amplexicaule*, *Ornithopus perpusillus*, *Veronica agrestis*. In subsequent years numbers fluctuated considerably and in 2006 none were seen. In 2012 a colony of approximately 70 specimens was found on and around the base of the rockery adjacent to the path where plants were first discovered. The park was laid out after the end of World War II and we are informed by the Friends of Homer Hill Park that 'red' (burnt?) pit mounds once stood on the site. Also recorded in B'ham in allotments, one plant in disturbed ground with *Gnaphalium uliginosum*, *Borago officinalis* and *Veronica agrestis* (SP115939, MWP, JWP & ICT, 2007). The first record in vc. 39 was for four weeds in a plant pot, in the garden of the then BSBI recorder in Tettenhall (SJ873002, BRF, 1995).

### Inula helenium L.
### Elecampane

2. Neophyte. A rare relic of cultivation. Four Oaks Common Allotments (SP105994, MWP, ICT & JWP, 2006); University Botanical Garden, Edgbaston (SP052838, MWP & JWP, 2007).

### Inula conyzae (Griess.) Meikle
(*Inula conyza* DC.)
### Ploughman's-spikenard

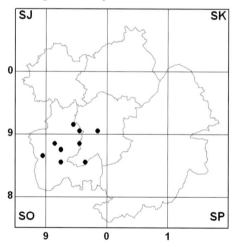

9. Native. Ax. Well drained, open, sunny, unshaded situations on derelict railway tracks and dry grassy slopes. A calcicolous species recorded from a handful of sites and represented by a very small number of records. A colony growing from brick mortar on the ledge of a canal bridge in Warrens Hall Country Park near Dudley (SO9588) has been known there for at least 25 years, but several sites seem to have been lost since the 1980s, including one at some distance from the present cluster at Coseley Road railway station embankment,

Bilston (SO945959, ICT, 1982). Ass: *Agrostis capillaris, Arenaria serpyllifolia, Catapodium rigidum, Coincya monensis, Erigeron acris, Helminthotheca echioides, Pteridium aquilinum, Veronica serpyllifolia.*

### *Pulicaria dysenterica* (L.) Bernh.
### Common Fleabane

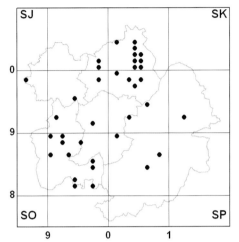

*37. Native. Ax. A perennial rhizomatous herb typically found in wet meadows, seasonally wet hollows and generally poorly drained areas on nutrient-poor to medium, moderately acidic to base-rich, often heavy clay or flushed soils. Some colonies can be quite large, but more often appearing in small isolated patches and frequently absent from apparently suitable habitats. Usually in semi-natural habitats, particularly commons, although these might be disturbed or neglected. Also tetrad SO99A. Ass: *Agrostis stolonifera, Carex leporina, Filipendula ulmaria, Juncus effusus, Juncus inflexus, Silene flos-cuculi.*

### *Solidago virgaurea* L.
### Goldenrod

1. Native. This species of hill woodland and grassy banks is probably now only found in our area at the northern tip of the Lickey Hills: greenspace off Leach Green Lane, Rubery (SO994768, JJD, 2001) and an old record nearby: Rubery Quarry (SO992778, AEEP, 1988). It was recorded in Sutton Park by Bagnall in 1868 and there are a few unconfirmed 1980s records from the Sandwell Valley (SP0293), Sedgley Beacon (SO9295), Rowley Hills (SO9788), Stourbridge Junction (SO9183) and the Bentley Canal (SO9599).

### *Solidago canadensis* L.
### Canadian Goldenrod

195. Neophyte. Canal and railway banks, neglected gardens, overgrown allotment plots, urban commons, usually in places with at least modestly fertile, dry or moist soils recovering from past disturbance

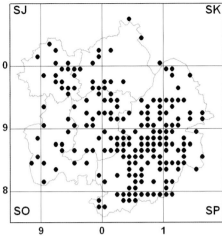

but not currently being disturbed. Regularly forming dominant patches from creeping rhizomes but often co-existing well with other members of the tall herb community. Frequently complementing Rosebay Willowherb in late summer where extensive areas of canal and railway bank are turned gold and purple with their flowers. Apparently even more abundant in B'ham than the Black Country. Despite its current frequency the first record for vc. 39 was in W'ton in 1972 (SO9098, 9198 & 9298) although in 1971 it was listed as abundant in B'ham in Cadbury *et al.*, the first record for vc. 38 being on waste land at Cannon Hill (SP0783?) in 1943. N America. Ass: *Artemisia absinthium, Artemisia vulgaris, Arrhenatherum elatius, Buddleja davidii, Chamerion angustifolium, Cirsium arvense, Heracleum sphondylium.*

### *Solidago gigantea* Aiton
### Early Goldenrod

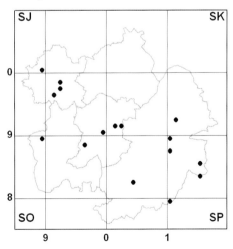

16. Neophyte. Naturalised in similar situations to *Solidago canadensis* and sometimes growing mixed in with it but in general much less common although it too can sometimes form large stands. Flowering earlier and forming small but persistent colonies on urban wasteland, canal and railway banks. Also tetrad SP09S.

▲ *Filago vulgaris*

▲ *Gnaphalium luteoalbum*

▲ *Inula conyzae*

Central N America. Ass: *Arrhenatherum elatius, Chamerion angustifolium, Poa trivialis, Solidago canadensis.*

## Aster spp.
### Michaelmas-daisies

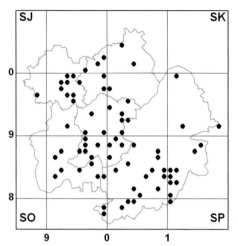

75. Neophytes. Very persistent perennial herbs often out-competing native vegetation to form large, long-lived colonies where left undisturbed, on railway, canal and roadside banks in well-drained, base-medium to base-rich, at least modestly fertile, dry to moist soils. A complex group which is further confused by the presence of garden varieties deliberately planted and relics of cultivation persisting on waste and disturbed ground. Identification is difficult and requires flowers which only appear very late in the season, hence a large number of records were not identified to species. The map shows all records within our survey period. Ass: *Arrhenatherum elatius, Artemisia vulgaris, Buddleja davidii, Chamerion angustifolium, Solidago canadensis, Tanacetum vulgare, Urtica dioica.*

## Aster × versicolor Willd.
(*A. laevis* L. × *A. novi-belgii*)
### Late Michaelmas-daisy

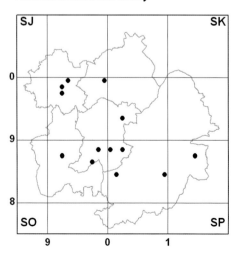

13. Neophyte. Less often recorded than some other *Aster* spp. but seen occasionally by several reliable recorders. Garden origin.

## Aster novi-belgii L.
### Confused Michaelmas-daisy
3. Neophyte. Sizable colony, waste land, Prescott Road, Stourbridge (SO913836, WAT, 2003); on derelict land by Stourbridge Canal (SO893857, APD, conf. CBW, 2008); Redswood Park to Bentley Lane (SO996994, MWP, 2010). N America.

## Aster × salignus Willd.
(*A. novi-belgae* × *A. lanceolatus*)
### Common Michaelmas-daisy

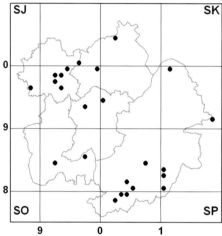

24. Neophyte. *A × salignus* is generally regarded as the most frequently encountered weedy-looking Aster, found naturalised in our area. In late summer large patches, frequently complementing *Solidago canadensis* and *Chamerion angustifolium* colonies, can be seen along many urban railway and canal banks. Garden origin.

## Aster lanceolatus Willd.
### Narrow-leaved Michaelmas-daisy
4. Neophyte. Very persistent and once established forming sizeable colonies. Less common than *A. × salignus*. Between Swan Pool & M5, Sandwell Valley (SP021923, MWP, 1998); Park Lane, Sandwell Valley (SP027907, MWP, 1999); N of Bourn Brook, Woodgate Valley (SO998834, JJD, 2003); raised bank, Hay Hall Rd (SP107843, MWP & JWP, 2006). N America.

## Erigeron glaucus Ker Gawl.
### Seaside Daisy
3. Neophyte. Roadside gutter, Stirchley (SP059808, MWP, 1999); Beaumont Road (SP043805, MWP, 2005); pavement seedling from nearby garden, Wylde Green (SP128943, MWP & JWP, det. EJC, 2007). California.

## Erigeron karvinskianus DC.
### Mexican Fleabane

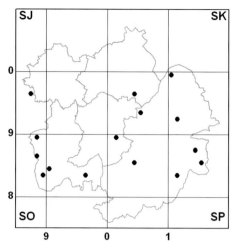

15. Neophyte. A procumbent to ascending perennial recently becoming established on garden walls and in paving below. It is also known from warm, sunny spots on a road verge, a concrete stream embankment and along the base of industrial buildings, where it has formed persistent colonies. Never found too far from habitation but apparently increasing in both B'ham and the Black Country. Mexico. Ass: *Dryopteris filix-mas, Pseudofumaria lutea.*

## Erigeron annuus (L.) Pers.
### Tall Fleabane
1. Neophyte. A tall, whitish-mauve-flowered fleabane found scattered over a wide area of the ironworks site of Foster, Rastrick & Co. on both sides of the Stour and hence in both vc. 39 and vc. 37 and a first vc. record in both (SO894848, APD, conf. ICT, 2011 and seen further N in 2012 on similar derelict land at SO895849). N America. Interestingly, the locomotive, the 'Stourbridge Lion', built on the Foster, Rastrick & Co. site, was the first to run commercially in North America. Could there be a connection?

## Erigeron acris L.
(*Erigeron acer* L.)
### Blue Fleabane
45. Native. Ax. An easily overlooked annual or perennial of dry banks, spoil mounds and artificially levelled post-industrial sites in open, sunny situations in well-drained skeletal, nutrient-poor and usually calcareous soils. Relatively uncommon but isolated individuals are often recorded. Perhaps most frequent in ballast or crushed cinder along railway tracks and in redundant sidings where it is known to form sizeable colonies. Ass: *Centaurium erythraea, Crepis vesicaria, Diplotaxis muralis, Festuca rubra, Hypochaeris radicata,*

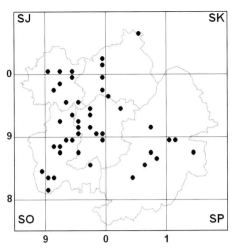

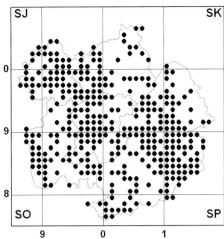

▲ *Erigeron annuus*

*Leucanthemum vulgare, Linaria vulgaris, Lotus corniculatus, Matricaria chamomilla, Medicago lupulina, Picris hieraceoides, Poa compressa, Senecio viscosus, Trifolium arvense, Trifolium campestre, Trifolium dubium, Trifolium medium.*

### *Erigeron speciosus* (Lindl.) DC.
### Garden Fleabane

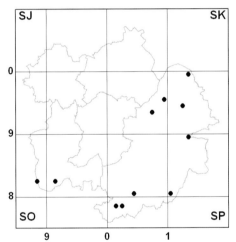

11. Casual. This showy daisy is commonly grown in gardens and occasionally spreads vegetatively or is self-sown onto garden walls and into paving cracks below. It is seldom, if ever recorded far from habitation. Plants discarded from gardens may persist for a season or two on spoil heaps and waste ground. Western N America.

### *Conyza canadensis* (L.) Cronquist
### Canadian Fleabane

354. Neophyte. A well established alien of roadsides, railways, gardens and urban commons and varying greatly in height from a few centimetres to over a metre. It is also a pioneer coloniser of patches of bare, compacted stony ground along paving and margins of shrub beds which have been irregularly treated with glyphosate, also one of the few plants able to grow between the paver bricks which are now

widely substituted for front gardens. Also SO99A. N America. Ass: *Arabidopsis thaliana, Conyza sumatrensis, Senecio vulgaris, Vulpia myuros.*

### *Conyza floribunda* Kunth
(*C. bilbaoana* J. Rémy)
### Bilbao Fleabane, Hispid Fleabane

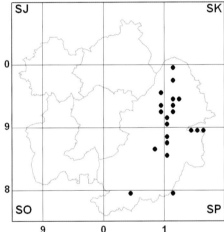

20. Neophyte. Recorded only towards the latter stages of the survey period from waste ground, roadsides and neglected gardens. Its preferred habitat would appear to be similar to that of both *C. canadensis* and *C. sumatrensis*, and on at least one site, it occurs with the latter. Almost certainly increasing in B&BC. S America.

### *Conyza sumatrensis* (Retz.) E. Walker
### Guernsey Fleabane

80. Neophyte. A plant of well-drained, open situations on banks, roadsides, gardens, paving and neglected bits of waste ground, similar to those exploited by *Conyza canadensis*, but many sites are perhaps less recently disturbed and slightly more fertile. A rapidly increasing, and without doubt under-recorded species in B&BC. Never recorded in the early stages of the project but towards the end it was encountered as frequently or more so than

▲ *Erigeron acris*

▲ *Conyza sumatrensis*

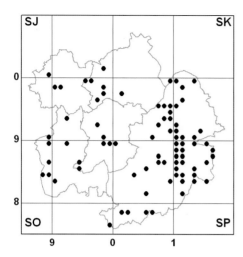

C. canadensis. Large colonies are often encountered on brownfield sites and in areas of dereliction and it often grows with or near to C. canadensis, possibly hybridising with it. S America.

### Conyza bonariensis (L.) Cronquist
### Argentine Fleabane

3. Neophyte. Another close relative of Conyza canadensis, reported from Wordsley (SO890868, CBW, 2006); Blakenhall (SO906970, CBW, 2006); roadside, Birchills Street, Walsall (SP006989, JEH, 2010). S America.

### Olearia × haastii Hook. f.
(O. avicenniifolia (Raoul) Hook. f. ×
O. moschata Hook. f.)
### Daisy-bush

1. Neophyte. St. John's Churchyard, Wednesbury. Spreading from an original planting (SO987947, MWP, 1997). Site now destroyed. New Zealand.

### Olearia macrodonta Baker
### New Zealand Holly

1. Neophyte. Shrub. By the canal, Spon Lock (SO997898, JJD, AWR & PLR, 2005). New Zealand.

### Bellis perennis L.
### Daisy

*675. Native. A very common perennial herb occurring in a wide range of managed grassland. Also a weed of roadside verges, paving and waste ground in open situations in all soil-types but avoiding the most acid. Often a dominant weed of poorly drained, compacted lawns and amenity grassland where it benefits from a frequent mowing regime and is extremely tolerant of trampling: in coarse vegetation it is out-competed by taller grasses and herbs. Ass: Agrostis capillaris, Festuca rubra, Lolium perenne, Plantago lanceolata, Poa annua, Prunella vulgaris, Taraxacum spp., Trifolium dubium, Trifolium repens.

### Tanacetum parthenium (L.) Sch.-Bip.
### Feverfew

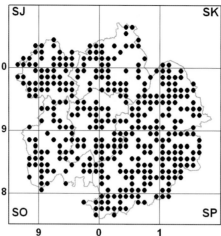

*384. Archaeophyte. An aromatic perennial herb often cultivated and seeding into garden borders, paths, allotments, disturbed and waste ground. Often one of the first plants to appear in paving after glyphosate treatment and can become abundant or dominant if left. Double-flowered plants are not uncommon. Ass: Epilobium ciliatum, Meconopsis cambrica, Sonchus oleraceus, Senecio vulgaris.

### Tanacetum macrophyllum (Waldst. & Kit.) Sch.-Bip.
### Rayed Feverfew

1. Neophyte. One plant self-seeded in flower border, B'ham Botanical Gardens (SP048854, JWP, MWP & EVJC, 2007). SE Europe.

### Tanacetum vulgare L.
### Tansy

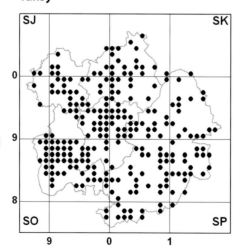

*252. Native. This aromatic perennial herb frequently forms large stands amongst other tall herbs and grasses on canal, railway and roadside banks, waste ground, hedgerows, neglected gardens and abandoned allotment plots. Found on a

wide range of reasonably fertile soils but avoiding the most acid or very dry. Also tetrad SO99G. Ass: Arrhenatherum elatius, Artemisia vulgaris, Buddleja davidii, Cirsium arvense, Heracleum sphondylium, Solidago canadensis, Urtica dioica.

### Artemisia vulgaris L.
### Mugwort

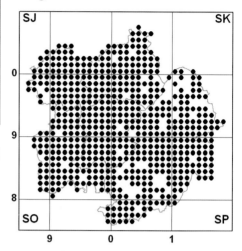

*610. Archaeophyte. An almost ubiquitous tall herbaceous perennial herb commonly found on canal towpaths, railway banks, roadside verges, waysides, waste ground, neglected gardens and a rapid coloniser on post-industrial and post-residential sites that remain undeveloped for more than a year. An important part of the tall-herb community in the urban area. Tolerant of some shade and found in a wide range of soil types but avoiding the most acid. Ass: Arrhenatherum elatius, Buddleja davidii, Cirsium arvense, Heracleum sphondylium, Rumex obtusifolius, Solidago canadensis, Urtica dioica; frequently growing with Artemisia absinthium in the Black Country.

### Artemisia × wurzellii C.M. James & Stace
(A. vulgaris × A. verlotiorum Lamotte)
### Wurzell's Mugwort

1. Endemic archaeophyte × neophyte. A 2m × 1m patch was discovered in 2006 growing along the roadside of Heartland Parkway, Nechells in the absence of both parents. A verlotiorum (Chinese Mugwort) is unknown in B&BC; the hybrid was first discovered in Middlesex and S Essex in 1987 and is clearly spreading although thought to be completely sterile. The site is between railway sidings and a desolate trunk road (SP109896, JWP, 2006).

### Artemisia absinthium L.
### Wormwood

*382. Archaeophyte. Aromatic perennial herb. Predominantly found in industrial areas: canal and railway banks, roadside verges, neglected and compacted waste

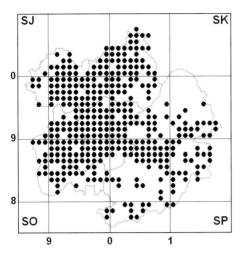

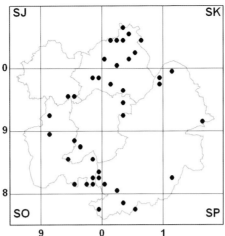

▲ *Tanacetum parthenium*

▲ *Artemisia* × *wurzellii*

▲ *Artemisia absinthium*

ground but also in unmanaged gardens and cleared post-residential areas, sometimes forming extensive stands. Typically in dry to moderately damp, usually base-rich and fairly nutrient-rich, but often rubbly or skeletal soils, avoiding shade. Formerly cultivated for its medicinal properties, there is no evidence to suggest that this has any relevance to its frequent occurrence. It is more regularly encountered in the W of the region and is generally regarded as a 'Black Country plant'. Ass: *Arrhenatherum elatius*, *Artemisia vulgaris*, *Cirsium arvense*, *Cirsium vulgare*, *Rumex obtusifolius*.

### Artemisia dracunculus L.
### Tarragon
1. Casual. A garden escape, in quantity, between 43 New Street and the chapel, Wordsley (SO891869, CBW, 2005). Russia.

### Santolina chamaecyparissus L.
### Lavender-cotton
1. Neophyte. Perennial garden escape, found on post-industrial site, Union Road, Oldbury (SO982908, MWP & T. Oliver, 2009). Mediterranean.

### Achillea ptarmica L.
### Sneezewort
*40. Native. Ax. An uncommon but widely distributed perennial herb of permanently moist and wet situations on heaths and in meadows and flood-plain grassland on nutrient-poor, usually slightly base-flushed soils in open situations. Occurring typically in small localised colonies and seldom in any great quantity. Absent from most of the urbanised areas and generally indicative of the presence of remnants of old, species-rich damp pasture, although, occasionally, double-flowered races, which are undoubtedly of garden origin, occur on recently disturbed post-housing and industrial sites, e.g. the cultivars 'Boule de Neige'

and 'The Pearl'. Also tetrad SO99A. Ass: *Cirsium palustre*, *Filipendula ulmaria*, *Galium palustre*, *Lotus uliginosus*, *Juncus acutiflorus*, *Juncus effusus*.

### Achillea millefolium L.
### Yarrow
*669. Native. A very common perennial herb of roadside verges, railway and canal banks, lawns, hedgebanks, post-housing and industrial sites and other disturbed and grassy places including old grasslands. In a wide range of soil types, avoiding only permanently waterlogged situations and very acid soils. Often abundant in amenity grassland and garden lawns where it is tolerant of mowing and trampling and is often one of the first spontaneous perennials to appear. Some pink-flowered plants on brownfield sites may derive from garden cultivars. Ass: *Agrostis capillaris*, *Bellis perennis*, *Festuca rubra*, *Hypochaeris radicata*, *Lolium perenne*, *Trifolium repens*.

### Achillea filipendulina Lam.
### Fern-leaf Yarrow
1. Neophyte. Self-sown outside a garden, Causey Farm (SO945816, MWP & APD, 2003). W & C Asia.

### Anthemis arvensis L.
### Corn Chamomile
1. Archaeophyte. EN. Formerly a rare annual or biennial weed of arable fields on light soils, now over-used in wildflower seed mixes. Phoenix Park, W'ton (probably in a seed mix) (SO918968, CBW, 2008). Older records: Sutton Park (SP0997, Bagnall, 1876); Sandwell Park (SP0291, A.J. Purcell, 1977); abundant on a re-seeded reclamation site at Fibbersley (SO9599, JPM, 1991); Clayhanger Village (SK046048, CW & PWS, 1987).

### Anthemis cotula L.
### Stinking Chamomile
2. Archaeophyte. VU. There is a scattering of records for this ancient annual weed

of crops in the 1980s and early 1990s, growing along waysides, canal sides and in waste places, but only two in our time period: Ryecroft Cutting (SP019998, S. Duke & P. Burkinshaw, 2002); without details (SJ80V, JVT, 2000).

### Anthemis tinctoria L.
### Yellow Chamomile
5. Neophyte. An attractive biennial to short-lived perennial herb occasionally appearing on land recovering from recent disturbance and in dumped soil. Plants are almost certainly of garden origin and seldom persist for more than a year or two. Many garden varieties are in cultivation but records mostly resemble the cultivar 'E. C. Buxton'. Pavement cracks, Coventry Road island (SP085861, MWP, 1997); Stourbridge Canal (SO896866, ICT, EVJC & J. Teall, 2001); disturbed land by Halfords, Bilston (SO943956, CBW, 2001); disturbed land, Ocker Hill (SO976937, JEH, 2007); herb garden, B'ham University Botanical Gardens, Winterbourne (SP052838, MWP & JWP, 2007). Europe.

### Glebionis segetum (L.) Fourr.
(Chrysanthemum segetum L.)
### Corn Marigold

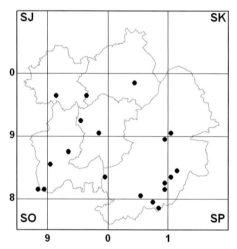

19. Archaeophyte. VU. A rare and declining annual, formerly a common weed of arable land. Occasionally colonies are found growing in cultivated and disturbed ground. Most, if not all of these are now no more than deliberate introductions in 'wild flower mixes' and are often growing with other cornfield annuals including Agrostemma githago, Papaver rhoeas and Centaurea cyanus, sometimes seeding and persisting for a year or two. However there are records from sandy arable land near Stourbridge at Iverley (SO889814 & SO891814, B. Westwood, 2000, but known thereabouts since at least 1989); scattered in sandy arable headland (SO899811, JJD, 2003);

earlier a few plants in an arable field off Racecourse Road, Norton (SO893825 & SO899822, WAT, 1990). These seem to be the last remnants of its presence in the arable flora in our area.

### Mauranthemum paludosum (Poir.) Vogt & Oberprieler
### Annual Marguerite
1. Neophyte. Garden annual; 50+ plants observed in cracks in concreted-over front garden in Poplar Road, Smethwick (SP0286, MWP, 2004). SW Europe.

### Leucanthemella serotina (L.) Tzvelev
### Autumn Oxeye
1. Neophyte. Rhizomatous perennial. Garden escape, recorded from waste ground just N of the B&Q roundabout off the Black Country Route, Bilston (SO9495, CBW, 2009). SE Europe.

### Leucanthemum vulgare Lam.
### Oxeye Daisy

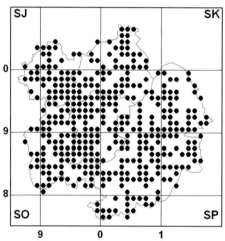

*391. Native. A cheerful perennial herb often flowering in great profusion along hedge banks, on waste ground and rough grassy areas along railways, canals, post-industrial land and in quarries. Thriving in nutrient-poor, well-drained or even droughty, slightly acid to calcareous soils, and favoured by occasional light disturbance. Abundantly sown in wild flower seed mixtures, but undoubtedly also a frequent member of the spontaneous flora, even, rarely, in old species-rich grassland. Ass: Centaurea nigra, Crepis capillaris, Festuca rubra, Linaria vulgaris, Rhinanthus minor, Senecio squalidus, Trifolium dubium.

### Leucanthemum × superbum (Bergmans ex J.W. Ingram) D.H. Kent (?L. lacustre (Brot.) Samp. × L. maximum (Ramond) DC.)
### Shasta Daisy
43. Neophyte. A perennial herb persistent where discarded or deliberately planted in

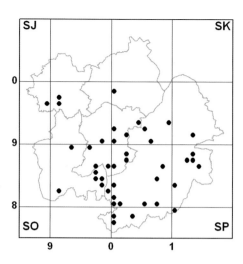

rough grassland and recently cleared post-housing sites, apparently commoner in the S and E. Garden origin.

### Matricaria chamomilla L.
(Matricaria recutita L.)
### Scented Mayweed

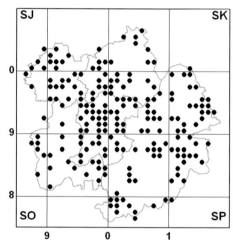

204. Archaeophyte. An aromatic annual of roadside verges, land recovering from recent disturbance, allotment gardens and traveller spoil banks. One of the pioneer colonists on newly formed roadside banks and other construction sites, often appearing in great abundance from long-dormant seed and usually flowering more rapidly from seed than Tripleurospermum inodorum. Dry to moist, fairly nutrient- and base-rich soil. Much of the distribution seems to be concentrated in the central urban areas. Ass: Capsella bursa-pastoris, Papaver dubium, Papaver rhoeas, Polygonum aviculare, Tripleurospermum inodorum, Veronica persica.

### Matricaria discoidea DC.
### Pineappleweed
*623. Neophyte. An erect, aromatic plant found almost ubiquitously in open, barish, compacted but base-rich and often fertile soils. A component of the pavement flora

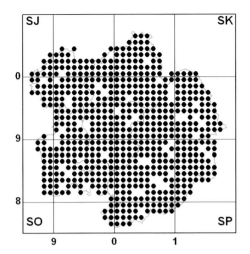

in urban areas where it is highly tolerant of trampling releasing its characteristic pineapple smell. Found in other bare, trampled places such as margins of earth paths, over-used playing fields, goal mouths on football pitches, etc. Asia and possibly N America. Ass: *Capsella bursa-pastoris, Plantago major, Poa annua, Polygonum aviculare, Sagina procumbens.*

Subsp. *discoidea* and subsp. *occidentalis* (Greene) P.D. Sell have not been distinguished but both may be present.

### *Tripleurospermum inodorum* (L.) Sch. Bip. **Scentless Mayweed**

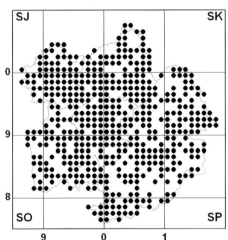

*494. Archaeophyte. Very common annual weed of disturbed and waste ground, gardens, roadside verges and margins of arable in open, sunny situations. A rapid coloniser of newly disturbed soil on post-housing, construction and industrial sites. Possibly more abundant than *Matricaria chamomilla* on richer and moister soil, although both often grow together. Ass: *Capsella bursa-pastoris, Matricaria chamomilla, Papaver dubium, Papaver rhoeas, Polygonum aviculare, Tripleurospermum inodorum, Veronica persica.*

### *Cotula coronopifolia* L. **Buttonweed**

1. Neophyte. A few plants persisting on derelict plant nursery site from former cultivation, Harborne Park Road Nurseries, Selly Oak (SP041829, MWP, 2004). S Africa & New Zealand.

### *Cotula squalida* (Hook. f.) Hook. f. **Leptinella**

2. Neophyte. A far creeping, procumbent perennial occasionally cultivated in borders and rockeries. Records are for colonies becoming well-established in lawn and mown grassland. Throughout a front garden lawn in Woodbourne Rd, Bearwood (SP011865, MWP, 1998); extensive patches in managed grassland, Lodge Hill Cemetery, Selly Oak (SP031823, DJA, 2000). First record for vc. 39: established on garden lawns, 84 Woodthorne Road South, Tettenhall (SJ873002, BRF, 1991). New Zealand.

### *Senecio cineraria* DC. **Silver Ragwort**

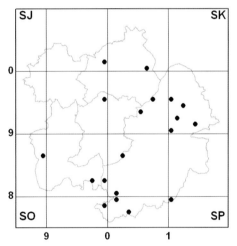

19. Neophyte. A frequently cultivated perennial herb used as a foliage plant in annual bedding plant schemes and generally discarded before flowering. A few records for odd plants in paving and neglected patches of waste ground, mostly in suburban residential areas and seldom found far from habitation. First seen in vc. 39 in 1992 on waste ground, Gorsebrook Road, near racecourse, W'ton (SJ909004, BRF). Mediterranean.

### *Senecio* × *albescens* Burb. & Colgan
(*S. cineraria* × *S. jacobaea*)

14. Alien × Native. A few records for individual plants of this fertile hybrid occurring along paving or on post-housing land in residential areas: two plants growing with *S. jacobaea* in rough

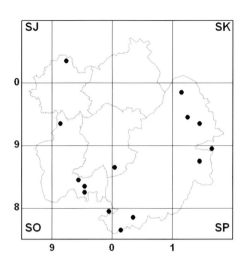

vegetation along The Fordrough, Sutton Coldfield, 2006.

### *Senecio jacobaea* L. **Common Ragwort**

*680. Native. 'Injurious weed'. A tall biennial or perennial found throughout the conurbation in all but the poorest or most ill-drained soils. Appears in fields, along roadsides, railways and canal banks, derelict and waste ground and frequently in lawns and amenity grassland, including road verge lawns, where it persists without flowering if regularly mown. Particularly prominent in heavily grazed pastures where it is avoided by rabbits and stock, to which it is poisonous, but it can also produce dense stands on ungrazed road embankments and unmanaged grassland from where it spreads effectively by reseeding into bare areas and open vegetation. Ass: *Arrhenatherum elatius, Cynosurus cristatus, Cirsium arvense, Festuca rubra, Lolium perenne, Plantago lanceolata, Plantago major.*

### *Senecio* × *ostenfeldii* Druce
(*S. jacobaea* × *S. aquaticus*)

1. Native. A somewhat fertile hybrid which occurs with the parents and might be under-recorded. Ancient pasture below reservoir dam at Bartley Green – both parents present and many intermediates (SP008815, CBW, 1998).

### *Senecio aquaticus* Hill **Marsh Ragwort**

*45. Native. Ax. An infrequent and possibly declining biennial to perennial herb found in marshy hollows, rush pastures, wet grassland, stream sides and woodland margins, usually in old pasture, encouraged by undergrazing, on moderately fertile and fairly base-poor, usually heavy soils. Still relatively common in a few places such as along stream margins in Sutton Park and the damper pastures of Walsall and Illey,

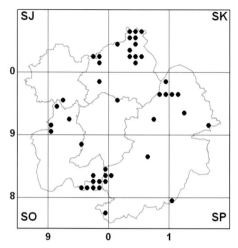

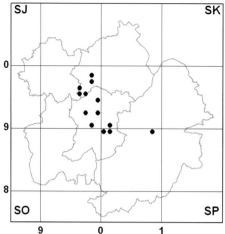

the early, annual-dominated stages of ecological succession in post-industrial clearance sites on fairly nutrient-poor but base-rich, often skeletal substrates. Its frequency dwindles to the E of the region where it appears to be less permanent except along railway corridors and it is quite scarce or even absent from some peripheral residential or countryside areas. A species possibly in decline as industry reduces. S Europe. Ass: *Artemisia absinthium, Artemisia vulgaris, Buddleja davidii, Medicago lupulina, Papaver dubium, Papaver rhoeas, Reseda luteola, Sonchus oleraceus, Trifolium arvense, Verbascum thapsus.*

### Senecio × baxteri Druce
(*S. squalidus* × *S. vulgaris*)
0. Alien × Native. Some, mostly tentative historical records: derelict hard tennis court, Edgbaston (SP08, R.C.L. Burges, 1945); a sterile plant was observed with both parent species on a traveller barrier on a construction site, Bilston Street (SO919875, ICT, 1982) but no specimen was taken; a plant at Pleck Gasworks could have been this, or *Senecio × subnebrodensis* (SP004974, JJB, 1989).

### Senecio × subnebrodensis Simonk.
(*S. squalidus* × *S. viscosus*)
2. Alien × Native. Alongside path, River Brook Drive, Stirchley (SP058816, MWP, conf. EJC, 2000); waste ground near Wednesbury Metro Station (SO9894, MWP, 2001). There are more old records: bombed site, B'ham (R.C.L. Burges, 1945); waste places at tennis courts, University of B'ham (SP0583, reported in Cadbury *et al.* 1971); common, with parents, railway line, Brownhills (SK052063, JPM, 1990); two, car park, Lower Forster Street, Walsall (SP015988, JPM, 1992).

### Senecio cambrensis Rosser
### Welsh Groundsel
0. Native. NT. First described from Flintshire (vc. 51) in 1948, it is a fertile 'new species' which arose naturally by the doubling of the chromosomes in a sterile *S. squalidus* × *S. vulgaris* hybrid. It appeared in school garden plots at Highfields School, W'ton, persisting for some years (SO880963, CBW, 1981).

### Senecio vulgaris L.
### Groundsel
*643. Native. An enthusiastic and tiresome weed in all sorts of recently disturbed and waste ground, arable land, garden borders, roadside verges and paving in a range of reasonably fertile soil types. Often abundant. Ass: *Capsella bursa-pastoris, Cerastium glomeratum, Euphorbia peplus,*

and largely confined to the countryside areas of B&BC. Ass: *Epilobium palustre, Galium palustre, Juncus effusus, Pulicaria dysenterica, Silene flos-cuculi.*

### Senecio erucifolius L.
### Hoary Ragwort

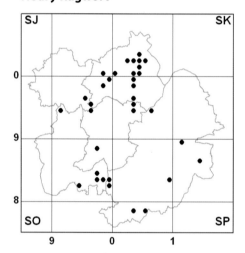

34. Native. Ax. A fairly uncommon perennial herb which is very occasionally locally abundant. Found as patches in meadows, field borders and grassy waste places, often (as in Walsall) by canal towpaths, on base-rich or calcareous soils of intermediate fertility. Sometimes associated with heavy winter-wet soils that dry out in summer. Some forms are very distinct from *S. jacobaea*, others less so. Recorded mainly from countryside areas, but occasionally found in Black Country 'tumbledown' pastures, old brickyards, etc. Ass: *Arrhenatherum elatius, Carex flacca, Lathyrus pratensis, Linum catharticum.*

### Senecio inaequidens DC.
### Narrow-leaved Ragwort
13. Neophyte. This potentially invasive perennial was first recorded in 2004 from canal towpath vegetation and in the brickwork of a nearby building along a 100m stretch of the Walsall Canal in

Moxley (SO969956, MWP, conf. EJC, 2004). The source of this concentration of plants has been tentatively attributed to seeds or seedling transference with shrub plantings nearby. In 2006 it appeared in the Albion Business Park, Spring Lane, Smethwick and on several other roadsides nearby (SP008896 & SP011896, PLR & MWP, 2006), close to the M5. Since these initial discoveries other well-established colonies have been found in car parks, along roadside verges and central reservations, around buildings, derelict gardens and on the bank of a canal. All finds so far have been from the Black Country apart from a solitary plant recorded from a roadside in Aston, B'ham (SP083895, D. Wall, conf. MWP & PLR, 2007). S Africa. Ass: *Conyza canadensis, Erigeron karvinskiana, Hordeum murinum, Senecio squalidus.*

### Senecio squalidus L.
### Oxford Ragwort

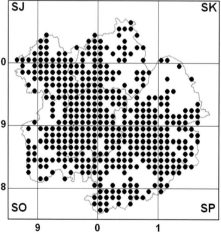

*457. Neophyte. A short-lived perennial herb found in disturbed ground, roadsides, railway ballast, mortared brickwork and other man-created substrates in open, sunny, exposed situations on well-drained soils especially those that are found around the more industrialised areas. Typical of

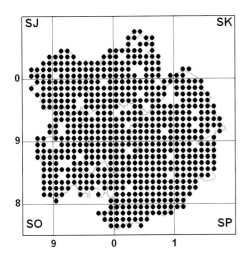

Senecio squalidus, Sonchus oleraceus, Stellaria media, Veronica persica.

All our records are thought to be for **subsp. vulgaris**. Ligulate forms are occasionally observed in B&BC. Four definitely ascribed to **subsp. vulgaris var. hibernicus** Syme are: (SJ80V, BRF, 1995); border of council house buildings (SP000882, MWP, 1998); Wednesfield (SJ931004, JEH, 2004); Wheeler's Lane Allotments (SP081814, MWP, ICT & EMP, 2008).

### Senecio sylvaticus L.
### Heath Groundsel

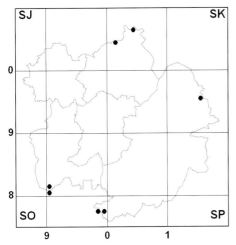

7. Native. Ax. In B&BC a very local annual found in open, well-drained, moderately acid, sandy soils only in the very periphery. Locally frequent on the gorse-dominated hillside and quarry slopes of Rubery Hill, at a few places on Pelsall Common and Brownhills Common and in more secondary sites in railway cuttings into sandstone in Stourbridge and by roadsides at Old Langley Hall in Sutton (SP150954, MWP, ICT & JWP, 2006). Also recorded in the early 1990s and possibly still present on the Ridge, Wollaston (SO8884), Highter's Heath (SP0779) and a single plant in the old Hawne Colliery workings (SO9584). Often appears after fires or disturbance.

Ass: *Aira praecox, Calluna vulgaris, Campanula rotundifolia, Danthonia decumbens, Deschampsia flexuosa, Digitalis purpurea, Festuca ovina, Ulex europaeus.*

### Senecio viscosus L.
### Sticky Groundsel

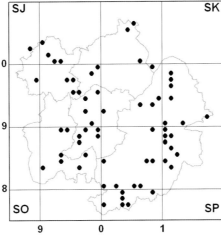

65. Native. Ax. An annual of open, sunny, well-drained situations. Often recorded in railway ballast, along canal towpaths and in sparsely vegetated banks and other bare places. Relatively infrequent but large colonies sometimes occur on derelict railway sidings with other annuals. Intolerant of competition from more aggressive species. Soils usually skeletal, base-rich and quite nutrient-rich. Also tetrad SO99D. Ass: *Arabidopsis thaliana, Artemisia vulgaris, Linaria repens, Linaria vulgaris, Medicago lupulina, Poa annua, Polygonum aviculare, Reseda lutea, Reseda luteola, Rumex acetosella, Vulpia myuros.*

### Brachyglottis × jubar P.D. Sell
(B. 'Sunshine'; ?B. laxifolia (Buchanan) B. Nord. × B. compacta (Kirk) B. Nord.)
### Shrub Ragwort
2. Neophyte. Shrub. A garden relic: cemetery, Brierley Hill (SO9386, A. Harris, 1998); huge bush where a road crosses a derelict railway, Tibbington (SO954934, JEH, 2007). Garden origin.

### Doronicum pardalianches L.
### Leopard's-bane
2. Neophyte. Remarkably, only two modern records for this attractive perennial which naturalised widely in the UK in shady places: railway bank opposite Poundland, Shepwell Green, Willenhall (SO974983, SJC & JaH, 2003); grounds of Woodbrooke, Bournville (SP0381, ICT, M. Kingsbury & S. Locke, 2008). Also only two older records; Tettenhall College woodlands (SO885995, DH, 1985) and by the M6 Motorway (SP042948, A. Black, A. Brown & TCH, 1987). W Europe.

No records either for the hybrids D. × willldenowii (Rouy) A.W. Hill or D. × excelsum (N.E. Br.) Stace.

### Tussilago farfara L.
### Colt's-foot

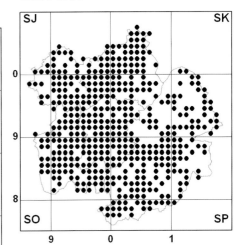

*469. Native. This rhizomatous perennial is a frequent feature along roadside verges, canal towpaths, banks, spoil heaps, wasteland, neglected gardens in heavy, poorly drained clayey, usually nutrient and base-medium soils in open situations. A pioneer plant, its flowers often appear alone on mounds of dumped road chippings, coal slack and other material. Forming large colonies when left undisturbed where its leafless yellow dandelion-like flowers carpet the ground in early spring before the characteristic leaves appear. It covered a large continuous area in old excavations at the rear of Ladymoor Pool, Bilston (SO943951) for many years. Ass: *Agrostis stolonifera, Chamerion angustifolium, Elytrigia repens, Equisetum arvense, Rumex obtusifolius, Salix caprea.*

### Petasites hybridus (L.) P. Gaertn., B. Mey. & Scherb.
### Butterbur

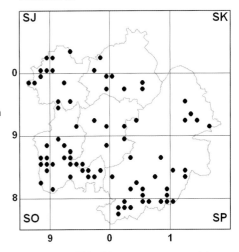

*79. Native. This rhizomatous perennial, once established, forms large stands, its leaves shading out all competition. A colonising plant of damp to permanently wet meadows, pool banks, streamsides and canal margins on heavy clay or silty base- and nutrient-rich soils in open to half-shaded aspects. Apparently not common in the urban core or the Walsall countryside. Some of the concentrations are associated with certain of the canal systems (where it can occupy large areas between towpath and water's edge) and river flood plains. Ass: *Aegopodium podagraria, Arrhenatherum elatius, Impatiens glandulifera, Phalaris arundinacea, Rumex obtusifolius, Urtica dioica.*

### *Petasites japonicus* (Siebold & Zucc.) Maxim.
### Giant Butterbur

0 Neophyte. Only an old record: Edgbaston Golf Course Complex (SP054841, BNHS, reported in Cadbury *et al.* 1971). Japan.

### *Petasites fragrans* (Vill.) C. Presl
### Winter Heliotrope

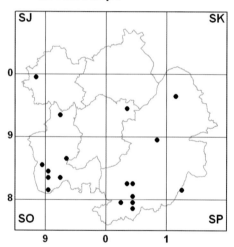

18. Neophyte. In few places in B&BC, mostly in the S. Usually in damp, shady places. Becoming very persistent once established and sometimes associated with the remnants of large estate gardens, e.g. at Wollescote Dingle. Records for woodland edge, streamside, overgrown gardens and roadside verges where it has spilled out from nearby gardens. N Africa. Ass: *Heracleum sphondylium, Impatiens glandulifera, Rubus fruticosus* agg., *Urtica dioica.*

### *Calendula officinalis* L.
### Pot Marigold

92. Neophyte. A frequently grown hardy annual, often seeding into nearby beds and paving near to its original planting. Solitary or small groups of plants are occasionally met with on recently created post-housing sites along with other garden

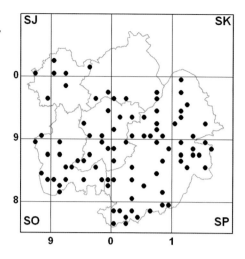

annuals. Seldom far from habitation and rarely persisting for more than a season or so. ?Garden origin. Ass: *Antirrhinum majus, Dactylis glomerata, Digitalis purpurea, Fallopia convolvulus, Lobelia erinus, Lobularia maritima, Meconopsis cambrica, Solanum nigrum.*

### *Ambrosia artemisiifolia* L.
### Ragweed

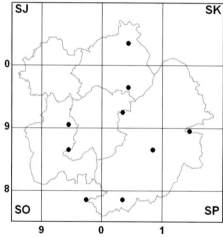

9. Neophyte. A summer-germinating casual annual found on newly created post-housing sites and on spoil mounds surrounding these sites, and on the land of a livery stables. Usually associated with discarded bird seed and other livestock food. First seen in 1996, more regular recent records (2005 onwards) suggest that this species may be on the increase. It is widely considered to be a serious pollen allergen. N America. Ass: *Avena sativa, Echinochloa crus-galli, Guizotia abyssinica, Hieracium* sect. Sabauda, *Panicum miliaceum, Phalaris canariensis.*

### *Ambrosia trifida* L.
### Giant Ragweed

0. Casual. Old record, on a railway track at West Bromwich (SO99, V. Jacobs, det. A.J. Wilmott. 1948). N America.

### *Iva xanthiifolia* Nutt.
### Marsh-elder

2. Neophyte, casual with us. A rare casual from animal or bird seed forming a colony of 20+ plants on an area of land recovering from disturbance, originally council housing and associated gardens, Oddingley Rd, West Heath (SP034786, MWP, conf. EJC, 2006). Also bird-seed alien, Sandwell Valley (SP035927, MWP, 1996). N America. Ass: *Ambrosia artemisiifolia, Avena sativa, Chenopodium album.*

### *Rudbeckia hirta* L.
### Black-eyed-Susan

1. Neophyte. A garden plant persisting on land recovering from recent disturbance, Oddingley Rd, West Heath (SP033786, JJD, 2006). N America.

### *Helianthus annuus* L.
### Sunflower

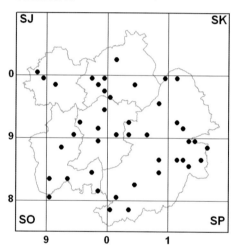

43. Neophyte. Resulting from discarded bird and animal feed, a frequently encountered casual of disturbed ground, gardens and traveller spoil banks. N America. Ass: *Chenopodium album, Lobularia maritima, Panicum miliaceum.*

### *Helianthus petiolaris* Nutt.
### Lesser Sunflower

4. Casual. Occurring rarely on disturbed and waste ground from discarded bird-seed. Possibly confused with small plants of *Helianthus annuus.* Sandwell Valley (SP035927, MWP, 1996); Greets Green (SO985917, MWP, 1997); Walsall canal (SO978928, E. McKay, 1997); Ley Hill Farm Road (SP0180, MWP, 2003). N America.

### *Helianthus × multiflorus* L.
(*H. annuus × H. decapetalus* L.)
### Thin-leaved Sunflower

1. Neophyte. Established as a mature plant on waste land, Gorge Road Allotments, Sedgley (SO926939, ICT, 2008) and an old record on waste land on the Lion Farm

Estate (SO980883, WAT, det. RM, 1992). Garden origin.

### Helianthus × laetiflorus Pers.
(*H. pauciflorus* Nutt. × *H. tuberosus*)
**Perennial Sunflower**

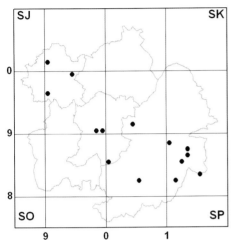

14. Neophyte. A tall perennial herb only rarely persisting as a garden discard in rough grassland and on post-housing land. There are no records from Dudley and only an old record (SJ902012, BRF, 1993) for Walsall. ?Garden origin.

### Helianthus tuberosus L.
**Jerusalem Artichoke**

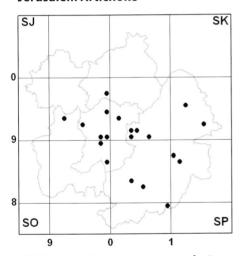

20. Neophyte. A minor crop grown for its edible roots and usually flowering too late in the year to produce viable seed. Very persistent where discarded or thrown-out along path margins and in neglected allotment garden plots from discarded tubers. N America.

### Guizotia abyssinica (L. f.) Cass.
**Niger**
4. Casual. A summer-germinating casual occurring rarely on post-housing land and disturbed soil and almost certainly always originating from discarded bird seed. Solitary plants or small colonies are usually

recorded with other bird-seed derivitives such as *Echinochloa crus-galli*, *Panicum miliaceum* and *Ambrosia artemisiifolia*. Sandwell Valley (SP035927, MWP, 1996); quarry (SO968878, ST, 1998); excavated soil (SP022802, MWP, 2005); post-housing site (SP033786, MWP & ICT, 2006). E Africa.

### Galinsoga parviflora Cav.
**Gallant-soldier**

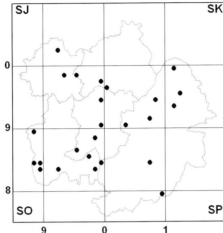

25. Neophyte. Cultivated ground, gardens and paving and a coloniser of allotment garden plots where its rapid growth and seed-set is perfectly suited to regular disturbance of the soil. Initial populations are likely to have originated from seed or immature plants being inadvertently introduced with potted plants from nurseries. S America. Ass: *Chenopodium album, Fallopia convolvulus, Lamium purpureum, Urtica urens, Veronica agrestis, Veronica persica.*

### Galinsoga quadriradiata Ruiz & Pav.
**Shaggy-soldier**

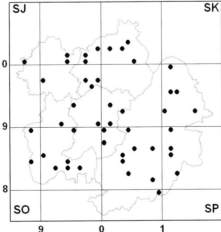

47. Neophyte. Cultivated ground, gardens and paving and particularly prevalent in some B&BC allotment gardens, where this and *G. parviflora* can be locally abundant and can become a problem, carpeting

▲ *Ambrosia artemisiifolia*

▲ *Iva xanthiifolia*

▲ *Galinsoga quadriradiata*

*Galinsoga parviflora* (by Anne Bebbington)

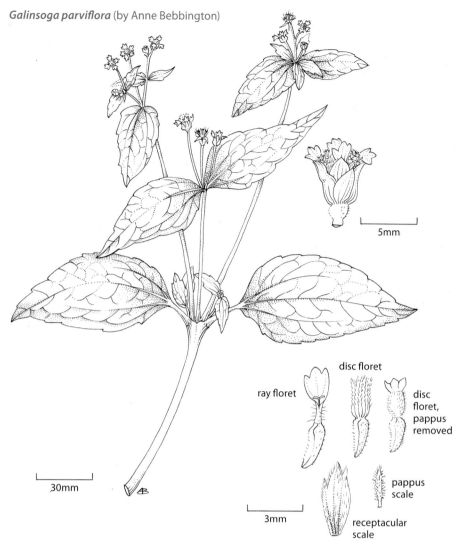

ray floret     disc floret

disc floret, pappus removed

pappus scale

receptacular scale

5mm

30mm

3mm

*Galinsoga quadriradiata* (by Anne Bebbington)

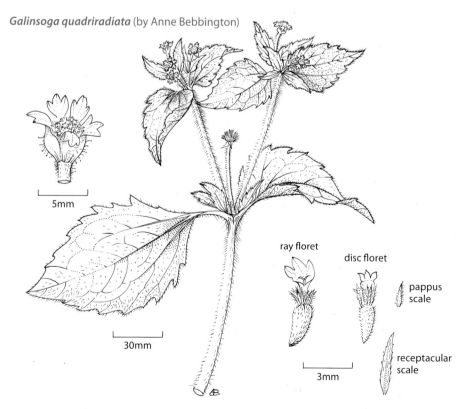

ray floret     disc floret

pappus scale

receptacular scale

5mm

30mm

3mm

the soil and scrambling up bean frames. Plants or seeds presumably arrived in the same way as *G. parviflora* with which it it is sometimes found. Now considered to be the commoner of the two *Galinsogas* in B&BC, although only *G. parviflora* is mentioned in Edees (1972), and not from B&BC. Nevertheless it was from B&BC that *G. quadriradiata* was first recorded in vc. 39 in 1968 (from a car park, Skinner Street, W'ton, SO9198, BRF & C.M. Hibbert). Both species are recorded from B'ham in Cadbury *et al.* (1971), but *G. parviflora* only from SP0588 and *G. quadriradiata* only from SP0386. S America. Ass: as *G. parviflora*.

### *Bidens cernua* L.
### Nodding Bur-marigold

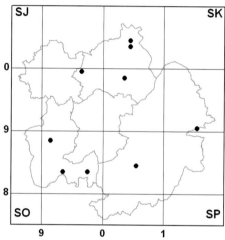

9. Native. Ax. An uncommon annual confined to a handful of records from the margins of small pools and large lakes on substrates with intermediate to fairly high base and nutrient status subject to fluctuating water levels. This species seems to be declining: records from Sutton Park have not been refound; there are Warks record centre records from Blackroot Pool (SP1097) and Powells Pool (SP1095) as recently as 1977 and in 1971 Readett recorded it in SP0995, SP0996, SP0998, SP1097, SP1195 and SP1196. It may also be lost from Clayhanger SSSI: last recorded there in 1986. On the other hand it recently appeared at Parkhall. Ass: *Bidens tripartita*, *Myosotis scorpioides*, *Persicaria amphibia*.

### *Bidens tripartita* L.
### Trifid Bur-marigold

28. Native. Ax. An annual of winter-wet hollows, wet meadows, muddy margins of ponds subjected to fluctuating water levels that often dry up in summer. Found in similar habitats to *Bidens cernua* and commoner, possibly persisting better in situations with less fluctuating water levels, but still probably declining due to habitat loss and replacement by *Bidens frondosa*

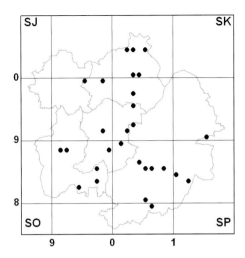

in recent years. The map suggests that it has been largely recorded by canals in B&BC, but there has been confusion with *B. frondosa* and some of the earlier records might be for that. Nevertheless it is still occasionally being reliably recorded by canals. Also tetrad SO99A. Ass: *Agrostis stolonifera, Bidens cernua, Carex otrubae, Myosotis scorpioides, Persicaria amphibia*.

## *Bidens frondosa* L.
## Beggarticks

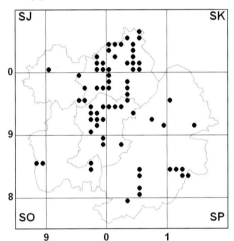

*70. Neophyte. A late summer-flowering annual thoroughly naturalised along the canal network throughout B'ham and the Black Country. It favours the canal-column brickwork and forms part of the community of plants growing just above the water-line where there is constant moisture. Also found amongst emergent vegetation in the margins of canals where it forms colonies on platforms of decomposing vegetation. Less tolerant of fluctuating water-levels than *B. tripartita* so rarely found around the muddy margins of pools but recently it does seem to be replacing *B. tripartita* around some of these, e.g. Edgbaston Pool. Despite the confusion with *B. tripartita*, this species was recognised in B&BC over

50 years ago: on the towpath between Landor Street & Saltley, B'ham, Grand Union Canal (probably SP0987, D.A. Cadbury, 1952) and its distribution is still centred in the West Midlands, although we have found it most frequently in the Black Country canals. It was first recorded in vc. 39 in a canal cutting near Hamstead (SP035939, WHH, 1954). N & S America. Ass: *Carex otrubae, Myosotis scorpioides, Oenanthe crocata, Phalaris arundinacea, Scutellaria galericulata, Sparganium erectum*.

## *Coreopsis tinctoria* Nutt.
## Tickseed

1. Neophyte. Annual, recorded from disturbed land and soil tip on building site, Heathland Avenue, Buckland End, B'ham (SP141890, JWP, 2007). USA.

## *Cosmos bipinnatus* Cav.
## Mexican Aster

5. Neophyte. A relic of cultivation, recorded in disturbed ground, mostly in allotments and gardens. Pool margin, Kingswinford (SO890893, MWP, 2007); waste land at Lane Avenue Allotments (SO9999, ICT & JaH, 2008); self-set at Harborne Lane Allotments (SP039831, MWP & PWS); Wheelers Lane Allotments (SP082814, MWP, ICT & EMP, 2008); Yardley Green Hospital grounds (SP115862, MWP, T. Oliver & L. Worledge, 2008); Bordesley Green Allotments (SP111869, ICT, 2008). Mexico, S USA.

## *Dahlia* × *hortensis* Guillaumin
## Dahlia

1. Casual. Relic of cultivation (SP0887, MWP, 2003). Mexico.

## *Tagetes patula* L.
## French Marigold

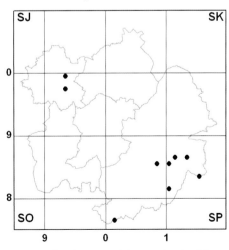

9. Casual. A frost-sensitive garden bedding plant, very rarely seeding into paving from nearby plantings. Mexico.

## *Helenium autumnale* L.
## Sneezeweed

1. Neophyte. One modern record. Several patches persisting from original garden plantings on an area of derelict housing land, Lichfield Rd (SP113992, MWP, JWP & PLR, 2006). N America.

## *Eupatorium cannabinum* L.
## Hemp-agrimony

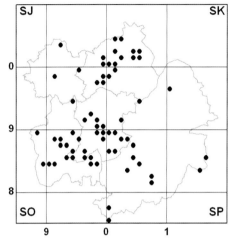

*66. Native. A fairly infrequently occurring perennial herb of base-enriched, moderately fertile, moisture-retaining and usually winter-wet soils in open and lightly shaded situations particularly along canals (favouring derelict sections and with some odd gaps in its distribution) and close to pools. Also, much less frequently, on rough ground, railway banks, and post-industrial sites. Mainly in the Black Country; much less common in B'ham and W'ton. Ass: *Angelica sylvatica, Epilobium hirsutum, Filipendula ulmaria, Phalaris arundinacea*.

▲ *Eupatorium cannabinum*

## 129. ESCALLONIACEAE

### *Escallonia macrantha* Hook. & Arn.
**Escallonia**

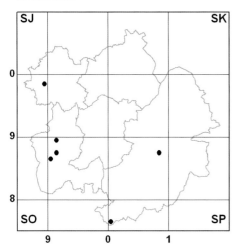

6. Neophyte. Evergreen shrub. Few records, probably all garden relics or discards: one bush in hedgerow, by canal, in derelict works grounds, rear of houses etc. First record for vc. 39 is from rough ground near to the canal, off Waldron Avenue, Brierley Hill (SO909868, APD, 2002). Chile.

### *Escallonia × langleyensis* Veitch
(*E. macrantha × E. virgata* (Ruiz & Pav.) Pers.)
2. Neophyte. Probably garden discards. In vc. 39: Dunstall Hill, W'ton (SJ916006, PN, 2005). In vc. 38 : near Hill Hook (SP105996, MWP, ICT & JWP, 2006). Garden origin.

## 130. ADOXACEAE

### *Adoxa moschatellina* L.
**Moschatel**

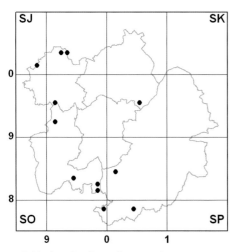

12. Native. Ax. An early-maturing rhizomatous perennial herb of woodland in shaded and semi-shaded situations on fairly moist, base- and nutrient-intermediate soils. Rare, and largely absent from the built-up areas; most post-1995 records are from woodland and dingles

around the margins of B&BC. Some of the populations have declined in recent years due to habitat loss but this low-growing, green-flowered plant is easily overlooked and in late spring quickly becomes overwhelmed by surrounding vegetation in its woodland habitat. Our most central record was from Sot's Hole, Sandwell Valley (SP011923), where it has not been seen since 1987. Ass: *Anemone nemorosa, Ficaria verna, Hyacinthoides non-scripta, Viola reichenbachiana*.

## 131. CAPRIFOLIACEAE

### *Sambucus racemosa* L.
**Red-berried Elder**
0. Neophyte. Deciduous shrub. One historical record from Merecroft Pool & Meadowland, Kings Norton (SP0478, BNHS, 1980). Europe.

### *Sambucus nigra* L.
**Elder**
*677. Native. Very common shrub or small tree in hedgerows, woodland, shrubberies, railway and canal banks and also a colonising weed of paving, gardens and waste ground in moist, fairly base-poor to base-rich, fertile to very fertile soils. Forms with dissected leaves (**forma laciniata** (L.) Zabel) or variegated leaves (**forma luteovariegata** (Weston) Schwer.) are occasionally found as is the green-fruited **forma viridis** (Weston) Schwer. Ass: *Acer pseudoplatanus, Corylus avellana, Crataegus monogyna, Ilex aquifolium, Prunus spinosa, Salix caprea, Urtica dioica*.

### *Sambucus canadensis* L.
**American Elder**
1. Neophyte. A shrub, predominantly recorded further N in the UK, with two records from Sandwell Valley where it was almost certainly originally planted: (SP034916, MWP, 1997); (SP037923, Sandwell Valley Naturalists, 1994). Eastern N America.

### *Sambucus ebulus* L.
**Dwarf Elder**
4. Archaeophyte. Ax. Large shrub-like herbaceous perennial. Three long established large patches, all by abandoned railway lines: along the old railway track, S of Pensnett High Street (SO913891, BRF, 1986, seen 2008); along the disused railway between Highfields Road and Lane Street, Bradley (SO949952, BRF, 1987, seen 2008); filled-in canal at Weddell Wynd, Prince's End (SO958945 to SO960944, CRP, 2000, seen 2008). There is also an old record from near Kings Norton Playing Fields (SP052794, B&BC Wildlife Trust, 1988).

### *Viburnum opulus* L.
**Guelder-rose**

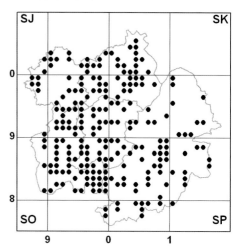

*227. Native; often introduced. Deciduous shrub, characteristic of old hedgerows and woodland margins in moist or damp or winter wet situations on soils of intermediate base status and fertility. Extensively planted in urban landscape schemes for its showy autumn display of leaves and fruit (although sometimes the sterile cultivar 'Roseum' (**Snowball-tree**) is planted, or possibly the allied species *V. sargentii* Koehne from Asia or *V. trilobum* Marshall from North America). Because of this the true native range in B&BC is obscure and it is no longer a reliable indicator of ancient woodland status in our area. Ass: *Alnus glutinosa, Cornus sanguinea, Corylus avellana, Fraxinus excelsior, Ribes nigrum*.

### *Viburnum lantana* L.
**Wayfaring-tree**

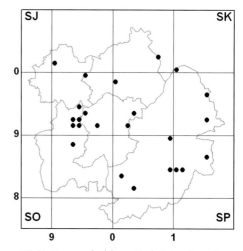

24. Native; probably entirely introduced in B&BC. A naturally occurring deciduous shrub of woodland edges, hedgerows, rough grassland in base-rich soils. It is recorded from parks, shrubberies, canal sides and occasionally from woodlands. It is beloved of landscape architects, and is occasionally introduced in habitat creation

schemes. There are no definite reports of seedlings and it appears always to be a remnant of planting or a garden throwout. It may just possibly be native on the limestone at the Wren's Nest, Dudley but it was definitely planted there in the 1980s. Ass: *Crataegus monogyna, Corylus avellana*.

### *Viburnum tinus* L.
### Laurustinus

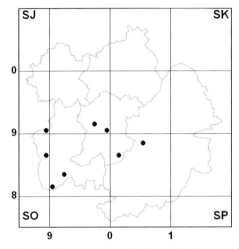

8. Neophyte. An extensively planted winter-flowering, evergreen shrub. Recorded as a persistent relic, seldom if ever regenerating from seed. S Europe.

### *Viburnum rhytidophyllum* Hemsl.
### Wrinkled Viburnum
2. Neophyte. Evergreen shrub; the only records are: one small plant self-seeded into paving along the approach road to Dudley Road Metro Station, West Bromwich (SO995919, MWP, 2004); perimeter of Phoenix Park, W'ton (SO9196, CBW, 2007). China.

### *Symphoricarpos albus* (L.) S.F. Blake
### Snowberry

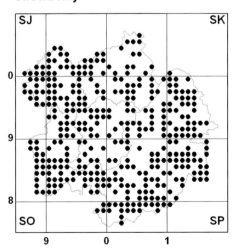

*374. Neophyte. A frequently planted, rhizomatous shrub, very persistent and extensively suckering to form dense thickets where left undisturbed. Also

appearing as isolated specimens on waste ground and in overgrown gardens, presumably as a garden discard; there are no definite records of seedlings. Preferring open to moderately shady situations, in slightly damp, fertile soils. A few records are from old woodland suggesting this species could be capable of invading semi-natural habitats. It was quite widespread in our areas of the 1971 Staffordshire and 1972 Warwickshire Floras but appears to be more frequent now. WN America. Ass: *Hedera helix, Rubus fruticosus* agg., *Solanum dulcamara, Urtica dioica*.

### *Symphoricarpos* × *chenaultii* Rehder
(*S. microphyllus* Kunth × *S. orbiculatus* Moench)
### Chenault's Coralberry

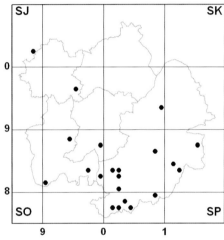

21. Neophyte. Frequently planted in shrubberies and occasionally persisting, also a garden discard in waste places by canals etc. Seedlings not recorded. A hybrid of garden origin.

### *Leycesteria formosa* Wall.
### Himalayan Honeysuckle, Flowering Nutmeg

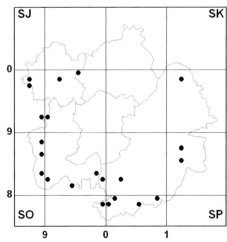

22. Neophyte. Deciduous shrub, occasionally persisting in overgrown shrub beds from original introduction, or as a

garden discard and only rarely in woodland. Occasionally thought to be self-sown close to gardens in pavements etc. Seldom far from habitation. Himalayas. Ass: *Fraxinus excelsior, Rumex obtusifolius, Urtica dioica*.

### *Weigela florida* (Bunge) A. DC.
### Weigelia
3. Neophyte. Deciduous shrub sometimes persisting as a relic from a former planting. Ancient churchyard, Wednesbury (SO987947, MWP, 1997) – now destroyed; by Grand Union canal (SP096891, PWS, 2002); by hedge, former sewage works, Woodsetton (SO928925, MWP & APD, 2004). China.

### *Lonicera pileata* Oliv.
### Box-leaved Honeysuckle

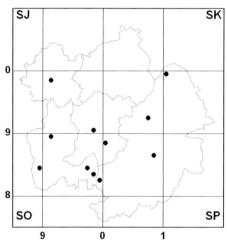

11. Neophyte. An evergreen shrub often found in mixed shrubbery plantings. Isolated plants occur rarely in hedgerows and woodland and are possibly bird-sown. Also recorded from SO99E and SO99I. China.

### *Lonicera nitida* E.H. Wilson
### Wilson's Honeysuckle

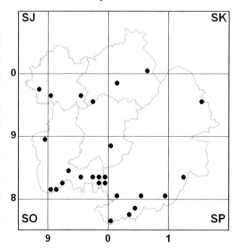

26. Neophyte. Evergreen shrub, regularly planted in shrubberies and sometimes planted alone to create a low garden hedge. The records, from hedgerows

and woodlands, may be relics of former plantings or bird-sown. China.

### *Lonicera tatarica* L.
### Tartarian Honeysuckle
1. Neophyte. Garden outcast, now a large shrub, Shenley Fields (SP016808, CBW, 1997). W & C Asia.

### *Lonicera henryi* Hemsl.
### Henry's Honeysuckle
1. Neophyte. Hill Hook LNR where a well-established plant has reached 20–30 feet, completely smothering a tree (SK105003, MWP & M. Yates, 2010). China.

### *Lonicera japonica* Thunb.
### Japanese Honeysuckle

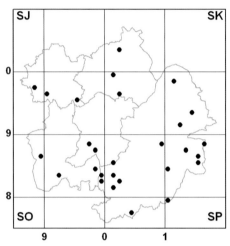

28. Neophyte. Records from hedges and tracks close to habitation where it has spread from nearby gardens. Sometimes rooting into grassy areas and climbing and scrambling extensively through nearby shrubs to form quite extensive patches and becoming quite persistent once established. There are further tetrad records from SO88Y, SO89Y & SO99D. E Asia.

### *Lonicera periclymenum* L.
### Honeysuckle

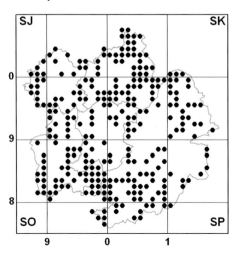

*282. Native. A sweet-smelling vine of woodland and hedgerows in semi-shaded, base- and nutrient-intermediate soils. Generally well distributed across the conurbation but some of the more inner city records may be confused with similar looking *L. × italica* of gardens. Ass: *Bryonia dioica, Hedera helix, Rosa arvensis, Rosa canina, Tamus communis*.

### *Lonicera × italica* Schmidt ex Tausch
(*L. caprifolium* L. × *L. etrusca* Santi)
### Garden Honeysuckle

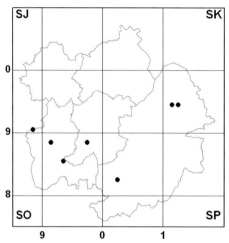

7. Neophyte. More than one species of garden-grown Honeysuckle are likely to be involved here and escapes are occasionally found in hedgerows and on rough ground, near to habitation. Some urban records for *L. periclymenum* could be for this. Garden origin.

## 132. VALERIANACEAE

### *Valerianella locusta* (L.) Laterr.
### Common Cornsalad

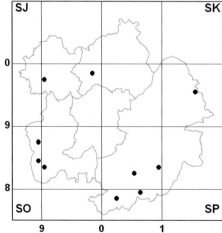

10. Native. Rare on walls and paving in open, sunny situations on neutral to weakly acid soils, mostly in residential or industrial areas. Ass: *Arabidopsis thaliana, Conyza canadensis, Rubus*

*fruticosus* agg., *Sisymbrium officinale, Veronica arvensis*.

### *Valerianella carinata* Loisel.
### Keeled-fruited Cornsalad

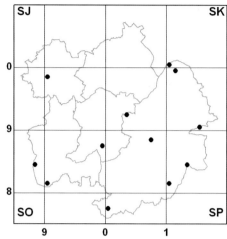

12. Archaeophyte. Walls and paving in similar situations to *V. locusta*. Mostly in residential areas but also twice on the banks of the River Tame, both in the Sandwell Valley (SP030925) and in Park Hall nature reserve (SP158909). Records suggest that of the two Cornsalad species found in the urban area this is slightly more frequent. Ass: *Arabidopsis thaliana, Cerastium glomeratum, Conyza canadensis, Sisymbrium officinale, Veronica arvensis*.

### *Valeriana officinalis* L.
### Common Valerian

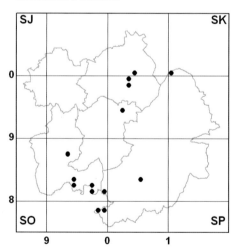

14. Native. Ax. Herbaceous perennial herb of woodland clearings, particularly along streams and ditches, occasionally in canal reedwamp communities, in permanently moist or damp soils of intermediate fertility and base status. This species seems to be declining generally in the English Midlands and particularly in B&BC. There are few modern records, and it was not recorded at many of the sites known from the 1980s in W'ton, the Walsall countryside, S

B'ham and Sutton Park. Possibly its love of streamside sites has made it susceptible to nutrient pollution, although its tendency to occur in small numbers may mean it has been missed. Ass: *Allium ursinum, Anemone nemorosa, Angelica sylvatica, Arum maculatum, Ficaria verna, Filipendula ulmaria, Hyacinthoides non-scripta.*

Two separate colonies of the larger **subsp. *sambucifolia*** (J.C. Mikan ex Pohl) W.R. Hayw. have been found on the Lye Close Brook (SO979824, JJD, 2003).

### *Valeriana dioica* L.
### Marsh Valerian
3. Native. Ax. Dioecious perennial herb of nutrient-poor but base-enriched flushes and mires. All confirmed modern records are from Sutton Park where there are thriving colonies near Little Bracebridge Pool (SP0998, most recently recorded in 2011) and N of Longmoor Pool in Longmoor Valley (most recently recorded in 2011 in SP0995 and SP0996). However it was not seen in SP1096 and SP1097, where it was recorded in Readett (1971), nor in SP0997, last recorded anonymously in 1859. There is also an unconfirmed record from the Leasowes in Halesowen (SO975840, H. Edwards, 2007). Ass: *Carex echinata, Comarum palustre, Dactylorhiza praetermissa, Dryopteris carthusiana, Juncus bulbosus.*

### *Centranthus ruber* (L.) DC.
### Red Valerian

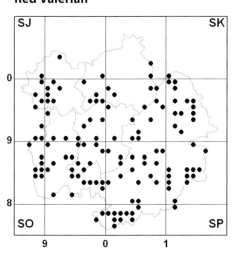

131. Neophyte. Railway and canal bridge brickwork mortar, garden walls and paving cracks below, in sunny, well-drained situations. Long-flowering throughout the summer months, locally common but seldom spreading far from habitation. White flowered forms are sometimes found. Mediterranean region. Also tetrad SO98J. Ass: *Anisantha sterilis, Anthriscus sylvestris, Dactylis glomerata, Galium aparine, Lamium album, Lamium purpureum, Lobularia maritima, Poa annua,*

*Rubus fruticosus* agg., *Rumex obtusifolius, Senecio squalidus, Urtica dioica.*

### 133. DIPSACACEAE

### *Dipsacus fullonum* L.
### Wild Teasel

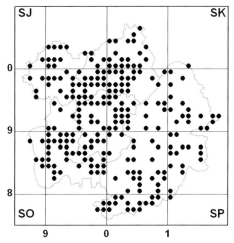

*250. Native. A tall biennial widely cultivated in gardens and allotments and colonising open situations on moisture-retaining and often richly fertile, neutral soils. Fairly common on roadside, railway and canal banks, wood margins and a rapid coloniser of overgrown gardens and neglected bits of waste ground. Ass: *Arrhenatherum elatius, Cirsium vulgare, Epilobium ciliatum, Rumex obtusifolius, Sinapis arvensis, Triticum aestivum.*

### *Dipsacus sativus* (L.) Honck.
### Fuller's Teasel
1. Neophyte. Allotments at Kings Heath (SP079802, JWP, conf. RM, 1995). Also an old record at Water Orton sidings (SP172914, HHF, 1973).

### *Dipsacus laciniatus* L.
### Cut-leaved Teasel
2. Neophyte. Road verge, Wall Heath (SO8789, CBW, 2006); several plants with *D. fullonum* in rough grassland near the New Hall Valley car park, Sutton Coldfield (SP129944, JWP, MWP, ICT, EVJC & JaH, 2007). Some plants at the latter site resembled ***Dipsacus × pseudosilvester*** Schur (*D. fullonum × D. laciniatus*).

### *Cephalaria gigantea* (Ledeb.) Bobrov
### Giant Scabious
4. Neophyte. A 2m tall rhizomatous perennial, establishing and spreading from garden rejects. Many plants along the banks of a disused railway cutting between Highfields Road and Lane Street, Bradley (SO949952, BRF & ICT, 1987, still large patches in 2008); a long established colony at the base of, and in the soil border on

▲ *Centranthus ruber*

▲ *Dipsacus fullonum*

top of a wall along the approach road into Sapcote Trading Estate, Powke Lane, Old Hill (SO958872, MWP, 1999); one patch in Druids Lane, King's Wood (SP069784, MWP, 1998); few plants in rubble, waste land behind Morrisons, Bilston (SO953960, ICT, 2004). An old record: about garden rubbish on waste ground at Wallbrook, Coseley (SO947935, WAT, 1987). Caucasus.

### Knautia arvensis (L.) Coult.
### Field Scabious

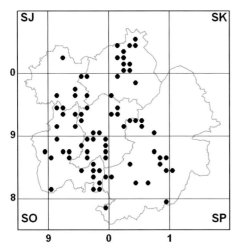

*78. Native. Perennial herb of well-drained open conditions in base-medium to calcareous, infertile soils, never occurring in great quantity but widely recorded across the region, with some concentration in the Black Country. A species of unimproved grasslands but also seen in old quarries on base-rich rocks and on dry roadside, railway and canal banks in light soils or spoils. An attractive plant, the origin of some of our records are likely to be from deliberate introductions in habitat-creation schemes. Ass: *Arrhenatherum elatius, Centaurea scabiosa, Crepis vesicaria, Leontodon hispidus, Picris hieracioides.*

### Succisa pratensis Moench
### Devil's-bit Scabious

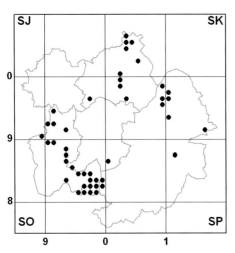

*45. Native. Ax. Perennial herb. Mildly acid, infertile, damp soils in open or partially shaded situations. A plant of unimproved, poorly drained rush-pasture and mire, and a good indicator of the presence of such, at least in remnant. There appears to be a steady decline in recent years, possibly due to habitat loss and deterioration, especially in the Walsall countryside and to some extent in Sutton Park. Ass: *Betonica officinalis, Carex nigra, Carex panicea, Juncus acutiflorus, Juncus conglomeratus, Juncus effusus, Potentilla erecta, Silene flos-cuculi.*

### Scabiosa columbaria L.
### Small Scabious

4. Native. Ax. A herbaceous perennial of dry, infertile calcareous grassland in open situations. Possibly native in calcareous grassland in the quarry, Wren's Nest NNR, Dudley (SO936920–937920), where it has been known since the 1980s. Very few other modern records: the Cracker, Tipton, in an area of limestone grassland, growing with *Plantago media* and *Poterium sanguisorba* subsp. *sanguisorba* (SO952928 & SO954928, MWP, 1997 & 1998) is probably an old introduction with limestone for iron smelting. The other two records, at Saltwells LNR (SO933877, J. Akers, 1999) and Phoenix Park, W'ton (SO918969, JEH, 2007) are probably deliberate introductions, the latter definitely. There are a few older records, of which the most likely is from the limestone quarry at Sedgley (SO920950, K. Hodge & G. Palmer, 1985), but it has not been seen there for many years. A record from Moor Hall Golf Course (SP127978, Natural England, 1982) has not been checked because we were refused access.

### 136. ARALIACEAE

### Hedera colchica (K. Koch) K. Koch
### Persian Ivy

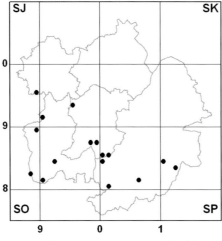

16. Neophyte. Long-persisting in shrubberies and on banks. All records are for spreading

patches from established plantings. Often with variegated leaves. Caucasus.

### Hedera algeriensis Hibberd
### Algerian Ivy

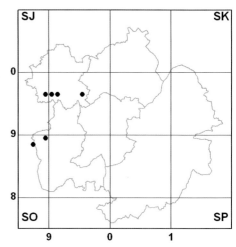

6. Neophyte. Usually grown indoors and fairly frost sensitive. Recorded only by CBW, it may well exist as a garden reject or escape elsewhere in B&BC. Churchyards and path-sides. Also tetrad record for SO98Y. N Africa.

### Hedera helix L.
### Common Ivy

*657. Native. Ubiquitous, in woodland, scrub, hedgerows, walls, railway, river and canal banks on basic to moderately acid soils in shaded to semi-shaded situations. Often carpeting the ground in secondary woodland as a monoculture. Many varieties are grown and some persist in derelict gardens.

### Hedera helix
### subsp. *poetarum* (Bertol.) Nyman
0. Neophyte. Old record, Highbury Park, Moor Green (SP069826, J. Turner & R.A. Jones, 1987). C & E Mediterranean.

### Hedera hibernica (G. Kirchn.) Bean
(*H. helix* subsp. *hibernica* (G. Kirchn.) D.C. McClint.)
### Atlantic Ivy

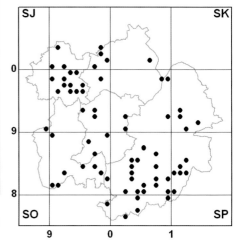

71. Native/alien. In similar situations to *Hedera helix* and sometimes displacing it. Not considered native in our area; all records are presumed to be for the cultivar 'Hibernica' (**Irish Ivy**). Recorders for the present survey have not consistently separated it from *H. helix* and some of those records might be for this. First record for vc. 39 was on rocks of a cutting of the A41, Tettenhall, W'ton (SJ887001 & SJ888005, BRF, det. A. Rutherford, 1975).

## 137. HYDROCOTYLACEAE

### *Hydrocotyle vulgaris* L.
### Marsh Pennywort

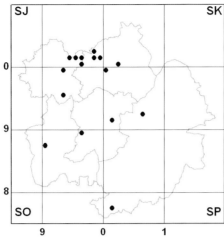

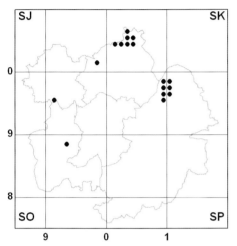

17. Native. Ax. A creeping, mat-forming perennial of infertile, water-saturated mostly peaty soils in open situations. Rare and becoming fragmented in its distribution in B&BC. Locally common in flushes and marshes in Sutton Park particularly near Little Bracebridge Pool and in the Longmoor Valley. Further colonies are found on Brownhills Common, Clayhanger, and one or two other sites in the N of the conurbation. Also reported from Cinder Bank, Saltwells and Park Coppice W'ton. In the past it has also been recorded at Moseley Bog (SP094819, CBW, 1989) and in a pond by the River Cole at Springfield (SP099826, JJD, 1993). Ass: *Carex panicea, Juncus bulbosus, Triglochin palustris, Valeriana dioica.*

### *Hydrocotyle ranunculoides* L. f.
### Floating Pennywort

16. Neophyte. Sch. 9 (invasive). An aggressive, invasive, N American aquatic perennial capable of rapidly forming dense stands on the surface of ponds, canals and ditches, typically completely suppressing other aquatic flora. First recorded in B&BC by MWP in 2004 (from the duck pond at Sandwell Valley and in ditches by the River Rea), during the later stages of Flora recording, its devastating impact on water-

bodies was becoming apparent. Parts of the Wyrley & Essington and Stourbridge canals were particularly badly affected and further colonisation was reported annually from pools and ditches across the region. Red Alert status is given for this species and the local Environment Agency or Centre for Aquatic Plant Management should be informed of any sightings. Recently, however, it may be retreating at some sites, possibly due to the application of effective control measures and/or a series of cold winters. N America.

### *Hydrocotyle sibthorpioides* Lam.
### Lawn Pennywort

0. Neophyte. One plant in fairly damp shade between paving slabs at Highfields School, W'ton (SO880963, CBW & BRF, conf. J.F.M. Cannon & A.O. Chater, 1983). First noticed in 1970 and persisted until the mid-1990s when it was shaded out by conifers. Tropics.

## 138. APIACEAE

### *Sanicula europaea* L.
### Sanicle

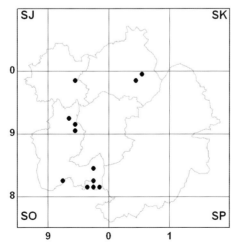

12. Native. Ax. A perennial herb of old deciduous woodland, dingles and copses on moist, neutral to calcareous soils of

▲ *Knautia arvensis*

▲ *Succisa pratensis*

▲ *Hydrocotyle ranunculoides*

intermediate fertility. Absent from much of the region due to scarcity of suitable habitats. Sometimes the populations are very fragmentary, persisting mainly by tracks and in other relatively bare places. It was recorded by Readett (1971) from SP1097 and SP1098 in Sutton Park and was still listed as present in 1991. The record in SO9498 is an introduction into a woodland planting which has persisted since the 1990s. Ass: *Circaea lutetiana, Galium odoratum, Lamiastrum galeobdolon, Melica uniflora.*

### *Astrantia major* L.
### Astrantia
0. Neophyte. One old record: a group of plants in rough grassland, Manor Farm Park, Northfield (SP024805, CBW, 1989). Europe.

### *Eryngium giganteum* M. Beib.
### Tall Eryngo
1. Neophyte. Perennial herb; several immature self-sown plants scattered throughout the site of an old garden in Ivyhouse Lane, Bilston, originating from a small, originally planted colony af mature plants (SO93989400, MWP, 2008). Caucasus.

### *Chaerophyllum temulum* L.
### Rough Chervil

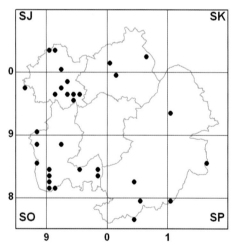

32. Native. Ax. Roadside verges, hedgebanks and wood borders and canalside hedges in fairly open to semi-shaded places on moist, base-intermediate soils of average to high fertility, avoiding acid soils. Occasional in the rural parts of B&BC but virtually absent from much of the urban area except along a few sections of canal. Also tetrad SO98E. Ass: *Anthriscus sylvestris, Arrhenatherum elatius, Fragaria vesca, Heracleum sphondylium, Rubus fruticosus* agg., *Tanacetum vulgare, Torilis japonica, Urtica dioica.*

### *Anthriscus sylvestris* (L.) Hoffm.
### Cow Parsley
*667. Native. Roadside verges, hedgerows, woodland margins, railway and canal

banks, meadows, rough grassland and waste ground in open and partially shaded, moist, fertile to very fertile soils avoiding only the most acid. Very common in tall herb communities along hedgerows and verges, in open woodland in more rural parts and an opportunist coloniser of fragments of waste ground and overgrown gardens in the densely populated areas, but sensitive to cutting and trampling. Not usual in old woodlands, but can invade along paths and in clearings, especially where there is an increase in rubbish dumping or disturbance. Ass: *Alliaria petiolata, Arrhenatherum elatius, Arum maculatum, Elytrigia repens, Heracleum sphondylium, Rubus idaeus.*

### *Anthriscus caucalis* M. Bieb.
### Bur Chervil
5. Native. A few recent records for isolated plants in paving and gravel paths in Stourbridge, B'ham and recently W'ton: Worcester Street, Stourbridge, gravelled area (SO899836, MES, 1997); Wood Street, Wollaston, pavements (SO889851 & SO889852, APD, 1998/99); 2 plants in pavement, Printing House Street, B'ham (SP072873, MWP, 1999); made-up canal bank, Ryder's Green, possibly introduced with builders' sand (SO986916, J. Little & J. French, 1997); base of wall of Midland Hotel, Berry Street, W'ton (SO917986, A.G. Blunt & ICT, 2011, site now destroyed).

### *Scandix pecten-veneris* L.
### Shepherd's-needle
0. Archaeophyte. Sect. 41, BAP, CR, Nationally Scarce. Edees (1972) recorded it from an old marl pit in West Bromwich in 1948; also a Bagnall record from Sutton Park (SP0997, Bagnall, 1876).

### *Myrrhis odorata* (L.) Scop.
### Sweet Cicely

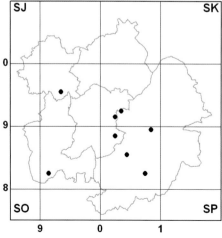

8. Neophyte. Remarkably few modern records for this species, which spreads so

enthusiastically in gardens. Almost all are isolated plants close to gardens or railway lines, but it is present in Ham Dingle (SO913827, B. Westwood, 2005), recorded there since at least 1974, and it has been recorded in Readett (1971) as present on the railway embankment at Sutton Park since 1941 (SP1097). Europe.

### *Coriandrum sativum* L.
### Coriander

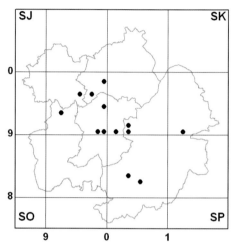

13. Neophyte. A frequently cultivated aromatic herb, in recent years blanket-sown in many urban allotment plots where it is usually recorded, as a casual. Also in pavement edges in residential areas. E Mediterranean.

### *Smyrnium olusatrum* L.
### Alexanders
5. Archaeophyte. Few records for this distinctive, yellow-flowered, perennial herb so abundant on the coast: two large plants on edge of public open space off Meadow Road, Hasbury (SO952832, AWR, WAT & CBW, 2001); a small colony established in canalside vegetation, Langley Maltings, Langley (SO995882, MWP, 2003); hedge, Chester Road (SP118927, MWP, ICT & JWP, 2007); Stevens Park, Wollescote (SO920834, APD, 2008); one plant at the bottom of a bank behind gardens in Temple Meadows Road, Sot's Hole, Sandwell (SP011923, MWP, 2009).

### *Conopodium majus* (Gouan) Loret
### Pignut
*204. Native. A widely distributed perennial herb of unmanaged, moderately acid, unimproved or semi-improved grassland, also on banks and in open woodland, on fairly dry soils of intermediate fertility. It occasionally forms extensive colonies in open grassland and light woodland. It can persist unnoticed for many years in old pastures incorporated into urban parks and kept permanently short-mown. Its

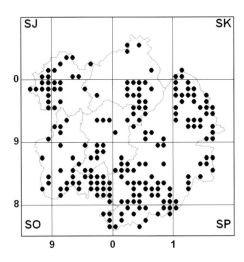

presence is often revealed when mowing has been relaxed following the flowering of Daffodil or Crocus planted in turf. Ass: *Anthoxanthum odoratum, Centaurea nigra, Festuca rubra, Ranunculus bulbosus, Trifolium dubium.*

### *Pimpinella major* (L.) Huds.
### Greater Burnet-saxifrage

2. Native. Rare and possibly introduced in our area. Large patch on raised bank, Ridgacre Canal, Black Lake, West Bromwich (SO999929, MWP, 2000); Rushall area, Walsall (SK0300, JEH, 2001). The latter record may be connected with the old one for Hawthorn Wood, Park Lime Pits (SK032001, P. Seccombe, 1984).

### *Pimpinella saxifraga* L.
### Burnet-saxifrage

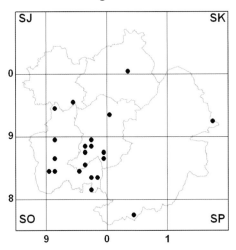

21. Native. Ax. A perennial herb of well-lit to partially shaded, calcareous to slightly acid, infertile soils in old well-drained, often sloping, species-rich grassland and also open wooded areas, quarry banks and grassy slopes. Stable populations occur at Park Lime Pits, Walsall and in neutral grassland at Lower Illey Meadows, Barrow Hill and Coopers Bank; large populations are recorded from old quarry sites on Rowley

Hills. Ass: *Agrostis capillaris, Anthoxanthum odoratum, Briza media, Centaurea nigra, Cynosurus cristatus, Festuca rubra, Hypochaeris radicata, Knautia arvensis, Leontodon hispidus, Linum catharticum, Prunella vulgaris.*

### *Aegopodium podagraria* L.
### Ground-elder

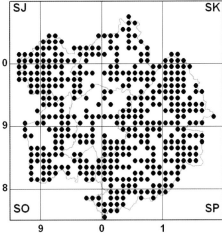

*452. Archaeophyte. A perennial with long, creeping rhizomes. Very common throughout B&BC, often forming pure continuous stands in intermittently disturbed, unmown rough grassland by roads, in hedges and woodland margins and on a variety of waste land. Quite shade tolerant (a native woodland plant in Europe) and favoured by the presence of nutrient-rich, base-intermediate or rich, deep, moist soils. A pernicious weed of gardens and allotments, from which it often colonises new areas in dumped material containing its rhizomes. Ass: *Anthriscus sylvestris, Arrhenatherum elatius, Dactylis glomerata, Galium aparine, Symphytum × uplandicum, Urtica dioica.*

### *Berula erecta* (Huds.) Coville
### Lesser Water-parsnip

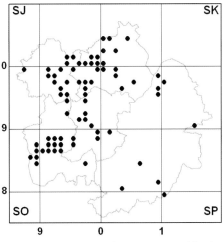

*74. Native. A stoloniferous perennial herb of constantly wet situations growing in

fairly base- and nutrient-rich mud and silt in the shallows of pools, lakes and streams and particularly associated with emergent vegetation along canals, particularly in the Black Country. Sometimes confused with *Apium nodiflorum* and frequently growing with it. Ass: *Alisma lanceolatum, Alisma plantago-aquatica, Apium nodiflorum, Carex otrubae, Glyceria maxima, Lycopus europaeus, Scutellaria galericulata.*

### *Oenanthe fistulosa* L.
### Tubular Water-dropwort

2. Native. Ax. Sect. 41, BAP, VU. A stoloniferous perennial herb associated with the winter-flooded 'draw-down zone' around still or slow-moving water relatively unenriched with nutrients, it is nationally declining and protected. It has been recorded in a number of B&BC sites in recent years, but the only modern records appears to be from pools remaining from Hadley's Brickworks, Bilston, where it was abundant around two tiny shallow pools (most recent records SO959978, PWS, 2000; SO960977, P.Wilkinson, 2000). It may now be lost from one, which was conserved in the public open space of a housing development partly to protect this species and has been unwisely used intensively for coarse fishing. One pond is within the fence of an electricity sub-station (SO959977) and *O. fistulosa* may still survive there. It seems to be gone from all its other sites, for which the last records are: Wyrley & Essington

▲ *Oenanthe fistulosa*

canal, W'ton (SJ943001, PWS, 1989); mire, Pelsall North Common, frequent (SK021045, CW, 1988); Clayhanger SSSI pool margins, abundant (SK035045, CW, 1990); Lindridge and Langley Pools (SP153967, Warks Wildlife Trust files, 1982). Ass: *Alisma plantago-aquatica, Bidens tripartita, Carex acuta, Bolboschoenus maritimus, Triglochin palustris, Veronica scutellata.*

### Oenanthe pimpinelloides L.
### Corky-fruited Water-dropwort

1. Native; presumed introduced in B&BC. Perennial herb largely confined to SW and S England. Our only records are for a small colony of 20 or so plants following the line of a small flush on a rough grassy bank to the rear of Ashfield Close, Ryecroft, Walsall. A further few plants were discovered a short distance away growing in rough grassland near the path in Mill Lane LNR (SP015998, MWP & JaH, 2001).

### Oenanthe lachenalii C.C. Gmel.
### Parsley Water-dropwort

0. Native. There is an old record for this plant, more usual in brackish coastal marshes, from a canal towpath at Brierley Hill (SO9287, FGB, 1980).

### Oenanthe crocata L.
### Hemlock Water-dropwort

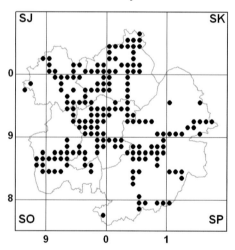

*191. Native. A robust perennial herb of sheltered situations on wet or moisture-retaining, fertile soils. Almost confined to canal margins in B&BC and one of the community of plants found in the constantly moist brickwork along the water's-edge. Also tetrad SO89Z. Ass: *Bidens frondosa, Carex otrubae, Lycopus europaeus, Rumex conglomeratus, Rumex hydrolapathum, Scutellaria galericulata.*

### Oenanthe aquatica (L.) Poir.
### Fine-leaved Water-dropwort

0. Native. This perennial of the draw-down zone of shallow ponds was recorded in

Wildlife Trust habitat surveys in the 1980s from the Walsall Canal (SO983976), the pond on Pelsall Common (SK021026) and The Slough, Brownhills Common (SK032053) but these records were not confirmed and the species was not seen in the present survey. It is however known from neighbouring rural areas.

### Aethusa cynapium L.
### Fool's Parsley

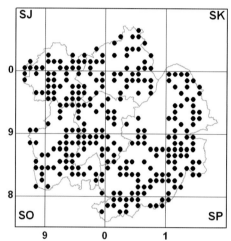

*293. Native. Annual, on recently disturbed ground in allotments, on spoil heaps, arable field margins, gardens and in neglected bits of waste ground near buildings, in dryish, open situations. Usually, but not always, on nutrient-rich and base medium soils. No distinction between the three subspecies has been attempted in the present survey. Ass: *Artemisia vulgaris, Euphorbia peplus, Poa annua, Senecio squalidus, Senecio vulgaris.*

### Foeniculum vulgare Mill.
### Fennel

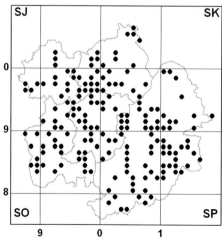

*182. Archaeophyte. A tall, distinctive perennial herb, frequent in open habitats such as sites recovering from recent disturbance, waste ground, allotments and gardens but also on factory wasteland in

industrial areas. On neutral to moderately calcareous, usually nutrient-rich soils but also in less rich situations such as pavement cracks, spoily waste, rubbly waste etc. Plants with bronze foliage occasionally occur. Ass: *Artemisia absinthium, Artemisia vulgaris, Arctium minus, Epilobium ciliatum, Melilotus officinalis, Oenothera glazioviana.*

### Anethum graveolens L.
### Dill

2. Casual. A glabrous annual cultivated for its leaves and fruits. Base of double hedgerow, RSPB, Sandwell Valley (SP035927, MWP, 1996); passageway between houses, Washwood Heath, B'ham (SP104884, MWP & JWP, 2006). Also older records from the towpath at Compton (SO885991, BRF, 1987); B'ham Canal (SP088863, S. Derry & PWS, 1987) and by a disused railway, Smethwick (SP017895, MWP, 1991). W & C Asia.

### Silaum silaus (L.) Schinz & Thell.
### Pepper-saxifrage

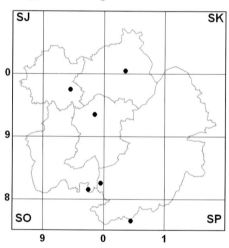

6. Native. Ax. The few modern records for this glabrous perennial are from damp, unimproved, moderately base-rich pastures at Illey meadows, Woodgate Valley Country Park, a pasture in the periphery of Hawkesley at Red Hill, and College Farm, Aldridge. The record from a post-industrial site in SO9893 is probably an accidental introduction and the one at Stow Lawn public open space in W'ton (SO940979, ICT, 2007) was from a deliberate introduction of hay from an old meadow at Askew Bridge in S Staffordshire (SO903914) in 1987; plants were still present there in 2010. There are records from the early 1990s from wider areas adjacent to Illey (SO9582, SO9681, SO9881, SO9983 & SO9978) some of which may still be extant, and similarly there are older records in the Aldridge area around Park Lime Pits (all in SK0300). Ass: *Achillea millefolium, Betonica officinalis, Centaurea*

*nigra, Dactylorhiza* spp., *Lotus corniculatus, Succisa pratensis.*

## *Conium maculatum* L.
### Hemlock

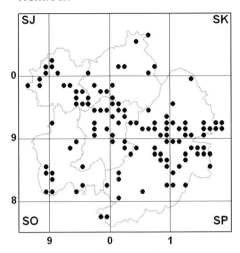

*119. Native. A tall biennial, frequent in open, moist, fertile or very fertile soils on the banks of canals, railways, roadsides and in old sewage beds. Also in rough grassland, waste and disturbed ground and motorway embankments in drier habitats. The distribution is unusual and suggests some association with the motorway system as well as some canals and river corridors, particularly the corridor of the River Tame. It was little recorded in our area by Cadbury *et al.* (1971) or by Edees (1972). Ass: *Arrhenatherum elatius, Artemisia vulgaris, Carduus crispus, Rumex obtusifolius, Urtica dioica.*

## *Bupleurum subovatum* Link ex Spreng.
### False Thorow-wax
0. Casual. Annual bird-seed alien with one old record: growing with *Solanum rostratum*, disturbed area, Ridgacre Road, Quinton (SP010847, MWP & LG, conf. A. Grenfell, 1989).

## *Apium graveolens* L.
### Wild Celery
3. Alien/native. Several plants in canal lock brickwork, Tat Bank Road, Oldbury (SO994889, MWP, 1998, still there in 2006). A seedling observed in a large area of houses cleared by demolition, corner of Old Heath Road, W'ton (SO937984, ICT & EVJC, 2004) was assumed to be the cultivated celery **var. dulce** (Mill.) DC., as was a record for Lee Howl Allotments (SO959927, MWP, 2008).

## *Apium nodiflorum* (L.) Lag.
### Fool's-water-cress
*174. Native. A perennial herb of canal margins, streams, ditches and shallows of ponds and lakes in nutrient-enriched,

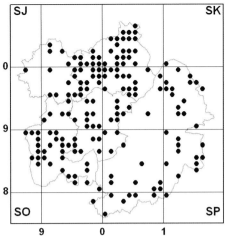

open situations. Generally common throughout B&BC in suitable habitats but apparently commoner in the Black Country than in B'ham, probably in association with the canals. A colony of a distinctive, variegated-leaved form was discovered in drying-out mud in Gannow Green Moat, Gannow Green (SO984783) in 2007. Ass: *Alopecurus geniculatus, Epilobium hirsutum, Glyceria fluitans, Myosotis scorpioides, Nasturtium officinale* agg.

## *Apium inundatum* (L.) Reichb. f.
### Lesser Marshwort
2. Native. Ax. A perennial herb of shallow, base- and nutrient-poor still or slow-flowing waters, it is present in wet pastures of Wood Farm, Rough Wood Wedge, Walsall, in a soakaway to the pool at N end of site by blocked branch of the Wyrley & Essington canal (SJ984019, ICT, 2008). This population was probably the one recorded by BRF in 1992: "occasional, pool margins, near canal, Short Heath, SJ9801". A further large population was recorded in an ephemeral shallow pool in unimproved pasture W of Brownhills Common (SK032061, ICT & SAHA, 2010). There are several other old records, one from Sutton Park (SP0997, Bagnall, 1875) and the rest from the Walsall area: locally frequent, pool margin, Clayhanger (SK033046, BRF, 1992); The Slough, Brownhills (SK032053, JJB, 1989). Also, in a nature trail guide for Brownhills: pond at SK0306, 1985, which may just be in our area and may be our extant record. Ass: *Callitriche* cf. *brutia* subsp. *hamulata, Eleogiton fluitans, Lemna minor, Lythrum portula, Mentha aquatica, Ranunculus aquatilis* s.s.

## *Petroselinum crispum* (Mill.) Fuss
### Garden Parsley
1. Archaeophyte. Biennial, self-seeded along path in allotment gardens, Allens Lane, Walsall (SK012026, MWP, SJC & JaH, 2004). E Mediterranean.

## *Sison amomum* L.
### Stone Parsley
2. Native. A hedgebank and roadside biennial with only casual-appearing records: half a dozen, by hedge, grassy waste area, N of Hayhead Wood, Walsall (SP040991, JEH, 2007); more than 20 plants, derelict front of house, pavement area, Kings Heath (SP078817, EMP, 2007 and again in 2008, when it was recorded independently by N. Walker, still there 2010).

## *Ammi majus* L.
### Bullwort
2. Neophyte. Annual; records can usually be traced back to bird seed or wool shoddy. One plant appeared alongside the path at the base of a recently cut-back double hedgerow, RSPB Reserve, Sandwell Valley (SP035927, MWP, conf. EJC, 1996); one plant in a derelict nursery, Warley Park (SP011861, CBW, 1996). S Europe.

## *Ammi visnaga* (L.) Lam.
### Toothpick-plant
2. Casual. Annual. 1 plant alongside the path at the base of a recently cut-back double hedgerow, RSPB Reserve, Sandwell Valley (SP035927, MWP, conf. EJC, 1996). Another 2m tall specimen appeared spontaneously in a shady shrub bed, Martineau Gardens, Edgbaston, B'ham (SP061843, V. Lawrie, B. Perry, S. Hill-Daniel & MWP conf. J Mason. 2011). Mediterranean.

## *Carum carvi* L.
### Caraway
0. Archaeophyte. Sect. 41, BAP, EN. Biennial of fields. One old record: 3 plants, Clayhanger Village (SK0404, JPM, 1991). Europe.

## *Angelica sylvestris* L.
### Wild Angelica

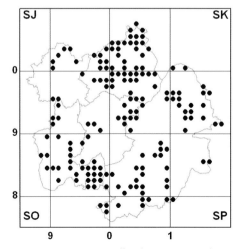

*164. Native. Ax. A tall, robust perennial of damp woodlands, woodland rides, river, pool and sometimes canal margins, poorly drained fields and meadows, often where there is a fluctuating water table. In semi-shaded to open situations in damp or wet soils of intermediate fertility and base status, particularly where a relative lack of disturbance has allowed the development of tall herb vegetation. The map seems to suggest that it is absent from much of the heavily built-up urban area and is a wetland indicator, concentrated in the main countryside areas and the river flood plains. Ass: *Cirsium palustre, Deschampsia cespitosa, Filipendula ulmaria, Galium palustre, Juncus effusus, Solanum dulcamara*.

### *Angelica archangelica* L.
### Garden Angelica
3. Neophyte. Perennial, appearing sporadically in B&BC, probably directly from cultivation, and with few modern records. Ettingshall Park Quarry, W'ton (SO924955, CRP, 2000); one probably planted, but with several self-sown, marsh at edge of field, Milking Bank Estate (SO922904, APD, 2004); River Rea corridor N of Fazeley Street, B'ham (SP081868, MWP, 2005). Continental Europe.

### *Levisticum officinale* W.D.J. Koch
### Lovage
4. Neophyte. Perennial, seeding from cultivation as a culinary herb. 2 or 3 by old filled-in canal, West Smethwick (SP002892, CBW, 1997); park near Woodbrook (SP030819, CBW, 1997); three plants in passageway to the rear of houses, Sutton Coldfield (SP103941, MWP, ICT, EVJC & JaH, 2006); by allotments, Allens Lane, Goscote (SK012026, MWP, JaH & SJC, 2004). Iran.

### *Pastinaca sativa* L.
### Parsnip

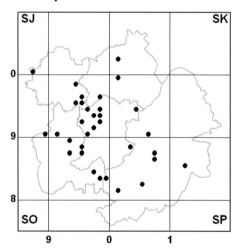

33. Native. Biennial. Roadside verges, waste ground and land recovering from disturbance in open, well drained, base-rich soils of intermediate fertility. Generally uncommon throughout the conurbation but found mainly on road, canal and

railway embankments and sometimes on old industrial land in the Black Country; locally frequent along some roadside verges. Ass: *Centaurea scabiosa, Dipsacus fullonum, Hirschfeldia incana, Sisymbrium orientale*.

Some of these records have been referred specifically to **subsp. *sylvestris*** (Mill.) Rouy & E.G. Camus (**Wild Parsnip**) usually from post-industrial sites. There are also a small number of records for **subsp. *sativa*** (**Cultivated Parsnip**) almost all self-seeded along paths in allotment gardens, but the majority of records did not distinguish the subspecies.

### *Heracleum sphondylium* L.
### Hogweed

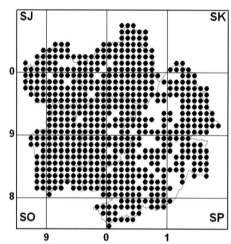

*621. Native. A very common perennial herb found in a wide range of habitats, which include canal and railway banks, rough grassland, roadsides, hedgerows and waste ground and particularly characteristic of the strip of vegetation developing in nutrient-enriched soil between roads and hedges. Tolerant of some shade but generally in well-lit situations in communities dominated by tall herbs and grasses and showing a preference for soils that are base-rich and fertile. Ass: *Aegopodium podagraria, Anthriscus sylvestris, Arrhenatherum elatius, Elytrigia repens, Rumex obtusifolius, Urtica dioica*.

### *Heracleum mantegazzianum*
Sommier & Levier
### Giant Hogweed
35. Neophyte. Sch. 9 (invasive). Colonies of this very large, distinctive, perennial herb from SW Asia can be found on waste ground, along banks of streams and rivers and in derelict gardens in open and partially shaded sites, usually in richly fertile and fairly base-rich, moist to damp soils. Prolific seeding can result in large localised populations forming when left

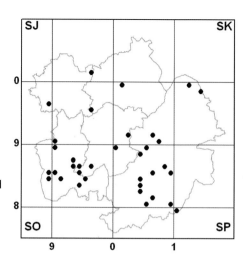

undisturbed, and it can in this way spread quite rapidly along roads and rivers. An extensive forest of Giant Hogweed once dominated the land on which the new Queen Elizabeth Hospital in Edgbaston now stands. The plant is notorious because, for some people, contact with the plant sets off a sensitivity to light which produces ugly and alarming skin blisters, weals and even long-term scarring. Therefore the plant is quite assiduously persecuted, and under the Wildlife & Countryside Act of 1981 it is an offence to "plant or otherwise cause Giant Hogweed to grow" in the wild. It is nevertheless not uncommon. SW Asia. Ass: *Arrhenatherum elatius, Artemisia vulgaris, Acer campestre, Galium aparine, Heracleum sphondylium, Impatiens glandulifera, Salix caprea, Urtica dioica*.

### *Torilis japonica* (Houtt.) DC.
### Upright Hedge-parsley

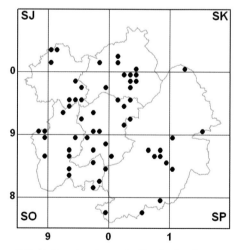

*59. Native. Ax. Annual of hedgebanks, roadside verges and rough grassland in open, moist soils of average fertility. The white-flowered successor to Cow Parsley (after Rough Chervil) along roadside verges but generally far less common in our area, especially in B'ham, although there are further tetrad records from vc. 37. Some records are by canals and in churchyards. Ass: *Anthriscus sylvestris, Arrhenatherum elatius, Chaerophyllum temulum, Heracleum sphondylium.*

### Daucus carota L.
### Wild Carrot

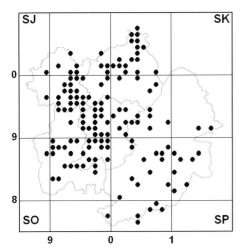

*141. Native. Ax. A biennial of railway tracks and sidings, canal towpaths, post-industrial sites, coal spoil, waste ground and dry grassy places in dry, open, fairly infertile, neutral to base-rich, often calcareous, well-drained, often drought-liable soils. Often a colonist in sparsely vegetated sites where little else will grow and discouraged by competition from other species. Sometimes included in wild flower seed mixes used in amenity areas, and can persist longer than many other species. Ass: *Carex flacca, Centaurium erythraea, Hypericum perforatum, Leucanthemum vulgare, Linum catharticum.*

All records are for **D. carota subsp. carota**; there are only two modern records of **subsp. sativus** (Hoffm) Arcang., the carrot of cultivation, as a casual in allotments, where it readily produces seed.

## MONOCOTS

### 139. ACORACEAE

### Acorus calamus L.
### Sweet-flag

24. Neophyte. A rhizomatous perennial, not fruiting in UK and spreading vegetatively. Well naturalised in a number of places in pool and canal margins but believed likely to have been originally deliberately introduced to many of them. Becoming more frequent along canals in the N of the conurbation, particularly Rushall and Wyrley & Essington, and associated with fairly base- and nutrient-rich waters, but forming pure stands in the much more acid shallow margins of Little Bracebridge

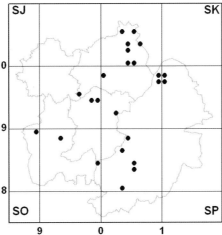

Pool, Sutton Park, from where it appears to be spreading into new squares. Asia & N America. Ass: *Crassula helmsii, Epilobium hirsutum, Iris pseudacorus, Mentha aquatica, Menyanthes trifoliata, Ranunculus lingua, Sparganium erectum, Typha angustifolia.*

### 140. ARACEAE

### Lysichiton americanus Hultén & H. St. John
### American Skunk-cabbage

2. Neophyte. A large perennial herb. Many hundreds of plants are thoroughly naturalised throughout wet to damp, probably semi-natural, Alder woodland to the S of Edgbaston Pool, spreading from original plantings in nearby Winterbourne Botanical Gardens. First recorded there 1955 (SP054841, B'ham Natural History Society), but not mentioned in Cadbury *et al.* (1971). Also recorded from the neighbouring square in a pool margin, Southbourne Close (SP055826, MWP, ICT, EMP & L. Bastin, 2007). W N America.

### Calla palustris L.
### Bog Arum

1. Neophyte. A small colony of this rhizomatous perennial was found along the margin of Edgbaston Pool, Edgbaston, near golf course (SP0584, JWP & M. Kingsbury, 2008). A plant at the side of Bracebridge Pool, Sutton Park recorded by BRF in 1979 persisted up to the mid 1980s but has not been refound in the present survey. It was also recorded as having been planted in a pond in Kings Heath Park in 1990 (SP067816, JB). Europe.

### Arum maculatum L.
### Lords-and-Ladies

*165. Native. A rhizomatous perennial shade-tolerant herb of hedgerows, woodlands, stream and river valleys, parks and estates in shaded places on moist, well-drained, reasonably base-rich and fertile soils. Excluded from the

▲ *Lysichiton americanus*

▲ *Arum maculatum*

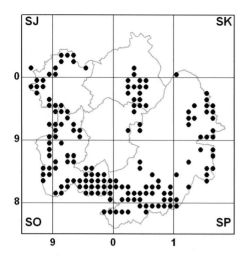

acid soils of N Walsall and Sutton Park, rare or absent from the more densely populated urban areas where suitable habitats are few. Presumably spread in bird droppings and by no means confined to ancient woods and hedgerows, but slow to colonise urban plantations. Its elaborate and fascinating inflorescences do not produce large numbers of seed and it has a prolonged juvenile phase in which it does not produce leaves for 2–3 years making it vulnerable to disturbance. Nevertheless it is initially dependent on moderate disturbance and shade to reduce competition and allow seedling establishment. Ass: *Geum urbanum, Hyacinthoides non-scripta, Hyacinthoides* × *massartiana, Mercurialis perennis, Stachys sylvatica, Viola riviniana.*

### *Arum italicum* Mill. subsp. *italicum*
### Italian Lords-and-Ladies

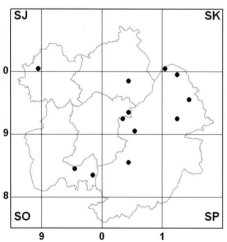

12. Neophyte. Our records are all for isolated patches or small groups of plants, in open woodlands, a pathside, a churchyard, on top of a soil heap and in neglected bits of waste ground to the rear of gardens. Very persistent once established but displaying little sign of natural increase. It was first recorded in vc. 39 as an escape from a wild garden, RSPB

Reserve, Sandwell Valley (SP036928, MWP, 1997) and it seems generally to be a recent arrival in our area. Europe.

### 141. LEMNACEAE

### *Spirodela polyrhiza* (L.) Schleid.
### Greater Duckweed

3. Native. Floating aquatic perennial, very rare and perhaps always casual in our area. A small colony in NE corner of pool, Lifford Reservoir (SP058799, JJD, 2001); ponds in Kings Heath Park (SP065817, JWP, 1995); in quantity in a small ornamental pool at Bantock House, W'ton (SO896980, ICT, 1999), lost in subsequent refurbishment of the garden.

### *Lemna gibba* L.
### Fat Duckweed

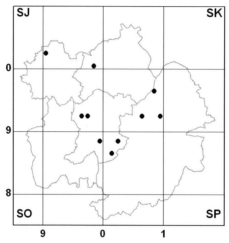

10. Native. Free-floating aquatic perennial, rather local and recorded rarely in the present survey from canals and pools, although when found it is usually in some quantity. The very few recent records suggest a decline in this species but it is easily overlooked when mixed in with *L. minor*. It is a species which appears to be highly tolerant of eutrophication and is usually in small, stagnant, nutrient-enriched water bodies. Readett (1971) listed it for Sutton Park from SP0995 & SP0996. Ass: *Lemna minor.*

### *Lemna minor* L.
### Common Duckweed

*240. Native. A free-floating aquatic perennial, found very commonly in still or very slow-flowing, usually sheltered situations in fairly or very base- and nutrient-rich waters and terrestrially on exposed mud. A rapid surface coloniser of pools, ditches, canals and smaller water-bodies such as water butts and garden ponds. Apparently less common in some central urban and drier residential areas. Ass: often in pure stands: *Azolla filiculoides,*

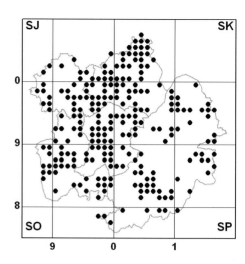

*Callitriche* spp., *Lemna minuta, Lemna trisulca, Riccia fluitans.*

### *Lemna minuta* Kunth
### Least Duckweed

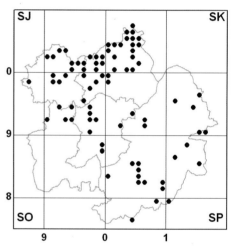

82. Neophyte. A free-floating aquatic perennial, an invasive coloniser of canals and margins and shallows of pools and lakes in both open water and those shaded by trees and woodland. First recorded in Britain in 1977, in recent years its rapid spread across the conurbation has resulted in a thick surface coverage forming across some smaller pools and sections of canal preventing light-penetration to the aquatic flora and fauna below. Often mixed in with *L. minor* but more shade tolerant and far more invasive and disruptive, it may be replacing *Lemna minor* in some areas. N & S America. Ass: *Lemna minor, Azolla filiculoides,* or in pure stands.

### *Lemna trisulca* L.
### Ivy-leaved Duckweed

*66. Native. A submerged aquatic found floating beneath the surface in still-water sites across the conurbation with intermediate levels of fertility. A locally frequent plant of canals and ponds, but nowhere really considered to be common

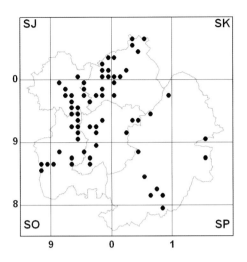

although it is often hidden under *Lemna minor* and can therefore be invisible. Apparently much commoner in the Black Country than in B'ham. Ass: *Lemna minor*, *Callitriche* spp., *Potamogeton natans*.

## 143. ALISMATACEAE

### *Sagittaria sagittifolia* L.
### Arrowhead

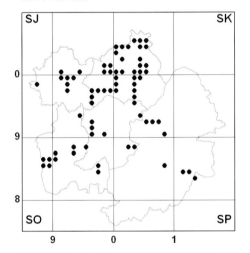

*72. Native. Ax. An emergent perennial herb of canal margins mainly in the Black Country, it has submerged and floating leaves, and is therefore favoured by clear water and sheltered conditions. Only really frequent along the Wyrley & Essington and sections of Walsall Canal less used by boat traffic, where it grows with other tall emergent species and is sometimes represented by large patches of submerged foliage in deep, clear water. Seldom in shallows of ponds and lakes where it is often deliberately planted as part of habitat creation schemes. Shows a preference for open situations in neutral substrates of intermediate fertility but moderately tolerant of eutrophic water. Ass: *Alisma lanceolatum*, *Butomus umbellatus*, *Iris pseudacorus*, *Potamogeton lucens*, *Sparganium emersum*, *Sparganium erectum*.

### *Luronium natans* (L.) Raf.
### Floating Water-plantain

6. Native. Ax. A protected species in UK and Europe, Sched. 8, Sect. 41, BAP, Nationally Scarce. Very rare and possibly extinct from most of its former sites due to eutrophication, disturbance, increasing water opacity and its inability to compete with more vigorous species. However in deeper water, submerged rosettes of leaves, rooting at intervals and forming extensive patches in the muddy substrate, may persist and go unnoticed for many years. It may therefore be under-recorded. Recent records are all from Walsall canals. It still extends into our area from the N in the Cannock Extension Canal, where it was recorded recently (C. John, 2007) throughout the middle part of the canal, between Pelsall Common bridge (SK019047), and the Wyrley and Essington canal junction (SK019044). It flowered quite profusely by the Pelsall Common bridge in 2011. Also in 2011 P. Wilkinson recorded it extending from the Cannock Extension Canal S and W into the Wyrley and Essington Canal, initially frequent in SK0104 and rare as far as SK015021. In 2011 it was also found east of the Cannock Extension in SK0405. Plants have also been reported within our time period growing quite far S in open water in the Rushall Canal (SP033960, CRP, 1998) although this record has still to be confirmed and more recently from further N in the same canal (SK048015, M. F. Godfrey, 2005). There is an undated but recent report from Friar Pool close to the canal junction at Pelsall (SK020043, DH) and there are older records from a wider extent of the Walsall canals: the Slough (SK032053, Wildlife Trust surveys, 1986 and 1989); Daw End Branch Canal (SK049047, G.J. Walker, 1989 and SK045038, CW, 1990);

and an unconfirmed report from Stechford Bridge Lake in B'ham (SP125876, CW, 1990). It is a plant of moderately acidic water low in nitrogen and phosphorus, on substrates of low fertility. Ass: *Ceratophyllum demersum*, *Myriophyllum spicatum*, *Nuphar lutea*, *Potamogeton pectinatus*.

### *Alisma plantago-aquatica* L.
### Water-plantain

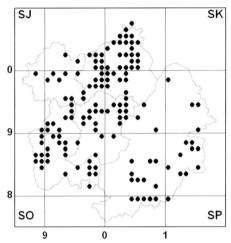

*142. Native. A perennial herb of the shallow margins of pools and ditches and often in the exposed mud of ephemeral pools. Also found along canal margins where it sometimes grows with, and possibly hybridises with *Alisma lanceolatum*. Preferring open habitats in moderately fertile muds of intermediate base status. Ass: *Bidens frondosa*, *Carex acutiformis*, *Glyceria maxima*, *Iris pseudacorus*.

Some plants along canal margins which are difficult to determine may be the hybrid *Alisma × rhicnocarpum* Schotsman (*A. plantago-aquatica × A. lanceolatum*) but currently we have no definite records.

▲ *Luronium natans*

## *Alisma lanceolatum* With.
## Narrow-leaved Water-plantain

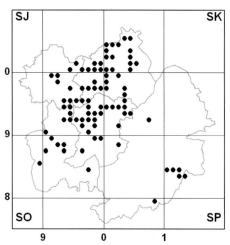

*87. Native. An emergent perennial herb almost exclusively confined to the margins of canals mainly in the Black Country, where it largely displaces *Alisma plantago-aquatica* and appears to show a higher tolerance to eutrophication and a preference for constant water-levels. Clearly relatively scarce in B'ham and not recorded in our part of vc. 38 in Cadbury *et al.* (1971). Mentioned in Edees (1972) only as a possible variant in *A. plantago-aquatica*, but Bagnall in 1901 made some vc. 39 records and reported that J. Fraser recorded it *circa* 1875 from Parkfield in W'ton (SO9296). The first more recent definite report from vc. 39 was from a canal at Smethwick (SP0189, C. Mansell, 1985). Ass: *Berula erecta, Bidens frondosa, Glyceria maxima, Iris pseudacorus, Phalaris arundinacea, Sparganium erectum, Typha latifolia.*

## 144. BUTOMACEAE

## *Butomus umbellatus* L.
## Flowering-rush

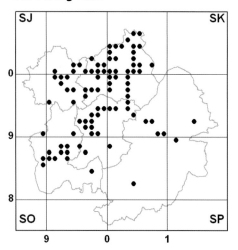

*92. Native. Ax. This submerged or emergent rhizomatous perennial is a feature of canals in our area particularly in the Black

Country, forming part of the reed-swamp community. Tolerant to some degree of eutrophication but favouring the cleaner waters associated with the rural parts of the conurbation and those with flows derived from high quality feeder pools such as Chasewater (SK00). Almost absent from ponds and lake margins but when it does occur it is usually part of a deliberate introduction in habitat creation schemes. Ass: *Alisma lanceolatum, Glyceria maxima, Iris pseudacorus, Sagittaria sagittifolia, Sparganium erectum, Typha latifolia.*

## 145. HYDROCHARITACEAE

## *Hydrocharis morsus-ranae* L.
## Frogbit
0. Native. VU. One old record for this floating aquatic perennial: Bentley Common (SO9899, C. M. Ashmore, 1973).

## *Stratiotes aloides* L.
## Water-soldier

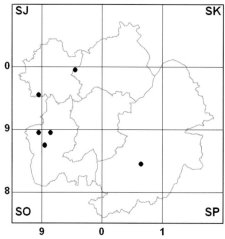

6. Native; introduced in B&BC. NT and Nationally Scarce. An aquatic perennial herb of rare occurrence in quiet canal basins and pool margins in B&BC, most likely always discarded from garden ponds. Most records are for one or two isolated individuals showing little signs of spreading, however, a substantial colony dominates the extreme northern end of the section of canal running parallel with the derelict railway walkway in Brockmoor, Brierley Hill (SO907878, B. Jones, 1999), where it has been established for many years. All our plants are female, reproducing vegetatively.

## *Elodea canadensis* Michx.
## Canadian Waterweed
*34. Neophyte. Sch. 9 (invasive). Formerly a very common aquatic perennial of canals and ponds throughout the conurbation but in recent years much declined or absent from most of its former sites and now

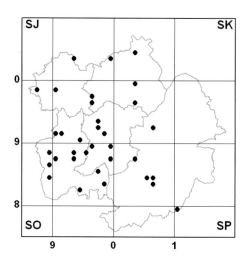

largely displaced by *E. nuttallii*, especially in the canal systems from where it has almost disappeared. Still present in some of the less polluted smaller ponds in the absence of *E. nuttallii*. N America. Ass: *Callitriche stagnalis, Elodea nuttallii, Myriophyllum spicatum, Potamogeton pectinatus.*

## *Elodea nuttallii* (Planch.) H. St. John
## Nuttall's Waterweed

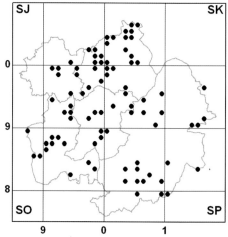

*85. Neophyte. Sch. 9 (invasive). A submerged aquatic perennial coloniser of canals, ponds and lakes and now virtually displacing *E. canadensis* throughout the canal system in B&BC. It was first recorded in vc. 39 from the B'ham canal in W'ton (SO917992, BRF & ICT, 1982). Tolerant of eutrophication and a highly successful coloniser of new habitats probably by fragment transference by birds. N America. Ass: *Elodea canadensis, Callitriche stagnalis, Myriophyllum spicatum, Potamogeton pectinatus.*

## *Lagarosiphon major* (Ridl.) Moss ex V.A. Wager
## Curly Waterweed
14. Neophyte. Sch. 9 (invasive). A submerged aquatic perennial widely available as an 'oxygenating' plant from aquatic stockists and rapidly outgrowing

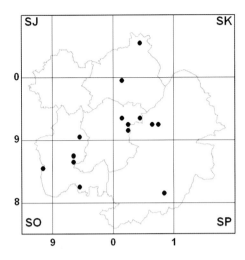

*Anagallis tenella, Carex echinata, Carex hostiana, Carex nigra, Carex panicea, Cirsium dissectum, Dactylorhiza* spp., *Eleocharis palustris, Juncus articulatus, Lycopus europaeus, Silene flos-cuculi, Typha latifolia.*

## 150. POTAMOGETONACEAE

### *Potamogeton natans* L.
### Broad-leaved Pondweed

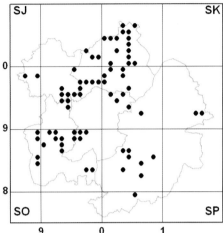

Park: (still present in SP0996, SP0998 and SP1096 in Readett 1971) and (SP0997, J. Stokes, 1787) also from Brownhills Common (SK037061, W. Prestwood, 1978). Ass: *Anagallis tenella, Carex echinata, Pedicularis palustris, Sparganium erectum, Veronica scutellata.*

### *Potamogeton lucens* L.
### Shining Pondweed

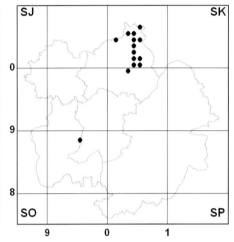

its intended location. Most of the records are for small patches spreading vegetatively in the margins of pools and especially canals and considered to be discarded material from aquariums and garden ponds or accidental introductions by water birds. Southern Africa.

## 148. JUNCAGINACEAE

### *Triglochin palustris* L.
(*Triglochin palustre* L.)
### Marsh Arrowgrass

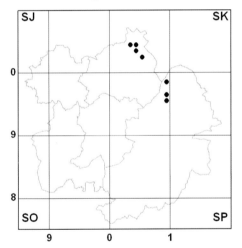

7. Native. Ax. A very local perennial herb of mires and base-enriched flushes in moderately acid, more or less infertile soils and muds in open situations. Frequent to locally common in parts of Sutton Park, particularly Longmoor Valley and near Little Bracebridge Pool. Also in pool margin at Clayhanger, wet pasture at Jockey Fields and King's Hayes farm, all in Walsall, also an old record on a post-industrial site: marsh around blast-furnace slag heap at Ladymoor Pool Bilston, last seen in 1980s. Numbers of records in vc. 38 seem diminished compared with Cadbury *et al.* (1971), similarly in vc. 39 compared with Edees (1972), who recorded it in 5 tetrads in SO99 and one each in SP08 and 09. Ass:

*73. Native. This floating-leaved, rhizomatous perennial herb occurs in many of the canals throughout the conurbation but generally as isolated patches and rarely in great abundance. A rapid coloniser of smaller ponds whose surface occasionally becomes totally covered when conditions are to its liking. Showing a preference for water of moderate depth so absent from many of the shallow pools and deeper lakes. It has a very wide ecological tolerance, found in base-poor to base-rich water over a wide range of substrates, but is nevertheless remarkably scarce in some parts of the conurbation. Readett (1971) recorded it from Sutton Park in SP0995, SP0996, SP0998, SP1096 & SP1097 but it was not recorded there in our survey. Ass: *Callitriche* spp., *Elodea nuttallii, Persicaria amphibia, Potamogeton crispus, Potamogeton pectinatus.*

### *Potamogeton polygonifolius* Pourr.
### Bog Pondweed
4. Native. Ax. Rhizomatous perennial herb of nutrient- and base-poor, acidic streams and flushes and shallow pond margins, on peaty substrates. Areas of fen and bog vegetation in Sutton Park: near Little Bracebridge Pool (most recently SP095982, MWP & ICT, 2005) and Longmoor Valley (most recently SP092963, MWP, ICT & PLR, 2006); a field pond, Lower Illey meadow (most recently SO977811, RM, 1997) and a pool in a field W of Brownhills Common (SK033064, ICT & SAHA, 2010). There are older records from other areas of Sutton

14. Native. Ax. A wholly submerged perennial herb of unpolluted, clear water. Infrequent, and now more or less confined to little used, nutrient-poor canals in the northern parts of the conurbation, where it is still locally frequent in places. Recently recorded in Rushall Canal, Wyrley & Essington, Anglesey Branch and Walsall Canals. Apparently more susceptible to eutrophication than *P. natans* with which it occasionally grows. It used to be present in two of the Fens Pools (SO9188) in Dudley in the 1980s, also it grew with *P natans* in a pond S of Dudley Road in Warrens Hall Country Park, Rowley Regis at approx. SO956885 until 1995. These were not refound during the present survey. Like most other *Potamogeton* species, its apparent decline in B&BC is a cause

▲ *Potamogeton lucens*

for concern. Ass: *Potamogeton crispus*, *Potamogeton natans*, *Sagittaria sagittifolia*.

### *Potamogeton alpinus* Balb.
**Red Pondweed**
0. Native. Only very old records from the Dudley Canal (SO9783) and from Bartley Green (SP0081), both by W. Mathews, 1881.

### *Potamogeton praelongus* Wulfen
**Long-stalked Pondweed**
0. Native. A specimen in Birmingham University Herbarium was collected by G.S. West in 1909 in Sutton Park. Both Cadbury *et al.* (1971) and Readett (1971) state "it was last seen in 1947", but neither give a grid reference.

### *Potamogeton perfoliatus* L.
**Perfoliate Pondweed**

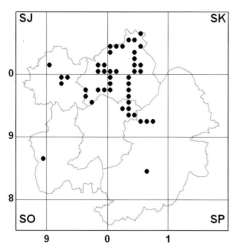

*46. Native. Ax. This rhizomatous submerged aquatic perennial is almost exclusively a plant of canals in the Black Country. It is most frequently recorded from Walsall, Wyrley & Essington, Tame Valley, Rushall & Hay Head Branch Canals, where populations appear to be relatively stable. Plants appear to be moderately tolerant of eutrophication making its apparent absence from many suitable habitats elsewhere in the conurbation rather puzzling. There were reliable records from a further eight 1km squares from the Dudley canal complex in the 1980s which were not refound in the present survey although it is present in the Stourbridge Canal on the Dudley boundary. Records lead us to believe that all *Potamogeton* species with perhaps the exception of *P. pectinatus* appear to be in decline in our area. Ass: *Ceratophyllum demersum*, *Myriophyllum spicatum*, *Potamogeton crispus*, *Potamogeton natans*, *Potamogeton pectinatus*.

### *Potamogeton friesii* Rupr.
**Flat-stalked Pondweed**
4. Native. NT. Ax. Very few recent reliable

records for this rhizomatous aquatic perennial. From the Stourbridge Canal (SO895850, JEH & APD, 2004) and several from the Wyrley and Essington Canal, all recorded by JEH (SK026043, 2001; SK014024 & SK015023, 2003; SJ944002 & SJ943002, 2004). There is an earlier record from the Stourbridge Canal at Wollaston (SO887859, WAT, 1990).

### *Potamogeton × lintonii* Fryer
(*P. friesii × P. crispus*)
**Linton's Pondweed**
5. Native. Ax. Characterised in Preston (1995) as most common in the English Midlands, with pre-1970 records from SO98, SO99, and SP08, in the present survey it was only recorded in SO99, from sections and branches of the B'ham and W'ton Canal: Deepfields, S of Coseley Tunnel (SO940944 to SO943935, S. Whild & AJL, 1998), and abundant nearby in the Wednesbury Old Canal (SO9494, S. Whild & AJL, 1998); scattered in the canal by Monmore Park Industrial Estate (SO930969, through SO9297 into SO9397, ICT & EVJC, 2001); frequent in the Loxdale arm of the same canal (SO945949, ICT, 1998). There are earlier records from this complex at Coseley (SO939949, BRF, 1993), and from the Titford Branch in Oldbury (SO989878 & SO995887, JJD, conf. C.D. Preston, 1987), and abundant in the pool area at the summit of this canal (SO987878, JJD, conf. C.D. Preston, 1987). It was also recorded from the Worcester and B'ham canal at Edgbaston (SP0484) by J. Keirnan (1961). Ass: *Potamogeton crispus*, *Potamogeton natans*, *Potamogeton pectinatus*.

### *Potamogeton obtusifolius* Mert. & W.D.J. Koch
**Blunt-leaved Pondweed**
2. Native. Ax. This rhizomatous perennial aquatic has been recorded only rarely during the recent survey: Moseley Golf Course, SW of Coldbath Pool (SP087817, JMP, 1996); pond at 15th hole, Moseley Golf Course (SP082816, EMP, 2008); Edgbaston Pool (SP054841, R. Duff & C. Walker, 1998, seen again 2009). There were no records from our area of vc. 39 in Edees (1972) and no old records in vc. 37, but it was reliably recorded in vc. 38 from Sutton Park in Wyndley Pool (SP1195, Cadbury *et al.* 1971), Readett (1971) also lists it for SP0997 & SP0998. There are also thirteen records from canals and anglers' pools across our area in the 1980s suggesting at least a sporadic occurrence here, although many of these records are unverified.

### *Potamogeton pusillus* L.
**Lesser Pondweed**
7. Native. Ax. Very few modern records for

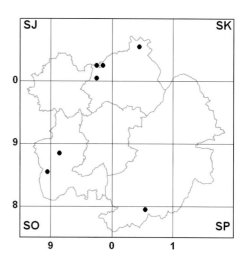

Fens Pools, Sneyd Pool, Lifford Lakes and Wyrley & Essington and Dudley Canals. There is also an old record from Edgbaston Pool (SP0584, D.A. Cadbury, 1935). Possibly overlooked but generally considered to be of rare occurrence.

### *Potamogeton berchtoldii* Fieber
**Small Pondweed**
4. Native. Ax. Recorded from Lindridge and Langley Pools near Sutton Coldfield (SP154968, MWP, ICT, JWP, JaH & M. Scholten, 2006); Edgbaston Pool (SP0584, MWP & JWP, 2007) and pools at Park Hall, Castle Bromwich (SP158908, ICT, MWP & JWP, 2006 and SP148905, SAHA, 2006) where small populations occur in the shallow margins. Readett (1971) recorded it in SP0998 in Sutton Park. Often confused with *P. pusillus*; small linear-leaved *Potamogeton* species are possibly overlooked but loss of suitable habitats seems to be the main factor causing their scarcity in B&BC. Also a tetrad record for SJ90A.

### *Potamogeton compressus* L.
**Grass-wrack Pondweed**
0. Sect. 41, BAP, EN, Nationally Scarce. All recent records for this species in our area are now thought to be erroneous, although Preston & Croft (1997) included B&BC in its distribution area. Bagnall listed it for Sutton Park in the 19th century.

### *Potamogeton crispus* L.
**Curled Pondweed**
*69. Native. Rhizomatous, submerged aquatic, found throughout the conurbation in ponds, canals, lakes, rivers and streams in mesotrophic or eutrophic waters but often absent from many apparently suitable habitats. More tolerant of eutrophication and pollution than most other *Potamogeton* species and along with *P. pectinatus* occurring in the more eutrophic waters of the more heavily used inner canals of B'ham as well as the

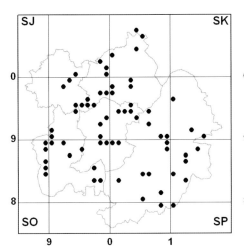

Black Country. Also tetrad SJ90A. Ass: *Ceratophyllum demersum, Myriophyllum spicatum, Potamogeton pectinatus, Potamogeton perfoliatus.*

### *Potamogeton pectinatus* L.
### Fennel Pondweed

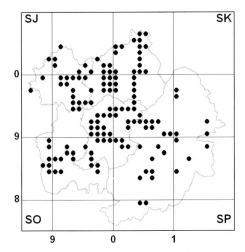

*136. Native. A submerged linear-leaved aquatic of canals, pools, and rivers and by far the commonest of the narrow-leaved *Potamogeton* species found in the urban area. Occurring in most of the more eutrophic canal bodies in the built-up areas of B'ham and Black Country even when quite well-used and often the only aquatic present. It is also a coloniser of many of the faster-flowing reaches of eutrophic rivers such as the Tame and Cole, again often in the absence of other aquatic species. Ass: *Elodea* spp., *Myriophyllum spicatum, Potamogeton natans.*

### *Zannichellia palustris* L.
### Horned Pondweed

13. Native. Submerged aquatic annual or perennial, locally frequent in the shallows of small to large ponds in a few places and also recorded rarely in canals where it is tolerant of eutrophication and sometimes occurs in some abundance. Also recorded

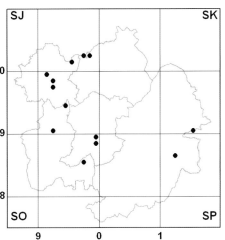

from shallow and nutrient-rich reaches of the River Cole in B'ham. Known from Sutton Park (SP0998) until at least 1991. Populations appear to fluctuate from year to year but unless deliberately sought after, plants are easily overlooked. Most likely under-recorded in B&BC but its distribution may well be sporadic. Ass: *Hippuris vulgaris, Potamogeton pectinatus.*

## 152. NARTHECIACEAE

### *Narthecium ossifragum* (L.) Huds.
### Bog Asphodel

0. Native. Herbaceous rhizomatous perennial, extinct in B&BC. Bagnall collected it in Sutton Park in 1873, and it was seen near Little Bracebridge Pool in the late 1940s (P. James, pers. comm.). Cadbury *et al.* (1971) mention a Withering record in 1787 from B'ham Heath (SP0488?). There are several historical records from our part of vc. 37: plants "near Rubery Hill on the Lickey" (SO9977, T. Purton, 1817) and it was recorded in the Moseley Common bogs (SP0982) up to 1838. Three historical records for "in the bog at the western foot of Rednal Hill, Bromsgrove, Lickey", SO9976, W. Matthews, from 1848, 1850 and 1856 may be just outside, and the site was destroyed by drainage around 1854.

## 153. DIOSCOREACEAE

### *Tamus communis* L.
### Black Bryony

*95. Native. Ax. A dioecious, tuberous climber in (usually old) hedgerows and in the margins, and sometimes further into, deciduous woodland on base-intermediate and nutrient-rich, moist and often clayey soils but avoiding water-logged conditions. Often non-flowering in denser shade, locally frequent and widely distributed, the map shows clear areas of concentration in parts of the Walsall countryside, the eastern fringes of Sutton and the ancient

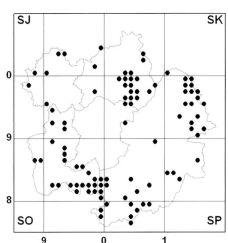

countryside of Halesowen and Woodgate and great similarity with the distribution of *Arum maculatum*. Like *A. maculatum*, it is possibly excluded from the central area by a lack of mature hedges and woodlands to colonise. Ass: *Crataegus monogyna, Lonicera periclymenum, Prunus spinosa.*

### 155. ALSTROEMERIACEAE

### *Alstroemeria aurea* Graham
### Peruvian Lily

2. Neophyte. Herbaceous perennial. Garden reject recorded near to Fens Pool at Fens Pools nature reserve, Dudley (SO913884, JEH, 2004); by recreation ground entrance, Oxbarn (SO8996, CBW, 2007). Chile.

### 157. LILIACEAE

### *Erythronium dens-canis* L.
### Dog's-tooth-violet

1. Neophyte. Bulbous perennial, quite well naturalised in several places in the graveyard, St. Michael and All Angels, Tettenhall (SJ891002, BRF, 1994, seen again 2008 but not found in 2011). S Europe.

### *Tulipa gesneriana* L.
### Garden Tulip

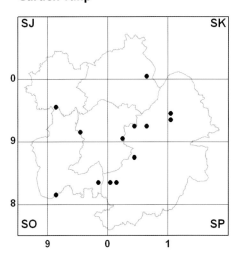

13. Neophyte. Bulbous perennial. Scattered records persisting from cultivation or as garden discard in grassland, scrub, waste land, roadsides, river banks. Some records as *Tulipa* sp. are almost certainly this and have been added. Also tetrad SJ90V. Garden origin.

### *Fritillaria meleagris* L.
### Fritillary

4. Native; introduced in B&BC. Bulbous perennial with a few records, semi-naturalised in (usually damp) grassland. Sheepwash Urban Park (SO976914, SO976919 & SO979914, MWP, 1998 &1999); Sandwell Valley (SP029913, MWP, 1998); grounds of Woodbrooke, Bournville (SP036814, AS, 1997, seen again 2008); St. Michael's Church, Boldmere (SP109939, SPG, 1998). Probably persisting from introductions in many parks and gardens.

### *Lilium martagon* L.
### Martagon Lily

1. Neophyte. Bulbous perennial, naturalised in woodland on limestone at The Gorge, Sedgley (SO928942, ST, 1989, seen again 2011) and probably a re-finding of WAT's first vc. record of 1986 from the same monad; old record from the grounds of Woodbrooke (SP036814, T. Thompson, 1985). Europe.

### *Lilium pyrenaicum* Gouan
### Pyrenean Lily

0. Neophyte. Bulbous perennial with one old record: three plants in small open area in tall grass/scrub community on W side of stream, Lutley Gutter (SO949839, WAT, 1989). Pyrenees.

### 158. ORCHIDACEAE

### *Epipactis purpurata* Sm.
### Violet Helleborine

3. Native. A perennial woodland herb, it appears to have a very sporadic existence around the edges of the conurbation. Four spikes seen in 2004 on footpath near Stourbridge Golf Course (SO901818, JJD, 2004). Two spikes recorded in The Dingle, Cotwell End Nature Reserve in a bare bank beneath Beeches (SO912925, M. Waller, 2010, seen again 2012); by the path in approach to Hodgehole Dingle, three clumps (SO924825, PWR, conf. APD, 2012). Old records from Hay Head Wood (SP042989, J. Beechy, 1989, seen again 1992 by DH, JPM & BRF) and Edgbaston Park (SP0583, Cadbury *et al.*, 1971).

### *Epipactis helleborine* (L.) Crantz
### Broad-leaved Helleborine

21. Native. Ax. Scattered records, but

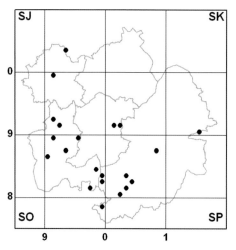

probably commoner in the S and W. Characteristically found in old mixed deciduous woodland on moderately base-rich and not very fertile soils, especially in streamside situations, but appearing, often only for a few seasons, in small numbers in a much wider range of usually shady habitats: plantations and naturally forming scrub in post-industrial sites, planted cuttings by canals and roads, even neglected gardens, planted shrubberies and school grounds. The immediate locality is often bare, but it has even been found in field layers dominated by ivy or nettles.

### *Epipactis phyllanthes* G.E. Sm.
### Green-flowered Helleborine

1. Native. Nationally Scarce. A population was seen in 2004 and 2005 (when there were *circa* 20 inflorescences) in scrub woodland in a neglected canal dry dock adjacent to the long-disused ironworks of Foster, Rastrick & Co, where the famous early steam locomotives 'Stourbridge Lion' and 'Agenoria' were built: Stour Valley, Wollaston, Stourbridge (SO894849, MES & AJR).

### *Neottia ovata* (L.) Bluff & Fingerh.
(*Listera ovata* (L.) R. Br.)
### Common Twayblade

1. Native. Introduced into a landfill haymeadow in Kitchen Lane (SJ963026, C. Young & F. McCullagh, 2000) in hay from Eades Meadow in Worcestershire; two plants flowered every year from 2000–2004, last seen in flower in 2008. Old record for Sutton Park (SP0997, Bagnall, 1868).

### *Gymnadenia conopsea* sensu lato
### Fragrant-orchid

1. Native. A record at SP049873 on a canal bank (Ms Bonham, 2002) has not been confirmed.

### *Dactylorhiza fuchsii* (Druce) Soó
### Common Spotted-orchid

39. Native. Ax. Tuberous perennial herb.

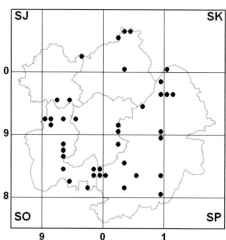

Old or semi-improved open pastures, quarries, brickyards, blast furnace spoil, road verges on relatively nutrient-poor and rarely very base-poor, usually at least intermittently damp soils, in the open or in very light shade, can withstand grazing and hay making, and even intermittent gang-mowing. It often grows with *D. praetermissa*, and sometimes seems to be represented only by hybrids with that species. Also recorded for tetrad SJ90V. Ass: *Anthoxanthum odoratum, Cynosurus cristatus, Carex leporina, Carex panicea, Dactylorhiza praetermissa, Festuca rubra, Galium palustre, Heracleum sphondylium, Hypericum perforatum, Juncus* spp., *Leucanthemum vulgare, Lotus corniculatus, Ranunculus acris, Stellaria graminea.*

### *Dactylorhiza × grandis* (Druce) P.F. Hunt
(*D. fuchsii × D. praetermissa*)

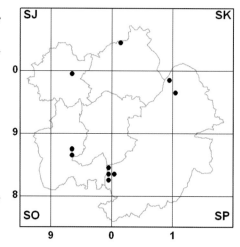

10. Native. Ax. Found with the parent species, or just with *D. praetermissa*, or occasionally alone, in wet pasture and flush habitats appropriate for *praetermissa*. Pelsall North Common; Sutton Park; Bowmans Harbour in W'ton; Saltwells LNR and Woodgate Valley Country Park. All records by RM or verified by I. Denholm (2008). There are older records for

Shireoak Quarry in Walsall (SK0603) and it is probably in other mixed *Dactylorhiza* populations.

## *Dactylorhiza maculata* (L.) Soó
### Heath Spotted-orchid

2. Native. Ax. Remarkably rare in B&BC, it seems only to be present in the Clayhanger/Brownhills area of Walsall, where it was recorded as a single plant in Birch/Oak woodland on Brownhills Common (SK035062, DH, 1998) and in the acid mire by the canal at the N end of Clayhanger Common (SK045052, AB, conf. JEH, 2006, seen again in 2008 and conf. I. Denholm). There are old records for Sutton Park (SP0997 in Readett 1971) which have been disputed and were not refound in the recent survey. Ass: *Agrostis stolonifera*, *Anagallis tenella*, *Carex echinata*, *Dactylorhiza praetermissa*, *Juncus articulatus*, *Lotus uliginosus*, *Molinia caerulea*, *Ranunculus flammula*.

## *Dactylorhiza incarnata* (L.) Soó
### Early Marsh-orchid

0. Native. Probably not present in B&BC. There are a few old records in Walsall, e.g. from Clayhanger SSSI (SK035045, J. Box, M.E. Evans & ICT, 1986), and Stubbers Green SSSI (SK046015, CW & S. Derry, 1987) but these have not been confirmed and are thought (including specimens from both sites seen by I. Denholm in 2008) more likely to be aberrant specimens of *D. praetermissa*.

## *Dactylorhiza praetermissa* (Druce) Soó
### Southern Marsh-orchid

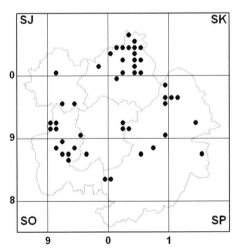

48. Native. Ax. Scarcely recorded in our area by Edees (1972) or Cadbury *et al.* (1971), but now quite common. It occurs characteristically in old wet pastures and flushes but also in quarries, especially claypit quarries, in the towpath edge and in drier reedswamps by canals, winter-flooded areas of abandoned railways, sometimes in quite dry and secondary

grasslands, rarely as a natural colonist of created hay meadows, on moderately to fairly base- and nutrient-rich substrates. It seems to be favoured by impeded drainage and the presence of bare surfaces, and often produces huge flushes when a quarry is abandoned which later subsides to a much smaller population. Ass: *Cirsium palustre*, *Epilobium hirsutum*, *Equisetum fluviatile*, *Festuca rubra*, *Glyceria maxima*, *Iris pseudacorus*, *Juncus effusus*, *Juncus inflexus*, *Lotus corniculatus*, *Plantago lanceolata*, *Potentilla reptans*, *Ranunculus acris*.

## *Dactylorhiza purpurella* (T. & T.A. Stephenson) Soó
### Northern Marsh-orchid

0. Native. Probably not present in B&BC. There are some old records from Brownhills Common (SK042063, JPM, 1990); Wyrley & Essington canal (SK050048, C. Hayes & W. Prestwood, 1977) and Doulton's Clay Pit (SO936871, Natural England Files, 1977), but they have not been refound. Possibly they were aberrant specimens of *D. praetermissa*.

## *Orchis mascula* (L.) L.
### Early-purple Orchid

0. Native. Probably not present in B&BC. Old records only, and all made in July and therefore possibly mistakes. Lazy Hill Wood (SK060029, E. Pulford, 1983); Tettenhall Wood (SO886995, DH & ICT, 1985); Daw End canal (SK049014, D. Sestakovs, CW & D. Withers, 1987 & SK046008, S. Derry & CW, 1987); Stubbers Green (SK046013, CW & S. Derry, 1987). None of these have been refound, although this species occurs just outside the W'ton boundary less than 3km from the Tettenhall Wood site. There is also a 1909 record by J. Amphlett & C. Rea from Illey (SO9881).

## *Anacamptis pyramidalis* (L.) Rich.
### Pyramidal Orchid

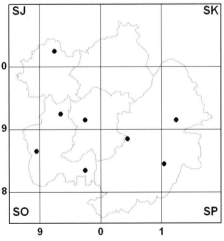

8. Native. Ax. A tuberous perennial herb of dry, open, nutrient-poor and base-

▲ *Epipactis purpurata*

▲ *Dactylorhiza fuchsii*

▲ *Dactylorhiza maculata*

rich limestone soils and rock exposures. There seem to be no old records in or around B&BC, but from 1999 there have been several widely scattered records across the area. The oldest record is from the Crown Tip, Leasowes Park (SO977839, AMG, 1999); most populations are on post-industrial sites – tips, old brickworks, canal sides – and it has also appeared in the old limestone quarry at the Wren's Nest (SO936921–2) from 2004. It was also established on Bushbury Hill (SJ925021) as a small flowering population in the mid-1990s from hay from Llanymynech strewn in 1987. It persisted there until at least 2005.

### Anacamptis morio (L.) R.M. Bateman, Pridgeon & M.W. Chase
(Orchis morio L.)
**Green-winged Orchid**
1. Native; introduced in B&BC. NT. Introduced to a capped landfill site in hay from Eades Meadow in Worcestershire in 1995, it first flowered there in 1999 and in 2012 it was still well established over about 0.3ha, Kitchen Lane, W'ton (SJ964026, CRP, 2000).

### Ophrys insectifera L.
**Fly Orchid**
0. Native. Old record: grounds of Oscott College (SP09, J. Caswell, 1880, in Herb. Bagnall).

### Ophrys apifera Huds.
**Bee Orchid**

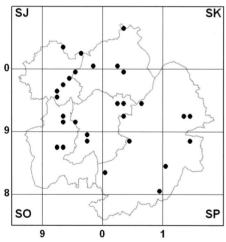

29. Native. Ax. Tuberous perennial herb. Not infrequent, but of sporadic occurrence throughout. Found typically in shallow, skeletal soil on limestone, or base-rich rubble or spoil, on outcrops, in quarries, playing fields, old gasworks sites, landfill sites, other areas of similar spoil, in one case in the conservation margin of a silage field. It has also colonised two created grasslands on landfill in W'ton (SO924955, 2007 & SJ963026, 2004) although thought

not to have been in the source hay or seed mixture. Presumably the hay meadow management suits it. Ass: *Blackstonia perfoliata, Briza media, Carex flacca, Centaurea nigra, Dactylis glomerata, Festuca rubra, Lathyrus nissolia, Linum catharticum, Plantago lanceolata, Potentilla reptans, Vicia cracca.*

## 159. IRIDACEAE

### Sisyrinchium montanum Greene
**American Blue-eyed-grass**
2. Neophyte. Perennial herb. Spreading patches, believed to be from an original introduction, in poorly drained, moderately acid grassland adjacent to Swan Pool, Sandwell Valley (SP0291, MWP, 1999), with *Carex flacca, Carex demissa.* Was still present there in 2012 but is extremely difficult to locate when not in flower. Also present in the open grassland on the old ironworks plateau at Pelsall Common (SK017045, Sandwell Valley Naturalists, 1992, seen again in 2002 by DH & JEH, when there were 60 flowering spikes, and in 2008). N America.

### Sisyrinchium californicum (Ker Gawl.) W.T. Ainton
**Yellow-eyed-grass**
2. Neophyte. Three plants in paving cracks at base of garden wall, Hundred Acres Road, Streetly (SP077968, MWP, ICT, JaH & PLR, 2006); spreading vegetatively, small clump on edge of pavement/waste site of post-housing site, Oddingley Road, Northfield (SP034786, JJD, 2006). Western N America.

### Sisyrinchium striatum Sm.
**Pale Yellow-eyed-grass**

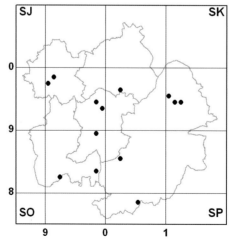

13. Neophyte. Perennial herb. A few records, mainly for single individuals or small groups of plants seeded along the base of garden walls where they meet the pavement. Parent plants are often

above or in a nearby garden. Maturity in this situation is rarely achieved due to the application of glyphosate along most of the urban roads throughout the spring and summer months. Also rarely persisting on post-housing sites as a garden relic or throw-out. One or two records from post-industrial sites. S America. Ass: *Campanula persicifolia, Filipendula vulgaris, Geranium pyrenaicum.*

### Hermodactylus tuberosus (L.) Mill.
**Snake's-head Iris**
1. Neophyte. Tuberous perennial, several plants recorded along a wire fence, Ridgacre, B'ham (SP010841, CBW, 1998). Mediterranean.

### Iris germanica L.
**Bearded Iris**

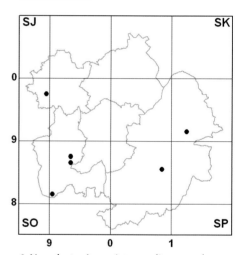

6. Neophyte. A persistent relic or garden throw-out. Very few records for individual clumps on waste ground, by a road, on a railway bank, a post-industrial site etc. Garden origin.

### Iris pseudacorus L.
**Yellow Iris**

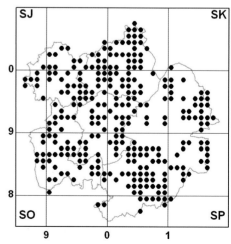

*294. Native. A rhizomatous perennial herb commonly occurring in open, unshaded margins of many of the canals, lakes and ponds throughout the conurbation where it frequently forms dense colonies. Also a popular introduction in planting schemes causing confusion as to its true native status in some places. Displays a wide degree of tolerance to water conditions and sometimes forms pure stands in the absence of other marginals, but apparently requires at least an intermediate base and nutrient status. Considerably more frequent than in the 1970s Floras. Ass: *Alisma lanceolatum, Butomus umbellatus, Epilobium hirsutum, Sagittaria sagittifolia, Sparganium erectum, Typha latifolia.*

### *Iris foetidissima* L.
### Stinking Iris

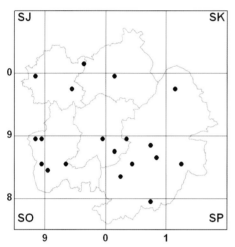

19. Native. A perennial herb, the few scattered records in isolation suggest this species is no more than an introduction in B&BC. Individual clumps or small patches have been recorded, sometimes but not always in the shade and on moderately fertile and base-rich soil, from municipal parks, waste ground close to gardens, track verges, hedgerows, several canal towpaths, banks of the Rivers Stour and Rea, Ham Dingle. Ass: *Brachypodium sylvaticum, Campanula trachelium, Conium maculatum, Dipsacus fullonum.*

### *Crocus vernus* (L.) Hill
### Spring Crocus

13. Neophyte. A cormous perennial herb. The most commonly grown species which includes several showy cultivars such as 'Pickwick', 'Remembrance', 'King of the Whites' and 'Little Dorritt'. Abundantly grown, and planted on many graves and often spreading into surrounding grassland in most of the churchyards throughout the conurbation, where, in early spring it displays showy patches of white, purple and purple-white, bi-coloured flowers. Also regularly discarded into grassy patches and bits of waste ground near houses where

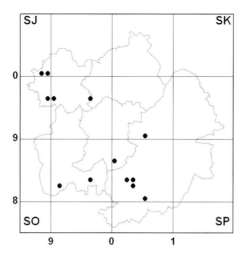

it persists without showing much sign of spread. Undoubtedly under-recorded due to the earliness of flowering and withering of foliage and doubts about whether plantings are deliberate. Many records for *Crocus* sp. belong here but have not been included in the map. S & C Europe.

### *Crocus chrysanthus* (Herb.) Herb.
### Golden Crocus

2. Neophyte. Cormous herb. Recorded, rarely, in sites marginal to cultivation. Naturalised in a churchyard, West Bromwich (SP0192, A. Underhill, 1996); plentiful in grassy verge, Woodlands Walk, Penn (SO895959, CBW, 2007). Balkans and Turkey.

### *Crocus tommasinianus* Herb.
### Early Crocus

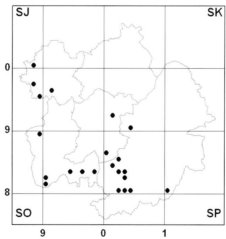

22. Neophyte. A cormous herb, readily spreading by seed from original garden plantings into grassy roadside verges, lawns, garden paths and paving, roadside banks and patches of woodland. Also a rapid coloniser from original plantings in grassy areas between graves in many of the churchyards in B&BC. Likely to be under-recorded due to the earliness of its flowering and withering of foliage later in

▲ *Ophrys apifera*

▲ *Sisyrinchium montanum*

▲ *Iris foetidissima*

the season. S Yugoslavia, S Hungary & NW Bulgaria.

### *Crocus × stellaris* Haw.
(*C. angustifolius* Weston × *C. flavus* Weston)
**Yellow Crocus**

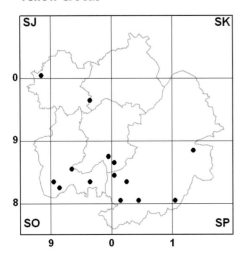

14. Neophyte. Most of the records appear to be for isolated plants or small patches on grassy banks and patches of ground to the rear of houses, where it has been discarded from nearby gardens or deliberately planted. Often persisting but showing little signs of natural spread. Garden origin.

### *Crocosmia paniculata* (Klatt) N.E. Br.
**Aunt-Eliza**
1. Neophyte. Perennial with corms, a garden reject. Kingswinford Railway Walk (SO899905, CBW, 2007). May be *C. paniculata × C. pottsii* (MacNab ex Baker) N.E. Br., according to Stace (2010).

### *Crocosmia × crocosmiiflora* (Lemoine) N.E. Br.
(*C. pottsii* (Macnab ex Baker) N.E. Br. × *C. aurea* (Hook.) Planch.)
**Montbretia**

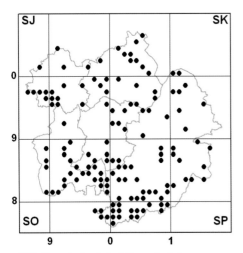

139. Neophyte. Sch. 9 (invasive). A persistent garden throw-out, very well naturalised, and sometimes forming

large patches, on grassy banks, waste ground and tracks to the rear of houses, hedgerows, stream and ditch sides, canal towpaths and even woodland in fairly dense shade where it can persist for many years without flowering. Spread is by increase of its basal underground corms. Usually in moist or damp, fertile and base-rich soils. Garden origin: parents from S Africa. Ass: *Anthriscus sylvestris, Dactylis glomerata, Hordeum murinum, Ilex aquifolium, Lamium album, Senecio jacobaea, Urtica dioica.*

## 160. XANTHORROEACEAE

### *Hemerocallis fulva* (L.) L.
**Orange Day-lily**
1. Neophyte. Rhizomatous perennial herb. One large flowering patch persisting from a former garden along the edge of a path on recently demolished council-housing estate, Ley Hill Farm Road, Northfield (SP0180, MWP, 2003). Garden origin.

### *Hemerocallis lilioasphodelus* L.
**Yellow Day-lily**
2. Neophyte. Perennial herb. Garden escape. Edge of Merrit's Brook, S of Shenley Fields (SP017802, CBW, 1994); edge of playing field, Wall Heath (SO8789, CBW, 2007). E Asia.

### *Kniphofia uvaria* (L.) Oken
**Red-hot-poker**
5. Neophyte. Densely tufted rhizomatous perennial. Goscote Sewage Works (SK019019, CRP, 1998); land at Queslett (landfill) (SP065943, SB, 2002); post-housing/industrial land, Seven Stars Road, Oldbury (SO992893, MWP, 2003). Another plant in a hedgebank at Manor Lane, Halesowen (SO981835, JJD, 2003); Union Road Oldbury (SO982908, MWP & T. Oliver, 2009). Almost certainly all relics of former plantings. S Africa.

### *Kniphofia × praecox* Baker
**Greater Red-hot-poker**
2. Neophyte. One patch in secondary woodland near buildings, Hill Top Golf course, Sandwell Valley (SP034917, MWP, 1997); roadside, near Woodsetton (SO934938, CBW, 2004). Almost certainly both relics of former plantings. Garden origin.

## 161. ALLIACEAE

### *Allium schoenoprasum* L.
**Chives**
11. Native (and Nationally Scarce) but also widely cultivated; entirely an introduction in B&BC. Perennial herb, with scattered

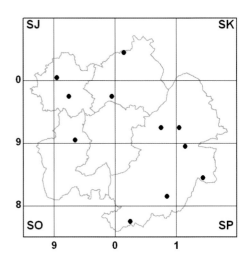

records mainly close to sites of cultivation: paving cracks in garden, base of garden wall along pavement, naturalised around allotments, but also several patches on post-industrial land to the N of Fort Parkway (SP115898, MWP, 2006).

### *Allium cepa* L.
**Onion**

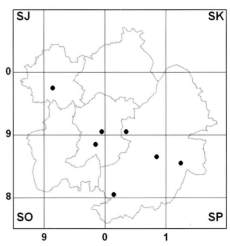

7. Neophyte. Only rarely occurring as isolated plants from original cultivation on post-housing site and neglected allotment gardens. Origin unknown.

### *Allium roseum* L.
**Rosy Garlic**
4. Neophyte. Perennial herb, few records: patches on derelict waste ground, Winson Green Road/Heath Street, Winson Green (SP044877, MWP, 1999); small patch in rough grassland to the rear of houses, Tile Cross (SP160863, MWP, ICT, JMP, JaH & SJC, 2007); Merrion's Wood (SP041960, SAHA, 2008); field margin by Walsall Golf Course (white-flowered) (SP036978, SJC, 2008). Mediterranean.

### *Allium moly* L.
**Yellow Garlic**
1. Neophyte. Bulbous perennial herb.

Large patches persisting and spreading vegetatively from original planting, in remains of old garden border. Site of former council housing estate to the E of Frogmill Road, Northfield (SP0078, MWP, 2003). E Spain & SW France.

### *Allium triquetrum* L.
### Three-cornered Garlic

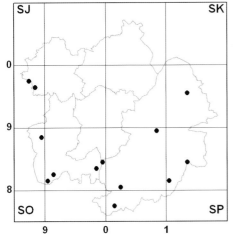

13. Neophyte. Sch. 9 (invasive). Bulbous perennial herb, with few records in pavement, rough grass and other neglected bits of waste ground, mainly in residential areas, but also occasionally in old woodland such as Ham Dingle (SO915825) and Leasowes Park (SO981837). W & C Mediterranean.

### *Allium paradoxum* (M. Bieb.) G. Don
### Few-flowered Garlic

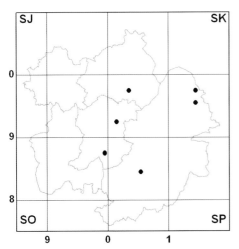

6. Neophyte. Sch. 9 (invasive). Bulbous perennial herb. Only a few records, establishing in field margins, roadside verges and also in damp woodlands, sometimes in steep, otherwise bare banks by streams. Possibly on the increase in B&BC, it can spread rapidly once established and is clearly capable of invading primary habitats here as at Sot's Hole, Sandwell Valley (SP0192, MWP, 2008). Caucasus & Iran.

### *Allium ursinum* L.
### Ramsons

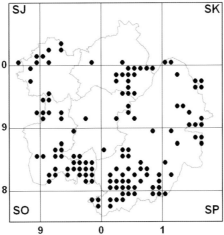

*133. Native. Ax. A bulbous perennial herb which seeds prolifically in favourable situations, found in moist woodland, hedge banks, by streams and on river banks, usually growing within the shade of trees and shrubs but occasionally spreading into more open situations in hedgerows or even along the margins of fields. Generally well distributed but becoming scarce in the most urbanised areas due to absence of suitable habitats. Mostly in, or expanding from, anciently wooded habitats, it grows typically in a specific zone on stream banks where it avoids both drought and waterlogging, often forming extensive carpets amidst which little else can grow. As a member of the woodland vernal flora, it is shade-avoiding, though it can in certain conditions persist under quite heavy shade. It seems to be spreading in many of its stations, but can sometimes surprise, being absent where conditions appear ideal yet persisting where apparently inimical such as in dry or open situations. Similar 1km square distribution to *Mercurialis perennis* in B&BC. Ass: *Ajuga reptans, Anemone nemorosa, Deschampsia cespitosa, Ficaria verna*, young *Fraxinus excelsior, Hyacinthoides non-scripta, Mercurialis perennis*.

### *Allium ampeloprasum* L.
### Wild Leek

3. Archaeophyte. Plants self-sown near original planting. Circular herb bed, B'ham University Botanical Gardens Winterbourne (SP0583, MWP & JWP, 2007); Coney Green Drive Allotments (SP015782, MWP, ICT, JJD, AWR, JWP & JaH, 2008); several well-established patches in rough grassland to the E of Brickhouse Road, Rowley Regis, spreading from an original introduction (SO965874, LG, 2007). All

▲ *Allium paradoxum*

▲ *Allium ursinum*

these records are believed to be **var. babingtonii** (Borrer) Syme.

### *Allium porrum* L.
### Leek
2. Casual. One plant in full flower, derelict allotment off Hob Moor Lane, Yardley (SP125855, CBW, 1997); one plant in disturbed ground next to lock S of Jones Road, W'ton (SJ911005, C. Young, 1998). Garden origin.

### *Allium sphaerocephalon* L.
### Round-headed Leek
1. Native, garden origin in B&BC. Established in the edge of a neglected lawn, Pensnett (SO912892, CBW, 2006).

### *Allium vineale* L.
### Wild Onion

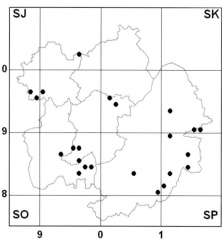

23. Native. A bulbous, perennial herb of infrequent occurrence, in rather dryish soils in open to semi-shaded situations. Small populations or few individuals occur in roughish grassland, roadside and railway banks and among canal towpath vegetation in neutral to weakly basic soils. Ass: *Arrhenatherum elatius*, *Galega officinalis*, *Ranunculus repens*, *Rubus fruticosus* agg., *Rumex obtusifolius*, *Urtica dioica*.

### *Allium fistulosum* L.
### Welsh Onion
1. Neophyte. Perennial, persisting from cultivation, Uplands Allotment Gardens (SP039909, MWP, 1998). Asia.

### *Agapanthus praecox* Willd.
### African Lily
1. Neophyte. Several patches showing little signs of spread on site of derelict garden. Lichfield Road, Four Oaks (SP113992, MWP, JWP & PLR, 2006). S Africa.

### *Tristagma uniflorum* (Lindl.) Traub
### Spring Starflower
2. Neophyte. Weedy bulbous perennial.

20 plants along back of pavement against fence, Watkins Gardens, Northfield (SP02997951, MWP, 2005); beneath street tree, Vauxhall Gardens, Dudley (SO95308915, MWP, 2008). S America.

### *Leucojum aestivum* L.
### Summer Snowflake
2. Alien/native. Bulbous perennial herb. Single discard plant in waste area, Ridgeacre (SP012844, CBW, 1998); record with no details (SO9995, A. Cole & E Barker, 2001); older record from the Ackers (SP105845, Wildlife Trust records, 1992). Subspecies not recorded.

### *Galanthus nivalis* L.
### Snowdrop

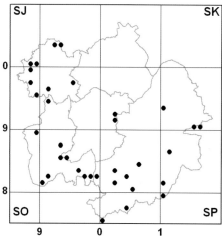

35. Neophyte. Bulbous perennial herb. Well-naturalised, long-persisting and spreading both vegetatively and from seed from original introductions and from garden cast-outs. Found in a wide-range of habitats including woodland, churchyards, roadside banks, streamsides, parks and estates. Also occasionally spreading into paving from nearby gardens in the urban area. Often *flore pleno*. Europe.

### *Galanthus elwesii* Hook. f.
### Greater Snowdrop
1. Neophyte. Bulbous perennial herb. Several plants seeded into surrounding grassland from an original grave planting, St Peter's Church, Old Church Road, Harborne (SP028840, MWP, 2011). SE Europe to Caucasas.

### *Galanthus woronowii* Losinsk.
### Green Snowdrop
1. Neophyte. Bulbous perennial herb. Naturalised in two places near graves in St Mary's churchyard, The Village, Kingswinford (SO984893, MWP, conf. PLR, 2011 & SO983893, CBW, conf. MWP & PLR, 2011). Found in the wild from an area

involving parts of Georgia, Russia and Turkey, where it occupies a wide range of habitats so has the potential to do well in the UK.

### *Narcissus* agg.

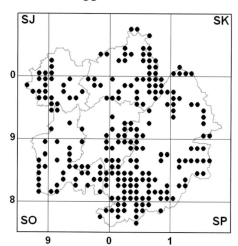

*236. Native and Neophyte. Originating from garden cast-outs and deliberate plantings and long-persisting in small clumps in all sorts of grassy places and wooded areas. Becoming naturalised and cheering up churchyards, woodland, hedge banks, roadside banks and verges, railway and canal banks, shrubberies and land recovering from recent disturbance with their display of golden-yellow flowers in early spring. The map suggests it is somewhat less frequently recorded in industrial areas. Most are thought to be **N. hispanicus** Gouan (*N. pseudonarcissus* subsp. *major* (Curtis) Baker) (**Spanish Daffodil**) from S France and the Iberian peninsula. A proportion have been assigned to particular species.

### *Narcissus poeticus* L.
### Pheasant's-eye Daffodil
6. Neophyte. A few records for isolated individuals or small groups of plants. Persisting from original planting or cast-outs, but seldom showing signs of spread. Unplanted group in Warley Park (SP009861, CBW, 1997); edge of Warley Wood (SP014857, CBW, 1997); banks of the Bourne Brook, Selly Oak (SP038833, CBW, 1997); post-industrial land N of Burnt Tree (SO957914, MWP, 2006); bank of Hillwood Common Road (SK117004, MWP, JaH, SJC & PLR, 2007). S Europe.

### *Narcissus* × *incomparabilis* Mill.
(*N. poeticus* × *P. pseudonarcissus*)
### Nonesuch Daffodil
6. Neophyte. A few records for deliberate introductions or garden throw-outs in churchyard, grassy area to the rear of

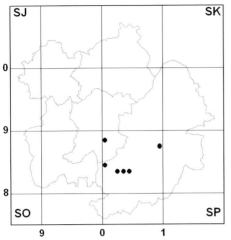

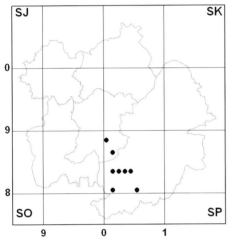

gardens, perimeter of recreation ground and at the sides of brooks. Garden origin.

## *Narcissus pseudonarcissus* L.
(*N. pseudonarcissus* subsp. *pseudonarcissus* L.)
**Daffodil**

8. Native. Well naturalised in parks, churchyards, hospital grounds and recreation grounds from original introductions. With introduced daffodil cultivars in grassland along the River Rea corridor to the south of Daffodil Way, Northfield where plants could possibly be relics of a native population that was at one time common in this area. Well established in woodland along the banks of Merritt's Brook in Manor Farm Park, Northfield where its native status has yet to be confirmed. Also tetrad SO99X.

## 162. ASPARAGACEAE

### *Convallaria majalis* L.
**Lily-of-the-valley**
23. Native, but introduced in B&BC. Rhizomatous perennial herb, with all records appearing to be deliberate introductions or plants spreading from original plantings in (mostly) secondary

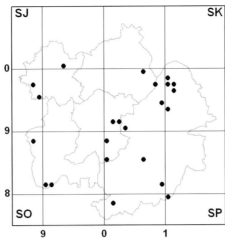

woodland, roadside verges, overgrown gardens and old railway sidings. Often forming extensive patches from a creeping rhizome once established.

## *Polygonatum multiflorum* (L.) All.
**Solomon's-seal**
2. Native. Rhizomatous perennial herb with unconfirmed modern records from Parish church, Short Heath, Walsall (SJ976009, SMP, 1998) and Highbury Park Allotments and Four Seasons Garden, Moseley (SP079824, A. Millward & EMP, 2006). It has also been recorded at Edgbaston Pool (SP055842, D.A. Cadbury, 1935, seen there in 1986) and listed by Cadbury *et al.* (1971) for both SP0583 and SP0584 ('Edgbaston Park').

## *Polygonatum* × *hybridum* Brügger
(*P. multiflorum* × *P. odoratum*)
**Garden Solomon's-seal**

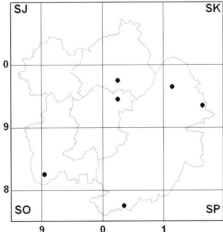

6. Neophyte. Rhizomatous perennial herb with a few scattered records for individual clumps or small patches in woodland, roadside hedgerow, grassy bank and wooded fringe near golf course. All almost certainly persisting from garden throw-outs or deliberate introductions. Garden origin.

▲ *Galanthus elwesii*

▲ *Galanthus woronowii*

▲ *Narcissus pseudonarcissus*

***Polygonatum odoratum*** (Mill.) Druce
**Angular Solomon's-seal**
0. Native. Old records from Wren's
Nest (SO937920, L. Southall, 1985); also
Erdington (SP19, B.F. Westcott, 1836).

***Ornithogalum umbellatum*** L.
**Star-of-Bethlehem**

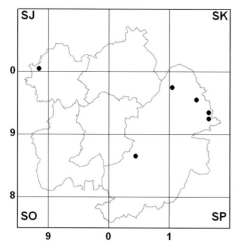

6. Neophyte. Persistent garden throw-
out or deliberate introduction. Very few
records, for individual plants or small
patches from a canal towpath, roadsides
and woodland. Our records have not
been assigned to either of the two
subspecies – subsp. *umbellatum* from
Europe and subsp. *campestre* Rouy
(*O. angustifolium* Boreau) which is
probably native in the Brecklands of
E England, but are most likely to be subsp.
*umbellatum*.

***Scilla siberica*** Haw.
**Siberian Squill**
3. Neophyte. Bulbous perennial herb
naturalised in grassland, St. Michael & All
Angels' Churchyard, Tettenhall, W'ton
(SJ891002, MWP, 1997); one plant self-sown
in tarmac paving, Oakham Road, Dudley
(SO957895, MWP, 2008); escaping from
garden into pavement, Yardley Wood
(SP101805, MWP, ICT, JWP & JaH, 2008).
There are two 1994 records from a wooded
bank, Cofton Park, Rednal (SP002766,
JJD) and scrubby road verge by golf
course, Frankley Beeches Road, Northfield
(SP004789, JJD). S Russia, Turkey & the
Caucasus.

***Scilla forbesii*** (Baker) Speta
(*Chionodoxa forbesii* Baker)
**Glory-of-the-snow**
4. Neophyte. Scattering of plants in
grassland from original introduction,
St. Michael & All Angels' churchyard,
Tettenhall, W'ton (SJ891003, MWP,
1997); Tettenhall (SJ885002, PN, 1999);
grass verge, Yew Tree Lane, Tettenhall

(SO872988, CBW, 2008); spreading out
from a garden into paving, Yardley Wood
(SP101805, MWP, ICT, JWP & JaH, 2008). W &
SW Turkey.

***Scilla sardensis*** (Whittall ex Barr) Speta
(*Chionodoxa sardensis* Drude)
**Lesser Glory-of-the-snow**
1. Neophyte. A few patches naturalised in
the grassland near the path, St. Michael
& All Angels' churchyard, Tettenhall
(SJ891003, MWP, 1998). W Turkey.

***Hyacinthoides non-scripta*** (L.) Chouard
ex Rothm.
**Bluebell**

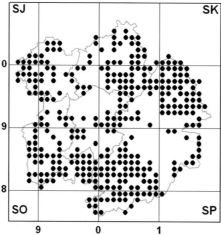

*346. Native. A bulbous perennial herb
of frequent occurrence in estates, parks
and churchyards and locally abundant
in many of the older deciduous
woodlands throughout the conurbation.
Also still relatively common in dingles,
river valleys and at the base of, and
spreading out from hedges, particularly
some of the older, species-rich
hedgerows still to be found in the rural
fringes. Becoming increasingly scarce in
the urban area and where present
usually occurring as tiny fragmented
populations in relic woodland and some
of the older gardens of Victorian and
Edwardian houses. Preferring neutral
to moderately acid, moist soils of
intermediate fertility in semi-shade. Ass:
*Alliaria petiolata, Ficaria verna, Hedera helix,
Holcus mollis, Pteridium aquilinum, Rubus
fruticosus* agg.

***Hyacinthoides* × *massartiana*** Geerinck
(*H. non-scripta* × *H. hispanica*)
159. Neophyte. Now considered to be
the commonly cultivated bluebell of
gardens, rapidly increasing by offsets
and forming extensive patches and once
established almost impossible to eradicate.
The hybrid is also fertile. Deliberately
planted in churchyards and parks and

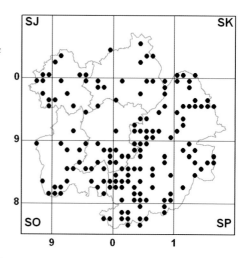

often discarded from gardens onto waste
ground, spoil heaps, wood margins and
hedge banks, where it readily becomes
established. Plants spreading into
woodland fringes containing native
bluebells are not uncommon and
introgressive hybridisation seems to
be taking place. Ass: *Alliaria petiolata,
Anthriscus sylvestris, Chamerion
angustifolium, Galium aparine, Geum
urbanum, Hedera helix, Holcus lanatus,
Muscari armeniacum, Rubus fruticosus* agg.,
*Urtica dioica, Vinca major.*

***Hyacinthoides hispanica*** (Mill.) Rothm.
**Spanish Bluebell**

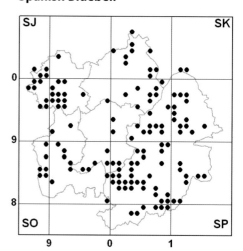

137. Neophyte. Confusion occurs and
recorders are in agreement that many
of the early records for this are now
believed to be in error for the hybrid
*H.* × *massartiana*. True *H. hispanica* is
now considered to be much rarer than
records suggest in B&BC. Portugal & W
Spain. The combined records for
*H. hispanica* and *H.* × *massartiana* are
shown in the map below and illustrate
the widespread nature of non-native
bluebells in B&BC, recorded for 255
monads, especially in W'ton and
B'ham.

## Hyacinthoides hispanica plus Hyacinthoides × massartiana

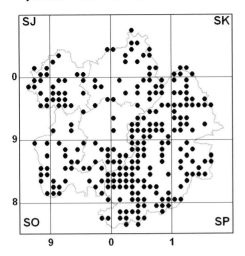

## Hyacinthus orientalis L.
### Hyacinth
1. Neophyte. The sole record is for a few plants on old graves, relics from original plantings. St. Mary's Church of England, Kingswinford (SO894893, MWP, 1997). SW Asia.

## Muscari neglectum Guss. ex Ten.
### Grape-hyacinth
3. Native; an introduction in B&BC. VU. One clump at base of old hedgerow, Robin Hood Crescent, Hall Green (SP101811, MWP, ICT, JWP & JaH, 2008), with *Muscari armeniacum*, *Cyclamen hederifolia* and *Helleborus foetidus*. This combination in the same hedgerow suggest it is no more than a deliberate introduction. Two other records are even more clearly introductions: paving below wall, New Rowley Road, Dudley (SO952892, MWP, 2008); Beacon View (SK063006, SMP, 2009).

## Muscari armeniacum Leichtlin ex Baker
### Garden Grape-hyacinth

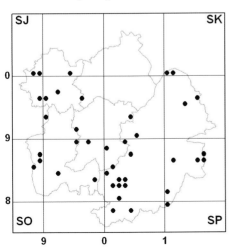

41. Neophyte. Bulbous perennial herb. A persistent garden throw-out becoming locally established along roadside verges and banks, around bases of street trees, on bits of neglected waste ground to the rear of houses and as a persistent garden relic on post-housing sites. Also sometimes seeding or vegetatively spreading from gardens into paths and nearby paving. Flowering early so undoubtedly more frequent than records would suggest. The Balkans, Turkey & the Caucasus.

## Muscari botryoides (L.) Mill.
### Compact Grape-hyacinth
1. Neophyte. An original planting showing little inclination to spread: two plants on an old grave, St Peter's Churchyard, Newtown, Great Bridge (SO981918, MWP, 1997). It was also recorded on Pelsall Common in 1991 (SK0104, JPM). S Europe.

## Muscari comosum (L.) Mill.
### Tassel Hyacinth
1. Neophyte. Key Hill Cemetery, Hockley (SP059881, CRP & J. Rau, 2002). Europe.

## Asparagus officinalis L.
(*A. officinalis* subsp. *officinalis*)
### Garden Asparagus

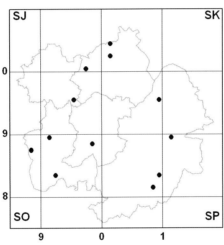

12. Archaeophyte. Perennial herb, with most records for self-sown plants or relics of former cultivation in neglected and overgrown allotment plots. Also rarely as isolated plants, on road verges and post-industrial land.

## Ruscus aculeatus L.
### Butcher's-broom
3. Native; an introduction in B&BC. Evergreen, rhizomatous shrub. Old woodland S of High Haden, Halesowen (SO965855, PWS, 1998); Penn Hall Wood (SO891955, PWS & T. Oki, 2000); amenity woodland planting, Bordesley Green Allotments (SP108871, ICT, 2008).

## Yucca gloriosa L.
(*Yucca recurvifolia* Salisb.)
### Spanish-dagger
1. Neophyte. Surviving in rough grassland, former Moat Farm site, Pinewoods, Woodgate Valley Country Park (SO991820, JJD, 2003). May have been lost in the hard winter of 2010–11, as was the case with many garden specimens in B&BC. South-eastern N America.

## 163. COMMELINACEAE

## Tradescantia virginiana L.
### Spiderwort
4. Neophyte. In paving just outside gardens or surviving from original garden plantings on post-housing sites. Edgbaston (SP0686, MWP, 2000); Pedmore (SO910819, JJD, 2003); Kingstanding (SP083943, MWP, ICT & JaH, 2006); Harborne (SP041828, MWP, ICT & PLR, 2008). N America. Some or all may be hybrids between *T. virginiana* and one or more other species.

## 165. TYPHACEAE

## Sparganium erectum L.
### Branched Bur-reed

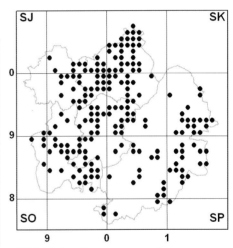

*202. Native. Emergent aquatic rhizomatous perennial herb, common in the margins of canals, ponds and to some extent by rivers and streams, rooted in base- and nutrient-rich muds. The map suggests canals are very important for this species. Ass: *Alisma plantago-aquatica*, *Glyceria maxima*, *Rumex hydrolapathum*, *Typha latifolia*.

Most recorders have not distinguished subspecies but **subsp. erectum** has been recorded in our parts of vc. 39 and vc. 38 and is probably the commonest subspecies. There are recent records for **subsp. neglectum** (Beeby) K. Richt. in the Walsall canals (e.g. SJ989016, JEH, 2006), and seven records (four within our recording period) in our part of vc. 37, in the complete range of habitats. JEH has recently recorded subsp. *oocarpum* (Čelak.) Domin., in the Anglesey Branch Canal (SK0407, 2010), just outside our area.

### *Sparganium emersum* Rehmann
### Unbranched Bur-reed

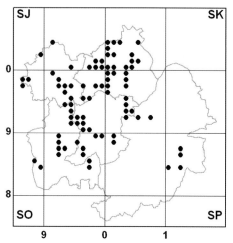

*83. Native. Aquatic rhizomatous herbaceous perennial. In our area a canal plant, growing in nutrient- and base-rich conditions in deeper water than *Sparganium erectum* and often producing floating leaves without flowering stems right across the canal where the water is reasonably clear. Seems to be scarcer in the busiest canals, and in many of the town centre parts and the B'ham canals as a whole. There are 1971 records from Sutton Park (SP0998, SP1096, in edges of pools). Ass: none or *Alisma plantago-aquatica, Glyceria maxima, Nuphar lutea*.

### *Typha latifolia* L.
### Bulrush, Greater Reedmace

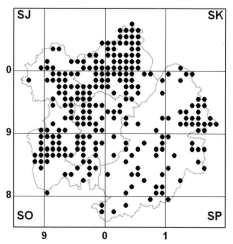

*259. Native. Emergent aquatic rhizomatous perennial, very common as a reedswamp plant, particularly in canals but everywhere in reliably wet, usually nutrient- and base-rich or even nutrient-polluted shallow water or bare mud situations (e.g. at sewage works), tolerant of disturbance and rapidly appearing from seed or rhizome fragments in new or disturbed wetlands, but intolerant of cutting and grazing. Quite invasive, but

often unwisely introduced in habitat creation schemes. Commoner in the Black Country than in B'ham. Ass: either growing alone or with *Glyceria maxima, Salix cinerea, Solanum dulcamara, Sparganium erectum*.

### *Typha × glauca* Godr.
(*T. latifolia × T. angustifolia*)
3. Native. Recorded twice in the River Cole area, one in a marsh in waste land E of Cole Hall Lane (SP147881, CBW, 1997) and another in a pond on the old course of the River Cole N of Kitts Green (SP154879, CBW, 1997), both without *Typha angustifolia*. Bracebridge Pool, Sutton Park, with *T. angustifolia* and *Menyanthes trifoliata* (SP098982, JWP, MWP & ICT, 2008).

### *Typha angustifolia* L.
### Lesser Bulrush, Lesser Reedmace

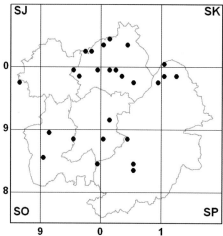

26. Native. Emergent aquatic rhizomatous perennial herb. Not common, forming often single-species reedswamps usually on fairly nutrient- and base-rich but not overly nutrient-polluted substrates and waters, in shallow to quite deep water where it can form semi-floating mats. Occasionally in canals but mostly in ponds, many of them ornamental and park ponds where it may well have been introduced. A record for SO9098 is a definite introduction. Quite widespread and well-established in several Sutton Park lakes, including the relatively base- and nutrient-poor Bracebridge Pool. Ass: *Acorus calamus, Carex paniculata, Juncus effusus, Menyanthes trifoliata, Persicaria amphibia, Ranunculus lingua, Solanum dulcamara*.

### 168. JUNCACEAE

### *Juncus subnodulosus* Schrank
### Blunt-flowered Rush
2. Native. There are old unconfirmed records of this perennial herb of calcareous mires from Pelsall Common (SK022045) and Radley's Walk (SP152239) but the

two current records in our area seem to be recent deliberate or accidental introductions: in a shallow pool on a large area of dumped rubble at Warley Woods (SP0086, ICT & EVJC, 2008) and forming a rush-marsh at the edge of two pools at Tansey Green (SO910899, ICT & B. Marsh, 2008).

### *Juncus articulatus* L.
### Jointed Rush

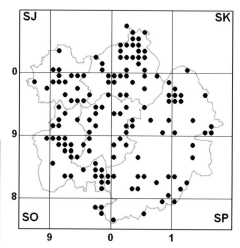

*144. Native. Rhizomatous perennial herb; a colonist of bare places in wet grasslands and mires, persisting in more closed, rush-dominated vegetation, also in bare mud around pools, by canals and in ditches. Mostly in base- and nutrient-medium situations, water table usually fluctuating but sites rarely drying out, common both in long-established and recently formed wetlands. Ass: *Agrostis stolonifera, Holcus lanatus, Isolepis setacea, Juncus effusus*.

### *Juncus × surrejanus* Druce ex Stace & Lambinon
(*J. articulatus × J. acutiflorus*)
4. Native. Recorded from mires in Sutton Park: (SP103954, ICT, MWP & JaH, 2005; SP096981, ICT & MWP, 2005; SP093962, ICT, MWP & PLR, 2006) and wet grassland at Kings Hayes Farm, Walsall (SK054027, ICT, 2008), but it is difficult to distinguish from the parent species, with which it often grows. Sometimes an 'acutiflorus/articulatus aggregate' has been recorded and the hybrid may be quite widespread in our area.

### *Juncus acutiflorus* Ehrh. ex Hoffm.
### Sharp-flowered Rush
*76. Native. Ax. Rhizomatous perennial herb often forming extensive stands in slightly flushed mires in heathland and old wet pastures, but also encountered, usually as much smaller patches or individual plants, in much more recent or disturbed, developing wetlands. Usually on peaty soils which are never nutrient-rich, usually

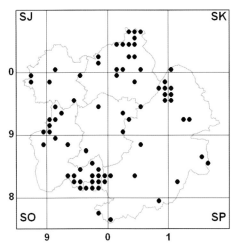

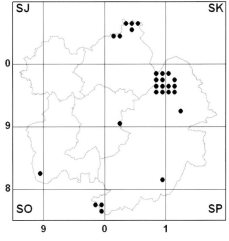

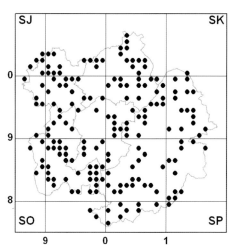

only slightly base-enriched and reliably wet although with a fluctuating water table; persisting into light shade. Ass: *Deschampsia cespitosa, Galium palustre, Juncus articulatus, Juncus conglomeratus, Juncus effusus, Molinia caerulea, Silene flos-cuculi.*

### Juncus bulbosus L.
### Bulbous Rush

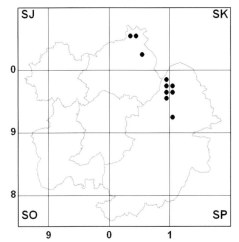

10. Native. Ax. Perennial herb recorded from the mires of Sutton where it is most abundant on bare areas and in short, open communities on reliably wet, nutrient- and base-poor peat. Also from wet pasture in Walsall. The plant from SP1092 was growing as a weed in a plant pot in a garden centre. The submerged aquatic variant does not seem to occur in B&BC. Subsp. *kochii* (F.W. Schultz) Reichg. has not been distinguished from subsp. *bulbosus* by our recorders. There is also a tetrad record: SP09E. Ass: *Carex echinata, Dryopteris carthusiana, Comarum palustre, Valeriana dioica, Veronica beccabunga.*

### Juncus squarrosus L.
### Heath Rush
*27. Native. Ax. A fairly uncommon perennial herb from wet or seasonally

wet areas in heaths on very nutrient-poor and very base-poor peats and gravels. Generally in areas kept open or short-turved by grazing or trampling. Abundant in Sutton Park, frequent on Pelsall Common, Brownhills Common and on Rubery and Rednal Hills, but often just one or two plants in quite tiny remnant fragments of suitable heath in commons, parks etc. Ass: *Calluna vulgaris, Erica tetralix, Molinia caerulea, Nardus stricta.*

### Juncus tenuis Willd.
### Slender Rush

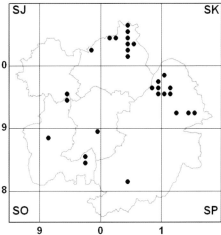

28. Neophyte. A perennial herb, increasingly commonly colonising semi-natural heathland, acid to neutral grassland, and damp places on canal towpaths, blast-furnace slag and coal spoil, on fairly or very base- and nutrient-poor soils, particularly along paths and similar moderately disturbed places. N & S America. Ass: *Festuca rubra, Juncus effusus, Juncus inflexus.*

### Juncus bufonius L.
### Toad Rush
*187. Native. A common short-lived annual colonist of bare mud, usually fairly base- and nutrient-rich, from the draw-down

zones of ponds to puddles by paths and tracks, in both built-up and more semi-natural situations throughout B&BC. Recorders have mostly not distinguished *J. bufonius* from *J. foliosus* Desf. or *J. ranarius* Songeon & E.P. Perrier (*J. ambiguus* Guss.) but there are no specific records of the latter two species. Ass: *Agrostis stolonifera, Gnaphalium uliginosum, Poa annua.*

### Juncus inflexus L.
### Hard rush

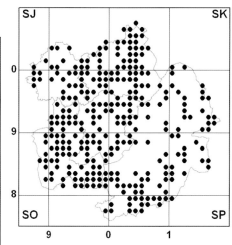

*306. Native. Densely tufted rhizomatous perennial herb from wet places in pastures, canal and stream banks, quarry floors, spoil tips, waterlogged areas on building sites. On nutrient-poor to -rich, base medium to rich, usually clay soils, tolerant of trampling and grazing but not shade. Frequent in the Black Country, less so in the urban core of B'ham. The hybrid with *Juncus effusus* has not been recorded. Ass: *Agrostis stolonifera, Carex hirta, Dactylorhiza fuchsii, Juncus conglomeratus, Juncus effusus.*

### Juncus effusus L.
### Soft-rush
*421. Native. Common and widespread densely tufted rhizomatous herb, often abundant or dominant in winter-flooded

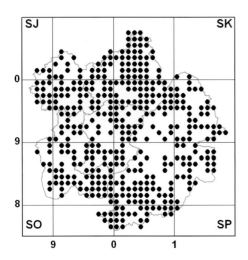

pastures and other wet grassy places recovering from disturbance, water margins, quarry bottoms, wet heaths, wet areas on waste land, and even, as isolated plants, in gardens and allotments, presumably as a relic of mulching with peat or the use of peat-based composts. Characteristic of fluctuating water tables, soils usually fairly heavy, base- and nutrient-poor to -medium. Tolerant of some trampling and disturbance and avoided by grazing stock. Ass: *Agrostis stolonifera*, *Deschampsia cespitosa*, *Holcus lanatus*, *Juncus conglomeratus*, *Ranunculus repens*.

### *Juncus conglomeratus* L.
### Compact Rush

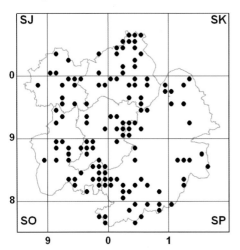

*132. Native. A densely tufted rhizomatous herb from a similar range of habitats to *Juncus effusus*, and often growing with it, but less common and more characteristic of rather base- and nutrient-poor wet grassland situations and possibly more confined to less built-up areas. Nevertheless it can sometimes be found in secondary mires developing on post-industrial sites. Ass: *Agrostis stolonifera*, *Carex nigra*, *Galium palustre*, *Holcus lanatus*, *Juncus acutiflorus*, *Juncus effusus*, *Molinia caerulea*.

### *Luzula forsteri* (Sm.) DC.
### Southern Wood-rush

0. Native. Shortly rhizomatous perennial of woodlands and other moist, sheltered places, at its northern limit here. Reported from just E of Moseley New Pool, Swanshurst Park (SP093816, P.G. Garner, 1993), not seen in present survey.

### *Luzula pilosa* (L.) Willd.
### Hairy Wood-rush

5. Native. Ax. A shortly rhizomatous tufted perennial, uncommon in B&BC, in open vegetation or bare surfaces on shady banks, typically above streams in old dingle woods, on moist soils of intermediate nutrient status and fairly poor to medium base status. Steep-sided stream valley, Lutley Gutter (SO943828, ST, 1998, also SP941823, WAT, 1990); Sutton Park (SP1095, SPG, 1998, seen again, 2004, also recorded from SP1196 by Readett in 1971); woodland bank, Rough Wood (SJ983010–SJ983009, ICT, MWP, SMP, AB & JaH, 2007). Also in a ruderal situation: established all along the border of a front garden – Vernon Avenue, Hamstead (SP047918, MWP, 2008). There are also some slightly older records from several dingles in the SW periphery of Dudley: Ham Dingle (SO916826, ST, 1986, also seen by WAT in 1990); Wollescote Dingle (SO923830, WAT, 1990), Illey Brook Dingle (SO9781, WAT, 1988); Breaches Dingle, the Leasowes (SO978837, WAT, 1990) and Cotwall End Dingle (SO912924, ST, 1986).

### *Luzula sylvatica* (Huds.) Gaudin
### Great Wood-rush

3. Native. Rhizomatous, densely tufted perennial herb. Found in UK in damp, acid, shaded habitats in woodland and moorland, it has a single old woodland station in B&BC at Ham Dingle, Dudley where it grows on the steep-sided bank in the northern arm of the dingle (SO916826, most recently seen in 1996, by CRP & A. Stanneveldt). Otherwise only established as an escape or introduction in gardens, where it is quite capable of maintaining itself vigorously: the B'ham Centre of the Earth (SP045881, CRP & AS, 1996); B'ham EcoPark (SP116860, MWP & JaH, 2004).

### *Luzula campestris* (L.) DC.
### Field Wood-rush

*218. Native. Shortly rhizomatous perennial, quite common throughout in garden lawns (especially those made from laid turf) and mown or grazed amenity grassland and pasture generally, on well-drained, dry to moist soils of average or low base status and quite low nutrient status. Probably under-recorded due to its

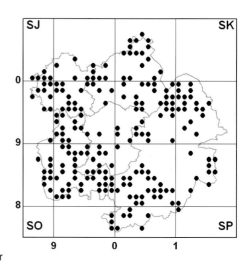

early flowering but may be less common in central urban areas. Ass: *Agrostis capillaris*, *Anthoxanthum odoratum*, *Bellis perennis*, *Festuca ovina*, *Festuca rubra*, *Hypochaeris radicata*, *Plantago lanceolata*.

### *Luzula multiflora* (Ehrh.) Lej.
### Heath Wood-rush

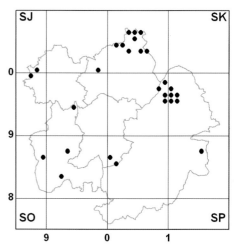

*28. Native. Ax. Tufted perennial, typically on reliably moist, base- and nutrient-poor peaty soils in mire, heathland and acid grassland, but also recorded from some less extremely acid grassland or woodland margin situations. Quite common in Sutton Park and Pelsall Common, where **subsp. congesta** (Thuill.) Arcang. is typical, and with scattered records elsewhere. There are some further, older records in vc. 37, notably from Rubery Hill (SO9977, JJD, 1992), but also from apparently secondary sites e.g. on an old tip on Mucklow Hill (SO9784, JJD, 1988). Ass: *Calluna vulgaris*, *Deschampsia flexuosa*, *Erica tetralix*, *Festuca filiformis*, *Juncus effusus*, *Molinia caerulea*, *Nardus stricta*.

### 169. CYPERACEAE

### *Eriophorum angustifolium* Honck.
### Common Cottongrass

11. Native. Ax. Long-rhizomatous perennial,

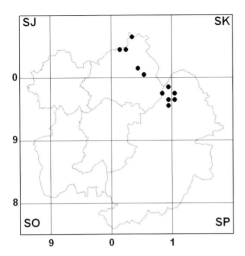

still quite widespread at Sutton Park, although apparently in fewer 1km squares than in the 1970s (eleven in Readett 1971) and at a very limited number of heathland sites in Walsall: Pelsall Common, Brownhills Common, Aldridge Station, Stubbers Green SSSI. Not recorded at Ketley Quarry (SO896888) or Turners Hill (SO908919) in Dudley where it was found in the 1980s. A plant of reliably wet, base- and nutrient-deficient, acid peaty mires in heathland, where it will colonise bare peat via its extensive rhizome system and persist in closed vegetation, even if the substrate becomes slightly less impoverished. At Stubbers Green it has colonised the margins of a subsidence pool, invading a moribund *Typha latifolia* reedswamp. Ass: *Calluna vulgaris*, *Eriophorum vaginatum*, *Hydrocotyle vulgaris*, *Molinia caerulea*, *Sphagnum* spp., *Vaccinium oxycoccos*.

### *Eriophorum vaginatum* L.
### Hare's-tail Cottongrass

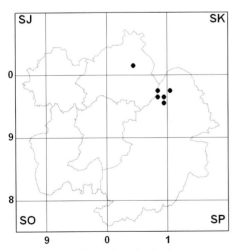

6. Native. Ax. Densely tufted, often tussock-forming, shortly rhizomatous perennial, seen mainly in Sutton Park in the present survey: Bracebridge and Blackroot Pool areas (SP1097, MWP & ICT, 2005); Longmoor Pool valley (SP092956,

MWP & ICT, 2005 & SP091965, MWP, PLR & ICT, 2006); damp heathland (SP087972, MWP, ICT & JaH, 2005); (SP086963, BL, 2010) and in fewer squares than in the 1970s (nine in Readett 1971) although one or two of the stands are quite extensive. Also recorded once in Stubbers Green 'bog' in Aldridge (SK046016, DH, 1996). A plant of damp or wet, base- and nutrient-deficient peaty mires in heathland, like *E. angustifolium*, but generally in relatively closed communities and not a colonist of bare peat. Ass: *Calluna vulgaris*, *Eriophorum angustifolium*, *Hydrocotyle vulgaris*, *Juncus effusus*, *Molinia caerulea*, *Sphagnum* spp., *Vaccinium oxycoccos*.

### *Trichophorum germanicum* Palla
(*T. cespitosum* (L.) Hartm subsp. *germanicum* (Palla) Hegi)
### Deergrass

0. Native. Recorded by Readett (1971) as present in SP0996, SP0997 and SP0998 at Sutton Park; not found in the present study.

### *Bolboschoenus maritimus* (L.) Palla
### Sea Club-rush

1. Native. Large perennial, known only from the main (coal-mining subsidence?) pool at Clayhanger SSSI, where it forms a substantial part of the reedswamp community which becomes exposed mud for much of the summer (SK034044, BRF, 1986, still frequent, 2006). Predominantly a plant of brackish coastal habitats it has a more limited inland distribution in water margins, presumably introduced by migrating birds. Clayhanger is not known to be saline; the mud is quite nutrient- and base-rich. Ass: *Hippuris vulgaris*, *Schoenoplectus lacustris*, *Typha latifolia*, and (latterly) *Crassula helmsii*.

### *Scirpus sylvaticus* L.
### Wood Club-rush

5. Native. Ax. Rhizomatous perennial, in a few widely scattered waterside wetlands, usually wooded, on deep, fairly base- and nutrient-rich silts. Goscote Valley (SK019022, PWS, TM & D. Jones, 2002); Buckpool Valley (SO899883, E. McKay, 1998); wetland S of Bourne Brook (SP042832, CRP, 1998, probably now lost); Edgbaston Pool, where it was first recorded by D.A. Cadbury in 1935 (refound at SP053843, ICT, T. Holland, PC & M. Kingsbury, 2009); Coldbath Pool (SP087818, JWP, 1996). It is also just outside our area at Northycote Farm (SJ9303). Older records from Walsall at the Duckery, Great Barr Park (SP051959, CW, 1990) and Aldridge Station (SK053005, CW, 1989) and from B'ham at Fox Hollies (SP128824, CBW, 1994) and

▲ *Juncus conglomeratus*

▲ *Eriophorum angustifolium*

E of the River Cole at Stetchford (SP124874, CBW, 1989) have not been refound. Ass: *Caltha palustris, Cardamine amara, Chrysosplenium oppositifolium, Filipendula ulmaria, Solanum dulcamara, Urtica dioica.*

### *Schoenoplectus lacustris* (L.) Palla
**Common Club-rush**

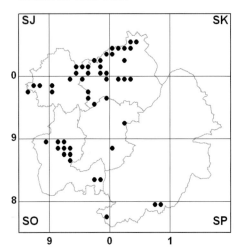

*50. Native. Large perennial, typically forming reedswamps or isolated clumps in quite deep, fairly base- and nutrient-rich, still or slowly moving waters, rooting in silt and mud. Sometimes persisting in less permanent water. Quite common in the canals and pools of the N and W, but much scarcer in B'ham. Sinker (1985) says it is susceptible to grazing, especially by Canada Geese – we have plenty of those in the Black Country! Ass: *Glyceria maxima, Typha latifolia*, but often in pure stands.

### *Schoenoplectus tabernaemontani*
(C.C. Gmel.) Palla
**Grey Club-rush**

2. Native. Large perennial with similar habitats to *Schoenoplectus lacustris*, but usually on the landward side of that species in shallower water, and much rarer. Currently the only reliable spontaneous record is from Wood Farm in Walsall (SJ985018, ICT, MWP, JaH, SMP & AB, 2007) where it forms part of the reedswamp community along the southern side of a pool beneath electricity pylons. There is a good stand in two quarry pools at Tansey Green, Pensnett (SO910899, ICT & B. Marsh, 2008) but there it appears to be a deliberate landscaping introduction. It was also recorded from the pool at Walsall Power Station (SO997999, J. Andrews, 1987; not seen there in 2006). Ass: *Eleocharis palustris, Glyceria maxima, Mentha aquatica, Rumex hydrolapathum, Typha latifolia.*

### *Eleocharis palustris* (L.) Roem. & Schult.
**Common Spike-rush**

*68. Native. Ax. Densely tufted perennial,

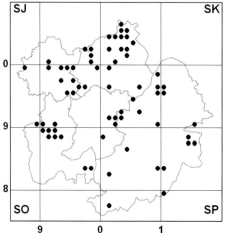

widespread but clearly not well-adapted to the built-up areas. In still, shallow water, typically in the margins of ponds and often forming extensive single-species stands, but also in marshes and reliably wet grasslands which are only sometimes quite species-rich. Especially on clayey or muddy substrates and discouraged by both base-poor and nutrient-rich conditions. Not persisting in shade and easily swamped by more bulky and taller water margin species, it is perhaps most typical of early stages in the colonisation of shallow pools for example in quarries and claypits and on coal spoil tips. Ass: *Agrostis stolonifera, Cardamine pratensis, Galium palustre, Juncus articulatus, Myosotis laxa.*

Most recorders have not distinguished the two subspecies, **subsp. *palustris*** and **subsp. *vulgaris*** Walters, but both were recorded as present in Sutton Park by Readett (1971).

### *Eleocharis quinqueflora* (Hartmann) O. Schwarz
**Few-flowered Spike-rush**

2. Native. Ax. Tufted perennial, from two monads in Sutton Park only: on reliably wet peat in acid but slightly base-flushed mires, Longmoor Valley (most recently SP092963, ICT, MWP & PLR, 2006) and Little Bracebridge Pool (most recently SP094983, ICT & MWP, 2005). There are older records for the intervening square SP0997 (Bagnall, 1872). Ass: *Anagallis tenella, Briza media, Carex hostiana, Carex panicea, Cirsium dissectum, Dactylorhiza fuchsii, Pedicularis palustris, Pinguicula vulgaris, Triglochin palustris.*

### *Eleocharis acicularis* (L.) Roem. & Schult.
**Needle Spike-rush**

0. Native. Sutton Park (SP0997, Bagnall 1876); also reported from the Park in 1987 by J.C. Bowra. Not seen in present study.

### *Isolepis setacea* (L.) R. Br.
**Bristle Club-rush**

22. Native. Ax. Small perennial, with

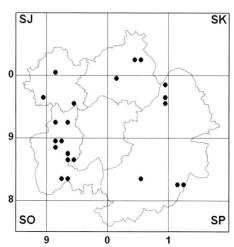

scattered records, mostly in open places in marsh or wet pasture or water margins of some age, but also a few records from similar but clearly secondary damp places in a quarry, a housing demolition site and a graveyard. A tiny plant, easily overlooked and probably under-recorded, it colonises bare mud and persists in short, open vegetation on relatively nutrient-poor and base-neutral damp or water-retaining peats and clays. Ass: *Agrostis stolonifera, Carex leporina, Dactylorhiza praetermissa, Galium uliginosum, Hydrocotyle vulgaris, Juncus effusus, Myosotis laxa, Silene flos-cuculi.*

### *Eleogiton fluitans* (L.) Link
**Floating Club-rush**

1. Native. Ax. Aquatic stoloniferous perennial, found in quantity in an ephemeral shallow pool, and a more permanent one close by, in old pasture W of Brownhills Common (SK032061 & SK033064, ICT & SAHA, 2010); it was also recorded in 1989 in a pool at the head of Wood Brook, Lodge Hill B'ham (in four monads: SP0281, SP0282, SP0381, SP0382, CBW, 1989, gone by 1997) and in 1990 in Friar Pool, Pelsall Common, Walsall (SK020045, JPM, 1990). Also old record from Sutton Park (SP0997, Bagnall, 1876). A species of clean, clear, nutrient- and base-poor water. Ass: *Apium inundatum, Lythrum portula, Ranunculus* subgenus *Batrachium.*

### *Cyperus longus* L.
**Galingale**

5. Native; but an introduction in our area. NT and Nationally Scarce as a native. Shortly rhizomatous perennial, with a few scattered records, usually but not always a clear introduction. It can be very persistent. By ponds: West Smethwick Park (SP004888, CBW, 1997); S of Chinn Brook (SP087799, JJD, 2000); Milking Bank Estate (SO922906, APD, 2004). By canals: silted-up former Halesowen Arm (SO973834, ST, 1997); Cocks Moors BMX Track pond (SP087799, CRP, 2002, possibly an

introduction). One record from a relatively dry garden situation at the foot of a wall, Tyburn Road (SO969973, MWP, 2004).

### Cyperus eragrostis Lam.
### Pale Galingale
3. Neophyte. Very shortly rhizomatous perennial with invasive potential. Wetland associated with the derelict Aldridge Railway Station (SK053005, DH, 2003); scattered as a pathside and also to some extent as a plot weed at a rather damp allotments site: Kent Road Allotments, Halesowen (SO981846, ICT & L. Worledge, 2008); one plant from grassed-over plot at Harborne Lane Allotments (SP040831, MWP & PWS, 2008). Tropical America.

### Cladium mariscus (L.) Pohl
### Great Fen-sedge
0. Native. Recorded by A.D. Skelding in 1978 in Willow carr by the River Cole at the Ackers, Tyseley (SP104843). Not seen in present survey.

### Rhynchospora alba (L.) Vahl
### White Beak-sedge
0. Native. Very old records from Moseley Common (SP0982, M.A. Beilby, 1836); B'ham Heath (SP08, W. Withering, 1787).

### Carex paniculata L.
### Greater Tussock-sedge

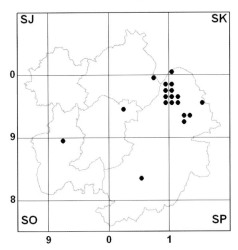

19. Native. Ax. Tussock-forming perennial, very scarce away from the NE. Reduced to a few moribund non-flowering tussocks in the alder carr S of Edgbaston Pool (SP055838, ICT, PC, M. Kingsbury & T. Holland, 2009), where it had been recorded by D.A. Cadbury in 1935. In our area it typically forms its spectacular tussocks in standing water over peaty substrates in the margins of large pools, forming part of the process of the succession to Willow and Alder woodland from open water. It will also grow along slow-moving streams. Many of our sites are now wooded, and in

a few places it seems to have persisted in drying out marshes. All these situations are to be seen in Sutton Park, and it seems equally happy there both in the more base- and nutrient-enriched Longmoor Pool and in the much more acid mires between the two Bracebridge Pools, where it forms extensive stands in *Betula pubescens* woodlands. Ass: *Alnus glutinosa, Betula pubescens, Carex pseudocyperus, Dryopteris dilatata, Hydrocotyle vulgaris, Iris pseudacorus, Salix cinerea, Solanum dulcamara, Typha angustifolia, Sphagnum* spp.

### Carex diandra Schrank
### Lesser Tussock-sedge
2. Native. NT. Perennial. A species of moderately base-rich wet mires previously recorded from two squares in Sutton Park: SP0997 (Bagnall, 1869) and locally frequent in a bog in SP0996 (Readett, 1971). It is still present in several patches, each several metres across, in the base-flushed mire N of Longmoor Pool (SP093959 & SP093960, T. Holland, conf. ICT, MWP & P. Coxhead, 2012). Ass: *Anthoxanthum odoratum, Comarum palustre, Carex flacca, Carex panicea, Carex rostrata, Galium uliginosum, Menyanthes trifoliata, Parnassia palustris, Silene flos-cuculi, Succisa pratensis, Triglochin palustris, Valeriana dioica.*

### Carex otrubae Podp.
### False Fox-sedge

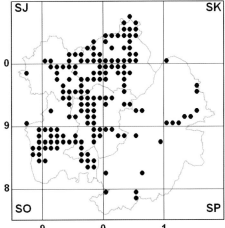

*163. Native. A member of the canal margin community, usually just out of the water. Also in quarries and along ditches in ill-drained pastures and post-industrial sites, usually on clay soils of intermediate base and nutrient status. Quite common in the Black Country, much scarcer in B'ham. Ass: *Deschampsia flexuosa, Juncus effusus, Juncus inflexus, Scutellaria galericulata.*

### Carex spicata Huds.
### Spiked Sedge
31. Native. Densely tufted perennial,

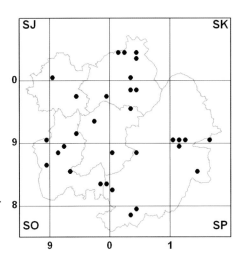

throughout, but quite thinly spread, in a variety of habitats, but mostly slightly damp rough grass or open grassland, including canal towpaths, road verges, abandoned railway tracks, in open or semi-shaded situations on soils of intermediate base and nutrient status. Ass: *Agrostis stolonifera, Alopecurus pratensis, Festuca rubra.*

### Carex muricata L.
### subsp. pairae (F.W. Schultz) Čelak.
(*C. muricata* L. subsp. *lamprocarpa* (Wallr.) Čelak.)
### Prickly Sedge

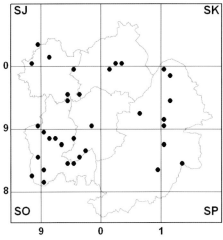

34. Native. Densely to fairly laxly tufted perennial, widely but thinly spread in B&BC, in a wide range of usually secondary situations including dry road and railway verges, churchyards, heathland margins and even marshes, occasionally but not typically in semi-shade, on moderately acid and nutrient-poor soils. Ass: *Agrostis capillaris, Arrenatherum elatius, Carex leporina, Festuca rubra, Juncus effusus, Vicia hirsuta.*

### Carex divulsa Stokes
### Grey Sedge
1. Native. The member of the *muricata* group most associated with disturbed, even cultivated situations, it was recorded on a grassy bank by the A38 at Northfield

(SP029806, CBW, 1996) also an old record at Water Orton sidings, probably just outside our area (SP172914, HHF, 1973). Our plant is **subsp.** *divulsa*.

## Carex arenaria L.
### Sand Sedge

0. Native, but introduced in B&BC. This long-rhizomatous perennial of maritime dunes was recorded twice here in the 1980s: on post-industrial land (former Triplex Lloyd site) close to the railway S of Junction 9 on the M6 at Wood Green Wednesbury (SO996965, C. Wilkinson & CRP, 1989), site now developed but material was dug up and moved to a site nearby but probably lost to scrub invasion. Also Bushbury railway sidings (SJ918019, C. Wilkinson, 1989), seen again in 1992 and 1994, site now inaccessible and repeatedly used for storing materials for railway track maintenance. Ass: *Blackstonia perfoliata, Centaurium erythraea, Cynodon dactylon, Erigeron acris, Pimpinella saxifraga*.

## Carex disticha Huds.
### Brown Sedge

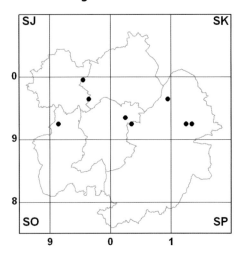

8. Native. Ax. Long-rhizomatous perennial, most of the records are from marshy areas in old grassland along stream valleys in relatively base-rich conditions but moderate nutrient status. A couple of records are from marshes by smaller ponds. Readett (1971) listed it for Sutton Park in bog and marsh in SP0998 & SP1095 where it was not seen in the present study. There is also a modern tetrad record for SO99A. Ass: *Alopecurus geniculatus, Filipendula ulmaria, Galium palustre, Silene flos-cuculi*.

## Carex remota L.
### Remote Sedge

*90. Native. Ax. Densely tufted perennial, typically in isolated tussocks in old deciduous woodland, usually on otherwise bare consolidated mud at the edge of streams and around shady ponds, on

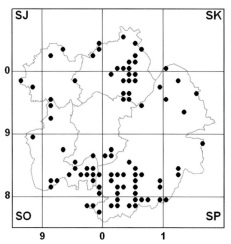

wet or moist soils which are not very acid or nutrient-rich. Very persistent in such places in the face of distubance but rarely in purely secondary sites and generally not common in built-up areas. Forms a very extensive single-species stand under willows NW of Edgbaston Pool (SP053843). Ass: *Cardamine flexuosa, Carex sylvatica, Chrysosplenium oppositifolium, Deschampsia cespitosa, Ficaria verna*.

## Carex leporina L.
(*Carex ovalis* Gooden.)
### Oval Sedge

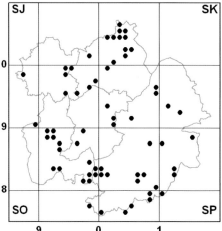

*65. Native. Densely tufted perennial, not uncommon in wet, often impeded drainage areas in grasslands, rush-dominated marshes and around ponds and along canals, but also sometimes in quite dry heathland. Mostly in remnants of unimproved farmland, but also in quite a few more recent sites in quarries and other post-industrial sites especially where they are of some age and subject to grazing and trampling by stock but rare in built-up areas. Soils reliably wet or with fluctuating water table, nutrient and base-poor to -medium. Also tetrad SO99A. Ass: *Agrostis stolonifera, Carex flacca, Carex panicea, Deschampsia cespitosa, Juncus effusus, Juncus inflexus*.

## Carex echinata Murray
### Star Sedge

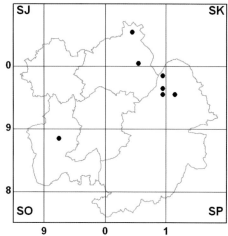

7. Native. Ax. This tufted perennial of base- and nutrient-poor mires in heathland is probably close to extinction in B&BC. Recorded as frequent in much of Sutton Park (6 monads) by Cadbury *et al.* (1971), is still present there but appears less common: mire above Longmoor Pool (SP093958 & SP092964, MWP, ICT, PLR & JaH, 2005 & 2006); wet scrub by Wyndley Pool (SP111958, MWP, JaH & ICT, 2005); locally common in boggy woodland clearings with base enriched acid flushes (SP096981, MWP & ICT, 2005); mire by Little Bracebridge Pool (SP095982, AB, 2007). Also a tiny population in the acid mire on Clayhanger Common (SK044052, ICT, 2008) and reported from close to the *Eriophorum angustifolium* mire at Aldridge Railway Station (SK053005, M. Robinson & H. Ball, 2007, seen again 2008). Also a record from Fens Pools (SO920887, PN & JVT, 2004). There is also an older record from the W bank of the B'ham Level Canal, Smethwick, in acid grassland with *Vaccinium vitis-idaea*, in a ditch at the base of the slope with cushions of *Sphagnum* moss (SP017890, TCH & CRP, 1987). Ass: *Anagallis tenella, Carex demissa, Carex nigra, Carex panicea, Eleocharis palustris, Dryopteris carthusiana, Juncus bulbosus, Molinia caerulea, Silene flos-cuculi, Triglochin palustris, Valeriana dioica*.

## Carex dioica L.
### Dioecious Sedge

1. Native. Ax. This tiny rhizomatous perennial sedge of slightly base-enriched flushes in heathland was recorded (as very rare) in Sutton Park from SP0995, SP0996 and SP0998 in Cadbury et al. (1971), and from SP0997 in 1872. Recently only seen (both male and female plants) in the mires above Longmoor Pool, both sides of the stream (SP093960 &SP093963, J. Bailey, ICT, B. Opara, C. Tinstell, N. Crowley, D. Mattley, A. Freeman & C. Tregaskes, 2011).

## Carex canescens L.
(*Carex curta* Gooden.)
**White Sedge**
2. Native. Ax. Shortly rhizomatous perennial of base- and nutrient-poor mires, usually in part shade. Currently only at Sutton Park, where it grows in the mire by Longmoor Pool (SP093959, MWP & ICT, 2005, also seen at SP094958 in 2011) and frequent in *Sphagnum* lawns in wet birch woodland and pool margins between Bracebridge Pool and Little Bracebridge Pool (SP097982, MWP, ICT & JWP, 2008). Previously recorded on Brownhills Common (SK034060, M.E. Evans & M.J. D'Oyly, 1983), not seen there in the present survey. Ass: *Molinia caerulea*, *Sphagnum* spp.

## Carex hirta L.
**Hairy Sedge**

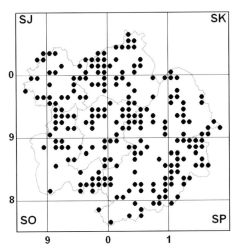

*227. Native. Far-creeping rhizomatous perennial, frequent in a wide range of under-managed grassy situations: heathland, marshy grassland (usually rank and often disturbed and trampled), rough grass on road verges and post-industrial sites, even football pitches and margins of allotments. Soil usually at least slightly damp, not very base-poor and usually fairly nutrient-rich. Ass: *Alopecurus pratensis*, *Arrhenatherum elatius*, *Dactylis glomerata*, *Deschampsia cespitosa*, *Lolium perenne*.

## Carex acutiformis Ehrh.
**Lesser Pond-sedge**
*80. Native. Ax. Tufted perennial with far-creeping rhizomes, quite frequent, and often abundant or dominant, in reedswamp by canals and around lakes and pools, in reliably wet hollows and ditches in flood-plain grasslands, on clay or peat substrates of intermediate or fairly high fertility and base status. Can stand a little grazing, and will persist in some shade but may fail to flower. Ass: *Epilobium hirsutum*, *Glyceria maxima*,

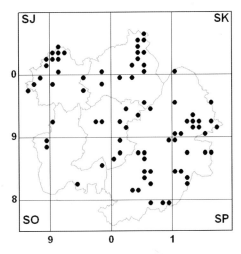

*Iris pseudacorus*, *Juncus effusus*, *Mentha aquatica*, *Sparganium erectum*.

## Carex riparia Curtis
**Greater Pond-sedge**

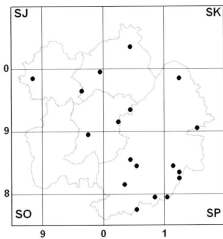

18. Native. Ax. Tufted perennial with far-creeping rhizomes, with only scattered records, mostly in reedswamps by canals or pools, also in ditches, much scarcer than *Carex acutiformis*, occasionally growing with it but more confined to more permanently flooded and deeper water situations and less tolerant of grazing or trampling. Ass: *Carex acutiformis*, *Epilobium hirsutum*, *Glyceria maxima*, *Iris pseudacorus*, *Nymphoides peltata*, *Phragmites australis*, *Ranunculus lingua*, *Sparganium erectum*.

## Carex pseudocyperus L.
**Cyperus Sedge**
37. Native. Ax. Tufted, shortly rhizomatous perennial, abundant along the Wyrley and Essington and Daw End canals in Walsall, and occasional along other canals; around pools, including in fairly shady Alder and Willow woodland by pools and, rarely, in similar places by streams. It grows in the very edge of the bank rather than as a reedswamp species and can also occur in the bare mud of draw-down zones

▲ *Carex disticha*

▲ *Carex echinata*

▲ *Carex pseudocyperus*

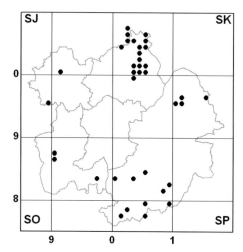

and other bare places in shallow water. Sometimes it occurs as isolated individuals, and it may sometimes operate as a pioneer species. Mostly substrates are nutrient- and base-medium to fairly rich organic muds and clays, but also present in much poorer substrates at Sutton Park. The records for SJ9100 and SO8995 are probably deliberate introductions into artificial ponds. Ass: *Alisma plantago-aquatica, Alnus glutinosa, Carex acutiformis, Carex otrubae, Carex paniculata, Carex pendula, Carex remota, Juncus effusus, Lycopus europaeus, Oenanthe crocata, Rumex conglomeratus, Solanum dulcamara, Typha latifolia.*

## *Carex rostrata* Stokes
## Bottle Sedge

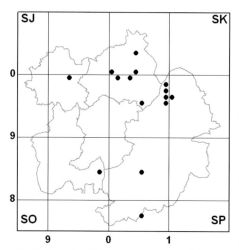

15. Native. Ax. Rhizomatous perennial, uncommon in mires and forming pure reedswamp stands in pools and canals but only on nutrient- and base-poor peaty substrates and in relatively unpolluted waters. Penetrates the urban area via the Wyrley and Essington Canal as far as Heath Town in W'ton (SO9399). Ass: *Acorus calamus, Equisetum fluviatile, Juncus inflexus, Menyanthes trifoliata, Sagittaria sagittifolia, Triglochin palustris.*

## *Carex pendula* Huds.
## Pendulous Sedge

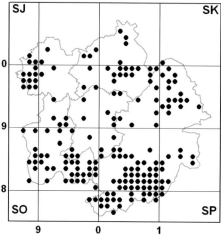

*188. Native, but often escaping from cultivation. Tufted, shortly rhizomatous perennial, not uncommon in flushes and streamsides in old woodlands on base-rich, moderately fertile heavy soils, but also frequently escaping from garden cultivation in residential areas and found in a variety of drier and often less shady positions. It seems to be much more common now as an adventive than in either Edees (1972) or Cadbury *et al.* (1971), although the distribution is still biased towards woodland sites and wooded areas. Ass: *Carex remota, Deschampsia cespitosa, Epilobium hirsutum, Epilobium montanum, Schedonorus giganteus, Urtica dioica.*

## *Carex sylvatica* Huds.
## Wood-sedge

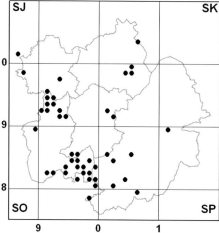

*46. Native. Ax. Tufted, very shortly rhizomatous perennial, from broad-leaved semi-natural woodlands, especially on moister and heavier base-medium to base-rich, moderately fertile soils. Sometimes in the open on limestone, and occasionally isolated individuals in tiny fragments of hedgerows and woodlands. Ass: *Anemone

*nemorosa, Brachypodium sylvaticum, Carex remota, Ficaria verna, Oxalis acetosella, Schedonorus giganteus.*

## *Carex strigosa* Huds.
## Thin-spiked Wood-sedge

2. Native. Ax. Tufted, with short stolons and rhizomes, only two modern sites in broad-leaved semi-natural woodlands: in flushed streamside areas in Ham Dingle (SO914827–SO916826, WAT, 1988, still there in 2005, and recorded from there by W. Mathews in 1881); stream banks in dingle woodland by the River Stour at Corngreaves (SO950849, ST & ICT, 1998). It should be carefully looked for in flushes in other dingle woodlands. There are old records, from Cradley Park (which was E of Lye in SO9384, S of the A458) originally made by W. Scott in 1832, and seen there again in 1909. Also from Bog Meadow Coppice, which was on the Bourne Brook near Harborne (SP0183, H.S. Thompson, 1909). Ass: *Carex pendula, Carex remota, Chrysosplenium oppositifolium, Deschampsia cespitosa.*

## *Carex flacca* Schreb.
## Glaucous Sedge

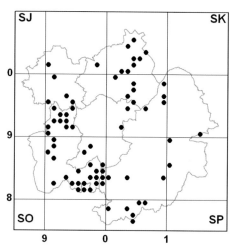

*72. Native. Rhizomatous perennial, not uncommon in a wide range of unshaded, mostly undisturbed grassy or 'sedgy' situations (although we found it completely dominant in a small urban front garden and pavement in Small Heath, SP1085 and it has also been recorded from steelworks spoil), from dry grassland to permanent flushes, but always in base-rich and usually nutrient-poor soils and not persisting in tall or rank vegetation. It may be more dependent on high base status in dry situations and sometimes forms part of the sedge assembly in mires even when only slightly flushed. Ass: *Briza media, Carex demissa, Carex panicea, Festuca ovina, Festuca rubra, Leontodon hispidus, Pilosella officinarum.*

### *Carex panicea* L.
### Carnation Sedge

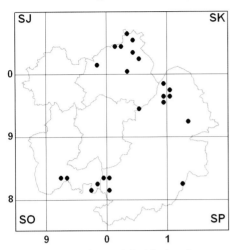

23. Native. Ax. Perennial with shortly creeping rhizomes, not very common, usually found in old, species-rich, open grassland and small-sedge mire communities on damp, slightly flushed nutrient-poor and fairly base-poor organic substrates in the periphery of the conurbation. Quite tolerant of light trampling and grazing. Ass: *Anagallis tenella, Briza media, Carex demissa, Carex hostiana, Cirsium dissectum, Cirsium palustre, Dactylorhiza fuchsii, Danthonia decumbens, Deschampsia cespitosa, Molinia caerulea, Nardus stricta, Pedicularis palustris, Pinguicula vulgaris, Triglochin palustris.*

### *Carex laevigata* Sm.
### Smooth-stalked Sedge

1. Native. Tufted, rhizomatous perennial, one plant in the edge of a drainage gully in quite dense shade in wet woodland close to the eastern edge of Sutton Park between Bracebridge and Blackroot Pools (SP106976, ICT & MWP, 2005). This species was last recorded in Sutton Park by Bagnall (SP0997, 1868). Ass: *Juncus articulatus, Juncus effusus, Ranunculus repens, Sphagnum* spp.

### *Carex binervis* Sm.
### Green-ribbed Sedge

6. Native. Ax. Tufted with short-creeping rhizomes, a plant of base- and nutrient-poor heathland, found in the transition between dry and wet communities. Five monads are from Sutton Park: (SP085963, MWP, ICT & JaH, 2005); (SP096969, CRP, 1999); (SP0998, S.F. Woodward, 1995); heathy grassland (SP100967, MWP, ICT, JaH & EVJC, 2005); shady heathland, track verge (SP110971, ICT, EVJC & SMP, 2005). Readett (1971) only listed it for two, different, squares: SP0997 & SP1097). Also a record from a tiny heathy flush in the Cotwall End valley in Dudley (SO909920, ICT, 2000, seen

again 2004, could not be found in 2009). Ass: *Calluna vulgaris, Erica tetralix, Juncus squarrosus, Molinia caerulea, Nardus stricta.*

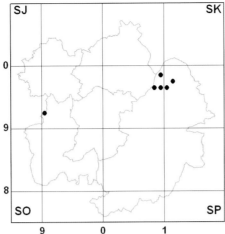

### *Carex hostiana* DC.
### Tawny Sedge

2. Native. Ax. Perennial with short-creeping rhizomes. A plant of nutrient-poor but quite strongly base-flushed mires, it has been currently recorded only in Sutton Park, from the Longmoor Valley (SP093962, ICT, MWP & PLR, 2006) and scattered by Little Bracebridge Pool (SP094983, ICT & MWP, 2005). Readett (1971) listed it for these squares and also for SP0997. There are older, unconfirmed records from Fens Pools (SO917885, ST, 1986) and Lower Meadows, Illey (SO976811, ST & CRP, 1986). Ass: *Anagallis tenella, Briza media, Carex panicea, Carex pulicaris, Cirsium dissectum, Dactylorhiza fuchsii, Eleocharis quinqueflora, Pedicularis palustris, Pinguicula vulgaris, Triglochin palustris.*

### *C. hostiana* × *C. demissa*

1. Native. Ax. Locally frequent with the parents in Longmoor Valley, Sutton Park (SP093962, ICT, MWP & PLR, 2006). Readett (1971) recorded it in SP0998 in 1951.

### *Carex lepidocarpa* Tausch
(*C. viridula* Michx. subsp. *brachyrrhyncha* (Celak.) B. Schmid)
### Long-stalked Yellow-Sedge

0. Native. JJD recorded it in 1988 in a marsh in Woodgate Valley Country Park, but it was not found there in 1992, 1994 or 2001. Also an unconfirmed record from the acid mire on Clayhanger Common (SK045053, DH, 2003).

### *Carex demissa* Hornem
(*C. viridula* subsp. *oedocarpa* (Andersson) B. Schmid)
### Common Yellow-sedge

17. Native. Ax. Fairly densely tufted, shortly rhizomatous perennial, from relatively open or even bare places in flushes in

▲ *Carex pendula*

▲ *Carex panicea*

▲ *Carex demissa*

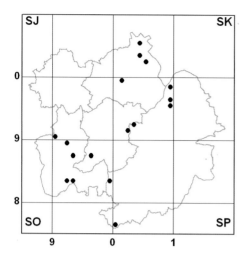

heathland, acid wet grassland, by pools, in quarries, sometimes on clearly secondary sites. Always in reliably wet, slightly base-flushed situations on nutrient-poor and acid peat or bare clay or even in trickles of water on rock surfaces. Seems to be much scarcer in Sutton Park than formerly: Readett (1971) also listed it for SP1096 & SP1195. Ass: *Carex flacca, Carex hirta, Carex nigra, Carex panicea, Cirsium palustre, Dactylorhiza* spp., *Drosera rotundifolia, Eleocharis quinqueflora, Juncus articulatus, Juncus bulbosus*.

### *Carex oederi* Retz.
(*C. viridula* subsp. *viridula*)
**Small-fruited Yellow-sedge**
2. Native. Tufted perennial, quite frequent in a stand of *Juncus inflexus* in a shallow-water temporary pool on clay at an old (Burbury) brickworks site (SP100834, ICT, conf. A.C. Jermy, 1995; SP099836, seen again by JJD, 2004). This population is unlike the typical prostrate lake shore form, being upright and *circa* 30cm tall. JJD described it as c.50 plants plus a few satellite colonies in a small sedge mire community along W side of a made path. There is also a very old record from the Birches, Hagley (SO8981, W. Whitwell, 1904).

### *Carex pallescens* L.
**Pale Sedge**
5. Native. Ax. Very shortly rhizomatous, tufted perennial, a plant in old unimproved marshy grassland on soils with moderate nutrient and base status in the S & W fringes. Marshy grazed margins to pond in field off Foxcote Lane, Lutley (SO937834, ST, 1998); marsh, Woodgate Valley Country Park (SO998834, JJD, 1988, seen 2003); unimproved grassland between Longdales Road and Redhill Road, Hawkesley (SP043769, JJD, 2000); Billesley Common (SP099817, JWP, 1996); in a small shady W-facing flush in the Cotwall End valley (SO9192, AMG, 1999; SO916924,

ICT & AMG, 2000; SO911921, AMG, 2002). There are slightly older records from wet grassland on Lickey Golf Course (SO994765, W. Watson, 1991); edge of Bourn Brook (SP014833, CBW, 1988, last seen 1994). Ass: *Achillea ptarmica, Ajuga reptans, Betonica officinalis, Carex nigra, Carex panicea, Caltha palustris, Hypericum tetrapterum, Silaum silaus, Succisa pratensis*.

### *Carex caryophyllea* Latourr.
**Spring-sedge**
4. Native. Ax. Loosely tufted, shortly rhizomatous perennial, from unimproved grassland on dry, shallow, nutrient-poor but fairly base-rich soils. A few records from old, species-rich grasslands (mostly pastures) in the Lapal and Illey area: Grassland on N side of Lapal Pool, Leasowes (SO980836, JJD, 2003); Manor Abbey Farm valley, scarp slope by stream (SO979823, JJD, 2003); streamside meadow W of Coopers Wood (SO984820, JJD, 2003) and records from the 1980s and early 1990s from SO975811, SO977811 & SO985827. Also a non-flowering plant in an unploughed bank in the grassland at Clayhanger SSSI in Walsall (SK035046, ICT & EVJC, 2006) could have been this. There are Sutton Park (SP0997, SP1097) records from the 1970s, not seen in the present study. Ass: *Agrostis capillaris, Alchemilla filicaulis* subsp. *vestita, Betonica officinalis, Briza media, Conopodium majus, Leontodon hispidus, Pimpinella saxifraga, Potentilla sterilis*.

### *Carex pilulifera* L.
**Pill Sedge**

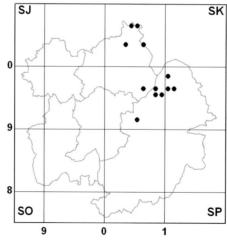

12. Native. Ax. Tufted, shortly rhizomatous perennial, on dry heathland and associated acid grassland, on very base- and nutrient-poor substrates, in open or short vegetation. Often seen by pathsides in heathland. Possibly commoner in Sutton Park than hitherto, it was only recorded in two squares there by Readett (1971). There are also new records for quite small

fragments of heathy vegetation in that general area. Surprisingly not recorded on Pelsall Common, although it is on Brownhills Common and Barr Beacon. It was recorded in heathy vegetation on Stourbridge Golf Course in 1992 (SO898825, WAT). Ass: *Calluna vulgaris, Deschampsia flexuosa, Festuca filiformis, Festuca ovina, Galium saxatile*.

### *Carex acuta* L.
**Slender Tufted-sedge**
3. Native. Ax. Tufted perennial with far-creeping rhizomes, known from two rather base-rich and nutrient-rich small pools associated with an old brickyard in Bilston where it grows in fairly pure stands (SO959977, J.A. Parris, 1988, last recorded 2000). The pools may be at the headwaters of the River Tame. Lost from at least one pool since 1997, trampled to death by anglers. It was also recorded at Stubbers Green SSSI on southern edge of the pool in 1999 (SK0401, Natural England record). Ass: *Agrostis stolonifera, Carex nigra, Deschampsia cespitosa, Eleocharis palustris, Glyceria fluitans, Oenanthe fistulosa, Persicaria amphibia, Typha latifolia*.

### *Carex nigra* (L.) Reichard
**Common Sedge**

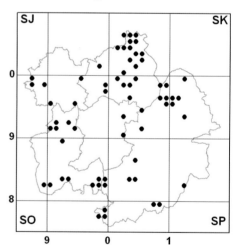

*66. Native. Ax. Perennial on typically far-creeping rhizomes, but very variable in habit and habitat, growing on damp or wet areas on a wide variety of heaths, grassland, mires and pond margins (where it can form marked tussocks). Occasional, usually in old or only semi-improved vegetation and always on fairly or very nutrient-poor and base-poor or only slightly base-flushed soils and peats, and rarely with a completely stagnant water table. Largely confined to the less intensively industrial and residential parts of B&BC. Ass: *Agrostis stolonifera, Agrostis vinealis, Carex echinata, Deschampsia flexuosa, Erica tetralix, Juncus*

conglomeratus, Juncus effusus, Molinia caerulea, Nardus stricta, Potentilla erecta.

### Carex pulicaris L.
### Flea Sedge
2. Native. Ax. A plant of short, open vegetation on quite base-rich but nutrient-poor, usually wet soils or peats, it was recorded from "two bogs" in Sutton Park (SP0996, SP0998) in Cadbury et al. (1971). Still present there, growing very locally in moderately base-flushed fen-like vegetation W and N of Longmoor Pool (SP093963, ICT, MWP & PLR, 2006) and in the mire by Little Bracebridge Pool (SP094982, C. Tregaskes, ICT, J. Bailey, B. Opara, C. Tinstell, N. Crowley, D. Mattley & A. Freeman, 2011). Ass: Briza media, Carex hostiana, Carex panicea, Triglochin palustris, Valeriana dioica.

### Carex morrowii Boott
### Morrow's Sedge
1. Neophyte. Perennial. Present as cultivar 'Evergold', a garden escape found on bank of River Rea, Eastside, B'ham (SP081868, MWP, 2005). Japan.

### 170. POACEAE

### Sasa spp.
### Bamboo

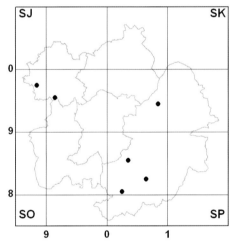

6. Neophytes. Mostly in parks or close to gardens, by lakes, in river corridors, usually in woodlands. The map includes a record for many large stands of **Sasa palmata** (Burb.) E.G. Camus (**Broad-leaved Bamboo**) from Manor Farm Park B'ham (SP029809, MWP, ICT, AWR, JWP, JaH, B. Rowe & L. Bastin, 2008). There is also an old record for the same species in the grounds of Moseley Hall, W'ton (SJ931037, JJB, 1989). Japan & Sakhalin.

### Sasaella ramosa (Makino) Makino
### Hairy Bamboo
2. Neophyte. A patch in rough grassland near to the path linking Sandwell Park

Farm and St John's Close (SP018913, MWP, conf. EJC, 1989 & 2000); rank vegetation, Mill Lane, River Rea corridor (SP021787, MWP, ICT, JWP, JJD, AWR & JaH, 2008). Japan.

### Pseudosasa japonica (Siebold & Zucc. ex Steud.) Makino ex Nakai
### Arrow Bamboo
3. Neophyte. The only recent records for this widely grown and recorded bamboo are: Cofton Park (SP005760, JJD, 1999); footpath off Grassmoor Rd (SP040787, JJD, 2001); Manor Farm Park (SP027808, MWP, ICT, AWR, JWP, JaH, B. Rowe & L. Bastin, 2008) and older records from Old Hill disused railway (SO926858, A. Black, A. Brown, TCH & ST, 1987). Japan & Korea.

### Nardus stricta L.
### Mat-grass

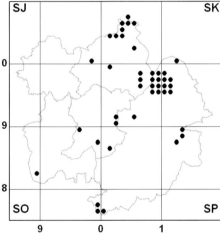

*43. Native. Ax. Densely tufted perennial, found in the main heathland areas, particularly in the transition between wet and dry areas and along paths – tolerant of trampling and disturbance. Also in acid grasslands which are relics of heathland and in grassland which has developed on coal spoil. Rarely abundant, but can be dominant in degenerate wet heath. Characteristic of well-lit, moist or moderately wet areas where raw acid humus, very poor in nutrients and bases, can build up. Ass: Calluna vulgaris, Deschampsia flexuosa, Galium saxatile, Juncus squarrosus.

### Nassella tenuissima (Trin.) Barkworth
### Argentine Needle-grass
4. Neophyte. Perennial, listed as a wool alien but frequently grown in gardens as 'Ponytails' and occasionally establishing, presumably from seed, in pavements and other habitats marginal to gardens. Pavement, Wyvern Road, Four Oaks (SP119971, MWP, ICT, EVJC, PLR & M.

Scholten, 2006); pavement, Swale Road (SP143942, MWP, ICT & EVJC, 2007); pavement and gutter, Pilkington Avenue/Money Hill Road (SP125945, PWP, JWP, ICT, JaH & EVJC, 2007); side of glasshouse, B'ham Botanical Gardens (SP048852, MWP, JWP & EVJC, 2007). Argentina.

### Oryzopsis miliacea (L.) Benth. & Hook. f. ex Asch. & Schweinf.
### Smilo-grass
2. Neophyte. By glasshouse, B'ham Botanical Gardens (SP048852, MWP, JWP & EVJC, 2008); in woodland at Lower Tinker's Farm allotments (SP017798, MWP & ICT, 2008). S Europe.

### Milium effusum L.
### Wood Millet

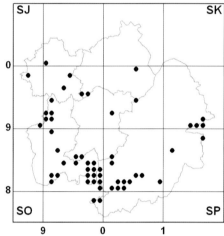

*55. Native. Ax. Tufted perennial, often abundant in old woodland but also often absent from apparently suitable places and largely in the periphery of B&BC. Can apparently spread into adjacent younger plantations and might sometimes be a relic of sowing, e.g. for pheasants, and latterly in habitat creation. Mostly in Oak woodlands in shade to deep shade on moist humus-rich soils with intermediate base and nutrient status. Ass: Carex sylvatica, Holcus mollis, Hyacinthoides non-scripta, Lamiastrum galeobdolon, Pteridium aquilinum, Rubus fruticosus agg., Stellaria holostea.

### Schedonorus pratensis (Huds.) P. Beauv.
### (Festuca pratensis Huds.)
### Meadow Fescue
27. Native, but often a relic of cultivation. Loosely tufted perennial, quite uncommon, in moist or damp, usually old grassland (but sometimes sown in leys and wildflower meadows), typically in flood plains and close to canals. Soils base- and nutrient-intermediate, often heavy or peaty. Tolerant of grazing and cutting and moderate trampling. Ass: Alopecurus

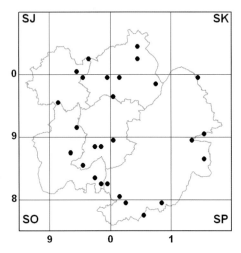

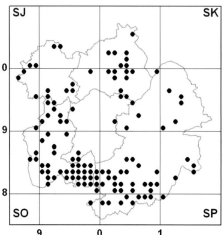

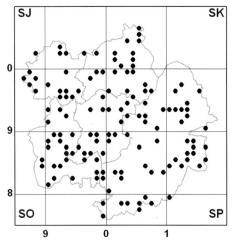

pratensis, Cardamine pratensis, Cynosurus cristatus, Lolium perenne, Ranunculus acris.

### Schedonorus arundinaceus (Schreb.) Dumort.
(*Festuca arundinacea* Schreb.)
**Tall Fescue**

*134. Native, but often a relic of cultivation. Densely tufted or tussocky perennial, quite frequent in rough grassland, especially on little-managed road verges and hedge banks, even appearing in abandoned or tree-planted amenity grassland throughout B&BC. Typically on moderately nutrient- and base-rich, moist soil. Probably always an introduction or an adventive in these habitats. Also a constituent of species-rich semi-natural grassland on damp, moderately base-flushed soils of intermediate fertility where it may be native. Tolerant of grazing, cutting and trampling but often only flowers if unmanaged. Ass: *Arrhenatherum elatius, Centaurea nigra, Dactylis glomerata, Deschampsia cespitosa, Ranunculus repens.*

### Schedonorus giganteus (L.) Holub
(*Festuca gigantea* (L.) Vill.)
**Giant Fescue**
*124. Native. Ax. Loosely tufted perennial, typically a plant of old woodland in semi-

shade, but also more widely in shady banks by water. On moist to damp, often heavy soils which are medium to rich in nutrients and bases. Ass: *Anemone nemorosa, Brachypodium sylvaticum, Bromopsis ramosa, Carex sylvatica, Filipendula ulmaria.*

### ✕ Schedolium loliaceum (Huds.) Holub
(✕ *Festulolium loliaceum* (Huds.) P. Fourn.;
*Schedonorus pratensis* × *Lolium perenne*)
**Hybrid Fescue**
2. Native. S of Bury Hill Park, Rowley Hills, in open grassland with both parents, not infrequent (SO975889, ICT, MWP, EVJC, JaH & EMP, 2007); canal towpath behind Walsall Art Gallery (SP009988, CBW, 2002). Probably elsewhere also: there are a few older records, all from vc. 37, usually with both parents: damp pastures in the Illey area (SO975811 & SO977829, WAT, 1988; SO985819, WAT, 1993); a road verge, Frankley Lane (SP008808, CBW, 1989); waste land, Highbury Park, Moor Green (SP068825, WAT, RM & JJD, 1993).

### ✕ Schedolium krasanii H. Scholz
(*Schedonorus arundinaceus* × *Lolium multiflorum*)
1. Native. A good stand reported in shade, with bird-seed wheat in a park, Sedgley (SO929935, CBW, 2008).

### Lolium perenne L.
**Perennial Rye-grass**
*696. Native. Ubiquitous non-rhizomatous perennial. In all kinds of grassland: old pastures, playing fields, lawns, self-generated grassland on waste sites, road verges. The species most commonly sown in lawns, amenity grassland and ley pasture and often naturalising from sowings. In base- and nutrient-medium to -rich, fairly moist soils. Where it is abundant it suggests a fertile soil. Tolerant of grazing, mowing, trampling. Ass: *Achillea millefolium, Bellis perennis, Cynosurus cristatus, Dactylis glomerata, Poa trivialis, Trifolium repens.*

### Lolium × boucheanum Kunth
(*L. perenne* × *L. multiflorum*)
**Hybrid Rye-grass**
3. Native × Alien. Probably as widespread as *L. multiflorum*, but difficult to distinguish from it, and in similar habitats; the two parents are interfertile and some varieties in cultivation (including those used as nurse crops in reclamation and habitat creation) are hybrids. River Tame by sewage works, Sandwell Valley (SP024947, MWP, 1998); (SP0293, MWP, 2001); (SP0885, MWP, 2003).

### Lolium multiflorum Lam.
**Italian Rye-grass**

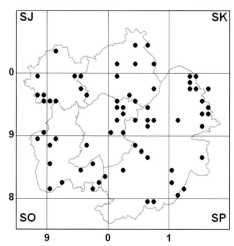

*68. Neophyte. Annual, typically an escape from cultivation in the edge of arable fields, habitat creation schemes, allotments, cemeteries, often somewhat moist to damp situations; also rarely in derelict land and in damp, coarse, semi-natural grassland. Soils nutrient-rich and base-rich. S Europe. Ass: *Arrhenatherum elatius, Dactylis glomerata, Rumex obtusifolius, Urtica dioica.*

### Festuca rubra L.
**Red Fescue**
*663. Native. Ubiquitous and often dominant, usually rhizomatous perennial in semi-natural grassland, sown lawns, road verges, blast furnace and coal spoil, canal banks, wherever there is well-drained, moist to dry soil of intermediate base- and nutrient-status. Tolerant of cutting and grazing, tends towards dominance where relative poverty or toxicity limits the growth of more competitive species but replaced by *F. ovina* on really impoverished sites. Almost all records are likely to be for **subsp. rubra**. Ass: *Agrostis capillaris, Anthoxanthum odoratum, Centaurea nigra, Cynosurus cristatus, Plantago lanceolata.*

### Festuca rubra subsp. juncea (Hack.) K. Richt.
1. Native, introduced here. Material from a gravel path in Collis Street, Amblecote was

taken into cultivation in 2003 & 2004 and was confirmed as this by C.A. Stace in 2008 (SO9085, MES, 2001).

### *Festuca rubra* subsp. *commutata* Gaudin
**Chewing's Fescue**
4. Native, but here always originating from seed mixtures. Non-rhizomatous perennial, recorded by roads and colonising amenity perennial and shrub beds. Presumably present in many sown lawns, but rarely distinguished by recorders. S of Warwick Road, Acocks Green (SP101838, CBW, 1996); Wednesbury (SO981946, ICT, EVJC, DJA & A. Ferguson, 2001); roadside, Bradley Lane (SO963953, MWP, 2004); pub car park, W'ton (SJ922014, ICT & EVJC, 2005).

### *Festuca rubra* subsp. *megastachys* Gaudin
**Strong Creeping Red Fescue**

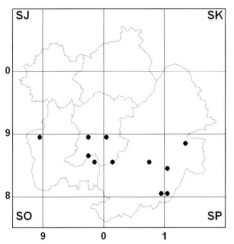

11. Neophyte. Probably common in B&BC and commoner than subsp. *commutata*. In sown lawns, as a pavement weed, in flower beds and on waste land, but not distinguished by most recorders. Europe.

### *Festuca ovina* L.
**Sheep's-fescue**

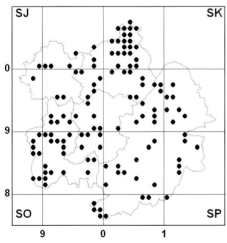

*126. Native. Densely tufted non-rhizomatous perennial from heathland,

acid grassland, rock exposures, quarry and coal mine spoil, sandy and stony banks including on limestone, in open and sunny situations. Also in fine, sown lawns. Not found to be common. Typically on light, shallow, impoverished, base-poor, drought-liable soils, but also on similar but base-rich soils. Tolerant of grazing and trampling. Ass: *Agrostis capillaris*, *Aira praecox*, *Deschampsia flexuosa*, *Pilosella officinarum*, *Rumex acetosella*, *Thymus polytrichus*.

    **Subsp. *hirtula*** (Hack. ex Travis) M.J. Wilk. Recorded as locally abundant in Sutton Park in Copson *et al.* (2008) and Falk (2009). This seems to date from a 1905 identification from SP0995.

### *Festuca filiformis* Pourr.
**Fine-leaved Sheep's-fescue**

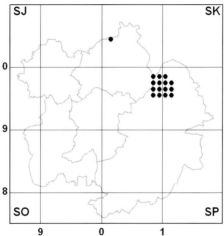

16. Native. Ax. Densely tufted non-rhizomatous perennial, recorded in heathland and acid grassland at Sutton Park, where it appears to be common, apparently almost (or entirely) completely replacing *F. ovina*. Also recorded from acid grassland, Pelsall Common (SK013046, R. Fussell, 1995, also SK011043, ICT, 2008 and spoil bank, SK015046, ICT, 2008). In heath and acid grassland on droughty, sandy or gravelly, base- and nutrient-poor soils. Ass: *Agrostis capillaris*, *Cerastium glomeratum*, *Danthonia decumbens*, *Juncus squarrosus*, *Nardus stricta*.

### *Festuca longifolia* Thuill.
**Blue Fescue**
0. Native. Said by W. Mathews (1897) to have grown on a wall at Dudley Castle, SO9490.

### *Festuca brevipila* R. Tracey
**Hard Fescue**
6. Neophyte. Densely tufted non-rhizomatous perennial, naturalising from seed mixtures, in well-drained situations, e.g. concrete edges to verges. Probably

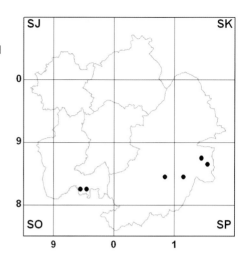

under-recorded: all records by CBW. Europe.

### *Vulpia bromoides* (L.) Gray
**Squirreltail Fescue**

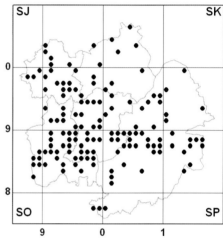

141. Native. Annual from bare places in sunny, dry, open, semi-natural grassland whether old or developing in quarries and on spoil tips. May also extend into more urban situations in similar habitats to those of *V. myuros*. Soils sandy, drought-liable, nutrient-poor, base-poor or -medium. Ass: *Aira praecox*, *Cerastium semidecandrum*, *Festuca ovina*, *Rumex acetosella*, *Senecio squalidus*, *Trifolium arvense*, *Trifolium dubium*, *Veronica arvensis*.

### *Vulpia myuros* (L.) C.C. Gmel.
**Rat's-tail Fescue**
221. Archaeophyte. Annual, often the only species in trampled, weed-killed, drought-liable sandy and gravelly urban situations whether industrial or residential; soils skeletal, base-rich, not fertile. Particularly abundant or dominant on railway ballast, but also by roads, in car parks, in fine, compacted rubble, even cracks in concrete, and no longer strongly associated with railways in our area. Some plants are difficult to separate from *V. bromoides*.

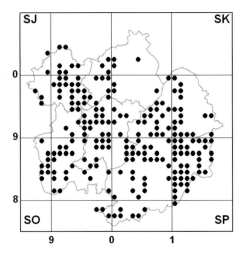

It was not recorded in our parts of vc. 39 or vc. 38 in the 1970s Floras. Ass: *Conyza canadensis, Geranium dissectum, Hordeum murinum, Lactuca serriola, Poa annua, Rumex acetosella, Sedum acre, Sisymbrium officinale, Sonchus oleraceus.*

### *Cynosurus cristatus* L.
### Crested Dog's-tail

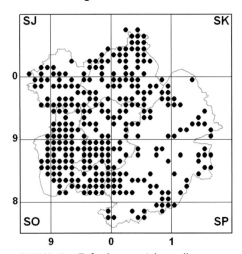

*317. Native. Tufted perennial, usually present in a monad, especially in the Black Country, but rarely common and surprisingly occasional in B'ham. A plant of at least modestly semi-natural and species-rich grassland but can coexist with quite competitive species provided that the management is fairly rigorous. Found on a wide range of soils but usually moist and never very acid or very fertile. Tolerates heavy trampling and/or grazing. Ass: *Agrostis capillaris, Centaurea nigra, Festuca rubra, Holcus lanatus, Hypochaeris radicata, Lolium perenne, Ranunculus acris, Trifolium repens.*

### *Cynosurus echinatus* L.
### Rough Dog's-tail

1. Neophyte. Annual, recorded from a bomb site in Summer Lane, B'ham (SP08, C.E.A. Andrews, R.C.L. Burges) in 1946. Unconfirmed records from a consultancy

report from grassland and fringes of hardstanding, close to canal, Havacre Lane/ Darkhouse Lane, Coseley (SO942946–8, H. Bowler & E. Lomas, 2004). Europe.

### *Puccinellia distans* (Jacq.) Parl.
### Reflexed Saltmarsh-grass

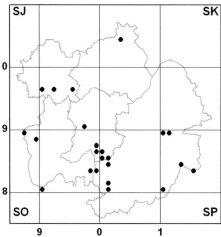

23. Native; introduced in B&BC. Tufted perennial, increasingly recorded from verges of busy roads and in the centres of dual carriageways and motorways subjected to winter salting and traffic damage. From single plants to plentiful, but still much less frequent than *Cochlearia danica*. Soils various, but always salty and usually heavily disturbed or gravelly or rubbly or even in cracks in bare concrete. Ass: *Agrostis stolonifera, Cochlearia danica, Plantago coronopus, Polygonum aviculare, Spergularia marina.*

### *Briza media* L.
### Quaking-grass

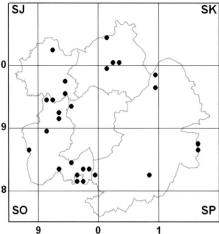

*27. Native. Ax. Loosely tufted, shortly rhizomatous perennial, a plant with several habitats, both wet and dry, but always nutrient-poor and fairly base-rich and usually semi-natural.

(a) Open grassland on shallow nutrient-poor and base-rich soils on limestone

outcrops and grassy railway embankments. Ass: *Arenaria serpyllifolia sensu lato, Brachypodium sylvaticum, Carex flacca, Festuca ovina, Linum catharticum, Ophrys apifera.*

(b) Old mesotrophic hay meadows – in artificially created examples in W'ton, but also in semi-natural grasslands in the Illey and Leasowes area. Ass: *Agrostis capillaris, Centaurea nigra, Festuca rubra, Leontodon hispidus, Rhinanthus minor.*

(c) Base-flushed peaty mires – only in Sutton Park in the survey period but also from the (probably) secondary mire around furnace slag at Ladymoor Pool in the 1980s (SO943951, J. Ashton, 1981, last seen 1989). Ass: *Anagallis tenella, Carex hostiana, Carex panicea, Cirsium dissectum, Dactylorhiza fuchsii, Pedicularis palustris, Pinguicula vulgaris, Triglochin palustris.*

### *Briza maxima* L.
### Greater Quaking-grass

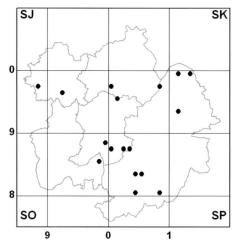

17. Neophyte. Annual; in our area mainly a casual of dry, fertile places associated with gardens such as gravel paths, unused planters, paving and gutters etc. Soils need not be particularly base-rich. Also in neglected fragments of waste ground where small colonies may persist for several years. Mediterranean.

### *Poa annua* L.
### Annual Meadow-grass

*698. Native. Ubiquitous and often abundant annual; recorded in nearly every square and probably present in all squares. Its main habitat is in trampled ground along paths but it also grows as a weed and colonist in gardens and allotments and on the edge of bare areas in all kinds of habitats, including lawns, especially where they are trampled and excessively mown. On a wide range of soils from compacted and stony to moist loams, usually nutrient-rich and not very acid. Not usually heavily shaded. Ass: *Capsella bursa-pastoris, Lolium* *perenne, Matricaria discoidea, Plantago lanceolata, Plantago major.*

There are no records of *Poa infirma* Kunth so far although it is present and expanding in vc. 38.

### *Poa trivialis* L.
### Rough Meadow-grass

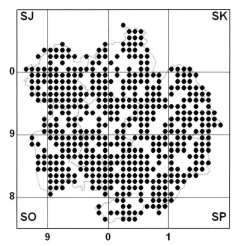

*515. Native. Shortly stoloniferous perennial, only differing in distribution from *P. pratensis* in detail, but probably commoner. Prefers moister habitats than *P. pratensis*, and extends into hedgerows, woodlands and a wider range of disturbed habitats, but particularly abundant in under-managed lawns, ley pastures and self-generating, 'tumbledown' grasslands on fertile soils from fairly base-poor to base-rich. Ass: *Poa annua, Lolium perenne, Ranunculus repens.*

### *Poa humilis* Ehrh. ex Hoffm.
### Spreading Meadow-grass

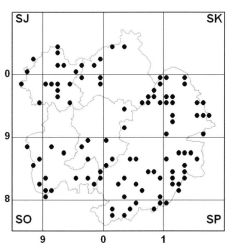

103. Native. Typically a long-rhizomatous perennial, probably under-recorded but map does suggest throughout our area. Probably widespread, but not sufficiently well separated from *P. pratensis sensu stricto* in the records. Plants with *P. humilis* characters are particularly common

associated with kerbstones and grass verges at the edges of roads; also in well-lit hedgebanks and in dry grassland. Soils may be drier and more nutrient-poor than those supporting *Poa pratensis*, and can be heathy and base-poor as well as base-rich. Also tetrad SP09E. Ass: *Agrostis capillaris, Agrostis stolonifera, Festuca filiformis, Festuca rubra, Galium saxatile, Nardus stricta, Phleum pratense, Rumex acetosella, Trifolium pratense.*

### *Poa pratensis* sensu lato
### Smooth Meadow-grass

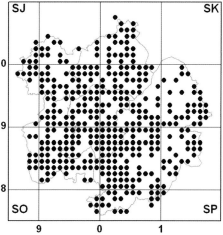

*450. Native. Rhizomatous perennial, very widespread in grasslands and grassy places in a variety of habitats, sometimes quite disturbed such as in rubble or on old walls, but *Poa pratensis* L. has usually not been distinguished from *Poa humilis* and recorders were given the opportunity to record *Poa pratensis sensu lato* on the recording sheet. Records specifically for *Poa pratensis s.s., Poa humilis* and *Poa angustifolia* have been added to this map. Plants grow in moist to fairly dry soils of intermediate base and nutrient status. Ass: *Achillea millefolium, Dactylis glomerata, Festuca rubra, Plantago lanceolata, Taraxacum* spp.

### *Poa angustifolia* L.
### Narrow-leaved Meadow-grass

5. Native. Ax. Shortly rhizomatous perennial. Mortar of an old brick wall, by road, Kings Heath (SP077815, CBW, 1999); bare ground by road at top of a dry canal bank, Merry Hill (SO933874, APD & ICT, 2002); bank with shrubs near railway platform, Four Oaks station (SP117980, MWP, ICT, EVJC & PLR, 2006); substantial colony in open grassland on water-stressed, dry quarry slopes, Rowley Hills (SO978890, MWP, ICT, EVJC, JaH & EMP, 2007); open vegetation on coal spoil plateau, Fens Pools (SO917886, ICT, 2007, known there since 1984). An extensive

population on an abandoned railway line in W'ton (SO914999, ICT, *circa* 1980) is now probably lost. Other old records are from Beaconhill limestone quarry: (SO920950, K. Hodge & G. Palmer, 1985) and Readett (1971) described it as locally abundant on the railway banks and in a waste place in SP0998 in Sutton Park. The records are from dry, skeletal, stony, base-rich but nutrient-medium soils with open vegetation, and the association in the literature with railway banks seems to hold to some extent in B&BC. Ass: *Arenaria serpyllifolia s.l, Festuca rubra, Hieracium* sect. Sabauda, *Hypochaeris radicata, Trisetum flavescens.*

### *Poa chaixii* Vill.
### Broad-leaved Meadow-grass

1. Neophyte. In a tree-shaded passage behind houses in a residential area by Perry Hall playing fields (SP055915, ICT, 2001, seen again *circa* 2003 but never in flower). S & C Europe.

### *Poa compressa* L.
### Flattened Meadow-grass

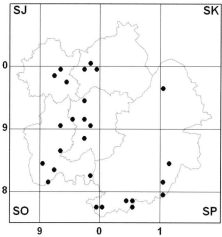

26. Native. Ax. Rhizomatous perennial; not uncommon. It tends to grow in open semi-natural grassland developing in sunny positions on dry, spoily post-industrial soils which are fairly nutrient-poor but base-rich. It can act as a colonist on bare spoil and will even grow in cracks in little-used pavements. Abundant in the old railway sidings next to the Wednesbury Parkway station (SO9794), it was also abundant on the Bilston Steelworks site not long after reclamation in the 1980s (SO9495). In B&BC less often found in the more classical habitats of quarry ledges and wall tops. It may sometimes be sown in 'reclamation' seed mixtures on urban sites. Ass: *Agrostis stolonifera, Aphanes arvensis, Catapodium rigidum, Centaurium erythraea, Cerastium glomeratum, Erigeron acris, Erodium cicutarium, Lepidium didymum, Matricaria*

*chamomilla, Sagina apetala sensu lato, Veronica arvensis, Viola arvensis.*

### *Poa palustris* L.
### Swamp Meadow-grass
0. Neophyte. Unconfirmed record from Quinton Meadows (SO994838, J. Price & AS, 1994). Site now destroyed. W Europe.

### *Poa nemoralis* L.
### Wood Meadow-grass

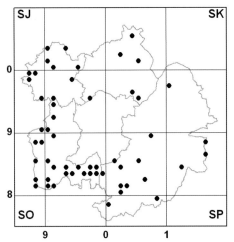

*56. Native. Ax. Loosely tufted, non-rhizomatous perennial, typically in relatively open vegetation in woodland. Sometimes in hedges or occasionally in more weedy habitats. Rarely abundant, commoner in the western and southern suburban and countryside periphery. May be sown in 'shady lawn' mixtures and sometimes persists. Soils dry to moist, base- and nutrient status medium. Usually in half shade but will grow in quite deep shade where it benefits from the lack of competition. Ass: *Geranium robertianum, Hedera helix.*

### *Dactylis glomerata* L.
### Cock's-foot
*705. Native. Almost ubiquitous, coarse, densely tufted perennial, not recorded from three squares which are almost entirely within Sutton Park. It bridges the gap between *Arrenatherum elatius*-dominated and *Agrostis capillaris–Festuca rubra*-dominated grassland but also common in grassy waste land, woodland margins, road verges and other uncultivated places. Can be naturalised from cultivation as a ley grass. Always most abundant in fertile and under-managed situations on dry to moist soils which are not base- or nutrient-poor. Intolerant of heavy grazing, cutting or trampling. Ass: *Arrenatherum elatius, Heracleum sphondylium, Holcus lanatus, Lolium perenne, Plantago lanceolata, Ranunculus repens, Taraxacum spp.*

### *Catabrosa aquatica* (L.) P. Beauv.
### Whorl-grass
2. Native. Ax. Stoloniferous aquatic perennial, only recorded recently in Sutton Park in the base-flushed nutrient-poor mires NW of Longmoor Pool, where it flowers in and around shallow muddy puddles (SP093958, ICT & MWP, 2005) and in similar vegetation by Little Bracebridge Pool (SP0998, S.F. Woodward, 1995, seen again in 2004). Readett (1971) listed it for four squares at Sutton Park (SP0995, SP0996, SP0998 and SP1095). These all seem to be rather nutrient- and base-poor sites for this species, which is generally described from ditches, pond margins and canal and river banks in Britain. A record from Kings Hayes Farm, Aldridge (SK0502, JPM, 1991) was not relocated in 2008 (the ditches had recently been dredged) but the habitat again is quite nutrient-poor and only moderately base-flushed wet pastures. It was however recorded in disturbed ground by the River Rea (SP035794, JJD, 1994) in what must have been a more nutrient-rich habitat. There is a very old record from Edgbaston Pool (SP054841, W. Withering 1801) and others, almost as old, from the Stourbridge area. Possibly this species is under-recorded.

### *Catapodium rigidum* (L.) C.E. Hubb.
### Fern-grass

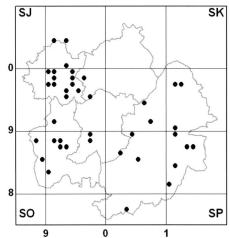

40. Native. Ax. A winter annual, in B&BC characteristically found on blast furnace spoil and soils derived from the same, but can appear on a variety of bared, skeletal stony soils, cinders, rubble, as a pathside weed and even in cracks in pavements, for example on edge of uppermost steps outside the Molineux football stadium, W'ton (SO913991, ICT, 2003–2006). Sometimes it can appear in quantity when soil is disturbed. Soils dry, nutrient-poor and base-rich. Ass: *Arabidopsis thaliana, Cardamine hirsuta, Conyza canadensis, Epilobium obscurum, Erophila* sp., *Poa annua, Sagina apetala sensu lato, Trifolium repens.*

### *Catapodium marinum* (L.) C.E. Hubb.
### Sea Fern-grass
2. Native. Locally common on rocks and walls by the sea, it is beginning to appear inland by salted roads. In B&BC, 50 or more plants appeared in 2012 in gateways and terraced house frontages (but not at the kerbside) scattered along the fairly busy Collis Street in Amblecote (SO900857, APD, 2012). Subsequent to this discovery a herbarium specimen from the furnace sand spoil tips E of the Coneygre Industrial Estate, Burnt Tree Island (SO957914, MWP, 2006) was confirmed as this species.

### *Avenula pubescens* (Huds.) Dumort.
(*Helictotrichon pubescens* (Huds.) Pilg.)
### Downy Oat-grass
3. Native. A loosely tufted perennial of old meadows on neutral or calcareous soils with only a few, possibly casual records in B&BC. An unlocalised record (SO9194, BH, 1999) might be from the limestone of Sedgley Beacon, but it has not been found there more recently. A single plant was found on the edge of a track at Warrens Hall Farm, Rowley Hills (SO956886, CRP, 2003). A record from Pelsall North Common (SK0104, JPM, 1991) has not been refound. A few plants have been found in the meadow created on landfill in Kitchen Lane using hay from Eades Meadow in Worcestershire (SJ963026, ICT, 2001, seen 2007). There is a tetrad record for SO98E.

### *Arrhenatherum elatius* (L.) P. Beauv. ex J. & C. Presl
### False Oat-grass
*688. Native. Very common loosely tufted perennial in under-used fertile land: rough grass, fencelines, edges of allotments, edges of shady places. Situations slightly protected from grazing, trampling, other forms of disturbance. Soil always moderately rich and usually well-drained. Scarce in some areas of Sutton Park. Ass: *Anthriscus sylvestris, Crataegus monogyna, Dactylis glomerata, Holcus lanatus, Lolium perenne, Rubus fruticosus* agg.

Most recorders have not distinguished **var. bulbosum** (Whilld.) St-Amans (**Onion Couch**), although it has been recorded and appears to be common.

### *Avena fatua* L.
### Wild-oat
69. Archaeophyte. Annual; not common, and rarely seen far from arable cultivation as a crop weed or in farmyards or on allotments (brought in with farmyard manure, or possibly in the soil seedbank?). Base- and nutrient-rich, well-drained, soil after disturbance. Also tetrad SO98E. Ass: *Anisantha sterilis, Fallopia convolvulus,*

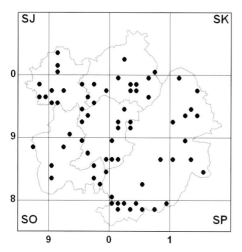

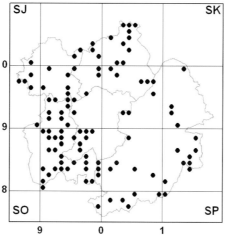

▲ *Catapodium marinum*

Lamium hybridum, Matricaria chamomilla, Papaver dubium, Papaver rhoeas, Persicaria maculosa, Persicaria lapathifolia, Tripleurospermum inodorum, Urtica urens.

### *Avena sativa* L.
### Oat

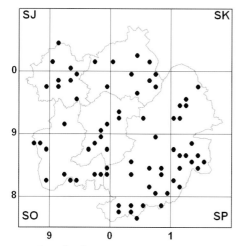

73. Casual. Infrequent annual, but commoner than Wild Oat, always as a casual in disturbed places, rubbish dumps, self-seeded in arable land, or as some of the associates suggest, in bird seed. In dry to moist, nutient-rich and base-rich loamy soils. W Mediterranean, possibly in cultivation. Also tetrads SO98E, SO99A. Ass: *Aethusa cynapium, Anagallis arvensis, Arrhenatherum elatius, Papaver rhoeas, Phalaris canariensis, Raphanus raphanistrum, Triticum aestivum, Viola arvense*.

### *Trisetum flavescens* (L.) P. Beauv.
### Yellow Oat-grass

*107. Native. Widely distributed but not very common, loosely tufted perennial, especially uncommon in the central and urban areas. Most often recorded, by a variety of recorders, in the Dudley area. Open, mostly dry grassland by roads and railway lines and in quarries and even on spoil, and in species-rich mesotrophic

or calcicolous grassland whether semi-natural or artificially created. Also scattered records in road verges and other sown grasslands. Soils dry, nutrient-poor and fairly to very base-rich. Tolerates occasional cutting, hay-meadow management and light grazing. Also tetrad SK00B. Ass: *Agrostis capillaris, Bromus hordeaceus, Festuca rubra, Plantago lanceolata, Ranunculus bulbosus*.

### *Deschampsia cespitosa* (L.) P. Beauv.
### Tufted Hair-grass

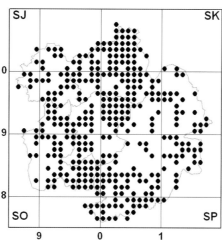

*366. Native. A densely tufted tussock-forming perennial, it occupies both its two main habitats in B&BC: impeded-drainage areas of unimproved wet pastures (especially but not exclusively old ones) and woodland, especially on limestone. It can however appear quite quickly where modestly fertile, poorly drained soils are allowed to develop grassland naturally with little management. It can also increase sufficiently to threaten diversity in unmanaged mires subject to a certain amount of nutrient pollution. Tolerant of some shade, intolerant of frequent cutting or heavy grazing or trampling. Ass: Wet pasture: *Alopecurus pratensis, Holcus lanatus, Juncus effusus, Juncus inflexus, Silene flos-cuculi*. Woodland: *Carex sylvatica, Mercurialis perennis*.

▲ *Arrhenatherum elatius* with smut fungus infection

▲ *Trisetum flavescens*

**Subsp. *cespitosa*** and **subsp. *parviflora*** (Thuill.) Dumort. were not generally distinguished in the Flora survey but both subspecies have been recorded, subsp. *cespitosa* throughout and subsp. *parviflora* in old woodland in Walsall, the Illey area and S B'ham.

## *Deschampsia flexuosa* (L.) Trin.
### Wavy Hair-grass

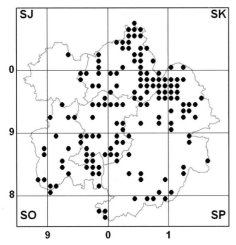

*154. Native. Ax. Loosely to densely tufted perennial, found most typically on various kinds of heath and acid grassland, but also coal spoil, whether shaded or not, shallow soils associated with rock exposures, leached soils on ancient hill forts and other steep, sparsely vegetated slopes, Birch or Oak/Birch woodlands. Typically, but not exclusively, dry soils and an indicator of low base status and relative nutrient poverty in soil. Also tetrad SO99A. Ass: *Aira praecox, Calluna vulgaris, Festuca ovina, Galium saxatile, Rumex acetosella.*

## *Holcus lanatus* L.
### Yorkshire-fog

*681. Native. An extremely common loosely or densely tufted perennial found in all but the most acid or driest grassland, tending to fluctuate in abundance, being much more abundant in wet seasons. Also a lawn weed, in wetlands, woodland margins and stands of tall herbs and a good colonist of disturbed habitats, especially on clay soils. On a wide range of moist to winter-wet soils, nutrient- and base-poor to rich. Tolerant of mowing, grazing, trampling and disturbance. Ass: *Agrostis capillaris, Anthoxanthemum odoratum, Deschampsia cespitosa, Festuca rubra, Juncus effusus, Juncus inflexus, Plantago lanceolata.*

## *Holcus mollis* L.
### Creeping Soft-grass

*408. Native. A rhizomatous perennial which is most common in a wide variety

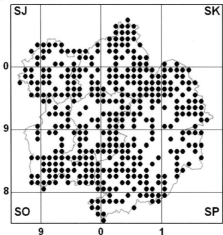

of shaded habitats, especially old oak woodlands, but also in coarse grassland, margins of heathland and can also be a bad garden and allotment weed. Soils low to medium in base and nutrient status. Ass: *Deschampsia flexuosa, Hyacinthoides non-scripta, Poa trivialis, Pteridium aquilinum, Stellaria holostea.*

## *Aira caryophyllea* L.
### Silver Hair-grass

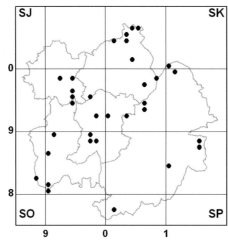

33. Native. Ax. A winter annual found in short, open, fairly long-established herbaceous vegetation on sites such as old railway cuttings, blast furnace spoil and rock exposures, typically on steep slopes exposed to the sun. The shallow, drought-liable soils and spoils it favours are nutrient-poor but at least moderately base-rich and sometimes unbalanced chemically. All these factors combine to prevent the vigorous plant growth and vegetation succession which would tend to exclude this species. Almost all the records are in the Coal Measures areas. Ass: *Agrostis capillaris, Aira praecox, Festuca ovina, Festuca rubra, Hieracium* spp., *Lotus corniculatus, Pilosella officinarum, Sagina apetala sensu lato, Sedum rupestre, Trifolium arvense, Vulpia bromoides, Vulpia myuros.*

## *Aira praecox* L.
### Early Hair-grass

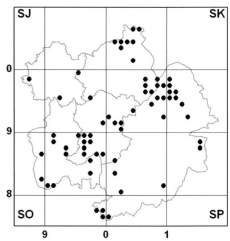

*66. Native. Ax. A winter annual found in short, open, usually long-established grassland associated with sunny, steep slopes and rock, sand and spoil exposures particularly in heathland, in quarries, on golf courses and on cinder mounds and coal spoil. Soils shallow, drought-liable, moderately or markedly acid and nutrient-poor. Records concentrated around Sutton Park, the Sandwell Valley, the Rowley Hills and the Walsall heaths. Ass: *Agrostis capillaris, Cerastium semidecandrum, Festuca ovina, Rumex acetosella, Spergularia rubra, Vulpia bromoides.*

## *Anthoxanthum odoratum* L.
### Sweet Vernal-grass

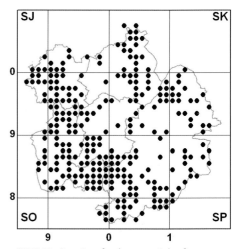

*279. Native. A tufted perennial, often abundant in semi-natural meadows and pastures and in artificially created versions of these, extending into heathland and open woodland and sometimes present in neglected fine-grass lawns. Very infrequent in typical amenity grassland, on recently created post-industrial sites and in residential areas. Soils well-drained to moist or damp, mostly moderately nutrient- and base-poor. Ass: *Agrostis*

capillaris, Festuca rubra, Luzula campestris, Plantago lanceolata, Trifolium repens.

### Phalaris arundinacea L.
### Reed Canary-grass

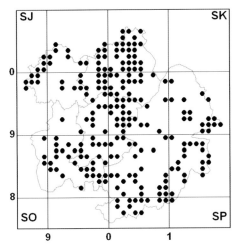

*230. Native. A perennial with extensive creeping rhizomes, found in ditches, water margins, especially stream and river banks subject to inundation but tending to dry out in summer, forming dense stands in suitable open habitats. Less continuous but thriving in similar wooded and scrubby areas. Also seen in apparently drier habitats, often where plants have been dredged out of ditches, but also occasionally forming patches on road and motorway embankments. Not in very acid or nutrient-poor soils. Discouraged by trampling or mowing. The variegated form **var. picta** L. (**Gardener's Garters**) turns up (but only apparently rarely) on newly created post-housing sites, spoil heaps and roadsides. Ass: Arrhenatherum elatius, Deschampsia flexuosa, Epilobium hirsutum, Glyceria fluitans, Salix cinerea, Solanum dulcamara, Urtica dioica.

### Phalaris canariensis L.
### Canary-grass

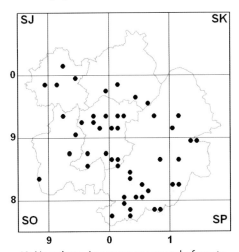

49. Neophyte. In our area a casual of waste and disturbed land and a pavement weed,

usually on fairly fertile soil and probably largely derived from bird seed. Also tetrad SO99D. Thought to be native in NW Africa & the Canary Isles.

### Agrostis capillaris L.
### Common Bent

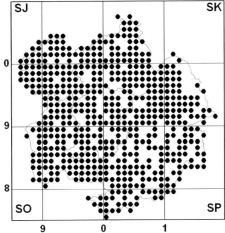

*552. Native. A shortly rhizomatous, tufted perennial found in both semi-natural and recent grassland and in many other grassy places: garden lawns and created meadows, invading mown amenity grassland, a characteristic component of old agricultural meadows and pastures, in marginal situations around heathland, in tumbledown grassland on waste land, in neglected gardens, spoil tips, road verges, young tree plantations etc. Frequently an abundant or dominant component of grassland and very tolerant of grazing, mowing and (to some extent) trampling and probably under-recorded in residential areas where close-mowing prevents flowering. Typically on well-drained but not very droughty, fairly base- and nutrient-poor soils. Tolerates light shade, intolerant of competition on fertile soils, can develop strains tolerant of heavy metal pollution. Ass: Festuca ovina, Festuca rubra, Holcus lanatus, Luzula campestris, Plantago lanceolata, Rumex acetosa, Rumex acetosella.

### Agrostis gigantea Roth
### Black Bent
*146. Archaeophyte. Rhizomatous perennial, from disturbed places and places recovering from disturbance; usually in tall-herb or rough grassland rather than as a primary colonist, although it can also be a persistent rhizomatous weed in allotments, gardens, and arable field margins. Thrives in moist but well-drained, nutrient-rich and base-intermediate soils. Intolerant of heavy shade, heavy grazing or frequent mowing. Also tetrads SP09E, X & Y. Ass: some vigorous forms of Agrostis

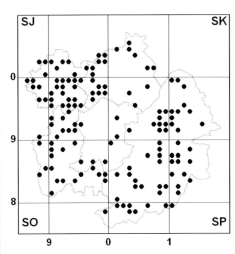

stolonifera, Arrhenatherum elatius, Artemisia vulgaris, Conyza canadensis, Elytrigia repens, Leucanthemum vulgare, Rubus fruticosus agg., Rumex obtusifolius.

### Agrostis stolonifera L.
### Creeping Bent
*665. Native. A ubiquitous stoloniferous perennial, a colonist of bare places, whether caused by disturbance or by flooding. It can grow out from its rooting position in pockets of better soil into quite inhospitable substrates by means of trailing stolons, invading paths, concrete and other rubble and even metalled roads and open water from the edges, cultivated land in gardens, allotments, farmland, bare areas in waste soil, rubble dumps and spoil tips; draw-down zones around ponds, streams and rivers and other periodically flooded or trampled places in grassland and wetland; an abundant or dominant component of semi-natural grasslands although it may be confused with Agrostis canina there. Typically growing in moist or damp, fairly fertile and base-rich soils. Easily suppressed by competition from other plants and intolerant of grazing. Develops many large and small genetically distinct but intergrading races adapted to local conditions, including heavy metal toxicity. Ass: Plantago major, Poa annua, Polygonum aviculare, but also Alopecurus geniculatus, Holcus lanatus, Juncus articulatus, Potentilla anserina.

### Agrostis canina L.
### Velvet Bent
30. Native. Ax. Stoloniferous perennial from grassland subjected to flooding, rush-dominated marshes and in the margins of wet woodlands, mostly in semi-natural situations with other nature conservation interest but also a few records by canals. Can form conspicuous or even dominant mats of (often non-flowering) leafy stolons beneath tussocks of rushes and other

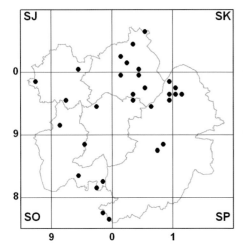

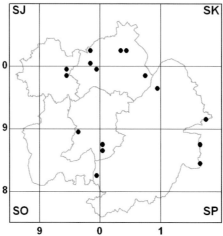

grasses where there is some shade, little grazing and only occasional trampling. Usually on reliably damp, moderately acid and infertile substrates but seems to appreciate slight flushing or occasional flooding. Tolerates light shade. Ass: *Cardamine pratensis, Cirsium palustre, Dryopteris carthusiana, Juncus articulatus, Juncus effusus, Luzula multiflora, Sphagnum* spp.

### *Agrostis vinealis* Schreb.
### Brown Bent

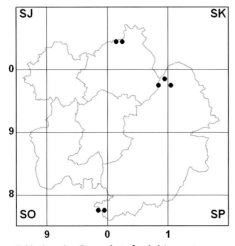

7. Native. Ax. Densely tufted rhizomatous perennial found in dry acid grassland, usually associated with heathland and (almost?) always in semi-natural vegetation. In open situations on moderately acid and nutrient-poor sandy or peaty soils, typically dry, but also recorded in drier parts of mires within heathland. Ass: *Agrostis capillaris, Calluna vulgaris, Deschampsia flexuosa, Galium saxatile*.

### *Calamagrostis epigejos* (L.) Roth
### Wood Small-reed

16. Native. Ax. Rhizomatous perennial, widely but sparsely distributed in damp or wet, unmanaged, usually self-generated grassland on old post-industrial sites and

in similar situations around reservoirs and in quarries where it tends to form fairly sharply delineated patches. Can tolerate half-shade. It was also recorded in Wychall Reservoir (SP0379) in the 1980s and in Fox Hollies Park (SP1282) in 1993. Ass: *Alopecurus pratensis, Arrhenatherum elatius, Deschampsia cespitosa, Epilobium hirsutum, Equisetum palustre, Holcus mollis, Juncus effusus*.

### *Calamagrostis canescens* (F.H. Wigg.) Roth
### Purple Small-reed

1. Native. Until recently this rhizomatous perennial persisted in Fens Pool at the eastern end of the northern shore in quite an extensive patch at around SO919887, last seen by ICT in 1999, and apparently now lost. Could this be the record in Edees (1972) from Pensnett Reservoir (Scott 1832)?

### *Lagurus ovatus* L.
### Hare's-tail

4. Neophyte. Annual, found in a planted grassland area, Goscote Wedge (SK019022, PWS, TM & D. Jones, 2002); dumped soil, derelict foundry site, West Bromwich Street (SO989899, MWP & PLR, 2008); a weed in planted Heather, Balmoral Road Wordsley (SO9996, CBW, 2007); on gravel car space by Spring Road, B'ham with *Vulpia myuros* (SP113829), where it was seen independently at this exact site in 1993 (P.G. Gardner), 1996 (F. Meeting) and 2007 (ICT). Old record: six plants, wall base, Brownhills (SK046053, JPM, 1991). S Europe.

### *Apera spica-venti* (L.) P. Beauv.
### Loose Silky-bent

4. Archaeophyte. Ax. NT and a Nationally Scarce annual. In our area essentially a rare casual species of disturbed sites, with records from the canal bank at Aldersley junction (SJ904011, F. McCullagh, R. Fussell & C. Young, 1997); a post-housing site, Ley Hill Farm Road, B'ham (SP0180, MWP, 2003) and waste ground in a Wordsley park (SO886871, APD, 2002). However recently

it was also found as an occasional member of the weed flora, with *Papaver argemone*, in a sandy arable field off Doe Bank Road, Pheasey (SP066967, MWP, ICT, PLR & JaH, 2008). There is an older record from waste ground near Fens Pool (SO916884, ST, 1986).

### *Apera interrupta* (L.) P. Beauv.
### Dense Silky-bent

0. Neophyte. A winter annual with a stronghold in grass/heath habitats in the Brecklands which has been considered a Nationally Scarce native plant (Stewart *et al.* 1994), but Preston *et al.* (2002) and Stace (2010) categorised it as an introduced species. It was recorded in the periphery of Round Oak and Bilston steelworks sites in the 1980s and early 1990s but not seen at either site within the survey period. The Bilston Steel sites have largely been developed, but the Round Oak site is part of Fens Pools LNR. It is a species thought to have a long-lived seed bank, so it might reappear. Large patch, disused railway ballast, Millfields (SO943961, BRF, 1976 to 1982); 50 plants, top of Round Oak Steelworks spoil heap by Middle Pool, Pensnett (SO917884, ICT & B. Jones, 1986); 25, waste ground, Bilston Steelworks (SO939954, BRF, 1993). BRF also showed ICT a population in open vegetation and bare areas on fine pale steelworks spoil, by the bridge on Coseley Road, Bilston (SO944957, *circa* 1993). S Europe.

### *Polypogon monspeliensis* (L.) Desf.
### Annual Beard-grass

1. Native; casual in our area. A native annual of barish places in the coastal regions of S and E England. Patch in paving alongside a wall, Handsworth (SP045890, MWP, conf. EJC, 2005); old record from spoil at Fens Pools (SO921890, ICT, 1986).

### *Polypogon viridis* (Gouan) Breistr.
### Water Bent

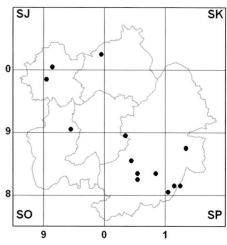

13. Neophyte. An annual or short-lived perennial, with growing number of records

from roadsides in urban areas, where it seems to be spreading steadily and often occurs over many hundreds of metres. Usually at the foot of walls delimiting roadside pavements. Also recorded from canal margin reedswamps. S Europe.

### *Alopecurus pratensis* L.
### Meadow Foxtail

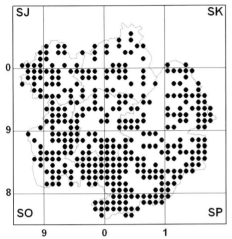

*380. Native. Tufted perennial, frequent but rarely abundant in moist semi-natural pastures and in hedgerows. Soon appearing and persisting in moist or damp areas cleared for development and on tips and dumps of quite nutrient- and base-rich soils. Tolerant of cutting and grazing but not of persistent trampling. Ass: *Arrhenatherum elatius*, *Dactylis glomerata*, *Holcus lanatus*, *Lolium perenne*, *Phleum pratense*, *Ranunculus acris*, *Sanguisorba officinalis*.

### *Alopecurus geniculatus* L.
### Marsh Foxtail

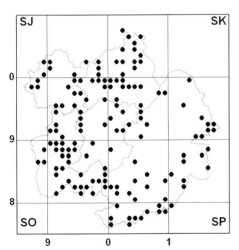

*146. Native. Tufted perennial, with flowering stems prostrate below and rooting at the nodes. Open grassland on sites of dried-up temporary ponds, other land subject to flooding, by ponds, slow-moving rivers, canal towpaths and also occasionally associated with cultivation.

Can initially be abundant or dominant under favourable conditions but may not survive drying out and competition with more vigorous species. On heavy or impeded-drainage soils, base- and nutrient-status intermediate to rich. Ass: *Agrostis stolonifera*, *Glyceria fluitans*, *Juncus effusus*, *Ranunculus repens*.

### *Alopecurus aequalis* Sobol.
### Orange Foxtail

0. Native. Annual or short-lived perennial from the draw-down zone around ponds and lakes, sometimes not seen for years in wet periods, in shallow water or exposed mud on moderately base-rich and nutrient-rich, typically clayey but humus-rich soils. Only pre-survey records in B&BC; not recorded here since 1991: a large population by Wychall Reservoir, Northfields (SP037792, RM & JJD, 1991); Ox Leys Pools (SP160951, JJB, 1990); Fens Pool (SO919886 & SO917885, ST, 1986); Sutton Park (SP0997, Bagnall, 1875).

### *Alopecurus myosuroides* Huds.
### Black-grass

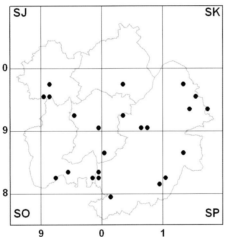

23. Archaeophyte. An annual, in B&BC predominantly a colonist of recently disturbed urban waste land, mostly as a casual and also occasionally an allotment weed. It has been an established weed of continuous cereal crops (its typical habitat elsewhere in UK) in SO9195 for at least 25 years. Seems best suited to well-drained but moist, fertile soils. Ass: *Agrostis stolonifera*, *Avena fatua*, *Epilobium ciliatum*, *Sagina procumbens*.

### *Phleum pratense* L.
### Timothy

*414. Native. A perennial grass found in a wide range of grassy places and in a variety of undermanaged semi-permanent pastures. In old grassland tends to be an indicator of past reseeding, and probably commonest in vegetation

▲ *Calamagrostis epigejos*

▲ *Polypogon viridis*

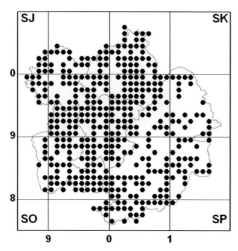

naturally regenerating after disturbance on moderately nutrient- and base-rich moist, loamy soils. Ass: *Lolium perenne, Plantago lanceolata, Poa trivialis, Ranunculus repens, Trifolium repens.*

### *Phleum bertolonii* DC.
### Smaller Cat's-tail

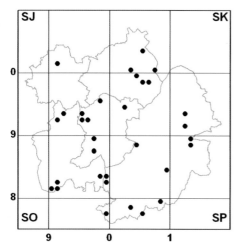

32. Native. Ax. Widely but sparsely recorded, mostly from permanent grassland, but some from more disturbed sites including quarries. Not consistently separated from *Phleum pratense*. Also tetrad records for SJ90Q, SK00A, SO98E & J. Ass: *Agrostis capillaris, Cynosurus cristatus, Festuca rubra, Hypochaeris radicata, Lolium perenne, Trifolium repens.*

### *Glyceria maxima* (Hartm.) Holmb.
### Reed Sweet-grass

*232. Native. Rhizomatous perennial, the characteristic reedswamp species of canals, but also forming reedswamps around ponds and other water bodies and usually a sign of fertile soils and eutrophic waters. It can dominate marshes winter-flooded by eutrophic water but very sensitive to mowing or grazing and much liked by stock. Typically in permanent shallow water, but it often persists on canal

dredgings dumped in hollows. Note the apparent scarcity away from the canals in B'ham. Ass: *Carex otrubae, Epilobium hirsutum, Oenanthe crocata, Sparganium erectum, Typha latifolia.*

### *Glyceria fluitans* (L.) R. Br.
### Floating Sweet-grass

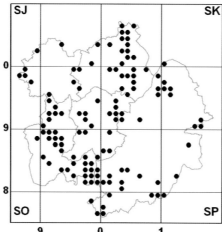

*122. Native. Loosely tufted perennial in pond margins and other waterside and wet situations with bare mud, often growing across shallow ponds, sometimes in canals and along streamsides, with a liking for quite fertile situations and eutrophic waters. Fairly tolerant of grazing and trampling, can stand some drying out in summer. Apparently not common in many areas of B&BC, possibly where suitable habitats are rare. Ass: *Agrostis stolonifera, Alopecurus geniculatus, Mentha aquatica, Myosotis scorpioides, Persicaria amphibia.*

### *Glyceria* × *pedicellata* F. Towns.
(*G. fluitans* × *G. notata*)
### Hybrid Sweet-grass

1. Native. Very large patch in marshy area S of little pool, Swanshurst Park (SP095815, CBW, 1999). Old records from Sutton Park: Readett (1971) described it as "frequent in

a mire" in SP1097, and Bagnall recorded it from SP0997 in 1892.

### *Glyceria declinata* Bréb.
### Small Sweet-grass

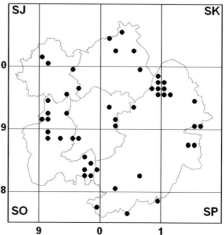

49. Native. Ax. Loosely tufted perennial, mainly from bare areas of pond margins, but also in bare parts of winter-flooded marshes, more confined to semi-natural situatations than *G. fluitans* or, probably, *G. notata* and rarely growing out into permanent water. Recorded in eight squares in Sutton Park. Usually on base-intermediate and only moderately fertile soils; tolerant of grazing and trampling. Also tetrads SJ90V, SK00B. Ass: *Agrostis canina, Agrostis stolonifera, Eleocharis palustris, Glyceria fluitans, Juncus acutiflorus, Juncus articulatus, Juncus effusus, Montia fontana, Ranunculus flammula, Stellaria alsine, Veronica beccabunga.*

### *Glyceria notata* Chevall.
### Plicate Sweet-grass

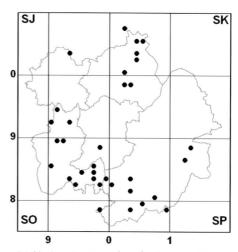

34. Native. Ax. Loosely tufted perennial, not common, usually in winter-flooded but permanently moist mud associated with ponds and slow-moving stretches of rivers and streams, often in sheltered and even shady situations, sometimes growing out

into permanent water. Substrate usually base- and nutrient-rich. Ass: *Agrostis stolonifera, Alopecurus geniculatus, Apium nodiflorum, Arrhenatherum elatius, Iris pseudacorus, Juncus effusus, Ranunculus repens, Veronica beccabunga.*

### *Melica uniflora* Retz.
### Wood Melick

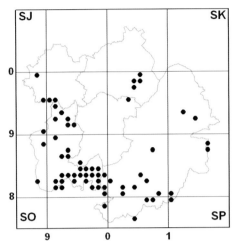

*64. Native. Ax. A rhizomatous perennial, almost confined to old woodland and hedgerows on nutrient-poor to -medium, fairly base-rich, soils in countryside areas. Soils typically loamy and moist but well-drained, and sometimes also on steep sandy banks and even rock outcrops if sufficiently porous and sheltered. Usually not in deep shade, and there are one or two records from plantations, grassland and even by a pond. Ass: *Anemone nemorosa, Brachypodium sylvaticum, Galium odoratum, Stellaria holostea.*

### *Bromus commutatus* Schrad.
### Meadow Brome

5. Native. Annual grass, which nationally can be both a weed of arable and a plant of old species-rich meadows and pastures. The only record from a meadow in B&BC is: frequent in meadow created on landfill in Kitchen Lane, W'ton by strewing hay from Eades Meadow in Worcs (SJ964026, CRP, 2000). Also a few casual records: from the foot of a wall in a residential area of Stourbridge (SO898841, MES, 1998); locally frequent in edge of a field of oats, near Halesowen Abbey (SO976830, WAT, 2002); road verge, B4187 (SO907810, JJD, 2003); Little Hardwick Road (SP071986, DH, 1995).

### *Bromus racemosus* L.
### Smooth Brome

4. Native. An annual grass, probably essentially a casual in B&BC. Recorded from a few sites mainly in the S: below the dam, Bartley Reservoir (SP009815, CBW, 1998); entrance to a car park off the Stourbridge

ring road (SO901844, APD, 1999); one plant in shrubbery, Maypole Grove (SP089786, JJD, 2001); grassland E of pond, Pinewoods, Woodgate Valley (SO990822, JJD, 2003); there are also older records from rough grassland by railway, near Stourbridge Junction (SO912830, JJD, 1991) and Park Lime Pits (SP029998, JJB & R.M. Busbridge, 1987).

### *Bromus hordeaceus* L.
### Soft-brome

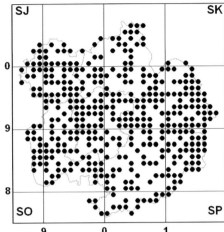

*409. Native. Very widespread annual in a wide range of non-intensively managed grassy situations. Annual, so needs some disturbance; colonises gateholes in pasture, edges of arable farmland, less intensively cultivated parts of allotments and. abandoned gardens, also sometimes in wildflower seed mixtures. Soils typically quite dry and often compacted, base and nutrient status medium. Encouraged by winter-trampling and tolerant of hay meadow management. Most records specify **subsp. *hordeaceus*** and there are no records for other subspp. Ass: *Alopecurus pratensis, Lolium perenne, Phleum pratense, Rhinanthus minor, Rumex acetosa, Trifolium pratense.*

### *Bromus × pseudothominei* P.M. Sm.
(*B. hordeaceus × B. lepidus* Holmb.)
### Lesser Soft-brome

2. Neophyte. Frequent in Yardley Cemetery (SP129846, CBW, 1997); dotted about in Lodge Hill Cemetery (SP026823, CBW, 1997), also two tetrad records from SO98E and SO99M. There are older records from bare places in the old Hawne Colliery site (SO957846, WAT, 1988); pathside of allotments, Cannon Hill (SP064832, CBW, 1989); bare footpath verge, acid grassland, Mucklow Hill (SO973847, WAT, 1992); bare ground by car park, Lye (SO922845, WAT, 1992). It was recorded in Cadbury *et al.* (1971) from SP0583.

### *Anisantha diandra* (Roth) Tutin ex Tzvelev
### Great Brome

0. Casual. An annual first reported in vc. 39 from a W'ton canal towpath (BRF, SO918988, 1988). Not recorded in B&BC since. Europe.

### *Anisantha sterilis* (L.) Nevski
### Barren Brome

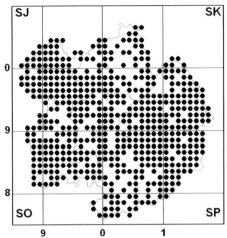

*549. Archaeophyte. Annual from road verges, disturbed hedgerows, frequently disturbed waste land especially around car parks and other areas maintained by irregularly spaced applications of glyphosate herbicides. Will persist in a wide range of substrates under these conditions and although favoured by sunny aspects, good drainage, and readily available moisture, nutrients and bases it is likely to be rapidly replaced by more competitive species on the richest soils. As an annual, it is intolerant of mowing. Mainly germinates in autumn and overwinters as seedlings. Ass: *Epilobium ciliatum, Galium aparine, Poa annua, Urtica dioica.*

### *Bromopsis ramosa* (Huds.) Holub
### Hairy-brome

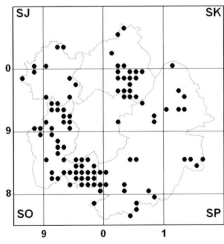

*104. Native. Ax. A tufted perennial in old, relatively semi-natural Oak and Ash woods and in old hedgerows and a useful indicator of such sites. On fairly base-rich, but not very nutrient-rich, moist, loamy soils. Ass: *Brachypodium sylvaticum, Carex sylvatica, Circaea lutetiana, Mercurialis perennis, Schedonorus giganteus.*

### *Bromopsis erecta* (Huds.) Fourr. Upright Brome

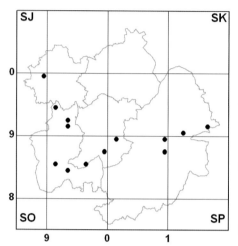

13. Native. Ax. Very shortly rhizomatous perennial, typically in limestone grassland on very dry, sunny, shallow, nutrient-poor soils associated with quarrying, where it can become dominant if not grazed. Has been found occasionally on limestone spoil and on other quite small fragments of dry shallow base-rich soil, e.g. persisting for many years in a fragment of rough grassland on the E side of the conglomerate outcrop in the middle of Barnford Hill Park, Langley Green (SO997874). Also sometimes as a wasteland casual, especially by canals. There are records in Edees (1972) from the Walsall limestone ("SK00F – Rushall etc.") but we do not have any records from there in the present survey. Also tetrad SO99L. Ass: *Arenaria serpyllifolia sensu lato, Centaurea nigra, Centaurea scabiosa, Galium album, Knautia arvensis, Linum catharticum, Picris hieracioides, Pimpinella saxifraga, Plantago media, Polygala vulgaris.*

### *Bromopsis inermis* (Leyss.) Holub Hungarian Brome

4. Neophyte. Annual, essentially an introduction into marginal habitats, usually as a patch in rough grassland where it can be quite persistent: canal bank, Netherton Tunnel Canal (SO969910, MWP, 1997); fenceline near B'ham University railway station (SP044836, MWP, 1998); rough grassland by Hafwen Close (SO998786, JJD, 2000); large colony in Aspen plantation in open space, Holly Drive (SO991786, JJD, 2000); on waste ground, Kendricks Road (SO985973, MWP & MHM, 2001). There

are further records from similar habitats (including one on railway ballast) from the early 1990s from SO9783, SO9981, SP0379 and SP0884. Some of the records are described as the European **subsp. *inermis***; there are no specific records for the N American subsp. *pumpelliana* (Scribn.) W.A. Weber.

### *Ceratochloa carinata* (Hook. & Arn.) Tutin California Brome

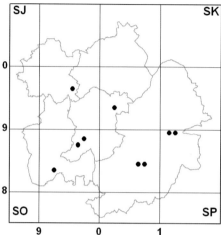

9. Neophyte. Annual or short-lived perennial. A few recent records as an adventive in rough grassland, by roads, on allotments, as a pavement weed but also in Wollescote Dingle (SO924830, T.D. Knight, RM & J.W. Meiklejohn, 2001). Occurrence sporadic, but at least one colony (SP021939 in the hedgerow by a disused road) might be persistent and another from wasteland and pavement in Balsall Heath (SP069845) was described as "clearly spreading" in 1997. Western N America.

### *Brachypodium pinnatum* (L.) P. Beauv. Heath False-brome

2. Native; introduced in our area. One large patch in the edge of the Staffs-Worcs canal, rooted between the coping stones on the tow-path side in between the Compton and Wightwick bridges at SO878984. Essentially a monoculture at this site, where it has been known since at least 1954 according to Edees (1972), most recently seen in 2007. There is also a record from Bloxwich (SJ995012, PN, 2007); a 1987 record on a disused railway at Clayhanger (SK037051, ICT) has not been refound.

### *Brachypodium sylvaticum* (Huds.) P. Beauv. False Brome

*156. Native. Ax. Tufted, weakly rhizomatous perennial, quite widespread in the field layer of semi-natural or at least old woodlands but also sometimes

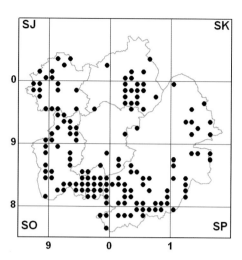

deliberately introduced in woodland field layer habitat creation schemes. As in rural areas it also exists as a component of limestone grassland vegetation. Not on poor acid or very sandy soils. Adversely affected by trampling, especially in the shade. Ass: *Arrhenatherum elatius, Bromopsis ramosa, Fraxinus excelsior, Schedonorus giganteus.*

### *Elymus caninus* (L.) L. Bearded Couch

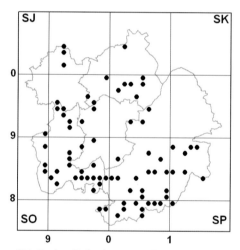

*79. Native. Tufted perennial. Woodland and scrub and other shaded or semi-shaded habitats which are usually but not always old. On dry to moist, base-rich and fairly nutrient-rich soils. Ass: *Alliaria petiolata, Brachypodium sylvaticum, Bromopsis ramosa, Hedera helix.*

### *Elytrigia repens* (L.) Desv. ex Nevski Common Couch

*587. Native. Pernicious rhizomatous perennial weed, very common in allotments, gardens, other cultivated land, road verges, waste land. Responds well to disturbance but not to mowing or shade. Dry to moist, fertile and fairly base-rich soils. Ass: *Arrhenatherum elatius, Cirsium*

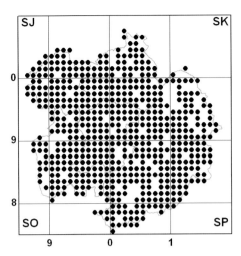

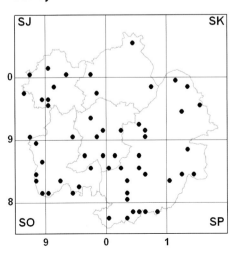

*arvense, Rumex obtusifolius, Taraxacum* spp., *Urtica dioica.*

### *Leymus arenarius* (L.) Hochst.
### Lyme-grass
2. Native. A large rhizomatous perennial grass, on railway bank E of New Street Station (SP081870, G.C. Slawson, 1998), known there since at least the 1970s (Charles Sinker pers. com.). Recorded from the canal bank at Winson Green (SP0488), most recently in 1998, but also SP045882 (J. Turner & CRP, 1987), SP043881 (JWP, 1987) & SP050880 (CRP, 1990).

### *Hordelymus europaeus* (L.) Jess. ex Harz
### Wood Barley
1. Native. A Nationally Scarce tufted perennial. Kitswell Dingle, Illey and associated strip of woodland along ditch W of M5 (SO985818, ST, 1986, most recently seen in 1998). A plant of ancient woodland, especially Oak-Ash, on moist, base-rich soils of medium nutrient status in half to full shade. It has also established itself (after deliberate introduction) in shady parts of the garden of one of the authors in SO8996 where it grows in cracks in concrete paving (2000–2011).

### *Hordeum vulgare* sensu lato
### Barley

56. Casual. On disturbed or cultivated soils in towns and as a short-lived relic of cultivation. All records which make the distinction are for **Hordeum distichon** L. (**Two-rowed Barley**) although *Hordeum vulgare* L. (Six-rowed Barley) is very occasionally seen in cultivation. Ass: *Agrostis stolonifera, Poa annua, Taraxacum* spp., *Triticum aestivum.* SW Asia.

### *Hordeum murinum* L.
### Wall Barley

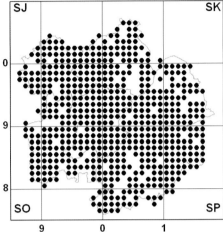

*590. Archaeophyte. Very common annual of grassy road verges, especially in under-managed amenity lawns and around lamp-posts, bases of telegraph poles, by walls, in crumbling pavements, in rubble etc., usually in sunny, sheltered situations. Soils well-drained, nutrient- and base-rich. Tolerant of trampling, disturbance and herbiciding. Ass: *Anisantha sterilis, Lolium perenne, Plantago major, Poa annua, Stellaria media.*

### *Hordeum jubatum* L.
### Foxtail Barley
1. Neophyte. Casual records with us: Self-set in gravel path close to planting at B'ham Botanical Gardens (SP049852, JWP, MWP & EVJC, 2007). There are also several 1980s Black Country records: blast furnace spoil at Ladymoor Pool (SO943950, ST, 1986); Great Bridge to West Bromwich Railway (SO985925, JJB, A. Black & TCH, 1987); on colliery waste, NW of Wallington Heath (SJ9803, R.N. Hill, 1988); more than fifty plants, waste pasture, Deepfields, Coseley (SO942947, BRF, 1991); eight plants, waste ground, river bank, Wood Green (SO997964, JPM, 1991). N America.

### *Hordeum secalinum* Schreb.
### Meadow Barley
12. Native. A tufted perennial, recorded from lawns laid as turf and occasionally in created amenity species-rich wildflower meadows. A constituent of unimproved

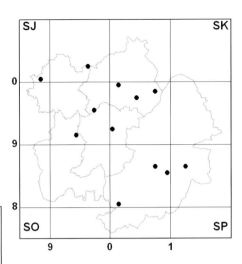

grasslands in England SE of a line from Flamborough Head to the Severn Estuary, which would just include our area, but probably always on secondary sites in B&BC.

### *Secale cereale* L.
### Rye
2. Casual. Mainly grown in allotments etc. as a green manure where it does not seem to persist or be recorded. May also be in bird seed mixtures. Two records from NW W'ton: bare ground, foot of a garden wall (SJ890004, C. Young & F. McCullagh, 1997); (SO894997, C. Young & F. McCullagh, 2000). SW Asia.

### *Triticum aestivum* L.
### Bread Wheat

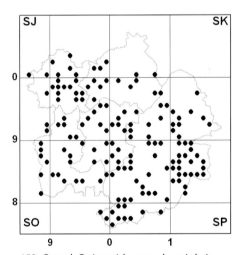

153. Casual. Quite widespread, mainly in disturbed soil in industrial and residential areas. Often beneath street trees, seeds deposited by birds. SW Asia. Ass: *Avena sativa, Brassica oleracea, Hordeum murinum, Hordeum vulgare, Lolium perenne, Stellaria media, Trifolium dubium.*

### *Triticum turgidum* L.
### Rivet Wheat
4. Casual. Generally growing from waste bird seed. Woodland, Griffins Hill (SP037815, CBW, 1997); Walmley (SP1493,

SPG, 2000); pavement, Brierley Hill (SO9188, CBW, 2000); pathside in park, Sedgley (SO929935, CBW, 2008). S W Asia.

### *Danthonia decumbens* (L.) DC.
### Heath-grass

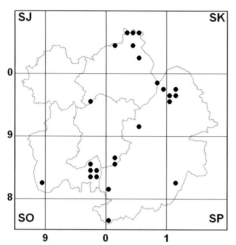

25. Native. Ax. Present in heathland and old heathy/acid grassland and usually in examples of some age. Soils dry or with impeded drainage, base-poor and very nutrient-poor. Elsewhere it is sometimes found in grassland on limestone but there seem to be no such records in B&BC. Ass: *Agrostis capillaris, Carex panicea, Deschampsia flexuosa, Festuca filiformis, Festuca ovina, Festuca rubra, Galium saxatile, Hypochaeris radicata, Nardus stricta, Rumex acetosella, Succisa pratensis.*

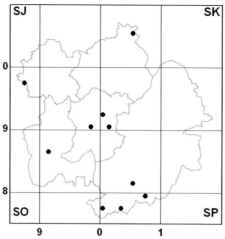

### *Cortaderia selloana* (Schult. & Schult. f.) Asch. & Graebn.
### Pampas-grass

10. Neophyte. Tussock-forming perennial. Distribution scattered, a relic of garden cultivation on waste land and canal side sites. S America.

### *Molinia caerulea* (L.) Moench
### Purple Moor-grass

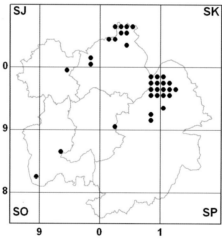

*34. Native. Ax. Densely tufted or tussock-forming perennial, found typically in heathland, mires and margins of acid woodlands on damp or wet peaty nutrient-poor and base-poor to -medium soils. Very rarely in grassland in B&BC. Intolerant of stagnant soil water and encouraged by falls in the water table in mires caused by drainage etc. Can appear, probably temporarily, in drier heathland after fires. Not at all common and more or less confined to semi-natural vegetation. It is not entirely absent in the S and there are further records from the early 1990s for Rednal Hill (SO9976) and Rubery Hill (SO9977). Also a tetrad record for SJ90A. Ass: *Calluna vulgaris, Erica tetralix, Eriophorum angustifolium, Juncus acutiflorus.*

### *Phragmites australis* (Cav.) Trin. ex Steud.
### Common Reed

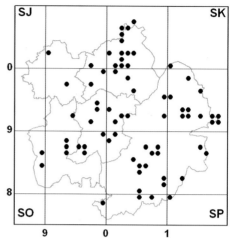

*73. Native. Scattered, occasional, reedswamp-forming rhizomatous perennial. In shallow water around large ponds and lakes, by canals and in river corridors, old beds at sewage works, rarely forming extensive semi-natural reedswamps in our area although often in pure stands. Will grow out of the water into marshes and fens, persisting quite a long time in drying sites. Now being much introduced by anglers, habitat creators and in attempts to purify nutrient-polluted streams. Soils organic or clayey, nutrient- and base-medium to very rich. Ass: *Epilobium hirsutum, Salix cinerea, Solanum dulcamara, Urtica dioica.*

### *Cynodon dactylon* (L.) Pers.
### Bermuda-grass

0. Native or alien, probably casual in B&BC. Perennial with stolons and rhizomes. Recorded from a little-used vehicle track alongside Bushbury railway sidings (SJ916021, BRF, 1992) and side of Gorsebrook Road sidings (SJ914004, BRF, 1994), both on sandy ash. Modern restrictions on access to railways have made it difficult to confirm the persistence of this species into our recording period but it is not thought to have survived. *Carex arenaria* was recorded at the same Bushbury railway sidings site.

### *Panicum capillare* L.
### Witch-grass

4. Casual. Annual contaminant of bird seed and grass seed and a garden escape found in disturbed places. A single plant was found with other bird-seed derivatives the summer following the cutting back of an overgrown double hedgerow near the site of the RSPB Visitors Centre in Sandwell Valley (SP035927, MWP, 1996); dumped soil, canal towpath, Little Bloxwich

▲ *Danthonia decumbens*

(SK007031, JEH, 2003); soil tip on building site, Heathland Avenue (SP142891, JWP, 2007); Bordesley (SP0886, MWP, 2003). N America.

### *Panicum miliaceum* L.
### Common Millet, Broomcorn Millet

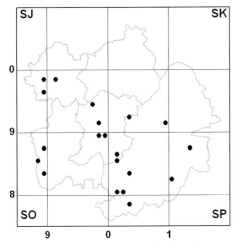

20. Casual. Annual on disturbed land: pavements, roadsides, roadside gutters, canal towpaths and becoming quite frequently recorded. Probably mainly originating from bird seed. Asia.

### *Echinochloa crus-galli* (L.) P. Beauv.
### Cockspur

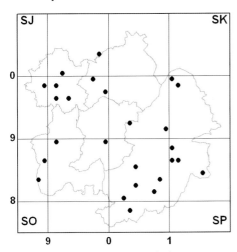

26. Neophyte. Annual recorded most frequently as a casual on urban pavements, also records on allotments and open areas on waste and disturbed land. Warm-temperate and tropical areas worldwide.

### *Echinochloa esculenta* (A. Braun) H. Scholz
### Japanese Millet

0. Casual. Only old records: waste ground, site of RSPB Centre, West Bromwich (SP035927, JPM, 1989); waste

ground, opposite school, W'ton Street, Bilston (SO943962, BRF, 1989). Japan (in cultivation).

### *Echinochloa colona* (L.) Link
### Shama Millet

2. Casual. Annual, for which the only recent records are in pavement cracks, Station Road, Erdington (SP109922, MWP & JWP, 2006); also a single plant with other bird-seed derivatives the summer following the cutting back of an overgrown double hedgerow near the site of the RSPB Visitors Centre in Sandwell Valley (SP035927, MWP, 1996). It was also recorded in a disused chicken pen at Highfields School, W'ton (SO880963, CBW, det. J.M. Mullin, 1987). Warm-temperate and tropical areas worldwide.

### *Setaria pumila* (Poir.) Roem. & Schult.
### Yellow Bristle-grass

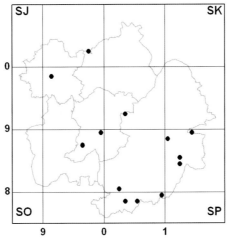

13. Neophyte. A few records as a casual from pavements, front gardens, foot of walls, quarries. Warm-temperate Old World.

### *Setaria verticillata* (L.) P. Beauv.
### Rough Bristle-grass

1. Casual. Annual; a few plants in path and edge of cultivated plot of an allotment, Gorge Road, Sedgley (SO926939, ICT, 2008). Also an old record from an Edgbaston garden (SP0583) in Cadbury *et al.* (1971). Warm-temperate Old World.

### *Setaria viridis* (L.) P. Beauv.
### Green Bristle-grass

15. Neophyte. The most commonly recorded *Setaria* species in under-managed gardens, at the foot of walls, in pavements, on waste land and in similar semi-disturbed sites. Not recorded as

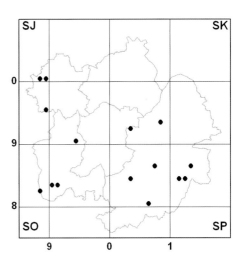

a weed of cultivation in B&BC. Warm-temperate Old World.

### *Setaria italica* (L.) P. Beauv.
### Foxtail Bristle-grass

3. Casual. A single plant was found with other bird-seed derivatives the summer following the cutting back of an overgrown double hedgerow near the site of the RSPB Visitors Centre in Sandwell Valley (SP035927, MWP, 1996); waste ground between railway and road near skip site, Warren Road, B'ham (SP101889, MWP, 1997); factory goods yard, base of tree, Ham Lane (SO892900, CBW, 2008). Warm-temperate Old World.

### *Digitaria sanguinalis* (L.) Scop.
### Hairy Finger-grass

2. Neophyte, casual in B&BC in disturbed situations. A single plant was found with other bird-seed derivatives the summer following the cutting back of an overgrown double hedgerow near the site of the RSPB Visitors Centre in Sandwell Valley (SP035927, A. Underhill, conf. MWP, 1996); Richmond Park Allotments (SO883898, ICT, 2008). S Europe, the Mediterranean & SW Asia.

### *Miscanthus sp.* Andersson
### Silver-grass

1. Neophytes. Introduced into the edge of a pool, Fens Pools (SO922887, MWP, ICT & A. Pritchard, 2008). Asia.

### *Zea mays* L.
### Maize

3. Casual. Three records of non-flowering plants in waste land close to habitations in B'ham: underpass near Snow Hill railway station (SP071872, MWP, 1997); front of neglected shrubbery, Heartlands Parkway (SP108896, MWP, ICT, JWP & PLR, 2006); Hawthorn Road, Kingstanding (SP081934, MWP, ICT & PLR, 2006). Mexico.

# Gazetteer

Sites, other localities and features of botanical importance mentioned in the text. Each grid reference gives a general location. Sites may include other squares. For localities outside B&BC the county is indicated as follows: Warks=Warwickshire; Worcs=Worcestershire; Shrops=Shropshire; Staffs=Staffordshire.

**Ackers, The** SP1084
**Acock's Green** SP1183
**Alder Coppice** SO9194
**Aldridge** SK0500
**Aldridge Common** SK0601
**Allesley** Warks
**Amblecote** SO8985
**Amos Lane Allotments** SJ9400
**Anchor Meadow** SK0500
**Ashen Coppice** SO9195
**Aston** SP0789
**Balaam's Wood** SO9978
**Balsall Heath** SP0784
**Barnford Hill Park** SO9987
**Barnhurst Bridge** SJ8901
**Barnhurst Sewage Works** SJ8901
**Barr Beacon** SP0697
**Barr Common** SP0799
**Barrow Common** SO9189
**Barrow Hill** SO9190
**Bartley Green** SP0081
**Bartley Reservoir** SP0081
**Basin Sidings** SO9794
**Beacon Hill Quarry** SO9194
**Beaconview Road** SP0293
**Bearwood** SP0286
**Beechcroft Wood** SO8799
**Beechdale** SO9999
**Bellevale** SO9584
**Bentley Heath Furnace** SO9899
**Bescot** SP0096
**Bescott Triangle** SP0096
**Billesley Common** SP0880
**Bilston** SO9496
**Bilston Steelworks** SO9395
**Birch Wood** SP0598
**Birmingham Airport** SP1685
**Birmingham Bull Ring** SP0786
**Birmingham East Side** SP0786
**Birmingham Heath** SP0487, SP0488
**Birmingham Heath Farm (Winson Green)** SP0387
**Black Cock Farm** SK0403
**Blackbrook Valley** SO9387
**Blackenall Heath** SK0001
**Blackheath** SO9786
**Blackheath Colliery** SO9686
**Blakenhall** SO9097
**Bloomfield Triangle** SO9592
**Bloxwich** SJ9901
**Blue Rock Quarry** SO9789
**Bordesley Green** SP1086
**Bordesley Green Allotments** SP1087
**Bournville** SP0481
**Bowman's Harbour** SO9399
**Bracebridge Pool** SP0998
**Bracebridge Pool, Little** SP0998
**Bradley Arm Canal** SO9595
**Bradnock's Hays** Warks
**Branton Hill Quarry** SK0600
**Brewin's Canal Section** SO9387
**Brick Kiln Lane** SO9091
**Brickhouse Road** SO9687
**Brierley Hill** SO9186
**Broadhidley Wood** SO9982
**Brockmoor** SO9187
**Bromsgrove Road Cutting** SO9783
**Bromwich Heath** SP0091
**Bromwich Wood** SO9981
**Brook Point Pool** SO9599
**Brownhills** SK0504

**Brownhills Common** SK0406
**Buckpool** SO9087
**Buckpool and The Leys** SO8987
**Bumble Hole** SO9588
**Burned Heath** SP0284
**Burnt Tree** SO9590
**Bury Hill Park** SO9789
**Bushbury** SJ9203
**Bushbury Hill** SJ9202
**Butterfly Meadow** SO9387
**Calthorpe Park** SP0684
**Cannock** Staffs
**Cannock Chase** Staffs
**Cannock Extension Canal** SK0104
**Cannock Plateau** Staffs
**Cannon Hill Park** SP0683
**Castle Hill** SO9491
**Castle Old Fort** SK0603
**Castle Vale** SP1490
**Castlebank Plantation** SK0603
**Chad Brook** SO0583
**Chase Road Pond** SO9190
**Chasewater** SK0307
**Chasewater and the Southern Staffordshire Coalfields Heaths SSSI** SK0406
**Cinder Bank** SO9388
**Cinder Hill** SO9294
**Clayhanger** SK0304
**Clayhanger Common** SK0405
**Clent Hills** Worcs
**Cock Heath** SO9795
**Cocks Moors Wood** SP0879
**Codsall Coppice** SO9585
**Cofton Common** SP0277
**Cole Valley** SP1587
**Colehall Farm Sewage Works** SP1587
**Coleshill** Warks
**Colton Hills** SO9095
**Compton Park** SO8899
**Coneygre** SO9591
**Cooknell Hill** SO8986
**Coombeswood North** SO9785
**Coombeswood South** SO9784
**Cooper's Bank** SO9190
**Cooper's Wood** SO9882
**Coppice Lane Wood** SK0305
**Coppice Road Wood** SO8897
**Coseley** SO9494
**Coseley Canal Cutting** SO9493
**Cotwall End** SO9192
**Cotwall End South** SO9091
**Cradley** SO9484
**Cradley Heath** SO9485
**Cressett Lane Bridge** SO9087
**Cuckoo's Nook** SP0598
**Cutler's Rough** SP0080
**Darby's End** SO9587
**Darby's Hill Quarry** SO9689
**Darlaston** SO9796
**Dartmouth Street** SO9991
**Daw End** SK0300
**Deritend** SP0886
**Digbeth** SP0786
**Dingle, The** SP0498
**Dingle View** SO9192
**Dingles, The** SP0980
**Doulton's Claypit** SO9387
**Dragonfly Pools** SO9387
**Druid's Heath** SP0678
**Druids Heath** SK0502

**Druids Heath (Golf course)** SK0601
**Druids Heath Farm** SK0602
**Duckery, The** SP0595
**Dudley Castle** SO9490
**Dudley Golf Course** SO9688
**Dunstall Hill** SJ9100
**Dunstall Park Racecourse** SJ9000
**East Park** SO9397
**Eastwood Road** SP0493
**Eccleshall** Staffs
**Edale** SO9789
**Edgbaston** SP0584
**Edgbaston Park Golf Course** SP0584
**Edgbaston Pool** SP0584
**Edgbaston Reservoir** SP0486
**Ellowes Road** SO9091
**Elm Road Pool** SP0481
**Elmdon** Warks
**Ettingshall** SO9396
**Ettingshall Park** SO9295
**Fallings Heath** SO9896
**Fens Pool** SO9188, SO9288
**Fibbersley** SO9699
**Finchfield Hill Cutting** SO8898
**Fordbridge** Warks
**Forge Lane Middle Wood** SP0291
**Forge Mill Lake** SP0392
**Foster, Rastrick & Co Ironworks** SO8984
**Four Oaks Common** SP1099
**Fox Hollies Park** SP1282
**Foxcote Meadows** SO9383
**Frankley** SP0080
**Frankley Beeches** Worcs
**Freehold Farm** SO9185
**Friary Road Allotments** SP0390
**Furnace Coppice/Hill** SO9684
**Galton Valley** SP0189
**Gas Street Basin** SP0686
**Gibb Heath** SP0488
**Glasshouse Hill** SO9083
**Glazeley** Shrops
**Goldthorn Wedge** SO9195
**Gorge, The** SO9294
**Gornal** SO9292
**Gornal Wood** SO9190
**Gornal Wood Common** SO9190
**Gorse Farm** SP0493
**Gorse Farm Wood** SP0493
**Goscote Valley** SK0102
**Gower Branch Canal** SO9890
**Grange Farm Wood** SK0303
**Gravelly Hill Junction** SP0990
**Great Barr** SP0494
**Great Barr Hall** SP0596
**Great Barr Park** SP0494
**Great Bridge** SO9792
**Great Bridge Canal Basins** SO9792
**Greet Common** SP0982
**Griff Chains** SO9386
**Grove Park** SP0383
**Grove Pool** SO9188
**Guns Lane** SO9991
**Haden Hill Park** SO9585
**Halesowen** SO9683
**Hall Green** SP1181
**Ham Dingle** SO9182
**Hamstead** SP0493
**Handsworth** SP0390
**Handsworth Heath** SP0590
**Harborne** SP0284

**Harborne Heath** SP0384
**Harborne Walkway** SP0385
**Hateley Heath** SP0093
**Haunch Heath** SP0780
**Hawne Colliery** SO9584
**Hawthorn Wood** SJ8900
**Hay Head Quarry** SP0498
**Hay Head Wood** SP0498
**Hayes, The** SO9384
**Hayes Cutting** SO9384
**Heath Acres (Darlaston)** SO9796
**Heath End** SK0202
**Heath Farm (Norton)** SO8983
**Heath Gate** SO8983
**Heath Green Road (Winson Green)** SP0487
**Heath Lane (Norton)** SO9083
**Heath Lane (West Bromwich)** SP0093
**Heath Pool (Norton)** SO8983
**Heath Road (Darlaston)** SO9897
**Heath Road (New Invention)** SJ9702
**Heath Road (Northfield)** SP0380
**Heath Street (Blackheath)** SO9786
**Heath Street (Winson Green)** SP0487
**Heath Town** SO9399
**Heath Way (Buckland End)** SP1389
**Heathbrook Farm** SO8789
**Heather Close (Moor Green)** SP0682
**Heathfield Hall (Handsworth)** SP0589
**Heathfield Lane (Darlaston)** SO9696
**Heathfield Road (Kings Heath)** SP0781
**High Haden** SO9685
**High Heath** SP1497, SK0302
**Highters Heath** SP0878
**Hill Commons** SK1100
**Hill Farm Bridge Fields** SP0395
**Hill Hook** SK1000
**Hilltop Golf Course** SP0391
**Hockley** SP0588
**Hodge Hill Common** SP1388
**Hodge Hole Dingle** SO9202
**Holder's Wood** SP0682
**Holdings, The** SJ9001
**Holland Park** SK0405
**Holloway Street** SO9191
**Holly Bank Common** SK0503
**Holly Wood** SP0594
**Hollybank Basin** SJ9700
**Holy Cross** Worcs
**Home Wood** SP1395
**Homer Hill** SO9485
**Horseley Fields** SO9298
**Horseley Heath** SO9692
**Hurst Hill** SO9293
**Hurst Hill Wood** SO9293
**Illey** SO9881
**Illey Brook** SO9781
**Illey Brook Tributary** SO9782
**Illey Meadows** SO9881
**Illey Pastures** SO9781
**Illey, Lower** SO9781
**Iverley** Staffs
**Ivy House Road** SO9788
**Jockey Fields** SK0403
**Jones's Wood** SP1393
**Juggins Wood** SP0082
**Ketley Claypit** SO8989
**Ketley Quarry** SO8989
**King's Hayes Fields** SK0502
**Kingfisher Country Park** SP1687
**King's Heath** SP0681

Kings Norton SP0379
Kings Norton Playing Fields SP0579
Kingsbury Warks
Kingswinford SO8888
Kitchen Lane SJ9602
Kitswell Dingle SO9881
Kitts Green SP1587
Knowle Hill SO9387
Lady Pool SK0200
Ladymoor Pool SO9495
Ladymoor Road SO9495
Ladywood SP0586
Langley SO9888
Langley Gorse SP1494
Langley Green Station SO9988
Langley Heath SP1494
Langley Mill SP1596
Lapal SO9883
Lapworth Warks
Lazy Hill Wood SK0602
Lea Marston Warks
Leach Green Quarries SO9977
Leasowes, The SO9784
Leasowes Canal Embankment SO9783
Leasowes Crown Tip SO9784
Leasowes Park SO9784
Leigh's Wood SK0501
Ley Hill Common SP1198
Lickey Hills SO9976
Lifford SP0580
Lifford Reservoir SP0580
Lime Pits Farm SP0399
Lindridge Pool SP1596
Little Bracebridge Pool SP0998
Little Heath (Buckland End) SP1489
Lodge Farm Reservoir SO9387
Lodge Hill Cemetery SP0282
Longbridge SP0077
Longmoor Pool SP0995
Lozells SP0689
Ludgbridge Brook SO9283
Lutley Gutter SO9584
Lutley Gutter South SO9483
Lutley Mill Road SO9584
Lyclose Meadow SO9882
Lye SO9284
Manor Abbey Woodland SO9782
Manor Farm Park SP0280
Marston Green Warks
Meers Coppice SO9284
Merecroft Pool SP0478
Merridale School Bog SO9098
Merrion's Wood SP0495
Merritt's Brook SP0180
Middle Pool SO9188
Middleton Warks
Mill Lane, Northfield SP0278
Mill Lane, Ryecroft SP0199
Mill Pool, Sandwell Valley SP0093
Minworth Sewage Works SP1692
Moden Hill SO9193
Monmore Green SO9297
Mons Hill SO9392
Moor Hall Golf Course SP1297
Moor Street Queensway SP0786
Moor Street Station SP0786
Moorcroft Pool SO9795
Moorcroft Wood SO9795
Moseley Bog SP0982
Moseley Common SP0982
Moseley Golf Course SP0881
Moseley Hall SJ9303
Mount Hotel Woodland SO8798
Mousesweet Brook SO9386
Moxley SO9795
Mushroom Green SO9386
Neachells Lane SO9498
Netherton SO9488
Netherton Hill SO9387
New Rowley Road SO9589

Newhall Valley SP1295
Newton Road SP0192
Newtown Pool SJ9904
Northfield SP0279
Northycote Farm SJ9303
Northycote Farm Coppice SJ9302
Northycote Farm Parkland SJ9303
Norton Covert SO8882
Oak Farm SO8990
Oak Lane Quarry SO8990
Oakwood Spinney SP1094
Oily Goughs SJ9801
Old Heath Colliery SO9398
Old Heath Road SO9399
Old Hill SJ8800
Old Town Gasworks SO9084
Old Wharf Road SO8984
Oldbury SO9989
Oldswinford Common SO8983
Ounty John Wood SO9081
Oxley SJ9001
Park Coppice SO9195
Park Farm SP0292
Park Hall SP1691
Park Hall Locks SP0396
Park Hill SO9195
Park Lime Pits SP0399
Parkhead Viaduct SO9389
Parson's Hill SP0578
Peascroft Wood SO9597
Peaseley's Wood SO8798
Pebble Mill SP0683
Pedmore SO9182
Pedmore Common SO8982
Pelsall SK0203
Pelsall Common SK0202
Pelsall Heath SK0203
Pelsall North Common SK0104
Pendeford Avenue SJ8901
Pendeford Mill Staffs
Penn SO8996
Penn Common Staffs
Penn Hall School Wood SO8995
Pensnett SO9189
Perry Barr SP0692
Perry Beeches SP0693
Perry Common SP0797
Perry Hall Bridge SJ9600
Perry Manor SP0591
Pest Heath SP0586
Pinewood Area SO9982
Pinfold Lane Quarry SP0696
Plantsbrook SP1492
Poplar Avenue Pond SO9899
Pouk Hill Quarry SO9999
Princes End Triangle SO9592
Priory Pool SP0979
Priory Woods SP0292
Pype Hayes Park SP1392
Queslett SP0694
Quinton SO0084
Quinton Meadows SO9983
Rakegate Wood SJ9102
Ray Hall Sewage Works SP0294
Reddicap Heath SP1395
Rednal SO9976
Rednal Hill SO9976
Ridgeacre Branch Canal SO9992
Rock, The, Tettenhall SJ8800
Rollings Heath SK0403
Romsley Worcs
Rough Wood Chase SJ9800
Round Oak Steelworks SO9287
Row Heath SP0480
Rowley Hills SO9788
Rowley Regis SO9687
Rubery SO9977
Rubery Cutting SO9977
Rubery Hill SO9977
Ruiton Quarry SO9191

Rushall SK0301
Saltwells SO9387
Saltwells Wood SO9387
Sandwell Hall SP0191
Sandwell Park Golf Course Woodland
    SP0290
Sandwell Priory SP0291
Sandwell Valley Birmingham SP0391
Sandwell Valley Country Park SP0392
Sarehole Mill SP0981
Sedgley SO9193
Sedgley Beacon SO9294
Sedgley Hall Farm Park SO9194
Sedgley Road East SO9691
Selly Oak SP0482
Shaw Street SO9893
Sheepfold Close SO9687
Sheepwash SO9791
Sheldon SP1584
Sheldon Heath Road SP1585
Shire Oak SK0504
Shire Oak Park SK0603
Shirley Warks
Short Heath SP1093, SO8983, SJ9700
Short Heath (Bloxwich Park) SJ9902
Small Heath SP0985
Smestow Brook, Compton SO8798
Smestow Valley SO8999
Smethwick SP0288
Smithy Lane SO9090
Sneyd Common SJ9802
Sneyd Reservoir SJ9802
Snow Hill SO9198, SP0687
Soho SP0389
Solihull Warks
Sot's Hole SP0192
Springfield SO9588
Springhill Wood SP1590
Springvale Park SO9295
St Margaret's Hospital Grounds
    SP0595
St Mary's Church Handsworth SP0590
St Peter's Church, Harborne SP0283
Stafford Road Cutting SJ9100
Staffs and Worcester Canal SO8899
Stambermill SO9184
Stocks Wood SP0481
Stonebridge Warks
Stonehouse Brook SP0182
Stour Valley SO9684 et seq.
Stourbridge SO9084
Stourbridge Common SO8884
Stourbridge Junction SO9082
Stow Heath SO9398
Stow Heath Colliery SO9397
Stow Lawn SO9497
Streetly SP0798
Stubbers Green SK0401
Sutton Coldfield SP1296
Sutton Park SP0997
Sutton Plateau SP0797
Swan Pool SK0401, SP2292
Tameside SP0792
Tansey Green SO9189
Tansley Hill SO9589
Temple Street SP0687
Tenterfields SO9783
Tettenhall SJ8800
Tettenhall Ridge SO8798
Tettenhall Road SJ8800
Tettenhall Wood SO8899
The Coldfield SP1094
The Heath SO9897
The Swag SK0401
Thimblemill Brook SP0086
Three Crowns Pasture SP0498
Tipton SO9592
Titford Pool SO9887
Tividale SO9790
Trittiford Pool SP0980

Turls Hill SO9293
Turner's Hill SO9091
Turner's Hill summit SO9688
Tyseley SP1184
Uffmoor Wood Worcs
Vale, The SP0584
Waddens Brook SO9599
Walkers Heath SP0578
Wall Heath SO8789, SO8889
Wallington Heath SJ9903
Walsall Arboretum SP0298
Walsall Power Station Pool SO9999
Walsall Wood SK0403
Walsall Wood Common SK0403
Walton Hill Worcs
Ward's Pool SO9696
Warley Woods SP0186
Warren's Hall SO9588
Warren's Hall Farm SO9588
Warren's Hall Park SO9588
Warren's Hall Woodland SO9589
Washwood Heath SP1088
Wast Hill Tunnel SP0477
Waterfall Lane SO9686
Wednesbury SO9895
Wednesbury Basin Sidings SO9794
Wednesfield SJ9400
West Bromwich SP0192
West Heath SP0277
West Park SO9099
Wheatmoor Wood/Plantation SP1398
Wheelers Lane Allotments SP0881
White Heath SO9786
Whiteheath Gate SO9887
Whitehouse Common SP1397
Wightwick Bank SO8798
Wightwick Court Woodland SO8798
Wightwick Manor SO8698
Wightwick Wedge SO8798
Wilderness Wood SP0495
Willenhall SO9698
Willenhall Memorial Park SO9598
Windmill Hill SO8798
Windmill Wood SO8798
Winson Green SP0488
Wishaw Hall Farm Warks
Withy Moor SO9185
Wollaston SO8984
Wollaston Common SO8885
Wollescote SO9283
Wollescote Dingle SO9283
Wood Farm SJ9801
Wood Green Road SO9996
Woodbrooke SP0381
Woodgate Valley Country Park
    SP0083
Wordsley SO8886
Wren's Nest SO9392
Wychall Lane SP0479
Wychall Reservoir SP0379
Wychbury Hill SO9182
Wyre Forest Worcs
Yardley Wood SP1080
Yardley Wood Common SP0979

# Index to fungi

Fungi species are arranged alphabetically by the species name (the specific epithet), with the genus name given after a comma. The page where each genus and class starts is also indexed.

# Index to lichens

Lichen species are arranged alphabetically by the species name (the specific epithet), with the genus name given after a comma. The page where each genus starts is also indexed.

# Index to bryophytes

Bryophyte species are indexed by the Latin binomial. The page where each genus, class and division starts is also indexed.

# Index to vascular plants

Vascular Plant species are arranged alphabetically both by the English name and the Latin binomial (***bold italic*** type). The page where each Genus and Family starts in the Atlas is also indexed as are the sections within *Hieracium*, *Rubus* and *Taraxacum*. Synonyms representing the more important name changes from the second edition of Stace are indexed in a *lighter italic* type. Page references to Chapter 8 are given in **bold**, those to chapters 1–4 in normal text.  Associated species are not indexed.